THE STANDARD
NATURAL HISTORY

6 £3 H. B. Whitmore.

18

July '45.

PRINTED IN GREAT BRITAIN

THE STANDARD NATURAL HISTORY

FROM AMOEBA TO MAN

CONTRIBUTORS :

G. J. ARROW, F.E.S.; M. BURTON, M.Sc.; W. T. CALMAN, D.Sc., F.R.S.
J. G. DOLLMAN, B.A., F.L.S.; F. W. EDWARDS, M.A., D.Sc.
C. C. A. MONRO, M.A., F.L.S.; J. R. NORMAN, F.L.S.
H. W. PARKER, B.A.; W. P. PYCRAFT, F.L.S.
N. D. RILEY, F.E.S.; G. C. ROBSON, M.A.
THEODORE H. SAVORY, M.A.

EDITED BY

W. P. PYCRAFT, F.L.S.

WITH TWELVE COLOUR PLATES
AND
OVER 900 ILLUSTRATIONS
IN THE TEXT

FREDERICK WARNE & CO., LTD.
LONDON AND NEW YORK

Pl. 1.   Frontispiece.

STARFISHES FROM TORRES STRAITS.

1, *Napanthia brevis* ; 2, *Tamaria tuberifera* ; 3, *Ferdina ocellata* ; 4, *Anthenea tuberculosa* ; 5, *Valvaster spiniferus* ;
6, *Linckia loevigata* ; 7, *Echinaster luzonicus* ; 8, *Nardoa rosea* ; 9, *Asterope carinifera* ; 10, *Fromia elegans* ;
11, *Bunaster uniserialis* ; 12, *Fromia milleporella* ; 13, *Ophidiaster granifer*.

PREFACE

ALMOST by common consent the term "Natural History" has come to stand for all that concerns living animals from the lowliest types to man himself. Books on this theme are almost without number, but these for the most part are devoted to special groups—Birds, Beetles, Butterflies, and so on.

The aim of the Publishers of the "Standard Natural History" has been to provide an adequate survey of the whole Animal Kingdom in a single volume.

This was a great undertaking, for the enormous variety of types between the lowest and the highest forms of animal life will be readily realised upon making only a cursory examination of the work.

Hence, the task of the Editor and his contributors was to seek to provide a balanced presentation of the Animal Kingdom such as would afford an easy, comprehensive survey of the classification of animals— that is to say, their relationship one to another by descent—and of the outstanding types which have come into being as the various creatures concerned adjusted themselves to the conditions of existence.

This intimate relationship between the forms and coloration of animals, and the shifts for a living they have to make, is the underlying cause of the wealth of variety which living animals present to-day, and this relationship should be constantly borne in mind by all who read these pages.

The wondrous story of Evolution thus unfolded is one that must afford unceasing interest to the general reader. In this volume he or she will find a comprehensive and lucid account of the Development of Species, from the Invertebrates to the Vertebrates, from the Protozoa to the Primates. At the same time pains have been taken to ensure a sufficiency of scientific detail to make this work an invaluable source of reference to the student.

The names of the contributors should inspire confidence, for they are men of world-wide reputation in their several subjects. Hence the work is not dependent upon, but is assisted by its illustrations. Well-known common types have been made to give place to the less familiar and more remarkable forms, and to secure these the authors' grateful thanks are due to the Trustees of the British Museum of Natural History, from whose specimens and publications the illustrations have been made. In addition, the authors wish to express their gratitude to the following Scientific Societies, Institutions, Publishers, and others who have so kindly given permission for the reproduction of various drawings and photographs.

To Messrs. George Allen and Unwin, Ltd., for Aurelia, from the *Text Book of Zoology*, by Sedgwick, p. 35. To the Council of the Ray Society for Foot of Nereis ; Hook of a Terrebellid ; Bristle of a Polynoid ; and Aphrodite, p. 44. Phyllodoce ; Lagisca ; Sacconereis, p. 45. Hetero-nereid, p. 46. Nereid, p. 47. Chaetopterus ; Sabellaria ; Branchiomma, p. 48. Hydroides, p. 49, and Nemertine, p. 58, from *British Annelids*, by Professor McIntosh. To the Institute of Oceanography, Monaco, for Tomopteris, from *Results of Scientific Campaigns*, by Malaquin and Curin, p. 45. To the Royal Swedish Academy of Sciences for Sipunculus and Priapulus, by Theèl K. Svensk, p. 54. To the Clarendon Press for Earthworm, from *Oligochaeta*, by Beddard, p. 50 ; Anodonta cygnea, from the *Manual of Elementary Zoology*, by Borradaile, p. 129 ; the Aesop Prawn, from the *Quarterly Journal of Microscopical Science*, coloured plate facing p. 174. Types of organs in antennae and Base of body of a Geometrid Moth, p. 205 ; Section through eye of a butterfly, p. 201, and Larva of Psychid, p. 266, from *Butterfly-lore*, by Eltringham. To the Cambridge University Press for Medicinal Leech, from *Parasitology*, by Harding, p. 52, and Dorsal view of King Crab, from *Zoology*, by Shipley and McBride, p. 380. To Messrs. Longmans, Green & Co., Ltd., for Philodina, p. 55, Pedalion and Melicerta, p. 56, from *Monograph on the Rotifera*, by Hudson and Gosse. To Messrs. Walter de Gruyter & Co., Berlin, for Gastrotrich, p. 57, and Kinorhynch, p. 58, from the *Handbook of Zoology*, by Kudenthal and Krumbach. To Messrs. Wilhelm Englemann, Leipzig, for Leptoplana, from the *Naples Monograph*, by Lang, p. 59 ; Geoplana and Mesostoma, from the *Monograph*, by Von Graff, p. 60, and Polystomum, from *Zoology*, by Zeller, p. 61. To the Liverpool University Press for Clonorchus, from *Annals of Tropical Medicine*, by Looss, p. 62. To the Egyptian Government School of Medicine, Cairo, for Strongyloides, from *Records of Egyptian Government School of Medicine*, by Looss, p. 65. To the United States Department of Agriculture for Cestode, from *Tapeworms of Poultry*, by Styles and Hassall, p. 62. To the United States National Museum for Scolex of Cestode, from *Cestodes of Dogs and Cats*, by Hall, p. 63. To Messrs. E. J. Brill, Leiden, for Rhabditis, by De Man, p. 64. To Mr. F. Martin Duncan for Lamp Shells, pp. 73, 75 ; Lesser Octopus, p. 103 ; and Common Cuttlefish, p. 143. To the Carnegie Institute of Washington for Starfishes, from *Echinoderm Fauna of Torres Straits*, by Clark (*frontispiece*). To Mr. Douglas P. Wilson for Egg-mass of Whelk, p. 118 ; Shore Crab casting, p. 151 ; Calanus, p. 159 ; Acorn Barnacles, p. 160 ; Nauplius, p. 161. To Messrs. A. and C. Black, Ltd., for figures from *Lankester's Treatise on Zoology*, viz. Proneomenia, p. 109 ; Nervous system of a Limpet, p. 113 ; Oncidium, p. 125 ; Anatomy of Dentalium, p. 127 ; Left Valve of Meretrix, p. 128 ; Glochidium, p. 135 ; Diagram of a Cephalopod, p. 139 ; Spirula, p. 142 ; Shells of Ostracoda, p. 158 ; Nebalia, p. 163 ; Anaspides, p. 164 ; Mysis, p. 166 ; Porcellio, p. 168 ; Gammarus, p. 169 ; Meganyctiphanes, p. 172 ; and Tawny Owl, from *Birds in Flight*, by Pycraft, coloured plate facing p. 724. To Messrs. Methuen & Co., Ltd., for Chirocephalus, p. 155 ; Cyclops, p. 158 ; Caligus, p. 159 ; Asellus, p. 167 ; Bopyroides, p. 168 ; and Talitrus, p. 170, from *Life of Crustacea*, by Calman. For Tachardia lacca, p. 197 ; Insect structure, p. 200 ; Types of Antennae, p. 201 ; Embia major, p. 232 ; Zorotypus, p. 233 ; and Pediculus, p. 236, from *Text Book of Entomology*, by Imms. To Mr. Jno. W. Taylor for Testacella, from *Monograph of British Mollusca*, by Taylor, p. 125. To Dr. Marie Lebour for Zoea larva, p. 173. To Mr. F. S. Russell for Common Prawn, p. 174 ; Common Shrimp, p. 175 ; and Larva of Spiny Lobster, p. 177. To Mr. Edward Step for Pond Snail, p. 123 ; Sponge Crab, p. 183 ; and Edible Crab, p. 185. To Mr. Ray Palmer for Comma Butterfly, p. 199 ; Leg of Honey-bee, p. 203 ; Louse of Vulture, p. 235 ; Ephemera danica, p. 237 ; White-fly, p. 256 ; Great Wood-ant, p. 335 ; Red Mason-bee, p. 343 ; Cells of Red Mason-bee, and Bumble-bee, p. 344 ; Cuckoo-bee, p. 345 ; and Syrphus, p. 353. To Mr. W. J. Lucas for Engrailed Moth, p. 198. To Mr. Hugh Main for Caterpillar of Early Thorn Moth, p. 198 ; Chironomus, p. 352 ; and Melophagus, p. 354. To the United States Department of Agriculture, Bureau of Entomology, for Stages in growth of American Locust, after Howard, p. 208 ; Yucca Moth, after Riley, p. 280 ; and Stages in growth of Chestnut Weevil, from the *Technical Bulletin, No.* 130, by Brooks and Cotton, p. 208. To the Entomological Society, London, for Ichneumon Wasp from *Trans. Ent. Society*, 1928, p. 196. To the Ministry of Colonies, Brussels, for " Nasute " worker, p. 230, and White Ant's nest, from *Les Termites*, by E. Hegh, p. 231. To Major R. W. G. Hingston, M.C., for Indian Harvester Ant, from *A Naturalist in Himalaya*, p. 334. To the Imperial Bureau of Entomology, London, for Figs. 7 and 8 in coloured plate facing p. 338, from *Locusts and Grasshoppers*, by Uvarov. To Messrs. Sidgwick and Jackson, Ltd., for Scorpion from Egypt, p. 381 ; Crab Spider, p. 384 ; Zebra Spider, p. 385 ; False Scorpion, p. 399 ; Harvester, p. 401, from *Biology of Spiders*, by Savory. To Mr. E. A. Robins for various Arachnida on pp. 382–384, 386–388, 391–393, 396–399. To Mr. J. Arthur Hutton for Scales of Salmon, p. 421. To the Editor of the *Fishing Gazette* for Salmon and Sea Trout, p. 438. To Dr. Schmidt for Metamorphosis of Common Eel, p. 446. To Mr. H. H. Goodchild for Metamorphosis of Plaice, p. 477. For various fishes from *Fishes of Great Britain* and *Indian Fishes*, by Francis Day, pp. 426, 427, 429, 430, 436, 445, 450, 451, 453, 454, 456–459, 461–463, 467, 469, 470, 472, 474, 475, 478–482. To the Government of the Philippine Islands, Bureau of Science, for coloured plate facing p. 460. To Dr. Rusconi for Development of Newt, p. 493. To Mr. L. A. Lantz for Salamander, p. 494 ; Mud Diver, p. 508 ; Green Lizard, p. 535 ; and Wall Lizard, p. 536. To Mr. Douglas English for Edible Frog, p. 501 ; Common Toad, p. 506 ; Slow-worm, p. 540 ; Grass-snake, p. 555. To Mr. E. W. Taylor for Grass-snake with Slough, p. 555. To Mr. D. Seth-Smith for various birds on pp. 577–580, 582, 584, 593, 594, 601–603, 606–609, 611, 612, 615–617, 618, 619, 621–623, 625, 629, 630, 634, 635, 640, 643, 648–654, 656, 657, 665, 669, 670, 672, 678, 685, 696, 700. Also for various mammals, pp. 788, 789, 792, 818, 825, 827, 838, 840, 842, 866, 877, 883, 902, 916, 917. To the Canadian Pacific Railway for Moose, p. 836 ; and to Dr. Marius Maxwell for African Elephants, p. 850.

ERRATA

P. vi, line 7, for Terrebellid read Terebellid.

P. 44, in caption under second illustration, for Terrebellid read Terebellid.

P. 211, line 4, for *Acerentomen* and *Eosentomen* read *Acerentomon* and *Eosentomon*.

P. 260, in caption under third illustration, for *senuhyalina* read *semihyalina*.

Pl. 5, in last line of caption, for 'dry' read 'wet' and for 'wet' read 'dry.'

P. 279, in caption under first illustration, for *Catacola* read *Catocala*.

Pl. 6, in caption, lines 1 and 2, for 'Mimicry of a Cockroach (*Leis dunlopi*, fig. 2) by a Ladybird Beetle (*Prosoplecta semperi*, fig. 3),' read 'Mimicry by a Cockroach (*Prosoplecta semperi*, fig. 2) of a Ladybird Beetle (*Leis dunlopi*, fig. 3)'; line 3, for fig. 4 read fig. 5, for fig. 5 read fig. 4, and for Sikkem read Sikkim; line 5, for 'swarming' read 'solitary,' and for 'solitary' read 'swarming'; line 7, for *Rigus* read *Rhigus*.

P. 340, in caption under first illustration, for *suleatus* read *sulcatus*.

P. 352, in caption under illustration, for *plumosus* read *dorsalis*.

P. 358, in caption under illustration, line 3, for Berlere read Berlèse.

P. 361, in caption under illustration, line 7, for *Amopheles* read *Anopheles*.

P. 366, line 6 from bottom, for 'acalyprate' read 'acalyptrate.'

P. 399, in caption under second illustration, for *Chalifer* read *Chelifer*.

P. 593, line 2, for Crozet read Crozier; line 3, for 1911 read 1902.

P. 594, lines 8 and 17, for Adeliae read Adelie.

P. 595, lines 15 and 25, for Adeliae read Adelie.

P. 647, line 22, for *mœgillivragi* read *macgillivrayi*.

P. 685, in caption under illustration, for *allinucha* read *albinucha*.

CONTENTS

CONTENTS

LIST OF COLOUR PLATES

TERMS USED IN CLASSIFICATION

The Animal Kingdom is, for scientific purposes, classified in the following order of terms:

Phylum
Class
Order
Family
Genus
Species

These divisions may, when convenience demands, be divided respectively into sub-phylum, sub-class, sub-order, etc.

Other terms frequently used, as, for example, Group and Division, are interchangeable terms and their value will be understood from the context.

In Class Aves the term " Legion " is used to comprise important groups of Orders, Sub-orders, etc.

THE STANDARD NATURAL HISTORY

INTRODUCTION

WHEN man came into his own, a part of his heritage was a brain capable of storing memories, of analysing the nature of his surroundings, and of drawing deductions from his observations. He developed, in short, a sense of " awareness," varying then, as it does to-day, in its acuity. The study of Natural History became for him a matter of necessity rather than choice. By trial and error he had to experiment with the herbs of the field and green things after their kind, and with the fruits of the earth in due season. Some he found indeed good, and some brought death in their train.

The sharpening of his wits by his conflict with the animal world called for a new courage, and that of no mean order. The spice of peril which this entailed gave him also, in his leisure moments, a feeling of exaltation, begotten by his triumph ; and in course of time he began to seek an outlet for his emotions in concrete form by carving images of his quarry on the walls of the cave which gave him shelter ; and it is to be noted that he selected, not the trivial creatures, but those whose capture afforded both excitement as well as danger—the big game animals—the ox, horse, and reindeer, the elephant and the rhinoceros. These ancient hunters were the first artists, and their achievements compare favourably with those of the most skilful of animal painters and sculptors of to-day.

Not until men had acquired ability to record their thoughts and impressions by writing do we get any insight into the conclusions at which they arrived in regard to animal life. Among them we find a strange mixture of fact and fable, into which we may not venture in these pages. But we find then, as now, that those who sought to obtain a grip of the welter of life around them found it necessary to adopt some sort of classification of the various creatures whose habits, or qualities, they desired to study. These early efforts naturally seem to us more or less crude, for primitive men had little but external characters to serve them as a guide in their attempts to form groups of various kinds of animals, according to their likeness to one another.

We are more fortunate. The heritage of the past is ours. A vast amount of knowledge of the structure of animals has been garnered ; and this has shown us that it is upon their anatomical structure, even more than on external characters, that we must depend in our efforts to trace the blood-relationship of the various types of animals one to another ; for no classification that has not this aim for its basis is of any value.

In the matter of structure, as well as of external form, we find large numbers of animals to all intents and purposes exactly alike, and their peculiarities are handed on from one generation to another.   Such entities, or groups of individuals, showing a common heritage and likeness, we call " species." We find groups of species differing one from another in no more than minor characters ; sometimes, indeed, they are so alike that only an expert can distinguish between them.   These we group together to form " genera." Similarly, genera are grouped together to form " families," while larger groups bearing certain characters in common are massed together to form " orders." All the species, genera, families, and orders representing one type of animal life are included in a " class."   The Mammals and the Birds, for example, form the class Mammalia and the class Aves respectively.

But the aim of this volume is not merely to furnish a concise account of the classification of animals.   As the different types are surveyed, it will be noticed that they present an almost awe-inspiring variety of form and size and coloration—the outward and visible signs of internal and often impalpable modes of growth.   What explanation have we to offer for these protean shapes ?

The answer to this is found in the study of haunts and habits, and the shifts for a living which all living things, whether plant or animal, have to make.   They have, as we say, to " adapt " themselves to the conditions of their environment, animate or inanimate.   These factors have given us the mole and the antelope, the bird and the tortoise, frogs and fishes, butterflies, crabs, sea-anemones, and jelly-fish.

But if we are to get a real insight into the moulding forces which have brought these varied and unlike types into being we must know something of the simpler, as well as the simplest, forms of life—mere specks of animated jelly.   And it is with these, therefore, that this volume begins. They reveal a positively astonishing wealth of types, showing that all animals, whether simple or complex, are capable of adapting themselves to the conditions imposed by the outer world, though the same conditions beget different results according to the inherent qualities of the stuff of which they are made.   Compare, for example, the common mole with the marsupial mole ; or the jerboa with the kangaroo.

Throughout the perusal of these pages this fact is to be borne in mind. Whether in discussing the beasts of the field, or the fowls of the air, the creeping things of the earth, or the dwellers in the great wide sea, all are witnesses, in their bodily shape, to this adaptability to their environment, that is to say, their special haunts.   Some, it is true, have contrived to express a certain amount of individuality in the form of ornament, or vivid colour, or exuberances of growth which seem to have no relation to the conditions of the environment, to be independent of this matter of haunts. This conclusion, however, is not really justified, for it shows that in such cases the conditions of environment are less strenuous than usual. Such resplendent individuals are they who have, so to speak, been born to a life of ease. The peacock, for example, and the argus-pheasant, have acquired their splendour because they happen to live where there is an abundance of food all the year round, obtainable on the ground, a congenial climate, and a freedom from enemies. Any marked change in these haunts, either in the physical conditions, abundance of food, or of enemies, would bring about their speedy extermination, for long flight, to escape these adverse conditions, would be impossible.

It will be unnecessary to enlarge upon these aspects of animal life, for the rest of this book is but a reiteration thereof. Were it possible to describe every known species of animal, it would be but a profitless and tiresome task; but here a selection has been made, designed, as far as possible, to illustrate and emphasise the undercurrent of forces which has found expression in the bewildering variety of forms which make up the Animal Kingdom to-day. Many gaps in our knowledge of living animals are filled by the study of their extinct ancestors, some of which carry us back to the oldest fossiliferous rocks. Such of these as help to explain the peculiarities of living animals will be mentioned here, but no more than these can find a place.

The usefulness and helpfulness of this volume will be immensely increased if it is constantly borne in mind that the bewildering variety of forms presented in its pages have all been derived from simple specks of protoplasm, or living jelly, which came into being in the remote past—a past which can be expressed but vaguely as " millions of years ago." That jelly, without definite form, or parts, possessed the tremendous potentiality of giving rise to more and more complex bodies, ranging to-day from Amoeba to Man.

We know nothing of the very earliest forms, for their bodies, having no hard parts, have left no records in the rocks. But it is to be remarked that the earliest known fossils were of the simpler, Invertebrate types, with the living forms of which, accordingly, this volume commences—to wit, the Protozoa, Sponges, Corals, Mollusca, the Arthropoda or jointed animals, such as the Crustaceans and Insects, the Echinoderms, and so on. Then came the Vertebrates, that is to say, the Fishes, Amphibians, Reptiles and Birds, and lastly Mammals. They appear in the records of the rocks in this order. That is to say, the early and lowly types of Invertebrates preceded the Fishes, and Fishes preceded the Amphibians. They were, each in their turn, the dominant types.

For long ages the Reptiles held this proud place, so that we speak of the

" Age of Reptiles." The Mammals are evidently descendants of the Reptiles. The earliest indubitable Mammals, preserved to us in the rocks, were small and lowly marsupial-types, represented to-day by the kangaroos, opossums, and so on. Ornithorhynchus and the Spiny Ant-eater (*Echidna*) to this day lay eggs like Reptiles. In this volume all these types will be surveyed, but it must be remembered that they are, so to speak, but the leaves of a living tree. We see nothing of the leaves shed in past years, though but for these the tree of to-day would not exist.

Not a little help towards gaining a grip of the unity inherent in the diversity of the various creatures described in this volume will be gained, if the adjoining diagrams representing the main groups or divisions and classes of the Animal Kingdom are carefully analysed, so as to fix in the memory their general relationship one to another. Each of these principal divisions we call a " phylum," from the Greek *phylon*, a tribe. In the various phylogenetic trees given in these pages an attempt is made to show the relationship of the several main branchings of these phyla, thereby rendering it easier to grasp the relationship of the several members of each of the various classes and orders, one to another. A glance at the phylogenetic tree of, say, the Fishes or the Birds, will suffice to make the purpose and value of such trees " leap to the eyes," and render a long and tedious explanation unnecessary.

PART I
SUB-KINGDOM INVERTEBRATA

SECTION I

Phylum PROTOZOA

By M. Burton, M.Sc.

AMOEBA : A LIVING UNIT

THE increasing interest in biology and biological problems has made the word " Amoeba " familiar to all, and the term " from Amoeba to Man " is accepted as a figurative sequence whereby, in the mind's eye, we pass from this minute organism, representative of the earliest manifestations of life, through a series of forms of increasing complexity till we arrive at man himself. It is doubly fitting, therefore, that a work of this nature should commence with a description of Amoeba before proceeding to a consideration of the rest of the Animal Kingdom.

Amoeba is an animal, about 1/100th of an inch in diameter, living amid the mud and vegetable debris at the bottom of ponds, and, according to some authors, in almost any fresh water exposed to the weather. So small a creature can only be seen with the aid of a microscope. It is no more than a tiny mass of protoplasm resembling, both in appearance and chemical constitution, the white of an uncooked egg. As we watch it, we see that it can gradually change shape and move about. Perhaps at first it is almost spherical, but, in a short while, blunt, finger-like processes, known as pseudopodia, or "false-feet," begin to appear on its margin. These slowly elongate, and, as they extend farther and farther, the rest of the body shrinks in proportion. The forward movement, initiated by the pseudopodia, is

5

communicated to the rest of the body, with the result that the whole moves
forward to the point reached by the pseudopodia.   The Amoeba has now
resumed its former more or less rounded condition.   Fresh pseudopodia
are again thrown out and the process is repeated.   By the repetition of these
movements the animal moves about in search of food.

Although so small, Amoeba is not so simple as is sometimes suggested,
since its protoplasm contains a number of structures, comparable with the
internal organs of higher animals, which play an important rôle in the life
of the creature.   The protoplasm is granular, resembling a jelly impregnated
with numerous fine solid grains, and as the animal moves about these fine
grains or granules stream in the direction in which the pseudopodia are
moving, so that not only does the body move as a whole, but the protoplasm of which it is composed is also in a state of constant movement within itself, the whole resembling the flowing of a drop of oil over a wet surface.   In fact, artificial Amoebae can be manufactured from various combinations of oils and fats which behave like true Amoebae, except that they cannot feed or reproduce themselves.

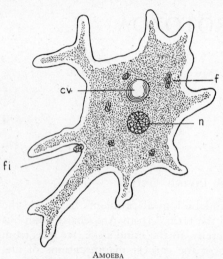

AMOEBA

fi, in the process of engulfing a particle of food; *n*,
nucleus; *cv*, the contractile vacuole; *f*, several food
particles already engulfed.

To return to the structures contained within the body of Amoeba, at the centre of the protoplasm forming its body is a spherical, semi-transparent structure whose outline can just be perceived in the living animal.   This is the nucleus, and herein is concentrated the whole vitality of the cell:
destroy it and the rest perishes.   Furthermore, it is the seat of control,
though its activities are very imperfectly understood, but they almost
certainly constitute the guiding influence in every action and movement.
With very few exceptions all living cells contain a nucleus, and even in
apparent exceptions it is claimed that the very high powers of the microscope
reveal faint indications of such bodies.   Embedded in the ground-substance
of the nucleus are a number of minute spherules which, on account of the
avidity with which they take up stains, are known as chromatin granules.
Although so insignificant in size and appearance, the chromatin granules
exercise an extraordinary influence on the organism itself, and on its progeny,
particularly in the transmission of characters from one generation to another.

The protoplasm surrounding the nucleus performs the function of feeding and excretion. The wanderings of Amoeba are definitely associated with a search for food. Moving as it does in a world consisting of fine grains of mud and organic debris, the animal is constantly coming in contact with small particles of animal and vegetable matter, which are engulfed by allowing the projecting pseudopodia to flow round them. Once within the protoplasm, each particle is surrounded by a cavity into which digestive juices are poured, reducing it to a fluid state so that it may be absorbed. By the movements in the protoplasm the indigestible residue is brought nearer and nearer to the outer limits of the body and finally voided by the simple process of the protoplasm flowing away from it. This is the most primitive method of digestion known. Any part of the protoplasm may act as a mouth, the digestive cavities are produced as and where they are needed, and waste matter is disposed of by merely moving away from it. In addition to these temporary digestive cavities, or food vacuoles, there is another permanent cavity which from its behaviour is called the contractile vacuole. This may be regarded as the counterpart of the kidney of higher animals, as it is the organ through which the body is rid of the waste fluids. It is very difficult to see, but as the waste matter collects in it, it gradually increases in size and forms, when fully distended, a conspicuous feature in the protoplasm. Then its walls collapse and its contents are squirted out to the exterior.

One point worthy of special note is the power of selection which so simple an organism as this possesses. Although constantly coming in contact with all kinds of solid particles, it will only take in those which are of food value : by which we may infer a dawning sense of taste, or what is known scientifically as a chemo-taxis. Further, should it come in contact with anything likely to prove harmful, it reacts by arresting its further progress and, reversing the flow of the protoplasm, moves away from it.

Reproduction in Amoeba is a very simple process. New Amoebae are formed, not by a process of " birth," but by a cleavage of the body into two, so that presently there are two individuals where formerly there was only one. In other words, there is neither parent nor offspring. In Amoeba, then, we are brought face to face with immortality in its simplest terms, for here there is neither birth nor death. The exact moment when the division of an individual takes place is probably determined by size. There is a limit to the size of any given species beyond which no individual of that species may go. When two new Amoebae are formed, they begin to feed, and, naturally, they too begin to grow. After a time, the limit of size is again reached, and a further division takes place.*

The method of locomotion in Amoeba is so characteristic that we speak of it as an " amoeboid movement," a useful term to remember since many

* Although sexual reproduction has not been observed in many species, it is more probable that in these the process is only resorted to at long intervals than that it never takes place at all (see p. 18).

of the cells of the Metazoa behave in exactly the same way. For example, our blood is composed of myriads of tiny cells suspended in a fluid contained within a closed system of tubes. These cells are of two kinds. The most numerous are the red corpuscles, disc-like bodies which carry oxygen and food all over the body to feed and maintain it, even to the outermost layers of the finger-tips. The others, the white, or colourless corpuscles, known as leucocytes, move and behave in exactly the same way as Amoeba, and form our greatest defence against disease, since they have the power of engulfing and digesting bacteria. Indeed, it was the study of these amoeboid cells in the blood which laid the foundation of the modern treatment of disease.

It may appear that undue consideration has been accorded this humble creature ; but a lengthy study of Amoeba affords a firm foundation for a study of the rest of the Animal Kingdom. Through it we can understand how the largest animals are built up of masses of cells ; and how each of these cells, as a living unit, contributes its quota to the life of the whole of which it forms a part.

There are many thousand kinds of animals in the world which, like Amoeba, consist of one cell only. All are moisture-loving. The majority live in the sea, in rivers, streams, lakes, or ponds ; some grow on damp soil, while many live in the bodies of larger animals. Some move about by pseudopodia ; but in others movement is effected by a single delicate thread of protoplasm forming a long whip-like flagellum, or by a number of short hair-like threads known as cilia. Some protect themselves with an outer coat or skeleton of silica, which is fashioned into most elaborate and beautiful shapes ; others construct a similar armour of limestone. No matter what their shape may be or what form their activities may take, their mode of living—their feeding, breathing, and reproduction—is fundamentally the same as that of Amoeba. Since it is from these simple animals, or something akin to them, that the rest of the Animal Kingdom is presumed to have evolved, they are called the Protozoa, literally, the first animals, and we speak of the Protozoa as constituting a phylum, or branch, of the Animal Kingdom.

This phylum is divided into four classes. The first includes those organisms which move by means of pseudopodia, and are known as the RHIZOPODA, or root-footed animals; the second, those with flagella, the MASTIGOPHORA, or whip-bearers ; the third, those with cilia, the CILIOPHORA ; and the fourth, the SPOROZOA, comprising Protozoa which have become permanently parasitic, and which reproduce by means of spores specially protected to withstand the weather and other destructive agencies. The last-named are a group of great economic importance, since so many diseases are due entirely to their presence.

Class RHIZOPODA

The members of the Rhizopoda, with the exception of a few forms like Amoeba, fall into two groups : those that have an external skeleton ; and those that take refuge in the bodies of larger animals, very much in the manner of the Sporozoa, and, like them, causing disease in some instances by their presence, although in no case do they reproduce by means of spores.

The skeletons of these simple organisms, when present, exhibit an almost bewildering variety of form, and many are of exquisite beauty. Some construct this skeleton of sand-grains and other solid matter, while others, by far the great majority, extract the mineral substances, lime or silica, dissolved in the water in which they live and deposit it in or around their own bodies.

In the Lobosa, Rhizopoda with thick, blunt pseudopodia, we find the earliest forms of protective covering. *Arcella*, a freshwater form, for example, secretes a simple plano-convex shell of a material resembling the tough outer skin or integument of chitin common to the insects. Sheltered within this shell, and fastened to it by delicate strands of protoplasm, *Arcella* protrudes part of its body, in the form of pseudopodia, through a small round hole in the under surface. *Quadrula*, another freshwater form, has gone one step farther and makes itself a delicate flask-shaped shell of neatly-fitting rectangular plates, while *Difflugia* secretes a gelatinous substance to which sand-grains become attached, so that in the course of time the animal acquires a shelter made from small particles picked up in the course of its wanderings. *Entamoeba*, on the other hand, has taken to a life of parasitism in the bodies of the higher mammals, and is the cause of dysentery in man.

From the human standpoint, the Foraminifera are of greater interest than any of the other Rhizopoda. With the exception of a few which live in fresh water, and one which lives in damp earth, all of the many thousands of species known are marine. None is naked : some construct shells of carbonate of lime, often of great complexity and beauty ; while others clothe themselves with sand-grains, sponge-spicules, and other debris picked up from the sea-bottom. These shells are built on one of two plans : those with a single opening through which the pseudopodia may protrude ; and those perforated all over with numerous small openings. Those built of carbonate of lime are frequently strengthened by supplementary layers of the same material which may, moreover, be produced into a number of long spines. Most of them consist, not of a single chamber, as in the Lobosa, but of a series of chambers gradually increasing in size, and connected one with the other by small holes, or foramina. Each chamber contains a mass of protoplasm, provided with one or more nuclei, in direct communication with those in each of the other chambers, so that the Foraminifera are not the simple animals we have seen in the Lobosa, but by reason of their multinucleate character have become more complicated in their structure.

Whether lying at the bottom or floating at various depths in the sea, the method of locomotion and feeding is always essentially the same. From the single opening in the shell, or from the numerous holes scattered over the surface, as the case may be, long thread-like pseudopodia protrude, branching and uniting in various ways to form a delicate network in which the small organisms required for food become embedded and ingested in the same way as in Amoeba. In a few Foraminifera the protoplasm flows out and invests the whole shell, while in one form this layer assumes a bubbly, or foamy, nature which probably helps materially in keeping the animal afloat.

Polystomella (highly magnified)

One of the most beautiful of the Foraminifera, and one very easily obtained from the waters around the coast of Great Britain.

At certain periods in their life the Foraminifera undergo a change by which the protoplasm within the shell breaks up into a number of small masses, or amoebulae, each with its nucleus. Sometimes the amoebulae move by means of pseudopodia, sometimes they develop a pair of flagella. Soon after their escape from the shell in which they have been living, often even before this takes place, each amoebula fashions itself a small shell of carbonate of lime, with either one or many openings. As growth proceeds a part of the protoplasm emerges from the shell which it is fast outgrowing, flows round the shell, and proceeds to build another larger shell which partially or entirely surrounds the first. So the process continues until a series of chambers of increasing size, all firmly joined together, is built up. The method of reproduction in which a whole family is produced by the simple breaking up of the adult involved is still of a very simple character, but is, even so, an advance on that seen in Amoeba.

As the new individuals are formed, and escape into the sea, or when an adult Foram dies, the empty shells drop to the bottom of the sea, where, in the course of years, they form deposits of finely divided calcareous mud, known as "oozes." By trans-formations in the earth's crust, the chalky oozes laid down by Foraminifera millions of years ago were raised high and dry, and formed, among other things, the chalk cliffs round our coasts, and the North and South Downs. The stone of which the Egyptian pyramids are built was formed from deposits of a particular kind of Foram known as *Nummulites*, remarkable among the Protozoa for its enormous size, which may be as great as a five-shilling piece.

A very interesting feature exhibited by many members of the Foraminifera is that known as the phenomenon of dimorph-ism: that is, where the same species presents two different forms. In the higher Verte-brates, we are familiar with a peculiar kind of dimorphism, known as sexual dimorphism, in which the male and the female differ considerably. In the

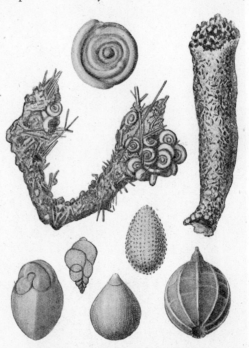

VARIOUS FORAMINIFERA (highly magnified)
A few only of the many beautiful forms which the shells of Foraminifera assume. Some, such as the two large specimens shown, clothe themselves with foreign particles such as sand-grains, sponge-spicules and the shells of other Foraminifera. (After Heron-Allen and Earland.)

Foraminifera, the two forms differ in size, shape, and mode of growth, but in these lowly organisms "sex," as we understand it, has not yet evolved. The small masses of protoplasm released by the breaking up of one form usually develop into individuals of the second form, thus producing an alternation of generations.

The Heliozoa, or Sun-animalcules, differ mainly from the Foraminifera in that the pseudopodia, still long and slender, are strengthened by a rod, apparently of firmer protoplasm, running down the centre and continuing into the body of the animal almost to the nucleus. They are mostly freshwater, and in their mode of life behave in much the same way as the Protozoa already considered. Most are naked; but some have the power of constructing a skeleton of needles of silica; while some form shells of agglutinated masses of sand-grains. One, at least, of the Heliozoa, builds a delicate perforated sphere of silica, very like the skeletons of the Radiolaria. In some cases, numerous individuals of the same species remain attached to each other, forming a compact colony.

In the next order, the Radiolaria, the protoplasm of the body is more complex. Specialisation is beginning to creep in, and we find it divided up into two or three concentric layers, with a large nucleus at the centre, each layer differing vastly from the others. The chief characteristic which divides this group of animals from all other Protozoa is that the central layer of protoplasm, with the nucleus, is enclosed in a chitinoid capsule, similar to the shell of *Arcella*. Perforations in this capsule permit of communication between the central layer and those surrounding it. In addition, many of the Radiolaria build another

RADIOLARIA (highly magnified)

The beauty of the skeletons of Foraminifera is rivalled by that of the Radiolaria. Their skeletons being constructed of silica, they assume a greater delicacy in design.

skeleton of silica, or of strontium sulphate, enclosing the whole of the body. This usually takes the form of a firm framework, globular, conical, stellate, or discoid in shape, variously ornamented with spines, and presenting a very complicated and beautiful object when seen under the microscope.

In this group of animals we are introduced, for the first time, to the phenomenon of symbiosis, where two animals, or an animal and a plant, live together to their mutual benefit, for most of the Radiolaria bear embedded in their protoplasm a number of very minute unicellular plants, called *Zoochlorellae*. As the result of digestion and respiration, the Radiolaria give off nitrogenous matter and carbon dioxide as waste, the two necessities of life to the *Zoochlorellae*. In return the minute plants give off, again as waste matter, oxygen, which the Radiolarian can use to great advantage. The whole process is one of mutual exchange.

Class MASTIGOPHORA

The Mastigophora embrace a great assortment of very perplexing organisms, considerably more advanced than the Rhizopoda ; all of them are characterised by the possession of one or more flagella. Usually they have one or two, but in rare cases they may have as many as eight. With a few exceptions they are smaller than Amoeba, and appear under the microscope as actively swimming specks moving through the water by lashing movements of the flagella which draw them along in much the same way as the propellor draws an aeroplane through the air. Possibly on account of their more active mode of life very few of them construct the type of skeleton so characteristic of the Radiolaria and other Rhizopoda. A few are able to throw out pseudopodia, in addition to the flagella, while others move with creeping, worm-like movements which suggest relationship with such forms as Amoeba.

The majority of the Mastigophora multiply by the simple process of splitting longitudinally. Before cleavage takes place the animal develops a double set of flagella, while nucleus and contractile vacuole divide also, so that when the animal itself has divided each of the two parts is complete. We meet now with a new phenomenon. Often it happens that two mature individuals will reverse this process and come together to unite so completely that only one remains in place of the original pair. This joining, or conjugation, is not the result of a chance meeting, but takes place only at certain periods and, we may assume, in response to definite stimuli, and is the first hint of sexual reproduction. In its more complete sense, sexual reproduction is the process by which a portion, always a single cell, from each of two bodies, called the " parents," come together and unite to form a fresh individual, called the " offspring." Further, the two cells or gametes which unite are usually of different sizes, the larger being regarded as the female, and the smaller as the male.

Asexual reproduction, on the other hand, is the formation of a fresh individual from a portion, consisting of one or many cells, of a single parent only. Many of the Invertebrates are able to multiply, and habitually do so, equally well by other methods. The splitting of the Amoeba into two, the budding of hydroids, polyzoa, and sponges are all examples of asexual reproduction. Although the union of two Protozoa may be regarded as a sexual process, the fact that the two cells taking part are alike is distinguished by the term "isogamy."

The Mastigophora are divided into two classes : the Phytomastigophora and the Zoomastigophora. The former have always been a source of perplexity. Although so like animals in most respects, they possess chromatophores, that is, masses of pigment very like the green chlorophyll of plants, by which they can elaborate food from the carbon dioxide dissolved in the water, in the same way as water-plants do. Moreover, the cell itself is frequently invested with a thin wall of cellulose, a typically vegetable substance. On the other hand, they are able to digest organic matter, which the lowly plants cannot, many of them having a special gullet for this purpose.

In a dipping taken from almost any pond we shall find two of these Phytomastigophora, *Chlamydomonas* and *Euglena*, in abundance. The former is pear-shaped, with two flagella at the pointed end. The major part of the cell is filled with a green chromatophore, while at the base of the flagella is a contractile vacuole and an eye-spot, a small patch of red pigment probably sensitive to light. The animal feeds in an essentially plant-like manner, manufacturing starch from the carbon dioxide dissolved in the water, yet in almost every other respect is most certainly an animal. Nobody seems to be able to decide whether it is plant or animal. To make decision more difficult, at certain times the *Chlamydomonas* passes into a colonial resting state, which resembles in every way certain of the Algae, the lowest form of plant life.

Euglena, on the other hand, is a minute, spindle-shaped organism pointed at one end. From the opposite, blunted end, springs a long flagellum directed forwards. At the base of the flagellum is a small tube-like channel, or gullet, leading down into the body of the cell with a contractile vacuole near the base. The body itself is coloured green by the presence of numerous small chromatophores. Sometimes the *Euglena* will be seen making its way slowly through the water by worm-like movements of contraction and expansion, at others by swift lashing movements of the flagellum.

In addition to being able to manufacture food by means of the chromato-phore, *Euglena* can take in food in solution, and, by the movement of the flagellum, small particles of solid matter are driven down into the gullet to be digested in the contractile vacuole. Even this brief description is sufficient to indicate how small is the gulf separating the two forms, *Chlamydomonas* and *Euglena*, the latter definitely accepted as an animal and the former always a subject of doubt, hence the difficulty of drawing a hard-and-fast line of demarcation between plants and animals.

Another member of the Phytomastigophora, *Gonium*, consists of four cells exactly alike, which live together in a small colony, always acting in unison, never separate, yet always retaining their individuality. Are we to regard this as a colony of four separate organisms, or as a single organism in which the four distinct individuals have joined forces ? Whatever view we adopt there is this to be said, that we have here a condition of things such as may originally have led to the banding together of unicellular organisms to form Metazoa.* In *Pandorina* the process is taken one step further. Here eight cells are permanently joined; but it is in *Volvox* that we find the closest approximation among the colonial Protozoa to the Metazoan condition.

Volvox is a small, green, hollow sphere of cells, barely perceptible to the naked eye, living in ponds. On a fine sunny day these minute globules may, with careful scrutiny, be seen slowly rising and falling vertically in the water, whence they may be taken by means of a dipping bottle. Each of the cells composing the sphere resembles *Chlamydomonas* very closely, except that instead of being pear-shaped the protoplasm of which it is composed is produced into a number of processes which give it a star-shaped appearance, and is joined to its neighbours by the points of the star, so that although feeding itself and being in most other respects independent, it forms a unit in a closely united family. The curious position is thus produced where a number of cells, each of which retains its individuality in almost all respects, is yet subservient as a whole to the individuality of the colony of which each forms a part. The result is a division of labour, a foreshadowing, withal, of that which obtains in the Metazoa where each set of cells is allotted one duty only, some to form the brain, some the digestive system, and so on.

In *Volvox* the division of labour goes no farther than the process of reproduction. Some of the cells migrate into the interior of the sphere, and enlarge considerably to form macrogametes, corresponding to the ova of the Metazoa; others to divide again and again to form microgametes, corresponding to spermatozoa. At the appointed time, a macrogamete is fertilised by a microgamete, and, after a short resting period, begins by a series of repeated divisions to form a mass of cells which eventually grows into a fresh colony. Even in the Protozoa, therefore, we find not only the rudiments of a sexual reproduction but also of a development by the repeated division of cells.

In *Dinobryon*, another freshwater form, a branching colony is formed. Each cell, again resembling *Chlamydomonas* in general form, is enclosed in an elongated, vase-shaped, gelatinous coat. When fully grown, the animal splits into two, and one of the newly formed individuals passes out of the gelatinous sheath, fixes itself to the edge thereof, and secretes itself a fresh gelatinous coat. Thus by repeated division is a branching colony produced.

---

* The term "Metazoa" is used to denote those animals whose bodies are multicellular, as opposed to the unicellular animals, or Protozoa.

The Dinoflagellates are an important group of the Phytomastigophora, since they form a large proportion of the microplankton: that is, the small, free-swimming creatures on which the larger animals in the sea feed. Each is enclosed in a cuirass formed of plates of a substance chemically allied to cellulose. These plates are usually very beautifully decorated. In this group, one flagellum is directed forwards, while the other is permanently lodged in a groove round the centre of the body.

The Zoomastigophora differ mainly from the Phytomastigophora in having no chromatophores ; their mode of feeding is, therefore, exclusively animal in nature. Some live in the sea, others in fresh water, while many are parasitic in the blood of the higher Vertebrates. They feed either by engulfing solid food, or by taking in substances in solution through the general surface of the body. The first group to be considered are the Choanoflagellates. These are sedentary, and are characterised by a funnel-like extension of the protoplasm around the base of the flagellum at the free end of the body. The lashing of the flagellum sets up currents in the collar which are undoubtedly concerned with nutrition. One view is that food is drawn into the collar by the action of the currents, and that waste substances are given off outside it, but according to other authorities the reverse may take place. However this may be, the chief interest of these strange creatures is centred in their resemblance to the collared-cells of sponges. In one genus, *Proterospongia*, the cells are invested in a mass of jelly, and resemble very simple sponges, so that it is thought probable that they represent a link between the Protozoa and the Sponges.

Three examples of
DINOFLAGELLATES

a, Ceratium ; b, Exuviella ; c, Dinophysis.

Some of the Flagellata are parasitic, and give rise to disease in those animals which they infest. For example, the Trypanosomes live in the blood and digestive tracts of the higher animals, including big game, and are responsible for various diseases, among them the scourge of sleeping-sickness. The Trypanosome causing this disease passes part of its life in the gut of the tsetse fly *Glossipina*, by which it is transferred to its Vertebrate hosts. It is harmless except in the case of man and domesticated animals. On the other hand, some Flagellates are indispensable to the well-being of the creatures in whose bodies they live. One, *Trichonympha*, lives in the gut of the termite, where it reduces the wood on which the termite feeds to a form which the insect can assimilate. Indeed, without the

Flagellate the termite is unable to live, and the partnership is one of mutual benefit.   Other partnerships of the same kind are known, and many others suspected where animals feed on matter which, to all intents and purposes, is indigestible.

Class CILIOPHORA

The Ciliophora, or Ciliates, are a large and complex group of Protozoa which differ from all other members of the phylum in that their bodies are covered, to a greater or lesser extent, by cilia, or fine protoplasmic hairs. It is not easy to make a distinction between cilia and flagella, both of which are slender extensions of the protoplasm ; but, broadly speaking, the former are small, short, and numerous, and maintain a constant to-and-fro movement throughout life, while the flagella are long, comparatively few in number, usually only one to each cell, and move in a rotary, whipping manner.   In many of the Ciliophora the whole surface of the body is covered by tracts of cilia ; in some the cilia are restricted to certain parts of the body ; and in others, the Acinetaria, they disappear altogether in the adult stages and are replaced by sucker-like processes.   Another feature which distinguishes the Ciliophora from all other Protozoa, is the presence of two nuclei, a meganucleus and a micronucleus ; the former large, often irregular in shape, and believed to be concerned largely with nutrition, the latter small, and probably controlling the remainder of the vital processes.

The majority of the Ciliophora live in fresh water, some swimming about. or creeping over the surface of the mud by means of their cilia, while others are stalked, and are attached to submerged vegetation, their cilia being used only as a means of obtaining food.   This consists of particles of decaying organic matter, bacteria, or even small Protozoa.   Many feed exclusively on decaying matter and bacteria, and are consequently abundant in foul ponds and rank ditches, their preference for infusions of decaying vegetation having gained for them the title, now no longer used, of Infusoria.   A few are marine, while others live in the intestines, bladder, or blood of higher animals, not parasitically, but, as often as not, exerting a beneficial rather than a harmful influence.

There are some who prefer to regard the Protozoa as noncellular, rather than unicellular animals, in which the differentiation of the body takes place without the intervention of cell-walls.   The best arguments in favour of such a view are to be found in the present group, as we shall see later.

One of the commonest of the Ciliophora, and the one most easily obtained, is *Paramoecium*, the slipper-animalcule.   A sample of water taken in a dipping-bottle from a shallow pond, partially filled with dead leaves, is certain to contain numbers of *Paramoecium*, which may be seen with the naked eye as white specks when the bottle is held up to the light.

The body of *Paramoecium*, unlike that of Amoeba, is constant in shape, although still flexible.   It is spindle-shaped, pointed at one end, and rounded at the other ; and is covered all over with longitudinal tracts of cilia whose constant movement drives the animal through the water with considerable rapidity. On the under-surface of the body, beginning at the front end, is a shallow groove, which extends about half the length of the body and ends in a funnel-shaped depression. Food trapped by cilia lining the gullet is carried into the body in the form of an intermittent stream of particles, where it is received into " food-vacuoles " which arise as required and travel slowly in procession round the body just beneath the surface. As a vacuole progresses round the body, the contained food is slowly digested, until by the time it has completed its circuit and reached a point just behind the gullet, only indigestible matter remains. This is discharged to the exterior, and the vacuole disappears as mysteriously as it arose.

At either end of the body is a contractile vacuole. The first is situated near the front end, and the other almost opposite the hinder limit of the gullet. These are permanent organs which collect the excretory products from the surrounding protoplasm and squirt them out to the exterior.

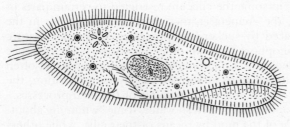

Paramoecium

When seen in the living state, the structure of *Paramoecium* is obscured by the coat of cilia covering the surface of the body. The example shown is seen in optical section.

The protoplasm of the body is differentiated into three well-marked regions : a central granular " endoplasm," forming the bulk of the body, surrounded by a clear " ectoplasm," which is bounded at the surface by a thin cuticle. Immediately beneath the cuticle is a layer of trichocysts, curious structures pointed at each end, concerning which very little is known except that, in response to certain stimuli, they are shot out in the form of long hairs. They may possibly be weapons of offence or defence, but hours of patient watching have revealed no evidence on which to form an opinion as to their true nature.

Reproduction in *Paramoecium* is of two kinds. In asexual reproduction the body divides into two, transversely, both nuclei taking part in the division. This normally takes place twice a day and appears to go on for about three months, by which time the stock begins to lose its vigour. Then, for a while, sexual reproduction takes its place. It seems to be a fundamental principle of life, that no matter how lowly an organism, and how readily it can reproduce asexually, there comes a time when sexual reproduction must take place, in order to rejuvenate the stock. There are instances among the Protozoa in which sexual reproduction has never been observed, but it seems fairly certain that it must take place, at some time or other, or the species would die out from sheer exhaustion of vitality.

Sexual reproduction in *Paramoecium* makes a nearer approach to that of the Metazoa than has been the case in any of the other Protozoa so far considered, and although not strictly comparable with that of the Metazoa, it is at least strongly suggestive thereof. When two *Paramoecia* come together in the sexual process, a mutual exchange takes place, the micronucleus of each divides into four portions, two of which disintegrate, and, of the remainder, one passes over into the body of the second individual while the other is retained. Ultimately, therefore, each individual possesses two micronuclei which later fuse together. The two individuals then separate to continue their normal, independent activities.

Another common Ciliate, *Vorticella*, the Bell-animalcule, is found growing on the stems and leaves of water-weeds. In this form the cilia are restricted to two circlets around the mouth, and the animal, instead of being free-swimming, is stalked. Its shape is that of an inverted bell with the rim fringed with a circlet of cilia, and the mouth closed, but for a crescentic slit on one side, by a disc bearing a similar, but smaller, circlet of cilia. The crescentic slit is the mouth of the animal and leads into a ciliated gullet.

The bell-like body is poised at the end of a long, slender stalk, which slowly contracts, as we watch it, into a corkscrew spiral, stays in this position for a while, then expands to its full length again. This expansion and contraction of the stalk is repeated at more or less regular intervals, and is brought about by the action of a contractile fibre running lengthwise through the stalk. The reason for the movement is unknown.

Asexual reproduction is effected by longitudinal division, in which one half of the bell splits off to swim away, develop a fresh stalk, and form a new individual. The sexual process is even more like that of the Metazoa than is the case in *Paramoecium*, since the two individuals taking part differ in appearance, and may be spoken of as male and female respectively. The male is smaller and free-swimming, and the female larger and stalked. For the rest, the process is the same as in *Paramoecium*.

In some Ciliates of the *Vorticella*-type, the individuals resulting from asexual division remain attached to each other, and form colonies.

The *Acinetaria* are Ciliophora in which the cilia are replaced, in the adult, by a few pin-like suckers. They are mostly stalked, and live mainly on the

Vorticella

FIG. 1.—*Mn*, meganucleus; *mn*, micronucleus; *g*, gullet; *f*, food-vacuoles; *cv*, contractile vacuole; *r*, excretory reservoir; *cf*, contractile fibre; *mf*, muscle fibres.

FIG. 2.—Showing the contractile movements of the stalk.

gills of aquatic animals and on water-weeds. They feed on smaller Protozoa, catching them by means of their suckers. In addition to the usual methods of reproduction, the *Acinetaria* can produce asexually-formed, internal buds, which break loose from the body of the parent and swim about by means of cilia, to settle down eventually as stalked, non-ciliated, suctorial adults. All the members of the group are ciliated in this way, in the early stages of their lives, the cilia being replaced later by suckers.

Class SPOROZOA

The last group of the Protozoa, the Sporozoa, which includes the malarial parasite and the Gregarines, exhibit such a diversity of structure, habits, and developmental characters that it is impossible to consider them in any detail here. The romantic discovery of the malarial parasite, and the manner in which it is transmitted by mosquitoes, has become almost everyday knowledge.

The Sporozoa are entirely parasitic and, as is the case with all parasites, have undergone considerable degeneration. They have no food-vacuoles, this being unnecessary since they feed by absorbing the nutrient fluids of their hosts ; the body is protected by a tough cuticle ; and organs of locomotion, in the shape of flagella, are present only at certain stages in their life-history.

Their developmental cycle consists of three phases. The first is devoted to feeding and growth, and is known as the vegetative or sporont stage. The second stage is one of rapid multiplication when the sporonts conjugate and ultimately divide to form innumerable spores. The spores are protected by a specially resistant coat to protect them from the vicissitudes of the third and last stage, in which they pass out of the body of the host to be transmitted to or picked up by a second host.

Three methods of infection are known. Sometimes the spores are accidentally swallowed by the host in its food ; at other times they are transmitted by an intermediate host, as in the case of the malarial parasite which is transmitted by the mosquito ; while, very rarely, infection is hereditary, the parasites penetrating the eggs of the host before they are laid.

Not all the Sporozoa are harmful to their hosts ; the majority of them are probably quite harmless, but others are capable of causing serious epidemics.

SECTION II

Phylum PORIFERA

(Sponges)

By M. BURTON, M.SC.

GENERAL CHARACTERISTICS

FOR a long time the exact nature of sponges was subject to doubt, and it was not until early in the last century that they were universally accorded a place in the Animal Kingdom. Aristotle was the first to give a scientific account of them, and both he and Pliny were undecided as to whether they were plant or animal. Eventually they came to the conclusion that they were neither, but something midway between. This uncertainty persisted for a long time, and was made the worse by the beliefs of the naturalists of the sixteenth and seventeenth centuries, of which the most fantastic was the suggestion that they were solidified sea-foam. Another curious belief, which arose from the fact that worms are often found sheltering in the canals of sponges, was that they were massive shelters built by the worms themselves as a refuge from their enemies.

The first real step towards an understanding was made by Dr. Robert Grant, a naturalist of the early nineteenth century, who took some soft shapeless crusts found growing on the rocks by the seashore, looking more like pieces of bread soaked in water than living creatures, and placed them in a dish of sea-water. To his surprise, the small round holes on the surface of the crusts proved to be active craters which belched forth jets of water. These crusts, now known as the " Crumb-o'-Bread " sponges, may be found at almost any point on the coasts of Britain, growing on rocks, pier-piles, seaweeds, and shells just below high-tide mark.   Since this sponge is so common that it may be seen and examined during even a casual walk on the seashore, and since it resembles in its anatomy the many thousands of different kinds of sponges found throughout the world, including the Bath Sponge, whose skeleton is in daily use throughout at least the civilised world, it will be convenient to study it in detail, in order to understand more exactly what a sponge is and how it lives.

THEIR CONSTRUCTION

The yellowish-white masses of the Crumb-o'-Bread Sponge bear at certain points on their upper surface a number of circular craters, or vents measuring about a quarter of an inch in diameter.   Scattered generally over the rest of the surface, but invisible to the naked eye, are thousands of minute pores. The pores open into minute canals which pierce the tissues of the sponge in all directions, branching as they go, converting the inside of the sponge into a labyrinth of branching canaliculi.   At a variable distance below the surface each of the finer subdivisions of these branching systems of canals ends in a spherical chamber known as a flagellated chamber,

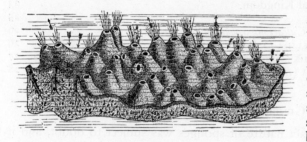

CRUMB-O'-BREAD SPONGE
The arrows indicate the manner in which the water enters through the pores scattered over the surface and leaves by the crater-like vents.

owing to its walls being lined with flagellated cells of a peculiar construction known as collared-cells.   Each collared-cell consists of a round body with a funnel-like collar at one end, from the bottom of which passes out a long, whip-like flagellum, the collar and the flagellum being merely extensions of the protoplasm from the body of the cell.   On the opposite side another minute canal leads away from the flagellated chamber, penetrating the tissues of the sponge before joining up with other similar canals to form larger canals, which in turn unite to form still larger canals that empty into a cloaca, and this communicates with the exterior by one of the vents already noted.   The canals travelling towards the chambers are known as inhalant canals, those away from them as exhalant canals.

In a living sponge, the flagella of the collared-cells are in constant motion, whirling round with a whip-like movement which draws a constant current of water through the sponge, the water being sucked in at the pores, drawn through the inhalant canals and flagellated chambers, forced through the exhalant canals, and out through the vents with considerable force. This stream of water is the life-stream of the animal, bringing in oxygen and the minute particles of organic matter on which sponges are believed to feed, and carrying out the waste substances.

The manner in which sponges feed is not yet completely known. In some the food-particles are caught in the collars of the choanocytes, while in others they are probably ingested by the cells lining the canals or by the tissues lying between the canals. There is reason to believe, also, that some sponges feed partially or wholly on substances in solution.

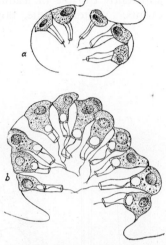

Sponges are singularly free from enemies, the animals which attack or feed on them being remarkably few in number. This freedom from competition accounts, doubtless, for the fact that they have survived from the very earliest geological times almost unchanged. The only adaptations they show are those which concern the situations in which they grow, adaptations which accommodate them to the nature of the sea-bottom, and to the strength and character of the currents to which they are exposed. It also accounts for the absence of any means of offence or defence, and probably, too, for

Flagellated chambers of (*a*) Crumb-o'-Bread Sponge and (*b*) a Freshwater Sponge (after Vosmaer).

the complete absence of any form of sense-organs. Indeed, nobody has so far been able with certainty to discover in them any form of nerve-cell, and only in a few isolated instances do they exhibit any response to external stimuli. The belief held by sponge-fishers that sponges will shrink as if in pain when plucked from the sea-bottom has been proved to be erroneous.

Relationship to the Animal Kingdom

The relationship of sponges to the rest of the Animal Kingdom is very obscure. Although they are usually regarded as Metazoa, the individualistic character of their cells shows that they are little more than colonies of Protozoa, similar to that seen in *Volvox*, and that they are not so much individuals as colonies of cells, in which each cell is more or less independent of the others, able to change its shape and function as the occasion arises, but in which all work together to make one harmonious whole. For this reason, among others, some authors prefer to regard them as constituting a separate sub-kingdom, the Parazoa.

Two things will serve to make more clear this conflict between the individualities of the animal as a whole and of the cells composing it. If a piece of living sponge be taken and pressed through a piece of fine muslin, the individual cells will be separated and will pass through the meshes of the muslin as a fine emulsion. Seen under the microscope, they are all alike, having taken on the form of an Amoeba discussed previously, and are all moving about quite freely and independently of each other, each one apparently capable of leading an independent existence, for a while at all events. After a time, however, the cells begin to reassemble in small masses which, by the coalescence of adjacent masses, eventually form a new sponge, still very small but complete in every detail. Bearing this independence of the individual cells in mind, it is of interest to contemplate the complete and harmonious co-operation of the cells of the beautiful Venus' Flower Basket, by which is built a skeleton so wonderful that it has been pronounced " the finest piece of engineering structure ever known, combining absolute efficiency with a minimum of material."

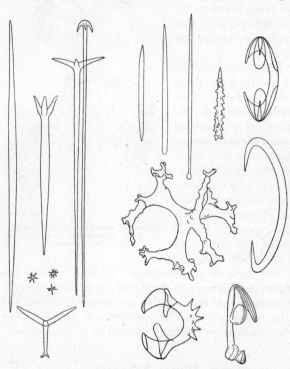

GROUP OF SPONGE SPICULES (highly magnified)

This group represents but a few of the many forms assumed by the spicules composing the skeletons of sponges.

Another difficulty in defining the relationships of the sponges concerns the tissues of which they are composed. In this respect, also, sponges have nothing in common with the rest of the Animal Kingdom. Most animals, in their embryonic state, possess an inner layer of tissue lining the whole of the digestive tract, called the endoderm, and an outer or surface layer, the ectoderm, while the muscles and other tissues between are formed from a third layer, the mesoderm. These three layers are quite definite and clearly defined even in the early stages of the embryo. The most primitive of the Coelenterata, the most lowly forms of animal life after sponges, have a well-defined endoderm and an ectoderm, and the beginnings at least of a mesoderm. Sponges possess an outer skin representing an ectoderm, and the water-canals are lined by a similar layer, but it is almost impossible to make anything in the nature of a comparison between the tissues of a sponge and those of other Metazoa.

Such loose agglomerations of cells as compose the bodies of sponges would never be capable of assuming the complicated shapes they do were it not that they are able to produce a skeleton for their support. This, like the cells which produce it, is a most adaptable structure, and consists either of an intricate system of horny fibres or of diversely shaped spicules composed either of silica or carbonate of lime. The spicules take the form of needles, crosses, anchors, stars, and so on, and are placed in such a position that they act as a scaffolding for the support of the cells. Many are microscopic in size, others are several inches long, while the curious *Monorrhaphis* has one spicule over a yard in length, which stands erect with its base buried in the mud and the sponge itself embracing the middle of the spicule. The materials necessary for their construction are extracted from the water, where they exist in such minute quantities that it is only by the most careful chemical tests that their presence may be detected.

How long sponges live is still largely a matter for speculation. Those living in fresh water, or in the shallow inshore waters round the coast, frequently die off as the winter approaches. Others are known to live for seven years or more ; while still others, judging by their large size, have probably lived for twenty years or so.

REPRODUCTION

At certain periods of the year germ-cells appear, ova and spermatozoa, or at least it is presumed that the latter are formed although their detection is no easy matter. How the ova are fertilised, moreover, is not precisely known, but it is presumed that the spermatozoa from a neighbouring sponge are carried in by the inhalant currents of water and wander through the body until they come in contact with an ovum. Once fertilised the ovum begins to divide, first into two, then into four, eight, and so on, until a spherical mass of cells is produced. This process of division, known as segmentation, is the usual method of growth in embryos throughout the Metazoa. The mass of cells so formed becomes ciliated and begins to revolve, moved round by the concerted action of the cilia. Later it finds its way out of the parent sponge into the surrounding sea, swims about for a matter of a few hours and settles down on the bottom to grow into a new sponge.

Often, however, small buds are produced on the surface of the sponge, by the simple growing-out of the cells in the immediate neighbourhood. When fully grown, they become constricted off and float away to settle down in their turn and grow into new sponges.

These simple organisms abound in great numbers in every part of the globe, from pole to equator, from between tide-marks down to the abysmal depths of the ocean. Round our own coasts they are most abundant where the shore is marked with rock-pools at low tide. The freshwater forms abound in rivers and lakes the world over, even in the lakes formed in the craters of extinct volcanoes which frequently lie as much as two miles above sea-level. Though often mere shapeless lumps, some assume a beautiful tree-like form, while others are shaped like cups, vases, goblets, or fans. Many, particularly the shallow-water sponges, are brightly coloured, yellow, green, red, orange, blue, and purple, and contribute in no small measure to the luxuriance of the so-called sea-gardens.

Sponges are divided into three orders :

Order CALCAREA

(*Calcareous Sponges*)

The first group, the Calcarea, with spicules of carbonate of lime, are rich in numbers though usually of small size, and are confined for the most part to the shallow seas. One of its members, *Leucosolenia coriacea*, looking like a low-growing tangle of orange or yellow threads, may be seen on rocks exposed at low tide in company with the Crumb-o'-Bread Sponge and the blood-red *Hymeniacidon sanguinea*. *Sycon ciliatum*, a tiny, exquisite vase-shaped sponge, with a fringe of shining spicules round the mouth, and measuring from one-quarter to three-quarters of an inch in length, may be found on the fronds of seaweed left stranded at low tide.

CARPENTER'S GLASS SPONGE

Is typical of the delicate beauty shown by the deep-sea Hexactinellida (one half nat. size).

Order HEXACTINELLIDA

(*Siliceous Sponges*)

The Hexactinellida, with skeletons formed of six-rayed spicules of silica, are typically deep-sea forms, rarely found above the 100-fathom line, but penetrating to waters four miles deep in some cases. This order contains some of the most beautiful of sponges, and includes the Venus' Flower Basket already referred to, the Glass-rope Sponge, Carpenter's Glass Sponge, and many other handsome forms. To this group belongs also the curious *Monorrhaphis* with the yard-long spicule.

Order TETRAXONIDA

(*Siliceous Sponges*)

The Tetraxonida, with four-rayed spicules of silica, are by far the most numerous, including the Crumb-o'-Bread Sponge already referred to, and *Chalina oculata*, a small tree-like form, both of which may be abundantly cast up by the sea after the autumn storms; the Neptune's Cup, a goblet-shaped sponge often reaching a height of four feet or more, and found abundantly around the coasts of the Dutch East Indies; the Sea-orange, *Tethya lyncurium*, probably the only sponge in which true muscle-fibre has been found; the fresh-water sponges, and the burrowing *Cliona celata*. The last two must be considered in slightly more detail. Freshwater sponges are greenish, somewhat slimy, masses found on lock-gates, on submerged sticks and leaves of the larger aquatic plants, and on the under-surfaces of stones. They are chiefly interesting in that, unlike all other sponges, they form resistant winter-buds, or gemmules, which sink to the bottom of the river or pond when the parent dies and in the spring grow out into fresh sponges. The gemmules are protected against the vicissitudes of the winter by a tough coat further strengthened by a layer of spicules.

Cliona celata, and its allies, bore into the shells of molluscs, particularly the oyster, and thereby do great damage to oyster-beds, although not actually attacking the animals living within, by rendering the shells unsightly and unfit for market. Oyster-shells with small round holes puncturing the whole of the surface may be found on the seashore at almost any point on our coasts.

Cliona—The Shell-boring Sponge

The centre figure shows a mollusc shell attacked by a Boring Sponge. The bottom figure shows an oyster shell with the galleries excavated by the sponge exposed. After a period of time spent within the shell the sponge grows enormously, forming a large yellow mass a foot or more in diameter, as shown in the top figure (much reduced).

B 2

Order Euceratosa
(*Bath and Commercial Sponges*)

The last order of sponges, and the most important to man, is that known as the Euceratosa, whose members possess skeletons of a fine network of spongin-fibres, and include the many different kinds of bath and commercial sponges. The main grounds for the world's supply of bath sponges are practically confined to two main centres, the Eastern Mediterranean and the West Indies. The sponges are gathered by divers, who detach them from the bottom with knives, or tridents. The first step in the treatment of a bath sponge is to get rid of the jelly-like flesh in which the skeleton is embedded, for the bath sponge, as we know it, is only the skeleton. This is done by leaving it exposed to the action of the sea until the flesh has rotted, when it is beaten and washed clean with hoses, and finally bleached. Bath sponges may be grown from cuttings, but since these take some seven years to mature it was not until the stocks began to show signs of depletion that sponge-farming, as an industry, was seriously considered. Nowadays, however, considerable progress is being made in this direction, particularly in the West Indies.

As has already been said, sponges have few enemies. This is not surprising in view of the hard and distasteful nature of their skeletons. On the other hand, we find them being used by all sorts of marine animals, worms, starfish, and various sorts of crustacea as shelters. Certain species of crab are permanently covered by sponges growing on their carapaces, a form which may be assumed to aid them in escaping their enemies or in catching their prey.

The influence of sponges on the lives of men goes farther than their use in surgery, in painting, and in the thousand and one ways in which they are used for cleaning purposes. Iodine, which is abundantly present in some sponges, was formerly obtained entirely from these animals. The extensive beds of flints in the Chalk which proved so useful to our early ancestors, and even now find their way into road-making, building, and pottery works, were, according to some authorities, formed from the dissolved skeletons of the siliceous sponges which flourished in the seas of earlier geological times. Nor must we forget that it was by a study of the behaviour of sponge-cells that Metchnikoff was led to his discoveries which to-day form the basis of the treatment of all bacteriological diseases.

SECTION III

Phylum COELENTERATA

(*Jelly-fishes, Sea-anemones, and Corals*)

By M. Burton, M.Sc.

GENERAL CHARACTERISTICS

ALL the members of the Coelenterata, however great may be the differences in their external appearance—and the group embraces forms as unlike as sea-firs, jelly-fishes, sea-anemones and corals—have two fundamental characters in common : the body has the form of a simple sac, with a single opening at one end, and its walls are composed of two layers of tissue only, an outer ectoderm and an inner endoderm. Between these two is a third structureless layer known as the mesogloea, but as this does not constitute a tissue in the ordinary sense of the word we speak of the Coelenterates as diploblastic, or two-layered, animals. This is important, as it constitutes a fundamental difference between them and the rest of the Metazoa, with the exception of the Sponges. From the latter they differ mainly in the possession of a definite, though simple, digestive cavity.

In addition, the Coelenterates are all, with the exception of the Ctenophora, armed with characteristic stinging-cells, known as nematocysts, or nettle-cells, a thing unique among the Metazoa. These nematocysts are rounded or oval capsules filled with a poisonous fluid, and containing a long, hollow thread. Each capsule is embedded in a cell of the ectoderm, bearing at its outer end a short bristle-like spine, which, when touched, contracts and causes the coiled thread to be shot out with considerable force, piercing the body of whatever has come in contact with it. The poisonous fluid flows down the hollow thread into the body of the captive, paralysing it or, in the case of a very small creature, killing it. Large animals so stung can, of course, wrench themselves free and make off, bearing the threads of the nematocysts still embedded in their tissues, but small animals are unable to escape, and are carried to the mouth and swallowed. The nematocysts serve as weapons of both offence and defence. Although the Ctenophora have no nematocysts, they are armed with cells of curious structure known as lassoo-cells, which serve the same purpose.

A fourth peculiarity of the phylum is that a large number of its members exhibit the phenomenon known as the Alternation of Generations, in which a sedentary or hydroid generation, sexless, and multiplying only by means of buds, alternates with a sexual, free-swimming, or medusoid generation, giving rise to ciliated larvae, as in the case of *Obelia*, which will be discussed later. The hydroid generation is a plant-like colony growing on rocks, or shells, from which medusae or small jelly-fish are budded off. The medusae swim about for a while and produce eggs and spermatozoa, by whose union ciliated larvae are formed, the larvae fixing themselves to the rocks and growing into a fresh hydroid generation. So the process goes on, each hydroid generation being succeeded by a medusoid generation and *vice versa*.

In some Coelenterates the alternation is incomplete, while in other forms one or the other generation is entirely suppressed, but even in those in which only the one generation persists, there is reason to believe that at one time they or their ancestors regularly completed the cycle.

NEMATOCYSTS

The nematocyst (*b*) contains a coiled thread-like tube which, as the result of appropriate stimulus, is shot forth (*a*); (*c*) shows how all the stinging cells are connected up by nerve-fibres.

There is yet another way in which the Coelenterates differ from the rest of the Metazoa, with the single exception of the Echinoderms : they are radiate, or radially symmetrical, animals. That is to say, no matter in what direction a Coelenterate polyp is cut through the centre, the two halves will always be identical provided the section is made vertically.

The Coelenterata are divided into four orders : (1) the Hydrozoa, including the Sea-firs, Portuguese Man-o'-War, and the Freshwater Hydra ; (2) the Scyphozoa, or Jelly-fish ; (3) the Anthozoa, including Sea-anemones and Corals ; and (4) the Ctenophora, or Comb-bearers.

Order HYDROZOA

(*Sea-firs, Portuguese Man-o'-War, and the Freshwater Hydra*)

The Hydrozoa are mostly of small size, and are distinguished by the predominance of the hydroid generation. The only other order with which they might be confused is the order Anthozoa, in which the hydroid generation only is represented, but from these they are separated by the complete absence of gastral filaments.

A typical member of this order is *Corymorpha*. In this the polyps shown in the adjoining illustration are solitary, each one borne on a short stem of which the lower end is buried in the fine sand of the sea-bottom. The mouth is surrounded by a ring of fine tentacles, and a second ring of larger, stouter tentacles is situated halfway down the body. Immediately above the second ring of tentacles is a cluster of buds, each of which will develop into a free-swimming, bell-shaped medusa such as those that are seen swimming around the polyps in the illustration. Some of the medusae will produce eggs; others produce spermatozoa which are shed into the sea to find their way to ova borne by the female medusae and fertilise them. By a process of cell-division the fertilised ova then develop into ciliated larvae which escape into the sea, swim about for a while by means of their cilia, and then settle down on the bottom to grow into fresh polyps. Thus is the alternation of generations completed.

The way in which *Corymorpha* lives may be taken as typical of all Coelenterates with the exception of the jelly-fish, which must be specially considered later. The tentacles, heavily armed with nematocysts, are continually waving about around the body of the polyp.

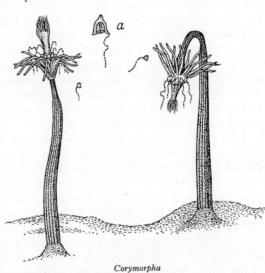

Corymorpha

Two individuals rising erect with their bases in the sand. Just above the ring of large tentacles is a group of medusa buds, while two medusae, recently set free, are swimming close by. (*a*) A medusa slightly enlarged.

Sooner or later a small organism, perhaps a crustacean, touches one or other of the tentacles as it swims past and is immediately stung and held captive by the threads of the discharged nematocysts, and carried over to the mouth, which protrudes slightly to meet it. Once inside the body the cells of the endoderm secrete digestive juices around it, and the prey is slowly assimilated, the indigestible parts and the waste matter arising from digestion being passed out again through the mouth. Respiration—the other important process necessary to life—goes on over the whole surface of the body. There are no definite sense-organs : and the movements of the tentacles and other parts of the body are controlled by nerve-cells scattered throughout the ectoderm.

The solitary condition of the polyps of *Corymorpha* is somewhat unusual among the Hydrozoa. In most cases they form colonies by budding. The original polyp formed from the ciliated larva gives off a bud, which, completing its growth, remains permanently attached to the parent and in turn gives off another bud, and so the colony grows. One of the commonest among these colony-forming Hydrozoa, and one of the most instructive, is the tiny *Obelia* found growing on rocks, shells, and seaweeds around our coasts. In this the colony consists of erect branches of about the thickness of sewing thread, with rows of tiny polyps on each side. The polyps themselves are very like those of *Corymorpha*, but have only one ring of tentacles corresponding to that around the centre of the body. They do not bear clusters of buds, but at certain intervals along the branches there are curious transparent structures shaped like tall Roman urns, with a rod of tissue running up the centre, directly continuous with the tissue of the rest of the colony. These are known as gonothecae, or reproductive cups. On the central rod, or blastostyle, small buds grow out. Beginning as minutest " pin-heads," they gradually increase in size, flattening as they grow, until finally they become saucer-shaped. They then become detached and escape through the mouth of the gonotheca as free-swimming medusae, which will in turn produce eggs and thus complete the cycle of generations.

Two very interesting things emerge from a study of *Obelia*. In the first place, a division of labour has been effected. Some of the polyps are entirely concerned with the nutrition of the colony, while the rest are entirely concerned with reproduction. The second point is more important. The medusae produced by *Obelia* are umbrella-shaped, with a ring of tentacles round the margin of the umbrella, and an elongated mouth protruding from the under-surface, where the handle of an umbrella would be. If now it were possible to take one of the nutritive polyps of the colony and stretch it out in the region of the tentacles so that the cylindrical body of the polyp became flattened or umbrella-shaped, we should have an exact copy of the free-swimming medusa. In other words, the medusa is a free-swimming polyp, but, nevertheless, slightly specialised to meet the more active nature of its career, in that it has developed several small balancing organs around the margin of the umbrella, and, further, the mesogloea has become considerably enlarged and encloses large cavities filled with a gas, giving added buoyancy and a more jelly-like appearance than the normal polyp. These facts will be seen to have considerable significance when we come to consider the true jelly-fishes or Scyphozoa.

A somewhat different type of colony is produced by *Hydractinia*, which habitually grows on the shell inhabited by a hermit-crab. Instead of forming an erect, branching colony, it coats the shell with a layer of tissue from which a number of polyps grow up. These are of two kinds, as in *Obelia*, nutritive and reproductive. The latter consist simply of a short stalk with a cluster of rounded capsules near the upper end, but no free-swimming medusae are formed, for the capsules are themselves degenerate medusae, which never become detached, but which produce ova and spermatozoa while still attached to the parent stock, the larvae developing direct from the eggs *in situ*.

In the green *Hydra* of our ponds and streams the medusoid phase has been completely suppressed and the eggs develop directly from the outer

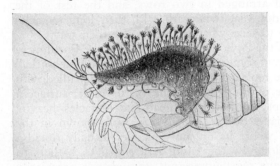

Colony of *Hydractinia* on the shell of a whelk inhabited by a hermit-crab.

layer of cells of the polyp, which, by its cylindrical body with a mouth at the upper end surrounded by a ring of hollow tentacles, bears a strong superficial resemblance to the sea-anemones. The absence of gastral filaments, however, marks it definitely as one of the Hydrozoa. Another hint as to its true relationship is given by the fact that it frequently gives off lateral buds which, were they to remain attached, would in course of time produce a colony simulating that of *Obelia*. Usually the buds become detached as soon as they attain the polyp stage with a mouth and a ring of tentacles, and begin to lead an independent existence. Nevertheless, this animal is of interest in showing how the alternation of generations is abridged and, at the same time, why Anthozoa, in which medusae are never developed, may be regarded as related to a form such as *Obelia* in which there is a very complicated life-cycle.

Physophora

With its double row of swimming bells above the group of nutritive polyps. The long stinging filaments below catch the prey, contract and carry it up to the nutritive polyps.

Hydra has a still further interest for the zoologist, for, as its name suggests, it has marvellous powers of regeneration. Not only can it replace mutilated, or completely amputated, tentacles, but if the body be cut into a number of small pieces, each piece will develop into a new polyp.

In addition to the colonies of Hydrozoa already considered, there are a number, known as the Siphonophora, which are always free-swimming ;

that is, in which the hydroid generation itself is free-swimming. The simplest among them is *Diphyes*. In this form two of the polyps have lost their tentacles and have become simply inverted bells, acting as floats to the rest of the colony, which consists of groups of nutritive and reproductive polyps depending from a slender stem hanging down from the floating bells. The next genus, *Physophora*, is very like *Diphyes*, except that the swimming bells are more numerous and arranged in two rows, and the rest of the polyps are bunched together immediately beneath, with their long tentacles trailing along in the sea ready to seize whatever may come their way.

Probably the best known of the Siphonophora is *Physalia*, the Portuguese Man-o'-War, or, as it is known in some parts of the world, " the Bluebottle." In this the swimming bells are replaced by an elongated bladder filled with gas that floats on the surface of the sea, carrying on its under-surface a number of flask-shaped polyps from which thread-like tentacles heavily armed with stinging cells hang down. *Physalia* is well known in the warmer waters of the world, where its ungainly bladder, usually tinted a delicate blue, gently borne along by the wind, is a signal to bathers to beware ; for its stings can have most unpleasant, though not necessarily fatal, results.

In the Siphonophora the medusoid generation is usually suppressed, the larvae developing in the reproductive capsules attached to the colony.

Order SCYPHOZOA
(*True Jelly-fishes*)

In the Scyphozoa, or true jelly-fish, it is the medusoid generation that predominates, the hydroid generation, although playing an important part, being subordinated to it. The common jelly-fish, *Aurelia aurita*, of the British coasts is a very good example of the order, for it is often to be seen during the summer months stranded in thousands on the beach as the tide goes out ; and there must be few who have not cautiously examined specimens as they lay on the sand. The smooth, gelatinous body is fringed round its margin with a row of delicate tentacles, while on the under-surface, near the centre are four opaque, horseshoe-shaped organs that show up clearly through the almost transparent body. These are the gonads, ovaries or testes, according to whether the jelly-fish is female or male, and are lodged in four pouches of the capacious digestive cavity which opens on the under-surface by a squarish, somewhat tubular mouth.

From the digestive cavity a number of faint lines radiate out to the margin of the body ; these mark food-canals, which empty into another canal running round the circumference of the umbrella, and serve for the distribution of food. Actually there are sixteen of these radial canals, although the manner in which some of them branch suggests that they are more numerous than this. Eight of them are unbranched, and divide the body into as many equal sectors, each of which is occupied by one of the other much-branched canals. At the middle point on the margin of each sector is a slight notch, where the sense-organs are lodged. Each of these contains a pigment-spot, probably sensitive to light, a " lithite," or concretion of limestone, which acts no doubt as a balancing organ, and a small depression or pit whose function is not properly understood.

If we turn the jelly-fish on to its back, we see that the corners of the mouth are produced into four fleshy tentacles, each consisting of a folded membrane abundantly armed with stinging cells. These probably serve as weapons of offence, as well as for the capture of prey, although there is good reason to believe that many of the Scyphozoa normally feed in a somewhat different manner from those Coelenterates we have already considered. As they move through the water by the rhythmic contraction and expansion of the body, induced by the action of bands of muscle-fibres running round the edge, numerous small organisms are caught within the umbrella and, becoming ensnared in a layer of mucus which coats the surface, are gradually brought together in small masses by the action of numerous cilia and passed on to the mouth.

Despite the presence of more complicated sense-organs and a more highly organised digestive cavity, a glance is sufficient to show

Aurelia Aurita

The common jelly-fish of the British coasts, viewed from beneath. *MA*, the four large oral tentacles; *GK*, the reproductive organs; *T*, fringe of marginal tentacles; *RG*, system of radical vessels; *GH*, openings of the subgenital pits; *RK*, sense-organs.

that *Aurelia* is just a larger edition of the individuals of the medusoid generation of *Obelia*. The hydroid generation, here called the scyphistoma stage, is, however, very much reduced.

When the horseshoe-shaped gonads are ripe, their contents are shed into the sea, where the eggs are fertilised. Each then develops into a hollow, ciliated larva which, after swimming about for a while, settles on the sea-bottom. Then a change takes place. The lower end becomes rather slender, and a mouth appears at the upper end, surrounded by a ring of tentacles, the scyphistoma so formed having much the appearance of a nutritive polyp of *Obelia*. The resemblance is heightened by the fact that a scyphistoma will occasionally multiply by budding. Usually, however, when it has reached a height of about half an inch, several constrictions appear running completely around the body beneath the ring of tentacles, and these become deeper and deeper until the body of the scyphistoma looks like a pile of saucers supported on a short stalk. In time their edges become deeply indentated, and, beginning at the top, each saucer in turn becomes detached, to swim away and grow eventually into a mature jelly-fish.

Rhizostoma is a close relative of *Aurelia*, differing mainly in the more complicated structure of the mouth-tentacles. It is an occasional visitor to our shores. In fact, all jelly-fish are very similar in structure, differing from each other in comparatively small details of shape and size. In some the body is helmet-shaped, in others it has the form of a hollow cube ; in some the tentacles are short, in others long, and so on. With the exception of *Craspidacusta*, which is freshwater, they are all marine and free-swimming, and the great majority are usually transparent, but the gonads, tentacles, and radial canals, or even the body itself, may be highly coloured. One form, *Pelagia noctiluca*, is phosphorescent.

Contrary to the conditions obtaining in the remainder of the Scyphozoa, one of its members, *Lucernaria*, is never free-swimming except in a limited sense. This is habitually fixed to the bottom of the sea, with the opening of the umbrella uppermost and the base constricted into a short stalk. As and when occasion demands it moves about by a sort of creeping movement.

The body of a typical jelly-fish consists of some ninety-nine per cent. of water ; a fact which can be readily demonstrated by leaving one of these animals on the seashore for a few hours, when it will disappear, leaving only the slightest traces of its former existence. Under these circumstances, therefore, it is not surprising that fossil remains are not frequently found. Nevertheless, very complete impressions of ancient jelly-fish, showing all the essential details of their structure, are found in the Upper Jurassic limestone of Solenhofen, Bavaria.

Order ANTHOZOA

(*Sea-anemones and Corals*)

The third order of the Coelenterata, the Anthozoa, is as well known as the Scyphozoa through two of its members, the sea-anemones and the corals. The most barren seashores, provided there is a small rock or a breakwater somewhere along its course, will yield a few sea-anemones ; while in the pools left by the receding tide on rocky coasts they form veritable sea-gardens. Perhaps in the sea-anemones more than in other Coelenterates we can appreciate the action of the early naturalists in including under the comprehensive title of Zoophytes a whole host of sedentary animals having a superficial resemblance to plants, for the sea-anemone, with its rosette of thick, fleshy tentacles, the whole brightly, often variously, coloured, does recall certain of our more familiar garden flowers, especially the dahlias and the like.

Sea-anemones present much the same plan of structure as the zooids of *Obelia*, or the scyphistoma of the jelly-fishes. There is the same cylindrical body, with a mouth at the apex surrounded by a ring of tentacles, the same simple digestive cavity, with a single opening, while the tentacles are armed with the characteristic nettle-cells. On the other hand, the capacity of the digestive cavity is considerably increased, and this is where the Anthozoa differ from all other Coelenterates, by the development of a number of mesenteries, or thin sheets of tissue which hang down from the roof of the cavity like curtains, thus offering a greater surface for the secretion of digestive juices, and the assimilation of the products of digestion. The medusoid generation has been entirely suppressed, the larvae developing directly from eggs and spermatozoa contained within the body of the hydroid generation.

The Anthozoa are mostly marine, a few only being found in brackish water, and include, besides the sea-anemones and corals, the sea-fans and sea-pens. The polyps, whether single as in the sea-anemone, or colonial as in the corals, are built on much the same plan, consisting of a cylindrical body with a slit-like mouth at the upper end, surrounded by one or more rings of hollow tentacles. The mouth leads, by a tubular gullet, into the interior of the body which constitutes a large gastral cavity, with the mouth as the sole opening. The compartments formed by the mesenteries communicate with each other or with the hollow tentacles, while the edges of the mesenteries are thickened to form digestive filaments. There are no special sense-organs, and the nervous system consists of a few isolated sense-cells.

The germ-cells develop on the mesenteries, and, when ripe, are shed into the sea where the fertilised eggs develop into hollow, ciliated larvae which swim about for a while before settling down to grow into adults. Thus there is no medusoid stage, the reverse to what is found among the jelly-fish, where the hydroid is almost lost. A few viviparous Anthozoa are known, and in these the eggs develop into larvae within the body of the parent.

The Anthozoa are divided into two groups : the Alcyonaria, with eight mesenteries and eight tentacles ; and the Zoantharia, with mesenteries and tentacles in multiples of six. These last, being the most important members of the group, must be described at the expense of the less important Alcyonaria, which include the strange Sea-pens, Sea-fans, and the precious Coral.

Sea-anemones, by reason of their flower-like form and brilliant colours, are among the best known and most abundant animals of the seashore. They must be few who have not found these brilliant, many-pointed stars in rock-pools. But as the tide goes out a big change takes place in their appearance, for, with tentacles drawn into the body out of harm's way and reduced to half their former size, they look like mere masses of coloured jelly.

Harmless as is the appearance of sea-anemones even when fully expanded, the batteries of nematocysts, or stinging cells, in the tentacles are a constant source of danger to the small creatures swimming around. Their potential aggressiveness has led to some curious cases of co-operation, or symbiosis, between sea-anemones and other animals. The hermit-crab, for example, frequently carries a sea-anemone on the disused whelk-shell which forms his movable home. The crab probably obtains a measure of protection from the presence of his formidable companion, while the anemone gains by being transported from place to place, and doubtless also by picking up stray fragments of the crab's meals.

Another interesting member of the Zoantharia is *Minyas*. In this animal the base of the body is converted into an air-chamber, enabling the animal to lead a free-swimming existence at the surface of the sea.

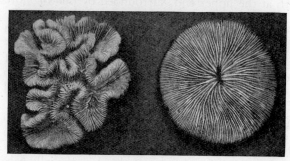

STONY CORALS

Three examples of the skeletons of stony corals, stripped of the living tissues.

In the Madreporaria, or White Stony-Corals, including the reef-building corals, the structure of the polyps is very similar to that of the sea-anemones. The most important difference lies in the fact that they build a skeleton of carbonate of lime for the support of their delicate tissues. While the reef-building corals are confined to the warm seas within 30° north of the Equator, and are therefore unknown in British waters, a few of the Stony-Corals are found in the waters of the North Atlantic. Such is the Devonshire Cup-Coral, a solitary coral resembling a sea-anemone in outward appearance. There is the same ring of tentacles enclosing a disc, with a slit-like mouth in the centre; but the surface of the disc is marked by faint lines which radiate from the mouth. If the surface of the coral be touched, it is found that these faint lines mark the edges of thin, stony plates. In effect, the polyp is seated on a stony cup of its own making whose cavity is

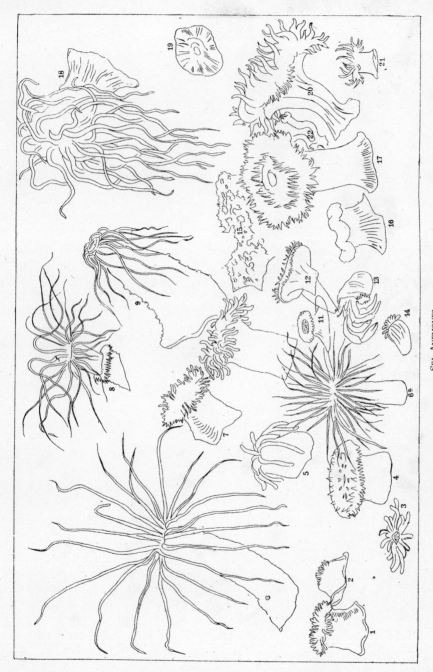

SEA ANEMONES.

1, 2. *Actinia equina.* 3, 5, 14. *Eloactis mazelii.* 4. *Ragactis pulchra.* 6, 6a, 8. *Cerianthus membranaceus.* 7, 19. *Actinia cari.* 9. *Cladactis cortae.* 10. *Cereactis aurantiaca.* 11, 12, 16, 17. *Heliactis bellis.* 13. *Adamsia palliata.* 15. *Astroides calycularis* (a coral). 18. *Anemonia sulcata.* 20. *Aiptasia mutabilis.* 21. *Bunodes.* 22. A Tubicolous Worm.

ood, and capable of being retracted into deep cavities at the sides of the y. The body itself is divided lengthwise by eight equal, crescent-shaped bands, along which are set rows of comb-like plates with fringed cilia which act as paddles, propelling the animal through the water.

At one end is a mouth leading into a gullet and a stomach, from which arise a number of blind canals underlying the comb-plates, while at the other end is a small balancing organ.

The majority of Ctenophora are more or less spherical, or oval, rarely helmet-shaped, but the beautiful, crystal-clear Venus' Girdle has the form of a ribbon. There are no stalked forms, and budding is quite unknown among them, as the young develop direct from eggs.

Although superficially resembling jelly-fishes there are a number of obvious differences. In the first place, they have no nematocysts, and this probably constitutes the biggest gulf between them and the remainder of the Coelenterates. Further, the mouth is not situated at the end of a manubrium as in the jelly-fish and other typical Coelenterates, and their method of progression shows no sign of the characteristic pulsations of a jelly-fish. On the other hand, they do show marked similarities to some of the Flatworms, particularly well shown in the Red Sea Ctenophoran, *Tjalfiella*, which, while retaining e peculiarities of the group, swims about only in the early stages of e, but becomes flattened later, forsaking its pelagic life to creep about a-bottom.

f the helmet-
d Ctenophora.
ongitudinal
ngs are rows of
arranged in a
of "combs,"
e vibrations of
the animal
s.

SEA ANEMONES.

Pl. 2.

filled with a system of vertical plates, or septa, whi
digestive mesenteries.

This system of radiating plates is characteristic
whether they be solitary, as the Devonshire Cup-Cora
colonies, as in the *Dendrophyllia*, or form massive colo
in diameter, and containing many thousands of polyp
Coral, where the cups have become united into mear

Coral-reefs are of three kinds : shore-reefs, fr
continents and islands ; encircling, or barrier reefs,
stretching for miles parallel with the coast, as in the
Australia ; and atolls, which are circular reefs en
great diversity in the form of the colonies, and the
together with the gaudy fishes, sponges, sea-cucumbe
with them, give the reefs a beauty which equals any
culturist's skill can produce on land.   In the words o
water being clear round the edges, a new creation .
to our view.   We had wheat-sheaves, mushrooms,
leaves, and a variety of other forms, glowing under
of every shade betwixt green, purple, brown, and w

The top of the living coral is covered with a co
which fall small organisms and particles of mud, bec
in it.   Such portions as are fit for food stimulate the
to movement, and are carried along to the mouth a
to the digestive cavity.   Unpalatable particles, o
carried away from the mouth.   By this selective
polyp fed, but the region round the mouth is kept c

Another group having much in common with
corals are the Antipatharians, or Black Corals, whic
whose branches, crowded with polyps, are strength
horny material, furnishing the black coral of comm

Order CTENOPHORA
(*Comb-bearers*)

The Ctenophora, popularly known as Comb-bea
provide at once an enigma and a possible link b
Coelenterates and the Flatworms.   They often
round our coasts, swimming near the surface of t
times, venturing too close inshore, they are caught
stranded on the beach by the receding tide.

Hormiphora, the common British form, has a
somewhat egg-shaped body about half an inch lon
phosphorescent in the dark—bearing a pair of
armed with numerous small suckers, or lassoo-cell

of f
bod

One o
shape
The
mark
cilia,
serie
by t
which
swim

all th
its lif
the se

SECTION IV

Group VERMES

By C. C. A. Monro, M.A., F.L.S.

(The term "Group" is applied to this Section because it embraces several phyla of worm-like animals of doubtful relationship.)

THE name "worm" is applied to almost any small elongated crawling creature, which cannot be recognised as belonging to some well-known group of animals. In Elizabethan times even a snake was called a " worm," and Shakespeare makes Cleopatra speak of the Egyptian asp, or viper, as " the pretty worm of Nilus, that kills and pains not." Unfortunately there are so many large and distinct groups of animals to which the name worm can be given that it has no longer any scientific meaning. Worms can be divided into six main groups :

1. The Annelida, or Ringed Worms.
2. The Gephyrea, or Bridge-worms, so called because they were once thought to bridge the gulf between the Ringed Worms and the group to which the starfishes belong.
3. The Nemathelminthes, or Round-worms.
4. The Platyhelminthes, or Flat-worms.
5. The Nemertinea, or Ribbon-worms.
6. The Rotifera, or Wheel-animalcules.

Phylum ANNELIDA
(*Ringed Worms*)

These are elongated, more or less cylindrical animals; the body is marked off externally into a series of rings which correspond internally with partitions dividing the cavity of the body into separate chambers. The *Annelida* are in their turn split up into the *Archiannelida* or so-called primitive Annelids, the *Polychaeta* or marine Bristle-worms, the *Oligochaeta* or land and fresh-water Bristle-worms, the *Myzostomata* or Sucking-mouth worms, and the *Hirudinea* or Leeches. The Annelida vary in length from a few millimetres to about two metres.

Archiannelida.—These are a small group of marine worms of simple organisation. There is little doubt that they are closely related to the marine bristle-worms. The simplicity of their organisation used to be regarded as a sign of their primitive character, but some recent authorities are inclined to attribute it in many species to retrogression. Complexity has been lost rather than never attained.

Protodrilus is a minute worm about 10 mm. in length; the majority of species are without bristles and crawl along by means of a ventral ciliated groove. They have two hollow tentacles which are inflated from an ampulla or bulb at their base in a fashion mechanically similar to the protrusion of a starfish's tube-feet. The normal individuals produce both eggs and sperm and are self-fertilising hermaphrodites, but there are in addition other forms of this species which carry no eggs and are known as complementary males.

Saccocirrus is a closely related genus in which the sexes are separate and all the individuals are provided with bristles.

Dinophilus is a curious form resembling superficially a Turbellarian. It has no bristles and moves by means of segmental bands of cilia or vibratile hairs.

Parergodrilus has the distinction of being the only Archiannelid that lives on land. It is found in humus and rotting leaves, especially beneath beech trees. It is provided with bristles and an eversible pharynx furnished at the end with a chitinous disc which it uses in crawling. It displays a pronounced tendency towards parthenogenesis. Some authorities claim that *Parergodrilus* belongs to the Earthworms.

There are a number of other genera of Archiannelids which do not require notice because they are of interest only to the scientific specialist.

THE POLYCHAETA
(*Marine Bristle-worms*)

The marine bristle-worms are a large and variable group, examples of which are found at all depths and in all seas. They are distinguished from the other great group of bristle-worms, the Oligochaeta, the vast majority of which inhabit the land and fresh water, by the possession of lateral expansions of the body wall in which the bristles are implanted, and of appendages of various kinds. In the Oligochaeta the bristles, which are comparatively few, are implanted directly in the body wall; there are seldom any appendages and hermaphroditism, which is rare in the Polychaeta, is the normal condition.

There follows a brief account of the external characters of the Polychaeta by which they may be recognised. The body may be divided into three regions, the head region or prostomium, or the region in front of the mouth, the body proper or metastomium, and the posterior end or pygidium. The prostomium and the following, or buccal, segment, which bears the mouth, are usually provided with a number of feelers, the palps, tentacles, and tentacular cirri. The body may consist of a number of similar segments or, as in the majority of sedentary forms, be differentiated into the thorax, abdomen, and caudal end. The shape also varies greatly in the different families; it may be long and vermiform or short and compressed. The body also carries various appendages, such as gills, cirri or finger-shaped tactile organs, and elytra, which are protective scales. The head varies greatly in shape in the different families; it may be simple or complex, square or cone-shaped, annulated or reduced to a minute lobe. Eyes, when present, range from pigment spots to elaborate organs with a crystalline lens. Associated with the wide differences in the shape of the head there is great variation in the number and shape of the cephalic appendages, that is to say of the feelers, and so on, round the head.

The feet, or " parapodia," are often very complex. Typically they are composed of two branches, a dorsal, called the notopodium, and a ventral, called the neuropodium.

If we take the foot of *Nereis* as a generalised type, we find a dorsal cirrus, two distinct lobes carrying bristles and each supported internally by one or more chitinous rods, the acicula, and a ventral cirrus. In addition we find in connection with both lobes a varying number of membranous expansions, the parapodial lips or languets. That the parapodia play an important part in the " shifts for a living " is shown by the fact that they are very variable, and in some of the sedentary forms are reduced to simple transverse ridges bearing uncini or hooks.

The bristles (chaetae) are chitinous structures which display an almost indefinite variety of ornamentation. They may be hair-like, spear-shaped, feather-like or comb-shaped: they may be simple or compound, composed of two articulating pieces. Perhaps the commonest type resembles a crochet-hook.

The uncini, or hooks, are small chitinous plates with toothed edges which occur in transverse rows on the ventral parapodial ridges of the sedentary forms.

The habit of building tubes is common among the Polychaeta, and is not confined to the sedentary forms. Tubes may be simple cylinders of hardened mucus or elaborate structures built up with shells and grains of sand; they

Parapodium or foot of *Nereis.* Note the dorsal cirrus, the upper and lower bristle-bearing lobes and the ventral cirrus.

Toothed hook of a Terrebellid Worm.

Bidentate bristle of a Polynoid Worm with rows of comb-like teeth on the shaft.

may be chitinous and transparent or stout and calcareous. Tube-formation will be described in greater detail when we deal specially with their builders.

We shall now give a brief review of the more important families with their main characteristics.

The *Aphroditidae* are worms with oval flattened bodies; the back is covered with elytra, or scales, and in addition to the bristles of the feet there is often a felting of fine hairs above the elytra.

The magnificent *Aphrodite*, or Sea-mouse, common on the British coasts,

Aphrodite: the Sea-mouse. The back has a felting of iridescent bristles.

is remarkable for its beautiful iridescent bristles which, as the body moves, change their colour from gold to peacock-blue. Many of the Aphroditids have their eyes on stalks. *Pontogenia* has wonderful scimitar-like bristles curving over its back.

The *Polynoidae* are recognisable by the longitudinal rows of scales on the back. These scales are often beautifully coloured and ornamented with various kinds of tubercles and spines. There are two pairs of black eye-spots which are not carried on stalks.

The *Amphinomidae* have transparent, glassy bristles and an elongated or heart-shaped crest behind the head, known as the caruncle. *Chloeia* is one of the most beautiful of all the marine worms; it has a purple or violet crest, violet markings on the back and on the gills, and white transparent bristles.

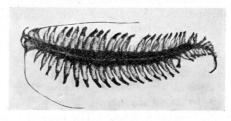

Tomopteris
A pelagic worm with long feelers.

Euphrosyne is remarkable in having the bristles and gills arranged in a series of transverse rows along the back.

The *Phyllodocidae* are long, slender worms with a body composed of numerous segments. They are recognisable by their large leaf-shaped cirri. Many are pelagic, that is to say, they spend their lives floating or swimming in the sea and not on the bottom.

The *Alciopidae* are also pelagic forms, transparent except for their enormous bright red eyes with large crystalline lenses.

Another pelagic family are the *Tomopteridae*; they have a pair of

Phyllodoce
A long brightly coloured worm with leaf-shaped dorsal cirri.

Lagisca
Note the rows of ornamental scales.

Sacconereis
The female of a Syllid, *Autolytus*. On the under-surface is a brood-sac within which the eggs develop.

exceedingly long feelers, sometimes three or four times as long as the body. The bristles have almost all disappeared, and the feet are provided with large flaps called pinnules.

The *Syllidae* are a large family of very small worms chiefly remarkable for their methods of reproduction. They may form chains of buds or young individuals from the hinder region of the parent individual. These young individuals are provided with long bristles and break off and swim away by themselves. In *Autolytus* the buds may not only display marked differences from the parent individuals, but a very distinct sexual dimorphism is evident. The females of *Autolytus* are called *Sacconereis* because of the remarkable sac, or pouch, in which they incubate their eggs. *Exogone* carries its developing eggs on its back.

Among the *Nereidae*, or Rag-worms, are found the commonest and best known of all the marine worms. They are active, voracious little animals with powerful jaws. The majority at the time of reproduction undergo

a kind of sexual metamorphosis known as epitocy. With the growth of the sexual products the middle and posterior parts undergo a sort of general degeneration involving the muscles and digestive tract. At the same time large flaps or lamellae are developed on the feet and the normal bristles are replaced by special oar-shaped swimming bristles. The head region is also changed, the eyes increasing in size and the feelers becoming longer. The sexually modified *Nereis* is known as a Heteronereid. When the transformation is complete, the Heteronereids swarm in immense numbers at the surface during the night, and after discharging their sexual products they usually die.

A curious case of parental care is recorded of *Nereis caudata*, which undergoes no sexual transformation. The male and female of this species live together in the same tube, which is formed of a transparent membrane strengthened by a thick

Heteronereid: the sexually modified form of *Nereis dumerilii*.

layer of sand and gravel. They occupy this tube, seldom leaving it, for several weeks. The eggs are laid and fertilisation takes place within the tube. The male then assumes the maternal rôle and incubates the eggs. First of all he arranges them in the tube with his proboscis and then begins to execute regular undulatory movements which create a current of water over the eggs. These movements are continued without interruption during the whole period of development, during the ten days before the hatching and the further time before the young leave the tube and fend for themselves. All this time the male does not leave his brood in search of food. There is only one thing which mars this picture of paternal devotion and that is the sad fate of the mother. Much weakened by the discharge of her eggs she is unable to defend herself, and within a few hours of laying she is usually devoured by the male.

Nereis dumerilii, another species of *Nereis* and one of the commonest worms found between tide-marks on our coasts, also has a strange history.

It is polymorphic, that is to say the individuals composing the species can be separated into a number of distinct types. There is a bisexual form which at maturity becomes a Heteronereid, another bisexual form which does not suffer this change, and a hermaphrodite form. The hermaphrodites may be divided into two sets of individuals, the small green ones filled with ripe sperm, which function as males, and the large yellow individuals filled with eggs, which function as females. In the body cavity of the males are also found a few eggs and in that of the females a few sperms. The eggs in the hermaphrodite males and the sperm in the hermaphrodite females tend to disappear as the time for sexual maturity approaches. As with *Nereis caudata* the eggs are laid in a tube and the male takes on the task of incubation. As before, the male sets up a respiratory current to aerate the developing young and does not abandon his task until they are old enough to fend for themselves. The female does not long survive the laying of her eggs, but the male lives on. He changes his sex and turns into a female. Some Nereids are found in brackish and even fresh water.

The *Nephthydidae* have a rectangular head and a large sickle-shaped gill curving down between the two branches of the foot. They are commonly used as bait by sea-fishermen.

The *Eunicidae* are a large family with strong complex jaws. *Marphysa sanguinea*, the handsome Red Rock-worm, which is much used for bait, is a member of the family, as is also the famous Pacific Palolo. The name " Palolo " is given by the natives of Samoa and the neighbouring islands to a headless worm which they collect in enormous quantities at the surface of the sea at certain fixed times of the year and which they use as food. It is, in fact, the posterior part of the body, filled with genital products, of *Eunice viridis*. This worm undergoes a sexual change analogous to that of the Heteronereids : the posterior part of the body degenerates into a sort of long sack containing the genital products and when the time comes this breaks away and swarms at the surface of the sea. In *Eunice viridis* and in a number of other worms there is a connection between the time of sexual activity and the phases of the moon, and changes similar to that of the " Palolo " are known to take place in several worms.

A typical Nereid.

Hyalinoecia, or the Quill-worm, builds a chitinous horny tube provided internally with mitre-shaped valves ; the tube bears a strong likeness to the quill of a feather.

The *Spionidae* are provided with a pair of long feelers. They live in the mud and sand and the majority build a delicate tube covered with a fine layer of these materials. *Polydora* is a rock-borer and makes small V-shaped tubes in rocks and shells. The majority of the family lay their eggs in their tubes. Some Spionids are remarkable in having little pockets along the side of the body formed from the cuticle or outer layer of the skin and containing the genital products. In some Spionids part of the developing eggs and young larvae serve as food for the other larvae growing up in the same tube, and in one species a portion of the mother's body degenerates and constitutes a pulp in which the larvae grow.

To the *Chaetopteridae* belong the large Parchment-tube-worm, which is highly phosphorescent and builds a stout leathery tube.

The *Cirratulidae* are distinguishable by their bunches of long thread-like feelers and rows of gills. Some Cirratulids, like certain Syllids, are viviparous and the young develop inside the parent. The majority are

Chaetopterus
A phosphorescent worm that forms a leathery tube.

Sabellaria
Note the crown of bristles in front of the head.

Branchiomma
A Sabellid with its plume of gills.

mud-dwellers and their gills wriggle about in the mud like so many pink worms.

The *Chlorhaemidae* are curious worms with a sort of cage of stout bristles growing forward in front of the head. They have green blood, and the whole of their skin is covered with papillae.

The *Opheliidae* have a conical head without any feelers. In many species there is a deep groove running the length of the ventral surface and a row of eyes along the side of the body.

The *Capitellidae* bear a general superficial resemblance to the common earthworms. They are among the very few Polychaeta in which there is an external distinction between the sexes in the form of a copulatory apparatus This is found generally in the males only, but in two genera both sexes are provided with it. In one of the *Capitellidae*, at the time of sexual maturity, the posterior portion of the body, filled with eggs, tears away from the anterior portion, which lives on and grows a new hinder end.

To the *Arenicolidae* belongs the common lugworm, one of the most popular forms of bait for sea-fishing. They live in the mud and sand in V-shaped tubes between tide-marks and exercise much the same beneficial action on the seashore as the earthworms do in the soil by continually turning it over and exposing new surfaces to the air.

The *Sabellariidae* are recognisable by their crown of concentric circles of broad-bladed bristles which lies in front of the head and is supported by two long stalks. This structure acts as a sort of stopper for their tubes, which are built of sand and gravel.

The *Amphictenidae* also have a stopper to their tube in front of the head, formed of broad bristles, arranged not concentrically, but in two opposite rows. The Amphictenids live completely buried in the sand with the head and wide end of their tube directed downwards. They build a conical tube open at both ends and formed of a single layer of fine sand and small shells. They use their stout anterior bristles for digging in the sand.

The *Terebellidae* are a large and striking group of worms distinguished by a handsome crown of tentacles which conceals the head. They build a membranous

Hydroides

A Serpulid with its gill-plume and spinous operculum or stopper to its tube.

tube encrusted with mud, sand and shells, and fixed to the substratum.

The *Sabellidae* have a beautiful multi-coloured plume of gills spreading like the corolla of a flower. They live in membranous tubes buried in the sand or attached to rocks. Some form quite temporary tubes which they leave to swim about; certain species swim tail first and have eyes on their hinder end to guide them.

The *Serpulidae* have also a beautiful gill-plume, and a calcareous stopper to their tube; this stopper is often rather fantastically ornamented with hooks and branching spines. They build chalky tubes of very different shapes, twisted or cylindrical. In the *Spirorbidae* the tubes are spiral.

THE OLIGOCHAETA
(*Earthworms*)

The few-bristled worms comprise the vast majority of freshwater worms and all the earthworms. Except in the very few genera in which gills or paired feelers are found, the body has no appendages and the bristles are embedded directly in the body wall. Of the land forms the common earthworm is a good example : in this the small rounded head is attached to a long cylindrical body composed of a series of segments separated by rings. An area near the anterior end where the skin is thickened marks the girdle which secretes a cocoon for the eggs. When the cocoon is made, the worm draws its body through it backwards laying its eggs in it at the same time. When the animal is clear of the cocoon, this automatically closes, and protects the developing eggs.

Earthworms are hermaphrodite, but not self-fertilising. In the aquatic forms asexual reproduction is found and chains of buds are sometimes formed : a number of new segments are budded and separation occurs in such a way that some of them form the tail end of the anterior animal, and the rest the head of the posterior. Except for the small aquatic forms such as the *Naididae, Tubificidae* and their allies, and a very few marine forms, all the Oligochaeta live in damp earth or decaying vegetation and are earthworms in the ordinary sense of the term. They are found all over the world and are recorded up to four or five feet in length. Outside the broad differences between the small aquatic and the larger land forms, one earthworm is externally very like another, and their classification, based mainly on the position and relation of the parts of the very complex reproductive system, is beyond the scope of this work.

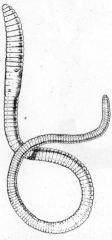

A typical terrestrial earthworm.

Darwin in his famous book, "The Formation of Vegetable Mould through the Action of Worms," brought to light a number of interesting facts about the effect of earthworms on the soil. They swallow large quantities of earth, digest any organic matter mixed with it and evacuate the earth in the form of worm-casts. In this way as much as ten tons per acre, or a layer one-fifth of an inch thick, may be turned up in a year and distributed by the weather over the surface. Their action is thus very beneficial to the soil because it brings to the surface the lower layers, and also buries decaying vegetable matter.

Earthworms are sensitive to vibrations, and on the approach of any heavy body they withdraw quickly into their burrows ; but some vibrations have the opposite effect, as may be seen when a stick is thrust into the ground and given a twirling movement. Earthworms will presently emerge in numbers in the immediate neighbourhood. Their burrows are often of considerable depth, because moisture is necessary to earthworms, and they will go down into the earth for some distance in search of it, when the surface of the ground is dry or frozen.

Although they have no eyes, Darwin showed that they will react to strong light. They have very little sense of smell, but considerable powers of taste.

The vast majority of earthworms are free-living, but mention may be made of the *Bdellodrilidae* (*Discodrilidae*), a family of small worms without bristles, which lead a parasitic existence on the gills of crayfishes.

A masterly account of the earthworms is contained in J. Stephenson's monograph, " The Oligochaeta."

MYZOSTOMATA

(*Sucker-mouthed Worms*)

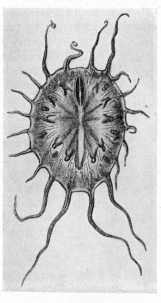

Myzostoma

These are a small group of flattened, disc-shaped worms which live as parasites on echinoderms, the vast majority being found on crinoids. The edge of the body is furnished with cirri and on the ventral surface are a number of parapodia provided with hooks. Myzostomids mostly occur on the disc and arms of their hosts, on which they often form cysts or galls. They are hermaphrodites; they function first as males when they are small; then as hermaphrodites, and finally as females.

They are closely related to the Polychaeta, but much modified by a parasitic existence.

THE HIRUDINEA

(*Leeches*)

From their association with man both as pests and as agents in medicine the leeches have acquired considerable human importance. They are for the most part cylindrical animals with a sucker at each end of the body. They are often brightly coloured, with the pigment distributed in elaborate patterns. The largest known leech is about one foot long. They are found all over the world in the sea, in fresh water, and on land. They are all either predaceous, that is to say they devour other small invertebrates such as earthworms and molluscs, or they are parasitic, that is to say they live by sucking the blood of other animals.

In addition to the grooves in the skin marking the limits of the segments, the body is further subdivided by a series of rings or annuli, of which there may be as many as fourteen to the segment. Except in *Acanthobdella*, which is regarded by some authorities as not being a true leech, there are no parapodia or bristles. Gills are sometimes found, and rows of small sense-organs called *sensillae*.

The suckers may be cup-shaped or scoop-shaped, and behind the head sucker there are usually several pairs of eyes. One of the most notable features about the leeches is the condition of their body cavity, or the space between the outer wall of the gut and the inner wall of the body. In the other classes of *Annelida* this consists of a series of more or less hollow chambers separated by partitions at the limits of the segments, but in the leeches it is filled with tissue which is pierced by a complicated system of canals.

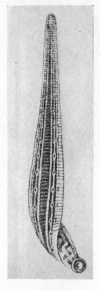

Nearly all land leeches progress by " looping " along, gripping alternately with the front and hind suckers, and many aquatic leeches swim after the fashion of an eel. They lay their eggs in cocoons secreted by the girdle in a manner analogous to that already described for the earthworms. W. A. Harding writes of the egg-laying of an aquatic leech as follows : " Shortly before a leech is ready to lay, it makes itself fast by its two suckers to some convenient object and the clitellum (girdle) becomes covered with a chitinous layer secreted by glands situated within its walls and destined to form the future cocoon. At first this layer is nearly white and somewhat viscous, but it gradually hardens and eventually assumes a more or less deep brown colour. The leech has now to with-draw the anterior part of its body through this cylindrical layer, having first discharged its eggs within it and caused it, by pressure, to adhere to the object upon which it rests. Swelling itself against the posterior extremity of its chitinous belt and dragging in the anterior extremity with it as it retires, this structure becomes invaginated until its two ends meet, thus preserving its contents from contamination by contact with the body passing through it. As soon as the cocoon is left free it evaginates itself and its extremities close up, leaving a small operculum (covering plate) through which, when hatched, the young leeches issue into the surrounding water." In some leeches the cocoon is attached to the ventral surface of the parent's body.

Hirudo medicinalis
The medicinal leech.

Leeches are hermaphrodite and in the *Hirudidae* reciprocal copulation takes place, but in the majority fertilisation is effected by means of hypodermic impregnation. One leech deposits a small packet filled with male element, or sperm, on the body of another leech. The sperms escape from their packet, penetrate the tissue of the leech and find their way to the ovarian pouches where fertilisation takes place. In some leeches the sperm-packets may be deposited anywhere on the body and the sperms find their way to the ova, but in others, the packets have to be placed in a special region of the body in the neighbourhood of the genital orifices, because the sperms can pass only through the special conductive tissue which underlies this region.

Apart from *Acanthobdella*, of which mention has already been made, the leeches are divided into two groups ; the *Rhynchobdellae*, marine and aquatic leeches with a protrusible pharynx and colourless blood, and the *Gnathobdellae*, jawed-leeches, with a fixed non-protrusible pharynx usually provided with toothed jaws ; with red blood. To this sub-order belong the true land leeches and a few aquatic forms, and it is they that have acquired an economic importance from their association with man.

Noxious Parasites

It is not generally realised that of all the external parasites in tropical countries the leeches are perhaps the most noxious. Travellers in tropical swamps and forests are unanimous in their testimony to the prevalence and ferocity of these creatures. The following passage from Haeckel, writing of the leeches of Ceylon, may convey some idea of their behaviour : " In some of the forests and particularly near the river banks and in the marshy jungles of the highlands and lower hills, it is impossible to take a step without being attacked by them. Not only do they creep along the ground seeking what they may devour—they are on every bush and tree, from which they frequently drop on the head and neck of the passer-by : they can creep up his legs, nay, they can even spring to reach their victim."

There are many confirmatory reports to show that this is not an exaggerated account. A leech bite is never specifically toxic, but their habit of fixing on to ulcers and diseased areas makes them very effective carriers of bacterial infections. Apart from their attacks on human beings they do considerable damage to domestic animals, baggage-carriers, and others ; and if the animals are in a weak or exhausted condition the leeches may even cause their death. In Asia Minor and Egypt there is an aquatic leech that lives in streams and ponds and is sometimes swallowed by men and animals in the drinking water. It fastens on the throat and nasal cavities of the host and causes constant haemorrhage. If it is not dislodged, it may kill its victim. This leech was a menace both in the Napoleonic and the recent campaigns.

The employment of leeches for the letting of blood is a time-honoured practice. It is mentioned by Pliny, and Sir Arthur Shipley showed that it was known in India and Arabia since the beginning of the Christian era. It reached the zenith of its popularity as a medical treatment in Western Europe in the early nineteenth century, when enormous quantities of leeches were cultivated on leech farms. Vast numbers were also imported from Russia, and the Russian Government in 1848 passed a special protective law prohibiting their collection during the summer months. Western medicine has to a great extent abandoned their employment in phlebotomy, but in India practitioners of the original native medicine still use them on a large scale.

Dr. J. P. Moore gives an account of the manner in which leeches are used in phlebotomy : " Only those leeches which have not been used for two or three weeks are applied to the part to be treated. If these have been well selected they begin at once to suck blood with avidity until they fall down filled, the amount of blood taken being three or four times the weight of the leech. Such leeches become very dull and inactive. They are rendered again serviceable by stripping with the fingers from tail to head, usually after pricking with a needle on the middle line of the back behind the head. Thus they are emptied of all the blood, and after rubbing thoroughly and replacing in the water usually recover, and after a rest of two or three weeks may be used again. Leeches thus regularly employed seldom live more than a year."

Phylum GEPHYREA

(*Bridge-worms*)

The Gephyrea is a loose term which embraces three distinct groups of worm-like animals, the *Echiuroidea*, the *Sipunculoidea* and *Priapuloidea*. Of these only the *Echiuroidea* show affinities with the Bristle-worms.

Echiurus is a sack-like creature six to ten inches long, with a spoon-shaped lobe in front of the mouth and a wide circle of hooks round the hinder end. It lives in burrows in the sand and mud.

Bonellia has the preoral lobe prolonged into an enormously long whip-like structure with a forked end. The male *Bonellia* is a minute worm-like creature living parasitically in the body of the female.

Sipunculoidea.—These are elongated, sausage-shaped animals, some of which may be almost a foot long. They have a circle of small tentacles in front of the mouth and the anus is found on the dorsal surface near the head end. They live in the mud and sand, in holes in the rock and often in the shells and tubes made by other animals.

Priapulus

A Priapulid with paired cauda appendages.

Sipunculus

Priapuloidea.—*Priapulus* is an enigmatic little creature about two inches long. The anterior end of the body is provided with circlets of chitinous hooks, and it has a caudal appendage like a bunch of grapes which serves as a gill. It lives in the mud and sand.

Phylum ROTIFERA

(*Wheel-animalcules*)

The Rotifers, or Wheel-animalcules, are small aquatic animals familiar to every student of pond life. They derive their name from the disc at the front end, around the margin of which are one or two rows of vibratile hairs or cilia : the continuous movement of the cilia gives the appearance of a rotating wheel. The disc is retractile within the body, and the bands of cilia are differently arranged in different groups. In *Philodina* they are interrupted above and below, and this produces the appearance of two rotating wheels ; and in the beautiful *Stephanoceros* the edge of the disc is produced into a number of processes.

The body may be divided into the trunk and the so-called foot. The trunk is often elongated, and contains the organs of digestion, reproduction, etc. The ventral mouth leads into the pharynx which is furnished with jaws or trophi ; behind this is a short tube leading into the stomach which is followed by a cloaca opening to the surface by a dorsal anus.

Philodina

The foot is often jointed, and ends in two movable toes : these are often perforated at the tips to allow the passage of a sticky secretion which the animal pours out to serve as an anchor.

In *Discopus* the end of the foot is expanded into a disc perforated by holes for the passage of the pedal-cement.

In the Bdelloid rotifers the foot has accessory pointed spurs, and the joints are retractile, one within the other, like the sections of a telescope.

In the *Triarthridae* there are movable pointed rods projecting from the body with which the animals can spring, and the *Pedalionidae* have six hollow appendages for jumping and swimming.

The Rotifers have various ways of moving. The Bdelloids can loop along like a leech, and the families with limb-like appendages use them for jumping. Swimming is effected by means of the cilia on the disc, which at the same time create a current carrying food into the mouth.

The sexes are separate and the males are rare and degenerate : in them the alimentary canal is usually vestigial or absent. The females are often viviparous and parthenogenesis is very common. The females carry two kinds of eggs, thin-shelled or summer-eggs, which develop without fertilisation, and thick-shelled or winter-eggs which last through the winter and are fertilised. The winter-eggs give rise to parthenogenetic females only. Fertilisation is either by true copulation, for the males possess a penis, or by hypodermic impregnation, when the body-wall of the female is perforated and the sperm released into the body cavity.

The Rotifers have a brain, or nerve-ganglion, lying dorsal to the pharynx, and usually one or two eyes above it. They have also feelers, usually three in number, from the tip of which project a number of delicate sense-hairs.

Many species build a gelatinous tube, a secretion from the skin, but *Melicerta* builds a chimney-like tube formed of small pellets cemented together.

In the *Loricata* the cuticle or external layer of the skin is hardened into a sort of outer casing, or shell, which is often ringed or sculptured; this may produce a misleading appearance of segmentation.

The great majority of Rotifers are aquatic; a few are marine. They are

Pedalion
Note the appendages used for jumping.

Melicerta
Note the chimney-like tubes, built up by the animals.

cosmopolitan in their distribution and are found wherever there is fresh water. Some swim or float near the surface and others inhabit the upper layer of the bottom deposit. Most of the tubicolous forms live on the stems of water plants and the Bdelloid rotifers on, or under, mosses. A few such as the marine *Seisonaceae*, ectoparasites on the Crustacean *Nebalia*, have adopted a parasitic mode of living.

The fascination that the Rotifera have always had for microscopists is easy to understand, for they are often beautiful and fantastic creatures. The following well-known passage taken from Hudson and Gosse's monograph gives an admirable picture of the animals in their natural habitat : " But if retaining sense and sight, we could shrink into living atoms and plunge under water, of what a world of wonders should we then form part ! We should find this fairy kingdom peopled with the strangest creatures—creatures that swim with their hair, that have ruby eyes blazing deep on their necks, with telescopic limbs that now are withdrawn wholly within their bodies and are now stretched out to many times their own length. Here are some riding at anchor, moored by delicate threads spun from their own toes ; and there are others flashing by in glass armour bristling with sharp spikes or ornamented with bosses and flowing curves ; while fastened to a green stem, is an animal convolvulus that by some invisible power draws a never-ceasing stream of victims into its gaping cup, and tears them to death with hooked jaws deep down within its body. Close by it, on the same stem, is something that looks like a filmy Heart's-ease. A curious wheelwork runs round its four outspread petals ; and a chain of minute things, living and dead, is winding in and out of their curves into a gulf at the back of the flower. What happens to them there we cannot see ; for round the stem is raised a tube of golden brown balls, all regularly piled on each other. Some creature dashes by, and like a flash the flower vanishes within its tube."

Phylum GASTROTRICHA

The Gastrotricha are minute freshwater animals about one-hundredth of an inch long. They are elongated and roughly circular in section, with a terminal mouth and a nearly terminal anus. Behind the anus is a short portion of the trunk which bears processes with openings for the secretion of a cement gland and therefore corresponds to the foot of the rotifers. The skin is chitinised in its outer layer and bears cilia, bristles, and curious scale-like structures.

The Gastrotricha have a cosmopolitan distribution, as far as is known, and live chiefly among Algae in conjunction with Protozoa and other minute organisms of a similar habitat. Their affinities are with the Turbellaria.

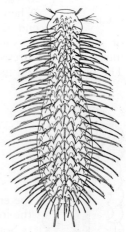

A spiny Gastrotrich.

THE KINORHYNCHA

The Kinorhyncha, represented by the genus *Echinoderes*, are a small isolated group of marine organisms less than a millimetre in length. They are found in shallow water and feed on organic debris. They have a hard chitinised cuticle divided into rings, and an eversible proboscis around which are two closely set circlets of spines. There are also spinous bristles ranged along the rings of the body and two long spines at the hinder end. The sexes are separate.

Phylum NEMERTINEA

(*Ribbon-worms*)

These are elongated worms, of which the great majority are marine. They have extremely contractile bodies, and a worm which may appear to be a few inches long will, when fully extended, reach a length of several yards. They are often very brightly coloured, and live for the most part in shallow water among seaweeds and corals. Some hide in the mud or sand of the sea-bottom and secrete gelatinous tubes which completely conceal them. The body is devoid of appendages, and the mouth is on the under surface of the front end. There is a straight alimentary canal ending in a terminal anus.

The Nemertinea have a remarkable proboscis. This lies in a sheath situated above the alimentary canal and running, in the majority of species, the whole length of the body. When retracted the proboscis lies in its sheath and its hind end is attached to the hind end of the sheath by a band of muscle. The sheath is filled with fluid, and the contraction of the muscular walls presses on the fluid which drives the proboscis forward. The proboscis and its sheath have been compared to the finger of a glove,

A Kinorhynch

A typical Nemertine

End of proboscis of *Tetrastemma* (enlarged).

the end of which is pulled in by a string tied to the tip on the inside.

Some Nemertinea have a chitinous stylet, like a thorn with a number of small reserve stylets to take the place, when required, of the principal stylet, situated at the end of the eversible part of the proboscis. Even when fully expanded a considerable part of the proboscis remains within the sheath.

Some Nemertines have stinging-cells, or nematocysts, similar to those found in the jelly-fish, on that part of the proboscis which is everted.

The nervous system is unusual in that instead of the usual loop joining the dorsal brain to the ventral nerve-cord and passing round the alimentary canal, the loop encircles the proboscis sheath only, and the nerve-cords are not ventral but lateral. The sexes are separate in the Nemertinea and a few forms are viviparous. They are not good swimmers on the whole, but the Indian Ocean form, *Pelagonemertes*, is pelagic. *Geonemertes* is a land form and certain species of *Tetrastemma* are found in fresh water. The principal food of Nemertines is tubicolous worms, which they extract with their proboscis.

Phylum PLATYHELMINTHES

(*Flatworms*)

The Flatworms are divided into the *Turbellaria*, the *Trematodes*, and the *Cestodes*.

The Turbellaria are flattened creeping forms that live in the sea, in fresh water, and on land. The body is often roughly leaf-shaped and the skin is covered with cilia and in some forms contains numerous rod-like bodies that are probably used as weapons. Eyes are present and the mouth often opens not at the front end, but in the middle or even the hinder end of the body. There is a mobile pharynx and often a sucker on the ventral surface. They are divided into the Polyclads or marine forms, with many branches to the intestine ; the Triclads, with three branches to the intestine ; and the Rhabdocoels, with a straight unbranched intestine. The Triclads and the Rhabdocoels are found in the sea, in fresh water, and on land.

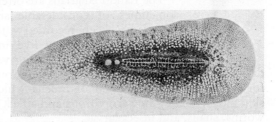

Leptoplana. A Polyclad

Leptoplana, which is fairly common between tide-marks on our shores, is a good example of a Polyclad. It ranges in size from half an inch to one inch in length : it lies like a flat film of tissue on rocks and stones and is capable of gliding along the substratum or even the surface film of the water. It can also swim by a flapping motion of the sides of the body. It feeds on other small marine animals sometimes larger than itself. Its method is to adhere firmly to its prey and to pour on to it the secretion of its salivary glands which softens the tissues and makes them easier to engulf.

Polyclads are, with few exceptions, shallow-water forms and often live in association with other marine animals. While creeping and swimming is the normal mode of progression, *Discocelis* has been observed to climb up the side of a glass jar by means of the expanded lobes of its pharynx.

They are probably all carnivorous and, as there is no anus, the faeces are periodically extruded through the pharynx.

The Polyclads are hermaphrodite and the male organs develop earlier than the female. Many Polyclads have more than one penis and *Polypostia* has as many as twenty of these organs. It is a remarkable fact that some Polyclads use their penes as weapons of offence, driving them into the skin of other Polyclads. True copulation has been observed in the group, but fertilisation is often effected by hypodermic impregnation.

The Triclads, which include the land and freshwater Planarians and also some marine forms, are distinguished from the Polyclads by their more elongated shape and the possession of a single genital pore as well as by their less complicated intestine. Of the freshwater forms *Polycelis nigra*, which is common in stagnant water, is a well-known representative. Freshwater Planarians have a very wide distribution, and are found even in mountain-streams at very high altitudes.

The Land Planarians are often very brightly coloured, and sometimes of considerable size. *Bipalium kewense* has been recorded with a length of over one foot. They live in dark places, under logs and in decaying vegetation. In dry countries they inhabit burrows in the ground, and make for themselves a sort of shell of mucus which keeps their skin moist. They are carnivorous and attack and eat earthworms, snails, and insect-larvae.

Geoplana
A Triclad.

All Planarians reproduce themselves sexually ; in the freshwater Planarians asexual reproduction also occurs. This is effected by the transverse division of the body into two parts, each part growing into an entire animal.

The Rhabdocoels, distinguished by the simplicity of their alimentary tract, are small active Turbellaria. The majority are marine, and representatives can usually be found on the seashore in pools, and among seaweed between tidemarks. Most of them are carnivorous, feeding on small Copepods and other Rhabdocoels ; and a certain number have taken to a parasitic mode of life. Both sexual and asexual reproduction are known to occur, and the genital system is very complex.

Mesostoma
A Rhabdocoel.

To the Rhabdocoels belongs the curious *Convoluta roscoffensis*, whose tissues contain a symbiotic green alga. The chlorophyll in this alga causes it to act as a special assimilating tissue by means of which *Convoluta* builds up carbohydrates in the manner of a plant. *Convoluta* has consequently abandoned the carnivorous habit and now lives entirely on the carbohydrates elaborated by the alga.

THE TREMATODA

The Trematodes form one of two main divisions of the parasitic flatworms : the other is the Cestodes. The Trematodes are split into two main groups, the monogenetic and the digenetic. In the monogenetic Trematodes the young do not require a second or intermediate host for their development, and they are often hatched as small editions of their parents. In the digenetic Trematodes there is a complicated life-history involving several remarkable changes of form, and the occupation of a host other than that inhabited by the adult form. The monogenetic forms are in the main external parasites and the digenetic internal parasites.

Of the monogenetic Trematodes the Temnocephalids are nearest to the Turbellaria. They occur for the most part on the outside of tropical freshwater crayfishes and crabs, adhering by their posterior sucker, and feed on Rotifers, Diatoms, and small aquatic organisms. The Tristomids and Polystomids, on the other hand, are parasitic on marine and freshwater fishes and Amphibia.

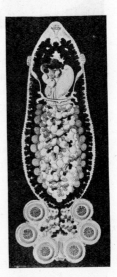

Polystomum
A Polystomid. Note the suckers.

Polystomum is found in the bladder of the frog. It is attached to its host by suckers at the hinder end and there is a sucker on either side of the mouth. This worm and its relatives live by sucking the blood and surface tissues of their hosts.

Polystomum and some other monogenetic Trematodes have free-swimming larvae, which, when hatched out, swim about till they find a suitable host on which to fix. Moreover, when their hosts come into contact, they transfer themselves from one to another.

The adult digenetic or endoparasitic Trematodes are parasites on vertebrate animals, and are usually found in the intestinal tract. They have complicated life histories and that of the liver-fluke, *Fasciola hepatica*, will serve as an example for the group. The adult Trematode lives in the bile ducts of the liver of sheep and certain other animals. Its eggs are passed out with the faeces of the host and after some weeks hatch out into a small ciliated embryonic creature known as a *miracidium*. If the *miracidium* is to survive it has to meet with a certain kind of pond-snail, in Europe *Limnaea truncatula*. Having met this snail, it bores its way into the tissues of the *Limnaea*, where it changes into a bladder-like organism called a *sporocyst*. Inside the *sporocyst* further changes take place, and a large number of small

creatures known as *rediae* appear.   Each *redia* may give rise by budding to
further *rediae* ; or to still another form called a *cercaria*.

The *cercariae* resemble the adult *Fasciola* with the addition of a tail.
They pass out of the snail and swim about by means of their tails until they
come to rest on a blade of grass.   They then lose the tail and surround
themselves with a protective cyst.   In this condition they remain until
they are swallowed by a sheep or some other suitable host, by whose
digestive-juices the cyst is
dissolved.   The young liver-
fluke then bores its way
through the tissues of its host
until it reaches the liver, and
eventually the bile-ducts,
where it develops into the
full-grown worm.   A large
number of sheep are killed annually by this fluke.

Clonorchus.   A digenetic Trematode

Some flukes have a second intermediate host (commonly a fish), in
addition to the first, which is, as far as our knowledge goes, always a
Mollusc.   They remain encysted in the second host, until it is eaten by the
final host.

The *cercariae* of the blood-flukes have the power of penetrating directly
through the skin and blood-vessels of their final host.

The well-known *Schistosoma* (*Bilharzia*), which causes disease in the
bladder and intestine of man, belongs to this group.

THE CESTODA
(*Tapeworms*)

Cestodes, or Tapeworms, are, with very rare exceptions, internal parasites in the alimentary canal of Vertebrates, but their larval stages are passed in animals
belonging to a variety of groups.   The great majority
are remarkable for the formation of a chain of similar
segments by the segmentation of the neck, the segment
farthest from the head being the oldest.   Each segment
contains both male and female reproductive organs and
self-fertilisation takes place.   These chains, which constitute the body, or *strobila*, of the Cestode, may reach a
length of several yards.   In a small number of forms this
chain-formation does not take place, when the animal is
not unlike a Trematode.   To secure the tapeworm to its
host, the head, or *scolex*, is provided with hooks or
suckers, or both.   The Cestodes have no mouth, nor
alimentary canal ; and are nourished by the absorption through the skin

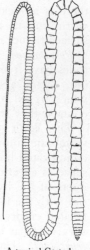
A typical Cestode

of the already digested food of their hosts. When a segment of the chain is ripe, it breaks away from the parent chain and continues to live as long as it remains in the intestine of the host. As the segments break away, each containing many thousands of eggs, they are passed out with the faeces.

Like the Trematodes, the Cestodes have a complicated life-history involving a series of changes. When the ripe segments filled with eggs —and these may amount to several millions—leave the final host, they are swallowed with the food of the intermediate host. Here the larvae from the developing eggs hatch, and burrowing into the blood-vessels are carried to various organs, where they are transformed into a *Cysticercus* or Bladder-worm, and grow the head of the adult form. When the intermediate host is eaten by the final host, the *cysticerci* fix themselves to the wall of the alimentary canal and develop into the adult tapeworm.

The Pork Tapeworm, *Taenia solium*, is a good example. The adult form lives in the intestine of man, and the intermediate host is the pig. The larva is hatched in the pig's gut, and being furnished with three pairs of hooks it burrows its way into the blood-system and establishes itself usually in the muscles. Here it turns into a small bladder-like organism, and the wall of the bladder opposite to the larval hooks turns inwards, and at the bottom of the pit thus formed four muscular suckers and a circle of hooks appear. This is the *Cysticercus* stage, and the

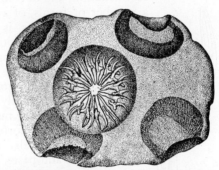

Scolex of a Cestode. Note the suckers and hooks.

suckers and hooks represent the head of the adult turned inside out. Now, if the muscle of the pig is eaten in a raw or uncooked state, the Bladder-worm turns its head inside out and fixes itself firmly to the wall of the intestine. It then begins to bud off a chain of similar segments, and the cycle may be repeated.

The Beef Tapeworm, *Taenia saginata*, has a similar history, but the ox and not the pig is the intermediate host.

Taenia coenurus is the tapeworm responsible for the disease known as the " gid " in sheep. The adult is a parasite in the intestine of the dog, and the bladder-stage known as a *coenurus* occurs in the brain of the sheep. If it presses on one of the cerebral hemispheres it may cause the animal to whirl round in circles till it falls. This parasite is responsible for a heavy mortality among the flocks.

Echinococcus uses man, among other animals, as its intermediate host. In its bladder-worm stage it is a dangerous parasite, forming hydatid cysts which may prove fatal. Its final hosts are the dog, and other *Canidae*.

Birds are often the victims of heavy infection by tapeworms, but they appear to suffer very little from the effects.

As is generally known, the formation of pearls by the oyster is often the response by this animal to the irritation caused by an internal parasite. One such parasite is a tapeworm-larva which lives in the soft tissues of the oyster. Should this larva die the oyster secretes a covering of nacre round it, and a pearl is formed.

Phylum NEMATHELMINTHES

(*Roundworms*)

The Nematodes are a very large group. Probably the majority are free-living, but a very large number are wholly or partially adapted to a parasitic life. They are rounded, vermiform-animals, without a trace of segmentation, and devoid of appendages, with the exception, in a number of forms, of a few hooks or bristles. One of their salient characteristics is the complete absence of cilia or vibratile-processes. With very few exceptions the sexes are separate. The free-living forms are found in every kind of habitat, on land, in the sea, and in fresh water. Many are predacious and live by attacking other small animals, others live more or less parasitically on the juices of plants, and others again feed on decaying matter.

Of the free-living forms perhaps the most common are the so-called " vinegar-eels " and the " paste-eels," which are found in old vinegar and paste.

Of the forms parasitic on plants we may mention *Tylenchus dipsaci*, which does much damage to a number of cultivated plants; *Tylenchus tritici*, which causes " ear-cockles " in wheat; and *Heterodera schachtii*, responsible for " beet sickness." *Heterodera radicicola* forms galls on the roots of a number of common food-plants.

Some Nematodes have an extraordinary power of remaining in a state of suspended animation. The galls of *Tylenchus tritici*, for example, are said to swarm with active larvae, when moistened, after being dried for twenty years.

Rhabelitis
A free-living Nematode.

The Ascarids, and the Hookworms, some of which are parasitic in man, make a complicated journey through the body of their hosts. The eggs of the larvae are passed out with the faeces of the host. The larvae of the Hookworms hatch in the open, and bore their way through the skin into the blood-vessels of the host. After passing through various organs they find their way to the lungs, and crawl up the trachea into the mouth, where they are swallowed, and so pass into the intestine. In *Ascaris*, when the eggs are swallowed they hatch in the intestine, and the larvae bore their way into the blood-stream and return *via* the lungs and the mouth into the intestine again.

Many Nematodes have an intermediate host in which they live in an encapsuled condition until eaten by the final host. Thus it is not uncommon to find encapsuled larvae in the muscles of fishes, the adult stage being passed in some animal that eats the fishes.

The larval stage of some Nematodes is passed in blood-sucking insects, by which they are transmitted to their vertebrate hosts. The Filariids, which are the cause of much disease in man in tropical countries, are thus transmitted. *Syngamus*, which is responsible for the disease known as "gapes" in chickens, lives in

Strongyloides. A Hookworm.

the trachea and suffocates its victims. The worm responsible in man and the pig for the disease known as *trichinosis*, is exceptional in passing both its larval and its adult stage in the same host. The common *Mermis*, which is often found in gardens after rain, is free-living in its adult stage and passes its larval stage as a parasite of insects. Finally, a few Nematodes have an alternation of parasitic and free-living generations.

The *Gordiacea*, or horse-hair worms, are probably related to the Nematoda; they occur abundantly in ponds and ditches, and have a life-history somewhat similar to that of *Mermis*.

Phylum ACANTHOCEPHALA

The Acanthocephala, or Thorny-headed worms, are a group of doubtful affinities. They are much modified in adaptation to a parasitic life, and have no trace of a gut, their nourishment being obtained by absorption through the skin. The adult worm lives in the alimentary canal of verte-brates, and the larvae in small invertebrates, often Crustacea, likely to be eaten by the final host. *Echinorhynchus* is a typical genus, and is found in its adult form in fishes.

Phylum CHAETOGNATHA

(*Bristle-mouthed Worms*)

By W. P. PYCRAFT, F.L.S.

Those who have to come to a decision as to the precise position among the Invertebrates of the "Chaetognatha," or, as they are commonly called, "Arrow-worms," from the fanciful resemblance they present to an arrow, are faced with an insoluble problem. All that can be said of these little creatures is that they are represented by some three-and-twenty species, divisible into three Genera—*Sagitta*, *Spadella*, and *Krohnia*. Their nearest relatives appear to be among certain aberrant Nematoda such as the Chaetostoma.

The " aloofness " these creatures display makes them, however, peculiarly interesting to those who find delight in the problems presented by the various types of animals, their responses to the external world, and their means of maintaining a hold on life. Measuring no more than an inch and a half in length, yet their frail, transparent bodies never come to rest; for their whole existence is passed at the surface of the sea, though at times they are taken at depths varying from 100 to 1000 fathoms. The causes governing these vertical movements are unknown.

But be this as it may, the " Arrow-worms " form part of that vast host of small creatures of many kinds — protozoa, jelly - fish, minute and lowly crustacea, such as " copepods," mollusca, and so on— which, drifting about with the currents of the sea, make up what is known as the " Plankton." Preying upon one another they are also preyed upon by hosts of fishes and other creatures.

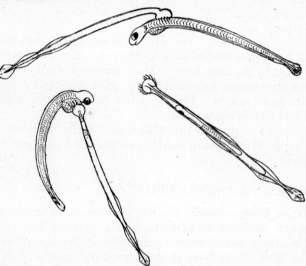

Arrow-worms attacking the larva of fish. Note the larva inside the worm in the centre.

But the " Arrow-worms " themselves play no insignificant part in this teeming welter of life. For at times they are found in such enormous numbers that the sea, on occasions, is " stiff with them "! This seething crowd is by no means an inoffensive one; for if they are furnishing food to larger creatures they are at the same time living like ravening wolves, seizing with their " mouth-bristles " jelly-fish, small crustacea, and larval-fishes. Thus do they turn upon their devourers.

Their bodies, it has just been remarked, are transparent; and in the matter of shape have been likened by some to an arrow, by others to a torpedo. For steadying purposes the sides of the body bear one or two pairs of small fins, while there is also a horizontal tail-fin: the membranes of these appendages being strengthened by fine rods. The small head bears in front a projecting hood, or shield, most prominent above and at the sides. Within the hood the head bears a number of sickle-shaped hooks—hence the name Chaetognatha, or "bristle-jawed"—whose points, when at rest, converge towards the mouth. But in feeding this hood is opened out when, automatically, the hooks are spread wide for the capture of prey. In addition to these hooks are a number of short, stout spines, borne on a semicircular area at the extreme front end of the middle-line of the hood. What function they serve is unknown, but they at least serve the systematist with a means of distinguishing genera and species, since their numbers are different, and constant within the different genera and species.

Some of the cells of the skin along the sides are modified to form sense-organs; while others project from the surface to form "adhesive cells." The muscular system is fairly well developed, forming along the trunk four separate bundles—two dorsal and two ventral. The musculature of the head is strongly developed to actuate the mouth-bristles.

The nervous system is concentrated in the head to form a thickened mass, or "ganglion," which gives off two lateral nerves to pass backwards round the gullet. Nerves from this ganglion are also given off to the eyes, olfactory organ, and muscles. There is also a ventral ganglion, and connected therewith a tangle of nerve-fibrils at the base of the ectoderm or outer skin. Groups of isolated cells, with long hairs, are scattered over the body and serve, apparently, as tactile organs.

There are no special respiratory or circulatory organs, and *Spadella mariona* alone shows any trace of an excretory organ. This takes the form of a glandular structure in the head, which, it is suggested, may be connected with the excretion of nitrogenous material.

The Chaetognatha are hermaphrodite. The paired ovaries lie in the trunk region of the body, and when mature they almost fill the cavity. The oviduct traverses the ovary, but how the ova find their way into it is unknown. But spermatozoa are sometimes found in it, so that it acts as a "*receptaculum seminis*." The oviducts open to the exterior at the upper surface of the lateral fin, just where the trunk passes into the tail.

Testes are located within paired cavities lying within the tail, and are formed from the cells lining the walls of the cavities, finally giving rise to the spermatozoa. These float about in the fluid of the body cavity and, through ducts, open to the exterior.

The fertilised ova float at the surface, and the development of the young is entirely embryonic, no larval stage being known.

SECTION V

Phylum POLYZOA

By M. Burton, M.Sc.

GENERAL CHARACTERISTICS

THE Polyzoa, or Bryozoa, are chiefly marine animals and, with one exception, live together in colonies which take the form either of flat incrustations on stones, shells, and seaweeds, or of erect growths, tree-like, fan- or cup-shaped. With the exception of the Lace-corals, so called because of a superficial resemblance to the true corals, they are dull and, for the most part, inconspicuous. As with several other groups of invertebrates, it is mainly under the microscope, when the numerous tiny creatures known as polypides (owing to a certain likeness to the polyps of the Coelenterates), of which they are formed, are revealed, that we find anything of interest or beauty in them.

FRESHWATER POLYZOA

One of the simplest among them, and one which helps us to understand the structure of the more complex forms, is *Paludicella*, one of the freshwater Polyzoa found in the rivers and lakes of the Continent. Each polypide is enclosed in an elongated chamber made of a tough, horny material, and joined to its neighbours at either end. Thus is formed a small moss-like growth, whose branches are composed of rows of polypides placed end to end.

The structure of a polypide is comparatively simple. The elongated chamber bears an opening near the front, or upper, end, through which protrudes the only part of the animal ever exposed, a mouth surrounded by a ring of hollow tentacles. The remainder of the body is entirely and permanently contained within the chamber, and consists, for the most part, of a U-shaped digestive tube which, commencing at the mouth, hangs down into the chamber. This tube arises in a muscular pharynx immediately below the mouth, and hangs down into the body-cavity in the form of a loop, the stomach being the lowest point, whence the tube turns upwards to open to the exterior quite near to the mouth. It is quite free except at one point where it is fastened to the body-wall by a double strand of tissue known as the funiculus.

Paludicella has no blood-vessels, the functions of a blood system being performed by a clear, colourless fluid filling the body-cavity, that is, the space between the digestive tube and the wall of the chamber. The nervous system consists of a small collection of nerve-cells situated near the mouth ; specialised sense-organs are entirely absent.

At the point where the funiculus joins the body-wall are two masses of cells which give rise, in the breeding season, to eggs and spermatozoa respectively. The fertilised eggs remain for a while in the body-cavity, where they undergo division and give rise to embryos. Frequently the final stages of development in the Polyzoa are completed in a special brood-pouch, situated near the base of the polypide. Eventually the embryos develop into ciliated larvae, which escape into the water and swim about for a brief period before settling down to form young polypides. Each new polypide so formed marks the beginning of a fresh colony, for when it has reached a state of maturity it gives off a bud which remains permanently and intimately attached to it. By repeated budding the colony grows in size, succeeding polypides being formed, as buds, from those already in existence. There are thus two methods of multiplication in the Polyzoa : repeated budding, by which the colony increases in size, and sexual reproduction leading to the formation of ciliated larvae which swim away to lay the foundations of fresh colonies.

Section of a polypide of *Paludicella*, with tentacles expanded. The most prominent organs are the U-shaped alimentary tract and the large band of muscle used in withdrawing the tentacles.

Paludicella enables us to grasp the meaning of the names by which the group to which it belongs is known. The grouping together of many animals to form a colony, so intimately connected as to give the impression of a single animal, suggests the name Polyzoa, while its moss-like form finds expression in the alternative name, the Bryozoa.

The polypides are without means of attack or defence, except in so far as they are covered with a tough coat into which they are able to retract the exposed crown of tentacles.

THE SEA-MATS

The various species of Polyzoa differ little from *Paludicella* so far as their internal anatomy is concerned. The majority of the marine species build bigger and more complex colonies, but the characters of the individual polypides vary little. The most notable differences between species concern the shape of the colony as a whole, the ornamentation of the outer covering of the poly-pides, and the structure of the mouth-opening. Reference has already been made to the different forms which the colony may assume. In some the outer horny cases of the polypides have been replaced by a thick, chalky layer, as, for example, in the Lace-corals. Among the larger Polyzoa are the Sea-Mats, whose dried remains, so abun-

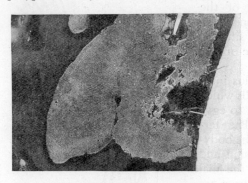

Portion of a SEA-MAT growing on a frond of seaweed

dantly found around our coasts, are usually mistaken for seaweeds.

The outer covering of the polypides is usually variously embossed and grooved, the patterns so formed having a delicate beauty of their own when viewed under the microscope. This ornamentation frequently extends round the mouth-openings, and has become variously adapted to give the enclosed animal a slight measure of protection; for while many of the openings are simple, more or less crescent-shaped slits, others are protected by small groups of blunt spines, and not a few are provided with a definite lid, or operculum.

SPECIAL STRUCTURES

An interesting differentiation occurs in some species where, although the majority of the polypides are quite normal, many have become modified to form curious avicularia, or "bird's-head organs." These have the appearance of "vultures' heads" mounted on slender necks, whose beaks snap viciously at anything coming within their reach, as the necks which bear them sway gently backwards and forwards. In yet other species their place is taken by long, whip-like organs, or vibracularia, which are constantly moving, lashing to and fro across the surface of the colony. In all probability these curious structures help to keep the colony clean, driving away small intruders and preventing sediment from settling on the surface.

Another difference between the freshwater and the marine Polyzoa is directly correlated with the more severe changes in their surroundings. These changes are climatic and the passage of the seasons necessitates some special method for carrying the species on from year to year. Such a method is found in the production of winter-buds, or statoblasts, consisting of groups of cells massed together and enclosed in a thick envelope. On the death of the colony, with the approach of winter, the statoblasts are released and sink to the bottom of the pond or stream. There they lie until the more genial conditions of spring stimulate the cell-mass to leave its protective coat and grow into a new colony, in much the same way as the larvae of *Paludicella* form new colonies.

Cristatella (enlarged)

a, a colony moving across the stem of a water-plant ; *b*, a stato-blast from which three young polypides have emerged.

Cristatella, another of the freshwater Polyzoa, deserves special mention because here the colony, contrary to the usual state of affairs, is mobile. It is flattened and slug-like, with the polypides protruding all over the upper surface, and is able to creep about over the stems and leaves of water-weeds by wave-like contractions of the under surface.

It is difficult to decide the exact position which the Polyzoa should occupy in the Animal Kingdom. Their likeness to some of the Coelenterates is superficial only, and is confined to the shape of the colony as a whole, and to the presence of a crown of tentacles. From the form of their larvae, and from other considerations, they are regarded by some as related to the Annelid-worms, and by others to the Mollusca. The most we can say is that they are animals of unusual structure which have probably arisen from the same ancestral stock as both the worms and the molluscs.

SECTION VI

Phylum BRACHIOPODA

("*Lamp Shells*")

By G. C. ROBSON, M.A.

THEIR ANTIQUITY

THE animals included in this group are popularly known as "Lamp Shells." Their soft parts are contained in a bivalve shell, one valve of which is shaped like an ancient Roman hand-lamp, of the kind which is saucer-like with one side flanged upwards to form a handle. In outward appearance the Brachiopods are very like bivalve (Lamellibranch) Molluscs; and they resemble those animals in another, perhaps more interesting, respect. We speak of the Mollusca as conservative animals, because they have preserved their main structural plan intact throughout a long evolutionary history. The Brachiopoda are still more conservative. The group is an extremely old one, and its representatives are found in the oldest fossil-bearing rocks of the Lower Cambrian. Nevertheless, some of the genera that appeared in early and middle Palaeozoic times have persisted in an unmodified condition down to the present day. In the course of many millions of years, during which time evolution has been active in modifying nearly all the groups of animals almost out of recognition, *Lingula*, which appeared in the Lower Ordovician period, and *Crania* and *Orbiculoidea*, which were evolved in the Upper Ordovician, have pursued the even tenor of their ways unchanged.

Few people will have had the opportunity of seeing a living Brachiopod, though *Lingula* will be perhaps familiar to some non-scientific readers on account of its unique history. A few species, such as *Terebratulina caput*

72

serpentis (the Snake-head) and *Terebratula capsula* are found in British seas. They live in rather deep water and do not form part of the familiar beach fauna.

In describing these animals we shall have rather more to say about the extinct forms than about the living members of the phylum. All that is now left of a once numerous and flourishing group of animals, of which over 2000 species were living in Silurian times, is a few families containing about 140 species. These animals are, as we have said, very like Molluscs in outward appearance, and for many years they were classed with those creatures ; but they are now recognised by most zoologists as a distinct phylum. They remain, however, a great source of interest to zoologists as their relationship to other animals is very obscure and puzzling. They have been placed with the Polyzoa in a phylum called Molluscoidea, and assumed to be more or less related to the Molluscs. Again, they have been treated as Annelids (Worms) ; and, finally, it was suggested that with the Polyzoa and the curious *Phoronis*, and two forms usually treated as degenerate Chordates, *Rhabdopleura* and *Cephalodiscus*, they should form a separate phylum known as the Podaxonia. None of these views has been largely accepted ; and it seems clear that a better knowledge of the embryology of these animals is required before we can decide their relationship to the other Invertebrata. At present it is best to consider them as a distinct phylum, with no particularly close relations, unless it be with the main Coelomate stock.

MODE OF LIFE

The Brachiopoda live exclusively in the sea. There are no records of freshwater members of the group ; nor do they even seem to become permanently acclimatised to brackish water. They are sessile in habit, *i.e.* they live permanently attached to the sea-bottom like an oyster. Next to the shell the stalk, or peduncle, by which they are anchored down, is the most striking feature in their external appearance.

The valves of the shell are mainly composed of either calcium carbonate or phosphate of lime,

LAMP SHELLS—Top and side view.

combined with small quantities of other substances. They are unequal in shape, one of them being usually larger than the other and having a prominent beak (rostrum). Unlike the shell of a Mussel or Cockle, in which the two valves are placed one on each side of the body, the valves of the Brachiopod shell are disposed one on the back (dorsal valve), the other on the front (ventral valve) of the animal, rather as the two parts of an old-fashioned cuirass were worn.   They are secreted by the surface of the mantle, as in the Mollusca.

On opening a modern Brachiopod it will be seen that the body occupies the hinder part of the mantle-cavity.   Posteriorly it is prolonged to form the stalk, or peduncle, which passes to the exterior usually between the valves.   The mouth is situated on the ventral surface of the body, and is overhung by a horseshoe-shaped disc (lophophore).   From this project into the mantle-cavity two elongate or coiled arms bearing tentacles.   These are beset with numerous fine processes like eyelashes (cilia) which vibrate and set up currents in the water.   By these currents minute organisms are driven towards the mouth.   The arms were originally supposed to represent the foot of the Mollusca, hence the name of Brachiopoda, or " Arm-Feet " (*brachion*, arm ; *pous*, *pod-*, foot).

Tethered to the sea-bottom, and depending for their food on the minute animals and plants which are drifted into the food-currents of the mantle-cavity, the Brachiopods are more helpless than the majority of Lamelli-branchs, and resemble the Oyster and the Spiny-Scallops (*Spondylus*) in their mode of life.   In fact, all these otherwise highly organised animals are not much more active than Corals and Sponges.

INTERNAL ANATOMY

The internal organs are suspended in a body-cavity (coelom) as in a Worm, or a Vertebrate.   There is a short gullet which is followed by a stomach.   The latter receives the ducts of the liver, which is the organ of digestion.   In one of the two main classes into which the phylum is sub-divided, the intestine is short and ends blindly.   In the other class (Ecardines) it is longer and ends in an anus.

The circulation system consists of a heart and blood-vessels.   The blood is oxygenated, not in gills, but probably in the thin inner surface of the mantle.   There are two pairs of kidneys in *Rhynchonella*, a single pair in all other forms.   The nervous system is very interesting, as it exhibits a peculiarity not usually found in highly organised invertebrate animals.   It retains the primitive connection with the skin usually found in lowly Invertebrates and in embryos.   Otherwise it is well developed, and consists of a ring round the oesophagus on which concentrated masses of nerve-tissue or ganglia are situated.   From these are given off nerves to the various organs.   In the adult there are no special sense-organs, such as eyes.

The sexes are separate in the Brachiopoda, and the occurrence of herma-phroditism which has been reported, *e.g.* in *Lingula pyramidata*, does not seem to be satisfactorily proved.   The reproductive glands (ovaries or testes) are four in number and discharge their products (eggs and spermatozoa) by the kidneys. The eggs are usually fertilised outside the body, in the sea-water, and development is thus external. In certain forms, however, (*e.g. Argiope, Cistella*), they undergo part of their development in special brood-pouches within the mantle-cavity of the female. In the course of development there is always a free-swimming larval stage, at the end of which the young Brachiopod settles down on the sea-bottom.

The Brachiopoda are found in practically all seas, usually at depths of less than 100 fathoms. A certain number live in much deeper water and some have been taken from depths close on 3000 fathoms. *Lingula* is not fixed permanently to the sea-bottom, but lives in a tube of sand which adheres to the lower end of its peduncle. Inside this tube it can stretch its shell upwards to the aperture of the tube so as to take water into its mantle-cavity. When it is disturbed, however, its peduncle contracts and withdraws the shell back into the tube. The rest of the living members of the phylum are permanently fixed to some solid object. They obtain the minute organisms on which they live, by opening the shell as widely as possible and admitting water into the mantle-cavity, where the cilia on the arms form currents which drive the food into

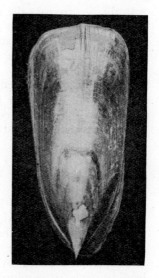

BURROWING LAMP SHELL (*Lingula*)

the mouth. Some of them, however, can unroll the arms and protrude them from the shell.

In this work the Brachiopods are treated as a distinct phylum, containing two classes, Ecardines and Testicardines, and four orders.

Class ECARDINES

Order ATREMATA

The Atremata are the most primitive order. The shell is either impregnated with mineral substance or horny. There is no special opening in the shell for the peduncle, the valves are not hinged, and the arms are devoid of skeletal supports. In the Cambrian period these forms predominated over the other types. The most remarkable family is the *Lingulidae*. This family, the members of which are recognisable in the Lower Ordovician, has persisted unaltered down to the present day. The living forms are found in the seas of China and Japan, off the Philippine Islands, and in Australian waters. The shell is thin, horny, and green in colour. The *Lingulidae*, as already explained, live in tubes of sand into which they can withdraw themselves. The Atremata fell into a kind of " decline " in the Silurian period, and gradually all the families (*Obolidae*, etc.), with the exception of *Lingula* and its allies, became extinct.

Order Neotremata

In the Neotremata the shell is frequently horny and is devoid of a hinge. They occur in Cambrian strata, and the modern *Craniidae* and *Discinidae* are first found in the Silurian. *Crania* is found in the Mediterranean, off the Hebrides and Shetlands. It has no peduncle and attaches itself by the ventral valve to rocks. The modern *Discinidae* have a wide distribution. Their shells are rounded and almost flat. *Discinisca atlantica*, a British form, was taken from the great depth of 2425 fathoms by the " Challenger " Expedition. These two families are the only representatives of the Neotremata that survived the end of the Palaeozoic.

Class TESTICARDINES
Order Protremata

The Protremata arose in the Cambrian and became practically extinct by the Carboniferous period, leaving only one family, the *Thecidiidae*, to survive to modern times. In these Brachiopods the shell-valves are hinged, and there is an aperture for the pedicle in the lower valve. *Thecidium*, like *Crania*, is fixed down by its ventral valve. Its eggs are incubated in a brood-pouch (marsupium) situated on the ventral side.

Order Telotremata

The Telotremata are the most highly organised Brachiopoda. They are represented at the present time by the *Rhynchonellidae* and *Terebratulidae*, representatives of sub-orders of which the former were in existence in the Ordovician period. These forms have a hard shell of mineral substance, the valves of which are hinged, and the arms of the lophophore are long and coiled very much. The arms are supported by a calcareous skeleton (brachidium). The *Rhynchonellidae* are represented at the present time by eight species. *Atretia gnomon* is found off the West Coast of Ireland in 650–1750 fathoms.

The evolutionary history of these animals suggests an interesting speculation. It is true that the living Brachiopods are the merest handful compared with the great number of extinct forms. When we look on the unchanging persistence with which *Lingula* and its living allies have remained true to type we are tempted to wonder if in another fifty million years or more they will be still unchanged, when more highly organised animals now living may have been long extinct. In short, we may ask, has *Lingula* the prospect of a future as long and as unchanging as its past ?

SECTION VII

Phylum ECHINODERMA

By C. C. A. Monro, M.A., F.L.S.

GENERAL CHARACTERISTICS

THE Echinoderma comprise five classes, the Starfishes (Asteroidea), the Sea-urchins (Echinoidea), the Brittle-stars (Ophiuroidea), the Sea-lilies, or Feather-stars (Crinoidea), and the Sea-cucumbers (Holothuroidea). They are radially symmetrical animals, living in the sea, or very rarely in brackish-water; and their skin is strengthened by a deposit of carbonate of lime. This deposit takes the form of small rods and plates, which in the majority of forms are joined together at the edges to form a continuous, firm outer-casing or shell; but in the Holothurians they are separately imbedded in the skin, and are known as " spicules." There is a spacious body-cavity, from which the internal organs are shut off, and the body is traversed by a series of canals which serve for respiration, or locomotion, or both. The outer casing is usually covered with tubercles and spines, from which the name echinoderm, or "hedge-hog skin," is derived.

The Echinoderms are the only large group of animals that is exclusively marine.

Class ASTEROIDEA

(*Starfishes*)

The Spiny Crossfish, or *Asterias glacialis*, common on the British coasts, may be briefly described as a star-shaped animal, with a central disc from which radiate five arms. In the Echinoderms the usual number of rays is five. The arms are not very distinctly marked off from the central disc.

On the under surface is the mouth, surrounded by a number of spines, and leading into a large sac-like stomach which occupies the greater part of the cavity of the disc. From the mouth to the end of the arms runs a groove, on either side of which is a series of small tubular bodies arranged in pairs. On the end of these tubular bodies are sucker-like discs. The animal can protrude or withdraw these tubes, and the suckers take a firm hold of any solid object in the neighbourhood. By means of these "tube-feet" the animal can either maintain its position or, by a combined action of the muscles of the arms and the tube-feet, move from place to place.

Asterias glacialis
The Spiny Crossfish.

The mechanism by which the tube-feet of a starfish are protruded and withdrawn is peculiar. It is essentially hydraulic pressure. In the cavity on the inside of the arm, between the plate of which they pass, the tube-feet are expanded into small, hollow, muscular bulbs. Each bulb, or ampulla, is connected by a small tube to a larger tube lying at the base of the arm-groove. This, in turn, is connected with a hollow ring round the mouth, to which are attached several bladders or reservoirs. This ring communicates with the exterior by a canal ending in a sieve-like plate on the surface opposite the mouth. Water passes through this plate down the canal into the circum-oral ring with its reservoirs, and from there, by way of the tubes, into the bulbs attached to the tube-feet. The muscular walls of the bulbs contract, drive the water into tube-feet and so cause them to expand. At the end of the arm there is a single tube-foot which is incapable of contraction. This is used as a sense-tentacle, or feeler, and above it is a small, red eye-spot.

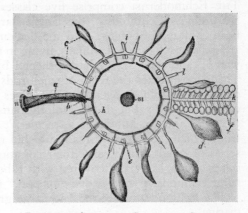

DIAGRAM OF AMBULACRAL SYSTEM OF A STARFISH

f, Small swellings connected with tube-feet; *k*, The radial canal with which they unite; *e*, Ring-canal into which the radial canals open; *c, d,* Membranous sacs that serve as reservoirs for water from radial canals; *a,* Stone-canal, leading from ring-canal to the madreporite, *n*; *m*, Mouth.

If we examine the upper surface of a Crossfish, we find that it consists of a network of plates, between which protrude little bladders of skin ; these are the papulae, and their function is to aerate the fluid of the body-cavity. The plates themselves are covered with a forest of spines. In the Crossfish these spines are all separate, but in many Starfishes they occur in clusters on a single stalk, like the bristles at the end of a paint-brush : these spine-clusters are known as paxillae. In the interstices of the plates are pads of skin covered with little white specks. Examined under a microscope these specks are seen to have the form of minute pincers, or scissors : these are the pedicellariae, and are used for catching hold of small objects. They can hang on to small food-particles, or be used as weapons of defence. Once the pedicellariae have gripped an object, escape is difficult, for the muscles attached to the handles of the pincers join below in a common band ; consequently the greater the pull away from the starfish, the greater the pressure on the handles of the pincers, and the tighter the grip of the jaws.

On the upper surface can also be seen the sieve-like plate through which the water passes into the canals leading to the tube-feet, and in some, but not in all, starfishes, a small aperture, the anus.

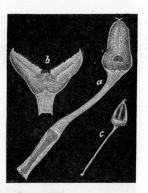

The sexes are separate ; and the gonads can be seen as long, feather-shaped bodies lying in the cavity of the arms below the paired out-growths of the stomach. The genital products escape through slits on the upper surface between the arms. Fertilisation takes place in the sea, and the eggs develop into free-swimming larvae and in about six weeks into small starfishes.

PEDICELLARIAE

a, Two-jawed, closed ; *b*, Two-jawed, open ; *c*, Three-jawed. (Enlarged.)

Only a small percentage of the larvae survive, for millions are eaten by fishes.

Starfishes are brightly coloured creatures, often with various shades of red, yellow, and purple. They are also very voracious feeders, eating almost any organic matter.

The favourite food of the Crossfish is mussels and kindred molluscs. Its method of feeding is to seize the mussel with its tube-feet, to hold it just below its mouth, and to arch its body and fold its arms over its prey like an umbrella. Its stomach is then forced through the mouth, inside out, to envelop its victim, until digestion has gone far enough for the edible parts to be removed from the shell. When dealing with large molluscs like the oyster it grips the sea-floor with the tube-feet at the end of the arms, and pulls the valves of the oyster apart with those along the middle of its arms. Although an oyster can resist a very considerable (about 4000 grammes) sudden pull, a long, continued pull exhausts it and forces it to open its valves; the starfish then thrusts in its stomach and pulls out the oyster.

Several species of starfishes eat oysters, and consequently cause much damage to oyster-fisheries. Dr. F. A. Bather writes, " No fewer than 42,000 bushels of starfish were removed from the oyster-beds of Connecticut in a single year, but not till they had done damage to the amount of 631,500 dollars. Crossfishes are also a great trouble to other fishermen, eating their bait, and even the fishes on the lines, and damaging the fishes in the nets. It is not to be wondered at that they have an evil reputation, so that in some parts they are called Devil's Fingers, and regarded with superstitious dread. To their credit it may be said that they are scavengers of the sea, and that their bodies make excellent manure."

Palmipes. A " Bird's-foot."

Besides the Common Crossfish (*Asterias rubens*) and the larger Spiny Crossfish (*Asterias glacialis*) found from the Arctic waters to the Cape Verde Islands, there are a number of starfishes common on the British coasts. *Asterina gibbosa* is a very small form, about an inch in diameter, with very short arms. The back is somewhat arched, and the under (oral) surface flat. Its eggs are very large, with much yolk, and the larva, instead of being free-swimming, as in most Echinoderms, remains on the bottom.

Palmipes placenta, a related form, is very flat, and looks like a pentagonal biscuit. It derives its name, " Bird's-foot," from the five radial ridges on the back corresponding to the arm-grooves beneath them. These, together with its yellow colour, suggest the foot of a goose.

Henricia sanguinolenta has a general resemblance to a Crossfish, but the arms are more heavily plated. Instead of shedding their eggs into the sea, the females fasten themselves to a rock by the tips of their arms, and arch their bodies into a dome in the cavity of which the eggs develop. The mother remains in this position, without food, until the young are able to provide for themselves.

Porania pulvillus, one of the starfishes called " Cushion-stars " by Forbes, is reddish-purple in colour, and has a thick body with short arms. The plates on the upper surface are sunk in a solid, gelatinous mass of tissue, so that the back is covered with smooth skin. The sides, however, are provided with conspicuous plates bearing spines.

Mithrodia has large blunt spines, bearing tiny spinelets.

The Sunstars (*Solaster*) are recognisable by their large number of arms which give them the appearance of a conventional picture of the sun. The spines are arranged in sheaves. They mostly inhabit Arctic waters, and live on other Echinoderms.

The Velata are a curious group of modified deep-water starfishes, which have their spines arranged in sheaves connected with webs of skin, so as to form umbrella-like structures. These webbed spine-clusters are usually separate, but in *Pteraster* the edges of the webs, or umbrellas, are joined together so as to form a tent-like covering over the whole back. In *Pteraster* the young develop beneath the tent, the space between it and the back being used as a brood-pouch. In the allied *Hymenaster* the under surface has long spines, and there is a wide membrane around the edges from which the animal derives its name.

In the *Paxillosa* the upper surface is closely set with free spine-tufts or paxillae.

Astropecten has very well-marked marginal plates, and neither vent nor suckers to its tube-feet. Having no suckers it cannot pull open molluscs, but has to swallow its prey whole. It lies, when at rest, half buried in the sand with only the middle of its back uncovered. It manages to breathe because its gill-sacs, or papulae, are situated in the part it leaves exposed. It has very muscular arms, and it can run along the sand on the tips of its pointed tube-feet.

Solaster. A Sunstar

Luidia is an allied form with seven or eight arms of unequal length. This starfish breaks off its arms, often into little pieces, on being in any way disturbed, and is consequently very difficult to catch intact. There is a vivid passage in Forbes' " History of British Starfishes " where he tells how he took with him a bucket of fresh water in which to put his catch.

" A *Luidia*," he continues, " came up in the dredge, a most gorgeous specimen. As it does not generally break up before it is raised above the surface of the sea, cautiously and anxiously I sank my bucket to a level with the dredge's mouth, and proceeded in the most gentle manner to introduce *Luidia* to the purer element. In a moment he proceeded to dissolve his corporation, and at every mesh of the dredge his fragments were seen escaping. In despair I grasped at the largest, and brought up the extremity of an arm with its terminating eye, the spinous lid of which opened and closed with something exceedingly like a wink of derision."

Starfishes have considerable powers of regeneration, that is to say, parts that are injured, or lost, speedily grow again. If one or more arms are lost, new ones grow in their place, but an arm will not give rise to a whole starfish unless it has attached to it that portion of the disc which contains the madreporite. There are forms with several madreporites; and if they split into pieces each piece containing a madreporite can grow into a whole starfish.

The order Valvata includes the starfishes in which the skeleton has no prominent spines, but is covered with minute granules. To it belongs *Linckia*, which often has the appearance of one long arm with four very short ones budding off from the end of it. This is known as the "comet-form": the long arm has been broken off from another *Linckia* and the four short ones represent a stage in the arm's growth into a complete starfish. The occurrence of many of these

"Comet" form of *Linckia*

"comet-forms" shows that *Linckia* easily loses its arms. *Culcita* is simply a pentagonal disc in which arms cannot be said to exist.

To the same group as the Crossfish, *Brisinga*, *Odinia*, and *Freyella* belong. These starfishes are characterised by their numerous, very long arms and tiny discs. Of these Dr. F. A. Bather relates the following story. "Dredging in the deep waters off Norway the poet Asbjörnsen brought up a phosphorescent starfish with small central disc and many long thin arms; impressed by its shining beauty, he called it *Brisinga*, after the breast ornament of the goddess Freya." The allied genera *Freyella* and *Odinia* are named after the Scandinavian deities.

Class OPHIUROIDEA
(*Brittle-stars*)

There is something to be learnt about this group of Echinoderms from a consideration of both its English and its scientific names. As "Brittle-star" suggests, they are very apt to break off their arms, much in the same way as *Luidia* and *Linckia* already described. Ophiuroidea, by its Greek derivation, means snake-tail, and is suggested by the animal's mode of locomotion, by the wriggling of its arms which recalls the movement of the tail of a snake.

If we examine a Brittle-star we notice at once that the arms do not grade into the disc, as they do in the starfishes, but are clearly marked off from it. The disc itself is circular. Moreover, the groove on the oral or under surface of the arms, which is a conspicuous feature in the starfishes, is not to be seen. It has been roofed over, and runs beneath its roof all the way to the mouth. Between the plates, which cover in the grooves on the ventral surface, short feelers protrude; these are the representatives of the tube-feet in the starfishes. If we open up an arm, we find that the cavity is to a large extent occupied by a series of small bones, or ossicles articulating with one another by interlocking facets and knobs; these ossicles are very like the vertebrae of a snake, and give the arm both flexibility and strength. They are continued to the mouth, at the border of which they are much modified, and join with the similar ossicles of the adjacent arms to form the mouth-frame. The plates projecting into the cavity of the mouth are known as " jaws," and on them is often a vertical series of so-called " teeth." Here is also attached a tuft of flattened spines known as tooth-papillae. The jaws and teeth are not used for breaking up food, but they act as strainers to keep out unwanted morsels. Some of the tentacles round the mouth are larger than the rest, and help the animal in feeding; they also clear away the remnants of undigested food rejected through the mouth, for the animal has no separate vent.

On the ventral surface, at the junction of each arm with the disc, is a pair of slit-like openings leading into pouches at the sides of the arms. These pouches function as respiratory sacs, for in the living Ophiuroid the disc alternately expands and contracts, by which means water is drawn in and forced out. The oxygen in solution in the incoming water passes through the thin walls of the pouches and is exchanged for carbon dioxide in the fluid of the animal's body-cavity. The carbon dioxide is expelled with the outgoing stream. In some forms these pouches serve also as brood-pouches, for they are in communication with the ovaries, and the eggs may develop in them. In others the eggs are discharged into the pouches and are carried to the exterior by the outgoing stream of water.

Ophiuroids feed on all kinds of small organisms, especially small molluscs: the deep-water forms feed mostly on the organic matter which is being continuously deposited from above on the ocean floor, where they have been found up to a depth of nearly four miles.

In opposition to the mode of locomotion of the starfish, which consists essentially in a slow protrusion and retraction of the tube-feet, the brittle-star moves by rapid muscular jerks of its arms. The effect is a sort of combination of wriggling and rowing.

Brittle-stars are often brilliantly coloured creatures: they are sometimes of the same colour throughout, and sometimes marked with a vivid pattern. The tropical forms especially are strongly pigmented. Moreover, phosphorescence is a common feature of these animals. It is the product of a special tissue, and whereas in the deep-water forms it occurs spontaneously, in the shore-living forms it only appears when the animal is irritated.

The power of regenerating lost parts, which has already been noted in the starfishes, is even more highly developed in the Ophiuroids. Some species are capable of reproduction by fission, that is to say, an individual splits into two parts and each part grows into a distinct individual.

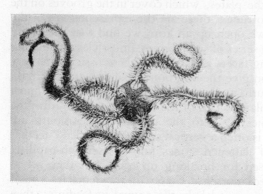

Ophiothrix.   A typical Brittle-star

There are between 1500 and 2000 species of recent Ophiuroids, and of these we can mention only very few.

Amphiura squamata is a small form, about a quarter of an inch across the disc. It is hermaphrodite and viviparous; the young develop inside the pouches of the mother. It has the power of throwing off the whole of the disc, except the mouth, and growing a new one. *Ophiactis* lives in crannies between stones and shells. The Mediterranean *Ophiactis virens* is much modified internally in relation to its habit of continually splitting into two and so multiplying. *Ophiacantha* has long spines, and *Ophiopholis aculeata*, very common at the mouth of the Clyde, displays a great variety of bright colours. Another very brightly coloured form is the common British *Ophiothrix fragilis* which occurs in swarms on the sea-bottom. *Amphiura* burrows just beneath the surface of the sea-bottom, and lies there with its long, thin arms stretched out. Thus hidden, it catches and devours small

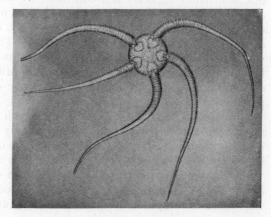

Ophiura.   A Sandstar

marine creatures, passing them to its mouth by its tube-feet. In some places it is so abundant that the ends of the arms of the one individual are almost touching those of its neighbours, and a sort of web of these creatures occurs on the sea-bottom.

The so-called Sandstars, of which *Ophiura* is an example, have very short spines lying close to the sides of the arms, and are consequently unfitted for climbing; they can, however, row themselves along quickly over a hard surface. They either scoop their food into their mouths with their arms, or manoeuvre so that their mouth is directly above their prey. *Ophiura texturata* has occasionally been found above the lower tide-mark; as the water retreats, it buries itself in the sand, but when it has been uncovered by the tide it comes to the surface and tries to make for the water again.

A star-shaped impression in the sand marks the place where it has been lying. Investigations into the rate of growth of this species show that it takes two years to reach sexual maturity, and three or more years to reach its full size.

The Ophiuroids, owing to their great abundance, play an important part in the economy of the sea, not only as consumers of a considerable portion of the available food-supply, but also as food for fishes and other animals.

Order EURYALAE

(*Gorgon-head Starfishes*)

Allied to the true Ophiuroids is an order variously known as the Euryalids, the branched *Ophiurae* (*Cladophiurae*), and the Gorgon-head Starfishes. The salient characteristic of the Euryalids is their habit of climbing up the stems of Sea-pens, or Gorgonid-corals, around which they coil themselves with some of their arms while with the others they catch any small organism that happens to be passing. In order to do this their arms have to move mainly in a vertical direction, winding and coiling upwards or downwards. This is made possible by the hourglass - shaped articulations of the " vertebrae," or ossicles of the arms. Moreover, the majority of forms have their five arms divided into many branches which fork again and again. In *Gorgono-cephalus caputmedusae*, known as the

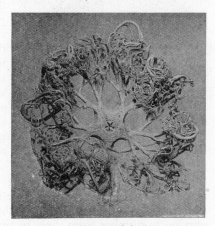

Gorgonocephalus
A Gorgon-head starfish.

Argus, the arms have the appearance of a dense coil of snakes, and their end-branches are said to number as many as 80,000.

In the Euryalids the upper and lower plates of the arms have either

disappeared altogether, or are vestigial, and the surface is covered by a skin which is either smooth or studded with granules. Moreover, the arm-spines are usually transformed into hooks, or spiny knobs. *Asteronyx loveni* is a good example of a Euryalid with unbranched arms. This is almost always found clinging to a Sea-pen in the manner already described, and it sometimes eats the polyps of the animal to which it clings. Of the species with branching arms, the Arctic *Gorgonocephalus eucnemis* may measure more than a foot from tip to tip of its arms.

Class ECHINOIDEA
(*Sea-urchins*)

The Echinoidea derive their name from the Greek word for a hedge-hog, because of the spines, or prickles, with which they are covered. With the exception of the *Echinothuridae*, or Leather-urchins, they have all a compact, hard skeleton of regularly arranged pentagonal plates, over which is a covering of skin. They are sometimes of considerable size, the body being six or seven inches in diameter. While the usual shape is that of an orange, or an egg, some forms are quite flattened and look like biscuits. The test, or skeleton, consists of ten double rows of plates. Five of these

double rows carry two series of pairs of small pores, each pair connecting one tube-foot with the water-vessel beneath the test. These pore-bearing double rows of plates are radial, and are known as the ambulacra; they correspond to the under side of the arms of the Star-fishes and Brittle-stars. The double rows of plates between the ambulacra are known as the inter-ambulacra; they are generally much broader than the ambulacra. In some Sea-urchins the plates of the ambulacra grow together to form compound-plates, but the

Test of edible Sea-urchin, with the spines removed from the left-hand half.

number of original or " primary " plates constituting the compound-plate can be distinguished by counting the pairs of pores, for each primary ambulacral-plate has a single tube-foot, and consequently a single pair of pores. In the compound-plates the tube-feet are arranged in regular arcs, varying in number from three to twelve.

In the middle of the upper surface of the test is a small, round area known as the apical system; it consists of ten plates, five from the ambulacra, and five from the interambulacra. The five ambulacral plates of the apical system are known as " oculars," because they are pierced by a small pore through which protrudes a tentacle, which does not, however, carry an eye-spot as does the tentacle at the end of a starfish's arm. The five interambulacral plates of the apical system are known as genital-plates, because they are pierced by a pore through which the genital products escape : one of these genital-plates is the equivalent of the sieve-like plate or madreporite of the starfish. Inside the apical area there is, in the round or " regular " Sea-urchins, a smaller region known as the anal area, for it contains the vent.

In the flattened, or irregular, Sea-urchins the vent is shifted to the edge of the test, or even to the under surface. In the round-urchins the mouth is situated in the middle of the under surface. The area round the mouth is covered with soft skin : this is often more or less filled with small plates, but sometimes is bare, except for the pore-plates of the ambulacra which meet at the mouth as in the starfish. The mouth itself is, in the regular forms, provided with five strong teeth ; these are continued beneath the test as long curved structures, attached to a curious framework of thirty bones connected by a complicated series of muscles. This five-sided framework is known as the " lantern of Aristotle," and is so called because the Greek philosopher of that name compared it to a ship's lantern of the type in use in his day. The Heart-urchins, or Spatangoids, have neither teeth nor dental apparatus.

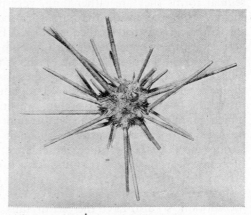

Cidaris. A regular Sea-urchin

The Echinoids are furnished with several different kinds of appendages, of which the most conspicuous are the spines. These are articulated with tubercles borne on the test ; and on the base of the spine is a ridge, or ring, to which are connected muscles attached to the test round the tubercle. By means of these muscles the spines can be moved in any direction. In the regular urchins the spines are arranged in an orderly series.

If we examine a simple form, such as the *Cidaris cidaris*, common on the west coast of Ireland, we find that each plate in the interambulacral areas is provided with one large tubercle to which a large spine is attached. These are the primary tubercles and spines. Each primary tubercle is surrounded by a circle of smaller tubercles bearing smaller spines, which are known as secondary spines ; and finally there are a large number of very small elevations dotted about the test : these are the " miliary " tubercles, and they are the sockets for an altogether different type of appendage, the pedicellariae. These are small pincer-like organs, with a head consisting usually of three valves, and a stalk to which the head is either directly attached by muscle-bands, or by means of a long, flexible neck. Each valve is usually provided with long, tactile hairs : if anything comes into contact with these hairs, the valves of the pedicellariae instantly close.

Another type of appendage is the " sphaeridia," which are small, oval, or rounded structures, situated on the ambulacra of the lower half of the test. They are regarded as organs either of balance or of taste.

Gills are absent in the irregular urchins, and in the Cidarids. When present, they are bush-shaped organs, surrounding the mouth ; and each interambulacrum carries one pair.

Among the appendages we must include the tube-feet. They vary considerably in shape in the various groups of Echinoids ; but in the regular forms they are rather long, very protractile, and end in a disc-like sucker. On the inside they are furnished with a skeleton of variously shaped calcareous rods, called spicules. Each tube-foot has normally two vessels or pipes connecting it with its bulb or ampulla beneath the test.

From the foregoing account of the external characters of Echinoids it will be seen that they are like starfishes that have grown in such a way that the ends of the arms are gathered together round the anus. If we look inside the test of a regular urchin, we find the mouth leading into a gut, which running almost all the way round the inside of the test turns back on itself to open to the exterior through the vent. It is held in place by strong sheets of tissue called mesenteries. The genital organs are, in the breeding season, large, tree-like structures lying in the interambulacra below the apical area. The water-ring lies just above the dental framework.

Just as the Starfishes and Brittle-stars each have their own method of locomotion, so also have the Sea-urchins. They either walk along on the tips of their spines, as on stilts, or pull themselves along by attaching the suckers at the end of the tube-feet, at the same time using their spines to balance themselves. The Cidarids, having poorly developed suckers on their tube-feet, move by means of their spines alone. Dr. Bather describes how a *Cidaris*, when placed upon its back on a smooth surface, pushes itself into an oblique position with the spines on one side, then throws the rest of its spines over towards the other side so as to displace the centre of gravity and thus roll over into its normal position.

The pedicellariae serve a variety of functions. They keep the test clean, removing particles of dirt, small organisms that settle on it, and any unwanted foreign body. On the other hand, they sometimes hold pieces of seaweed, etc., over the test in order to conceal it, a type of camouflage not confined to Sea-urchins. But their most important function is defence, for the so-called gemmiform pedicellariae are provided with a poison gland which secretes a toxic fluid into the wound caused by their bite. These pedicellariae will seize an enemy and hold on until they are torn from the test. In an account of a fight between a starfish and a sea-urchin the author describes how the urchin seized the tube-feet of the attacking starfish with some of its gemmiform pedicellariae. The starfish retreated, and in doing so dragged from the test all these pedicellariae. The attack and retreat were repeated until all the pedicellariae were pulled out of the test. The starfish then enveloped the urchin with its extruded stomach.

The pedicellariae are also useful to the animal in holding small creatures until they can be seized by the tube-feet and passed by them to the mouth.

The natural relationships of the Echinoids are still in some respects a matter of controversy. Of all the urchins the Cidarids are probably the most primitive; they have a rounded body with stout primary spines covered with a special outer layer beset with hairy outgrowths. The secondary spines are usually flattened, instead of round. A *Cidaris* which occurs off the North of Scotland is known as the Piper, because the round body, and the spines, remind the country people of a bagpipe with its drones. Cidarids are found all over the world.

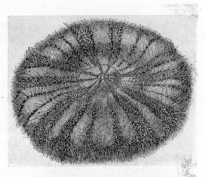

Echinothurid. A Leather-urchin

The Echinothurids, or Leather-urchins, have a flexible test. This is due to the presence of thin slips of soft body-wall between the skeletal plates. They are generally large, brightly coloured creatures which in the preserved state have the appearance of a tam - o' - shanter. They are deep-sea forms, and Wyville Thompson gives a vivid account of the dredging of one of the first specimens on record. " As the dredge was coming in we got a glimpse of a large, scarlet urchin in the bag. As it was blowing fresh, and there was some difficulty in getting the dredge capsized, we thought it would be crushed to pieces. We were somewhat surprised, therefore, when it rolled out of the bag uninjured ; and our surprise increased, and was in my case mingled with a certain amount of nervousness, when it settled quietly in the form of a rounded red cake, and began to pant—a line of conduct, to say the least of it, very unusual in its rigid undemonstrative order."

The Echinothurids have poison-sacs at the bases of some of the spines, and can inflict a very painful sting. The Saleniids are small deep-water forms with long, slender, usually thorny, spines.

Of the Arbaciids *Arbacia lixula*, a common Mediterranean form, has been much studied. It has a conical test, and moves by means of its oral or lower tube-feet exclusively. Whatever the stimulus applied to the animal, the spines always converge, so cannot be used in locomotion. Moreover, the skin is not, as in most urchins, covered with vibratile hairs, so that the faecal matter deposited on the test is not removed in the usual manner by the divergence of the spines and the sweeping action of the vibratile hairs on the skin. The animal overcomes this difficulty by living near the shore where the wash of the waves keeps it clean.

Coelopleurus floridana is a large deep-sea form from the West Indies; it has long, curved, and pointed red spines. The Diadematids, or Turban-urchins, mostly live in shallow water among the rocks. They have long, extremely sharp, and sometimes poisonous spines which they point at anything approaching them. They are very sensitive to light and shade, and move quickly on their long spines. They occur in enormous numbers on the Great Barrier Reef of Australia.

To the Echinids belongs the common British *Echinus esculentus* and a number of other well-known forms. *Echinus esculentus* is thickly covered

Diadema. A Turban-urchin

with short spines of a reddish colour, with violet tips; the test itself is globular in shape, and bright red. It has long tube-feet, with strong suckers. The spines are very little used in locomotion, but the animal besides pulling itself along by its tube-feet can, owing to the flexible nature of the mouth-area, protrude its teeth and use them to drag itself along. It owes its specific name to the fact that its ripe ovaries are regarded as a delicacy all round the shores of the Mediterranean.

Echinus acutus is a variable species, much smaller than *Echinus esculentus*, and with longer, and fewer, primary spines; it also lives in deeper water, being abundant at one hundred fathoms. *Paracentrotus* has five or six pairs of pores in its ambulacral plates, instead of the three found in *Echinus*.

Paracentrotus lividus, or the Purple Egg-urchin, is a somewhat flattened, greenish form, about two inches in diameter, with spines about an inch long. It occurs in very great numbers off the south and west coasts of Ireland, and also in the Mediterranean. It bores deep, basin-shaped cavities in the rock, and covers itself with pieces of seaweed, etc.; it prevents itself from being dislodged by the waves by wedging its spines tightly against the sides of its hole. It lives in large colonies, the rocks in certain places being honey-combed with these strange cavities, each with its occupant. The method of excavation is not certainly known, but it is probably effected by the continual scratching of the spines and teeth.

Strongylocentrotus drobachiensis is another rock-borer. It is a handsome, shore-dwelling species, with a wide distribution in the colder seas of the

Northern hemisphere. It has a greenish-brown test, and greenish or reddish spines with white tips. Its favourite food is said to consist of Hydroids.

Heterocentrotus and *Colobocentrotus* are tropical shallow-water forms, with very stout primary spines, triangular in section ; between the bases of these the tips of the secondary spines are expanded umbrella-fashion, to form a covering or cuirass to protect the animals from the waves.

The *Clypeastroidea*, or Cake-urchins, are much modified in relation to life on a sandy bottom. They live normally in shallow water just beneath the surface of the sand, and the test is much flattened to prevent them from sinking, or from being turned over by the waves. The centre of the test is more or less raised, and slopes down to a thin, expanded edge. On the upper surface are five sunken areas, shaped like petals, the edges of which are marked by large slit-like pores ; these are the ambulacra, and the slit-like pores are the holes through which pass the long tube-feet, which protrude above the sand and act as gills. In addition to these respiratory tube-feet are a great number of small locomotor tube-feet, scattered all over the upper surface and concentrated, in some forms, on the under surface in ten branching grooves which meet at the mouth. These locomotor tube-feet are small, and feeble in comparison with those of an *Echinus* ; but in loose sand a large number of feeble pulls from the whole surface is more effective, as a means of locomotion, than the action of a much smaller number of more powerful tube-feet.

Clypeaster. A Cake-urchin

The test is covered with a forest of small, velvety spines, which on the upper surface are all furnished with vibratile hairs ; these cause a continuous flow of fresh sea-water to pass over the respiratory tube-feet. Moreover, the anus has moved from the centre of the upper surface to the edge of the under surface, so that the water flowing over the gills is free from defilement. The Clypeasters swallow great quantities of sand, and obtain their nourishment from its organic inclusions ; the teeth, in relation to this, act simply as sand-shovels, and can no longer bite or chew. The gut coils inside round the test as near to the edge as the flattening will allow, and the spaces not occupied by the gut and the other internal organs are filled by supporting pillars or walls of calcareous matter, which serve to keep the upper surface of the test from crushing down on to the lower.

Echinarachnius parma is a very flattened form, almost circular in outline, and is known as the Sand-dollar. It is common on the east coast of North

America and derives its name from its supposed resemblance to the American silver dollar.

Rotula, or the Wheel-urchin, has the edge of the skeleton drawn out into

a number of finger-shaped processes recalling the spokes of a wheel.

In *Mellita* these processes join at their tips and so leave spaces or " lunules " which appear as perforations in the test. This formation of finger-shaped processes and " lunules " is essentially an attempt to reduce the size of the skeleton, for in the very flattened forms this tends to become disproportionate to the size of the soft parts of the body.

The Spatangoids, or Heart-urchins, are modified in a different direction, and the common British *Echinocardium cordatum* is usually selected as a good example of the order. *Echinocardium* lives at the bottom of a burrow, about nine inches below

Rotula.   A Wheel-urchin

the surface of the sand ; and there is a kind of chimney leading from the burrow to the surface.   The animal digs its way into the sand by means of

Spatangus.   A Heart-urchin

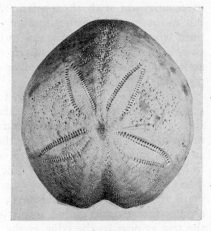

Spatangus
A Heart-urchin with its spines removed.

its flattened spines, which also serve to keep the walls of the burrow from collapsing inwards.   The chimney is cemented with mucus.   The test, instead of being flattened, is elongated, and oval in outline.   The mouth is on the under surface, towards the front end of the test, and is a transverse slit with a projecting lip ; there are neither teeth nor jaws. The anus has moved to the hinder end.

As in the Clypeasters there are five petals with pores for the feet functioning as gills, but the anterior ambulacrum, or front petal, has passing through it a number of enormously long tube-feet, which extend right to the top of the chimney, where they gather up any edible substances within their reach ; they pass any particle they may have seized down to the shorter tube-feet near the mouth, and they, in their turn, convey the food into the mouth. Many Spatangoids have special bands of small dark spines covered with vibratile hairs, which drive a current of water over the respiratory tube-feet, and remove the faecal matter from the vicinity of the anus. In most Spatangoids, on the under side, behind the mouth, is a specially modified area known as the " plastron," or " sternum," from its resemblance to a ventral shield, and it is this area which carries the spade-shaped digging spines.

Not all Heart-urchins have a chimney from their burrow to the surface. Some forms that live in loose, clean sand are able to do without it.

The fossil record of Sea-urchins is rich ; and has afforded material for much study. The Druids regarded them as serpent's eggs, possessing magical properties, and treated them as objects of veneration, as they did the mistletoe.

Class HOLOTHUROIDEA
(*Sea-cucumbers*)

The Holothurians have a very different appearance from the Echinoderms so far considered. They are sausage-shaped, or vermiform creatures, usually with a thick, leathery skin. The calcareous skeleton is not, as in other Echinoderms, a solid frame, but consists of innumerable microscopic rods and plates embedded in the skin. In some forms these rods and plates, which are known as spicules, are so numerous, and closely packed, that their presence makes the skin hard and stiff ; and in the Psolids they are modified into large overlapping scales ; in a few species they are altogether absent. The mouth is at one end of the body, and the anus at the other. The mouth is surrounded by a circlet of tube-feet modified into feelers which show great diversity in structure, and are important in classification.

As in other Echinoderms there are five radii, marked by five bands of longitudinal muscles running beneath the skin. Associated with these there are, in most forms, five radial water-canals which send branches to the tentacles, traverse the length of the body, and are connected in front with a ring-canal which surrounds the gullet ; the radial water-canals sometimes give off five double rows of tube-feet, which are never in grooves, but come directly from the surface. The tube-feet are not, however, very often arranged in five regular series, but spread all over the ventral surface, and even all over the body. The water-vascular system instead of communicating with the exterior through a sieve-like plate or madreporite, as it does in other Echinoderms, in most Holothurians opens into the body-cavity. In many forms the body is somewhat flattened, the under side being used as a walking surface, and has three of the radii forming what is known as the " trivium "; while the upper, or dorsal, side has two radii and is known as the " bivium."

Just in front of the ring-canal, surrounding the gullet, is the calcareous ring, which consists of five radial and five interradial pieces. These pieces differ considerably in the various groups, and are much used in classification. The radial pieces are usually distinguished from the interradial pieces by the presence of a notch in front, through which the radial muscle and the radial nerve pass.

The mouth leads into the gullet, behind which is a long tube, the gut :

Holothuria forskali.   " The nigger."   A sea-cucumber

this turns back upon itself in an S-shaped loop. Before reaching the anus it widens into a rectum, or cloaca, which is attached to the body-wall by a large number of muscles. The cloaca is important for the part it plays in respiration. As the muscles contract, it opens widely and a quantity of water is drawn in ; relaxation of the muscles causes it to close, and the water is driven out. This bellows-like method of breathing is made more effective by the presence in the body-cavity of most Holothurians of paired, branching tubes coming off the cloaca ; these are filled and emptied of water by the pumping action just described.

Close to these branching tubes, which are known as respiratory trees, and like them attached to the walls of the cloaca, are a number of small, worm-like tubes which secrete slime. These tubes form very singular weapons of defence, for if the animal is attacked, or irritated, the circular muscles of the body-wall contract and force the liquid in the body-cavity against the walls of the cloaca, which burst as a consequence of the pressure of the liquid so that the tubes, together with a considerable portion of the viscera, are extruded. In the sea-water the slime secreted by the tubes swells and becomes a mass of long, sticky, white threads in which the enemy is entangled. Even so formidable an animal as a lobster is known to have been rendered quite helpless by this sticky secretion. These slime tubes are not present in all Holothurians ; the " Cotton-spinner," or Nigger (*Holothuria forskali*), common on the British coasts, derives one of its popular names from its habit of throwing out these remarkable slime threads.

The genital organs are situated on the upper side of the body : they consist of a number of long tubes, usually branching, and open to the exterior by a duct at the base of the upper tentacles. In a few forms the passage is continued to the tip of one of the tentacles. In most Holothurians the sexes are separate, but a number are hermaphrodite ; the eggs and sperm, however, develop at different times, so that the hermaphrodite forms are alternately male and female. A few Holothurians are viviparous, that is to say, the young develop in the body of the mother, and of these the European *Leptosynapta minuta* is a good example.

Holothurians have great powers of regeneration, and readily renew the lost parts of the body. In fact, the majority, when irritated, violently contract the circular muscles of the body and expel their viscera either through the anus, or through a rupture in the wall of the cloaca. They then grow another set of organs within a few weeks. The Synaptids sometimes contract themselves in such a way that the body is torn across in two ; the anterior end will then grow another hinder end. A few forms normally multiply by the division of the body into two, and the growth into a complete animal of each part. This has been observed in *Cucumaria lactea* and a number of other forms. *Cucumaria lactea* also multiplies by budding, the anterior end of a new individual growing out of the side of the body near the head of the parent.

The Holothurians are, on the whole, sluggish creatures, lying on the bottom or creeping about by the contraction of the body-muscles. The tube-feet are little used as organs of locomotion, but rather as a means of attachment to rocks, etc. Their food consists either of the organic matter contained in the mud and sand of the sea-floor, or of the small floating organisms, either living or dead, in the sea-water. The shape of their tentacles, or feelers, is closely connected with their method of feeding. The mud- and sand-eaters have stout feelers, with short branches, with which they shovel into their mouths quantities of the bottom material : these have shield-shaped feelers. Those, on the other hand, that feed on floating organisms have feelers with long, slender branches covered with slime, in which their food becomes entangled : they are the *Dendrochirota*, or tree-feelers. There are three orders of bottom-feeders, the *Aspidochirota*, the *Elasipoda*, and the *Molpadonia*. Of those with long, bushy tentacles there are two orders, the *Dendrochirota* and the *Apoda*.

The *Elasipoda* are deep-sea forms, living in the ooze. The under side is often modified into a creeping sole and the tube-feet of the dorsal surface are long, stiff, pointed processes that act as gills. They must sink to some extent in the soft ooze, and the dorsal tube-feet project above its surface and so help the animals to breathe. The *Elasipoda* have often very strange shapes. In *Peniagone* the dorsal tube-feet are united by a web, and form a large sail-like organ above the front end. In *Psychropotes* they are fused to form a long tail.

In *Laetmogone* the ventral tube-feet are arranged in rows at the side of the body, and are like stumps on which the animal walks. In *Scotoanassa*, an active swimmer in the depths of the sea, the lateral tube-feet are confined to the hinder end and united to form a fringe. In *Oneirophanta* the back is covered with long, horn-like processes. Allied to the *Elasipoda* are a few forms that abandoned the bottom and took to the open sea. *Pelagothuria* has a great superficial likeness to a jelly-fish. The bases of the feelers have grown out into long processes connected in their upper part

Scotoplana. A deep-sea Holothurian

by a web ; the mouth, with its circlet of feelers, is above the web. They swim and float about the oceans, catching small organisms in their feelers.

The *Aspidochirota* are distinguished from the *Elasipoda* by the presence of respiratory trees. They live on firmer ground than the *Elasipoda*, and with their shield-shaped tentacles shovel the mud and sand into their mouths. To this order belongs the Cotton-spinner and its allies. *Stichopus* has the ventral tube-feet confined to the radii, and a neck-like prolongation of the front-end. The *Synallactids* are rather large, deep-sea forms, and a number of them have the habit of sticking shells, pieces of sponge, etc., to their skin. This appears to be a form of camouflage.

The *Aspidochirota* include among their numbers the edible forms known as Trepang or Bêche-de-mer. The Chinese make a soup of the dried bodies of these Holothurians. Those with the viscera intact, and with the smallest quantity of calcareous spicules, are the most highly prized. The catching of these edible forms on the Great Barrier Reef of Australia and in the Malay Archipelago constitutes a considerable industry.

The *Molpadonia* are burrowers, living buried in the ground, and are modified in relation to their mode of life. They have thick, sausage-shaped bodies, and a kind of tail at the end. They have simple finger-shaped feelers, and the tube-feet are reduced to five small papillae round the anus. They apparently live with their tails projecting from the mouths of their burrows for breathing purposes.

The *Dendrochirota* fish in the water for any small passing creature with their long, bushy feelers, and when they have caught it bend the feeler in which it is entangled down to the mouth, suck it off and straighten out the feeler.

Cucumaria and its allies have more or less cylindrical bodies, and the tube-feet are often confined to the five radii. *Cucumaria crocea* is an Antarctic form which holds its young on its back by its tube-feet, which are evenly distributed all over the surface. Some Dendrochirotids cling to the rocks or corals with their tube-feet, and others form burrows in the mud. *Ypsilothuria* is a V-shaped creature which lives buried in the mud, except for its two ends. In another burrower, *Rhopalodina*, from West Africa, the two ends have come together, so that the animal is like a bulb at the end of a stalk.

Psolus is a very curious form. There is a flattened, ventral sole to which the tube-feet are confined, and on the back the spicules are developed to form a sort of armour-plating of scales. In the Antarctic *Psolus ephippiger* the dorsal scales are modified to form a brood-pouch in which the young develop. The mouth, and sometimes the vent, is also protected by scales. The Psolids cling to rocks and stones by means of their ventral sole which acts as a sucker. *Psolus phantapus*, however, lives buried in the mud with only its two ends protruding.

The *Apoda*, or Synaptids, have lost their tube-feet, usually their radial canals, and their respiratory trees. This condition is associated with their burrowing mode of life. They have feather-shaped tentacles for catching floating particles of food, and a thin skin through which they breathe by diffusion. Their appearance is very like that of a worm. *Leptosynapta inhaerens* is a species common on the west coasts of England and Scotland. The majority of Synaptids

A PLATED HOLOTHURIAN
(*Psolus*)

Some plates of the back, above the brood-pouch, are removed (enlarged).

have spicules in the shape of anchors embedded in the skin, and these they use in locomotion. The handle-end of the anchor is attached to an anchor-plate by a kind of loose joint. When the animal extends its body and the skin is taut, the anchor is pressed against the plate and the flukes cause a multitude of tiny projections of the skin which grip in the sand. When the animal relaxes its muscles the flukes of the anchor are lifted from the anchor-plate and thus the creature drags itself along. *Leptosynapta besselii* is a giant form, which reaches a length of six feet.

Class CRINOIDEA
(*Sea-lilies*)

The fossil record of the Crinoids is extensive, and until recently the living forms were regarded as the impoverished survivors of a once numerous and powerful group. There were several reasons for this view. The number of shore-living forms is very small compared with other Echinoderms in countries where the littoral fauna is systematically studied. The number of species known was very small, partly because Crinoids are brittle and difficult to collect intact, and partly because they are not easy animals to study. The high percentage of inorganic matter in the body makes it a very suitable subject for fossilisation, and consequently the palaeontological record is very abundant. Our ideas, however, on the superiority of fossil over recent Crinoids must undergo a considerable change when we hear from Mr. A. H. Clark, whom we have to thank for much of our knowledge of recent Crinoids, that a ship in the North Pacific on which he was naturalist had, on more than one occasion, her forward deck buried under several tons of individuals belonging to a species larger than any fossil form, and that on the voyage he handled tens of thousands of specimens.

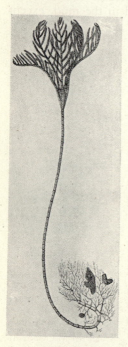

Rhizocrinus
A stalked Sea-lily.

The Crinoids are cup-shaped, or flower-shaped animals with feather-like branching arms. They are attached to the ground by a jointed stalk, either throughout life, or in the young stage only. The animal is so orientated that the ventral side is turned upwards, and the stalk is attached to the dorsal or under surface.

If we examine an adult stalked Crinoid, for example an *Endoxocrinus*, we find a stout, pentagonal stalk built up of small segments held together by a number of strands, and pierced by a canal containing a nerve. At intervals the stalk bears whorls of appendages called cirri, which can catch hold of rocks and other solid objects, for they are the animal's means of attachment. The cup to which the stalk is attached is, on its outer or dorsal surface, made up of strong, regularly arranged plates. From the sides of the cup spring five arms, which may fork once or many times ; consequently the number of end-branches to the arms varies widely in the different forms. The arms, like the rest of the skeleton, are made up of a series of plates jointed together. Each arm-plate has a side-branch, or pinnule, and these are arranged in an alternating series on both sides of the arms. From the ends of the arm-branches and pinnules run grooves which eventually meet in five channels passing to the mouth : these are lined with vibratile hairs driving a stream of water containing food-particles into the mouth. The latter is usually in the middle of the upper or ventral surface of the cup (the disc) and leads into a coiled gut, which opens to the exterior by a vent situated on a conical elevation near the mouth.

The food-grooves are lined with tube-feet arranged in a series of groups of three along the sides. The water-canals connected with the tube-feet meet in a ring round the mouth. There is no madreporite, but a number of small pores leading into the body-cavity, and also a number of small passages from the ring-canal. The tube-feet are not used for locomotion, but for respiration. The genital organs stretch from the body down the arms into the pinnules, where their products ripen and escape through an opening at the side. The stalked Crinoids live a stationary life attached to the sea-floor, sometimes by the cirri, and sometimes by root-like processes or incrusting expansions at the bottom of the stalk. They occur at considerable depths, and live by spreading their arms to collect the food-particles which are swept down the food-grooves into the mouth. The stem is flexible, and can bend with a current : it breaks most easily just below one of the whorls of cirri, so that the animal can readily attach itself again.

There is a rare and much modified Crinoid called *Holopus* found in shallow water in the Caribbean Sea. It is a reef-dweller, and the stem is so much reduced that the under or dorsal surface of the cup itself appears to be fixed to the rocks on which it lives. It hangs upside down on the roofs of caverns and clefts in the rocks.

The Comatulids, or unstalked forms, constitute the great majority of living Crinoids. Traces of the stem remain in the form of a large plate or knob with a circlet of cirri in the middle of the cup. Their normal habit is sessile, or stationary, attached to some suitable object by their cirri, but if need be they can both creep and swim. Creeping is effected by a combination of a pulling and a pushing with their arms. Two or three of the arms are extended to their fullest, and the nearest object is grasped, partly by the hooks at the end of the pinnules, and partly by means of a sticky secretion of the skin. As they hold on with one set of arms, they bend the others underneath the cup, and push in the direction of the object to which the extended arms are attached. This is not a rapid means of locomotion : an individual with arms about ten centimetres long, in an aquarium, was observed to cover about forty metres in an hour. Swimming is accomplished by an alternate bending and extension of the arms and pinnules.

They are for the most part shallow-water forms, and the common *Antedon bifida*, or Rosy Feather-star, of the British coasts, is a good example of the group. Except in the absence of a stalk its structure resembles that already outlined for the stalked Crinoids. It is found at depths varying from two to a hundred fathoms, and the deep-water specimens are larger than those in shallow water. The difference is considerable, for a shallow-water specimen measures about twelve centimetres across, while a deep-water specimen attains to about twenty-two centimetres. In Crinoids generally the average size increases gradually from the shore-line to the hundred-fathom line ; this size is maintained to about six hundred fathoms. Below the six-hundred-fathom line the size gradually decreases, until below the two-thousand-fathom line only a very few Crinoids of minute size are known.

For this variation in size with depth A. H. Clark has an interesting explanation which throws a light on the conditions of life of Crinoids. The upper layers of the sea are rich in small floating organisms, which, when they die, fall to the bottom and form a continual rain of dead organic matter. These small organisms, dead or alive, are the food of the Crinoids ; and near the surface the latter must depend on what drifts past their arms and pinnules. In rather deeper water they have both the living organisms and the rain of the dead. Below the hundred-fathom line the living organisms are said to begin to disappear, but this is compensated for by the great increase in the rain of the dead forms. This is maintained up to about six hundred fathoms ; below this the gradual decomposition of the dead forms lessens their food value, and there is consequently a gradual diminution in the size of the Crinoids feeding on them.

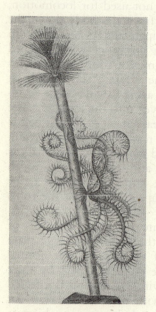

Antedon bifida
The Rosy Feather-star clinging to
the tube of a Sabellid worm.

A. H. Clark's contention that size varies with the food supply is borne out by a number of considerations. The common Arctic, circumpolar comatulid, *Heliometra glacialis*, shows a sudden great increase in size in two places, off the west coast of Greenland, and in the northern part of the Sea of Japan. Now, the west coast of Greenland has a large number of fiords which continually release vast masses of freshwater ice, and so kill off countless small organisms which cannot withstand the change in salinity. These fall to the bottom and supply the Crinoids with a very abundant supply of food. In the Kara and Barents seas there is no similar infiltration of fresh water to cause a change of salinity and kill off the floating life ; consequently the Crinoids are smaller. The giant North Japanese forms are accounted for in a rather different way. The Karo-Shiwo, or Japanese warm-current, mixes in its northern part with the cold water of the Bering and Okhotsk seas, and the change of temperature is fatal to enormous quantities of floating life, and so increases the food supply of the Crinoids.

In apparent contradiction to the general rule that between the hundred and the six-hundred-fathom line is the belt of maximum size for the Crinoids, in certain parts of the tropics and particularly in the East Indies, very large Crinoids are found in very shallow water, decreasing in size with depth. The suggested explanation is that the very hot sunlight causes rapid evaporation at the surface water, especially in shallow water, and a consequent mortality among small organisms. Moreover, when the tide comes in over the shallows there is a mingling of warm with comparatively cool waters, which destroys organisms incapable of enduring a change in temperature ; furthermore, the torrential tropical rains would change the salinity of the surface water and thus might kill off the more delicate of the floating life. A combination of all these factors might account for the great size of the Crinoids in the shallow waters of these regions.

Young comatulids pass through a stage in which they have a stalk, and lead a stationary existence similar to that of the stalked forms. The discovery, a little more than a hundred years ago, of a minute stalked Crinoid, that J. V. Thompson showed to be a young *Antedon*, led to the realisation of the affinities of stalked and unstalked forms. The larva of the young *Antedon* is a barrel-shaped creature, with separate rings of vibratile processes (cilia), by means of which it swims about. Inside the larva the skeleton develops in such a way that the stalk is in the anterior end, and the cup in the posterior, so that the front end of the larva becomes the hinder end of the adult. After swimming for a few days the larva fixes itself on a piece of seaweed or other object, by its anterior end, and after certain changes the cup opens, the arms are spread out, and the animal begins to feed. By the time that a couple of whorls of cirri have been developed, the young *Antedon* breaks away from its stalk and attaches itself to some anchorage by its cirri.

Most Echinoderms have a free-swimming larval stage in which they are carried along by currents until they develop into the adult form. By this means they can begin their adult life at some distance from their parents, and overcrowding is, to some extent, prevented.

Echinoderm larvae are distinguished by the band of vibratile processes which furnish their means of locomotion. Beginning as a simple band round the mouth, it forms complicated folds and out-growths, by which the larvae of the various classes may be recognised. Crinoid-larvae, however, differ from the rest in having a number of separate rings instead of one continuous band.

SECTION VIII

Phylum MOLLUSCA

By G. C. ROBSON, M.A.

CHIEF CHARACTERISTICS OF THE GROUP AND ITS SUB-DIVISIONS

THE name "Mollusc" almost inevitably suggests to our mind's eye a soft, sluggish creature, and when we survey the great phylum or group known as the Mollusca, we see that this mental picture is not inapt. It is true that many other invertebrate (backboneless) animals are equally soft and sluggish, some, indeed, even more so than the majority of Molluscs. But the slug and the snail, which are typical Molluscs, seem to typify slowness of movement more than the others.

Nevertheless it would be wrong to brand all these creatures with this stigma. One whole class of Molluscs, the Cephalopoda, are active animals, strong swimmers, and as savage in their way as the tiger or the cobra. Even among the snails and whelks, we find lively and carnivorous species : creatures which pursue and attack their prey in a most remorseless manner. Besides being less sluggish than they appear the Mollusca have great staying powers. They can survive all kinds of adverse conditions, and some of them can go without food for a long time. They are also a very ancient group. They have come down to our times from a very remote period in the world's history and their shells are preserved in the most ancient fossil-bearing rocks. One might with justice call them a conservative group of animals in regard to their habits. Only one section of this phylum has ventured on to dry land. The rest keep to a life in water, and the majority have not left the ancestral home in the sea in which we believe they, like all other organisms, first appeared. However, as if to show their

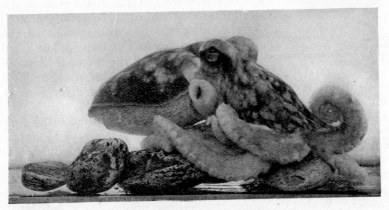

LESSER OCTOPUS (*Eledone cirrosa*)
A typical Cephalopod mollusc.

very marked adaptability, those which have become terrestrial have flourished exceedingly, and the land snails constitute one of the largest groups of land animals.

The conservatism of this phylum is shown in another way. It includes such apparently diverse animals as the snail, the slug, the oyster, the cuttlefish, and the octopus. But, although these animals are superficially very unlike, their underlying structure is similar ; this uniformity of structural plan is rigidly maintained.

The outstanding feature of the Mollusca is the hard shell which envelops them. It is present in all the five classes ; and though in certain cases it is degenerate, or even, as in some slugs, entirely absent, it was present in the ancestors of such forms. Now, the hard skeleton of a mammal, such as a dog or a man, is internal and provides a flexible support for the body, and surfaces of attachment for the complicated system of muscles which effect the movement of the limbs. In the Mollusca, on the contrary, the skeleton (for so we may term the shell) is external, and its object is to protect the soft parts of the animal against carnivorous enemies, accidental blows, and, in the case of such forms as the snails and bivalves which can withdraw themselves into the shell, against excessive heat and drought.

The shell is made up principally of lime-salts and is formed (secreted) by the mantle. The latter is a sheath of skin which envelops the soft parts and hangs down round the body like a skirt, enclosing a space (mantle-cavity) between itself and the body, in which are situated the breathing organs. The under surface of the Mollusc's body is very muscular and is the organ of locomotion, the foot.

Left valve of *Meretrix*

a, Anterior ; *b,* Posterior end ; *d,* Ventral margin ; *m,* Anterior adductor scar ; *m',* Posterior adductor scar ; *n,* Pallial sinus.

It will be noticed that in the table of classification at the head of this chapter the Mollusca are divided into five main groups or classes. The detailed character of these will be described in due course. For the moment let us direct attention to the essential characteristics of these classes so that it may be easy to see the main lines of divergence in the phylum.

The best known of these classes is that which includes the limpets, periwinkles, whelks, snails, and slugs. It is the largest class of Molluscs, and its members are called " Gastropoda," or " belly-footed " Molluscs. These animals are mainly aquatic, but one very large sub-order and several families live on land. They have a distinct and well-formed head which carries eyes placed at the base or at the tips of tentacles. Within the mouth is a peculiar ribbon-like organ known as the radula, or tongue, beset with numerous rows of teeth, presenting an astonishing range of difference in number, form, and arrangement, and furnishing very beautiful objects when seen under the microscope. The radula is used for rasping the food. Its actions can be easily seen in any water-snail living in an aquarium as it makes its way up the glass side, browsing on the minute plants that adhere to the latter. The shell of Gastropods is usually coiled into a spiral, and the body is likewise spiral. The internal organs are not symmetrically disposed as they are in other Molluscs.

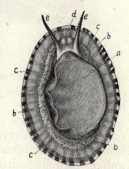

LIMPET : under surface

a, Foot ; *b,* Mantle ; *c,* Gills ; *d,* Mouth ; *e,* Tentacles.

Let us now consider the Lamellibranchs, so-called because their gills are usually in the shape of broad plates (Latin *lamella*, plate). The body is enclosed in a shell formed of two pieces (valves) ; hence they are sometimes known as bivalves. They afford a striking contrast in their habits and structure to the Gastropods. They, indeed, are far more sluggish than the latter. Some of them live either temporarily or permanently fixed to solid objects ; others burrow in sand or mud. They have no definable head, and their food is usually brought to them in the shape of microscopic plants and animals that float in the water. Their activities are limited, and their range in the adult stage is very circumscribed. They are indeed " chained to the soil " like an ancient serf. The Lamellibranchs mainly live in the sea, but a few families have taken to a life in ponds, lakes and rivers.

Squids, cuttlefishes, and octopods are examples of the third largest class of Molluscs—the Cephalopoda. These animals are mostly vigorous and aggressive, and in accordance with the freedom of their movements they have a more muscular body usually unhampered by a rigid shell. In the matter of size they include not only the largest Molluscs, but also the largest living invertebrate animals.

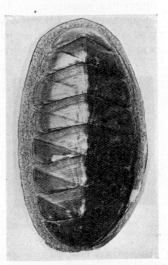

An important point in the anatomy of the Cephalopods is that the head is fused with the foot (hence the name Cephalopod, or " Head-Foot ") to form a single mass, though the process by which this fusion has come about is too complicated to be discussed in these pages. Thus it comes about that one may say that an octopus walks on its mouth, for the mouth is in the centre of the under surface of this " head-foot." Around the mouth are placed long arms and tentacles furnished with suckers, by which the prey is grasped. Other characteristic features of these animals are the ink-sac, from which they pour a cloud of black fluid (ink) into the sea-water in order to baffle

COAT-OF-MAIL SHELL (*Chiton nobilis*)
A typical Amphineuran mollusc.

their enemies, and the " siphon," or funnel, a special organ of locomotion not found in other Molluscs.

The two remaining classes are smaller, and less important for our immediate purposes, as they comprise more or less unfamiliar animals. The Amphineura, which are mainly represented by the Chitons, or Coat-of-Mail Shells, have the distinctive feature of a shell divided into eight plates, while the Scaphopoda, or Tusk-Shells, have a tubular shell.

Having now traced in broad outline the more striking features of the Molluscs we may pass to consider the surprising variety of form, coloration, and habits which they display. We have seen that in their general structure the Molluscs are remarkably uniform. This uniformity is, however, very largely masked by the truly surprising amount of variation in the external parts. This often leads to marked differences from the average or normal members of a group. Thus Gastropods are usually small animals which secrete a solid coiled shell. Nothing could be more unlike the typical Gastropod than *Pterotrachea*, with its slender, gelatinous body, long snout, and flat fin-like foot. It has no shell, and at the posterior end is a long thread-like appendage. *Aplysia* is likewise a remarkable-looking creature. It is a large fleshy animal (the shell being internal) with two pairs of prominent tentacles, and the margin of its foot is expanded to form large swimming-lobes. When at rest it looks like a crouching hare. *Tethys*, which has its tentacles expanded to form a great fringed cowl, and the Eolids, whose slug-like bodies are densely covered with numerous finger-like appendages, are further examples of the wonderful plasticity of the Gastropod body. But these divergences from the normal Gastropod type are " put into the shade " by certain parasitic Gastropods, *Entoconcha* and *Enteroxenos*, which live inside the bodies of Echinoderms. For, as a consequence of this mode of life, they have degenerated into worm-like creatures with no trace of Molluscan organisation in the adult state.

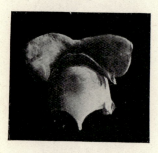

SEA BUTTERFLY (*Hyalaea tridentata*)

The shells of many Gastropods are adorned with spines, ridges, and tubercles, often attaining a fantastic degree of development, but whether these exuberant growths are of any use to the animal is a matter for speculation. So large and numerous are the knobs (denticles) around the shell-mouth of sundry land-snails that one is tempted to wonder how the animal can ever get out of the shell. Nevertheless, Dr. C. Boettger has shown that in one species at least (*Otala tigri* of North Africa) these denticles are of great use as they serve as a defence against the attack of carnivorous beetles (*Carabus*). A whelk of the genus *Thais* uses such a tooth on its shell-mouth as an oyster-knife. This mollusc preys on bivalves, and forces open the two valves of its victim's shell by inserting the tooth between them. Perhaps the elaborate fringed and pointed spines of certain rock-whelks (*Muricidae*) are of service to these molluscs in protecting them against carnivorous fish. A special device which may have a similar result is seen in the case of the curious Carrier-Whelks, which attach pieces of foreign shell, stones, etc., to their shells, which must act as an effective disguise. Other remarkable protective devices, more fully described on later pages of this work, are to be seen among the *Eolids*, in the use of the ink-sac of Cephalopods, and in the dual-purpose breathing organs of *Ampullaria*.

A point to remember in the life-history of the Mollusca is that many of them undergo a change of form in the course of their development, not unlike the metamorphosis of insects. In the viviparous pond-snail (*Vivipara*) the young snails are incubated in the mother's body until they are able to look after themselves. The land-snails and slugs generally lay eggs (sometimes enclosed in a hard shell) from which the young emerge in a completely formed state only differing from their parents in size. It is interesting to note that the eggs of certain " Bulimoid " forms (*e.g. Borus*) are over an inch in length and are, therefore, larger than those of many birds. The majority of marine molluscs, however, pass through what is known as a larval stage before they attain the adult condition. The ferti-lised eggs float about in the sea-water and develop into tiny objects known as " Trochophore " or " Veliger " larvae. These have a rudiment of the gut and other organs of the adult, but their most striking feature is a girdle of fine hairs (cilia) which, by rhythmical lashing movements, propel the little molluscs through the water. Such larvae stand in the strongest possible contrast with the adult forms—Gastropod or Lamellibranch —which they are destined to assume. These little creatures appear in the sea in countless myriads in certain seasons of the year, as each pair of adult molluscs usually produces a vast quantity of eggs. Most of them, however, are doomed to an early death, as they are swallowed by larger animals or washed away to places unsuitable for their further development.

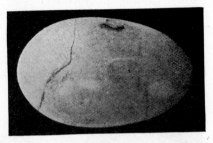

EGG OF A GIANT SNAIL

Class AMPHINEURA

(*Polyplacophora*=*Chitons or Coat-of-Mail Shells ;* *Aplacophora* =*Solenogastres*)

It is sometimes possible for the seashore naturalist to obtain from the surface of large stone, or in the hollows of rocks, a small oblong animal about an inch long, covered with eight narrow, shelly plates. It has a vague resemblance to a woodlouse, and the resemblance is heightened by the fact that the animal can roll itself into a ball just as the woodlouse can. This creature is *Chiton cinereus*, the common " Coat-of-Mail Shell." The Chitons are the most common representatives of the Amphineura, and are found in nearly all seas, and sometimes at very great depths. Over three hundred living species of these animals have been described. Associated with them in classification, but bearing very little external resemblance to them, are certain animals of worm-like shape known as the Solenogastres. These are much less common and are found on muddy bottoms in rather deeper water.

These two groups, the Chitons (or Polyplacophora) and the Solenogastres (or Aplacophora) are united in the class Amphineura. They agree in having an elongate and symmetrical body with the mouth and anus at opposite ends, and in their skin are embedded a number of horny or calcareous spicules. Although superficially very unlike the Chitons, the Solenogastres can be derived from the Chiton type of structure, and, indeed, the less specialised members of the group preserve an important indication of their Chiton-like ancestry.

Sub-class *POLYPLACOPHORA or CHITONS*

The shell of the Chitons is divided transversely into eight separate plates. The latter are pierced by holes through which project a number of minute eyes (" shell eyes "). The Chitons are peculiarly sluggish animals. They live on or under rocks and stones where they browse on algae, etc. They are mainly found in the shallow water of the littoral zone, but some (*e.g. Lepidopleurus*) are found at greater depths, even deeper than two thousand fathoms. Among the more interesting forms are the *Cryptoplacidae*, in which the mantle tends to grow over the shell-valves and cover them in till the shell is scarcely visible. In some genera the valves are very much reduced in size (*e.g.*

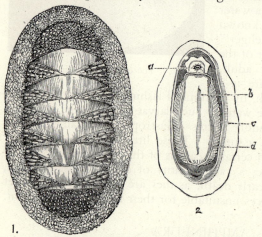

COAT-OF-MAIL SHELLS, or CHITONS

1, *Chiton squamosus* (upper surface).　2, *Chiton elegans* (lower surface) : *a*, mouth ; *b*, foot ; *c*, mantle ; *d*, gills.

Cryptoplax) and the animal tends to appear worm-like. In this family is placed the Giant Coat-of-Mail Shell, *Cryptochiton stelleri*, which attains a length of ten inches, and is found on the north-west coasts of America. Another interesting family is the *Mopaliidae*. The part of the mantle which is not covered by the valves at the sides is in this family given a hairy appearance by numerous fine spicules, a condition also seen in *Tonicia*, in which the girdle is quite shaggy. In the matter of their reproduction these creatures show some striking differences. Thus *Ischnochiton magdalenensis* lays its eggs in a long string in which as many as 200,000 eggs are contained. In *Callistochiton viviparus* the young are developed in the mother's body, and in some other forms, *e.g. Hemiarthrum*, they are incubated in the mantle-cavity.

Sub-class *APLACOPHORA* or *SOLENOGASTRES*

The Solenogastres are divided into two sub-orders, the Neomeniomorpha and the Chaetodermomorpha. The first of these are found crawling over or adhering to corals and hydroids, on which they feed. They are somewhat less specialised than the Chaetodermomorpha and they retain definite trace of their Chiton-like ancestry.

We have seen that in certain Chitons the mantle tends to grow over and enclose the shell-valves. In some it also extends downwards and rather inwards, towards the foot which is narrow, and is restricted to the median line of the under surface. It is believed that this process has been carried to an extreme in the Solenogastres, and the foot has been obliterated by the downgrowth of the mantle. In the Neomeniomorpha, however, an indication of the foot is still found in a median ventral furrow. The arrangement of the gills is in striking contrast to that found in other molluscs, since the gills are situated in a special cavity or " cloaca " at the posterior end of the body. These animals are hermaphrodite, and the kidneys serve as ducts for the passage of the eggs and spermatozoa. There are about twenty-five different genera, of which *Neomenia*, *Rhopalomenia*, and *Myzomenia* occur in British waters.

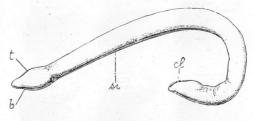

Proneomenia gerlachei
A shell-less relation of the Coat-of-Mail Shell (Chitons). *b*, mouth ; *cl*, cloaca ; *si*, foot-groove ; *t*, head.

The radula is absent in certain forms (the *Neomeniidae*, etc.).

The Chaetodermomorpha are entirely worm-like in shape and are devoid of the ventral groove. As in *Neomenia* and its allies, there is a posterior (bell-shaped) cloaca in which the gills are contained. The sexes are separate in this group. The Chaetodermomorpha feed on microscopic organisms such as Diatoms, Protozoa, etc., and are found crawling on muddy bottoms. It is customary to recognise only two genera, *Chaetoderma* and *Limifossor*, in this group, and there are only a few species.

Some Continental zoologists believe that the Solenogastres should not be included in the Mollusca, as they are deemed to resemble certain primitive worms more closely than they do the Mollusca. Satisfactory proof of this theory is, however, not forthcoming, and in the meantime the evidence of the Molluscan affinity of these animals must be regarded as more conclusive.

Class GASTROPODA

(Snails, Periwinkles, Slugs, Limpets, etc.)

The limpet, the periwinkle, the common snail, and the slug are familiar examples of Gastropod Molluscs. The group is an enormous one, and must contain between thirty and forty thousand different species. These live in practically all parts of the world, in the sea, in fresh water, and on land, and in a great variety of habitats. They are most usually found on and under plants, as the majority of them are vegetable eaters. In the sea, the shallow water of the littoral zone, and between tide-marks, where there are abundant masses of seaweed, algae, etc., is their favourable habitat.

COMMON WOOD SNAIL of the British Isles (*Cepea hortensis*)

Here they may be found crawling over rocks in search of encrusting plants, or on the fronds of *Laminaria* (brown algae), *Fucus* (bladder wrack), or *Zostera* (eelgrass). Some of them eat planttissue in a more decayed condition, and consequently are to be found on bottoms at a greater depth to which the decaying debris of plants has been washed by currents.

On the land they are to be seen in hedgerows, fields, woods, among the lichens growing on rocks, or in the dense growth of jungles. Some tropical groups are almost entirely restricted to trees ; and there are many of our British snails to be found climbing in similar places. However, the group is exceedingly adaptable, and its members may be found in more out-of-the-way places. Some of the marine forms are found in the great abysses of the ocean. Deep-sea forms must inevitably be carnivorous, as at great depths, beyond the reach of sunlight, there are no green plants. Other marine forms burrow into corals (*Magilus*) or are parasitic on starfishes and other Echinoderms (*Stylifer*, etc.).

There are many species which inhabit brackish and fresh water. They are found in mangrove swamps, tidal ditches, rivers, streams, and ponds. A few genera, such as *Cremnoconchus*, live in torrents, and species of *Melanopsis* are habituated to hot springs. On the land they have become accustomed to the arid conditions of deserts, and are found at the edges of glaciers and on sand-dunes. This great diversity of habitat stands out in sharp contrast to the conservative mode of life followed by all the other molluscs.

In addition to the deep-sea forms already mentioned, many families are carnivorous. The marine Whelks prey on bivalve molluscs ; and the Eolids eat Hydroids and other Coelentera. Among land-snails and slugs, the *Streptaxidae*, *Testacellidae*, and *Oleacinidae* feed on their own kind, on earthworms, millipedes, and other small animals.

The shell is the chief means of protection which these animals possess. They can withdraw the body completely inside it, and the aperture of the shell is then effectually sealed by a hard plate (operculum) carried on the back of the foot by one large group (Streptoneura), or by a temporary shield (epiphragm) secreted by the foot. They are thus secure against enemies or intense heat and drought.

The Gastropoda are distinguished from other molluscs by the shell, which is usually formed in a single piece and spirally twisted. This shape is, however, subject to a good deal of variation, and the spire may become more or less unwound. In some families it is tubular, and in others plate- or cup-like. However, in these groups it is spirally coiled in the embryo. In some exceptional cases (*e.g.* certain slugs) the shell is absent altogether. This loss of the shell is foreshadowed in several shell-bearing families, and is, indeed, not uncommon among the Mollusca. It is due to the mantle growing up the

Starfish with *Thyca*, a parasitic gastropod, attached.

sides and spreading over the shell which it ultimately encloses. The Cowries (*Cypraea*) are a good example of Gastropods with partly covered shells.

The class is further distinguished by the asymmetrical organisation of their internal parts. This is seen in the fact that they usually have only one kidney, one gill, and one auricle of the heart ; and the nervous system in one main sub-division is affected by a marked twisting. They are, however, descended from symmetrical ancestors, and the more primitive living Gastropods show distinct traces of symmetrical organisation. The anatomy has the usual Molluscan characteristics. The internal organs are sheathed in a fleshy sac which forms the muscular foot underneath, the mantle above, and the head in front. The latter is very highly developed in Gastropods and bears sense-organs and tentacles. The cavity between the mantle and body (mantle-cavity) is open, and contains the gills in aquatic forms. In land-snails it is almost completely closed in and forms a lung. The radula (rasping tongue) is very well developed, and one sub-class is sub-divided according to the form and arrangement of the teeth with which it is furnished.

The Gastropoda are sub-divided into two sub-classes—the Streptoneura which contain a number of primitive and other forms; and the Euthyneura, which on the whole are more specialised.

Sub-class *STREPTONEURA*
(*Limpets, Cowries, Periwinkles, etc.*)

Order ASPIDOBRANCHIA
(*Limpets, Top Shells, etc.*)

The first order, the Aspidobranchia, are with few exceptions marine Gastropods in which the nervous system is but little concentrated, and the gills are of the primitive Molluscan type, *i.e.* they are feather-shaped, consisting of a central axis with numerous filaments disposed down opposite sides. The most familiar group in this order are the *Patellidae*, or Limpets. Together with a few less known groups (the *Acmaeidae*, or False Limpets, etc.) they form a sub-order known as the Docoglossa, so-called because the teeth of the radula are shaped like beams (Greek *dokos*, beam). The shell of these forms is not spirally coiled in the adult, but is flattish and plate- or saucer-like. Traces of coiling are, however, to be found in the young stages of *Acmaea*.

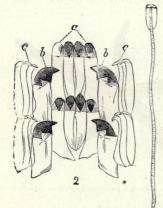

1, Radula of the Common British Rock-Limpet (*Patella vulgata*), natural size. 2, Two transverse series of teeth : *a*, median teeth ; *b*, laterals ; *c*, uncini, or marginals. (Enlarged.)

Sub-order *DOCOGLOSSA*
(*Limpets*)

The true Limpets (*Patellidae*) are found in nearly all parts of the world. They live on rocky shores, adhering to the flat surfaces of rocks, or creeping over the latter in search of algae and seaweeds on which they browse. They adhere to the rock-surface by means of the sucker-like foot, which has an adhesive power so strong that it can develop a resistance equivalent to lifting sixty-two pounds or about 1900 times the limpet's own weight. This energy is required to prevent them from being dislodged by the action of the waves and washed away to unfavourable situations. It is also no doubt serviceable in preventing them from being pulled off the rocks by seabirds and other enemies. On certain rock surfaces where limpets have been in occupation for some time it is possible to see the holes excavated by the acid secretions of the foot. Continued observation has shown that the Common Limpet (*Patella vulgata*) has a well-developed "homing instinct," and will return to its hole with considerable regularity.

The Common Limpet ranges from low- to high-water mark in the British Isles ; but below this level it is replaced by another species, the Horse Limpet, or Flither (*Patella athletica*), which in certain parts is especially sought for bait, though it can only be caught at the low water of spring tides. Limpets vary in size from small forms like *Lepeta* to the large *Ancistromesus mexicanus* of Western Central America, which occasionally is nearly a foot in length. The *Acmaeidae* have a single true gill ; but in the *Patellidae* the true gills are replaced by numerous plate-like outgrowths of the mantle, which can be seen between the foot and the edge of the shell. *Lepeta coeca*, a deep-water form from the North Atlantic, has no eyes. Other deep-sea Limpets are *Bathysciadium*, in which the foot is transformed into a sucker, and *Lepetella tubicola*, which has been obtained from a depth of over two thousand fathoms.

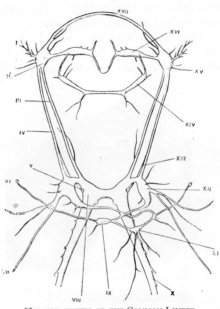

NERVOUS SYSTEM OF THE COMMON LIMPET
(*Patella vulgata*)

I, tentacular nerve ; II, left cerebral ganglion ; III, cerebro-pedal connective ; IV, cerebro-pleural connective ; V, left octocyst ; VI, left osphradium ; VII, pallial nerve ; VIII, anterior part of pedal cord ; IX, supra-intestinal ganglion ; X, pedal cords ; XI, abdominal ganglion ; XII, pleural ganglion ; XIII, otocystic nerve ; XIV, stomato-gastric ganglion ; XV, optic nerve ; XVI, labial commissure ; XVII, cerebral commissure.

Sub-order RHIPIDOGLOSSA

(*Ear-Shells, Top Shells, etc.*)

The second sub-order of the Aspidobranchs consists of the Rhipidoglossa. In these the teeth of the radula are arranged like the sections of a fan (Greek *rhipis*, fan). It is a larger group than the Docoglossa and includes some peculiar primitive forms. The *Pleurotomariidae* are a very interesting family. They first appeared in the very remote Silurian Period and became a very flourishing group comprising several hundred species. At the present time they are represented by five species only. These " living fossils," as they have been called, are found off the coasts of Japan, the Moluccas, and the West Indies. The *Pleurotomariidae* have two gills and other indications of a primitive status. Their handsome shells are much sought after by collectors, and high prices have been paid for the few examples which are known.

The Ormers (*Haliotidae*), or " Ear-Shells," are found in many parts of

E

the world. *Haliotis cracherodii* of the west coast of America is a large form which goes by the local name of "Abalone" and is caught for food and also for its handsome "mother-of-pearl" shell. The smaller *Haliotis tuberculata* of the Channel Isles is also eaten by the inhabitants of these islands. It is, in fact, an important article in their diet, and in recent years, owing to a failure of the "fishery," has been the subject of an official inquiry made by the Government of the Islands. The *Haliotidae* have two gills, a primitive trait. The spire of the shell is very much reduced and the last whorl is very large.

The *Fissurellidae*, or "Key Hole" Limpets, may be regarded in certain respects as the most primitive of living Gastropods. In many Rhipidoglossa there are two gills and two auricles, but the right-hand gill and auricle show some sign of reduction and are smaller than the left. In the *Fissurellidae* the gills and auricles are equal and symmetrical, and the heart is in the middle of the body, and not as in other Streptoneura, displaced to one side. The shell is not spiral but broadly conical, and in the living animal the mantle completely covers the shell. At the apex is a hole, the persistent relic of a slit seen in the shell of *Pleurotomaria* and a series of holes found in the body whorl of that of *Haliotis*. This slit and the holes in the shell correspond with a similar slit or holes in the mantle, and is found in archaic Gastropods. It may indicate that the mantle in the primitive Gastropods was actually double in origin, or it may be a secondary development, perhaps an adaptation to enable the contents (stale water, faeces, etc.) of the mantle-cavity to be expelled more rapidly.

Pleurotomaria adansoniana

Other interesting families are the *Trochidae*, or Top Shells, many representatives of which are found on British shores, the *Neritidae*, which includes some freshwater forms ; and the *Helicinidae*, which live on land and have the mantle-cavity transformed into a lung. The *Titiscaniidae*, represented by a single genus *Titiscania*, found in the Pacific Ocean, have entirely lost the shell and are elongate and slug-like.

Order PECTINIBRANCHIA
(*Periwinkles, Cowries, etc.*)

The Pectinibranchia constitute the second and larger order of the Streptoneura. They are distinguished from the preceding order by the structure of the gill in which the filaments are found on one side of the main axis only and are disposed down the axis like the teeth of a comb (Latin *pecten*, comb), by the regular absence of a second auricle and gill, and other features indicative of more complete asymmetry than is found in the Aspidobranchia. The Pectinibranchia are sub-divided into two sub-orders, the Taenioglossa and Stenoglossa, according to the structure of the radula.

Sub-order *TAENIOGLOSSA*

(*Periwinkle, Cowry, and River Snail, etc.*)

The Taenioglossa contain some well-known molluscs, *e.g.* the Periwinkle, Cowry, and River Snail. The *Viviparidae* (River Snails) are found in many parts of the world, there being two species found in the British Isles (*Vivipara vivipara* and *V. fasciata*). In this family the young do not undergo the early stage of their development as helpless larvae, floating in water, but are incubated in the mother's body in a special brood-pouch, and are born as young snails.

The *Ampullariidae* next attract our attention. These are known as Apple Snails, from the resemblance of their round greenish shell to an apple. *Ampullaria* lives in the rivers and marshes of Central and South America ; and the allied *Pila* and *Lanistes* in the Old World. These forms are very interesting, as they have both a gill and a lung, and are amphibious. When they are in the water they can use the gill and shut off the lung from contact with the water, and, conversely, when they are at or near the surface they can shut up the gill chamber and breathe by means of the lung. Some of them have a long siphon attached to the entrance of the lung by which they can draw air into the latter when actually under water.

Two allied families, the *Cyclophoridae* and *Cyclostomatidae*, live entirely on land, and the mantle chamber is accordingly converted into a lung. The common British *Pomatias elegans*, which is found plentifully in chalky districts, is a representative of these " land periwinkles." The true Periwinkles (*Littorinidae*) themselves include some forms which are virtually amphibious. The common periwinkle of our own coasts (*Littorina litorea*) is often found some distance from the sea, living the life of a land animal. Its mantle-cavity shows signs of becoming a lung, as the gill-filaments are prolonged across its surface as a vascular network, like that of a lung. A similar " halfway house " towards the acquisition of a lung is seen in *Cerithidea* and *Hypsobia*. The process of lung-formation in these aquatic molluscs is carried furthest in *Cerithidea ;* and it has been found by experiment that *Hypsobia* can live for about three months out of water.

The *Naticidae* are marine Taenioglossa which are interesting for two reasons. In the first place the foot is very large and is expanded so as to cover the shell in front and behind. The anterior expansion (propodium) is, no doubt, of service to the animal as it spends its life digging in sand in search of small clams on which it preys.   In relation to this carnivorous and aggressive mode of life the mouth region is highly modified.   During a survey of the animal life on the Dogger Bank, Captain F. M. Davis found that a high percentage of the empty shells of the clam, *Spisula subtruncata,* bear the small hole drilled by *Natica alderi,* through which it sucks out the

SHELLS OF THE AMERICAN SLIPPER LIMPET
(*Crepidula fornicata*)

unfortunate bivalve.   The hole is made principally by the acid secretion of a special gland on the proboscis of the *Natica.*

The *Calyptraeidae* contain some curious forms, the shells of which are cup-like, or conical, and have practically no spire, thus resembling Limpets or the *Fissurellidae.   Crepidula fornicata,* the American Slipper Limpet, is a form which has attracted much attention in recent years.   It was imported accident-ally into English waters with American oysters and has spread with great rapidity round the south and east coasts of England, so that its character-istic slipper-like shell can be found at suitable places between the Naze (North Essex) and Poole (Dorset).   Moreover, it has increased to such enormous numbers that it has become a serious pest in certain oyster beds.   Tons of these animals are removed from the beds every year.   The Slipper Limpet is interesting owing to the fact that it undergoes a change of sex in its lifetime.

The *Valvatidae,* a small family, are important from the evolutionary point of view, as they retain the primitive type of gill with two rows of filament seen in the Rhipidoglossa.   They live in fresh water and are hermaphrodite.

The *Vermetidae,* or " Worm-shells," at first sight are singularly unlike their relatives, for the shell is uncoiled and like the tubes made by certain marine worms.   The animal, fixed down by the shell to a rock or coral, often forms large encrusting masses.   The eggs are attached to the inner surface of the mother's shell where they are incubated.

Tiara amarula
With egg capsules on the surface of the shell.

The *Hydrobiidae* are a family including many genera that live in brackish and fresh water.   *Hydrobia jenkinsi* is remarkable as being the only mollusc which is known to be parthenogenetic, *i.e.* which lays eggs that develop without fertilisation.   Certain related genera are restricted to Lake Tanganyika in Central Africa.

The *Melaniidae* (or *Tiaridae*) are a large family in which the shell is usually elongate and very dark in colour. They inhabit tropical and sub-tropical countries, and, like the *Viviparidae*, their young are incubated in the mother's body.

The shell of the *Coecidae* is very remarkable, being almost completely uncoiled and forming a tube divided into compartments by transverse partitions (septa) rather like that of the primitive Cephalopod *Nautilus*.

The *Cypraeidae*, or Cowries, are a well-known group. The shell is highly polished, and is often very beautifully coloured. It is further remarkable for its shape and structure. At first sight it does not appear to be spiral, but to be globular on one side and flattened on the other, with the aperture showing as a long slit down the flat side. Actually the last whorl is very large and, so to speak, rolled round the rest of the shell; and the inner wall separating the successive whorls is obliterated.

The *Eulimidae* include forms which pass a normal free-living existence, and others which live as parasites in the digestive tract of Echinoderms.

The *Entoconchidae* are entirely parasitic; and their structure is very degenerate, the sense-organs, gills, and anus being absent.

Unlike the rest of the free-living Taenioglossa, the last group we have to consider, the *Heteropoda*, have the foot flattened from side to side like the fin of a fish, as an aid to swimming. These small marine molluscs are transparent and live at or near the surface of the open sea. They are carnivorous, and their eggs are embedded in a gelatinous secretion which serves as a float.

Sub-order STENOGLOSSA
(*Whelks*)

The second sub-order of the Pectinibranchs, the Stenoglossa, have a narrow " tooth-ribbon," or radula (Greek *stenos*, narrow, *glossa*, tongue),

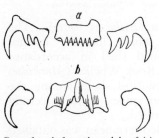
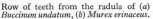

Row of teeth from the radula of (*a*) *Buccinum undatum*, (*b*) *Murex erinaceus*.

A GIANT GASTROPOD (*Megalotractus aruanus*)

usually with only three teeth in a row. These teeth are, however, very strong, and serrated, and together with the development of a proboscis and a poison-gland are an adaptation to a carnivorous mode of feeding.

The *Fasciolariidae* include some very large forms. *Fasciolaria gigantea* and *Megalotractus aruanus*, from South Carolina and North-West Australia respectively, attain a length of nearly two feet. Certain secretions of the African *Fasciolaria tulipa* are used by native tribes as dyes. The Whelks (*Buccinidae*) are a large family mainly restricted to Northern waters.

The egg capsules of the Common Whelk (*Buccinum undatum*), deposited in horny, semi-transparent masses, are familiar to all visitors to the seashore. A more remarkable type of egg-mass is formed by the American *Busycon perversum*. The eggs in this form are laid in biscuit-like capsules, each containing numerous eggs. The capsules are strung together in " roulettes," a single roulette containing as many as 140 capsules. The Dog Whelks (*Purpuridae*) are common objects on parts of the British coast,

EGG-MASS OF THE COMMON WHELK

EGGS OF *Busycon perversum*

where the common and highly variable *Purpura lapillus* is found. The *Coralliophilidae* contain some remarkable forms which, like the Taenioglossate *Vermetus*, have a more or less uncoiled shell in accordance with their habit of burrowing in corals. The Rock Whelks (*Muricidae*) include some of the most remarkable and beautiful shells among the Gastropoda, which are ornamented with ribs and spines, these, in certain species, becoming long and delicate or elegantly frilled.

The purple dye of the Tyrians of the eastern Mediterranean was obtained from *Murex trunculus* and *brandaris*, and dumps or middens of the empty shells of these molluscs are still to be found on the sites of the ancient Phoenician cities.

The *Olividae* mainly live below the level of the sand into which they burrow. The mantle is turned back over the shell and is ornamented with flag-like processes. The shell is in most forms highly polished, and often beautifully ornamented. That of *Oliva porphyrea* has a truly astonishing pattern arranged like a picture of mountains executed in the Chinese manner.

The *Conidae* are mainly inhabitants of tropical seas. The shell has its spiral structure obscured by the growth of the last whorl. During the lifetime of the animal the shell is covered by a thin, horny skin (the

FRILLED ROCK WHELK

Scaphander lignarius

periostracum), which in many species conceals a very elaborate and beautiful colour-pattern. Were such patterns exposed during life they would, no doubt, be explained as of protective or warning value to the animal by those anxious to discover an adaptive meaning in every type of colour-pattern. The *Conidae* have a highly developed poison-gland, the secretion of which, injected by a bite from the animal, causes violent pain and swelling in human victims.

Sub-class *EUTHYNEURA*
(Including the Land Snails and Slugs)

The second great sub-class of the Gastropoda, the Euthyneura, include such familiar forms as the Snails and Slugs, and many less well-known but more remarkable types. They are distinguished from the Streptoneura by certain anatomical features which need not be described here. They are all hermaphrodite, and with a few exceptions they have no operculum. The sub-class is divided into two orders—the Opisthobranchia and Pulmonata.

Order OPISTHOBRANCHIA

(*Sea Slugs, etc.*)

The Opisthobranchia live in the sea and have gills and an open mantle-cavity. In the more specialised forms the original symmetry of the Molluscan body is re-established, though the lost members of originally paired organs (gills, kidneys, auricles) are not recovered, and the shell tends to disappear entirely.

The *Bullomorpha* are the least specialised of these Gastropods. The shell is well developed, and the gill and mantle-cavity are normal. The head is provided with a " digging-shield "; and in many of them the foot is modified for swimming. They are mainly swimmers or burrowers.

Tethys leporina
A Nudibranch. Note the cowl-like expansion in the head region.

The *Aplysiomorpha* include very curious forms. The shell is very much reduced, or even lost; and the margins of the foot form very elaborate swimming lobes. The *Aplysiidae* are called " Sea Hares " because the high visceral sac and large tentacles give the animal a marked resemblance to a crouching hare. There are probably two species of *Aplysia* in British seas.

Allied to the two groups last named are two interesting tribes which are usually called collectively the Pteropoda, but should more strictly be called by separate names, as they are structurally dissimilar, though they have similar habits and distribution. These are the Gymnosomata and Thecosomata. They are small pelagic animals, *i.e.* they live permanently floating in the open sea. They are found, sometimes in dense masses, in most seas, and constitute an important part of the plankton or floating marine life. So numerous are they, indeed, that in certain areas the bottom deposits of the sea are mainly composed of the shells of Thecosomata. Some idea of their prodigious numbers may be gained from the fact that about 500,000 square miles of the sea-bottom is covered by their empty shells which form what is known as the " Pteropod Ooze." These deposits occur at about a depth of 1500 fathoms.

Among the Thecosomata *Limacina* and *Peraclis* have coiled shells. The *Cymbuliidae* have no true shell, but a kind of false shell (pseudo-conch) is formed. Among the *Cavoliniidae*, *Clio* and *Creseis*, which are representative genera, have very much expanded, wing-like lobes formed from the foot, on account of which they are sometimes called Sea Butterflies, a name they fully deserve. The Gymnosomatous Pteropods have neither shell nor mantle; they resemble the Thecosomata, however, in having the foot expanded to form fins. Certain of them (the *Pneumodermatidae*, for example) are furnished with a proboscis which can be thrust out for the purpose of sucking, and is supplied with suckers, a feature which for a long time caused them to be classified as Cephalopods (*q.v.*). These animals are carnivorous, and feed on other minute marine animals and their larvae. Some of them are cannibals, for they attack and eat their own kind.

Included in the *Pleurobranchomorpha* is the curious *Umbraculum* (or *Umbrella*, as it used to be called), which has a flat external shell rather like a Chinese umbrella in shape. This mollusc has a very remarkable radula, or tooth-ribbon, which bears as many as 750,000 teeth, the largest number of teeth in any known mollusc.

The remainder of the Opisthobranchia constitute the Nudibranchia. These are called the Sea Slugs, as they have an elongated, naked, slug-like body. The shell is entirely absent in the adult (unlike some of the true Slugs). The Nudibranchia are more or less symmetrical, though in some forms the anus is on the right side. They are a marine group, but certain forms come into brackish water to lay their eggs. The group as a whole is a very striking one as far as bodily form is concerned and contains some of the most remarkable types

A COMMON NUDIBRANCH (*Rizzolia peregrina*)

of Mollusca. The *Phylirrhoidae*, which occur in most warm seas, are said to be phosphorescent. The body is laterally compressed and is transparent.

Most of the Nudibranchs have rows of appendages arranged along their backs, and in *Scyllaea*, another pelagic form, these are broad and leaf-like. *Tethys* and *Melibe* (*Tethyidae*) are very remarkable in appearance, and extremely unlike the forms of Gastropods with which we have been dealing. The head in these animals is surrounded by a large hood or cowl-like structure formed from the anterior tentacles. *Tethys* has neither jaws nor radula, while *Melibe* has only a pair of jaws. The habits of *Melibe leonina*, which lives on the Pacific coasts of North America, have been carefully studied of recent years. The animal seems to live on plankton, which are swept into the capacious funnel-like hood and thence are passed to the mouth. The eggs of these molluscs are laid in a very peculiar cluster.

The *Eolidomorpha* are distinguished by the fact that the liver is contained in a series of long appendages placed along the back. Each appendage contains a section of the liver which is continuous with a main liver duct.

These animals are often very brilliantly coloured, and the appendages are very curiously shaped.

The *Eolidae* are a very large family of small forms. They feed upon various Hydroids, and make use of the waste products from their food in a very singular fashion. Hydroids are, as is well known, furnished with stinging-cells of a complex form known as nematocysts, which contain a coiled-up thread furnished with a barb. When an appropriate stimulus is applied the barbed thread is shot out; and this barb, if it comes into contact with the skin of any soft-bodied animal, effectually acts as a sting. Now, when the tissues of Hydroids which are eaten by Eolids are digested, the nematocysts escape digestion, and are stored up in special sacs situated at the tips of the dorsal appendages (cnidosacs). If the Eolid is disturbed or attacked, the nematocysts are expelled from the appendages, and their barbed threads are liberated to serve as a defence against enemies. The Eolids have the power of casting off the appendages at will, as may be easily seen, if they are placed in some acid reagent. These animals mainly live in shallow water, and a good many species can be obtained in pools on British coasts.

Among the last section of the Nudibranchs, the *Elysiomorpha*, which are distinguished from their relatives, *inter alia*, by the peculiar form of the radula, the rows of which have only a single tooth, we must note the *Limapontidae*. These animals have no dorsal appendages, and the body is very like that of a land-slug.

Order PULMONATA

(*True Snails, Land Slugs, etc.*)

The second order of the Euthyneura is constituted by the Pulmonata or Lung-breathing Snails. This is the largest order in the Mollusca, and is indeed one of the most flourishing groups in the Animal Kingdom. Its members are principally land animals, but there are some families which live in fresh water, and a few are marine.

It has been already seen that several families of Streptoneura, *e.g.* the *Helicinidae* and *Cyclophoridae*, live on land, and have accordingly developed a lung for breathing air. In the Pulmonata the lung is developed as in other terrestrial Gastropods from the mantle-cavity. The anterior edge of the mantle, which is free in aquatic forms, becomes fused in air-breathing Gastropods with the neck and sides of the body, a small contractile orifice, the pneumostome, remaining open to admit air into the cavity of the mantle chamber. The Pulmonata are, however, distinguished by other special features. Besides their other typical Euthyneuran characteristics (loss of operculum, hermaphrodite reproductive system), the nervous system is highly concentrated; the kidney usually has a long duct (ureter),

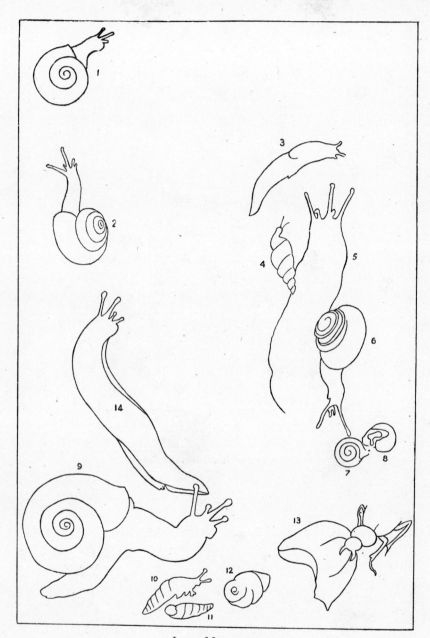

LAND MOLLUSCS.

1, 2. Varieties of *Helix hortensis*.   3. *Agriolimax agrestis*.   4. *Buliminus moutanus*.   5. *Limax maximus*.
6. *Helix nemoralis*.   7, 8. *Helix personata*.   9. *Helix pomatia*.   10, 11. *Clausilia ventricosa*.
12. *Cyclostoma elegans*.   13 14. Varieties of *Arion empiricorum*.

Pl. 3.

LAND MOLLUSCS.

and there is no free larval stage of development. Most of the terrestrial genera have the power of hibernation and estivation (winter and summer sleep).

Sub-order BASOMMATOPHORA

(*Freshwater Snails, etc.*)

The Pulmonata are divided into two sub-orders, the Basommatophora and the Stylommatophora. The former include the familiar Ram's Horn Snail (*Planorbis*) and the Pond Snails (*Limnaea*). Examples of the latter are the Land Slugs (*Arion, Limax*, etc.), and the True Snails (*Helicidae*).

The first sub-order (Basommatophora) contains almost exclusively aquatic forms, the *Auriculidae* being the only terrestrial family. The eyes

COMMON POND SNAIL (*Limnaea peregra*)

RAM'S HORN SNAILS
(*Planorbis corneus*)

are borne on the base of the tentacles of which there is a single pair. The *Auriculidae*, though terrestrial, may be described as maritime, for they are always found near the shore at about high-water mark. Some of them are said to travel down shore as the tide ebbs and to reascend as it rises. *Cassidula* and some other tropical genera live on or about the roots of mangroves. Certain of these forms, *e.g. Leuconia, Melampus*, and *Pedipes*, have the foot divided transversely, and probably all such genera move by contracting the two sections of the foot alternately. The *Siphonariidae* and *Gadiniidae* are sometimes called the Limpet Snails. They have flattened, limpet-like shells; but the latter can be distinguished from those of the true limpets by the presence of a scar, or groove, on the inner surface. These molluscs live between tide-marks on rocks.

The *Planorbidae* and *Limnaeidae* are two widely distributed families of freshwater Gastropods. It is generally believed that they are Pulmonates which have reacquired the faculty of living in water. They have a lung cavity and can breathe air, but can also obtain their oxygen from water. This they do by means of secondarily acquired respiratory organs developed from the mantle near the pulmonary orifice.

The *Planorbidae* have a spiral shell which is, so to speak, flattened so that all the whorls are in one plane. There are species of *Planorbis* in the British Isles, of which the common Ram's Horn Snail (*P. corneus*) is the most common. It is found in ditches, ponds, and streams. The *Limnaeidae* have a spiral shell and are very plentiful in this country, *Limnaea peregra* being found in a great variety of habitats. This family is indeed very adaptable. It is almost world-wide in its occurrence, and species of *Limnaea* are found as far north as Greenland. One species (*L. hookeri*) is found at a height of over 17,000 feet in the Himalayas ; and others occur in brackish water, in sulphur-springs, and in the depths of large lakes such as the Lake of Geneva. The freshwater Limpets (*Ancylidae*) also claim our attention. *Ancylus* has no lung-cavity, and the shell exhibits no traces of spiral structure, being conical and like that of a true Limpet. There are two species of *Ancylus* in the British Isles, one of which lives in rapidly flowing water, the other in slower streams and in lakes.

Sub-order STYLOMMATOPHORA
(*Land Slugs, True Snails, etc.*)

The Stylommatophora (second sub-order of the Pulmonata) are an enormous group, and constitute the bulk of the order. They all live on land, with the exception of the *Onchidiidae* and one or two amphibious genera. They differ from the Basommatophora in that they have two pairs of tentacles, and that the eyes are borne on the tips of the hinder pair of these. Both pairs of tentacles can be withdrawn into the head. This group is not only a very large one, but it has also diverged along several evolutionary paths which have led to substantial differences of habit and structure. It is not possible, however, in a work of this size to discuss the complex and interesting question of their evolution.

A certain number of them are carnivorous. Chief among these are the *Oleacinidae*, of which there is a single European species, *Glandina algirae*. These forms feed on other snails and on slugs, and it will be realised that it must be very quick and active for a mollusc, as it preys on creatures which can withdraw

A CARNIVOROUS LAND SNAIL
(*Glandina guttata*)

into their shell.   Apparently they attack their prey, *e.g.* a snail, when it is fully extended.   The head is seized, and the *Glandina* follows the snail as it withdraws into its shell.   The snail-slugs, *Testacellidae*, elongate forms with a small flat shell placed on the tail end, are likewise carnivorous, and prey on earthworms and other small invertebrata. Three species of *Testacella* are found in the

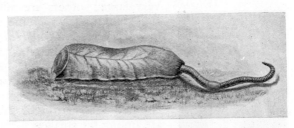

The carnivorous Land Snail (*Testacella*) eating an earthworm

British Isles.   These are relatively common and may be often found in gardens after dark.   The curious *Enneadae*, the aperture of whose shells is guarded by a palisade of teeth, and the *Streptaxidae*, the axis of whose shell is inclined from the vertical, are also carnivorous.

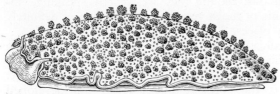

THE MARINE SLUG (*Oncidium tonganum*)
Left-side view.   (After Quoy and Gaimard.)

Under the general term Land Slugs may be considered several families, not all of which are immediately related.   In these the shell is either entirely absent or represented by a very degenerate plate or some granules under the skin.   The *Limacidae* still retain the shell, but it is either wholly or partly covered over by the mantle and is not spiral except in *Parmacella*. There are many species of *Limax* in the British Isles, of which *Limax flavus*, the Yellow Slug, and the small Field Slug, *Agriolimax agrestis*, are the most familiar.   In the *Arionidae* the shell is still further reduced.   For example, in *Arion ater*, the large Black Slug of this country, the only trace of the shell is an irregular calcified mass which lies in the skin of the " shield " (the ovoid patch of raised skin at the head end which represents the

Papuina hedleyi
An arboreal snail from New Guinea.

mantle).   The tropical *Veronicellidae* and the marine *Oncidiidae* (of which the remarkable genus *Peronia* has eyes all over its back) are entirely devoid of a shell.

The *Helicidae*, or True Snails, are an enormous family containing a large number of genera.   Some of these, such as *Orthostylus* and *Helicostyla*, are

very large ; others are minute.   There is also considerable variation in the shape of the shell which may be lens-shaped (*Helicina lapicida*), formed like that of a *Trochus* (certain species of *Papuina*), or elongate (*Cochlicella*).   The *Achatinidae* of Africa, which have large ovate shells often handsomely coloured, the *Bulimulidae*, and the long, slender *Clausiliidae* are large families with wide distribution.   The *Pupidae* are among the smallest forms of molluscs (and, indeed, of invertebrate animals), some species of *Pupa* rarely exceeding a few millimetres in length as adults.   The Amber Snails (*Succineidae*) are often found on submerged plants and twigs, and may be regarded as amphibious, though they are, strictly speaking, inhabitants of moist vegetation rather than of definitely watery places.

Finally, we must allude to the *Janellidae*, which are slug-like forms with air tubes (tracheae) leading into the adjacent tissues from the pulmonary cavity. This is the only mollusc which has developed tracheae, structures otherwise characteristic of certain Arthropoda.

Rhodea gigantea
A remarkable Central
American Land Snail.

Class SCAPHOPODA

(*Tusk Shells*)

The third class of the Molluscan phylum has received its scientific name Scaphopoda, or " Boat Foot " (Greek *scaphos*, boat, and *pous*, *pod-* foot), because these molluscs possess an elongated and rather cylindrical foot shaped somewhat like the hull of a boat.   To the ordinary observer, however, the shell is perhaps a more peculiar feature, as it looks like an elephant's tusk in miniature, and the group well deserves the popular name, " Tusk Shells."

ELEPHANT'S TUSK SHELL (*Dentalium*)
A Scaphopod mollusc.

The Scaphopods are burrowing molluscs, and spend the whole of their adult life half buried in the sand of the sea-bottom.   They are admirably adapted for their burrowing operations.   The body is long, slender, and cylindrical.   The mantle-flaps are not free as in the Gastropods, but are united under the foot to form a tubular sheath for the body.   The shell receives its tubular form from the mantle and is a hollow tube with orifices at the small (posterior) and large (anterior) end.   The head is imperfectly marked off from the body ; it carries, however, two special lobes from which project a number of delicate sensitive filaments (captacula).   The foot and the captacula project from the broad end of the shell.

When the Scaphopod is burrowing and when it is at rest in the sand, it keeps itself in a more or less upright position with the broad end below the sand, and the small (posterior) end above the level of the latter.   The aperture at the small end thus has to serve for the intake of food and water and for the expulsion of waste products.   The internal anatomy of these animals is simpler in some respects than that of the Gastropods, for example.   They have no gills, and no heart, and the vascular system is

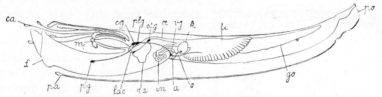

Anatomy of *Dentalium*, seen in longitudinal section, left-side view.   *a*, anus ; *ca*, captacula ; *cg*, cerebral ganglion ; *f*, foot ; *go*, gonad ; *in*, intestine ; *k*, left kidney ; *la.c*, labial commissure ;   *li*, liver ;   *m*, mouth ;   *o*, orifice of perianal sinus ;   *oe*, oesophagus ; *pa*, mantle ; *pg*, pedal ganglion ; *plg*, pleural ganglion ; *po*, posterior orifice ; *ra*, radular sac ; *stg*, stomato-gastric ganglion.

scarcely more than a series of irregular cavities.   The eggs and spermatozoa are discharged through the right kidney as in some of the primitive Gastropods.

There are two families of Scaphopoda—the *Dentaliidae* and *Siphonopodidae*. Both of these groups live in sand and feed on minute organisms such as Diatoms and Protozoa.   In the *Dentaliidae* the foot is rather pointed or prow-like ; but in the *Siphonopodidae* it ends in a sucker-like disc.   By thrusting this disc in a contracted condition into the sand and expanding it, the members of this family can pull themselves along through the sand or burrow vertically.   Among the *Siphonopodidae*, *Pulsellum* has the disc of the foot furnished with a long, thread-like appendage.

The Scaphopoda were once classified as Annelids (Worms), but they have long been recognised as true Molluscs.   They seem to be more closely related to the Gastropoda than to the other groups of Mollusca, in spite of the ventral fusion of the two mantle-flaps, which is a feature in the organisation of some Lamellibranchs.

Class LAMELLIBRANCHIA
(*Cockles, Oysters, Mussels, Scallops, Clams, etc.*)

The bivalves, or Lamellibranchia, are the second largest class of the Molluscs. The Cockle, the Oyster, and the Mussel are well-known examples of this group of animals. At first sight they would seem to have little structural resemblance to snails, periwinkles, and slugs (Gastropoda). But on opening the two valves of which the shell is composed we find that the body is arranged on the same essential plan as that of any other mollusc, as it is divided into a visceral sac covered by the mantle, and a foot, the mantle enclosing the characteristic mantle-cavity, in which the gills are suspended.

The Lamellibranchia are aquatic animals and live in the sea and in fresh water. Although several members are able to live out of water for a considerable time they have never succeeded in populating the land. This is due to the fact that their method of feeding is highly specialised and can only be carried out in water. They are, nevertheless, a large and flourishing group and constitute a marked feature of the animal population of most shores. They are world-wide in distribution and have been obtained from very great depths in the sea. The number of families that have taken to a life in fresh water is not very great,

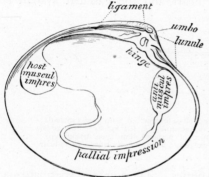

Left valve of *Meretrix*, seen from the inside, to show nomenclature of various parts.

but one of these, the River Mussels (*Unionidae*), is very large and contains over 1400 species.

These molluscs are sedentary, slow-moving animals. A few genera, such as *Lima* and *Pecten*, can indeed dart rapidly through the water by abruptly snapping the valves of the shell together, and *Tellina* and *Yoldia* can leap by rapid contractions of the feet. The Cockles (*Cardium*) are said to perform similar leaps. But the majority live buried in sand and mud, or else they attach themselves to rocks and other solid objects by a bunch of glutinous adhesive hairs (the byssus) secreted by the foot. Some of them are permanently fixed down by one valve (True Oysters, *Spondylus*), and others burrow into rock or wood (*Pholas, Teredo*).

This sedentary life is intimately associated with their peculiar and very specialised mode of feeding and with highly characteristic structural features. The Lamellibranchs, unlike the rest of the Mollusca, have a very imperfectly developed head. They have no organs of mastication (radula and jaws), and they feed on microscopic organisms and minute particles.   These are driven towards the mouth by currents set up by minute hair-like processes (cilia) on the gills.   The latter, which are situated in the mantle-cavity, are specially modified to serve not merely to utilize water for respiratory purposes, but also as an apparatus for sieving out the nutritious particles which float in the water and for passing them to the mouth.   The modification of the gills is very diverse, and becomes very complex in the more highly evolved kinds of Lamellibranchs.   Consequently, it is very useful in classification.   As the shell covers the main mass of the animal and the head is so little developed, eyes are rarely found on the anterior end of its body.   Instead they are developed on such parts as project from the shell, e.g. the edge of the mantle and siphons.

A point in the natural history of these animals that is often lost sight of is the fact that many of them, at least among the marine families, are not so inert as their burrowing, sedentary habits would lead one to suppose. In order to avoid being washed away to unsuitable places as rough seas shift the surface layers of sand in which they burrow, they must expend a great deal of energy in burrowing and adjusting their position. On exposed beaches the young of many burrowing forms seem to anchor themselves to masses of sand-granules by means of the byssus.

In order to maintain connection with the water while they are burrowing, the majority of Lamellibranchs are provided with

Anodonta cygnea

The Swan Mussel removed from its shell and lying on its right side with a large part of the left lobe of the mantle cut away.

a.ad., anterior adductor muscle ; *a.r.*, anterior retractor ; *d.s.*, dorsal siphon ; *f.*, foot ; *l.i.g.*, left inner gill ; *l.ml.*, remains of left mantle lobe turned back ; *l.o.g.*, left outer gill ; *l.p.*, labial palps ; *p.ad.*, posterior adductor muscle ; *p.r.*, posterior retractor ; *pro.*, protractor ; *r.ml.*, right mantle lobe ; *r.ml.'*, thickened edge of the same ; *v.s.*, ventral siphon with papillae.

tubes (siphons) by which they can draw fresh water into the mantle-cavity and expel the waste water, faeces, etc.   These siphons are formed by the edge of the mantle.   The latter hangs down on each side, and in many families the free edges are joined together at one or more points.   One or more orifices are thus formed which lead into the more or less enclosed mantle-cavity, and the lips of these orifices are often extended to form the long siphonal tubes.

The shell is the form of two valves joined together by a ligament along the upper edge and by interlocking " teeth " situated along their inner surfaces of that edge.   The animal is attached to its shell by adductor muscles, which serve to close the valves together.   The shell-valves of a dead Lamellibranch nearly always gape, *i.e.* open, because the ligament which served to pull them apart no longer has the resistance of the adductor muscles to overcome.

The class is divided into four orders, according to the structure of the gills. This classification has been criticised, especially by students of fossil forms ; and an alternative scheme has been proposed which depends on the structure of the shell. It is not, however, desirable to discuss the merits of these schemes in this work.

Order PROTOBRANCHIA

This order is a small one, and contains scarcely any forms which are familiar to the ordinary observer. It is, however, a highly interesting group as it contains the most primitive and least specialised forms. Its distinctive characteristic is the possession of gills which resemble those of primitive Gastropods and, we must assume, represent the archaic Molluscan type of breathing organ. The gill consists of a more or less feather-like structure, a pair of which project from the wall of the mantle-cavity, one on each side of the body. It consists of a simple axis which contains a blood-vessel, carrying delicate filaments set on opposite sides of the main axis. The filaments are broad and plate-like, and their outer ends are free. The Protobranchia have a flat surface to the foot, reminiscent of the flat creeping sole of Amphineura and Gastropods. The gut is slightly dilated just behind the mouth, possibly an indication of a former pharyngeal mass. As in other primitive Molluscs the ova and spermatozoa are discharged through the kidneys, there being no special generative ducts.

Nucula cumingii
A representative of the oldest group of Lamellibranchia.

The *Nuculidae* are the more interesting Protobranchs. Like *Pleurotomaria* among the archaic Gastropods, which we have spoken of as a " living fossil," they were far more numerous in early times than they are to-day. They have the edges of the mantle entirely free. *Yoldia*, *Solenomya*, and *Leda* are other examples of this order.

Order FILIBRANCHIA
(*Mussels, Scallops, Pearl Oysters, etc.*)

This order includes the Common Mussels, the Scallops, and Pearl Oysters. The gill shows a considerable advance in specialisation on that of the Protobranchia. The filaments lie parallel to each other and are more or

less vertical in direction, and each filament is bent on itself and is thus
sub-divided into two sections. That section of each filament which is
next to the axis is called the direct limb ; that which lies beyond the bend,
the reflected limb. The whole series of filaments of one side thus forms
a double plate (lamella) consisting of the direct lamella (all the direct limbs)
and reflected lamella (the reflected limbs). The reflected limbs are bent
upwards so that in section each gill looks like a W. Adjacent filaments
are locked together by cilia (small hair-like processes) arranged in bunches
down their sides, the cilia of one fila-
ment fitting into those of its neighbour
as the bristles of two brushes fit when
the brushes are pressed together. The
byssus is well developed in most
Filibranchs.

The *Anomiidae* have pearly shells of
a peculiar structure. The right valve
is perforated by a hole through which
the byssus passes. The latter structure
is large and calcified so that it affords a
strong means of adhesion. The pinkish-
brown and pearly shells of *Anomia
ephippium*, which are sometimes used
for making the petals of artificial
flowers, can be found on many parts
of the English coast. An allied form,
Placuna, has a very thin, flat, and transparent shell, and is used in some parts
of the East for glazing windows.
Hence it is known as the " Window
Pane Oyster." The *Arcidae* or "Ark-
shells " live in sub-tropical and tropical
seas. They have heavy brown shells
with numerous teeth along the hinge-
line. *Scaphula*, which lives in rivers of
India, is a freshwater form. Another
Indian form, *Trisidos* (or *Parallelepipe-*

Upper and lower valves of *Anomia ephippium*, the
" saddle " oyster. Note the notch in the lower
valve through which the byssus passes to
anchor the animal down.

dum), has a very remarkable shell, the front end of which is twisted to the
left and the hind end to the right. Allied to the *Arcidae* are the *Trigoniidae*,
which, like the archaic Gastropod *Pleurotomaria*, may be called " living
fossils." Only six species of this genus, *Trigonia*, are known, all of which
are found in Australian seas. In Secondary times they were far more
numerous, and they flourished abundantly in the seas of Jurassic times.
Trigonia has the power of jumping by abruptly snapping the valves of its
shell together.

The Mussels (*Mytilidae*) form a very large family with representatives in cold, temperate, and tropical seas. *Mytilus edulis*, the Common Mussel, lives attached by its byssus to rocks, shingle, etc., in large beds (" scaups ") often covering several acres. Mussels are eaten by man in many parts of the world, and are also preyed on by other enemies. In the British Isles the Dog Whelk (*Purpura lapillus*) is an inveterate enemy of Mussels, through the shells of which it bores and afterwards sucks out the flesh by means of its proboscis. *Lithodomus*, which is related to the true Mussels, has a long cylindrical shell and bores into coral and other limestone rocks by means of an acid secreted in a gland of the mantle.

ARK SHELL: external and internal view
(*Arca ventricosa*)

The *Aviculidae* include the Wing Shells (*Avicula*), the Pearl Oyster (*Margaritifera*), and the Hammer Oysters (*Malleus*). The shell of *Avicula* has a very long posterior extension (auricula) which gives it the appearance of a swallow in flight. These Molluscs seem to live in rather intimate association with Coelentera in warm and tropical seas, and the colour of *Avicula radiata*, which lives on Sea Fans (*Gorgonia*), is said to blend with the branches of the *Gorgonia* and to afford it protection from enemies. The shell of Pearl Oysters (*Margaritifera*) differs from that of *Avicula* in that the wings (auriculae) are not so long. The genus is widely distributed through warm and tropical seas. It is fished commercially for the sale of

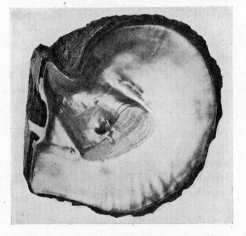

ORIENTAL PEARL OYSTER (*Margaritifera margaritifera*)

the brilliant nacrous shell, and the pearls that are often found inside the latter.

The chief centres of the pearling industry are in Ceylon, India, Japan, and North-West Australia. The Pearls found in the Pearl Oyster are of several kinds, of which the large, spherical, " orient " type is the most valuable. The formation of these and other kinds has been the subject of a good deal of inquiry and controversy. The latter seems now to have narrowed down to the question as to the initial cause of pearl-formation. One theory is that the pearl is formed round a nucleus consisting of a parasitic (Cestode) worm, by which the oysters are infested. Another theory is that " orient " pearls can be formed round other foreign bodies—such as grains of sand, or diseased tissue in the animal's tissues. Whatever the original nucleus is, however, the fact remains that " orient " pearls are formed of concentric layers of nacre (mother of pearl) deposited round some solid object in the mollusc's tissues which served as a stimulus for shell-deposition. Japanese cultivators have taken advantage of this knowledge, and have produced " culture pearls " by a grafting operation.

The Hammer Oysters (*Malleus*) have a very singular shell, usually shaped like a thick T. This shell may be derived from one like *Avicula*, if we realise that the horizontal stroke

WING SHELL (*Avicula brunnea*)

Trigonia margaritacea

An Australian Filibranch. This genus was more widely spread and more abundant in the seas of the Jurassic period. At present only six species are known.

of the T represents the auriculae of *Avicula* and the vertical stroke the main part of the shell. *Malleus* lives in the East and West Indies, Indian seas, and the Pacific. *Vulsella* is another curious form allied to the *Aviculidae* which lives embedded in sponges.

The Scallops (*Pectinidae*) are peculiar anatomically on account of the high degree of complexity which their eyes attain. The latter are borne on short tentacles which hang down in a fringe from the outer edge of the mantle. They have a retina, lens, and cornea, and resemble in certain respects the eyes of the Vertebrates. The Thorn Oysters (*Spondylidae*) are closely related to the Scallops and are remarkable for the brilliant colouring of their shells which are fixed down to rocks, etc., permanently by one valve.

Order EULAMELLIBRANCHIA
(*True Oysters, Cockles, River Mussels, etc.*)

This is the largest order of the Lamellibranch class. It is divided into nine sub-orders and includes such familiar molluscs as the True Oyster (*Ostraea*), the Cockle (*Cardium*), the River Mussels (*Unionidae*), and a variety of forms known as clams (*Mactra, Psammobia*, etc.). The filaments of the gills are united by permanent vascular junctions and the whole lamellae are also joined by similar unions. The gill is usually thrown into a series of folds (this feature also being seen in certain Filibranchs). The inferior edges of the mantle are usually fused at one or more points.

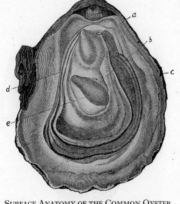

SURFACE ANATOMY OF THE COMMON OYSTER

a, position of mouth ; *b*, mantle ; *c*, gills ; *d*, junction of mantle-lobes ; *e*, adductor muscle. (Nat. size.)

The *Ostraeidae* (True Oysters) are fixed to the bottom in adult life by the left valve. The foot in accordance with this sedentary mode of life is superfluous and much reduced in size. Some species of *Ostraea* are hermaphrodite, while some undergo a change of sex during their lifetime. The cultivation of oysters of various kinds for human consumption is world-wide and of considerable antiquity. The *Pinnidae* are a related family of which certain species grow to a very large size. *Pinna nobilis* of the Mediterranean is sometimes over two feet in length. These forms have a byssus composed of fine silky hairs which has sometimes been made up into a material for human use.

The *Dreissensiidae* contain the single genus *Dreissensia* (" Zebra Mussels "). These are freshwater forms which inhabit rivers, lakes, and canals. On occasions they have invaded water-mains, in which they have been a considerable source of trouble, as masses of their shells have obstructed the flow of water through the mains. *Dreissensia polymorpha* is said to have been imported from Russia into England, into which it migrated from the Caspian Sea, about 1824. The *Carditidae* include the very remarkable genus *Thecalia*, in which the lower edges of the shell-valves are folded in to form a cup-like recess in which the eggs are incubated.

The *Galeommidae*, which are usually placed in the same sub-order as the last-named genera, are a very interesting group, as in some members of this family the mantle has more or less completely grown up over the shell, which is thus internal as in the *Lamellariidae* and certain Pulmonates

Unio tuberculatus, a freshwater oyster

There are over 1400 species of these oysters which have become of commercial value in North America.

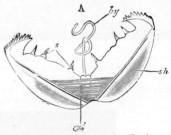

" Glochidium " larva of the Freshwater Mussel (*Anodonta*) when free-swimming.

ad, anterior adductor muscle ; *sh*, shell ; *s*, teeth of the shell ; *by*, byssus.

among the Gastropods. *Scioberetia*, which is placed in this family, is hermaphrodite and lives commensally (in close association with and sharing the same food) with an Echinoderm, *Triphylus*. *Entovalva*, an allied form, illustrates a more extreme state of association, as it lives as a parasite in the alimentary canal of another Echinoderm, *Synapta*. The *Cycladidae* are a family of freshwater forms which include our common British *Cyclas* and

SHIPWORM (*Teredo navalis*)

e.s., exhalant siphon ; *f*, foot ; *i.s.*, inhalent siphon ; *p.*, one of the pallets ; *s.*, one valve of the shell.

Pisidium. The latter is sometimes known as the Pea-Clam. Some of the species of this genus are excessively minute, even as adults.

The *Unionidae* (Freshwater Mussels and Oysters) are a very large family. There are over 1400 species of *Unio*, and of these the greater number live in the river systems of North America. In that country they are cultivated for the purpose of obtaining supplies of shell for button-making.

The most remarkable feature of these molluscs is certainly their larval development. The young are incubated between the gill-plates, which

are in certain species specially modified to form brood-pouches (marsupia). They ultimately escape from the maternal body as larvae with a triangular shell, the edges of which are prolonged into hooks (" Glochidia " larvae). These larvae swim by snapping the valves of their shells, and if they come into contact with

Valves and pallets of the Shipworm (*Teredo navalis*), above. Below: Burrows in timber. Note the shelly lining of the burrow.

a fish they attach themselves to the skin or the gills of the latter by means

The WATERING-POT SHELL (*Brechites*)

THE " ROSE " OF THE WATERING-POT SHELL

of the hooks. If they settle on some soft spot of the fish, the skin forms a capsule (cyst) round the Glochidium, and inside the cyst the young mussel undergoes further development and eventually escapes by the breaking of the cyst.

Among the Veneracea, of which the handsome *Veneridae* are typical, are placed the *Petricolidae*. These live in holes which they bore in rocks. *Petricola pholadiformis*, which may be found on British coasts, was originally confined to American waters, but has spread to European waters.

The Common Cockles (*Cardiidae*) are inhabitants of sandy bays and estuaries. They have a long foot bent in the middle, so that it seems to have a knee. Allied to these familiar forms are the Giant Clams, *Tridacnidae*, which inhabit warm seas. *Tridacna gigas*, the largest species of living Lamellibranchs, sometimes attains a length of three feet and a weight of 500 lb. The *Solenidae*, or Razor Shells (Myacea), have elongate narrow shells with an aperture at each end. They live in sand in a vertical position and burrow to a considerable depth.

In the Adesmacea are placed a number of genera which burrow into wood or rock. The Shipworm (*Teredo*) is the most remarkable of these. In this genus the body is long and worm-like, and consists very largely of the enormous siphonal tube. The shell is reduced to two small valves which cover only a small part of the body. Shipworms bore into submerged timber and used to cause much damage to wooden ships. They secrete a kind of secondary shell which serves as a lining to the burrow. Another group of elongate forms are the *Clavagellidae*. The most remarkable example of these is *Brechites*, the Watering-Pot Shell, which has a long calcareous secondary shell with the valves of the true shell embedded in it, and an expanded structure at one end very like the rose of a watering-can.

Order SEPTIBRANCHIA

The last order of the Lamellibranchs contains very specialised marine forms. They live in very deep water beyond the reach of sunlight and consequently of plant life. As a result they are carnivorous, and perhaps more strictly, carrion-eaters. The gills have become transformed by the development of muscular tissue in their substance into a pumping mechanism by which large particles can be drawn into the mantle-cavity. Respiration is effected at the inner surface of the mantle-cavity instead of by special gills. There are only three small families of these molluscs, the *Poromyidae*, the *Cetoconchidae*, and *Cuspidariidae*, of which the first and last have representatives in British seas. The *Poromyidae* are the least specialised; and vestiges of the original gills are found in their mantle-cavity. They can be derived from certain groups of Eulamellibranchia, in which an increase of muscular tissue is observable in the gills.

Class CEPHALOPODA
(*Squids, Cuttlefishes, and Octopods*)

The most familiar examples of this class of Molluscs are the Cuttlefish, the Squid, and the Octopus. These animals have always been a subject of fascination for imaginative people. Their bizarre appearance, and their strength and ferocity, and the great size to which some of them grow have made them the subject of legend and story. Heroes fight with gigantic Octopods, enormous squids overwhelm boats (and even full-rigged ships !), and the Kraken (probably a reminiscence of the Atlantic *Architeuthis*) looms in the mist of Norse mythology. The Cephalopoda, however, has other claims on our attention than their sinister appearance and the aggressiveness of some of the species. They stand out from the rest of the invertebrate animals on account of their highly efficient organisation and large average size. Actually the Giant Squid is the largest invertebrate animal, fully grown specimens having been obtained which span fifty feet in total length (including the tentacles). One might say, with truth, that they are the rivals of the Vertebrates in strength, swiftness, and efficiency.

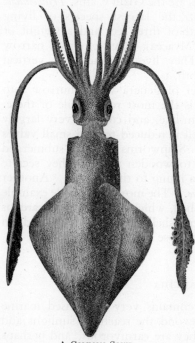

A COMMON SQUID

The name given to this class of Molluscs is derived from two Greek words, *cephalé*, head, and *pous*, pod- foot, and indicates the essential peculiarity of these animals. In a typical Cephalopod, such as the Squid or Cuttlefish, the head and foot, instead of being distinct structures, as in a snail, are merged into a single mass. From the edges of this mass extend the long arms beset with suckers which constitute their weapons of offence.

At first sight it may seem strange that these animals are placed in the same phylum as sluggish creatures such as snails and oysters. Their structure also seems at first sight very unlike that of the latter. It is possible, however, to show that their main structural plan is like that of a snail or mussel. To explain this, however, it would be necessary to go into certain questions of comparative anatomy which are outside the scope of this work.

Perhaps the thing which most impresses us in the structure of these animals is the extremely active, mobile arms. They are not jointed and bony as in a Vertebrate, but they are, nevertheless, very efficient. They are beset with numerous suckers, small cup-like organs which adhere to the prey that comes within their grasp. In some forms (the Decapoda) two of the arms are specially modified for snatching and grasping. These forms may indeed be said to have hands, as the

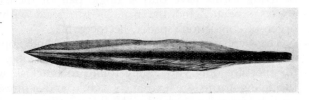

"PEN" OF THE SQUID

suckers are concentrated in an expanded palm at the tip ; and in some there is a remarkable device for locking the hands together at the wrists to increase the power of their grip.

The most primitive Cephalopods have an external shell coiled somewhat like that of the Water Snail ; but in nearly all living forms the shell is degenerate and concealed within the body. In many forms fins are developed on each side of the body. There is a further organ of locomotion known as the funnel. This takes the form of a muscular tube, opening into the mantle-cavity at one end, and into the exterior at the other. Water is drawn into the mantle-cavity through its wide aperture, held there under strong pressure (the mantle aperture being then closed by a special "adhesive apparatus"), and then forcibly driven out in a jet from the funnel. The ejection of this jet drives the animal backwards, and by its means it can make rapid darting movements.

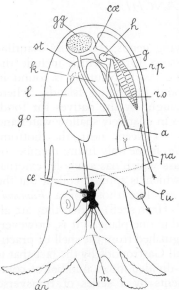

Diagram of the structure of a Cephalopod, as seen from the left side. *a*, anus ; *ar*, arms ; *ce*, central nervous system, with eye ; *coe*, coelom ; *fu*, funnel ; *g*, gill ; *gg*, gonad ; *h*, heart ; *k*, kidney ; *l*, liver ; *m*, mouth ; *pa*, mantle ; *r.o*, renal orifice ; *r.p*, renopericardial orifice ; *st*, stomach.

The mouth of a Cephalopod is furnished with a pair of horny jaws which look like those of a parrot. With these they crunch their prey, holding it against the jaws with their sucker-bearing arms.

A characteristic organ, the ink-sac, opens into the rectum. In this is secreted a dark fluid ("ink") which can be poured into the sea-water, where it forms a cloud and serves as a means of concealment and escape from enemies. This "ink" is manufactured into the *sepia* paint used by artists and draughtsmen.

The circulatory system is distinguished from that of other Molluscs by the fact that the blood is largely contained in closed vessels. There are four gills and four kidneys in primitive Cephalopods ; but the majority of living forms have only a single pair of these organs. The sexes are always separate, and the male is furnished with a highly characteristic organ of copulation (spadix, hectocotylus).

The Cephalopoda are marine animals and appear to be incapable of accommodating themselves to water of less than normal marine salinity, for they are only very rarely found in brackish water. The majority of the living forms are extremely active and aggressive creatures and prey on fish, crustacea, and other Molluscs. Some of them hunt in mid-water, while others keep more closely to the sea-bottom. The earliest traces of fossil Cephalopods are found in Cambrian rocks.

The class is divided into two sub-classes — the more primitive Tetrabranchia and the Dibranchia.

Sub-class *TETRABRANCHIA*
(*Nautilus*)

This group is represented by a single living genus, the Pearly Nautilus (*Nautilus*), and a very large number of extinct forms which include the familiar fossils known as Ammonites. The Pearly Nautilus is found in the seas around New Caledonia, the Fiji and Philippine Islands, where it is caught by the natives for food.

It lives in relatively shallow water and seems to keep near the bottom. *Nautilus* is the only living member of the class which has a wholly external shell which is spirally coiled, but the coils are like those of a *Planorbis* (Ram's Horn shell) in that they are all wound in one plane. It is, however, distinguished from the shell of practically all Gastropods by the fact that it is sub-divided into a number of compartments by a series of transverse septa (walls).

SHELL OF THE PEARLY NAUTILUS
The most primitive of living Cephalopods.

Nautilus is the sole survivor of a large and thriving group of Cephalopods which flourished in the seas of the Palaeozoic period. We should note that the earliest of these, the Cambrian *Orthoceras* and *Piloceras*, had straight cone-like shells ; and there is little doubt that the true *Nautili* which appeared in the Eocene period were evolved from these straight-shelled forms.

Nautilus manifests its primitive nature in other structural features. It has, as we have said, four gills and four kidneys, the funnel is not a complete tube, but is composed of two separate flaps, and it has no ink-sac. The head-foot bears a circlet of numerous short tentacles borne on special lobes. They are prehensile, but have no suckers such as are found in Squids and Cuttlefishes. *Nautilus* is nocturnal in its habits, and seems to live in shoals and may be gregarious.

Related to the living and extinct Nautiloids and constituting a second order of Tetrabranchs are the Ammonites (already referred to). These are an extinct group which was exceedingly common in late Palaeozoic and Secondary times. Fossil-beds of certain epochs in Jurassic times are crowded with their shells, and it is a matter of interest to speculate why so flourishing a group became extinct. Some students have sought an answer in the evolution of the Ammonite shell. The group first appeared in the Devonian period, and it is not easy to distinguish the early Ammonites from the contemporary Nautiloids, as they seemed to have come off the same primitive straight-shelled stock. They became progressively more and more coiled, and at the same time the partitions in the inside of the shell (septa) became thrown into elaborate folds and the outer surface became covered with knobs and ridges. With progress of time this ornamentation and the folds of the septa became more and more complex. Then, according to some authorities, a process of degeneration set in. About Middle Cretaceous

AN AMMONITE (*Criocerus emericii*)

times there was a gradual return to a more simple structure : the shell became uncoiled, and ultimately straight forms reappeared. It has been thought that the Ammonite stock actually lost its old vigour and exuberance of growth and ultimately degenerated. It seems, however, more likely that this is a superficial view and that the whole group of Ammonites was not subject to this degeneration. In all probability they became extinct owing to some great change in their environment to which they could not adapt themselves.

Before leaving this interesting group it should be pointed out that they are ranked as Tetrabranchs along with *Nautilus* and its extinct allies on account of the structure of the shell. The structure of their soft parts is, of course, unknown, though Dr. G. Steinmann has claimed to have recognised certain features in their shell structure that suggest that they should more properly be ranked in the next sub-class as Octopods.

Sub-class *DIBRANCHIA*
(*Squids, Cuttlefishes, and Octopods*)

The Squid, Cuttlefish, and Octopus are representatives of this class which contain about 140 living genera and a very large number of fossil ones. The chief feature of the sub-class is the reduction of the shell. The external surface of the body is completely naked, except in *Spirula*. This is due to the fact that the mantle has grown round and over the originally external shell and covered it in, so that it has thus become internal and very largely degenerate. In addition, the funnel of the Dibranchia is always a closed tube, and the arms are reduced to five or four pairs. These are always furnished with suckers. The Dibranchia are distinguished from the preceding sub-class in having only two gills (as their name denotes) and two kidneys. Finally, we should note that an ink-sac is always found, except in certain specialised deep-sea forms.

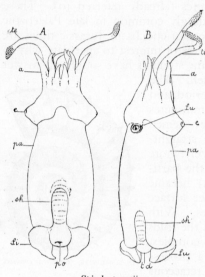

Spirula peronii

A ten-armed Cephalopod, in which part of the shell is still exposed. *A*, dorsal aspect; *B*, ventral aspect; *sh*, shell; *e*, eye; *fu*, funnel; *fi*, fins; *a*, arms; *pa*, mantle; *te*, tentacular arms; *po*, posterior fossa; *td*, terminal pallial disc. (After Chun.)

When a squid or an octopus is attacked or disturbed, it pours out into the water the dark ink secreted in the ink-sac. Primarily the dark cloud thus formed in the water serves as a means of concealment. It is a smoke-screen like that formed by a modern warship in order to conceal its movements from the enemy gunners. There is some question, however, whether it does not also provide a different means of escape. The ink, in some forms, seems to remain as a more coherent mass in the water. The enemy (*e.g.* a fish) mistakes it for the squid or cuttlefish, which, executing one of the remarkable colour-changes to be described immediately, becomes more or less invisible and darts off in a different direction.

The Dibranchia have, embedded in their skins, certain highly complex cells containing masses of diverse colours, known as chromatophores. By the contraction and expansion of these, the various colours can be masked or displayed, enabling the animal to change its colour at will. Some of these colour-changes are undoubtedly of protective value, as the common Octopus, for example, has been seen to assume the colour of its background so effectively as to delude a human observer.

The sub-class is divided into two orders—the Decapoda, which include the Squids and Cuttlefishes ; and the Octopoda, in which are placed the Octopus and its allies.

Order DECAPODA

(Squids and Cuttlefishes)

It is not part of the scheme of this work to dwell at length on extinct forms of life. But, as in the case of the Nautiloids, a word must be said concerning the forerunners of the Decapoda as the evolutionary history of this group is very interesting. Many non-scientific readers will be familiar with an odd cigar-shaped fossil known as a Belemnite. These fossils are actually the shells of the extinct ancestors of our modern Squids and Cuttlefishes. At about the time known to the geologist as the Upper Trias, the shells of these forms show indications of the great change which

COMMON CUTTLEFISH SWIMMING

was to take place in Cephalopod structure. Whereas the Nautiloids and Ammonites continued to secrete a true shell, the early Dibranchiate shell consists of an additional layer secreted round the true shell and known as the guard, and later on a second, additional shelly layer, the proostracum, appears. In the course of time the true shell (phragmocone) is reduced to a mere vestige and is entirely replaced by these secondary growths. This process of shell-reduction was due to the mantle growing over the original shell, enclosing it, and secreting secondary layers which ultimately replaced it.

F

This process is associated with the changes in habit and structure that produced the muscular, rapidly swimming Squids and Cuttlefishes of to-day. The Palaeozoic Cephalopods, like our *Nautilus*, were slow-moving animals which kept near the bottom. By the reduction of the heavy chambered shell, and the conversion of the body into a muscular tube with "stream-lines," the great mobility and aggressive habits of the Dibranchia became possible.

SHELL OF *Spirula peronii*

A, complete specimen. *B*, section of shell showing, *a*, septa; *b*, siphuncle.

The sub-order Sepioidea contain living forms which still retain the shell in some semblance of entirety. Of these *Spirula* is certainly the most interesting. This animal has had a curious history. For many years it was only known from a very few more or less incomplete specimens, though the shell is to be found in great numbers on tropical and sub-tropical beaches. In 1922, however, a Danish expedition obtained a large number of the living animal off the West Indies and in the Atlantic Ocean. It seems that *Spirula* lives

COMMON CUTTLEFISH (*Sepia elegans*)

"BONE" OF THE COMMON CUTTLEFISH

in mid-water, and at very considerable depths. It has a coiled and chambered shell like that of *Nautilus*. But the shell is almost completely covered over by the mantle, and inasmuch as we have reason to believe that it is descended through forms with less coiled shells (*Spirulirostra*) from straight Belemnite-like ancestors, it would seem that the coiling is not primitive. Our modern Cuttlefishes (*Sepiidae*) again have a substantial portion of the original septate shell, though it is very much modified.

The Cuttlefishes are a world-wide group, and comprise several genera and many species. They are mostly found in shallow water near the coast, and they usually come into in-shore water to deposit their eggs. The latter are small, dark, grape-like objects which are laid in clusters on submarine plants, etc.

Idiosepius pygmaeus is a curious little cuttle-fish which is found in far-eastern waters. It has recently been described by Dr. M. Sasaki as exhibiting the strange habit of adhering to fronds of the seaweed *Ulva* by a kind of adhesive organ developed on its back.

The Teuthoidea, or Squids, are a large and diverse group containing many strange and interesting forms. They are characterised by the almost complete absence of the original shell, the horny " pen " (gladius) found in the muscles of their back being an aftergrowth. The *Architeuthidae*, or Giant Squids, are one of the most striking families. There are some twelve species of these Giant Squids, the largest of which, *Architeuthis princeps*, lives in the North Atlantic, and sometimes attains a total length of over forty feet (including the long tentacles). Although stories are current of their ferocity, their attacks on man seem, on examination, to be limited to occasional onslaughts on fishing boats, when they have been netted or otherwise disturbed. They form part of the food of toothed whales, and the skin of the latter is sometimes found scored by the suckers of these Squids, so that we assume that they fight desperately with their enemies. A certain number of small squids, the *Thauma-*

Stenoteuthis caroli

A Giant Squid, a specimen of which was stranded on the coast of Yorkshire in 1925.

tolampadidae and *Pyroteuthidae*, some of which have been obtained from very great depths, have special organs situated around the eyes, on the mantle, and inside the mantle-cavity, from which light is given out. *Lycoteuthis*

MOLLUSCA

diadema, which was obtained in about 1600 fathoms in the Southern Ocean in 1899, is the most remarkable of these luminous squids.

The Cranchias form a separate group within the Teuthoidea to which the name *Consuta* or *Egopsida Consuta* is given. They are all distinguished from the other Teuthoidea by the fact that the edge of the mantle is permanently fixed to the head. All the Cranchias are small animals, living a more or less floating life, and should be classed with the Pteropods and other " drifting " organisms as plankton. Some very peculiar forms occur in this group. *Pyrgopsis* has its eyes and arms situated at the end of a long thin neck. *Sandalops* has enormous eyes at the end of long stalks ; and *Bathothauma* has a long, pillar-like neck, minute arms, and a globular body. The bizarre form and curious modification of the head and arms of these forms has so far received no satisfactory explanation on adaptive lines.

Order OCTOPODA
(*Octopods*)

The Octopoda are provided with eight arms, the prehensile tentacles of the Decapoda being absent in this group. The shell is reduced to a plate or hoop-like rudiment or the so-called " stylets," which are a pair of delicate rods embedded in the dorsal musculature. The Octopoda, with a few exceptions, live on or near the sea-bottom. The majority are active, powerful animals, in some cases attaining a total span of over ten feet. Specimens of *Octopus apollyon*, the Giant Octopus of the Pacific, have been recorded with a span of nearly thirty feet. Our own *Octopus vulgaris* sometimes spans twelve feet. These animals feed principally on crabs. Previously to

Octopus medoria, a typical octopod

dismembering its victim with its arms and beak, the Octopus paralyses it by injecting a poison (secreted by its salivary glands) into its gill-chamber. The true Octopods (*Octopodidae*) are of world-wide occurrence. They mostly live in shallow water, on reefs, etc., but the *Bathypolypodinae*, like the allied Cirromorpha, are inhabitants of deeper water. They have no ink-sac, probably because in the lightless depths beyond three hundred fathoms the ink-cloud would be of no use for protection.

A few words must be said concerning the Paper Nautilus (*Argonauta*), one of the most remarkable of the Cephalopods. This animal, which must be distinguished from the Pearly Nautilus, is found in nearly all warm and sub-tropical seas. Unlike the rest of the Octopods the female has an external shell of elegant and delicate texture and construction. It is not a true shell, *i.e.* developed from the shell glands of the mantle.

SHELL OF THE PAPER NAUTILUS

This shell is not the same as that found normally in molluscs, but is a special growth developed from the dorsal arms. It is used as a brood-chamber. Note the cluster of eggs on the left-hand side.

It is formed from the skin of the two dorsal or uppermost arms. The early Greeks called this animal " Nautilus," or " the Sailor," because they believed it paddled about in the shell, raising its membranous arms as sails. But as Professor T. H. Huxley remarked, the shell is not a boat, but a perambulator ! It is, in fact, used for containing the developing eggs. In it they are cradled until the young Argonauts are ready to take on a free-living existence. The male Argonaut is a tiny dwarf, very much smaller than the female.

SECTION IX

Phylum ARTHROPODA

(*Jointed Animals*)

CHAPTER III

CHAPTER IV

CHAPTER V

CHAPTER VI

INTRODUCTION

By W. T. Calman, D.Sc., F.R.S.

In systems of zoological classification down to the beginning of the nineteenth century the name Insecta was commonly applied to one of the main divisions of the Animal Kingdom, comprising crabs and lobsters, spiders and scorpions, centipedes and millipedes, as well as the endless variety of winged and wingless creatures related to the beetles, butterflies, bees, wasps, flies, and the like. Nowadays the name Insecta is usually restricted to the last of these assemblages, and the comprehensive group is known as Arthropoda, a name indicating that they are animals with "joined legs."

The feature alluded to by the name is not quite distinctive, for other animals, such as the Vertebrata, have also jointed limbs. While, however, the body and limbs of a Vertebrate are supported by an internal skeleton of bones surrounded by the muscles which move them, the skeleton of an Arthropod is on the outside and encloses the muscles. This external skeleton is formed by a kind of outer skin, the cuticle, which is soft and pliable at the joints, but elsewhere is hard and shelly, and encases the body and limbs as if in a suit of plate-armour. Thus the body is enclosed in a series of rings or body-segments which are very plainly seen, for instance, in the body of a centipede, or the tail of a lobster, but tend to become soldered together, especially in front.

The limbs, of which there is typically a pair to each body-segment, are also divided into segments by movable joints and may have the form of walking-legs, swimming-paddles, or weapons for attack or defence, or be modified for various other uses. It is very characteristic of the Arthropoda that some of the limbs in the neighbourhood of the mouth are turned inwards to work against their fellows and serve as jaws. The jaws of an Arthropod—a lobster or a beetle, for instance—thus work from side to side, not up and down like those of a vertebrate animal. In front of the head one or two pairs of limbs usually form long, many-jointed feelers or antennae. Thus the antennae, jaws, legs, and swimming-paddles of a lobster all belong to the same series of limbs, and they can be shown to be all constructed on the same plan. Possibly, though this is more doubtful, even the movable stalks on which the eyes of the lobster are set are also modified limbs. When different parts of an animal belong to the same series and are constructed on the same plan, although they may differ greatly in form and in use, they are said to be homologous. It is to be noted that the wings of an insect are not homologous with the legs and other limbs;

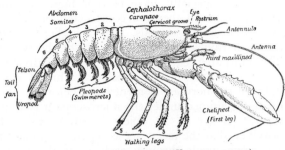

Diagram of the Common Lobster (*Homarus gammarus*)
Female, from the side.

they are not in series with them and are constructed on a different plan.

The outer skin or cuticle which forms the exoskeleton is quite continuous over the surface of the body and limbs, and, since it is not composed of living matter, it cannot grow. As the animal increases in size, therefore, the exoskeleton must be periodically shed and replaced. This process of moulting is very characteristic of the Arthropoda and can sometimes be watched in a crab kept in an aquarium. The shell splits across the back, and the animal slowly and painfully extricates its body and limbs, leaving the old shell quite complete down to the smallest detail. The new cuticle which had previously formed under the old one is at first quite soft, and the crab is for some days defenceless and hardly able to move. Gradually, however, the shell hardens, and the animal is seen to be considerably larger than the case from which it escaped. The whole growth of the animal thus takes place in the intervals after emergence from the old shell and before the new one has hardened.

SHORE CRAB CASTING ITS SHELL

The possession of a rigid exoskeleton, forming a system of jointed levers moved by muscles, has enabled the Arthropoda to qualify themselves for a much more active and varied life than any other invertebrate animals.

F 2

In particular it has allowed them successfully to colonise the dry land and become adapted for breathing air, so that the insects have become by far the most numerous and in many ways the dominant land animals.

In connection with this active life the Arthropoda have developed an increasing elaboration of the nervous system and of the sense-organs. The eyes, especially, have become highly complex and efficient organs of vision, although they are constructed on quite a different plan from the eyes of vertebrate animals. In the higher Crustacea and Insects, where they are most fully developed, they are of the type known as compound eyes. The transparent cuticle covering the eye is divided into a number (sometimes many thousands) of facets, each of which forms a lens to concentrate the light on the nervous element lying below it. When the cuticle is stripped off and examined under the microscope it is seen that each facet can form a separate image of an object in front of it. It must not be supposed, however, that the facets act as separate eyes and that a fly, for instance, sees a separate image through each of its thousands of eye-facets. It can be shown that each eye acts as a whole and that the separate elements co-operate to build up a single picture.

The classification of the Arthropoda is somewhat complicated and cannot be fully explained without going into details of structure that it is not possible to describe here. It may be useful, however, to mention some of the more striking features by which members of the principal classes into which the group is divided may, as a rule, be recognised.

Insects have the body usually divided into three parts, head, thorax, and abdomen. The head bears a single pair of antennae, or feelers, and there are three pairs of legs attached to the thorax. Wings (one or two pairs) are commonly present in the adult insect on the upper side of the thorax.

Centipedes and Millipedes have a distinct head with one pair of feelers. The body-segments are numerous and all nearly alike. There is a large number of legs, all alike, and extending the whole length of the body. The Centipedes have one pair of legs to each body-segment, the Millipedes two pairs.

The Arachnida have the head nearly always coalesced with the thorax, but the abdomen distinct. There are no feelers, and the thorax carries four pairs of legs besides another pair of limbs in front which often look like legs.

The Crustacea have the head not distinct from the thorax and carrying two pairs of feelers. The legs may be very few or very numerous, but they are rarely all alike.

Insects, Centipedes, Millipedes, and Arachnids are air-breathing animals and nearly all live on land. The Crustacea, with few exceptions, live in water and breathe by means of gills.

CHAPTER I

Class TRILOBITA

By W. T. Calman, D.Sc., F.R.S.

Among the animals whose remains are found as fossils in the older rocks of the geological series there are many Arthropods which differ greatly in structure and appearance from any now living. The best-known of these, and in some ways the most interesting, are the Trilobites, which are generally ranked as a distinct class. They are interesting because they come nearer than any others to what we suppose the primitive Arthropoda to have been like, and they have been regarded as the ancestral stock from which many, possibly all, of the existing classes have been derived. Whether this be so or not, they are among the very oldest animals of which we have any definite knowledge, some of them being found in rocks of the Lower Cambrian age, at the very beginning of the geological record. They died out, as far as we know, at the close of the Palaeozoic era. In many places their remains are very abundant, and they are familiar to every collector of fossils.

The general shape of a typical Trilobite is very characteristic. They are flattened, not unlike a woodlouse in outline. The head is covered by a broad crescentic shield which bears a pair of compound eyes on the upper surface. This is followed by a series of body-segments, the last few of which are often soldered together to form a tail-shield. The name of the group alludes to the fact that the body is nearly always divided into three lobes by a pair of furrows which run down the length of the back. It is very rare to find specimens that show anything of the under surface, and for a long time no trace of legs or other appendages could be discovered. It is now known, however, that the head carried a single pair of antennae and that the remaining limbs were all alike, two-branched, the inner branch forming a leg while the outer branch carried what seem to be gills. All the legs had jaw-like lobes at the base on the inner side and seem to have helped in passing food to the mouth. Many species could roll the body up into a ball, as some woodlice do when attacked, and they are often found preserved in this rolled-up condition.

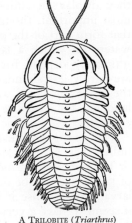

A Trilobite (*Triarthrus*)
(From Beecher.)

Although Trilobites are very common fossils in many of the older rocks, it is very rare to find specimens with any of the limbs preserved. This specimen shows the antennae in front of the head and the two-branched legs at the sides of the body.

CHAPTER II

Class CRUSTACEA

(Shrimps, Barnacles, Woodlice, Prawns, Lobsters, Crabs, etc.)

By W. T. Calman, D.Sc., F.R.S.

The Crustacea have been called the " Insects of the sea," and the name indicates aptly enough that the part which they play in the life of the sea is not unlike that which the true Insects take in the life of the land. From the pools of the shore down to the deepest abysses of the great oceans they are present everywhere, often in countless multitudes, swimming or creeping, lurking in the mud or drifting idly at the surface. They range in size from the microscopic water-fleas to the great crabs and lobsters, and they display an almost endless diversity of shapes and of habits. The most important, though not the most conspicuous, are the minute kinds that form part of the plankton, the assemblage of floating life in the surface waters on which a large proportion of the other inhabitants of the sea ultimately depend for food. In fresh waters the smaller forms at least are hardly less abundant, and nearly every pond or ditch contains some of the many kinds of water-fleas. Some Crustacea have even invaded the land, and the woodlice so common in gardens and the land-crabs of tropical countries have become true air-breathers.

The young of Crustacea, when hatched from the egg, are usually very unlike their parents, and reach the adult form after passing through a more or less complicated metamorphosis. Some of the more remarkable forms of the larvae will be described later, but mention may be made here of one larval type because it is found in so many widely different Crustacea that it seems to have a very special significance. This is the form known as the " nauplius." It has an oval, unsegmented body with three pairs of limbs surrounding the mouth on the under side and a single simple eye in the middle of the head. Crustacea of many different orders, which when full-grown are exceedingly unlike one another, begin life as nauplius larvae.

The Crustacea are classified in five sub-classes, each of which is divided into a number of orders. In the following pages an account is given of each of these sub-classes. Since, however, the majority of the larger and better-known Crustacea belong to the Sub-class Malacostraca, and in particular, to the Order Decapoda, that order will be described in fuller detail.

Sub-class *BRANCHIOPODA*

(Fairy Shrimps, Brine Shrimps, Water-fleas, etc.)

The Crustacea that are grouped together as Branchiopoda present great differences in external form, but they all agree in having the limbs, which are sometimes very numerous, flattened and fin-like or gill-like, whence the name Branchiopoda, which means " gill-feet." Practically all of them are inhabitants of fresh water, and in many ways they are the most primitive or old-fashioned of living Crustacea.

Order ANOSTRACA
(*Fairy Shrimps, Brine Shrimps*)

The Fairy Shrimp, which is sometimes to be found in ponds and rain-puddles in the South of England, is a representative of the Order Anostraca. It is a beautiful shrimp-like animal about an inch long, transparent and tinged with red on the limbs and tail. There is no carapace or shield on the back, the whole body being divided into segments like the body of a worm. The first eleven segments behind the head have each a pair of fin-like feet, but the hind part of the body has no feet and ends in a forked tail. The head carries a pair of large black eyes each set on a movable stalk, and there is a pair of thread-like feelers in front. The females can be recognised by having on the under side, just behind the last pair of feet, a large pouch for carrying the eggs. The males have, on the under side of the head, a pair

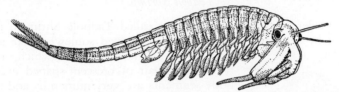

A FAIRY SHRIMP (*Chirocephalus*), male enlarged. (After Baird.) The " claspers "
are folded up under the front of the head.

of large " claspers," each shaped somewhat like a hand with webbed fingers, which are used for seizing the females.

The Fairy Shrimp generally swims back-downwards, with a graceful rhythmical movement of the feet. It feeds on small particles floating in the water, which are drawn with the currents caused by the feet and passed forwards towards the mouth.

Like many of the Branchiopoda, the Fairy Shrimp is usually found in quite small ponds which are liable to be dried up in summer. When this happens the eggs lie dormant in the dried mud, ready to hatch when rain again fills the pool. Some of the dried mud from a place where Fairy Shrimps have been living, if placed in an aquarium, will often give rise to swarms of tiny larvae which grow up in a few weeks to the adult form. The larvae, to the naked eye, appear only as dancing specks, but under the microscope are seen to be of the type described above as the nauplius. They moult their skins repeatedly, the body lengthening and becoming segmented, and the limbs appearing in regular order till the adult shape is reached.

The Fairy Shrimp is the only one of the Anostraca now found in England, but another species was formerly found at Lymington in Hampshire and other places where salt was made by running sea-water into shallow ponds, and allowing it to evaporate by the heat of the sun. This was the Brine Shrimp, which is still found on the shores of the Mediterranean and in other parts of the world where salt is made in this way, as well as in salt lakes, such as the Great Salt Lake of Utah. It forms one of the few exceptions to the statement that the Branchiopoda are freshwater animals, for it flourishes only in concentrated brine, where few other animals can live. It is similar to the Fairy Shrimp, but less than half its size, and is faintly tinged with reddish colour. Since it usually occurs in dense swarms, it causes the water to appear as if stained with blood. The Brine Shrimp is remarkable, among other things, for the fact that, in many places, only females are found and that it may reproduce by parthenogenesis, that is, by the development of unfertilised eggs.

Order NOTOSTRACA

(*Tadpole Shrimps*)

In the Order Notostraca (sometimes called Tadpole Shrimps) the back is covered by a broad shield or carapace shaped somewhat like a horse's hoof-print, in the middle of which, near the front, are a pair of crescent-shaped eyes. The body-segments are very numerous and the pairs of leaf-like limbs more numerous still. The end of the body carries a pair of long whip-like appendages corresponding to the forked tail of the Fairy Shrimps.

One of the NOTOSTRACEA
(*Lepidurus productus*)

Apus cancriformis was formerly found in various localities in the South of England, but it had not been seen for nearly half a century and was supposed to be extinct in this country when, in 1907, it was discovered in marshy pools in the South of Scotland. In the following year it was searched for in the same locality without success, and it has not been met with since anywhere in the British Isles. Such sudden appearances and disappearances are often observed in the Branchiopoda and seem to be due to the eggs being carried in mud adhering to the feet of birds. Probably the Scottish colony had developed from eggs introduced in this way from the Continent by migrating birds. In *Apus*, as in the Brine Shrimp, many colonies consist exclusively of females, and males are rarely seen.

Order CONCHOSTRACA

(*Clam Shrimps*)

In a third order, Conchostraca, the carapace forms a bivalve shell, like that of a Mussel, and the animals are therefore sometimes called Clam Shrimps. The shell completely encloses the body and limbs, and the resemblance to a small Mussel is increased by the concentric " lines of growth " with which the valves are marked. Several species of Conchostraca are found on the Continent of Europe, but none in the British Isles.

Order CLADOCERA

(*Water-fleas*)

The members of the Order Cladocera are known as Water-fleas and are abundant everywhere in ponds and ditches. They are all of small size and can only be studied with the aid of the microscope. As in the Conchostraca, the carapace forms a bivalve shell, from which, however, the head projects in front, bearing a pair of large two-branched antennae. By repeated backward strokes of these antennae the animal swims with a peculiar jumping motion which is alluded to in the popular name. Under the microscope, the transparency of the shell allows much of the internal structure to be studied in the living animal. The four to six pairs of feet are seen in constant motion, causing a current of water to enter between the valves of the shell bearing with it the minute floating particles which serve as food.

In the front of the head is a large single eye. Near the back the heart can be seen beating, and just behind it is a space between the body and the shell which serves, in the female, as a brood-pouch and is usually occupied by a number of developing eggs. These eggs develop without being fertilised, and, during the greater part of the year, no males are found. At certain seasons, however, males appear, and the females produce another kind of egg which requires fertilisation.

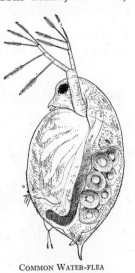

COMMON WATER-FLEA
(*Daphnia pulex*)

Female with eggs in the brood-chamber. (Much enlarged.)

These eggs are enclosed in a thickened part of the shell and are thrown off in their protective case when the shell is moulted. They lie dormant for some time and can be dried without injury. In this condition they may be transported from one pond to another entangled in the feathers of birds or even blown by the wind. Unlike the other Branchiopoda, the Cladocera have, as a rule, no larval stages, the young leaving the brood-pouch as miniature adults. Some species of Water-fleas are not more than one-hundredth of an inch in length, and are thus the smallest of living Crustacea.

Sub-class *OSTRACODA*

The Crustacea belonging to this sub-class are nearly all microscopic in size and are very abundant both in fresh water and in the sea. Like the

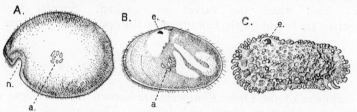

SHELLS OF OSTRACODA. (After Brady and Norman and Müller.)

B is a freshwater species, the other two are marine. *C* shows how the shell is sometimes elaborately sculptured. (All much enlarged.) *n.*, notch characteristic of the myodocopa ; *e.*, the median eye ; *a.*, mark of attachment of the muscle connecting the two valves of the shell.

Conchostraca and Cladocera they have a bivalve shell which, however, encloses the head and is not marked with lines of growth. In many marine species the shell is elegantly sculptured. The limbs are leg-like, and there are not more than one or two pairs behind those that are connected with the mouth. Parthenogenesis is even more common than it is among the Branchiopoda. A freshwater species has been cultivated in an aquarium for over thirty years without males appearing, and there are some species of which the males have never been seen.

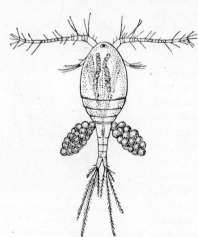

Cyclops albidus

A species of Copepod found in fresh water. (After Schmeil.) Female, carrying a pair of egg packets. The actual length is about one-tenth of an inch.

Sub-class *COPEPODA*

(*Cyclops, Fish Lice, etc.*)

Even more abundantly distributed than the Ostracoda, both in the sea and in fresh water, and much more diversified in form and habits, are the microscopic Copepoda. The genus *Cyclops*, of which some species may be found in almost every pond, is a fairly typical example. It has a pear-shaped body, tapering and segmented behind and ending in a forked tail. There are two pairs of antennae, the first pair very long, and behind the jaw-limbs there are four pairs of two-branched, paddle-shaped, swimming feet, from which the name of the group ("oar-feet") is derived. In the front of the head there is a single red eye. The female is often found carrying a pair of oval egg-packets, from which the young hatch in the form of typical nauplius larvae.

Calanus finmarchicus

A species of Copepod which is often found in vast numbers at the surface of the sea, and forms an important food of the Herring and other surface-feeding fish. (Enlarged.)

Many of the marine Copepods live at or near the surface of the sea, where they form an important part of the plankton. They feed on the minute floating plant-life and in their turn form the food of many kinds of surface-feeding fish and even of the great whalebone whales. Sometimes these plankton Copepods are so abundant as to discolour the water for many miles. In northern seas the most plentiful is a species called *Calanus finmarchicus*, which forms the main food of the Herring and Mackerel.

Besides the free-swimming Copepoda there are a large number which live as parasites on other aquatic animals. Many are found on fishes and are known as Fish Lice. Some of them are not very different in structure from the free-living species, except that they have flattened bodies and are provided with hooked claws to enable them to cling closely to the skin of their hosts while they suck their blood. Others are very strangely modified, becoming, when full-grown, shapeless sacks, incapable of movement and having lost most of their limbs. The parasites of the Salmon, known to anglers as " Sea Lice " and " Gill Maggots " respectively, are examples of these two types.

Caligus rapax

A common Fish Louse found on marine fishes. The two sausage-like packets of biscuit-shaped eggs are often longer than shown in this specimen (enlarged). (After Wilson.)

A common parasite on all kinds of freshwater fish in this country is the so-called Carp Louse (*Argulus*), which resembles in general shape some of the Copepod Fish Lice, but has a pair of large compound eyes and differs so much in many other details of structure that it is very doubtful whether it is at all closely related to the Copepoda.

Sub-class *CIRRIPEDIA*
(*Barnacles*)

The typical forms of this class are the Barnacles which cluster on floating logs of driftwood and are the chief cause of the fouling of ships' bottoms on long voyages, and the Acorn Shells or Rock Barnacles which cover the rocks just below high-water mark on our own coasts.

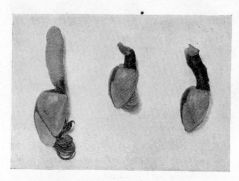

GOOSE BARNACLES (*Lepas anatifera*)
The fleshy stalk is sometimes much longer than in these specimens. (Half natural size.) 1, Legs fully expanded; 2, Legs half out; 3, Shell closed.

At first sight the common Ship Barnacle, or Goose Barnacle, shows little resemblance to a Crustacean. It is rooted to its support by a long muscular stalk which bears at the free end a shell composed of five plates hinged together. From a slit on one edge of the shell there can be protruded six pairs of long curled feet, each of two branches fringed with stiff bristles. When spread out these feet form a kind of casting net which sweeps the water for the capture of minute floating prey, and is then withdrawn into the shell. The stalk is, in fact, the greatly elongated front part of the head, and the remains of the minute first pair of antennae can be discovered embedded in the cement which fixes it to the support. Huxley described a Barnacle as "a Crustacean fixed by its head and kicking the food into its mouth with its legs." The Acorn Shells are constructed on the same plan as the Ship Barnacles, but they have no stalk, and the conical shell, not unlike that of a limpet, is cemented directly to the rock. At the top of the shell is an opening, closed by two pairs of valves between which the feet are protruded.

ACORN BARNACLES (*Balanus balanoides*)
(Slightly reduced.)

The shells of the Barnacles give them so great a resemblance to Mollusca that it is not surprising that the older naturalists classified them in that group. In 1830, however, J. Vaughan Thompson, a naval surgeon at Cork, discovered their larvae and showed that they were Crustacea. He found that they are hatched from the egg in the form of a nauplius which differs only in minor details from the nauplius larvae of many other Crustacea which, when full-grown, have not the slightest resemblance to barnacles. After swimming at the surface of the sea for some time the nauplius changes into another larval stage, also free-swimming, which, from its resemblance to certain Ostracods, is known as the Cypris larva. It has the body enclosed in a bivalved shell, within which six pairs of swimming feet can be seen, and in front bears a pair of curious antennae with suckers which serve to attach the animal when it has found a suitable object on which to settle. The bivalved shell is then thrown off, and the form of the adult is gradually assumed.

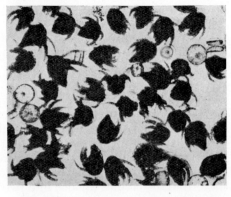

NAUPLIUS LARVAE OF ACORN BARNACLE. (Enlarged.)

In the Middle Ages, when Natural History was largely a matter of legends and marvellous stories, a very curious myth grew up about the Barnacles. There were different versions of the story, but they all told how the Barnacle developed into a sea-bird, the so-called Barnacle Goose. This bird is a winter visitor to our shores, and its Arctic breeding-places were then, and for long afterwards, unknown.

The sub-class Cirripedia also includes some strangely modified forms which live as parasites on other animals, and have even less resemblance to ordinary Crustacea than have the Barnacles. Not unfrequently crabs of various kinds are found which carry under the abdomen or "tail" what looks like a soft fleshy tumour. This is a degenerate Cirripede known as *Sacculina*, and it is attached to its host by a

A SHORE CRAB which bears under its tail a degenerate parasite, Cirripede *Sacculina carcini*.

short stalk from which fine root-like threads branch throughout the body of the crab and penetrate even to the tips of its legs. Through these roots the *Sacculina* absorbs nourishment from its host, for it has no mouth or food-canal, no jaws or legs, and when it is mature it is little more than a bag of eggs. There is nothing to show that it is a Crustacean or even an Arthropod at all. Yet the larvae that hatch from the eggs are typical nauplii, and they develop into Cypris larvae that hardly differ from those of ordinary Barnacles except that, like the nauplii, they have no mouth or food-canal. These Cypris larvae settle on a crab, and, after a further series of extraordinary changes, appear as the fully-formed *Sacculina* on the under side of the crab's body.

Sub-class *MALACOSTRACA*

(Woodlice, Sandhoppers, Shrimps, Prawns, Crayfishes, Lobsters, Crabs, etc.)

This sub-class includes a far greater variety of forms than any of the other sub-classes. The features that they have in common and that justify their being brought together in a single sub-class, though very important, are not, for the most part, very conspicuous, and cannot be fully explained without going into details of structure that would be out of place here. One character that is generally fairly obvious, however, is that the body, apart from the head, is divided into two regions commonly known as thorax and abdomen, although they have no relation to the two regions so named in a mammal, for instance. The thorax carries eight pairs of appendages, some or all of which are often walking legs. The abdomen has six pairs of appendages and is usually divided into six segments, with, very rarely, a seventh, besides an end-piece or " telson " which carries no appendages.

There are reasons for believing that the ancestral Malacostracan was a prawn-like form which had a carapace enveloping the thoracic segments, and in which the eyes were set on movable stalks. The antennules (or first antennae) were two-branched and the second antennae had a flattened plate (representing the outer branch) which served as a balancer in swimming. The eight pairs of thoracic legs had each a whip-like outer branch serving as an oar in swimming, and the same purpose was served by the abdominal limbs which were flattened two-branched " swimmerets." The last pair of abdominal appendages were larger than the others and spread out on either side of the telson to form with it a fan-like tail-fin, which the animal no doubt used in making sudden backward jumps through the water by bending the abdomen downwards and forwards.

The reasons for supposing that the ancestral Malacostracan was something like the type here sketched are, first, that in each of the chief divisions of the sub-class there are forms coming near to this type in their shape and structure, from which the other members of the division may be supposed to have been derived by changes associated with their peculiar habits of life ; and, secondly, that the earliest fossil Malacostraca, found in rocks of the Carboniferous period, were mostly of this general type.

The classification of the Malacostraca, as given below, shows them arranged in eleven orders which are grouped in five divisions. Some of the smaller orders are not of much general interest, and their names can only be mentioned here. The Order Decapoda, however, including most of the larger and more familiar Crustacea, will be dealt with in greater detail.

Division *PHYLLOCARIDA*

Order NEBALIACEA

The best-known representative of this small division is a little shrimp-like Crustacean found in the sea on our southern coasts and in many other parts of the world. Its special interest lies in the fact that it has been supposed to form a link between the Malacostraca and the primitive Branchiopoda. It has a bivalve shell somewhat like that of the

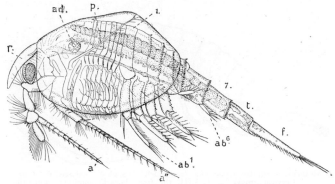

Nebalia bipes, a representative of the PHYLLOCARIDA. (Much enlarged.) (After Claus.) *a'*, antennule ; *a''*, antenna ; *ab¹–ab⁶*, the abdominal limbs ; *ad*, muscle joining the two valves of the shell ; *f*, tail-fork ; *p*, palp of maxillula ; *r*, rostral plate ; *t*, telson ; 1–7, the seven somites of the abdomen.

Conchostraca, and its thoracic feet instead of being walking-legs are flattened and leaf-like, resembling the typical Branchiopod limbs. The abdomen is unlike that of the other Malacostraca in having seven distinct segments, and the telson ends in a " tail-fork." There are certain fossil Crustacea known from rocks as early as the Cambrian period that may be related to *Nebalia* and confirm the view that it is the most old-fashioned of the Malacostraca.

Division *SYNCARIDA*

Order ANASPIDACEA
(*Mountain Shrimps*)

About thirty-five years ago a curious Crustacean, to which the name of " Mountain Shrimp " was given (*Anaspides tasmaniae*), was discovered in rocky pools of mountain streams in Tasmania. It is a brownish animal about an inch and a half long, having very much the prawn-like form described above as that of the primitive Malacostracan, except that it has no carapace and the body is completely divided into segments. At the base of each of the thoracic legs, besides the whip-like swimming branch, there are two leaf-shaped gill-plates. In many other points of its structure the Mountain Shrimp differs from all other living Crustacea, but it was soon noticed that it resembled in a remarkable way certain fossil forms that had been described from Carboniferous rocks in Europe and America. The fragmentary remains of these fossils, to which the name Syncarida had been given, are very hard to decipher, and their structure is as yet only imperfectly known, but they resemble the Mountain Shrimp in having a fully segmented body, no carapace, a tail-fan, and swimming-branches on the legs. There is little doubt, therefore, that the Mountain Shrimp is a surviving representative of

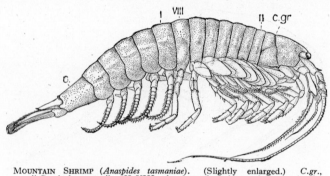

MOUNTAIN SHRIMP (*Anaspides tasmaniae*). (Slightly enlarged.) *C.gr.*, " Cervical groove "; II–VIII, the free thoracic somites; 1–6, the abdominal somites.

this very ancient group of Crustacea which were once distributed over a great part of the world.

A few other species of living Syncarida have since been discovered in Australia and Tasmania, but the most interesting is one that has been found in Europe. Some twelve years before the discovery of *Anaspides*, a zoologist who was investigating the water of wells in the city of Prague observed two specimens of a minute Crustacean which he was quite at a loss to classify. From his description and from a re-examination of one of his specimens which had fortunately been preserved, it was pointed out many years later that this Crustacean, to which he had given the name *Bathynella*, was in many ways like *Anaspides*, but the animal was never seen again until 1914, when it was found in a well in Switzerland and its structure fully investigated. Since then two other related species have been found in the subterranean waters of caves and wells in various parts of Europe. They are of microscopic size (about 1/25th of an inch in length), colourless, without eyes (like many other subterranean animals), and with the various appendages somewhat simplified in correspondence with their minute size. In all essentials, however, they agree with the larger Syncarida, and there can be no doubt that they are survivors that have lingered on in their subterranean retreats while their relatives have disappeared from the surface of the earth, except in the far-off Australian region. Quite recently, the gap in the distribution of the group has been partly bridged by the discovery of a fourth species of the family *Bathynellidae* in a cave in the Malay Peninsula.

Division *PERACARIDA*

(*Woodlice, Freshwater Shrimps, Sandhoppers, etc.*)

Unlike the two divisions discussed above, the Peracarida present a great diversity of general form and habits. They are grouped into six orders, linked together by certain peculiarities of structure, of which the most striking is the possession by the females of a brood-pouch on the under side of the thorax in which the eggs and young are carried. This brood-pouch, to which the name of the division (" Pouched Shrimps ") alludes, is formed by a series of overlapping plates attached to the bases of the legs. The eggs pass into it from the oviducts and undergo their development there, the young emerging only when they have assumed practically the form of the adult. There are no free-swimming larval stages (except in some highly modified parasites), and the development is said to be " direct."

Order MYSIDACEA

(*Opossum Shrimps*)

The members of this order are sometimes known as Opossum Shrimps. They are mostly graceful, transparent, shrimp-like forms, with stalked eyes, a carapace covering the thorax, feathery swimming-branches on the legs and a tail-fan. Most of them are found in the sea, and they may often be seen in rock-pools, hanging suspended in the water with the swimming-branches of the legs in constant rhythmical motion, or darting backwards with a flick of the tail-fan. It has recently been shown that the ceaseless beating of the swimming-branches is at least as much concerned with feeding as with locomotion. The whirling movement of each feathery filament draws in a current of water which passes between the bases of the legs and forwards along a groove on the under side of the thorax. A comb-like row of hairs on one of the pairs of jaws strains off from the water the minute floating particles, which are then pushed into the mouth. In addition, however, the Opossum Shrimp can seize and devour larger masses of food.

When an Opossum Shrimp is examined under the microscope, a pair of curious organs can be seen in the inner side-plates of the tail-fan. Each consists of a rounded cavity within which lies a button-shaped, glass-like object supported on a ring of hairs. These were formerly supposed to be organs of hearing, but they are now known to be concerned in maintaining the balance of the animal in swimming.

Nearly all Mysidacea live in the sea, but a few are found in freshwater lakes, and their story is rather a curious one. In some of the lakes in countries surrounding the Baltic, in Scandinavia, Finland, and North Germany, as well as in parts of the Baltic itself, there is found a small Opossum Shrimp (*Mysis relicta*) which is not closely related to anything now living in the North Sea, but seems to be a variety of a species which is abundant in the Arctic Ocean. In some of the lakes it is accompanied by other Crustacea similarly related to Arctic marine forms. It is known from geological evidence that the Baltic was once an inlet of the Arctic Ocean which extended across Northern Russia, and the ancestors of these Crustacea must have entered it at that time. Later, the connection with the Arctic Ocean was cut off, and the Baltic became an inland lake, the water of

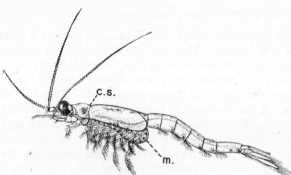

OPOSSUM SHRIMP (*Mysis relicta*). (Enlarged.) (After Sars.) This freshwater species is found in lakes in Northern Europe, but many closely similar forms are found in the sea. *cs*, cervical groove of the carapace ; *m*, brood-pouch.

which was gradually diluted by the influx of fresh water from rivers. *Mysis relicta* and some of the other marine animals were able to adapt themselves to living in the fresh water. The lakes in which they are now found were once fjords, or gulfs of this inland sea, from which they have been cut off by elevation of the land. Only at a later period did the Baltic become connected with the North Sea between the Danish islands, and its waters again became salt. A similar process must have happened elsewhere, for *Mysis relicta* is found in Lough Neagh and some other lakes in Ireland, and in the Great Lakes of North America.

Orders CUMACEA, TANAIDACEA, AND THERMOSBAENACEA

The next three orders of Peracarida include forms of inconspicuous size and less general interest. The Cumacea and Tanaidacea are found in the sea, mostly burrowing in mud, and are in some respects transitional between the primitive shrimp-like Mysidacea, and the more specialised orders to be discussed presently. The Order Thermosbaenacea includes only a single species recently discovered living in the water of a hot mineral spring in Tunis. It is noteworthy, among other things, because it lives in scalding hot water at a temperature of 48° C. in which few other animals could survive.

Order ISOPODA

(*Woodlice, etc.*)

This is the largest and most varied order of the Peracarida. The majority of its members have a characteristic general shape which is seen, for example, in the common garden Woodlice. The body is flattened from above downwards and is completely divided into segments, there being no carapace covering the thorax. The abdomen is short, and the abdominal appendages are broad plates serving (in those Isopods that live in water) as gills. The eyes are not mounted on stalks but are set on the sides of the head. The legs are used for crawling and do not have swimming-branches.

The families included in this order are numerous, but only a few typical forms will be described here. Most Isopods are found in the sea, but some inhabit fresh water and an important group of them have even invaded the dry land.

In ponds and ditches in this country two species of the genus *Asellus* are common. They are little, flattened, brownish animals about half an inch long, with long antennae and with a pair of forked spikes at the hind end of the abdomen. A third species, blind and colourless, has recently been discovered in the water of a well in the New Forest.

Many kinds of Isopods may be found in rock pools between tide-marks, swimming or creeping among weeds. *Sphaeroma* has the power of rolling up into a ball

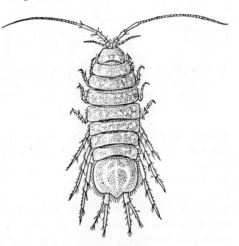

Asellus aquaticus

A common freshwater Isopod (enlarged). (After Sars.)

when touched. *Idotea* and its kindred are long narrow forms, often olive-green in colour, matching the seaweeds to which they cling. The *Cirolanidae* are " savage devourers of fish and not to be held in the human hand with impunity." A little species of this family, *Eurydice achatus*, about a quarter of an inch long, is very common in sandy bays, swimming actively, and pinching most unpleasantly the skin of bathers or paddlers. *Cirolana* sometimes attacks in shoals the fish hooked on fishermen's lines, till nothing is left but skin and bones. Some related families comprise blood-sucking parasites of fish, the larger kinds of Fish Lice. They are found clinging to the skin with their strong hooked claws, often under the fins or within the gill-covers, and sucking blood with a sharp, piercing beak. Some of these fish parasites are known to change their sex in the course of their life-history. When young they are actively swimming males, but later in life they settle down on the skin of a fish and become females.

A very curious group of Isopods are found as parasites on other Crustacea.

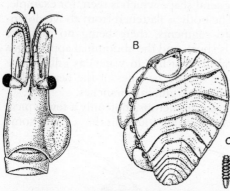

A PARASITIC ISOPOD (*Bopyroides hippolytes*). *A*, the front part of the body of a species of Prawn (*Spirontocaris polaris*) having on one side of the carapace a tumour-like swelling containing the parasite. *B*, the female *Bopyroides* further enlarged. *C*, the male parasite on the same scale as the female. (After Sars.)

It is not unusual to find specimens of the Common Prawn which have on one side of the carapace a rounded swelling, like a boil. If this be opened, it will be found to enclose a curiously distorted object, hardly to be recognised as an Isopod, with a large brood-pouch filled with innumerable eggs. To the under side of the body of this female a microscopic male may be found clinging, like a secondary parasite, on its mate.

The most familiar of all Isopods are the Land Isopods, or Woodlice, which are common in every garden. They are of particular interest because they are the only Crustacea that have become completely adapted to spend the whole of their life on land. The largest British species is the Sea Slater, *Ligia oceanica*, which is abundant on rocky places on the seashore, living just above high-water mark, within reach of the salt spray. It is said sometimes to enter the water of rock-pools, and it is thus intermediate in habits, as it is to some extent in structure, between the marine Isopods and those that are more exclusively terrestrial. It is about an inch long, with a thin, flattened body enabling it to slip into narrow crevices so that it is difficult to catch.

One of the commonest species found in gardens is *Oniscus asellus*, which has a brownish body with two rows of yellowish spots on the back. Equally common is *Porcellio scaber*, which is bluish-grey in colour. If the under side of a living *Porcellio* be examined with a lens, a white spot will be seen on the outer plates of each of the first two pairs of abdominal appendages. These white spots are tufts of fine branching tubes in the interior of the appendage. The tubes are filled with air and open to the outside by a minute pore, and they enable the animal to breathe air. They represent, in fact, the beginnings of a "tracheal system" like that which

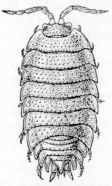

WOODLOUSE (*Porcellio scaber*) (enlarged). (After Sars.) This is one of the commonest species of land Isopods found in gardens.

constitutes the means of respiration in Insects and some other air-breathing Arthropoda. It is impossible to suppose, however, that the Woodlice are in any way closely related to the Insects, for instance, and their tracheae must be imagined as having arisen independently from those of the Insects. Such instances of independent origin of similar structures are of great importance in their bearing on general theories of evolution.

Oniscus and *Porcellio* are usually found in damp places, under stones and the like, but some species are more independent of moisture. The common Pill Woodlouse, *Armadillidium*, may often be seen crawling actively about on rocks in hot sunshine. Its name is derived from its habit of curling into a ball when touched, in which condition it was formerly used in popular medicine as a ready-made pill.

A small, colourless, blind Woodlouse is occasionally found in the nests of ants in the South of England. It has the rather cumbrous name of *Platyarthrus hoffmannseggii*, and it is one of the curious " guests " the presence of which in the nests is tolerated by the ants, although they do not appear to be of any service to their hosts.

Order AMPHIPODA

(*Freshwater Shrimps, Sandhoppers, Whale Lice, etc.*)

This is also a very extensive order, although it does not present such a wide range of structure as the Isopoda. Its members, like the Isopods,

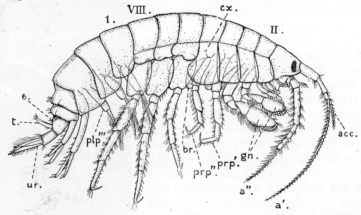

A COMMON MARINE AMPHIPOD (*Gammarus locusta*) (enlarged). (After Sars.) The freshwater *G. pulex* is very similar to this. *a'*, antennule ; *a''*, antenna ; *acc*, accessory (inner) flagellum of antennule ; *br*, gill plate ; *cx*, coxal plate ; *gn*, the two pairs of gnathopods ; *plp'''*, abdominal appendage of third pair ; *prp'*, *prp''*, first and second paraeopods, or walking legs ; *t*, telson ; *ur*, uropod ; II–VIII, thoracic somites ; 1–6, abdominal somites.

have a segmented body, without a carapace, and sessile (not stalked) eyes, but the body is nearly always flattened from side to side, and the abdomen is often bent forwards under the thorax.   The gills are under the thorax, attached to the bases of the legs.

An Amphipod which is very common in fresh water in this country is

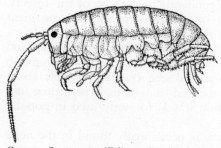

COMMON SAND-HOPPER (*Talitrus saltator*) (enlarged).
(After Sars.)

Gammarus pulex, sometimes called the " Freshwater Shrimp." It is about half an inch long, of a greenish-brown colour, and is important as food for trout and other freshwater fish. Numerous species of this and related genera are found in the sea. Perhaps the most familiar Amphipods, however, are the Sandhoppers (*Talitrus* and *Orchestia*), which every one has seen leaping in myriads about high-water mark on sandy beaches.

They jump by suddenly straightening the bent abdomen. They are more or less amphibious animals, and in this country they are rarely found far above high-water mark.   In tropical countries, however, some species live in damp forests at great distances from the sea.   Some of these " land-hoppers " have been found living in hothouses in this country, having been imported in the earth round the roots of tropical plants.

A number of Amphipoda belong to the subterranean fauna that inhabits the underground waters in various parts of the world. One of these is found not uncommonly in the water of wells in the South of England, and is known as the Well Shrimp.   It is closely related to the freshwater *Gammarus*, mentioned above, but it is much more slender and delicate, and like most subterranean animals it is colourless and quite blind, the eyes being reduced to inconspicuous vestiges.

Many Amphipods are found swimming freely at the surface of the sea, where they form part of the plankton.   Especially characteristic of this habitat are the members of the Sub-order Hyperiidea, which have the eyes, as a rule, enormously enlarged so

SKELETON SHRIMP (*Caprella*).

that they cover the surface of the large head.   Specimens of *Hyperia* are very commonly found in British waters sheltering under large jelly-fishes.

Very different in general form from the other Amphipods are those belonging to the Sub-order Caprellidea, sometimes called Skeleton Shrimps.

With the body drawn out to the slenderness of a thread, the abdomen reduced to a mere stump, and two pairs of legs generally missing, while their gill-plates remain, these grotesque animals are found clambering slowly among the branches of zoophytes or seaweeds. One family of this sub-order, the *Cyamidae*, or Whale Lice, are parasites of whales. They have the body broad and flattened, and the legs have sharp hooked claws with which they anchor themselves to the skin of their host. They do not suck blood, but seem to feed by gnawing the skin. In one respect they are unlike all other Crustacean parasites, for they are without the power of swimming at any stage of their life. They can only pass from one whale to another by actual contact. The young settle down close to their parents and seem to move very little, so that masses of thousands of individuals are found packed close together, and covering large patches on the skin of the whale.

Division *EUCARIDA*

Order EUPHAUSIACEA

The Division Eucarida comprises only two orders, and these are of very unequal size and importance. The Euphausiacea, which form the first order, are small, transparent, shrimp-like animals found swimming at or near the surface of the sea, forming part of the assemblage of floating life already referred to as the plankton. From the fact that they possess swimming-branches on the legs they were formerly grouped together with the Mysidacea, but they are distinguished from them by having no brood-pouch and by many other less obvious details of structure. Like most Eucarida, they have free-swimming larvae, but in this order the series of larval stages is unusually long, most species hatching from the egg as a nauplius which differs little from the nauplius stage of a Copepod or a Branchiopod.

The Euphausiacea are remarkable for the complicated system of light-producing organs which they possess. Many marine animals, including Crustacea of various orders, have the power of emitting light like glow-worms or fire-flies, but in most cases they do so by certain skin-glands which discharge a luminous secretion. In the Euphausiacea, however, the light-organs are constructed like tiny searchlights, each with a reflector and a lens to concentrate the beam. If a jar of sea-water in which some of these Euphausids are swimming be taken into a dark room, stirring the water or even tapping on the glass will cause the light-organs to flash out like a row of tiny lamps along the side of the body. It is hard to guess what the use of these light-organs may be. Many Euphausids descend to depths in the sea where little light, if any, can penetrate from above. They usually swim in shoals, and the light which they emit may help the members of a shoal to keep together; it can hardly enable them to find their prey, for most Euphausids feed by sifting out from the water the microscopic plant life of the plankton.

Some Euphausids are of importance as food for surface-feeding fish. The herrings in Loch Fyne in Scotland are said to owe their exceptional quality to the fact that they feed largely on a species of Euphausid,

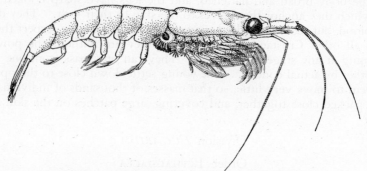

LUMINOUS SHRIMP (*Meganyctiphanes norvegica*).   (Twice natural size.)

Meganyctiphanes norvegica, which is abundant in the deeper waters of the loch. Both in the Arctic and the Antarctic regions Euphausids form the chief food of some of the larger whales, and their vast shoals which discolour the sea for miles are known to the whalers as " whale-feed " or " kril."

Order DECAPODA

(*Prawns, Shrimps, Lobsters, Crabs, etc.*)

The second order of the Eucarida, the Decapoda, not only vastly exceeds any other order of Crustacea in the number of known species, in the range of their structure, and the variety of their habits, but it includes all the larger and more familiar examples of the class.   For these reasons it will be dealt with in fuller detail.

The more primitive Decapoda have the general shrimp-like form already described and resemble somewhat closely the Euphausiacea.   They are distinguished, however, by the fact that the first three pairs of thoracic limbs, which, in the Euphausiacea, resemble the legs of the following pairs, are more or less completely modified to serve as jaws, and are known as " maxillipeds," or " foot-jaws."   The remaining five pairs of thoracic limbs are legs (hence the name of the order, " ten feet "), but nearly always one or more pairs end in pincer-claws (chelae) and are used for seizing food. The gills, which lie at the bases of the legs on each side of the thorax, are enclosed in a pair of gill-chambers by the overlapping side-plates of the carapace.   In the lower Decapoda the abdomen is large, and its appendages, the " swimmerets," are the chief organs of locomotion.   In the higher forms, the Crabs, the abdomen is small and tucked up under the thorax, and the animals crawl instead of swimming. In nearly all Decapods the eggs are deposited on the abdominal appendages and are carried adhering to them until hatching takes place.

Most Decapoda pass through a series of free-swimming larval stages in the course of their development, but there are great differences in the character of these larvae. Only a few of the more primitive forms (*Penaeidea*) are hatched from the egg in the form of a nauplius. In the higher Decapods, particularly in the Crabs, the earliest larva has a very characteristic shape and is known as a zoea. In the zoea there is a short helmet-shaped carapace, often with large spikes projecting in front, on the back, and at the sides; the eyes are large but not yet set on stalks, the maxillipeds are the only thoracic limbs developed, and there is a slender, flexible, segmented abdomen, ending in a tail-fork.

The classification of the Decapoda is somewhat complicated. The very numerous species and genera are arranged in some forty-six families, which again are grouped in tribes, sections, and sub-orders. For the sake of simplicity, however, it is convenient here to adopt a system of classification which differs somewhat from that given in more advanced works. On this system three sub-orders are recognised :

Sub-order Macrura (" long-tailed "). Prawns, Shrimps, and Lobsters. The abdomen is long, with a tail-fan, and the abdominal limbs are well-developed.

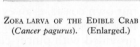

ZOEA LARVA OF THE EDIBLE CRAB
(*Cancer pagurus*). (Enlarged.)

Sub-order Anomura (" irregular-tailed "). Hermit Crabs, etc. The abdomen is twisted or partly folded under the body. There is nearly always a tail-fan, but the abdominal limbs are often reduced.

Sub-order Brachyura (" short-tailed "). Crabs. The abdomen is small, folded under the body. There is no tail-fan, and the abdominal limbs are much reduced.

In each of these sub-orders only the more important groups will be mentioned.

Sub-order MACRURA

(*Prawns, Shrimps, Lobsters, Crayfishes, etc.*)

The Macrura might be roughly divided into the prawn-like forms, active swimmers, with a relatively thin " shell," and the more heavily armoured Lobsters and their kindred which crawl on the bottom of the sea.

Of the prawn-like forms, one large group is the Tribe *Penaeidea*, which comprises most of the larger Prawns of tropical seas. These may generally be recognised by having the first three pairs of legs provided with pincer-claws (chelae) and nearly alike in size. Swimming-branches are often present on the legs, although they may be reduced to tiny rudiments. In many ways the *Penaeidea* resemble the Euphausiacea, and, as in that group, some are hatched from the egg in the form of nauplius larvae, being the only Decapods in which this primitive type of larva occurs. The later larval stages in some species have a very remarkable appearance, the carapace being armed with great branching spines. Certain pelagic species further resemble the Euphausiacea in possessing complicated light-organs dotted all over the body and limbs. Some of these organs are so placed as to illuminate the interior of the gill-chambers. What use they can have in that position it is impossible to guess.

Many of the larger species of *Penaeus*, which are common in the warmer seas and may reach the dimensions of small lobsters, are used for food, and

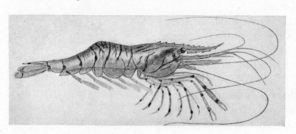

COMMON PRAWN (*Leander serratus*). (Reduced.)

the fishery is of considerable importance, especially in India, Japan, and the southern United States. *Penaeus caramote* is a common Mediterranean species highly esteemed for the table.

The Tribe *Caridea*, including the common Prawns and Shrimps of our own coasts, is an even larger and more diversified group. Its members may usually be distinguished by having only the first two pairs of legs provided with pincer-claws. Some species, belonging for the most part to the fauna of the deeper waters of the ocean, retain the primitive swimming-branches on the legs, but as a rule these are lost in the adult although they are present in the larvae. Some of these deep-sea species also possess light-organs.

The Common Prawn of our coasts (*Leander serratus*) is a typical example of the *Caridea*. It is easily recognised by the great length of the sabre-shaped, saw-edged beak or rostrum which projects from the front of the carapace. The first and second legs have small but distinct pincer-claws. The Pink Shrimp (*Pandalus montagui*), often to be seen in fishmongers' shops, is very like the Common Prawn, but is a little smaller. It has no apparent pincer-claws on the first pair of legs and very minute ones on the second pair, which are unequal, many-jointed, and curiously flexible.

Among weeds in rock-pools the little Aesop Prawn (*Hippolyte varians*) is very common. It is only about an inch long, and its English name alludes

Pl. 4.

AESOP PRAWNS (*Hippolyte varians*).

Showing colour changes : 1, on brown seaweed ; 2, on green sea-grass ; 3, night coloration.

to the hunchback-shape produced by the sharp downward bend of the abdomen. It is remarkable for the variety of colours which it shows and for the closeness with which these match the weeds on which it is found. Thus, on green weeds the prawns are bright green, on brown weeds they are olive brown, and on red weeds they are red. When the weeds to which they are clinging are branching and feathery the prawns are correspondingly barred or lined with colour. Whatever the colour during the day all the prawns become a beautiful transparent blue at night, resuming the colour of the surrounding weed in the morning. When hatched, the prawns are colourless and transparent, and swim at the surface of the sea. After passing through their larval stages they approach the shore and settle down among the weeds to which they remain clinging, moving little for the rest of their life. Shortly after settling they begin gradually to assume the colour of whatever weed they may have happened to settle on; and if they do leave it or are washed off by the waves, they seem to select weed of the same colour to cling to. If they are forced to shelter among weed of a different colour in an aquarium, they change their colour to that of their new home in the course of a few days. These changes of colour are produced by the movements of pigment within minute pigment-cells scattered over the skin, but the mechanism whereby they are adapted to produce so close a resemblance to their surroundings remains a mystery.

COMMON SHRIMP
(*Crangon vulgaris*).
(Reduced.)

The Common Shrimp (*Crangon vulgaris*), which is very abundant in sandy bays all round our coasts, differs from the prawns in having the rostrum reduced to a little spike between the eyes and the body slightly flattened instead of compressed from side to side. It is of a translucent greyish colour, speckled with brown so as to resemble closely the sand on which it lives, and its concealment is helped by its habit of lying half-buried in the sand. In a pool left by the tide on the sand, nothing living may be visible, but if the water be disturbed, half a dozen greyish shadowy forms will dart away to settle on the bottom again and disappear each in a little puff of sand.

There are many other kinds of *Caridea* even in British waters, while in the warmer seas their numbers are endless. In this country there are no truly freshwater species, although the little Ditch Prawn (*Palaemonetes varians*), common in the brackish ditches of salt marshes, is often found in places where the water is almost or quite fresh, and in the Norfolk Broads the larger *Leander longirostris* is equally at home in salt and in fresh water.

In tropical countries, however, freshwater prawns of many kinds are abundant. The larger kinds belong to the genus *Palaemon*, and are very

G

similar to our Common Prawn, differing chiefly in having the legs or claws of the second pair very large, sometimes as long as the body. Some species grow to a foot or more in length (without the claws) and are often mistaken for Crayfishes. They may easily be distinguished, however, by the compressed, saw-edged rostrum, and by the fact that the large claws are the second instead of the first pair of legs.

The lobster-like Macrura are grouped in three tribes, of which the first, the *Eryonidea*, comprises a small number of curious blind inhabitants of the deep sea. They have flattened bodies, and their eyes are represented only by the vestiges of the stalks on which they were once supported.

SEA CRAWFISH OR SPINY LOBSTER (*Palinurus vulgaris*). (Much reduced.)

They are distinguished from all other Decapods by the fact that the first four, and sometimes all five, pairs of legs have pincer-claws. They are interesting because they were well-known as fossils long before they were discovered surviving as living animals in the deep sea. The *Eryonidea* in the early part of the Secondary period lived in shallow water, and some of them at any rate had well-developed eyes. In the early part of the Cretaceous epoch they disappear from geological history, apparently because they left the shallow waters for the depths of the ocean where they still survive.

Some members of the next tribe, the *Scyllaridea*, are much more familiar. On the southern and western coasts of the British Isles, the large Spiny Lobster, Rock Lobster, or Sea Crawfish, the *Langouste* of the French (*Palinurus vulgaris*), is common. It is occasionally to be seen in the fishmongers' shops, although it is not so much used for food in this country as it is in France. It is distinguished from the Common Lobster by its prickly carapace, with no rostrum in front, by the thick and stiff feelers or antennae of the second pair, and by the fact that none of the legs have large pincer-claws, although the hindmost pair have small pincers in the female. The larva of the Spiny Lobster is very remarkable. It has a broad, flattened body, as thin as paper and as transparent as glass, long spidery legs, and large black eyes set on long stalks. In the British species the oldest larva is only about half an inch long, but in tropical seas larvae of two and even three inches in length are met with. These larvae were known long before

their relation to the Spiny Lobsters was suspected, and they were supposed
to be independent species of Crustacea to which the generic name of
Phyllosoma was given and the
English name of Glass Crabs.

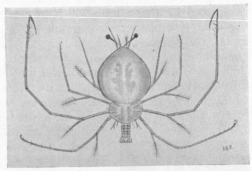

Phyllosoma larva of the Spiny Lobster. (Much enlarged.)

The Spiny Lobsters are
especially characteristic of the
warmer seas. They include
the largest of living Macrura,
and several of them are used
for food in various parts of
the world. Closely allied to
them are the Flat Lobsters,
which have the body broad and
flattened, often with a rough
warty surface, and the second
antennae replaced by shovel-
like plates which have been stated, perhaps wrongly, to be used for
burrowing in sand. A small species, *Arctus ursus*, is found occasionally on
our southern coasts, and some of the larger species,
by their strange shapes, attract collectors of
curiosities in tropical seas.

The Tribe *Nephropsidea* includes the true Lobsters
and the freshwater Crayfishes. These are distinguished by having the first three pairs of legs
provided with pincer-claws, the first pair being large
and massive, the rostrum short and more or less
flattened, and the second antennae slender.

The Common Lobster (*Homarus gammarus*) is
well known, in general appearance at least, to most
people. It is found on the coasts of Europe from
Norway to the Eastern Mediterranean, usually in
rocky places. It shelters in crevices, crawling forth
in search of food, and shooting backwards through
the water, when alarmed, by powerful strokes of
its broad tail-fan. Its colour, dark blue to nearly
black on the back with a good deal of red or orange
on the under side, is due to pigment in the shell,
and therefore does not change much or rapidly
during life, unlike the colour-changing prawns
mentioned above, in which the colour resides in
living cells of the underlying tissues. The two

COMMON LOBSTER (*Homarus gammarus*). (Much reduced.)

great claws are unlike in size and shape, the larger, which may be the right
or the left, having the fingers armed with blunt knobs adapted for crushing
the shells of mussels and the like, and the smaller claw having saw-edged

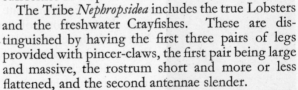

fingers for holding and tearing the prey. Lobsters, like most of the larger Crustacea, readily throw off a limb that is seized by an enemy or injured in fighting. The limb parts at a special " breaking-joint " near the base, and is replaced by a new limb which grows in its place but only reaches full size after several successive moults. It often happens that lobsters are found with one claw much smaller than the other, the smaller claw in such examples being in process of regeneration.

The newly-hatched larvae of the lobster are transparent little creatures that swim at the surface of the sea by means of the swimming-branches with which the legs are provided. There are no swimmerets, the abdomen has a row of spines on the back, and the telson is forked. After moulting several times, the larva loses the swimming-branches, the swimmerets and tail-fan are developed, and the young lobster seeks the bottom to assume the habits of the adult.

NORWAY LOBSTER (*Nephrops norvegicus*). (Much reduced.)

On the Atlantic coast of North America another species is found which is very similar to the Common Lobster and, like it, is the object of an important fishery.

The so-called Norway Lobster, or " Dublin Prawn " of the London fishmongers (*Nephrops norvegicus*), is unfortunate in its English names, since the Common Lobster is often imported from Norway, where it is abundant, while the Dublin Prawn, which was formerly brought from the Irish Sea, is now chiefly caught in the North Sea. It is much smaller than the Common Lobster and is distinguished by its long slender claws and large, kidney-shaped eyes. When alive it is of an orange colour, beautifully marked with red and white. It lives in deeper water than the Common Lobster, on a muddy bottom, and is usually caught by trawling.

In the deep sea several species of blind lobster-like Crustacea are found. The most remarkable are two species of the genus *Thaumastocheles*, which have one of the claws enormously enlarged, sometimes as long as the body of the animal, with long slender fingers set with teeth like those of a rake. It is supposed that this extraordinary claw may be used for raking the mud for the small animals on which the *Thaumastocheles* feeds.

Closely allied to the Lobsters are the freshwater Crayfishes, of which there are two families inhabiting the rivers and lakes of the Northern and Southern Hemispheres respectively. Unlike the Lobsters, but like many other freshwater animals, they have no free-swimming larval stages, the young hatching from the egg in a form very similar to that of the adult, and

remaining clinging to the swimmerets of the mother until they are fully developed and able to shift for themselves.

The Common Crayfish, *Astacus pallipes*, is found in many rivers and streams in England and Ireland, but not in Scotland. It is about three to four inches long and generally of a brownish green colour. It hides in crevices or makes burrows in the banks of the stream and is said sometimes to leave the water at night and make short excursions on land. It is little used for food, preference being given to the larger red-clawed species, *Astacus fluviatilis*, which is imported from the Continent.

The geographical distribution of Crayfishes is remarkable. The Northern Crayfishes, forming the family *Astacidae*, are found in Europe, extending east to Turkestan, in the basin of the Amur River, Korea and Northern Japan, and in California. All these belong to the genus *Astacus*, but east of the Rocky Mountains they are replaced by the genus *Cambarus*, with many species in the United States. The Southern Crayfishes, of the family *Parastacidae*, occur in Australia and New Zealand, Madagascar, and parts of South America. No Crayfishes are found in Africa or Southern Asia. Except in Europe, it does not seem that Crayfishes are much used for food. Some species of *Cambarus* are eaten in the southern United States, and the large *Astacopsis*, known as the Murray River Lobster, is sold in Sydney and Melbourne.

A few species of Crayfishes have become almost land animals, although they are probably always confined to marshy or damp places. This is true of some species of *Cambarus* in North America and also of the *Engaeus* of Tasmania, which burrows in the earth in damp forests and is known as the Land Crab.

The well-known Blind Crayfish of the Mammoth Cave in Kentucky is one of several species of *Cambarus* living in subterranean waters in the United States. Like most subterranean animals they are colourless and blind, the eyes being quite atrophied and only the vestiges of the eyestalks remaining.

Sub-order *ANOMURA*

(*Hermit Crabs, etc.*)

Forming in some respects a link between the Macrura and the Anomura, but now usually classified with the latter, is the Tribe *Thalassinidea*. They are mostly soft-bodied, loosely-built, lobster-like animals, with small and imperfect eyes, living in burrows in mud at the bottom of the sea. Several species are found on the British coasts, one of the most curious being *Callianassa*, which has one of the claws of the first pair greatly enlarged and oddly shaped.

The Tribe *Paguridea*, comprising the Hermit Crabs and some allied forms, is a large group with varied and interesting habits. Nearly all its members have the habit of using as portable shelters the empty shells of Gastropod

Molluscs, and their structure is remarkably modified to fit them for this mode of life.

The Common Hermit Crab (*Eupagurus bernhardus*) is often to be seen in rock-pools, scrambling actively about and carrying with it a whelk or peri- winkle shell into which it retreats when alarmed.   If extracted from its shell, a matter of some difficulty, it is seen to have the abdomen soft and twisted to fit into the spiral shell and the tail-fan formed into an apparatus for wedging the end of the body into the cavity.   The pincer-claws of the first pair of legs are very unequal, the larger forming a stopper for the opening of the shell when the animal withdraws into it.   The next two pairs of legs are long and slender and used for crawling, while the last two pairs are short, with roughened pads at the end which grip the inside of the shell and hold the body in place.   The swimmerets are present only on one side of the abdomen and are conspicuous only in the female, where they serve

for carrying the eggs.   As the Hermit grows, it is necessary for it from time to time to change its dwelling for a larger one.   When it finds an empty shell of suitable size it carefully explores it with its claws, and if it proves satisfactory quickly inserts its body into the new habitation.

Many Hermit Crabs are of special interest because they live in more or less constant association with certain other animals.   Very often this association is of the kind that is termed " commensalism," the partners being rarely found sepa-

COMMON HERMIT CRAB (*Eupagurus bernhardus*) in the shell of a whelk.   (Reduced.)

rately and each apparently deriving benefit from the presence of the other. Several species of sea-anemones are found only on shells inhabited by Hermit Crabs.   Thus the full-grown specimens of the Common Hermit Crab which are found below low-water mark frequently have a sea- anemone (*Calliactis parasitica*) attached to the shell, sharing the crumbs from the crab's meals and no doubt giving its host some measure of protection by reason of its stinging powers.   A third partner is often present in this association, for a bristle-worm (*Nereilepas fucata*) shares the inside of the shell with the Hermit, living in the upper whorls and thrusting out its head when the crab is feeding to snatch morsels from its very jaws.

Another common British Hermit Crab (*Eupagurus cuanensis*) is found inhabiting a spiral cavity in a sponge, *Suberites*.   When young, the crab lives in a small Gastropod shell on the outside of which the sponge settles. The growth of the sponge keeps pace with that of the crab, so that the latter

never needs to change its lodging. In other species, the size of the shell is similarly increased by the growth of a horny crust formed by Hydroid Zoophytes or by Polyzoa. Even this does not exhaust the possibilities of these strange associations, for a Hermit Crab living in the shell of a Gastropod mollusc, carrying a sea-anemone and sharing its lodging with a bristle-worm, may have an Isopod parasite on its gills, and a group of Cirripedes, allied to *Sacculina*, under its abdomen.

The Hermit Crabs of our coasts never voluntarily leave the water, but on tropical beaches species of the genus *Coenobita*, which may be called Land Hermits, lead an almost completely terrestrial life, travelling far inland and only returning to the sea to breed.

Like our common Hermits they carry Molluscan shells as portable shelters, and the finding of these shells scattered about far inland has some-times puzzled observers until it was noticed that they had been brought by crabs.

The Land Hermits often climb into bushes in search of food, but their climbing is on a small scale when compared with that of the great Coconut Crab or Robber Crab (*Birgus latro*). The statement that it climbs lofty palm-trees to get the coconuts was made by some of the early naturalists, and, although doubt has been cast on the story, the crab has been seen and photographed in the act. *Birgus* is very closely related to *Coenobita*, but it grows to a foot in length of body, and, perhaps on account of its great size, it has given

COCONUT CRAB (*Birgus latro*). (Much reduced.)

up the use of a portable shelter. Its abdomen, which is carried partly bent up under the thorax, is not soft and fleshy like that of the ordinary shell-inhabiting Hermit Crabs, but has the back covered by shelly plates. It is furthermore not twisted but symmetrical, although it preserves a trace of its derivation from the twisted abdomen of the normal Hermit Crab in having swimmerets only on one side.

The Coconut Crab is easily recognisable for a modified Hermit Crab, but the resemblance is much less close in the case of the Stone Crabs, of which one species, *Lithodes maia*, is common in the North Sea. It looks at first sight not unlike one of the spiny Spider Crabs, to be described later, but it may be easily distinguished by having only three instead of four pairs

of walking legs behind the pincer-claws. The fourth pair of legs are not lost, but they are slender, and, as in the Coconut Crab, folded away out of sight in the gill-chambers. The small size of the abdomen and the fact that it is carried closely tucked up under the thorax give the Stone Crabs a close resemblance to the true crabs of the Sub-order Brachyura, but the abdomen is often unsymmetrical, and the swimmerets, which are present only in the female, are confined to one side of the abdomen. They are the only Anomura that have no tail-fan. Some of the Stone Crabs have the carapace and legs even more spiny than our British species, and one, found in Japanese seas, looks like a Crustacean hedgehog. Another very large Japanese species is the object of an important fishery, and its canned flesh is largely exported.

STONE CRAB (*Lithodes maia*). (Much reduced.)

The Tribe *Galatheidea* comprises the Squat Lobsters and the Porcelain Crabs, in both of which the last pair of legs are feeble and usually folded up in the gill-chambers. They have a well-developed tail-fan. Squat Lobsters of the genus *Galathea* and Porcelain Crabs (*Porcellana*) are common under stones between tide-marks on our coasts.

The members of the Tribe *Hippidae*, known as Mole Crabs, are found abundantly burrowing in the sand on tropical beaches. They are curiously modified, with spade-like feet adapted for digging, and some

SQUAT LOBSTER (*Munida rugosa*). (Reduced.)

of them have long, stiff antennae which keep open a tubular passage in the sand for the purpose of breathing.

Sub-order BRACHYURA
(Crabs)

The True Crabs, which form this sub-order, have the carapace often broader than long, the abdomen reduced to a tail-flap tucked up under the thorax, no tail-fan, or the merest rudiment of one, and the jaws enclosed in a " mouth-frame " closed below by a pair of folding doors formed by the flattened third maxillipeds. The swimmerets are only well developed in the female and serve for the attachment of the eggs when the crab is, as the fishermen say, " in berry." The newly hatched young have usually the form of the typical zoea larva described previously, and a later larval stage is known as the megalopa, in which the general form of the adult is assumed, but the abdomen is large and extended and the swimmerets are used in swimming.

The number of genera and species is very large, and they are grouped in some twenty-six families. Here again, without attempting a strictly scientific classification, we can only mention a few of the more striking forms in each of the principal groups.

The *Dromiacea*, or Sponge Crabs, receive their name from the habit of carrying a cloak formed of a piece of sponge, the test of a sea-squirt, or some

SPONGE CRAB (*Dromia vulgaris*)
carrying on its back a cloak of the sponge, *Clione celata*.
(Reduced.)

such object, held by the last pair or the last two pairs of legs, which are short, elevated on the back, and end in pincers. In many details of structure the *Dromiacea* are the most primitive of the Brachyura, some of them having, for instance, a vestige of the tail-fan in the form of two small plates interposed at the sides between the last two segments of the abdomen. Many of them are plump furry crabs, like *Dromia vulgaris*, which is found, although not commonly, on the south coast of England.

The *Oxystomata*, sometimes called Sand Crabs, although many others share their habit of burying themselves in sand, are distinguished by the triangular shape of the mouth-frame which is narrowed in front and extends forward between the eyes. This peculiarity is associated with the sand-burying habit, for the breathing-channels at the sides of the mouth are carried forward so that the crab can breathe with only the tip of its snout at the surface of the sand. The only *Oxystomata* found on British coasts

are the little Pebble Crabs (*Ebalia*), whose general appearance is sufficiently indicated by their English name.   In the warmer seas the group is more abundantly represented, and includes some very odd-looking forms.   The Masked Crabs (*Dorippe*) have the back of the carapace sculptured into the likeness of a grotesque human face.   The last two pairs of legs are small, elevated on the back, and used, as they are in the Sponge Crabs, to carry a piece of sponge, a Molluscan shell, or some other object by which the body is concealed.   The Cockscomb Crabs (*Calappa*) get their name from the high serrated crests on the large claws which fit neatly against the front of the carapace.   The carapace is broadened behind to cover the legs, so that the crab, when at rest, presents no vulnerable points to an enemy. The Oxystome Swimming Crabs (*Matuta*) have the legs flattened into paddles for swimming and also for digging in sand.

The *Oxyrhyncha*, or Spider Crabs, are mostly long-legged, more or less spiny crabs, with a beak or rostrum, often double, projecting between the eyes.   The Spider Crabs have the interesting habit of masking themselves with pieces of living seaweed, sponge, or other marine growths.   They pluck these from their surroundings with their claws and plant them on the back of the carapace and the legs, where they are held by the little hooked hairs with which the body is covered. The weeds or sponges continue to live and grow so that the whole crab becomes covered with a most effective disguise, and as the Spider Crabs are slow-moving animals this concealment no doubt saves them from many enemies.   The crabs can to some extent adjust their disguise to their surroundings.   If a crab covered with seaweed be placed in an aquarium with sponges it will pick off the weed from its back and legs and replace it with pieces of sponge.

SPIDER CRAB (*Maia squinado*),
dressed with fragments of weed.   (Reduced.)

A number of kinds of Spider Crabs are found on our coasts.   Most of them are of small size, and they generally have an untidy appearance owing to their being dressed in the way just described.   The Large Spider Crab (*Maia squinado*), which is common on the south coast of England, and is occasionally used for food, grows to a size of about six inches across the carapace.

By far the largest, not only of the crabs, but of all living Arthropoda, is the Giant Spider Crab of Japan.   In this species the carapace may be some fifteen inches long by over a foot wide, while the claws, which, as in many

Oxyrhyncha, are greatly elongated in the male sex, may span as much as eleven feet when stretched out.

Looking very different from the other Spider Crabs are the members of the little family *Parthenopidae*, which have a triangular carapace, broadened behind to cover the short legs, and the claws very long and massive. The carapace is often very rugged and pitted, so that the crab looks like a worm-eaten fragment of the coral among which it lives.

In the remaining families of Crabs the carapace is not narrowed in front, and there is no projecting rostrum. They are sometimes grouped in two divisions, the Round-fronted and the Square-fronted Crabs, but the limit between the two is hard to define. The Round-fronted Crabs usually have the carapace broader than long and more or less transversely oval. The Edible Crab (*Cancer pagurus*) of our coasts is familiar to most people. Like the Lobster it is usually found in shallow

GIANT JAPANESE CRAB
(*Macrocheira kaempferi*).

The scale of the figure is shown by the two-foot rule placed below the specimen.

water among rocks, and young specimens are often met with between tide-marks. It may grow to a weight of as much as twelve pounds.

The Furrowed Crabs (*Xantho*), of which three species are found on our south coast, represent a family of which the members are very abundant in tropical seas, where they are often brilliantly coloured. The Giant Crab of Tasmania (*Pseudocarcinus gigas*) may measure a foot in width of carapace and has one of the claws enormously large and massive. Next to the Giant Spider Crab it is the largest among living Crustacea.

COMMON EDIBLE CRAB (*Cancer pagurus*). (Much reduced.)

One little crab of this group deserves mention on account of its very unusual habits. This is *Melia tessellata*, which is found in the Indian and Pacific Oceans. Its claws are feeble and apparently ill-adapted for use as weapons, but it is usually found

holding in each claw a living sea-anemone, which it has picked from its attachment and carried about with it to use not only as a weapon, but also as a means of collecting food. The fingers of the claws are armed with hooked teeth which give them a grip on the slippery anemone. In the instances described above of partnership between sea-anemones and Hermit Crabs the benefit appeared to be mutual, but in the case of *Melia* it would seem as if the anemone had much the worst of the bargain.

The Masked Crab (*Corystes cassivelaunus*) is common on sandy beaches round our coasts. It gets its name, like the Oxystome Masked Crabs already mentioned, from the resemblance of the markings on the back of the carapace to a human face. The male has very long and slender claws, while those of the female are quite short. The antennae, which are very short indeed in most crabs, are here long and stiff, and when they are brought together the hairs with which they are provided form a tube through which the crab can breathe when it is buried in the sand.

SWIMMING CRAB (*Portunus depurator*).   (Reduced.)

A large and important family in this group is that of the Swimming Crabs (*Portunidae*), which have the end joints of the last pair of legs formed into broad flat paddles. A number of species are found on the British coasts. The largest has a furry carapace, handsomely marked with red and blue, and is known as the Velvet Crab. It is used for food in some places, as, for instance, in the Channel Islands.

The Common Shore Crab (*Carcinus maenas*), known to every seaside visitor, belongs to the same family, although its hind legs are not distinctly paddle-shaped and it is not a good swimmer. It is a particularly hardy and adaptable animal, able to live for long periods out of the water.

Many kinds of Swimming Crabs are sufficiently large and abundant to be used for food in various parts of the world. The Blue Crab of the Atlantic coast of the United States is especially esteemed as a delicacy when in the soft-shelled state after moulting. A large species, *Neptunus pelagicus*, is caught and eaten in large numbers from the Red Sea to Japan. In recent years it has invaded the Eastern Mediterranean through the Suez Canal and is now regularly caught by the fishermen of Palestine and Egypt.

One family in the Round-fronted group which is of special interest is that of the River Crabs (*Potamonidae*). These are found throughout the tropics, and one species extends its range into Southern Europe. They

live in rivers, lakes, and swamps, and many of them are amphibious in their habits, spending much of their time on land, so that they deserve the name of Land Crabs as much as the members of the group to be described later to which that name is commonly restricted. Like many other groups of freshwater animals, the Crayfishes, for instance, they have no larval metamorphosis, the young on hatching being provided with all the appendages of the adult and leaving the shelter of the mother's abdomen as fully-formed little crabs. The European species, which is found in Italy and Greece, was well known to the ancients and can be recognised on certain Greek coins.

A little crab found on our south coast may be mentioned here because it belongs to one of the families that serve to link the Round-fronted with the Square-fronted group and form an obstacle to their easy classification. This is the Angular Crab, whose long slender arms, long eyestalks, and rhomboidal carapace are defined by mostly straight lines to form a kind of cubist pattern.

The crabs of the Square-fronted group are mostly inhabitants of the warmer seas, though many of them penetrate into brackish or even fresh water. The more typical members may be recognised by the more or less square outline of the flattened carapace.

The species of *Grapsus* and several related genera are the commonest shore crabs of the warmer seas, leaving the water readily and running with great activity among the rocks. *Sesarma* and its allies, some of which are known as Mangrove Crabs from their abundance in mangrove swamps, are not only amphibious in their habits, but are particularly characteristic of brackish water and extend up estuaries to the fresh waters of rivers and lakes.

The little Gulf-weed Crab is found throughout the tropics clinging to floating weed and the like in the open ocean. It is especially abundant in that part of the Atlantic known as the Sargasso Sea, where the sight of it is said to have led Columbus to the too-hasty inference that he was approaching land.

On sandy beaches in the tropics a great variety of crabs are found living a more or less amphibious life. Above tide-mark the Swift-footed Crabs (*Ocypoda*) live in burrows. They are almost land animals, breathing air by means of their swollen gill-chambers which serve for lungs. Lower down on the beach, sand-feeding crabs like *Scopimera* emerge from their burrows when the tide is out to scoop up the surface sand, which they chew for the sake of the organic matter in it and spit out the rest in little round pellets scattered round the mouth of the burrow.

On muddy flats and in salt marshes in the tropics the Calling Crabs or Fiddler Crabs are found in swarms. The females are very ordinary-looking little crabs, with small claws, but the males have one of the claws of relatively enormous size, often larger than the body of the animal. These large claws

are often brilliantly coloured, and have been supposed to serve to attract the females, but they are also used as weapons in the combats of the males.

A very peculiar family of the Square-fronted crabs is that of the little Pea Crabs which live

WEST INDIAN LAND CRAB (*Gecarcinus ruricola*).   (Reduced)

within the mantle-cavity of bivalve molluscs such as oysters, mussels, and the like. They are hardly parasites in the strict sense, since they live by stealing a share of the food brought in by water-currents into the mantle-cavity of their host, but it is difficult to refuse the name of parasite to others of the same family that live in the terminal part of the food canal of sea-urchins and sea-cucumbers.   The males of the Pea Crabs are more active than the females which, when they have entered a mollusc's shell, settle down for life, become bloated and soft-shelled, and devote themselves to producing vast quantities of eggs.

Another family of special interest is that of the Land Crabs (*Gecarcinidae*), which are conspicuous inhabitants of many tropical countries. These are to a large extent air-breathing animals, the gill-chambers (as in some other instances mentioned above) being distended and the lining membrane richly supplied with blood-vessels to act as a lung. They are never found at very great distances from the sea, however, for their young stages are marine, and it is necessary for the crabs to visit the shore at the breeding season. In some species at least, this migration to the sea takes place annually, the crabs moving across country in great swarms.

MANTIS SHRIMP (*Squilla mantis*).
(Reduced.)

Division *HOPLOCARIDA*

Order STOMATOPODA

(*Mantis Shrimps*)

This division comprises only a single order, that of the Mantis Shrimps, so-called from the resemblance of the great claws to those of the Praying Mantis Insect. They have a more or less flattened body, the abdomen very large, and the

small carapace leaving the last four thoracic somites uncovered. The eyes are stalked, and they, like the antennules, are carried by separate movable segments of the head, a peculiarity not found in any other Crustacea. The large claws (the second pair of thoracic limbs) are not pincer-claws, but so constructed that the last segment, often armed with strong teeth, shuts down, like the blade of a clasp-knife, on the preceding segment.

Most of the Mantis Shrimps live in burrows in sand or in crevices of rocks or coral, whence they issue to seize the passing animals that form their prey. One species, *Squilla desmarestii*, occurs, but not commonly, on the south coast of England. It is about three inches long, but in the tropics, where they are abundant, some species grow to more than a foot in length. The Mantis Shrimps, in the course of their development, pass through a long series of larval stages, mostly distinguished by the large size of the carapace which sometimes envelops the whole body. These larvae are often abundant in the plankton of the warmer seas, where their large size (some are two inches long) and glassy transparency make them very striking objects.

CHAPTER III

Class PROTOTRACHEATA

(*Peripatus*)

By N. D. RILEY, F.E.S.

THE Arthropoda, with their hard bodies and jointed legs, occupy a conspicuously isolated position in the Animal Kingdom. Their segmented bodies, each segment bearing, usually, a pair of legs or appendages of some kind or other, find a counterpart only amongst the more highly organised Worms. From somewhere about the point of separation of these two stocks it seems probable that *Peripatus*, the sole representative of the Class Prototracheata, has arisen, for it combines some of the characters of each.

Peripatus was first found in 1826 in the island of St. Vincent, West Indies. The discoverer regarded it as a slug. Subsequently, other species of the genus were met with in Central and South America, in Africa, and also in Australia and New Zealand. Such a wide distribution points clearly to considerable antiquity, especially when considered in conjunction with the fact that all the species bear a very close resemblance to one another.

Some fifty or sixty different species are now recognised, the best known being *Peripatus capensis*, which is found in South Africa. This is a cylindrical, soft-bodied creature, very worm-like or caterpillar-like in general appearance,

with a single pair of moderately long but very stout antennae on the head, peculiarly suggestive of the tentacles of a slug.   In addition to the antennae, the head bears a single pair of jaws, a pair of eyes, and a pair of papillae in the neighbourhood of the mouth upon the surface of which open the slime glands.   From these organs *Peripatus* can, when alarmed, eject a highly viscous substance, which would appear to be utilised not only as a means of defence, but also for the purpose of securing the small insects upon which it feeds.   In some ways this fluid is analogous to the silk spun by insects and spiders ; it is ejected with great force, being thrown sometimes a distance of nearly a foot.

The body, in fully grown individuals, may be as much as three or four inches in length, and, although distinctly worm-like in shape, is covered by a skin of remarkable beauty.   Soft and velvety in texture, delicately coloured in dark green (*P. capensis*), bluish-grey, brown, blackish, or even reddish orange, it compares in general attractiveness with that of any other

member of the Animal Kingdom.   The under surface of the body is nearly always paler than the upper and somewhat less arched. The segmentation of the body is not apparent, but the number of segments can be determined by counting the legs.   All the segments from head to tail are similar—there is no thoracic region such as

A *Peripatus* from South America.   (Natural size.)

that which characterises the insects and the legs are all alike, hollow, each bearing a pair of claws.

The structural characters that have decided zoologists to place *Peripatus* in the Arthropoda, but as a distinct class, sometimes called the Onychophora, are mainly concerned with details of internal anatomy.   The most important link is afforded by the fact that respiration takes place by means of a system of air-tubes, as in Insects.   The arrangement of these tubes does not follow that found in Insects, however, as the minute tracheae open upon the surface of the body in a very large number of places.   The presence of jaws, also, which may be regarded as modified appendages, is indicative of Arthropodan affinity.   Other details of internal structure point just as definitely to a close relationship with the Annelid worms, so that *Peripatus* is to be regarded without doubt as a very primitive form.   It stands absolutely alone as a kind of halfway animal, a link between the Arthropods, more especially the Myriapods perhaps, and the Annelid worms.

All the species of the group, so far as observed, are extremely sluggish, moving with great deliberation and carefully picking their course.   They

live beneath the bark of rotten trees, under stones, or in the crevices of rocks, using their eyes, apparently, only as a means of avoiding light, and investigating the ground with their extraordinarily sensitive antennae. The food, so far as is known, consists of animal matter—minute insects principally, which they tear up with their jaws, afterwards sucking up the juices. They have the power of extruding the jaws from the mouth, and of working them backwards and forwards.

The breeding habits of *Peripatus* are unusual for so lowly a creature. It has been stated that one of the Australian species lays eggs, but the statement lacks confirmation. Otherwise, all the species are viviparous. " The young of *Peripatus capensis* are born in April and May. They are almost colourless at birth, excepting the antennae, which are green, and their length is 10 to 15 mm. A large female will produce thirty to forty young in one year. The period of gestation is thirteen months, that is to say, the ova pass into the oviducts about one month before the young of the preceding year are born. They are born one by one, and it takes some time for a female to get rid of her whole stock of embryos. The mother does not appear to pay any especial attention to her young, which wander away and get their own food." Sometimes, however, they may be found creeping about upon the velvety back of their mother.

Outwardly the males and females are not distinguishable. The method by which the eggs are fertilised appears somewhat obscure. The male deposits small bundles of spermatozoa, in the form of oval, white spermatophores, indiscriminately upon the body of the female, most commonly towards autumn. It is assumed that from this position the spermatozoa make their way through the body wall and the tissues of the body till they reach the ovary.

CHAPTER IV

Class MYRIAPODA

By T. H. Savory, M.A.

General Characteristics

The Class Myriapoda contains the Centipedes and Millipedes, which include some thousands of species, distributed throughout the world, in hot and cold countries, in barren and in fertile districts. They are all terrestrial, but a few species live on the shore, between the tide-marks, and are able to survive long immersion. They are animals whose bodies are composed of well-defined rings, or segments, each segment behind the head bearing one or two pairs of legs.   In this similarity of all the segments and in the possession of legs on the hinder segments of the body, the Myriapoda resemble *Peripatus*, and differ from the Insects and Arachnids.   In some genera the legs are quite long, and give a spider-like appearance to the creature.   The head is always distinct from the body-segments, and it probably consists of several segments fused together.   It bears a pair of antennae in front, and the mouth-parts below, the latter consisting of a lip, a pair of toothed jaws or mandibles, and one or two pairs of maxillae.

Myriapoda, as would be expected of a large and widely distributed group, show much diversity in size and colour.   They range from species scarcely visible to the naked eye, to others that are over six inches long ; the numerous reports, in the classics and elsewhere, of Centipedes a yard long are either exaggerations or are due to confusion of Myriapods with other animals. Some Centipedes are short and squat, others have more than a hundred segments ; some have bright streaks of colour, but the majority are tawny, or black.

With the exception of a few small families, Myriapods are very clearly divided into two orders, the Centipedes, or Chilopoda, and the Millipedes, or Diplopoda.   The Centipedes are flattened, possess a pair of poison-fangs, and bear one pair of legs on each segment of the body.   The Millipedes are more rounded, have no poison-fangs, and each segment after the fourth bears two pairs of legs.   Centipedes are carnivorous, generally predatory, active animals, while all Millipedes are vegetarians, and usually move but slowly.   Compared with Insects, or with Mites, Myriapods are of small economic importance, but some Millipedes, including our familiar Wireworm, do much damage by gnawing the tubers and roots of crops.

Order CHILOPODA

(*Centipedes*)

The active brown Centipede, so common in all our gardens during the summer, by name *Lithobius forficatus*, is the most familiar example of this order, and illustrates the characteristics already mentioned.   It lives under leaves and heaps of garden rubbish, and in the winter buries itself in the earth.

The food of *Lithobius* consists of Insects and their larvae, and occasionally it kills worms and other small creatures.   The prey is seized by the poison-fangs, and a droplet of poison injected into it, killing it instantaneously. Even such an active creature as a Bluebottle fly is sometimes seized by a *Lithobius*, which creeps up behind it.   In some of the larger Centipedes the bite is dangerous to man.

In this country *Lithobius* lays its eggs from June to August ; its breeding habits have been described by Sinclair.   The genital opening is on the last segment.   The extrusion of the egg follows some convulsive movements of the hinder part of the body, and when it appears it is received by two small hooks on the under side of the last segment. If the male sees the egg at this critical moment he rushes at the female, seizes the egg, and eats it. In more fortunate circumstances the female clasps it, and hurries away from the male's presence. The egg, which is a small sphere, is coated with a sticky liquid secreted by large accessory glands contained in the Centipede's body, and the female, using the hooks and her hind legs, rolls the egg over and over so that it gets completely covered with earth. It is then indistinguishable from a particle of soil and is free from the male's cannibal attentions. The young Centipede that hatches from the egg is already in possession of its poison-fangs and of six pairs of legs. In growing, fresh segments make their appearance just in front of the last segment.

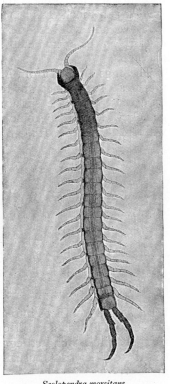

Scolopendra morsitans

A Centipede common in all tropical countries. (After Koch.)

At least one British Centipede, *Geophilus electricus*, found not uncommonly in Cambridgeshire and in Epping Forest, has the remarkable property of being phosphorescent at night. The light is quite bright, like that of the glow-worm, and of unknown function, but it probably enables the males and females to find each other.

A remarkable feature of Centipedes is their apparent indifference to temperature. Sinclair has described how in Cyprus he found a species of *Lithobius* and another of *Scolopendra* to be plentiful in the hot luxuriant districts of the plains, and that when he climbed Mount Troodos, the ancient Olympus, he found the same two species quite as common and quite as active among the snows.

Order DIPLOPODA

(*Millipedes*)

The small black Wire-worm, so common in our gardens and wherever crops are grown, is undoubtedly the most frequently met with British Millipede. Its name is *Julus terrestris*. It is not so active as a Centipede, despite the greater number of its legs. Its food consists exclusively of the underground parts of cultivated plants. Millipedes, being vegetarians, are not possessors of poison-fangs ; they can protect themselves, however, by a fluid, secreted by their " stink-glands," that contains prussic acid and has a most unpleasant odour. Practically all Millipedes, except a few cave-dwelling species, possess these glands.

Julus is a much easier creature to keep and observe in captivity than is *Lithobius*, and will breed readily if well fed. The cages should have a layer of earth on the bottom and the food should be sliced apple, chopped leaves, and grass.

The eggs are laid from May to July, and before their arrival the female prepares a sort of nest for their reception. She first of all buries herself a little way below the surface of the earth, and secretes from her salivary glands, which now become unusually active, a sticky fluid which she mixes with small bits of earth. She fashions these little dabs of " mortar " with

A Sumatran Millipede, *Platyrrhachus mirandus*. (Natural size.)

her jaws and front legs into a small spherical nest, smooth inside, but rough outside. There is a small opening on the top, through which she passes from sixty to a hundred eggs. The oviduct of a Millipede opens on one of the front segments, usually the seventh, and not on the last segment, as in Centipedes.

The eggs are tiny, and are stuck together by a viscous fluid. When all are laid the female closes the nest with more of the paste of earth and saliva, and abandons it. The eggs hatch in about twelve days and the young on emergence have but three pairs of legs. As they grow, more legs appear, in batches of ten.

CHAPTER V

Class INSECTA

By N. D. RILEY, F.E.S.

INTRODUCTION

IT is not perhaps generally realised that the total number of different species of insects at present known to science exceeds half a million, nor that, at a moderate estimate, fully as many more remain to be discovered. The largest collection anywhere in existence, that at the British Museum (Natural History), is estimated to contain 8,000,000 specimens ; but it is admittedly very incomplete. To attempt to summarise in a few words the immense variety of form and structure, and the behaviour when living, of this enormous number of creatures, is therefore manifestly to attempt the impossible.

Insects are as nearly ubiquitous as it is possible for air-breathing animals to be. Their very perfect means of locomotion, more particularly their power of flight, and the wide ranges of substances upon which they are able to subsist, have no doubt contributed very largely to the remarkable success they have attained in the struggle for existence. The specialisation of the functions of the different stages, as so frequently happens—the caterpillar doing the feeding and growing, so that the resultant butterfly can concentrate upon reproduction, for example—must also have played no inconsiderable part in this same struggle. To their powers of locomotion, however, must in the main be attributed the fact that they have, and no doubt had already ages ago, established themselves in almost every terrestrial situation in which animal life can exist at all.

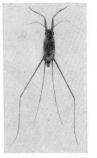

Halobates flaviventris
One of the very few known marine insects; collected off the coast of Ceylon.

Numerous species have taken to life in fresh water and many consequential adaptations have had to be acquired, and perfected, before life in these altered circumstances could be successfully maintained. The great variety of devices for obtaining a supply of air amongst the fresh-water Insects will be realised from the following pages, and affords clear evidence that the habit of living in water is not a primitive one amongst insects. In view of the large measure of success insects have achieved in colonising rivers and ponds, it is curious how little they have been able to adapt themselves to sea-water. Although many species exist that live within tide limits, and are capable of surviving frequent immersion by the tides, hardly any are entirely marine—a few bugs (*Halobates*), and a species of gnat recently collected in tow-nets off the island of Samoa, make up the entire list. Caves have been more successfully invaded, and there are many hundred species known only from caves in various parts of the world, most of them quite blind.

One may divide insects into two large classes, in accordance with their feeding habits. The larger class, in all probability, consists of those that are directly dependent upon plants for their food. Amongst these it is easy to trace a complete chain of relationships, from the insects that feed upon almost any kind of vegetable matter, to those that confine their attentions to one or two plants only, or one portion of the plant only, as, for example, the leaves, the stems, or the roots of herbaceous plants, or the wood of trees ; many insects even restrict themselves to the petals, pollen, and nectar of flowers alone.

The other large class is carnivorous, either promiscuously so, like the Praying Mantids, or with well-marked predilections in favour of certain groups of species. The latter class may be typified by the larvae of the Hover-flies and Lady-bird beetles that feed upon Aphids ; an extreme case is that of the Australian Lady-bird Beetle, *Novius cardinalis*, which apparently will eat nothing but the Fluted-scale Insect, *Icerya purchasi*, and is therefore an invaluable creature in the control of this dangerous pest. From these two large groups have been developed, on the one hand those amazing associations between insects and flowers that are a constant source of wonder, and on the other the parasitic habits which, if less attractive, are no less remarkable. Between them lies another comparatively large and certainly important group that feeds indiscriminately upon all kinds of decaying matter, both vegetable and animal. To it belong such creatures as the Spring-tails, the Burying-beetles, Dung-beetles, Blowflies, etc., all of which really perform most valuable services as general sca-vengers.

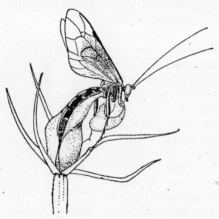

The male of the Ichneumon Wasp (*Lissopimpla semi-punctata*), with its abdomen inserted in an Australian orchid, and clasping the labellum. The pollinia become attached to the insect's body and are transported from flower to flower.

Several examples of the adaptation of plants and insects for mutual benefit will be dealt with in the succeeding pages—the Yucca-moth which fertilises the Yucca-plant in order that its larvae should have food ; the Madagascan Hawk-moth upon which the fertilisation of an orchid depends ; the fertilisation of the fig, dependent upon a minute wasp, and an Australian orchid, dependent upon a male Ichneumon-wasp that appears to mistake the flowers for its own female, and so on. But the lines along which the elaborate behaviour of parasites has been developed are less obvious. One is apt to speak of all creatures that live on, or within, any other, as parasites ; yet when an attempt is made to classify them according to their habits difficulties at once arise. The flea is some-times called a parasite ; yet it sucks blood only in the adult stage, and there-fore is no more a parasite than are mosquitoes and other blood-sucking flies. The Bird-lice are also generally called parasites ; actually they are only scavengers, feeding on the bits of loose skin, hair, and feathers of the creatures upon which they spend their whole lives.

There is another large group, which merges imperceptibly into those

to which the term " parasite " is usually restricted, known as " predators."
In the widest application of the word, a predator is any insect that seeks and
devours any other insect ; but there is a large group of them, known as
" special predators," that confine their attentions to one or a few species
only. Such creatures are the large, solitary Scoliid-wasps, the females of
which search out grubs and lay their eggs upon them. It is no great jump
from this state of affairs to that in which the egg is laid inside the grub,
the wasp-grub devouring its host from the inside, and being, in fact, a
typical internal or " endo-parasite." Further discussion of parasitism will
be found in the chapters on Hymenoptera, Coleoptera, and Diptera, the
three orders to which all the highly specialised forms are confined.
Immense as is the toll of insect life continually being taken by birds,
reptiles, small mammals, and other such creatures, it is yet doubtful whether
it approaches that exacted by the parasitic members of their own class. For
upstart man it is most fortunate that there are these means for maintaining
the balance of nature, for otherwise he would very quickly vanish before
the attacks of the insect hordes. As things are, it is only by resort to a great
variety of protective devices that many species
succeed in holding their own against their innumerable enemies.

PROTECTIVE DEVICES

Protective devices may be of many kinds. The
most obvious, and one that is very common, is
that which depends upon the construction of a
shelter, either in the form of a case, such as that
of the Caddis-fly grub or the Psychid caterpillar,
into which the individual can withdraw when
threatened, or in the form of a nest, like those of
the Termites, which forms a kind of fortress-
stronghold for an entire colony. In the majority
of cases these coverings are composed of extraneous matter held together merely by silken
threads, but frequently saliva also enters into their
composition, especially in the formation of the
harder substances. Sometimes, however, insects
rely solely upon their own secretions, for example,
the " wool " of the Woolly Aphis, and the scales
of all Scale Insects. It is not improbable that
many internal feeders (stem- and root-boring
grubs, etc.) have been forced to adopt this mode

A portion of a twig encrusted
with *Tachardia lacca*, the Lac
insect. A typical Scale Insect.
(After Imms.)

of life primarily for protective purposes. Frequently, protection of the
kind just referred to is supplemented by resemblance to inanimate objects

that form part of the insect's normal environment; this is known as protective resemblance.

In the foregoing examples protection is obtained simply by the use of extraneous substances that form part of the creature's natural environment. Matters are, however, fundamentally different in those very numerous instances in which the insects themselves come to bear so close a likeness to the objects upon which they rest, or live, that their detection is a matter of extreme difficulty to the unpractised eye. Well-known examples are furnished by the "looper" caterpillars of the Geometrid moths, by these moths themselves when they rest upon tree trunks with the mottled sur-

The Engrailed Moth, *Tephrosia bistortata*, at rest.

Caterpillar of the Early Thorn Moth, *Selenia bilunaria*, in resting attitude.

faces of which their own colours so beautifully harmonise, by the Stick Insects and the leaf-like Praying Mantids, and by the Indian Leaf Butterfly and its numerous allies—but examples could be multiplied indefinitely. The principle is almost the rule rather than the exception, especially amongst those insects that are readily devoured by birds and other insect-eating animals. Probably not even a tithe of the ingenious devices that fall into this category have yet been recognised.

When resemblances of this order have for their models animate creatures, such as other insects, they are said to be due to "Mimicry"—a word of somewhat unfortunate choice, on account of its implication of conscious effort, which is, of course, entirely absent. In all these cases, which are very numerous, insects of one group come to resemble, to the point of deception, insects in another group usually by no means closely related to themselves; and in the process their whole appearance departs widely from that which is normal to their nearest relations. The theory is that the " model " is a specially fortunate insect in that it is not attacked much by insectivorous creatures, and that, by resembling it, the mimic shares some of these privileges. Many instances of this fascinating subject will be dealt with in the succeeding pages, particularly amongst the Lepidoptera. A very closely related phenomenon is that of " warning colours." The majority of " models," it has been noted, are conspicuous insects that live openly, without any attempt at disguise. Experiments have shown, in certain instances, that they are, in fact, distasteful to insect-eating creatures, and, therefore, it is argued, their bright colours are virtually an advertisement of this fact and a warning of their unpalatability.

The Comma Butterfly, *Polygonia c. album*, at rest.

Many other very interesting aspects of insect life might be dealt with in these introductory remarks, but unfortunately the limitations of space preclude it. The origin and development of social instincts, so powerful in certain groups, so lacking in others, in spite of the fact that few orders are without some species that exhibit at least a tendency in this direction, provide a subject with many aspects of intense interest, both biological and philosophical, that has been very much studied of recent years. So much more attention has latterly been devoted, however, to the examination of insects in relation to man, either as pests of his crops, or as carriers of disease, that what amount almost to separate sciences, economic and medical entomology, has grown up around these branches of insect behaviour, attaining such proportions that to do them justice a separate volume for each would be required. These aspects of entomology will be alluded to in the following pages, in connection with species that illustrate them. In the meantime, it will be as well to examine briefly the main features of insect structure and development that are common to the whole class.

By the older naturalists all those creatures that compose the great

Arthropod phylum were called Insects—crabs and woodlice, scorpions and spiders, mites and ticks, centipedes and millipedes, bees and beetles, butterflies, moths, etc.   The application of the term has, however, become narrowed by usage, so that nowadays the Insecta, or *Hexapoda* as they are sometimes called, may be defined as " those Arthropods that in the adult stage have the segments of their bodies arranged in three distinct groups : (*a*) the head, which bears a single pair of feelers (antennae) and, as a rule, three pairs of appendages (jaws, etc.), around the mouth ; (*b*) the thorax with three pairs of jointed legs and, at most, two pairs of wings ; (*c*) the body or abdomen, which is devoid of legs."   Immature forms of many insects naturally will not readily fall within such a definition.

STRUCTURE

The Insect-body consists essentially of a series of tough, chitinous rings, jointed together and bearing appendages.   According to the theory that the original number of these rings was twenty, as in a very large number of the Crustacea, then the *head* would be composed of the first five segments fused together, the *thorax* of the next three, and the remaining twelve, reduced in number, would form the *abdomen*.

It is, of course, quite impossible in an adult insect to recognise any division of the head capsule into segments. The evidence in support of its evolution by fusion from a number of segments is, however, very strong.   In the developing embryo, in fact, there are usually six divisions recognisable, one of which, situated in front of the mouth, is here neglected. Many authorities also argue

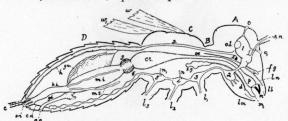

INSECT STRUCTURE

Section of a hypothetical winged insect.   *A*, head ; *B*, neck ; *C*, thorax ; *D*, abdomen ; *a*, aorta ; *an*, anus ; *cr*, crop ; *g*, gizzard ; *g.d, g.n, g.p*, genital organs ; *h*, heart ; *h.i*, hind intestine ; *l1, l2, l3*, legs ; *lb*, labrum ; *lm*, labium ; *m*, mandible ; *m1*, maxilla ; *m.i*, stomach ; *o.o*, eyes ; *oe*, throat ; *p*, mouth ; *s.g*, salivary gland ; *w, w*, wings ; 1, brain ; 2–6, other ganglia of the nervous system.   (After Imms.)

that the eyes have been evolved from a pair of primitive appendages and that they therefore represent yet another segment.   On the basis of five segments, however, the case is fairly plain.   The first segment bears the feelers (antennae) ; the second, in a certain number of embryos, has been observed to bear appendages, subsequently lost, corresponding with the second pair of feelers in Crustacea and with the chelicerae of Arachnida ; the third bears the mandibles ; the fourth and fifth, the other two pairs of mouth-parts.

The variation of the head structures, as will be seen in the succeeding pages, is very considerable.   From the simple thread-like feelers, found in the more primitive orders of Insects, all manner of extraordinary structures have been evolved.   The club-shaped antennae of the butterflies, the feathery organs found in so many moths, the curiously expanded, sometimes fan-shaped antennae that occur so frequently amongst the beetles, and the elbowed antennae of the bees, to mention only a few, must all have been derived from simple types in which all the segments were alike.

After the antennae, the next most conspicuous objects on the head of an insect are the eyes.   Examined with a lens, their surface presents the appearance of a honeycomb, being divided into a number of six-sided figures, each of which is called a facet.   In the cockroach the number of these facets is about 1800, but some of the dragon-flies, and also certain

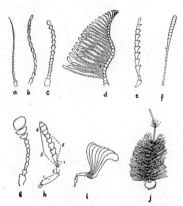

VARIOUS TYPES OF ANTENNAE

a, Cockroach (simple) ; *b*, Ground Beetle ; *c*, a Termite ; *d*, a Saw-fly ; *e*, a Click-beetle ; *f*, a Butterfly ; *g*, a Burying-beetle ; *h*, a Chalcid wasp ; *i*, a Cock-chafer ; *j*, a Gnat.   (After Imms.)

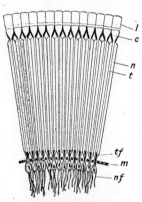

Diagram of a section through part of the eye of a butterfly. *l*, outer lenses ; *c*, cones, surrounded by dark pigment ; *t*, transparent rods ; *n*, nerve-cells ; *tf*, branches of the trachea ;   *m*, membrane between eye and brain-chamber; *nf*, nerve-fibres leading to brain.

Hawk-moths, have been shown to have upwards of 20,000.   If a section be cut vertically through the eye, a very remarkable structure is disclosed. The facet is seen to be composed of two transparent lenses beneath which, with its base applied to them, is a crystalline cone, surrounded by dark colouring matter and supported at its apex by a long narrow transparent rod.   Surrounding the rod are narrow, elongate nerve-cells, again filled with colouring matter (pigment) and connected by nerve-fibres to the brain. The nerve-cells, apparently, correspond with the retina of the human eye and are spoken of as retinulae.

The mouth parts are not objects that lend themselves to ready observation, but nevertheless from the point of view of classification they are of the greatest importance.   In the very primitive *Thysanura* they are remarkably similar in many respects to those typical of the Crustacea—clear evidence of a common origin—and include an extra pair (*maxillulae*) which is absent in all other insects. In general, throughout the other orders of Insects the mouth parts consist of (1) a pair of simple biting jaws (mandibles); (2) a pair of somewhat complicated appendages called the maxillae, which consist essentially of two lobes and an antenna-like organ (the palp), mounted on a basal portion; (3) a pair of similar organs, usually somewhat simplified by fusion of the parts, called the labium.

From these " standard " structures, as they might be termed, an extraordinary diversity of organs has been evolved. The " horns " of the

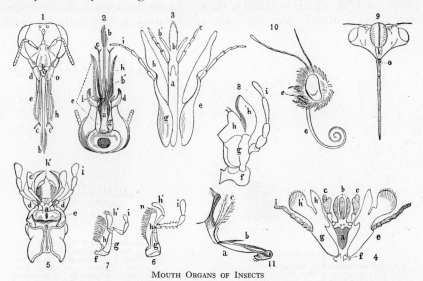

MOUTH ORGANS OF INSECTS

1, head of honey-bee, from the front; 2, head of humble-bee, from below; 3, maxillae and labrum of a bee (*Andrena*); 4, maxillae and labium of saw-fly (*Cimbex*); 5, lower view of head of carnivorous beetle (*Procrustes*); 6, maxilla of carnivorous beetle (*Cicindela*); 7, maxilla of cock-tail beetle (*Staphylinus*); 8, maxilla of locust; 9, head of bug (*Cicada*), from the front; 10, head of butterfly; 11, head of horse-fly (*Tachina*).

Labium—*a*, mentum; *b*, ligula; *b'*, paraglossae; *c*, palp; *d*, mandible.   *Maxilla* (*e*), with *f*, cardo; *g*, stipes; *h*, lacinia; *h'*, galea; *i*, palp; *k*, head-plate; *n*, teeth on lacinia.

Stag-beetles are enormously developed mandibles; many insects, on the other hand, such as Moths, May-flies, and Caddis-flies, that feed by suction, or take no food in the adult state, have no mandibles at all. In Bees they are club-shaped, and used for kneading the wax; and in insects such as Aphids and Bugs they are modified to form lancets for piercing plants so that the food may be absorbed by suction. The proboscis of the Butter-flies and Moths, on the other hand, is formed from a part of the maxillae, from which also are developed the piercing organs of many blood-sucking flies. The labium also undergoes its share of change; as a rule its parts are much fused together and collectively form the " lower lip," but in the

Bugs they form a flexible sheath for the protection of the piercing organs to which allusion has already been made, and from it, in the case of the two-winged flies, the proboscis has been built up. The proboscis, by the way, should not be confused with the tongue, which is an entirely different structure readily recognisable in some insects, but not in the majority.

The thorax is attached to the head by a delicate flexible neck. The three segments of which it is composed are usually firmly welded together, particularly in winged insects, less so in those that live upon the surface of the ground or in water, for the latter are without the powerful muscles needed for flight. Variation in this part of the insect's body is, in fact, mainly a matter of detail in accordance with the locomotive needs of the species, for to the thorax are attached the three pairs of legs and the wings.

What might be called the normal insect leg is a comparatively simple structure, and wonderfully uniform in basic features throughout the class, in spite of its many interesting modifications. It consists of four main sections, the haunch (coxa), the thigh (femur), the shin or shank (tibia), and the foot (tarsus). The foot consists of five small jointed sections

LEG OF AN INSECT

a, coxa; *b*, thigh; *c*, shank; *d*, foot (note the 5 joints) ; *e*, claws; *tr*, trochanter.

terminated by the claws, and in between the haunch and the thigh is a further small joint called the trochanter. The first pair of legs is the most often subjected to modifications. In burrowing beetles, and in the Mole Cricket, for instance, creatures belonging to widely different orders, they are immensely and somewhat similarly widened in correlation with the similarity of habits. In the Praying Mantids they are pincer-like in form, and armed with ferocious-looking spines, devices for the seizing of prey. Frequently they bear "combs," used for the cleaning of feelers, the most perfect examples of which are to be found in the Bees. The middle

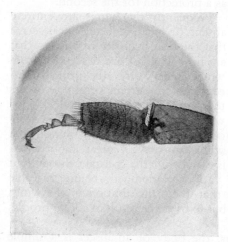

Hind-leg of the Honey-bee, showing pollen-brush, auricle, etc. (Much enlarged.)

and hind pairs of legs are usually more normal, but the pollen-brushes borne by bees on their hind-legs probably represent the most remarkable development of all. The little pad, called the *pulvillus*, that lies between the claws of the foot also occurs in a considerable variety of forms, chief among which is that which enables flies and other insects to walk up a window-pane. The pad in these cases is soft, and bears numerous minute, sticky hairs by means of which a grip is maintained; when not wanted the pulvillus can be withdrawn to avoid injury.

When a butterfly emerges from its chrysalis its wings are hardly noticeable; they hang like two little sacks on each side of the thorax. As they expand the upper and lower surfaces come together, eventually closing so tightly that microscopic examination is necessary before the two sheets can be detected. Between these run nervures, often spoken of as veins, which serve to strengthen the wings and to carry air-tubes. The actual surface of the wing is usually naked, but in Butterflies and Moths it is characteristically covered with innumerable coloured scales, arranged as are the tiles on a roof. Variation in the shape and texture of the wings is considerable, but principally it is in the direction of a thickening of the first pair so that they can be used as a protection for the second.

WING SCALES

Part of the lower surface of a wing of the Red Admiral Butterfly, much enlarged, showing the overlapping of the scales that cover it.

Frequently the wings are entirely absent, or much reduced, but it seems that the vast majority of insects that are now wingless are descended from winged ancestors; the principal exceptions are certain primitive orders that appear never to have developed wings at all. From the point of view of classification and evolution the wings are of very great importance; for the arrangement of their nervures is extraordinarily constant throughout large groups. The same nervures, variously modified, being traceable throughout the orders, it is obvious that their distribution in the wings of any given species is not haphazard, but fixed as the result of a long process of evolution.

Compared with the other portions, the body of an insect is a simple structure, consisting of a number of closely similar segments one behind the other. However, in the reproductive organs which it contains, it really guards the most vital possessions of any insect. Upon these, and the discharge of their proper functions, depend the survival of the species : to them really all other parts of the creature's anatomy are subservient.

Within the body, lying along its lower surface, is the central nervous system, consisting typically of a chain-like arrangement of nerve-centres (ganglia) corresponding with the segments and connected by nerve-cords. In fact, however, there are never as many centres as segments, their number being frequently much reduced. Commencing with a distinct brain and a ring around the mouth, the system extends with numerous ramifications throughout the thorax and the body right to the extremity of the latter. It is of interest to contrast the position of this system with that found in the higher animals, in which it runs along and above the backbone. To it are connected the various organs of sense, the eyes, ears (when present), the organs of touch, taste, and smell, and even, it has been suggested, some others that seem to have no counterpart in the human body. Ears have not been recognised, so far, in a very large number of insects ; but they are notably present in those that are capable of producing sound. In Grasshoppers and Crickets they are situated on the shins of the front legs ; in Locusts, and another group of Grasshoppers, on the first

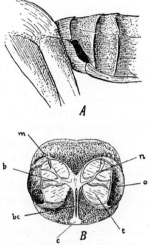

A, base of the body of a Geometrid moth, showing opening of " ear." *B*, the " ear " (in section)—*o*, external opening ; *t*, tympanum ; *b*, protective bar ; *n*, nerve and connective tissue ; *bc*, *c*, nerves ; *m*, muscle.

segment of the body, in which situation, or on the thorax, they occur also in a good many Moths. In Gnats and Midges they are developed in the basal segments of the feelers, and in the Blowfly beneath the bases of the wings. In all cases, however, the structures are in the main similar. A cavity of some kind is formed, across the inner surface of which, usually at or near the orifice, is stretched a delicate membrane forming a kind of drum-head, with which are associated the ends of special nerves, and behind which there is also a space filled either with air or a fluid. Delicate rods are also often present in the cavity, and there appears to be no doubt that the whole apparatus is especially suitable for the perception of sound, though probably serving other purposes as well.

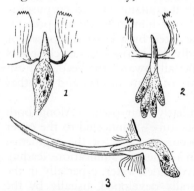

Three types of organs found in the Antennae of Lepidoptera. 1 and 2, which are sunk in pits, are believed to be organs of smell ; 3, an organ of touch. The attached nerve-cells are shown. (Greatly enlarged.)

The organs of smell appear to be seated in the feelers ; indeed, this fact has been established now almost beyond dispute. The actual organs are formed by minute pits, of which there may be a thousand or more on a single antennal segment. These pits are filled with fluid, and contain rod-shaped cells connected to the nervous system.

That the sense of touch, seated also in the feelers and in the palps, is acute and of very great importance to an insect can be seen by watching one of these creatures as it feels the surface upon which it walks. The actual operating medium is no doubt supplied by the delicate sensory hairs which are distributed over the surfaces of the feelers, the palps, and also, as a rule, of certain areas of the feet. Organs somewhat similar to these, and situated in, or in the neighbourhood of, the mouth, almost certainly serve the purpose of distinguishing the different tastes of the various substances that compose the insect's food.

Recently there has been discovered situated on the top of the head in Moths, in the neighbourhood of the eyes, a pair of minute organs, which also, to judge by their structure, are of a sensory nature. The purpose for which they are used, however, has not yet been ascertained. The same applies to the deep pit at the extremity of the palp, also assumed, on account of its structure, to be a sense-organ. The study of these organs, and of many others which are all equally unexplained, is, indeed, a most fascinating one, and, diligently pursued, should help very materially to elucidate some of the unsolved problems of insect life.

A few other important features of insect anatomy still remain to be mentioned. Contrary to general ideas, an insect has both blood and a heart. True it is that neither compares at all closely with those of the higher animals, but yet they serve a similar purpose. The blood may be colourless, but is more often green, and although it contains no red corpuscles, bodies comparable with the white corpuscles of human blood are present. It bathes all the internal organs, and is circulated by a heart composed of a tube-like vessel lying along the back, and divided into a series of chambers by a number of valves ; the flow is from the tail towards the head, and can readily be seen in the translucent caterpillars of many moths, and in other insects.

Respiration in insects is on a plan peculiarly their own. Along both sides of the body run comparatively large air-tubes, connected to the outer air by openings called spiracles, which occur on most of the segments. Inwardly these tubes (tracheae) branch off in a series of ramifications leading to all parts of the body. In insects that live under water, especially in the larval or immature stages, gills are generally developed, usually by the outward growth of the tracheal system from the spiracles ; and it has even been argued that from such outgrowths the wings have been evolved.

The food-canal exhibits remarkable uniformity throughout the whole of the Insects. From the mouth the gullet leads into the crop ; this in turn leads to the gizzard, thence to the stomach and intestines. The gizzard is often furnished with teeth, hard ridges of chitin, and hairs, considered formerly to serve for grinding the food, but now recognised to function as a strainer to prevent solid food not digested in the crop from passing into the stomach, which simply diffuses the digested food through its walls into the blood. In insects that take only liquid food the gizzard is devoid of these structures, and the gullet may be modified to form a suction pump ; in Bees it forms the honey-stomach, which is capable of being shut off at will from the real stomach.

Reproduction, in the vast majority of cases, is of the usual sexual type, by the union of the male sperm-cell with the female egg-cell. The eggs, after formation in the ovaries, pass downwards and are fertilised in the genital pouch by sperm-cells that have been stored in a special reservoir during sexual union. The commonest exception to this rule is a method of reproduction called parthenogenesis, and exhibited by Saw-flies, very many Aphids, and numerous other insects, and even occurring exceptionally in species usually reproducing in the normal manner. In these cases the eggs laid by virgin females, and therefore not fertilised by the male, develop

Gynandromorph Gipsy Moth. The left half is male, the right female in character. The reproductive organs in such individuals, if composite, are functionless ; more often they are female and functional.

and give rise to fresh individuals capable of reproduction. In some species this is so much the established rule that no male has yet been discovered. But in most cases there appear to be definite circumstances under which normal fertilisation is necessary to ensure the continuance of the species. True hermaphrodite reproduction is exceedingly rare ; there are, in fact, only a few very abnormal flies in which it occurs. *Termitoxenia*, for example, normally has both sperm- and egg-cells in the same individual, so representing a condition only generally found in creatures much lower down in the scale.

INSECT METAMORPHOSIS

Most people are sufficiently familiar with the development of a butterfly—egg, caterpillar, chrysalis, and adult insect—for it to be unnecessary to recapitulate it. There are, however, certain variants of the process that help materially to an understanding of the evolution of insect metamorphosis, and therefore need brief mention.

In the group of primitive insects known as the Apterygota it is often difficult to distinguish the young from the adults except by their size. As they grow they moult, but the moults do not disclose alterations in the external appearance of the insect. In the next sub-class are grouped insects which change their outward appearance at each moult, attaining

H

the winged condition at maturity, but yet remaining active throughout their development.   To this great group (Exopterygota) belong the Earwigs, Cockroaches, Grasshoppers, and Locusts, Bugs and various kinds of Lice, Stone-flies, May-flies, and Dragon-flies.   In reality, of course, the apparently very great differences between these two types of development are less important than they seem, for they are due mainly to the conspicuous development of the wings.   The fundamental distinction between the two groups lies in the fact that in the one wings have never been evolved, in

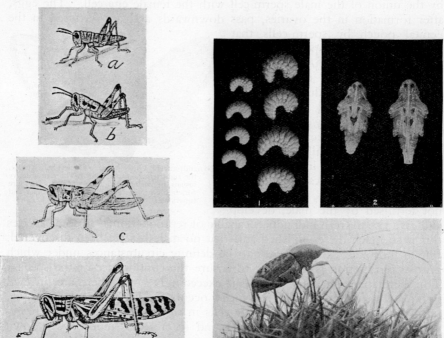

Stages in the growth of an exopterygotous insect, the American Locust, *Schistocera americana*. *a*, young hopper ; *b*, second stage ; *c*, fourth stage ; *d*, adult insect.

Stages in the growth of the Chestnut Weevil, *Curculio proboscideus*, an endopterygotous insect.   1, Larva ; 2, pupae ; 3, perfect insect.

the other they have, but, in certain cases, as for instances in the lice, have been lost again later.

The third sub-class (Endopterygota) departs materially, however, from the other two, in that the wings do not develop externally but internally. After an active, feeding stage (caterpillar or larva) there follows a resting stage (chrysalis or pupa), during which no food is taken and the tissues of the body undergo a complete reorganisation.   The emergence of the adult insect from the chrysalis is then the last moult.   Certain of the exopterygotous insects, notably the Dragon-flies and Cicadas, approach this type by having a resting stage before arriving at maturity, and they are consequently said to have an incomplete metamorphosis; they forecast, in fact, the development of the higher insects, and perhaps show the lines along which evolution has taken place.

From insects in which the development of the wings and other structures peculiar to the adult occurs simultaneously throughout their lives it is possible to form a complete chain of slightly varying types, leading up to the most perfect, in which development is subordinated to growth in the early stages, and followed by a period of outward passivity but internal transformation. These variations will be dealt with more fully in the succeeding pages.

The classification of Insects follows the usual practice. The grouping of the orders is based in the main upon the structure of the wings and of the mouth-parts, and also to a large extent upon the manner in which they develop. The sequence of orders in the succeeding pages begins with:

Sub-class *APTERYGOTA*

The three orders that compose this sub-class are mainly of interest on account of the light they shed upon the probable origin of Insects. They are active little creatures, living generally in obscure places under stones, dead leaves, etc., and are mostly of too small a size to attract much attention. They never exhibit any traces of wings, have no metamorphosis, are distinctly segmented, and in general appearance suggest rather the immature than the adult forms of other insects. Two features of their mouth-parts show very decided affinity with the Crustacea: the mandibles, which are almost exactly like those of the Crustacea, and the maxillulae, which are not found in any other order of Insects.

The fact that they have a wider range of distribution upon the earth's surface than other insects, being found in the Arctic and Antarctic regions, and on all the intervening lands, is in itself a clear indication that they must have been in existence throughout a very long period of time. And the argument that this is indeed probably the case has recently been strengthened by the discovery of fossil remains, in the Rhynie Chert beds (Old Red Sandstone) of Scotland, that are almost certainly to be attributed to this sub-class. Should the interpretation of these fossils be correct, they would afford remarkable confirmation of the assumptions, made upon other grounds, as to the age of the Apterygota, and prove them to be not only the most primitive of existing insects, but also actually the oldest of which we have knowledge.

To speculate, before the Devonian period, in which these creatures lived, " the ancestors of Plant-life dwelt in the sea, and the ancestors of the Insects were almost certainly marine and lived alongside them, possibly feeding on them.   When the plants came out of the sea, and began to live on the land, they had to adapt themselves to their new mode of life.   It does not require any great stretch of imagination to see an analogous adaptation to their new surroundings in the case of the . . . first true Insects.   It would seem highly probable that the first step in the evolution of true insects, from some marine form of Arthropod, was taken through an association with the special group of plants which first made good their footing on the dry land ; most probably the Arthropods fed on them, and evolved with them, changing their mode of life and their form, as their food-plants changed theirs.   From this simple beginning, through many millions of years, a closer and closer association of the two great groups of plants and insects has gradually grown up, culminating in some of the most perfect and wonderful adaptations of living organisms to one another for mutual benefit '' (Tillyard).

Order THYSANURA

(*Bristle-tails*)

To the Bristle-tails belongs the most familiar of the wingless insects, the Silver-fish (*Lepisma saccharina*), often met with amongst old books and papers in houses.   It is typical of the order in having three bristle-like tails, and small paired limbs on a number of the segments of the body, in addition to the usual three pairs on the thorax.   In *Machilis*, of which genus one species is quite common on sea-shores, there are associated with these limbs curious little extrusible sac-like organs, the exact function of which is not known.   In both *Lepisma* and *Machilis* the body is covered with scales, and rather humped up in the middle, in a manner vaguely suggestive of a shrimp.   *Campodea* represents another section of the order that is found throughout the world, even in caves, and on mountain-tops, under stones, and in loose soil; these have no eyes, their blindness being apparently compensated by unusually well-developed feelers.

The Silver-fish, *Lepisma saccharina*. (After Lubbock.)

Order PROTURA

The minute creatures that compose this order were first recognised only so recently as 1907.   They occur under stones and the bark of trees, in peat and moss, and other similar situations.   In shape they are long and narrow.   One of their most notable features is the entire absence of feelers, the first pair of legs being carried in such a manner as in some measure to perform the functions of these organs. But more remarkable still is the fact that the number of their abdominal segments is increased during growth, a kind of transformation found nowhere else in the whole class of Insects. The best-known genera are *Acerentomen* and *Eosentomen*.

Order COLLEMBOLA

(*Spring-tails*)

The Spring-tails are all furnished on the under surface of the first segment of the body with a curious tube or sucker, generally called the ventral tube. The forked tail is usually turned forwards, and held in position under the body; when released, it springs back, and, striking the surface of the ground, causes the insect to leap into the air. These little creatures live under stones, leaves, etc., large numbers of them often being associated together. They are moderately common, the best-known genus being *Podura*.

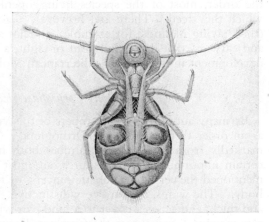

A common British Spring-tail, *Papirius fuscus*. Ventral aspect, showing the " Spring."

Sub-class *EXOPTERYGOTA*

Order ORTHOPTERA

(*Earwigs, Cockroaches, Stick Insects, Locusts, Crickets*)

If this order is not very rich in species, it has at any rate made a bold bid for first place in the number of its individuals, for such ubiquitous creatures as the earwig, the cockroaches (including the domestic " black-beetle "), the grasshoppers, crickets, and locusts belong to it. In distribution it is world-wide; and geologically it is certainly the oldest of the winged orders of Insects. With the exception of the possible Devonian fossils referred to under the Apterygota (p. 209), the first clear evidences of insect life occur in the Carboniferous formation of the Primary period. Here we find insects closely resembling in bodily structure the cockroaches of to-day, but bearing two pairs of similar wings. And as in the Triassic and Jurassic rocks of the Secondary period insects intermediate in wing-structure between these two are found, the line of descent is quite clearly defined.

The species that compose the order can easily be separated from all other insects by a few simple characters. The mouth-parts are of the biting type; the two pairs of wings are veined in a highly complex fashion, and the anterior pair is thickened to form a protection, when all are closed, to the much thinner, larger, and much folded hind wings; the three segments of the thorax are readily distinguishable; and the body is almost invariably composed of ten segments and bears at its extremity two short, stiff tails known as cercopods—a feature more common in the Crustacea than the Insects. In habits there is a considerable degree of uniformity throughout the order, most of the species living openly amongst the herbage upon which they feed. There are, however, a good many carnivorous species (the Praying Mantids, for example), and not a few, such as the cockroaches and earwigs, that live mainly out of sight, a habit that reaches its extreme development in the entirely subterranean Mole Crickets.

Family Forficulidae (Earwigs)

By many authorities the members of this very compact family are treated as an order distinct from the Orthoptera. They do, in fact, differ rather markedly from all the other families both in outward appearance and in certain important internal features, amongst the former of which may be mentioned the very characteristic pincers, or forceps, at the extremity of the body. The wings, too, are very distinctive. The front pair are very short and thick, and act as a cover to a hind pair which are folded in a most intricate manner. Sometimes the Common Earwig may be seen flying, though it is by no means a common sight. If seen on the wing it should be watched closely; almost as it alights, it shuts up the hind-wings like a pair of fans, folds them over twice, and then, with the aid of its forceps, tucks them under the firm basal pieces, the whole being in turn slid under the front pair.

It seems barely credible that the forceps' only function should be that described above, but it is perhaps stranger still that no definite evidence exists as to their use for other purposes. Various theories have been advanced: that they are defensive or offensive weapons; that they are actually pinching organs (some species have been observed so to use them); or that they have the effect of scaring off enemies by their terrifying aspect when curved up over the back in a poor imitation of a scorpion. In the males they are generally much better developed than in the females, and frequently they are not symmetrical. Their origin is fairly clearly shown by the fact that in some tropical species they only appear at the last moult, being transformed from a pair of jointed tail-like organs (cercopods) such as are found in other Orthoptera.

Not a great deal is known about the habits of these creatures. In the case of the common British species (Forficula auricularia) the diet is almost entirely vegetable matter, and the habits mainly nocturnal. They are of great interest, however, in that, lowly as they are in the insect scale, they yet show clearly the beginnings of social instincts. Kirby, one of the fathers of British entomology, wrote many years ago of the Common Earwig :

"This curious insect, so unjustly traduced by vulgar prejudice—as if the Creator had willed that the insect world should combine within itself examples of all that is most remarkable in every other department in nature—still more nearly approaches the habits of the hen in the care of her family —she actually sits upon her eggs, as if to hatch them—and guards them with the greatest care. Degeer, having found an earwig thus occupied, removed her into a box where there was some earth, and scattered the eggs in all directions. She soon, however, collected them, one by one,

The Common Earwig, *Forficula auricularia*, with wings expanded.

with her jaws, into a heap, and assiduously sat upon them as before. The young ones, which resemble the parent, except in wanting elytra and wings,

Hemimerus

An aberrant Earwig. From a balsam preparation.

and, strange to say, are, as soon as born, larger than the eggs which contained them, immediately upon being hatched creep like a brood of chickens under the belly of the mother, who very quietly suffers them to push between her feet, and will often, as Degeer found, sit over them in this posture for some hours."

Even more remarkable than this in some ways, considering the simplicity of the organisation of Earwigs in other respects, is the behaviour of the related genus *Hemimerus*. These are structurally somewhat degenerate and very rare creatures, one of which at least lives among the hairs of a rat. They are blind and wingless, yet the eggs are hatched within the body of the mother, and the young are born one at a time, after they have grown to quite a respectable size. How this very rare type of development should have arisen in such simple creatures is very difficult to explain. No doubt it is an adaptation to, or at any rate the result of, a very peculiar mode of life, and in this connection it is interesting to note that exactly the same thing has come about in the case of certain degenerate flies with similar parasitic habits.

Family Blattidae (Cockroaches)

Like the other families of the Orthoptera, the *Blattidae* form a very homogeneous group, not very rich in species, perhaps, but abundantly represented in individuals. They are essentially inhabitants of the tropics, about 1200 different kinds being known, but a certain few have been distributed by the agency of man throughout the world. In general appearance all the species are very much alike. The body is broad and flat and always has a pair of cercopods. The thorax is similarly widened and prominent, and bears powerful legs such as one would expect in such swift-running creatures. The antennae are usually very long and thread-like, composed sometimes of as many as a hundred joints.

A point of interest is that the simple eyes are often absent, their positions being marked by pale oval spots, devoid of lenses and called fenestrae. With what particular habit the loss of these eyes is correlated is not known; the creatures are certainly the reverse of light-loving, so possibly they have no need of them and they have become atrophied. No particular investigation of the subject, however, appears to have

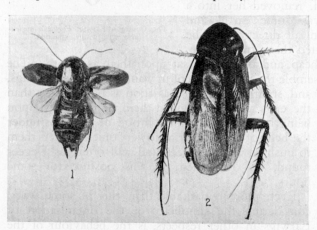

Two common Cockroaches, usually called "Black-beetles." 1, *Blatta orientalis;* 2, *Periplaneta americana.*

been made. Very often the wings are absent entirely, or less developed in the females than in the males. When present they are carried flat over the back, the lower ones, on account of their size, folded fan-wise. In Upper Carboniferous times the *Blattidae* appear to have been easily the predominant insects, as approximately ninety per cent. of the fossil insects found in those beds are referable to this family. Since those remote times they have dwindled greatly, so that now they comprise barely one per cent. of the world's insect fauna.

The best-known species is no doubt the common "Black-beetle" (*Blatta orientalis*) of kitchens and domestic situations generally. Together with *Blattella germanica* and *Periplaneta americana* it shares the honour of inhabiting ships and buildings throughout the world. It has, in fact, become domesticated and adapted to life in artificial conditions; it is no longer possible to do more than conjecture its true home and natural surroundings. In food habits it is particularly partial to sweet, starchy matter, but will attack a great variety of substances in addition, often doing more damage by the mess it creates than by the amount it consumes. The wild species probably feed upon decaying matter, both animal and vegetable, in the main, and live on the surface of the ground amongst dead leaves, under stones, etc. Some even burrow in the soil, thus showing a tendency to adopt the mode of living peculiar to their cousins the Mole Crickets.

The process of egg-laying in the family is somewhat specialised. When the eggs have been passed down from the two ovaries into the genital pouch of the female, there is formed around each a kind of casing. Further eggs are added to this, in series, each with its casing, until the full number has been dealt with. The complete egg-carrying structure so formed is conveniently called an ootheca, and resembles a purse divided longitudinally into two chambers each having a number of pockets in which the eggs are contained. The whole ootheca being often of considerable size it generally happens that the first-formed portion protrudes from the insect's body before the other end is com-

[An Australian Cockroach, *Panesthia lata*. Note the development of the legs in correlation with the burrowing habit of this insect.

pleted ; and it may even be carried about in this position for some time whilst the bearer searches for some convenient spot in which to deposit it. When the young nymphs are ready to emerge the case splits along the back, and they struggle out.

In some species, as, for example, the Australian representatives of the genus *Panesthia*, which burrow in the soil, the process is carried a stage further, the ootheca being dispensed with, and the female bringing forth the young nymphs alive. The Panesthias are also of especial interest in that they exhibit the beginnings of a form of social life. They live in their burrows in strict family communities composed of an adult male, a female, and their offspring in various stages of growth. And to facilitate life in their burrows the adults, soon after reaching maturity, deliberately bite off their own wings.

Family Mantidae (*Praying Insects*)

The members of this family are easily recognisable by the remarkable form of the first pair of legs, which are modified for the purpose of seizing the other insects that form their food. The lower edge of the thigh is furnished with numerous sharp, sabre-like teeth directed forward in such a manner that when the shin, which is also provided with spines, is folded

H 2

back upon it any small insect that is unlucky enough to find itself between the two is caught and held firmly between them. Another conspicuous feature is the greatly elongated first segment of the thorax. The fore-wings (tegmina) are usually coloured like the rest of the insect, generally some shade

Mantis religiosa
In this figure of the Praying Mantis, the strangely developed and heavily spined grasping fore-legs are conspicuous.

of green, that renders it not easily seen amongst the foliage of the trees and shrubs in which it lives; but the hind wings are frequently very brightly coloured, and always very much larger.

An admirable picture of these tigers of the insect world is given by the late Professor Lefroy:

" There are few more striking insects than a Mantis in its natural habitat waiting for food; balanced on the two pairs of legs, it looks from side to side, turning the head with quick motions and seeming to look intently from the large eyes; the antennae active, moving constantly, the fore-legs drawn up under the head but ready to dart out; the creature is so intent, the attitude so expectant and yet suggestive of cunning; in an instant it stiffens, becomes rigid, every part still, the long fore-legs extended; should its prey alight near, it moves stealthily, stalking it as a cat does a bird, gradually drawing nearer till its fore-legs strike and the insect is held securely, drawn up to the mouth and devoured." Sometimes it would seem as if these creatures kill for sport almost, so little of their catch do they consume.

The attitude of these insects, with the vicious-looking raptorial fore-legs held up as if in prayer, has given rise to quite a host of super-stitions in the countries they inhabit.

Mantis religiosa
The Praying Mantis of Southern Europe, with wings expanded.

In the East it is held that they always face towards Mecca; in other countries they are regarded as saints or soothsayers—the latter term often being given in text-books, by the way, as a popular name for the group; and even the ancient Greeks attributed to them supernatural powers. All the species are admirably coloured and adapted for concealment, some even to the extent of resembling flowers, both in colour and in form, by which means flower-haunting insects are deceived and fall into their clutches. Others have the sides of the thorax and the limbs developed in the form of leaf-like expansions, as, for example, in *Deroplatys*, that cause them to harmonise with their surroundings with surprising accuracy.

As a family they appear to be very successful, being spread throughout the warmer countries of the world. Their stealthy habits and cryptic form and colour no doubt contribute largely to this, deceiving alike both friend and foe—there is an authentic record of one of the large South American species catching and beginning to devour a small bird!

Like the Cockroaches, the Mantids enclose their eggs in oothecae, which are attached to sticks, twigs, stones, etc., but the manner in which these egg-cases are formed differs somewhat. The eggs are laid and simultaneously surrounded with a frothy substance that hardens on exposure to the air, but before this takes place the mass is moulded into a shape peculiar to the species by the action of the tips of the wings. It has been observed that the young mantids, immediately after hatching, hang suspended by silken threads that are extruded from the neighbourhood of the tip of the body,

A species of *Deroplatys*
From Singapore. A Praying Mantis, showing leaf-like expansion of the thorax and of the second and third pairs of legs.

and remain in this position until after the first moult. The capacity for producing silk seems to disappear after this stage and not to be redeveloped; in any case, however, its production, especially in this region of the body, in an order that otherwise is without it, is a very remarkable fact.

Family Phasmidae (*Stick Insects*)

To this family belong some of the largest living insects, more than one of the species measuring over a foot in length when fully grown. They resemble, fairly closely, the members of the preceding family, the *Mantidae*, but are readily distinguished from them by having all three pairs of legs normal and alike. Further, whereas in the Praying Insects the first segment of the thorax is the longest, in these the middle one exceeds either of the others in length, in spite of the fact that as a rule all three are moderately large. The front pair of wings (the tegmina) are always much smaller than the other pair, and the latter are composed of two sharply differentiated parts, a thickened anterior portion which resembles in colour and texture the front pair, and a thinner portion which is often very brightly coloured. When the insect is at rest the brightly coloured portion is folded beneath the thickened part and is invisible, so that only those portions are exposed that harmonise with the general coloration of the insect. In many species the wings are entirely absent, rendering it a difficult matter to distinguish the adults from the immature forms.

In marked contrast to the Praying Insects, the Stick Insects are strict vegetarians; and they feed principally under cover of night. During the day they rest amongst low-growing foliage, grasses, etc., and in these positions are amazingly difficult to detect. The first pair of legs is held close together to the front, continuing the narrow line of the slender body; and the other two pairs, when stretched out unsymmetrically from the body, as they almost invariably are, look exactly like twigs or the stems of leaves. One section of the family, however, has developed in a rather different direction, although only following a trend indicated just as prominently in the Praying Insects and even in other Orthopterid families, and by virtue of immense lateral expansions of the body and of the legs has deservedly earned the designation of "leaf-insects." The Oriental genus *Phyllium* is one of the best known of these, as it is also one of the best examples of the group—its wings are so coloured, veined, and marked as to look exactly like leaves. Indeed, in some species of this section the simulation of leaves goes so far that holes, dark spots, rings, and similar markings occur, giving a most realistic impression of damage caused by insects and fungi.

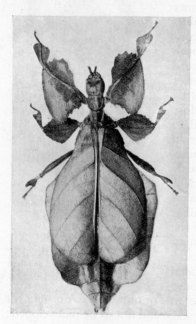

Phyllium scythe

An Indian Stick Insect in which the leaf-like appearance has reached a very high stage of development, even the legs bearing leafy lateral expansions.

Unlike most other Orthoptera, the Stick Insects lay their eggs singly in a seed-like capsule dropped haphazard amongst the herbage, dispensing altogether with the usual ootheca. They present several other features of interest. For example, parthenogenesis—that is to say, virgin reproduction —is very common amongst them. The common European *Dixippus morosus* illustrates this very well; it is commonly bred in captivity, and may go through scores of generations without ever producing a male. The power of regeneration is also very strong in them, a fresh limb being grown to replace one accidentally shed ; results are not always altogether happy, however, as sometimes a lost antenna may be replaced by a leg, which can hardly be regarded as adequate restitution.

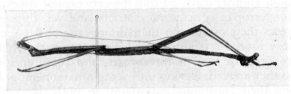

The remaining families of the order are all characterised by having very long and powerful hind-legs, specially adapted for leaping. They are also remarkable in having

The Stick Insect of Southern Europe, *Dixippus morosus*. The figure represents the very rare male of this species. The shape of the extremity of the abdomen is characteristic of the sex.

very well-developed sound-producing apparatus and ears. Collectively they are sometimes spoken of as the *Saltatoria*, the preceding families, on account of their more ordinary methods of progression, being called the *Cursoria*.

Family Acridiidae (*Locusts and Short-horned Grasshoppers*)

The Locusts and Short-horned Grasshoppers form a readily recognised, compact family, distinguished by the short feelers, the three-jointed feet, and the short, stout ovipositor of the female. The organs of hearing are situated on either side of the first segment of the body, immediately behind the thorax, and are visible externally as two crescent-shaped pits. The sound that these organs are doubtless intended to receive is produced by structures situated on the wing-covers (fore-wings or tegmina) and legs. This stridulating mechanism, as it is called, consists of a row of raised knobs, situate on the inner side of the haunch of the hind-leg, and of a strengthened and otherwise altered nervule on the tegmen, the two portions being so arranged that the edge of the tegmen can be drawn across the row of knobs and, by them, be set in such a state of vibration as to produce the familiar chirping.

The habits throughout the family are remarkably uniform. By means of her stout ovipositor the female lays her eggs, as a rule, at some little depth in the ground, in a mass, surrounded by some kind of protective covering. The young, when hatched, resemble the adults fairly closely, except for the lack of wings. They are generally known in this stage as " hoppers," their wings developing slightly at each stage until the adult " flyer " stage is reached.

Among the many interesting species that compose this numerous family are the Locusts. No one who has ever seen a swarm of locusts in flight is likely to forget the sight.—" The swarm was visible while still far off, in its thickest part like a black nimbus or a pall of sooty smoke. Everywhere the sky was alive with insects. On all sides were millions of fluttering wings, closely packed where the cloud was dense, but still crowded even at the outskirts of the flight."—But to suffer their depredations is quite another story. From the very earliest times they have been a by-word for terror in agricultural districts, and yet, through all those thousands of years their origin and their disappearance has remained a mystery. They may invade a country and lay their eggs there, they may even overrun a country for two or three years, and yet suddenly vanish as mysteriously as they arrived, leaving only a nightmare memory behind them. Considering their enormous importance in both the Old World and the New, and the amount of ingenuity that has been expended upon their control, it seems almost incredible that these all-essential points in connection with their life-histories should have remained so long without elucidation. It has, however, in the end fallen to the lot of an entomologist within the last decade to solve the mystery. It amounts, quite simply, to this, that the swarming locusts of one year are just ordinary solitary grasshoppers the next!

The Common Locust of the near East, *Locusta migratoria*.

The best-known Locust of South-East Europe and Western Asia is *Locusta migratoria*. One year this species occurred in enormous swarms in the Northern Caucasus. These swarms were very carefully observed, particularly in respect of the exact areas in which they laid their eggs. When these hatched the following year they produced chiefly individuals like their parents, but with them there appeared a very considerable admixture of quite different-looking individuals that had previously always been regarded as belonging to a different species, *which had been entirely absent from the district the previous year*. Subsequent breeding experiments carried out in laboratories confirmed these facts and showed quite clearly that the two supposedly distinct species, one a swarming locust, the other a grasshopper living a solitary life, were actually one and the same species. The locusts, therefore, do not disappear from a district they have invaded; they give rise to a generation having such entirely different habits, form, and colours, that they are no longer recognisable. And it is not surprising that even now some entomologists throw doubt upon these facts, so entirely different, typically, are the two forms.

In the adult swarming phase (*migratoria*) the general coloration is pretty uniform, whereas in the other phase (*danica*) much greater variation occurs, and the relative sizes of the wing-covers, haunches of the hind-legs (femora), and parts of the thorax also differ markedly. Even internally there is a difference, the relative sizes of the air-sacs not being the same. The greatest contrasts, however, are shown in the early stages. The young *danica* " hoppers," as they are called, exhibit an almost endless variety of colours, being usually either grey, green, fawn, brown, or even black. *Migratoria* hoppers, on the other hand, have constant colour characters in each stage, always some combination of black with orange, red, or yellow.

We are confronted, therefore, with a state of affairs similar in a way to that found amongst certain species of butterflies that inhabit the tropics, in which the broods occurring in the dry season have an utterly different appearance from those met with in the wet season. A most interesting fact ; but how can it be explained ? What has just been shown to occur in *Locusta migratoria* has, within the last three or four years, been found to be true of other locusts, *e.g.* the Desert Locust (*Schistocerca gregaria*, probably the locust of the Bible), *Schistocerca paranensis* in Mexico, and *Locustana pardalina* in South Africa, and probably also occurs in the Rocky Mountain Locust (*Melanoplus spretus*). The phenomenon is, therefore, widespread.

Breeding experiments have shown that if individuals of these species are overcrowded in their cages, then they tend to develop the swarming phase. The insect appears to need overcrowded conditions in order to produce this phase. It is not difficult to visualise the solitary phase occupy-

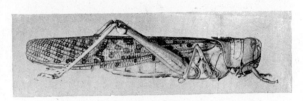

Schistocerca gregaria
The Desert Locust ; probably the Locust of the Bible.

ing an area in which conditions are so favourable that it breeds and multiplies to an extent sufficient to cause overcrowding ; immediately this occurs the mechanism giving rise to the swarming phase is released, and, once released, inevitably increases in intensity through the stages, even through a second generation perhaps, and so may lead eventually to the formation of one of those very large swarms which alone migrate any considerable distance.

The evolution of this remarkable capacity in these few species would form an interesting study. Fortunately we know of cases amongst the ordinary solitary grasshoppers that show its beginnings. Some of these, for example, occur from time to time in incredible numbers, and it has been frequently observed that under these conditions they very often, during their early stages, gather together to form compact moving bands ; and even at times something like the flight of one of the really migratory species has been observed. The potentiality therefore exists, less developed, in these solitary species, and similarly is stimulated in them by overcrowded conditions.

Family Tettigoniidae (Long-horned Grasshoppers)

The Grasshoppers of this family, sometimes called Tree Locusts, bear a considerable superficial resemblance to their cousins the *Acridiidae*, but are readily distinguished by the great length of their feelers. These are usually carried curved over the back, in which position they frequently extend well beyond the tip of the body. The females can be very easily recognised by the very long, narrow, and usually slightly curved ovipositor that sometimes exceeds in length the whole of the abdomen. The wings are carried pent-house fashion over the back, the tegmina being as usual narrower and stouter than the other pair. Both sound-producing and sound-receiving organs are present, but situated quite differently from those of the Short-horned Grasshoppers. The ears, similar in general features to those of the other grasshoppers, are placed on the shins of the first pair of legs.

Tanusia brullei

A S. American Long-horned Grasshopper. The apparent imperfections should be noticed in the tegmina, which normally are folded back and cover all but the tips of the hind-wings.

The mechanism for sound-producing (stridulating apparatus) is near the base of the tegmen, and consists of a transverse file on the under surface of the left tegmen that can be scraped across a sharp ridge on the upper surface of the right tegmen. One species, *Tettigonia viridissima*, can sometimes be heard in the southern counties making a loud and distinctly unmusical chirping with this apparatus; but some of the foreign species have quite a reputation as songsters, such, for example, as the North American Katydids, which are stated to call "Katey did! she did! she did!" The chirping is generally louder and more prolonged in this than in the other family of Grasshoppers.

There is considerably greater diversity in structure, habits, and development in this family than in the *Acridiidae*. Leaf simulation, as in the South American genera *Pterochroza* and *Tanusia*, is carried to such lengths that even the mines made by small caterpillars within the leaf-tissues are faithfully reproduced; mimicry, too, is exhibited of animate creatures, the young larval forms of the South African *Myrmecophana* being so exactly ant-like as to defy recognition except by an experienced entomologist.

In another direction there occur the extraordinary creatures known as Cave Locusts, which have neither ears nor sound producing apparatus, are entirely wingless, and have very short bodies and excessively long legs and antennae.

A species belonging to this group, and very common in New Zealand, is *Pachyrhamma fascifer*, which measures eight or nine inches from the tip of the antenna to the end of the hind-leg ; yet another species, *P. acanthocera*, also found in New Zealand, far surpasses it by measuring twelve to fourteen

Anastostoma australiae
The Australian King Cricket.

inches. The Wetas of New Zealand and the King Crickets of Australia represent yet another section, characterised by their enormous jaws—almost suggestive of Stag Beetles—lack of wings, and generally ferocious and repulsive appearance. They are heavy, stout creatures, and in a way seem to show some affinity with the next family, for not a few of them burrow in the ground. The actual King Crickets belong to the genus *Anastostoma*. It is unfortunately true that many of these remarkable insects of the Antipodes are very nearly extinct.

Family Gryllidae (*Crickets*)

The Crickets, more familiar to the ear than to the eye as a rule, may be considered as a specialised off-shoot of the last family. They differ from them in having the tegmina (fore-wings) bent in such a manner that one portion of each lies flat along the back, the other vertically against the side of the body. The sound-producing apparatus is also more elaborate, though essentially the same, there being a file or rasp on the under surface of each tegmen. The volume of sound produced by this mechanism is remarkable, even as exemplified by the common European *Gryllus domesticus*, but this species is far out-distanced by some of the tropical kinds, one of which, *Brachytrypes megacephalus*, is stated to be audible at a distance of a mile ! The hind-wings often project beyond the tegmina, and the ears are on the shins of the fore-legs—both of which characters are also found in the Long-horned Grasshoppers.

Not a great deal is known about the life-histories of the Crickets in general, but in the main it may be said that they most closely resemble the *Tettigoniidae.* The common *Gryllus domesticus* is indeed almost a domestic animal, so much so, in fact, that its natural habitat is quite unknown. Crickets occur all over the world, and have been found fossil in the Lias, so they are no doubt a comparatively ancient group.

Gryllus domesticus
The Common
House-Cricket.

A curious form of variation occurs in the family that seems clear evidence of an evolutionary trend. The hind-wings, which are usually moderately large and often have their tips rolled up so that they look like cercopods, are sometimes very much smaller and completely hidden by the tegmina until these are moved. Such individuals were formerly regarded as distinct species, but it is now known that this is not the case. The condition appears to represent a stage in a process that will ultimately lead to the complete loss of these wings.

Family *Gryllotalpidae* (*Mole Crickets*)

The Mole Crickets—most aptly named—can be at once distinguished from the true Crickets by their short antennae (composed, however, of numerous segments), the huge, smooth, convex first segment of the thorax, and the burrowing fore-legs; sound-producing organs are sometimes present. They have indeed an appearance that distinguishes them at sight. The manner in which the fore-leg is adapted to the burrowing subterranean habits of these creatures is very remarkable. All the joints are very much expanded and flattened, the shin widens out from the base towards the extremity, and is

Gryllotalpa gryllotalpa. The Mole Cricket. The specimens figured are from the New Forest, Hampshire. The wings are normally folded over the back, as shown in the upper figure.

there produced to form four large, strong teeth spread out like the fingers of the hand ; and, in addition to this, the first segment of the foot is modified in the form of a blade, much like that of a penknife. The result is that not only can the creature dig readily and powerfully, but, by means of moving the blade of the foot over the teeth of the shin it is provided with an instrument resembling a pair of wire-cutters, and most effective for the purpose of severing roots.

The family is not numerous in species, but, in spite of their furtive habits, its representatives have succeeded in establishing themselves throughout the world. They are in the main carnivorous, but probably consume a certain amount of vegetable matter as well—some even burrow in the stems of plants instead of the soil.

The next six orders to be dealt with, and also one or two others, used formerly to be regarded in the main as families of the old Order Neuroptera. Their superficial resemblances, however, due chiefly to their rather similar transparent much-veined wings, only disguise the many fundamental differences that divide them up into the well-marked orders nowadays recognised.

Order PLECOPTERA

(*Stone-flies*)

The adult Stone-flies are mostly rather sombre creatures and sluggish. They have long thread-like feelers like those of most Orthoptera, which order they also resemble in having the fore-wings narrower than the hind-wings, and the latter with a wide inner portion (against the body) that folds up fan-wise. The wings are, however, entirely membranous and have the nervures arranged in a very definite system. Little fusion of the segments of the thorax occurs, all three being easily distinguished.

The immature stages are aquatic, and in this connection are of great interest on account of their various adaptations for obtaining a supply of air. The usual spiracular openings of the air-tube (tracheal) system along the sides of the body are absent. In their place are developed gills, formed either by outgrowths of the same system (on the

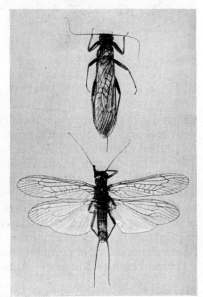

Two specimens of the British Stone-fly, *Perla carlukiana*, from the River Usk. In the upper specimen the wings are in normal resting attitude.

thorax), or from modified appendages (on the body), and resembling in appearance minute fern-like structures or bundles of delicate tentacles. These may be present on the sides of the thorax, or on the side or around the extremity of the body. In the last case they form a rosette. In some species, however, gills are entirely absent; and in these breathing takes place *via* the extremity of the abdomen through the walls of the hind parts of the gut. The eggs are washed off in masses by the female, in running water, and have to take their chance of adhering to some submerged stick, or stone, such as the young larval forms like to cling to, for these are sluggish creatures which spend much of their time in apparent inactivity, although some are active enough. Their food consists principally of minute particles of vegetable and animal matter, but some of the more active kinds prey upon other small aquatic creatures.

A large Stone-fly from Siberia, *Pteronarcys retic*

Apart from these various adaptations to an aquatic life, the Stone-flies are of considerable interest in several other respects. Allusion has already been made to the many points in which they resemble the Orthoptera, a true affinity which is emphasised superficially by the brightness of the coloration—with red and purple hind-wings, etc.—of the members of the essentially Australian family *Eustheniidae*. In another direction the Stone-flies forecast the manner of development of the higher insects, for, just prior to their final moult, they pass through a brief resting period that may be likened to the pupal or chrysalis stage of butterflies and moths. They are world-wide in distribution and of some considerable antiquity, large numbers of their fossil forbears, classed as *Protoperlaria*, having been disinterred during the last few years from the Lower Permian beds of Kansas, in North America. No comprehensive account exists of the thirty odd species that are to be found in Great Britain.

Order ISOPTERA

(*Termites, or White Ants*)

The Termites are popularly known the world over as White Ants, and no doubt this term will always be applied to them, for it is too aptly descriptive to be readily supplanted by the more technical word. It is, perhaps, unfortunate, for it is based on an entire misconception, although a readily excusable one, of the nature of the insects to which it is applied. The Termites are about as closely related to the ants as are mice to man. On the other hand, they have developed a social life and organisation rivalling, and parallelling in many of its most minute details, that of the true ants. Professor Wheeler has very succinctly summed up the state of affairs in a sentence : " It is as if we had found, when Australia was first explored, the kangaroos and opossums enjoying a social organisation like that of man."

Termites abound throughout the tropics, and occur also in many of the temperate regions. The number of species at present known probably does not exceed a thousand, only two of which are commonly met with in Europe. They are mostly amazingly prolific, however, thereby amply making up for their deficiency in species. They live always in communities in termitaria of various kinds, some quite small, others housing upwards of half a million individuals. Probably as a result of their entirely subterranean existence the vast majority of Termites are entirely devoid of pigment in their very thin, delicate, and flexible integument. The covering of the head alone is at times moderately hard, that of the body little more than a membrane.

Winged sexual form of the South Indian White Ant, *Termes taprobana*.

Five different castes are distinguished in each species, three of which are capable of reproduction, the other two being sterile. The reproductive castes are either fully winged, short-winged, or devoid of wings ; the others are always wingless. Of the reproductive kinds the fully-winged caste is undoubtedly the most important. In them the body is usually quite strongly chitinised and therefore, for a Termite, comparatively firm ; the compound eyes are fully developed ; the brain large ; the sexual organs better developed than in the other castes ; the colour often quite dark ; and the wings ample with both pairs alike. It is this caste that periodically issues from the nest in the vast swarms so often referred to in accounts of animal life in tropical countries. Major Hingston gives a very excellent account of a swarm which he witnessed, emerging an hour or two before sunset, one evening in the Hazara valley in Kashmir :

" The main body, after crawling for a few minutes about the opening, scramble up the stems of the bushes or the blades of grass and then take wing into the air. . . . The sharp eye of an insectivorous bird soon detects them and they are instantly devoured. Other Termites follow, but their enemies have found them out. Birds great and small come flocking to the scene ;

little chats and bulbuls vie with hawks and pariah kites in the work of carnage. All nature appears set on their extinction. Round about the nest the crows and mynas congregate in hundreds, devouring the living morsels as they emerge into the light. Those that succeed in escaping into the air are seized by drongos, shrikes, or bulbuls—swifts and swallows meet them at higher altitudes, and kestrels swoop down on them from above. I carefully noted the fate of fifty consecutive termites as they embarked into the sky, but not one of them succeeded in travelling thirty feet before it was devoured. I could not see a single insect escape. A filthy scavenger-vulture was swallowing them greedily from off the ground, and those which I protected at the mouth of the nest were being attacked by a host of carnivorous ants, to be dragged again beneath the soil . . . I do not believe that in the broad daylight a single one would ever have escaped its enemies. It was the darkness of night that saved them. In the fading light of the evening I saw numbers hovering over the grass in my garden."

The Termites Major Hingston saw at dusk were no doubt alighting and

setting about the work of forming fresh colonies. The whole swarming process is indeed often spoken of as the nuptial flight, for it has no other purpose than the union of the sexes. Often all the colonies over a wide area will send forth their winged sexual forms at the same time. Whatever

Winged sexual form of a West African White Ant, *Termes nigeriensis*. Near the base of the frail wings can just be seen the suture where they break off after flight.

mysterious factors control, or stimulate, this remarkable synchronisation of flights from totally unconnected nests, there can be no doubt that for the species it must be highly beneficial. It almost certainly ensures the mating of members of different colonies, and so tends strongly to prevent the inbreeding that is always detrimental to the production of healthy offspring.

Almost immediately on the return of the winged forms to earth, which often occurs suddenly, as if they were incapable of further flight, the wings are shed, not from the base, but across a definite suture near the base so that the stumps remain. The insects seem then to segregate in pairs and to commence burrowing into the ground, and about this time, or probably when they are at a safe distance from the surface, union appears to take place, whereupon the female, or " queen," commences to undergo a remarkable change. Her body begins to expand, and many of her muscles degenerate, but her ovaries and other internal structures connected with the production of eggs develop to an amazing extent, so that eventually she becomes a white, membranous, bolster-like object some two to six inches long, with diminutive head and thorax attached at one end, and with the harder portions of her integument that formerly fitted together lying scattered like islands upon the billowy expanse of her abdomen. Correlated with this development there naturally takes place a corresponding extension of the nervous and vascular systems, and of the food canal. Everything is directed to the production of eggs; and so successfully is this achieved that the output is known in some cases to reach the colossal figure of 30,000 eggs every twenty-four hours. The male, or "king," undergoes no such change.

Less is known about the other two reproductive castes; both live entirely subterranean lives, taking no part in the nuptial flights. In the short-winged variety the body is much weaker than in the fully-winged reproductive caste just dealt with; the eyes are less developed, and this is also true of the brain and the sexual organs. Precisely what rôle this caste plays in the economy of the community is at present not fully understood. It is certain, however, that in the event of disaster overtaking the royal couple, individuals of it are capable of assuming their functions, although not so fully; it is possible, too, that they take some part in the work of the community. The third caste is entirely devoid of wings and is usually quite colourless, and not met with at all in the species that may be described as highest in the Termite scale. Even less is known of its functions than of the other lesser caste; its complete absence in certain groups seems to indicate, perhaps, that it is a survival from a period when termite organisation was at a lower level than it is now, and that it is in process of extinction.

The sterile castes are two, workers and soldiers. They are always wingless. The workers form the largest section of the population. In appearance they are soft, white creatures, rather resembling the immature stages of the reproductive castes. Their compound eyes are reduced to vestiges, but their jaws are strongly developed. Practically the whole work of the colony depends upon them; they feed the queens, forage for food, build the nest and repair it when necessary, and take care of the eggs and young. It is this caste that does the damage to books, woodwork, telegraph poles, railway sleepers, furniture and other fabrics, that has earned for the order such an unenviable reputation. Except amongst the more primitive species they work entirely in the dark, constructing roofed galleries or tunnels for their protection in the event of their desiring to cross places exposed to the light.

Small as they are, they work with incredible speed; they have been known, in a night, to devour entirely a pair of muddy boots, leaving only the mud standing, and there is an authentic case in India of their having destroyed, in a night, the bedding on which the prisoners in a Bengal prison were sleeping. These unfortunate occurrences, however, annoying as they may be, are but due to man's folly in putting temptation in the way of the termites. Their food is cellulose, which they obtain from dead wood and decaying vegetable matter, and, therefore, under natural conditions they are, in fact, highly beneficial creatures, performing a work similar to that of the earthworms in breaking down ground-litter and converting it into material that can be at once utilised by growing vegetation. The renewal of the tropical forests of the countries in which they are so excessively abundant must therefore, in a large measure, depend upon their activities.

Of the soldiers there are two principal types, developed in accordance with the form of defence adopted, but not occurring together in the same species. In the commoner type the head is very strongly chitinised, and

the jaws large and powerful, sometimes grotesquely so; in the other type, called "nasuti," the head is shaped like a retort, and the creature can squirt from its tip a jet of re- pellent fluid. Ants are amongst the bitterest enemies of Termites, and against their attacks the "nasuti" seem much more effective than their heavy-jawed relatives; the latter, indeed, seem to rely more upon their aggressive appearance than upon their courage.

A soldier of the African White Ant, *Termes lilleborgi*, from S. Nigeria. Note the enormous head and large jaws.

The general sub-divisions of the Termites are thus seen to be almost identical with those of the Ants, with the important difference that any individual of any caste may be of either sex.

The feeding habits are highly complicated. From the simple habit of devouring dead woody substances, each individual supplying his or her own needs, the Termites have developed a very elaborate system of feeding one another, by a variety of means. Saliva, food that has been swallowed and brought up again, and substances that have passed completely through the food canal, are all utilised; but not content with this they also derive nutrition by licking from each other's skins the fatty exudations to be found there. It is stated that the different castes have differently flavoured exudates (by which, perhaps, they are recognised), and that the most sought after is that supplied by the queen. Although similar feeding habits occur in other orders of Insects, in none of them is it pushed to such lengths as in the Termites. The members of the colonies, as Professor Wheeler remarks,

A " nasute " worker of *Eutermes usambarensis*, so called on account of the retort-shaped head.

" may be said to be bound together by a circulating medium of glandular secretions, fatty exudates, and partly and wholly digested food; just as the cells of the body of a higher animal are bound together as a syntrophic whole by means of the circulating blood."

Great variety is shown by the Termites in the form of the nest they build. Some of the lowlier forms, indeed, hardly build any, being content with rough galleries about the surface of the ground, but from these to the most highly specialised types one can trace a gradually increasing architectural skill. Having withdrawn from the world to a life of cloistered isolation and darkness, they would soon be exterminated but for the erection of strong fortifications. The bricks are bits of earth and wood, the mortar saliva, and from these materials nests are built so strong that they will turn the blade of an axe. Most of them do not conform to any particular shape ; the commonest form is a cone or tower built up above the original sub-terranean nest, often reaching a consider-able height.

The tallest are those made by a species of Australian *Eutermes*, which may reach a height of twenty feet. Ten or twelve feet is quite ordinary. More unusual are the wedge-shaped structures, running north and south and known as compass termi-taria, and the little mushroom-shaped nests found in Central Africa. Or the nest may be constructed in a tree, quite clear of the ground, much in the manner that certain wasps adopt. In every case, however, the royal chamber is situated somewhere about the centre of the complex ramification of tunnels, galleries, and chambers that honeycomb the whole nest. Many species use these chambers for the storage of food supplies, grasses, etc., but some of the most specialised kinds, again taking a leaf out of the book of the ants, grow

A White Ants' nest, or termitary, in the Uele Forest, Belgian Congo.

fungi in them upon which they feed the reproductive castes and the young.

Considerable light has been thrown upon the origin of the Termites by the discovery in Australia of a genus called *Mastotermes*, which has many features of strong resemblance to the cockroaches, and seems to indicate that both have been derived from the same ancestral stock. This genus differs, in fact, so widely from all other Termites that it is usually placed in a family by itself. The remainder are divided between three families, *Protermitidae*, *Mesotermitidae*, and *Termitidae*, the sequence representing progressive stages of specialisation.

Order EMBIOPTERA

The insignificant little creatures that compose this order, although they have been known to science for about a hundred years, have not been very much studied, probably because none seems to have any practical interest. They are seldom as much as half an inch in length, and decidedly narrow, somewhat suggestive of a frail earwig or a termite—indeed, by many scientists they are considered to be but a branch of the Isoptera, or termites. The females are wingless, and distinctly rare; the males are much more common, often flying to lights in the moist tropical districts to which they are confined. The wings in the latter sex are developed gradually, as usual in the exopterygotous orders, and after the final moult resemble those of the Termites in their lack of differentiation (both pairs being alike), but

1   2

Embia major

A comparatively large Indian species. (1) The male; (2) the female, which is wingless. (Much enlarged.) (After Imms.)

differ from them in being smoky black; they are very delicate, and set wide apart.

A feature that serves to distinguish all the Embiids very readily is to be found in the swollen basal segment of the tarsi of the first pair of legs. It is in this very unusual situation that these creatures carry the gland that produces the silk with which they construct their tunnels. The species are sometimes solitary, but more usually they live gregariously in small colonies. *Embia major*, a comparatively large Indian species, makes a nest of silken galleries that usually communicate with one or two small subterranean chambers.

The purpose of these tunnels is not clearly understood ; it is assumed that they are for protection either against predacious enemies, or against changes of humidity (the insects are extremely frail), but in any case this species invariably constructs them, and is able to move backwards or forwards within them at considerable speed. They are built up very rapidly by a kind of weaving motion performed by the first pair of legs, and, as each leg may produce, so it appears, up to seventy-five or eighty threads simultaneously, the rapidity of the operation can easily be appreciated. Although many hundred individuals sometimes inhabit a common nest, there are no castes, nor any social organisation, like that of the Termites. The female, however, has been observed to exercise the same maternal care for her young as the female earwig and some few other lowly insects already dealt with.

Although only about sixty species of Embioptera are at present known, distributed throughout the tropics, the order appears to be a comparatively ancient one, for fossil wings, clearly of the same lineage, have recently been discovered in the Lower Permian beds of Kansas.

Order ZORAPTERA

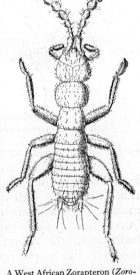

This order of minute insects has only been known to science eighteen years, having been recognised first in 1913. Its members are very minute, to judge from the six species that have so far been discovered, being only about 2–3 mm. in length. They live in rotting wood, and also have been found in Termite nests. Formerly they were thought to be wingless, but more recently winged forms have been found in a species having also wingless forms. It is considered now, indeed, that, in the case of this species at any rate, a simple community system has been evolved consisting of winged sexual forms and sexless workers—a state of affairs also found in the Termites. The winged forms, however, have a type of wing quite unlike that of the Termites, and closely resembling the Psocopterid wing (see next order). The order may be considered, therefore, as a connecting link between the Termites and the Psocoptera, its

A West African Zorapteron (*Zorotypus guineensis*), the first species to be discovered. (Much enlarged.) (After Imms.)

interest, apart from this, lying principally in the apparent social organisation that it exhibits.

Order Psocoptera

(*Psocids, Book-lice*)

The Psocids are small, or very small, insects with rather soft, plump bodies, sometimes, but by no means always, provided with delicate, little-veined wings. As an order they are easily characterised by the development in the mouth-parts of a pair of chisel- or gouge-like organs (styliform appendages of some authorities, modified laciniae of others) used for digging into the bark of trees, or breaking up the food before it is taken into the mouth. The winged forms are also readily recognisable by the special and rather peculiar arrangement of the wing-nervures.

Of the wingless species the best known is undoubtedly *Troctes divinatorius*, the minute little white creature that is an inhabitant of old books and rubbish, and is, in fact, *the* Book-louse. This tiny insect is often spoken of as the Death-watch. That so small an animal—it seldom exceeds one millimetre in length—should be thought capable of producing so much sound seems

Psocus lineatus (enlarged)
The largest European Psocid.

hardly believable. Yet most circumstantial and detailed accounts have been published that seem beyond question to inculpate it. One of the earliest was that by the Rev. W. Derham, who, some two hundred years ago, gave an account before the Royal Society. He stated that he had not only observed the creatures in the act of ticking, but could, by suitable tappings, induce them to respond. It is a pity that no recent investigations of this problem appear to have been made; it is quite possible that the earlier observations were made upon wrongly identified insects.

Atropos pulsatorius and *Lepinotus inquilinus* are two other very common book-lice—not distinguishable from *Troctes* except by very close examination—that share with it the odium of being serious pests of libraries and museums. The paste of books, paper, dry and decaying collections of insects not properly cared for, the straw of mattresses, etc., often suffer badly from the attentions of these and related species. Most species, however, live in the open, on or under the bark of trees, on walls, etc., but nearly always where there is a growth of lichens or fungi, upon which many of them feed. One British species, for example, *Caecilius flavidus*, is common on diseased branches of trees, feeding apparently on fungi, but it seems to negative any beneficial result that might be expected as a consequence of this habit, by carrying the spores of the fungus about on its body and thereby helping as a distributing agent.

Some of the larger winged species are quite prettily coloured and attractive insects, looking almost like small moths, and are sometimes to be found gathered together in large groups on the trunks of trees. The rare Lepido-psocids, indeed, carry the deception further, for their wings bear a covering of scales similar at first sight to those of the Lepidoptera. The occurrence of such scales is rare, but the presence of hairs on the wing-nervures is much more commonly met with.

Some three hundred different species of Psocids are known, distributed amongst eight families. Formerly they appear to have been very common creatures, their remains having been frequently met with in amber, and, more recently, in the Lower Permian of Kansas.

Order ANOPLURA

(*Lice*)

The Lice fall naturally into two sub-orders, Mallophaga, or Biting Lice, and Siphunculata, or Sucking Lice. Formerly these were regarded as distinct orders, but recent research, stimulated perhaps by the discovery of the importance of certain species as carriers of disease, has shown that they possess so many fundamental characters in common that they can best be regarded as specialised branches arising from a common stock. The very obvious difference between the two sections lies in the mouth-parts. In the Mallophaga these are of a more or less normal, biting type ; whereas in the Siphunculata they are modified to form a sucking tube—a feature which led to their association by many authorities with the true Bugs.

Sub-order *MALLOPHAGA*

(*Biting Lice*)

These are the small, flattened, wingless insects, seldom as much as a quarter of an inch in length, sometimes of consider-able breadth, that principally infest birds —for which reason they are often spoken of collectively as the Bird-lice—but also mammals, to some extent. They spend the whole of their life upon their host, feeding upon fragments of feathers, hair, and skin. The injury they do results not so much from their feeding-habits as from the scratching action of their claws as they move about upon the body of the host.

The louse of the Vulture (*Conocephalum flavescens*). (Much enlarged.)

Not infrequently their presence is highly injurious, and

may even cause death. Some of the commonest and best-known species are *Menopon gallinae* on chickens, *Philopterus dentatus* on ducks, *Trichodectus canis* on dogs, and *T. bovis* on cattle. A louse of some kind seems to have been recorded from most birds of any size, but, curiously, amongst the mammals it appears to be the domesticated kinds that suffer most.

Close study of the sub-order during recent years has revealed a remarkable association of closely related species of lice with closely related groups of birds. The facts are now well established in many cases, and can only mean that as the birds evolved into different species from a common stock, so their parasites followed suit. Conversely, it may be argued that the occurrence of closely related species of lice upon birds not usually regarded as having any great affinities might be taken as an indication that our classification is at fault. This suggestion has indeed already led to the supposition that the New Zealand Kiwi is more closely related to the Rails (because their lice are similar) than hitherto supposed—a surmise that has, in fact, met with some support on other grounds. Close investigation of these lice may quite possibly prove of considerable aid in the study of the phylogeny of their hosts.

Sub-order SIPHUNCULATA
(*Sucking Lice*)

The same close relationships exist in this sub-order as in the Mallophaga.

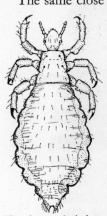

Pediculus, the genus to which the human body- and head-lice belong (*P. humanus corporis* and *P. humanus capitis*), apart from man, occurs only on apes and certain monkeys; *Haematopinus* is confined almost entirely to Ungulates; *Polyplax* to rats and mice; *Echinophthirius* to marine mammals, and so on, thus emphasising the blood-relationships of their hosts. All the species live by sucking the blood of their hosts after puncturing the skin; comparatively few occur on domestic animals, the majority living upon other mammals. No doubt many remain to be discovered, as they are not easy creatures to collect.

By far the most important species from the human standpoint is *Pediculus humanus*, which is a proved carrier of typhus fever, and an indirect transmitter of " trench-fever " and relapsing fever.

The human body-louse
(*Pediculus humanus*).
(Much enlarged.) (After Imms.)

Order EPHEMEROPTERA
(*May-flies*)

The short antennae, large, triangular, much-veined fore-wings and very small hind-wings, together with the long body and its three long, thin tails, should enable the insects of this well-defined order to be recognised without any difficulty. Its members are scattered throughout the world and represent an order that in former times was considerably more abundant than now. They can be traced back among the fossils to the Lower Permian, the wings showing less and less disparity in size the further back one goes ; before that time they seem to have emerged from certain forms prevalent in the Carboniferous period. Nowadays they are familiar insects in the neighbourhood of streams and lakes, to which places they are confined. In colour most May-flies are grey, pearly, or brownish, with the transparent wings occasionally faintly tinted, or with dark markings.

The life-history exhibits several points of interest. The eggs are laid

A common British May-fly, *Ephemera vulgata.*

Ephemera danica
A May-fly common in the British Isles, at rest.

in water, either loosely or in compact masses—exceptionally the females are viviparous, though this is very rare—and give rise to small, active aquatic nymphs that feed mostly upon minute vegetation, though occasionally predacious. At first the nymphs appear to absorb through the skin a sufficient supply of oxygen from the water for their needs, but later they develop gills in various situations according to the species, usually in the form of abdominal processes, the function of which is to extract air from the water and pass it into the tracheal system.

Morphologically these nymphs exhibit another peculiarity, for their mandibles are of the Crustacean type, found elsewhere in the Insects only in the primitive wingless orders—a feature which points clearly to their great antiquity. The nymphal stage is generally very prolonged, and may last as long as three years, thus forming a very marked contrast to the exceedingly brief life of the fully developed May-fly. After many moults a stage is reached in which rudimentary wings are present. When full-grown the nymph climbs to the surface of the water, the skin breaks along the back, and there emerges the sub-imago, a fully winged stage unique amongst insects. This creature flies away, often a hundred yards or more, settles, and then sheds another delicate skin before attaining complete maturity. These sub-imaginal skins may very often be seen on fences and posts in the neighbourhood of streams, sometimes in great abundance, complete with legs, antennae, and wings. No attempt appears to have been made to explain the processes by which this very remarkable metamorphic stage has been evolved in this alone of all Insect orders.

It is curious that, like the winged Termites which have such a brief span of life in the outside world, the May-flies nearly all emerge and take to the air in the evening, and that, like them again, very large numbers often emerge on the same evening. Possibly there is an adaptation here for the same ends, namely cross-breeding on the one hand and protection from enemies under cover of darkness on the other, so that reproduction may be secured. Their principal enemies whilst the insects are on or near the surface of the water are undoubtedly fish, especially trout—the " Green Drake " of fly-fishers is modelled on the sub-imago of the common British May-fly, the " Grey Drake " upon the adult, and many other " duns " and " spinners " are similarly modelled on other May-flies ; but birds, too, attack them. Sometimes they emerge in vast swarms, and are attracted to lights, in the neighbourhood of which they may at times be observed indulging in aerial " community " dances, that consist of a fluttering upward movement followed by a slower descent. They are largely crepuscular. Their brief adult life is truly ephemeral, and may be no longer than three or four hours, or at most two or three days. So short is it, indeed, that they take no food, and their mouth-parts and food-canal, no doubt as a direct consequence, are functionless.

Order ODONATA

(*Dragon-flies*)

Dragon-flies have a world-wide distribution, some 2500 species being known, but they are most abundant in tropical regions. They are deservedly noted for their brilliant colours, skilful flight, and graceful form. The body is relatively longer than in any other group of insects ; wings are invariably present, the two pairs approximately alike, hard and glassy, and always having a very large number of nervures, the majority of which are short and run transversely across the wing. A very characteristic feature of a dragon-fly's wing is the node—a slight re-entrant angle on the anterior edge of the wing from which arises a strong cross-nervure. The head is very freely movable and carries a pair of very large compound eyes, a pair of short feelers, and strong biting jaws, the other mouth-parts being modified to form a kind of trap for catching the small insects upon which dragon-flies feed. The short, rather spiny legs are also used for this purpose to a great extent, especially for catching and holding larger insects; they are little used for walking purposes. The arrangement of the thorax is also peculiar, the segments sloping forwards and downwards so that the legs come to lie in a very forward position, almost beneath the head, and the wings to rest naturally along the back. The situation

Libellula quadrimaculata

A frequently migratory Dragon-fly occurring both in Europe and in N. America.

of the male genital armature, on the second segment of the body, is unique amongst the known orders of Insects.

Development is of the kind sometimes called "incomplete metamorphosis"; it has certain features in common with that of moths and butter-

A strangely marked African Anisopterid Dragon-fly, *Rhyothemis fenestrina*.

flies. The eggs are sometimes laid in slits cut in aquatic plants by the ovipositor of the female; sometimes in masses enclosed in a gelatinous string that adheres to submerged objects; sometimes scattered on the surface of the water, or washed out from the abdomen of the female as she dips it, whilst flying, into the water. They hatch out into tiny swathed creatures called pro-nymphs, which cast off their skins almost immediately and appear as free-swimming nymphs or naiads. This stage may last anything from twelve months to two, three, or even five years, the whole of which time is spent in the water.

Breathing takes place during the larval stages by means of tracheal gills

I

hidden within the extremity of the abdomen (Sub-order Anisoptera), or through three suitably modified tail processes (Sub-order Zygoptera); but it has been shown that the nymphs can, in many cases, survive periods of drought, due to the drying up of their watery surroundings, as frequently happens in tropical regions, with complete equanimity. In habit they are entirely carnivorous, feeding principally upon May-fly larvae, mosquito larvae, and the like, although little seems to come amiss to them in this respect, even tadpoles and small fish being attacked by some of the larger species. They are able to adapt their coloration to their surroundings to a certain extent, and generally lie concealed in some manner or other waiting for any small creature that may come within range. When this occurs, the dragon-fly nymph shoots out its "mask" at it, and secures it. The "mask" is a characteristic structure developed from the lower lip and peculiar to the nymphs of dragon-flies. It is an arm-like organ that bears at its extremity a pair of curved, jaw-like spines with which the prey is seized; when folded up it is hidden beneath the head, the lower surface of which it completely conceals.

A British representative of the large and widespread genus *Sympetrum, S. striolatum.*

The nymphs moult, as a rule, a dozen or more times, but the wing-sheaths never assume large proportions. When fully grown they become tense and appear swollen, especially about the thoracic region. When the perfect insect is about to emerge the nymph climbs up the stem of a plant above the surface of the water. The skin dries, and soon begins to crack along the middle of the thorax; the thorax appears through the cleft, and, swelling up, causes it to extend; the head is next disengaged and the legs withdrawn from their sheaths. The insect then throws its head farther and farther back, and by this means gradually frees the hinder part of its body, with the exception of the last few segments, which still remain enclosed in the nymphal skin. After a while it suddenly bends its body forward, grasps the sides of the sheath with its legs, and, doubling up its abdomen, finally extricates the rest of its body. The wings quickly expand, dry, and harden; but the mature coloration is not immediately developed, and the insects may fly for some while in a teneral, or not fully mature, condition.

Dragon-flies play an important part in the destruction of small winged insects, especially flies, their appetite being apparently insatiable. It has often been observed that each individual has its own beat, and it is a fact that when they are abundant each confines its operations to a definitely restricted area, returning to rest on the same twig. Sometimes they migrate in swarms, certain species, as, for example, the European *Libellula quadrimaculata,* having strong migratory propensities. There is no doubt that the dragon-fly population of Great Britain receives frequent accessions from the Continent. Certain Oriental species have a habit, most unusual amongst such sun-loving creatures, of flying at night, and are said to be addicted to the highly beneficial practice of preying upon mosquitoes.

Of existing species the largest is no doubt *Megaloprepus caerulatus,* a rather frail creature with an excessively long body that inhabits Central and South America and has a wing expanse of $7\frac{1}{2}$ inches ; but this is a mere dwarf compared with the giants of the Carboniferous period, some of which measured a good two feet across the wings. The order is divided into two sub-orders, based upon the characters of the nymphs and of the adults.

Sub-order *ANISOPTERA*

This group includes the largest and most robust species, in which the hind-wing is markedly broader at the base than the fore-wing. Two clearly defined families are recognised, which include such well-known genera as *Anax, Aeschna, Rhyothemis, Cordulegaster, Libellula,* and *Sympetrum,* all with representative species in Great Britain.

Sub-order *ZYGOPTERA*

These are the more delicate dragon-flies, in which the bases of all four wings are quite narrow. They are divided into three families which may be typified by *Calopteryx* (the very

The Damsel-fly from the New Forest, *Calopteryx splendens.* The areas shown dark on the wings are brilliant metallic blue.

beautiful Damsel-flies), *Lestes, Platycnemis,* and *Agrion,* all of which have British representatives.

Order THYSANOPTERA

(*Thrips*)

The tiny Insects that compose this order are often to be met with in profusion in flowers, although they occur almost as plentifully on the foliage of plants, and also amongst dead leaves, fungi, etc. They are narrow and elongate, varying in size from 1/50th to half an inch in length, and as a rule winged, the wings being excessively narrow, with only one or two nervures and wide fringes of hair. The antennae have six to nine joints and the mouth-parts are peculiar in being asymmetrical. The front of the head slopes downwards and backwards so that the mouth-parts, much as in the Bugs, come to lie beneath the thorax. Similarly, too, they are adapted for piercing and sucking.

Heliothrips haemorrhoidalis
The Black-fly.

The development shows an interesting approach to the " complete metamorphosis " type of the higher insects. Except for the absence of wings, the young, when they emerge from the egg, resemble their parents. After two or three moults the wing-pads make their appearance, and at this stage the young Thrips of many species retire below ground and remain more or less quiescent in small earthen chambers of their own construction. After a while this " pro-nymphal " condition, as it is called, is terminated by a moult that discloses the true nymph or pupa, which is a true resting stage, during which no food is taken. The wings, of course, are developed externally.

Many Thrips are now recognised as of economic importance, such as *Heliothrips haemorrhoidalis* (the " Black-fly " of greenhouses), the Wheatthrips (*Frankliniella tritici*), the Corn-thrips (*Limothrips cerealium*), and the Grass-thrips (*Anaphothrips striatus*) which, when prevalent upon the spikelets of oats, produces sterility. Some are confined to individual species of plants, but more ordinarily they are distinctly catholic in taste. Many are helpful in securing the fertilisation of plants, by disseminating pollen, but it appears that on the whole the harm they do outweighs any benefits they may confer. Virgin reproduction (parthenogenesis) is of frequent occurrence throughout the order; males are seldom anything like so common as females, and in some species excessively rare. Thrips occur throughout the temperate and tropical regions, sometimes in countless numbers. They probably form quite a high proportion of the minute winged life that is so little studied. The winged species, in certain cases, appear to migrate. Only a few hundred species have been described, principally from Europe, Australia, and North America—very many more must await discovery, for they have so far been very little investigated.

Limothrips cerealium
The Cornthrips.

Several schemes of classification have been proposed for them, the most natural dividing them into three sub-orders (or super-families) according to the number of spiracles, the number of nervures on the wings, and the shape of the extremity of the abdomen. The *Tubulifera*, in which the tip of the body is tubular in both sexes, feed mainly on dead leaves, fungi, etc., some of the Australian species departing so far from this habit, however, as to form galls. To the *Terebrantia*, which feed upon the tissues of living plants, other than fungi, belong the giants of the order, including *Idolo-thrips spectrum*, which attains a length of half an inch, and was first found in Australia by Charles Darwin during the voyage of H.M.S. " Beagle."

Order HEMIPTERA

(*Bugs*)

The numerous insects included in this order exhibit great differences in their external form, and while some, such as the *Flatinae*, rival the butter-flies and moths in the beauty and delicacy of their colours, others are amongst the most loathsome of creatures. But whatever be their form or colour, all agree in two essential characters, the first consisting in the fact that their development takes place without a complete metamorphosis ; and the second that all have the mouth taking the form of a symmetrical beak, or rostrum, adapted for piercing and sucking. The beak consists chiefly of the lower lip (labium), which is long and narrow, composed of three or four joints, and grooved along the whole length of its upper or anterior surface. This groove forms a sort of sheath in which are lodged four long, slender blades, corresponding to the mandibles and maxillae of other insects, but here transformed into piercing organs. All these parts are covered at the base, in front, by the narrow and slightly elongated upper lip (labrum). From the structure of their mouth, which is fitted only for the reception of liquid nutriment, it is easy to infer that these insects live by piercing the tissues of plants and animals and extracting the juices.

The larvae differ little from the adults except in size, the absence of wings, and their usually shorter and more slender antennae. In many species, however, the females are without wings at all stages ; and in some cases both sexes are thus unprovided. When wings are present, they may be all of similar texture, or the front pair may be somewhat stiffer and less membranous than the hinder. Wings of both these kinds are found in the Sub-order Homoptera. In other cases, while the hind-wings are entirely membranous, the front pair are stiff and horny for some distance from their base, and thin and membranous towards their extremities. Such wings, which characterise the Sub-order Heteroptera, are known as hemi-elytra. Over thirty thousand species are already known. The earliest undoubted fossil remains of the order are found in the Lower Permian beds of Kansas ; in strata of the Jurassic epoch they are comparatively common, and become tolerably abundant in amber and beds of Tertiary age.

Sub-order *HETEROPTERA*

(*True Bugs*)

All the Heteroptera, no matter how different they may be in external form or mode of life, are termed bugs, although this name was originally applied only to the bed-bug and a few closely allied species. Most are winged insects, in which the fore-wings, known as hemi-elytra, or simply as elytra, always have the form described above. Their antennae are either short and inconspicuous, as in the water-bugs, or distinctly visible as in the land-bugs, and are generally composed of a small number of joints. As a rule they have two compound eyes, and often two or three ocelli. The first segment of the thorax is usually large, with the head sunk deeply into it. The abdomen generally has an oval, flattened form, and the legs are mostly slender. With few exceptions bugs are characterised by a peculiar and somewhat unpleasant odour, which arises from a liquid secreted by special glands placed in the front part of the abdomen, and opening to the exterior by means of two small ostioles on the ventral surface of the metathorax.

Of a group so large as this, and exhibiting such variety of structure, habits, and adaptations to differing environments, an attempt to give a general account would present such difficulties that it will probably be best to treat its main sub-divisions one by one. Here, again, obstacles are at once encountered, for owing largely to the intensive investigations of the last quarter of a century the classification has been rendered much less stable than formerly appeared to be the case. Two main divisions are, however, still generally accepted ; (*a*) Gymnocerata (sometimes called Geocorisa) in which the antennae are conspicuous and freely movable in front of the head ; (*b*) the Cryptocerata (or Hydrocorisa) in which they are on the under side of the head, or in grooves beneath the head.

Division *GYMNOCERATA*

(*Land-bugs*)

Here seven series of families, or super-families as they are more generally termed, can be recognised, leading gradually in habits, if not so much in structure, to the Cryptocerata, which are in the main Water-bugs. In this group development is of a very simple order. The young seldom resemble the adults very closely on emergence from the egg, except in general outline. They undergo, as a rule, four or five moults, each of which may be accompanied by a change of colour or pattern, varying in extent according to the species, the wings meanwhile gradually developing. Although the environment selected by the larval forms may often differ considerably from that of the adult, and, in consequence, the nature of the food as well, the process of development is continuous, and there is no resting (pupal or nymphal) stage.

The Pentatomoid, or Shield-bug group of families, is composed of a very large number of species, almost entirely plant-feeding, in which the beak is long and straight, extending between and well beyond the bases of the first pair of legs. In some few that have departed from the normal habit and become carnivorous, the beak stands out a little from the head, no doubt to facilitate attack. The typical Shield-bugs (*Pentatomidae*) can readily be recognised by the strongly developed scutellum, or backward prolongation

1   2   3

TYPICAL SHIELD-BUGS

1, *Catacanthus incarnatus*, from Burma.   2, *Datanes limbata*, from Tonkin.   3, *Runibia decorata*, from Bolivia.

of the thorax, a development that reaches its maximum in such genera as *Coptosoma* in which the whole of the body and the wings are covered so that the insects look at first sight like Chrysomelid beetles, a delusion which is heightened by their metallic bronze and greenish colours, their small size, and their similar habits of living, often gregariously, exposed on plants. None of these extreme forms occurs in England—they are commonest in the East, but the more ordinary Shield-bugs are well represented. These are very generally brightly coloured and conspicuous insects, red and black being a common combination; but blue, green, and metallic colours are not infrequent.

     Although so widely distributed and abundant, the Shield-bugs do very little serious damage to crops, probably because they keep on the move from plant to plant, seldom staying long enough anywhere to suck sufficient sap to harm the plant. There are, of course, a few exceptions, such as the Hottentot-bug (*Eurygaster maurus*), a dark brown species with two clear spots on either side, at the base of the scutellum,

A Shield-bug from Uganda, *Ceratocoris horni*, closely related to *Coptosoma*, in which the shield is so developed as to cover the whole of the abdomen.

which in some parts of Europe occasionally proves a pest on wheat: also the aptly so-called Harlequin-bug (*Murgantia histrionica*) of America, and the Cabbage-bug (*Eurydema oleracea*) of Europe, both of which attack cabbages and related plants. Curiously, there is quite a large number of plant orders that are virtually shunned entirely by all the true bugs. Butler, for instance, in his admirable account of the British Heteroptera, gives a list of over twenty orders of plants which are apparently absolutely free from the attacks of these insects, at any rate in so far as their British representatives are concerned.

A Shield-bug, *Pectocoris lineola.* A pest of cotton in Queensland.

Closely related to the Pentatomids are the Coreid bugs, which include the Squash-bugs of American writers, the Gum-tree bugs of Australia, and the very injurious Rice-bug (*Leptocorisa*) of India and the East. They are mostly rather elongate insects with the antennae placed on the upper side of the head, and the wings with numerous nervures. In coloration they are mainly "pro-cryptic," that is to say, adapted to assimilate easily to their surroundings, leaf-like or green, often with lateral expansions of the limbs. This latter development is sometimes carried to great lengths; certain African species that inhabit desert regions are almost as thin as paper, and have their sides fantastically cut up and spined so that they resemble almost exactly the bracts of the desert plants upon which they feed. The Lygaeids, though extremely numerous, are

The Hottentot-bug of Europe, *Eurygaster maurus.*

The Harlequin-bug of N. America, *Murgantia histrionica.*

Leptocorisa geniculatus
A species of Rice-bug which occurs in the Philippine Islands.

neither conspicuous nor important. They are mostly of dark coloration, and generally live about the surface of the ground, under stones, dead leaves, etc. They are of interest in that many species have both winged and wingless forms, a phenomenon very rare in the Heteroptera though of very wide occurrence in the Homoptera to be dealt with later.

The Fire-bugs (*Pyrrhocoridae*), so called on account of their almost invariable fiery-red colour, relieved only by black spots, are highly important, the species of the genus *Dysdercus* being the "Cotton-stainers" that are such serious pests of cotton wherever it grows. It is of great interest to note that the Trinidad species has a definite migratory phase comparable with that of the migratory locusts. When it begins to move about in swarms, as it not infrequently does, urged no doubt by hunger, it has been observed that all the individuals comprising the swarm are smaller, and very much darker in colour than is ordinarily the case with individuals enjoying more normal conditions.

Helcomeria spinosa, an unusual type of Coreid bug with leaf-like expansions of the legs and thorax.

The Tingoid and Aradoid groups include only a small number of species, readily recognised by their characteristic form and structure. In the former the hemi-elytra are large, and have a net-like appearance on account of which they are generally called Lace-bugs; in the latter they are small, simple, and never completely cover the broad, flattened abdomen.

The Assassin-bugs (*Reduvoidea*) present an interesting departure from their vegetarian allies, being very largely carnivorous. The beak is short and stout, not pressed close to the under side of the head, but standing out

A common European Fire-bug, *Pyrrhocoris apterus*. (Three times natural size.)

One of the " Cotton-stainers," the E. African species, *Dysdercus cardinalis*.

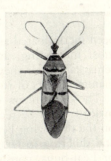

A Reduvoid bug, *Phonoctonus nigrofasciatus*, which closely resembles the Cotton-stainer superficially, and preys upon it.

well away from it. They exhibit, too, an interesting variety of form, tending in very many cases most strongly, even deceptively, to resemble species upon which they prey; but to what extent this may be regarded as mimicry, whether protective or offensive, does not appear to have been investigated. An example is afforded by the members of the African genus *Phonoctonus*, which are red and black and quite extraordinarily similar to the Cotton-stainers (*Dysdercus*), which form their normal food; others, however, are mimetic of Braconid wasps, from which they are only to be distinguished by a close examination. To the species belonging to the Sub-family *Emesinae*, however, must undoubtedly be awarded the palm, for not content with aping the Mantids by using their fore-legs as pincers, some species have succeeded in resembling stick insects, others mosquitoes, and not a few would at first sight be mistaken for Daddy-longlegs. The last-mentioned type is found in caves in East Africa and Assam, running about on the walls in complete darkness. Many of the larger species are capable of causing a distinctly painful wound, especially the members of the genus *Triatoma*, and one of these has, indeed,

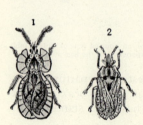

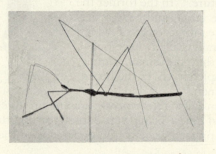

Two common British Lace-bugs: (1) *Tingis affinis*; (2) *Aradus corticalis*.

An Assassin-bug from Guatemala, *Emesa longipes*, bearing a striking resemblance to a Praying Mantis.

A Burmese Assassin-bug, *Triatoma rubrifasciatus*.

been incriminated as a carrier of disease. The family is thus, on the whole, most interesting, and one that well repays study; even the young are remarkable, for they have a habit of " camouflaging " themselves with all manner of bits of rubbish, so that they may escape notice.

Those members of the Miroid series of families that have wings (the majority) can be recognised at sight by the *cuneus*, a smaller triangular area on the fore-wing between the outer membranous and inner harder portions, and differing in texture from both. The very numerous family of Capsid-, or Leaf-bugs, consists entirely of rather fragile insects, seldom more than half an inch in length, of strictly herbivorous habit. They are often brightly coloured and usually common. Some few are of economic importance: *Helopeltis theivora*, an inconspicuous little creature, is the " Tea-mosquito " of the East; *Lygus pratensis* is a troublesome insect wherever it occurs, and in England does a good deal of damage to chrysanthemums.

It is curious how the same modifications in certain definite directions

crop up in widely different groups.   It was pointed out that some of the
Shield-bugs closely resembled Chrysomelid beetles ; in India there is a
small dark shining Leaf-bug, called *Halticus minutus*, a pest of oranges,
that looks almost exactly like a Halticid beetle (the *Halticidae* and *Chrysomelidae* are very closely related), and completes the resemblance by having
the faculty of leaping into the air just after the manner of its supposed
" model."   The Flower-bugs are even smaller than the Capsids, and are
to be sought chiefly, as their popular name indicates, on flowers, where they
may be found feeding on pollen, thrips, and sometimes green-fly.   The

1   2   3

TYPICAL CAPSID-BUGS

1. A " tea-mosquito " from Ceylon, *Helopeltis antonii*.   2. A common British species, *Lygus pratensis*.
(Much enlarged.)   3. *Halticus saltator*.

best-known genus is *Anthocoris*.   The wingless Bed-bugs (*Cimicidae*) complete this series.   They need little comment.   All are parasitic blood-
sucking creatures, found principally upon birds, apart from the two detest-
able species associated with man and too well known to need further
description.
    Of the Land-bugs there remain now only two of the major groups to
deal with, both of which show stages in the adaptation to an aquatic life.
The Shore-bugs (*Saldidae*) are dark-coloured and very active little creatures,
predacious, and in habit rather resembling Tiger-beetles.   They are to be met
with on the seashore, amongst the low-growing herbage of salt marshes,

and the mud and mosses around streams and lakes. *Salda littoralis* is shown in the accompanying illustration. The Water-striders and Pond-skaters (*Gerridae, etc.*) have gone a step further, and live actually on the surface of the water, being kept dry by the velvety pile that clothes their lower surfaces. In them the three pairs of legs are modified for different purposes : the first pair for seizing the small insects that form their food, the

A Cimicid bug, *Antho-coris nemorum.* Known amongst hop-growers as the Needle-nosed Flea.

The Bed-bug, *Cimex lectularius.*

A Shore-bug, *Salda littoralis.*

A common British Pond-skater, *Gerris paludum.*

second pair for rowing, and the third for steering. They occur in both running and stagnant waters, those inhabiting the latter having, as a rule, much longer legs. To this group belongs the genus *Halobates* containing the Sea-skaters, almost the only insects known that are able to support life entirely upon the surface of the ocean, often hundreds of miles from land.

Division CRYPTOCERATA

(*Water-bugs*)

In all the true Water-bugs the antennae are hidden in cavities under the head.

The Water-scorpions (*Nepidae*) can be recognised at once by the long breathing tube made of two interlocking portions and situated at the extremity of the abdomen. They are excessively rapacious creatures, with fore-legs like those of the Praying Mantids, and they attack all and sundry, being popularly known in Australia as " Toe-biters " or " Needle-bugs," owing to their habit of attacking bathers and inflicting painful stabs with their beaks. They inhabit the muddy and weedy bottoms of ponds, are broad, flattened, and oval in shape, usually dark brown in colour, and frequently two inches or more in length, apart from the breathing tube or siphon. *Nepa* is probably the best-known genus, though *Ranatra*, which is more elongate and cylindrical in shape, is almost as familiar. The Giant

Water-bugs (*Belastomatidae*) are very closely allied to the *Nepidae* but lack the long conspicuous siphon, and have one more joint (four in all) in the antennae. They have almost identical habits and include the largest known bugs. The Giant Fish-killer (*Lethocerus indicus*) may be as much as four inches in length: it is of a dull brown colour, not infrequently flies great distances, and, being often attracted to light, has earned the name of Electric-light-bug. It is found throughout the East, from India to Australia.

Whereas the insects just referred to are, in the main, inhabitants of tropical

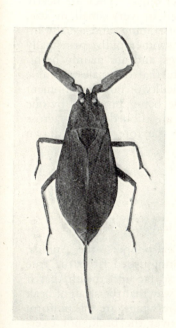

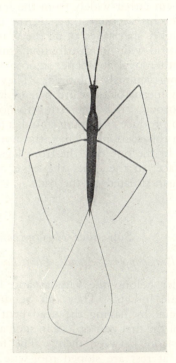

A British Water-scorpion, *Nepa cinerea*.

A Water-bug from Ceylon, *Ranatra elongata*.

The Water-boatman, *Notonecta maculata*.

and subtropical regions, the Water-boatmen (*Notonectidae*) are primarily inhabitants of more temperate zones, all the largest and most conspicuous species being found in those regions. They can be recognised at once by the fact that they swim upon their backs. They occur on the surfaces of ponds and streams throughout the world, and must surely be familiar to any ordinarily observant person. On the under side of the body there is a long keel, with a trough on either side of it. When the insect submerges, air is enclosed within this trough by means of hairs so arranged as to cover them, and upon this supply of air the insect depends whilst below the surface of the water. The Water-boatmen are carnivorous in habit, being especially partial to a diet of the grubs of mosquitoes and other small flies.

The *Corixidae*, or Water-crickets as they are sometimes called, differ from the foregoing families in that the back of the head overlaps the first segment of the thorax (prothorax), and when viewed from above completely hides it. Various other characters also separate them and tend to detach them rather widely from the remainder of the group, and on this account they are, in fact, regarded as the most highly specialised of all the Water-bugs. They are nearly world-wide in distribution, small or very small in size, rather oval in shape, smooth or shining, and usually inconspicuously coloured. They swim rapidly, principally by means of the third pair of legs, and are mainly herbivorous. It is interesting to note that the males are able to produce a chirping sound, a faculty of rare development in this section of bugs, the noise being produced by one of two methods. In the one case the front legs are rubbed rapidly across the front of the face, in the other the edge of the fore-wing is drawn over a rasp-like organ situated on the back.

A British Water-cricket, *Corixa geoffroyi*.

Sub-order *Homoptera*

(*Cicadas, Leaf-hoppers, Aphids, Plant-lice, and Scale Insects*)

To this sub-order belong the Cicadas and Leaf-hoppers, the Aphids, Plant-lice, and Scale Insects. They can be distinguished from the true bugs, or Heteroptera, by having the head bent so far underneath that it touches the bases of the first pair of legs in such a way that the straight beak appears to spring from between them. The fore-wings are of uniform texture, and when at rest are sloped roof-wise over the back, not overlapping and flat. The first two or three joints of the antennae are generally thickened, the remainder forming a bristle. The latter character, however, applies more strictly to the second division of the sub-order, the Sternorrhyncha, in which the feet are composed of one or two joints only, and the beak always seems to arise from between the legs rather than obviously from the head, as it does in the Auchenorrhyncha, the first division. With the exception of one or two families, the Homoptera exhibit a most remarkable internal adaptation for the digestion of the plant-juices upon which they feed. The food-canal contains a perfect " by-pass " arrangement, which conducts the liquid portions of their food direct from the crop to the hind-gut, only the more solid matter passing through the mid-gut.

Division *AUCHENORRHYNCHA*

(*Cicadas, Leaf-hoppers, etc.*)

The families that belong to this division, in addition to the characters already mentioned, always have three segments to the feet. They include the Cicadas and the Leaf-hoppers.

Cicadas (*Cicadidae*) are stout-bodied insects with a short, broad head, bearing prominent lateral compound eyes, and three distinct simple eyes which are often brightly coloured and resemble tiny jewels set near the middle of the forehead. The thorax is short and very broad, and stretches back some distance behind to form a kind of shield. The wings are moderately large, extending well beyond the tip of the abdomen, glossy and transparent, but sometimes finely coloured and more or less opaque. Cicadas develop slowly, a long period being spent in the immature stages. One of the North American species, *Tibicina septemdecim*, is, indeed, popularly

The N. American " 17-year locust," *Tibicina septemdecim.*

The New Forest Cicada, *Cicadetta montana.*

known as the Seventeen-year locust, since that period is the interval between one generation and the next. Practically the whole of this time is spent below ground, for although the female Seventeen-year locust is at great pains to make incisions in the twigs of trees in which to place her eggs (thereby causing the twigs to die), the young grubs immediately they hatch drop straight to the ground and burrow into it. There they make themselves little underground chambers in which they live, feeding upon the sap of roots.

The song of the Cicada is so well known, especially in tropical countries, that it is hardly necessary to refer to it ; only the males sing, possibly, as Xenarchus hinted, in their happiness at having " voiceless wives." The seat of the highly complex apparatus that produces, in some species, such an astounding volume of sound, is at the base of the abdomen, just where it joins the thorax. Only one species, *Cicadetta montana*, occurs in England, in the New Forest district.

The Frog-hoppers (*Cercopidae*) are a large family of small bugs that must be familiar to most people. They are very commonly found on garden plants, and when disturbed leap considerable distances to get out of harm's way. Their larvae form the frothy masses known as " Cuckoo-spit," with which they surround themselves. On account of this habit the generic name *Aphrophora* (froth-bearing) has been given to one of the principal genera. There is another section, however, in which the larvae live

The Alder Frog-hopper,
Aphrophora alni.

entirely below ground, like the young Cicadas, but even so they line their chambers with a frothy liquid similar to that produced by members of the first section.

Very similar in habit to the Frog-hoppers are the Devil-hoppers (*Membracidae*), mostly rather small creatures inhabiting the tropics (only two species occur in England), in which the back of the thorax is produced in various ways, and extends a considerable distance over the abdomen. Other portions of the thorax as well are very frequently modified in all manner of extraordinary ways, so that one is seldom at fault in diagnosing any utterly bizarre bug as a Membracid. In other directions they are of interest in that, like the plant-lice, their " honey-dew " is much sought after by ants, which in not a few cases have learnt how to stroke them so that they will produce a tiny droplet of this much-prized sticky fluid. The Leaf-hoppers (*Jassidae*) again are very similar in habits. They are great leapers, very much like the Frog-hoppers, but usually more slender, and sometimes occur in incredible numbers upon grasslands and forage crops, doing considerable damage.

The Lantern-flies and their allies (*Fulgoridae, etc.*) comprise the remainder of the Auchenorrhynchous Bugs, and consist of a heterogeneous

Two views of a grotesque S. American Membracid, *Membracis expansa*, in which the thoracic " shield " entirely overshadows the rest of the insect.

crowd of creatures that have so far defied satisfactory classification. Most of the true Lantern-flies are quite large insects with ample wings, frequently very attractively coloured. In many species the head is greatly produced in front, and forms thus a lantern-like structure, frequently, but apparently groundlessly, alleged to be luminous, from which the family takes its name. In some cases this " lantern " is curiously marked, as in *Laternaria*, one of the largest South American kinds, in which the side view presents a picture of a crocodile's head faithful in every detail. The *Flatinae* are creatures with ample wings very suggestive of butterflies when in flight. Many are coloured in delicate shades of pink and green and have been observed to

A handsome bright red Jassid from Borneo, *Tettigoniella addita.*

An oriental Lantern-fly, *Fulgora spinolae.*

rest upon the stems of plants clustered together in such a manner that the group resembles a flower-spike, the coloured specimens at the bottom resembling the flowers, the green ones above them suggesting the unopened buds.

Division *STERNORRHYNCHA*

(*Leaf-suckers, White- or Snow-flies, Plant-lice, Scale Insects*)

The four families that make up this division have either two-jointed feet (Leaf-suckers, White- or Snow-flies, and Plant-lice), or one-jointed feet (Scale Insects). They are all minute insects living entirely upon plant-juices, many being restricted to a single " host-plant," and often highly specialised. The *Psyllidae*, or Leaf-suckers, sometimes called Jumping Plant-lice, resemble minute Cicadas in appearance. Generally they are green or brown in colour, and very active, combining flying with leaping, though not capable of prolonged flight. The rather long antennae should serve to distinguish them from the Leaf-hoppers which they otherwise rather closely resemble, both in habits

Psylla genistae
The Psyllid of the Broom.

and superficial appearance. They do a good deal of damage to crops in various parts of the world, the most notorious kinds being the Apple- and Pear-suckers (*Psylla mali* and *P. pyrivora*), and not a few species are productive of galls upon the plants they attack. A typical *Psylla* is illustrated on this page.

White- or Snow-flies, *Aleurodidae*, like the remaining families of this division, have no power of leaping. They are attractive little creatures, like minute snow-white moths, the common little *Asterochiton vaporarium* being familiar to most people as a general inhabitant of greenhouses, where it frequently does a certain amount of damage, especially to tomatoes. Its life-history is interesting in that it shows a transition from the normal Leaf-sucker kind towards the highly complex types of the Plant-lice and Scale Insects. Both sexes are winged. The eggs are laid with little supporting stalks, after the fashion of those of the Lace-wings, and the young, when they hatch, are very flattened oval creatures with their legs quite hidden beneath them. After the first moult the legs and antennae degenerate; after the second moult the wings begin to show; but the

The White-fly of greenhouses, *Asterochiton vaporarium.*

creature has yet to pass through a pupal stage, during which it looks not at all unlike a scale insect adorned with spines, before emerging in the adult winged form.

Plant-lice, Green-flies, or Aphids (*Aphididae*) as they are called, scarcely need any introduction. Apart from their very great economic importance (*e.g.* the *Phylloxera* of the vine), interest in them principally centres around their peculiar modes of development and their polymorphism—many species exhibit quite a number of types so different that until comparatively recently they were considered to be distinct species. Their alternation of habits is also of much interest. The phenomenon of virgin reproduction (parthenogenesis) is very commonly exhibited, and is associated with the occurrence of generations in which the sexes are very unequally represented (summer broods), the males being very rare or absent ; the females, too, although capable of adopting the normal practice of laying eggs, are more frequently viviparous, or vary from brood to brood. Structurally the main variations affect the wings and the mouth-parts, both of which may be either present or absent in members of the same brood ; the sexual forms are the more often without functional mouth-parts; wings appear principally to be the prerogative of the migratory forms and of the males.

It is a very common thing for a species to pass part of its life reproducing parthenogenetically upon one host-plant, and then to migrate by means of its winged forms to another kind of plant, there to repeat the process disguised as a different species ; one may even have the two different strains, derived from common parents, pursuing their courses side by side. A tremendous toll is taken of these creatures by their numerous enemies, and it would seem as if nature has specially conferred upon them these manifold methods of reproduction and their amazing fertility as a means of withstanding them. Under favourable conditions a complete life-cycle may be passed through in seven to eight days.

The Cochineal Insect, *Dactylopius coccus*. (1) Male ; (2) Female. (Enlarged.)

The Scale Insects (*Coccidae*), although, like the Aphids, they are in the main very serious pests, yet have a few redeeming features. They give us lac (from *Tachardia lacca*) and cochineal (from *Dactylopius coccus*) and other dyestuffs, and in some few cases wax in sufficient quantities to be of commercial value. These scarcely off-set, however, the damage done by such species as the San José Scale (*Aspidiotus perniciosus*) the Fluted-scale (*Icerya purchasi*), and the Mussel-scale (*Lepidosaphes ulmi*). The young larvae are very similar to those of the White-flies (*Aleurodidae*), but they very soon degenerate. After the second moult the females rarely move, the scale characteristic of the family forms over them, they lose eyes and legs (they never had wings), and remain fastened to their host-plants by their beaks. The males, on the other hand, after the second moult enter a pupal stage from which they emerge as winged insects, but devoid of mouth-parts and with only one pair of wings; their sole function is to fertilise the females so that these can deposit their eggs beneath the shelter of their scales.

Sub-class *ENDOPTERYGOTA*

Order NEUROPTERA

(*Lace-wings, Ant-lions, Alder-flies, Scorpion-flies, etc.*)

With the Neuroptera begins the series of orders classed together as the Endopterygota, on account of the fact that the wings develop internally.

The larval forms are generally specialised, and very different from the adults, the insects passing through a complete metamorphosis, including a resting pupal (chrysalis) stage.

The Neuroptera of Linnaeus consisted of all the transparent-winged, much-veined insects such as May-flies and Dragon-flies, as well as those dealt with here. Even as restricted, however, the order is far from homogeneous, and is best considered as covering a number of compact and rather isolated groups, evolved along three or four different lines, and composed, to a considerable extent, of relics of ancient and formerly more abundant orders. For example, the earliest known fossils in the whole of the Endopterygota are Scorpion-flies, which belong to this order. These were found in the Lower Permian, and it seems not improbable that from the same immediate group have been evolved the Caddis-flies (Trichoptera), the Butterflies and Moths, and also the Diptera.

All the families of Neuroptera agree in possessing biting jaws and, with few exceptions, four nearly similar wings with complicated veining— a very common feature of the fore-wings is the number of short nervures that run at right angles to the front edge upon which they end. The wings are held roof-wise over the back during rest, as in Caddis-flies and the smaller moths. The larvae are generally of the active, predacious type, variously modified; but some are so sluggish that they rely upon their prey falling into their jaws; others are aquatic; but all have a definite chrysalis stage. The important families differ so much from one another that it will be best to deal with each in turn.

The sole British representative of the *Sialidae, Sialis lutaria,* the Alder-fly.

The Alder-flies (*Sialidae*) are represented in England by a single species, *Sialis lutaria,* found not uncommonly along the banks of quiet streams. It is a dark, heavy, rather clumsy insect with brownish, black-veined wings, rather less than an inch in length; its antennae are long and thread-like. Its eggs, packed together like a number of minute gas-cylinders on end, are often to be seen on plants near the water's edge. Its larva is aquatic and actively predacious, breathing by means of jointed filaments that arise from the sides of its body; it has no spiracles. On attaining maturity it leaves the water and, burying itself in the soil, turns into a chrysalis which is sufficiently capable of movement to be able to reach the surface of the ground to allow of the emergence of the adult. The best-known representatives of the family in other parts of the world are the Old World genus *Neuromus* and the *Corydalis* flies of North and South America, which sometimes have a wing-expanse of as much as three or four inches, and, in the males, have jaws nearly half as long as the body.

In the Snake-flies (*Raphidiidae*), the first segment of the thorax is so prolonged that, together with the head, it nearly equals in length the rest of the thorax and the body. The four wings are almost exactly alike. The larvae are active and predacious, living principally in rotten wood. Only four species occur in England, and none outside the temperate regions of North America and the Old World. Few species are known.

The adult Ant-lions (*Myrmeleonidae*) are sometimes mistaken for Dragon-flies, which superficially they very closely resemble, though rather more delicate in build. Their short but prominent feelers will serve at once to distinguish them. Their popular name is based on the behaviour of the larvae, which have the habit of constructing little conical pits in sandy soils, at the bottom of which they lie buried with only their jaws protruding. Small insects that step on the sloping sides of the pit usually roll down, and are then seized and sucked dry by the Ant-lion, whose jaws are grooved so as to carry the liquid direct to the gullet. The flies themselves are mainly nocturnal,

One of the four British species of Snake-fly, *Rhaphidia notata*. Note the long first thoracic segment, the so-called "neck."

and occur throughout most of the tropical and temperate regions, though absent from England. The best-known genera are *Palpares*, which is mainly African, and the smaller, clearer-winged European *Myrmeleon*.

Closely allied to the Ant-lions are the Ascalaphus-flies (*Ascalaphidae*), more stoutly built insects, with quite long club-ended antennae. On the wing they look more like slow-flying, rather heavy moths than anything else, and are commonly to be met with in the South of Europe, and throughout most warm-temperate and tropical regions. The larva is a stout, rather flattened, slightly hairy creature, with prominent head and jaws, just like the Ant-lions, predacious, but not forming pits. The closely allied Nemopterid flies need passing mention, as they are most attractive little creatures. The fore-wings are more or less normal, but the hind-wings are produced in the form of long, narrow filaments, expanded at the extremity like the blade of an oar, the whole often exceeding two or three times the length of the fore-wings. The grubs, too, are remarkable. The body is like that of an Ant-lion, but the head is carried at the end of a long and extremely narrow, rigid neck, jointed at the thorax, and often longer than the whole of the creature's thorax and abdomen put together. They are found in the Mediterranean region,

A Spanish Ascalaphid, *Ascalaphus longicornis*. The wings are black and bright yellow with some transparent areas, presenting a very striking appearance when in flight.

Africa, India, and even Chile, and seem to be essentially desert creatures, the grubs having been found principally lying buried in the fine, dusty sand of caves, and similar situations, waiting for their prey.

The False Mantids (*Mantispidae*) are of interest in showing how homo-

A typical Nemopterid from Spain, *Nemoptera bipennis*.

A Nemopterid from Asia Minor, *Kirbyina sheppardi*, in which the filamentous hind-wings are much expanded towards the tips. These expansions are always twisted.

logous structures can be modified in totally unrelated groups of insects to precisely similar ends. Their fore-legs resemble so exactly those of the Praying Mantids (Order Orthoptera) that the earlier entomologists con-

An Indian False Mantid, *Mantispa senuhyalina*. The fore-legs are set in an unnatural attitude, but they show the grasping arrangement of spines very clearly.

sidered them to belong to the same family. The same modification also occurs elsewhere, as has been noted, for example, in the Water-scorpions (Order Hemiptera). The False Mantids are rare insects, but have a wide distribution. The larvae show an interesting tendency towards parasitism, or perhaps one should say a transition from general to specialised predaciousness. They hatch as normal active grubs, but do not feed; later they enter the nests of spiders, or wasps, and devour the developing young, themselves changing in form and assuming an appearance something like that of a cockchafer grub—a fat, sluggish creature with quite diminutive legs.

Silveira marmorata, from Mashonaland, is a member of the family

Osmylidae, represented in England by only a single species (*Osmylus chrysopa*). Closely related to these are the Lace-wings (*Chrysopidae* and *Hemerobiidae*), which are familiar insects with a world-wide distribution. The adults are frail insects, with very much veined, delicate wings and rather long antennae. Some species emit a rather pungent and unpleasant odour. They are valuable creatures, however, as their grubs consume enormous numbers of small soft-bodied insects such as Aphids, Scale Insects, Thrips, and small Leaf-hoppers, and their presence is to be encouraged. The grubs are usually greenish, mottled with brown, and they can be recognised

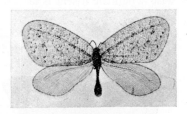

An E. African Osmylid, *Silveira marmorata.* Very moth-like in appearance.

by their prominent jaws and rather stout, but tapering bodies. The egg-laying habits of the female are probably unique. With each egg a sticky substance is first exuded, which is applied to the leaf and then drawn up as a tall thread ; it hardens in the process, and the egg is carried on the top of it.

With the minute *Coniopterygidae* the account of this order must close.

Osmylus chrysopa, the comparatively rare British representative of the *Osmylidae*. The specimen figured is from Newton Abbot.

Chrysopa vulgaris, the Lace-wing fly.

These are minute, fragile insects, rather like Aphids superficially, but, of course, having biting jaws. They differ from all other Neuroptera in having the hind-wings very much smaller than the other pair. Little is known of their habits, but they would appear in the main to be beneficial, as their food seems to consist principally of Scale Insects.

Order TRICHOPTERA

(*Caddis-flies*)

The Caddis-flies form a moderately well-defined order nearly related to the Lepidoptera (Butterflies and Moths), to some of which they bear a very close superficial resemblance. The surface of the wings, and of the insect's body, is covered with fine hairs. The fore-wings are long and narrow, very frequently shaded and mottled in grey and brown, and the hind-wings are much more ample, the portion nearest the body folding fan-wise when the insect is at rest. The feelers are long and thread-like, often

longer than the wings, and the mouth-parts imperfectly modified for sucking. In the neighbourhood of ponds and streams, in which the early stages are passed, Caddis-flies are often abundant. They fly fairly readily, making much more use of their legs when alighting, or taking wing, than do moths; in their resting attitude the fore-wings are sloped over the back roof-wise, with the long antennae curved back above them. From Stone-flies, which also resemble them superficially, they can readily be separated by their large haunches set close together.

Adult Caddis-fly.

The eggs, which are enclosed in a jelly-like substance, are dropped by the female into water. The young grubs are active, and rapidly construct about themselves the characteristic cases which distinguish them as Caddis-worms. The different families and genera, sometimes even the species, can be recognised by the particular fashion of construction of the case. This consists of a foundation of silk to which are attached fragments of sticks, stones, leaves, stalks, shells of small water-snails and similar objects. The majority of the larvae feed upon plant tissues; they are entirely beneficial, for if they are not engaged in this occupation they are probably serving as food for fishes. When full-grown the grub closes its case and turns into a chrysalis that is, however, capable of considerable movement; for when the time comes for the emergence of the winged insect, it bites through the case and either climbs or swims to the surface of the water. If the latter method of progression is normal for the species, the middle pair of legs is modified by expansion and a clothing of long hairs to form a pair of quite respectable oars.

A Caddis-fly larva that constructs a case entirely from small shells, within which it lives.

From the foregoing it will readily be remarked that there are several points of obviously close affinity between Caddis-flies and the less specialised Moths. In addition, the manner in which most of the nervures of the wings run longitudinally, and often branch, should be noticed; the hairy

Pl. 5.

TROPICAL INSECTS, I.

1. A South American Syntomid Moth (*Chrysocale ignita*).   2. An East African Hawk-moth (*Leucophlebia xanthopis*).
3. A Swallow-tail Butterfly from New Guinea (*Papilio weiskei*).   4. A Short-horned Grasshopper from Palestine.
5. A South American Bee (*Exaerete frontalis*).   6. The horned male of a Central African Bug (*Ceratocoris cephalicus*).   7. A tropical American Shield-bug (*Pharypia pulchella*).   8 and 9. Mimicry in South American Beetles: the Tortoise-beetle (*Mesomphalia auricoma*) mimicked by the Longicorn Beetle (*Ites plagiatus*).
10. A tropical American Dragonfly (*Lais pudica*).   11. A moth-like Flatid Bug from Kenya Colony (*Ityraea speciosa*).   12. A West African Shield-bug (*Glaucias guineensis*).   13. A Nymphalid Butterfly from the Amazon Valley (*Agrias sardanapalus*).   14 and 15. Seasonal variation in *Teracolus achine*, an African Pierid Butterfly; fig. 14 shows the dry, fig. 15 the wet season form.   Both in the resting attitude.

covering of the wings too—the scales of the butterflies are but modified hairs—is another feature of correspondence ; and the presence in some Caddis-flies of structures designed to secure the close co-operation of the wings on either side, like the " jugum " of Moths, together with the frequent occurrence of scent-organs, which, in their minute detail, closely resemble the analogous organs so common in the Lepidoptera, also serve strongly to emphasise the close relationship. Indeed, between the lowest Moths and the most specialised Caddis-flies there is, in the adult stage, only a very small gap indeed.

The order is represented throughout the world, about two hundred species occurring in Great Britain. Of the British species, however, only some of the larger kinds are at all commonly seen, most of the small species being so retiring and sluggish in habit as to escape notice.

Order LEPIDOPTERA

(*Butterflies and Moths*)

The attractive and frequently very beautiful insects that comprise this order are sufficiently familiar to need no lengthy introduction. Their usual division into two sub-orders, Rhopalocera, or Butterflies, and Heterocera, or Moths, although convenient and in very general use, is yet in reality more popular than scientific ; for the moths are themselves divisible into a number of sections each fully as important as the butterflies with which they are contrasted. A very good idea of the inequality of the two groups is afforded by a glance at a list of British butterflies and moths. This will show that whereas there are at most sixty-eight different kinds of butterfly to be found in the British Isles, the number of moths exceeds two thousand.

Pseudosphex polistes   *Sphecoma angustata*

Two Clear-winged moths that strongly resemble wasps.

Another familiar and in some ways better division of the order recognises two groups, one called the Macro-lepidoptera, *i.e.* the butterflies and the larger moths, the other the Micro-lepidoptera, or small moths ; but in this arrangement the implication of size is unfortunate, for it does not hold good throughout, although applying fairly well in the majority of cases.

Butterflies and moths are readily distinguished from all other orders of Insects by the innumerable, minute, flattened scales that clothe their wings and give rise to their characteristic coloured patterns. These scales exhibit great variety of shape and structural detail, and even furnish characters of value in the recognition of species ; they are, as already noted, in reality modified hairs. They are arranged upon the wing-surface like tiles upon a roof, and this, combined with the colouring matter they contain, gives them the appearance, when seen under a lower power of the microscope, of a mosaic. Sometimes the presence of pigment within the scale is combined with a special minute structural formation of the scale itself, the two features together having the effect of acting upon light rays so that only those of certain wave-lengths are reflected. In this manner the brilliant metallic blue colours of the *Morpho* butterflies, unfortunately so popular just now for ornamental jewellery purposes, appear to be produced.

A common British Geometrid moth, *Hybernia defoliaria.* (1) Male; (2) Wingless female.

As with all other large orders of Insects, so it is with the Lepidoptera ; one has only to mention one of their principal characters and any number of exceptions are at once brought to mind. There are many butterflies and moths that have no scales upon their wings, or the greater part of them, and there are also not a few moths that are wingless. The former are principally day-flying moths that mimic bees and wasps, or butterflies that inhabit dense and therefore dark tropical forests ; while the wingless forms may be the females of many Geometrid moths, or Bag-worms belonging to the family known as *Psychidae*. It is interesting to find that wing-transparency has been attained along at least two different lines of evolution. In the case of the two species of Bee-hawk moth occurring in the British Isles— both stout, hairy-bodied insects which look when in flight amazingly like bumble-bees—the wings, at the time of the emergence of the insect from the chrysalis, are almost entirely clothed in scales, but these are so loosely attached that at the first flight they are nearly all shaken off. The case

A male Psychid moth, *Clania ceronia*

of the forest-haunting butterflies is quite different, for in these the scales are actually modified and reduced to minute spicules, readily observable with a good lens. Reduction of the relative size of the wings is of frequent occurrence in the order. There is, for example, the beautiful New Guinea Bird-winged butterfly, *Ornithoptera paradisea*, black, green, and translucent gold in colour, in which the hind-wings in the male are not much more than one-third as large as the fore-wings ; and the South African Burnet-moth, *Semioptila fulveolans*, which is associated with termites, has almost thread-like hind-wings which are seven or eight times as long as the insect's body. But reduction to the point at which flight becomes impossible is rarer.

Several species exhibiting this modification occur in England, and are principally to be found during the winter months. *Cheimatobia brumata*, the Winter-moth, is one. The male is an inconspicuous, delicate insect, measuring about one inch across the wings, and grey in colour, that often flies to lights in houses during December and January. Its female has but the merest stumps of wings, barely discernible. It may be that her wings

Papilio chabrias
A small jet-black and golden Swallow-tail butterfly from the Amazon Valley.

Semioptila fulveolans
An African Zygaenid moth exhibiting a very unusual modification of the hind-wings.

have gone because they were a positive disadvantage to her in her business of egg-laying, on twigs and buds, during stormy winter weather. The female of the little brown Vapourer-moth, of which so much has latterly been heard in connection with Hyde Park, London, is a similar creature. She never moves from the cocoon from which she emerges and upon which she deposits her eggs. As a natural consequence of this enforced immobility one would expect to find that eventually the legs as well were lost ; this condition actually occurs in the genus *Epichnopteryx*. In all these abnormal cases, however, the creatures can still be recognised as lepidopterous, either by means of the hair-scales that cover the body, or by the proboscis.

The proboscis, when not in use, lies coiled up like a watch-spring against the lower surface of the head. It is a conspicuous feature of all butterflies, and of most moths, but in certain families of the latter, as in the May-flies, it is vestigial ; these, however, take no food in the perfect state, relying upon the reserves stored up when they were caterpillars. At first sight the proboscis appears to be a simple tube ; but closer examination will show that in reality it is composed of two tubes, which are so shaped that by interlocking they form a third. Through this third, central, false tube the food is drawn up by the sucking action of a kind of bladder within the head. The outer, real tubes contain the muscles that coil and uncoil the proboscis and also air-tubes and nerve fibres that run to the microscopic sensory papillae, which are situated at their extreme tips, and serve, presumably, as organs of taste.

Flanking the proboscis on either side, and serving to protect it in a measure, are the palpi, short, hairy, upturned structures the function of

The larva of a species of Psychid moth in its case. The female never leaves the case, even depositing her eggs within it.

The Convolvulus Hawk moth, *Herse convolvuli*, with the proboscis fully extended.

which, though no doubt sensory, is not understood. Some of the most lowly forms of moths have a second pair of these palpi, and some even have mandibles, a character so little in harmony with general conditions amongst the Lepidoptera that it has been suggested they should be relegated to a separate order. It is such species, however, that serve to emphasise the extraordinary homogeny of the whole Class Insecta. Troublesome as they are from the point of view of classification, they are of the greatest interest when the relationships of the different orders are considered.

Simple eyes (ocelli), though always present in caterpillars, are often absent in the perfect insects. The compound eyes, however, are always present. A brief account of these will be found in the introductory remarks. In butterflies they are obviously of considerable value, as demonstrated by the skill and ease with which these creatures can avoid obstacles and even the collector's net. It is difficult to estimate, however, the actual nature of the image perceived. There is no focussing mechanism. Each facet of the eye is so arranged that little more than the light rays from objects directly in front of it can reach the sense-nerves at its base; and so it would seem that the butterfly's picture of the outside world must be made up of light and dark dots arranged like the "half-tone" illustrations in a newspaper.

Although it has been argued that all insects are colour-blind, a moment's thought will suffice to show that this cannot be so. Why should the brilliant blue *Morpho* butterfly descend from the tree-tops it usually haunts to examine a dead and dried specimen of its own kind fastened to the ground? The appeal could be to no other sense but vision, and the shape of the specimen in this case could be of no importance. A certain amount of experimental evidence also exists to confute the supposition that butterflies cannot appreciate colours.

If a butterfly's antennae are removed it cannot control its flight; but the static function these organs are thereby shown to possess is in reality only a small part of their usefulness. A minute examination of them reveals the presence of innumerable microscopic pits, each containing a little projection, or bristles, that can only serve some sensory purpose. Some, no doubt, are olfactory; others, perhaps, are tactile, and it should be borne in mind that in either case these senses may be developed to a degree far surpassing anything with which we are familiar. A sense of touch may be so delicate as to appreciate changes of air pressure when approaching solid objects. Smell might be so keen that it would account for the proven fact that the males of some species, especially those with very bushy, feathery antennae, can detect the females at very considerable distances.

The collector's trick of "assembling" is based upon this last phenomenon. A freshly emerged female is exposed in some convenient position, and before long males will almost certainly reach it, although none may ever have been observed anywhere in the vicinity. Another fact well known to collectors provides evidence that moths are also capable of detecting sound vibrations. When they are massed together on a patch of "sugar" (made of stale beer, molasses, etc.), upon a tree trunk at night, they may decamp at once on the snapping of a twig or the rustling of leaves, although quite undisturbed by many much louder noises. Similarly, the firing of a rifle had no effect upon butterflies settled on an African veranda, though they took to flight at once when a light rustling noise was made. They must, therefore, have ears of some kind, capable, perhaps, of appreciating a certain range of vibrations differing from that which the human ear can detect. Indeed, a pair of organs suitable for the purpose exists on either side of the body, close to the thorax, in many moths, and probably awaits discovery in very many more. They can be seen fairly easily in the

Brimstone moth, a sulphur-coloured species about one inch across the wing, which is common in most gardens towards June.

The green, grey, and white butterflies of the S. American genus *Ageronia* are locally known as Click Butterflies, on account of the clicking noise they make when in flight. The specimen figured is *A. guatemalena* from Costa Rica.

Each consists essentially of a thin membrane in connection with the nervous system, and stretched within a cavity that opens to the air by means of a slit in the side of the body-wall.

In other orders of insects it will have been noticed that, as a rule, the possession of ears has been nearly always associated with the presence of organs capable of producing sound. This faculty, however, appears to be comparatively rare in Lepidoptera. The most familiar example is afforded by the Death's-head Hawk-moth, which produces a squeaking noise by forcing air through its proboscis. The male of the Camberwell Beauty (called in Germany the Mourning Cloak, on account of the white border to its otherwise black wings), is also said to make a faint sound by rubbing the veins of the fore-wing over one of those on the hind-wing, when circling round the female. The large, mottled, lichen-like *Ageronia* butterflies of tropical America make a very distinct clicking noise, when in flight, by means of a projection near the base of the fore-wing, which strikes against a double hook on the body.

A more elaborate apparatus, however, is found in the Australian Whistling-moth (*Hecatesia*), the sound being produced by means of a large, roughened, scaleless area on the fore-wing. Instances could be multiplied, but taken together they would still represent only a very small number

The Javan Skipper Butterfly, *Ismene oedipodea* (*Hesperiidae*). (1) Male ; (2) Female. The male exhibits very clearly a large patch of androconia on the fore-wings which is a common secondary sexual character in Lepidoptera.

relatively; no doubt their paucity is to some extent due to lack of observation. In most instances, it may be remarked, the capacity for producing sound is an adaptation peculiar to the male, as is, indeed, the case in most insects, and it is therefore to some extent justifiable to class it amongst the sexual characters that occur so abundantly throughout the order, especially in that sex.

Such sexual characters are usually termed " secondary," because, although not essential to the pairing of the sexes, they are yet ancillary to that process. Most commonly they take the form of pencils of hair (modified scales), associated with patches of scales adapted for the production of scent. A simple arrangement consists of a pencil that rests, normally, flat along the surface of the wing in contact with a patch of these glandular scales, and is capable of being erected and opened fan-wise, presumably for the purpose of diffusing the scent. Such an arrangement is very general amongst the tropical members of the family to which the " Meadow-brown " butterflies of this country belong (*Satyridae*). Much more widely spread amongst the butterflies is the far simpler arrangement in which the brushes are absent, and the scent-scales (androconia) are scattered all over the surface of the wing, or, as is frequently the case, gathered in dark patches along, or between, the veins.

In very many, probably the majority of the butterflies belonging to the *Pieridae* (the " Whites," *e.g.* the Large-white and the Cabbage-white), the former arrangement exists ; the latter prevails in many *Satyridae*, as in the Meadow-brown itself and in the genus *Argynnis* (*Nymphalidae*) to which the Fritillaries belong, and provides a ready means of determining the sexes. In the *Danaidae*, to which family belongs the Milkweed-butterfly, a rare visitor to these shores, the glandular scales in some species are contained in a perfect little pocket in the membrane of the hind-wing (the lowest black spot in the figure of *Danaida chrysippus*, p. 273), and it seems that the scent is diffused by the application of brushes situated in the extremity of the body. Frequently the whole shape of the wing may be altered for the purpose of accommodating these appliances, so that the outline of the male is quite unlike that of its female. Not infrequently the legs, and various parts of the body, may be the seat of these brushes and scent-glands, or even, though rarely, the antennae.

But common as are secondary sexual characters of this type in the Lepidoptera, they are not nearly so widespread as ordinary sexual dimorphism, in which the sexes appear in different forms. Strictly speaking, any creature in which the sexual attributes are carried by different individuals must be dimorphic, but in insects the term is used to denote an obvious outward difference of shape, colour, or pattern. As might be expected, the phenomenon is much more common in butterflies and day-flying moths than in night-flying species, natural selection having doubtlessly worked most, in the case of these species, upon those features that are of importance during the hours of daylight. To a less extent sexual dimorphism is quite well shown by several common British butterflies. The female of the

Small-white, for instance, has much larger black markings on the upper surfaces of its wings than the male ; and the female Orange-tip entirely lacks the large, bright orange patch on the fore-wing that characterises the male. Both these belong to the *Pieridae ;* in the *Lycaenidae*, to which family belong the " Blues," it is always the male that has the brilliant blue upper side, the female being as a general rule plain dark brown on this surface, though resembling the male exactly on the under surfaces of the wings.

The same applies, as a general principle, throughout the family, both in

A South American Erycinid Butterfly exhibiting considerable sexual dimorphism. (1) Male ; (2) Female.

A Pierid Butterfly from Ceram, *Delias stresemanni*, exhibits strong sexual colour differences. The male (1) is white above, the female (2) is blackish ; beneath both are alike.

the " Blues," which are mainly inhabitants of temperate regions, and in the " Hairstreaks," which produce so many brilliant metallic species in warmer and tropical regions. In fact, this brilliance of the male is the rule of sexual dimorphism in Lepidoptera. The largest known butterflies, the Bird-winged Swallow-tails of the East, of which some thirty or forty species are recognised, exhibit it as intensely as any other group. In this genus (*Ornithoptera*) the males, always smaller than the female, are strong-flying, handsome insects with a wing expanse of as much as seven or eight inches, whose dominant hue is black, contrasted, however, with large areas of glistening blue, green, yellow, or translucent gold. The females are always simply black and white. The beauty of the males is comparable with that of the Birds of Paradise that inhabit the same regions as these giant butterflies, and it has been argued that, similarly, it is due to Sexual Selection.

Such evidence as exists in support of this theory is far from convincing, however, if not directly contradictory, so that it seems more likely to have been developed for quite different reasons. Most of the pigments that form the basis of these brilliant colours have originated, it appears, indirectly from the waste products of digestion ; it has been suggested that as their utilisation for the adornment of the wings has not proved a positive disadvantage to the insects concerned, for in this case they would have come under the axe of Natural Selection, their development has proceeded unchecked, and has produced results which, at any rate to the human eye, are highly attractive. Somewhere between these two views the truth should be sought, but it is unlikely to be found until a very great deal more is known of the intimate relations of these insects to their environment, both animate and inanimate.

A typical example of the *Ithomiinae*, *Leucothyris aegle*, peculiar to the tropical forest regions of Central and South America. The wings, where not transparent, are black and red.

Sexual dimorphism, dimorphism that is confined to one sex only, as, for example, when the female of a species occurs in two different forms, and polymorphism, when either or both sexes occur in many different forms, are intimately connected with " mimicry," to which brief reference has been made already in the introductory remarks, and also in the accounts of several of the other orders of Insects. As the mimicry theory owed its inception, however, to a study of the Lepidoptera, it is perhaps justifiable to treat of it at greater length under this order than elsewhere.

The celebrated naturalists, H. W. Bates and A. R. Wallace, share between them the credit for the conception of the idea upon which the theory of mimicry is based. The former made his observations in the Amazon Valley, and the latter in the East Indies ; but it fell to the lot of Bates to publish the theory. In the Amazon Valley, and throughout tropical America, are to be found large numbers of butterflies in which both the wings and the body are unusually long and narrow. They belong to the sub-family *Ithomiinae*. In colour they are mainly black and brown, or else they have transparent wings marked round the edges with black, red, and silver. In habit they are very lazy ; they often congregate in large numbers upon low-growing foliage, and show little inclination to take alarm. They appear to be very little sought after by insect-eating birds and lizards ;

K

in fact, they really seem to lead charmed lives, immune from attack, although surrounded by a host of potential enemies.

Amongst these individuals, and resembling them to the point of deception, Bates discovered, rarely, odd specimens of other butterflies belonging to entirely different families. Thus there were some belonging to the *Pieridae* (the Whites), some belonging to the *Erycinidae* (a family closely related to the *Lycaenidae*), some very nearly related to the Fritillaries (*Eresia*, etc.), and not a few belonging to various families of Moths. All these infrequent specimens had departed entirely in appearance, both in colour and pattern, and often also in shape, from the normal members of the families to which their structure showed them to belong. It was as if a duck had come to look so like a seagull that the difference between them could only be ascertained by a study of anatomy. The explanation he offered was that these rare " mimics," by getting themselves mistaken for their careless and abundant " models," enjoyed the same benefits, and that the immunity of the models was due to some actual distastefulness they possessed.

This mimicry of a distasteful species by an edible one has since become known as " Batesian mimicry." Its complement is found in what is known as " Müllerian mimicry," in which two or more distasteful species come to resemble one another, so that the benefits each formerly held are spread more evenly over both, to their consequent benefit. If two dissimilar species vary so that eventually they look like one species, both being distasteful, the chances of any individual of either species being eaten by insectivorous birds, or other enemies, must be approximately halved. In either kind of mimicry the approach in pattern and colour of one species towards another is, of course, not in any sense conscious, but to be attributed entirely to the action of Natural Selection, which would operate by permitting the survival of those individuals which showed the greatest variation, in the matter of shape and coloration, towards the " model," whilst killing off those showing least or no tendency in this beneficial direction.

The theory of mimicry has in the past been much scoffed at, and even to-day there are doubters. But thanks to the patient observations of innumerable naturalists in all parts of the world, the evidence in support of it is now overwhelming. Besides, what other means are there of explaining those numberless resemblances that will deceive at first even the trained eye of the skilled entomologist, both in the field and in the Museum? Critics are apt to forget that Natural Selection works upon a system of averages. Because a bird has been seen to devour one individual of a protected species (a thing that is bound to happen more or less frequently), the whole theory does not fall to the ground. Under the stimulus of hunger birds, admittedly, will eat nauseous insects, but experience has shown that they will not touch them save under dire necessity. Butterflies have inhabited the earth longer than Man ; they have passed through millions of generations, each one of which has been perhaps the gainer to some infinitesimal amount through the action of Natural Selection. The cumulative effect of such action throughout immense periods of time is not disproportionate to the perfection of adaptation exhibited by mimetic butterflies.

No account of mimicry would be complete without some reference, however brief, to the African Swallow-tail butterfly, *Papilio dardanus*, which in many ways is the most remarkable butterfly in the world. The male of this species measures about five inches across the wings, and is plain yellow with a wide black border, particularly on the hind-wings, which have the usual short tails. One may assume for the sake of brevity that it is constant in pattern throughout Africa south of the Sahara, and in Madagascar. It is not distasteful. Three of the commonest African butterflies, all of them markedly and demonstrably distasteful, none of them having tails, are *Danaida chrysippus*, a brown species with a few black markings, *Amauris niavius*, a white species with wide black borders, and *Amauris echeria*, a black species spotted with yellow. All are rather smaller than the male *dardanus*. Throughout the areas occupied by these distasteful " models " the females of *dardanus* occur in forms exactly mimicking each. The tails have gone and also the yellow colour of the male ; instead are reproductions, faithful in every detail of colour and pattern, of these other butterflies belonging to a widely separated family.

An African mimetic butterfly, *Pseudacraea poggei* (lower figure), and its model, *Danaida chrysippus*. The latter species is exceedingly common and distasteful to insectivorous animals ; the former is rare, local, and belongs to a different family.

In most parts of Africa this polymorphism is now so fixed that intermediates are unknown, but in Kenya and Abyssinia they still occur, and help to show us the lines along which evolution has taken place. Thus in Kenya females sometimes appear that have a considerable amount of the yellow pigment of the male ; and in South-West Abyssinia they are met with, very rarely, still in mimetic garb, but having tails like those of the males. In other parts of Abyssinia again, and in Madagascar, the female is always yellow, and tailed. One can therefore, with justification, assume that the ancestral female was like the male, and that the intense competitive life upon the African continent has resulted in the production of the mimetic females by a process that in Kenya is still going on actually before our eyes. This single butterfly thus presents us with all the stages of a complete chapter in evolution. A whole volume could be written upon this single species ; indeed, one has already been published upon the mimetic butterflies of the continent of Africa.

The type of mimicry exhibited by *Papilio dardanus* is, of course, Batesian. A very good example of the Müllerian type, in which all the species associated together are distasteful, is afforded by butterflies belonging to the very group (*Ithomiinae*) that caused Bates to put forward his theory. This group is composed of a number of genera apparently possessing varying degrees of distastefulness. But although the genera are fairly numerous, the different types of colour-markings are comparatively restricted, and recur over and over again throughout the genera. The species of similar pattern, though structurally dissimilar (they belong to different genera) apparently associate together, the benefits accruing to the one pattern being shared by the numerous species wearing it. Into this same association also enter a certain number of other butterflies belonging to another group, the *Heliconiinae*, which also enjoy a degree of immunity from attack by insectivorous animals. But, fascinating as is the subject of mimicry, we must leave it in order to deal with others no less attractive.

Seasonal variation is well shown by the undersides of these male Bath Whites. All came from Mesopotamia. The top figure shows the winter form, the bottom figure the extreme summer, and the middle figure an intermediate form.

Reference has already been made to the sexual dimorphism exhibited by our common Small-, or Cabbage-white butterfly. There is another kind of dimorphism exhibited by this same species that is in some ways even more remarkable. The butterfly first appears on the wing about May. The dark markings of the wings characteristic of the species, in individuals of this brood, are greyish and rather small ; the under side of the hind-wing is very dusky green. The brood that results about July, from eggs laid by females of this spring brood, is composed of individuals that are usually larger and have all the dark markings larger, and blacker, and the under surface of the hind-wing rather less grey. This kind of dimorphism, being related to the time of year at which the forms appear, is known as "seasonal dimorphism," and is of very wide occurrence in butterflies. One might almost say that, at any rate in the temperate regions, a majority of the butterflies that are normally double-brooded show some constant, though often very slight, differences between the two broods.

In England the Holly Blue, so common in London gardens in early spring, the Green-veined White, the angular Comma-butterfly, and several other species, including some of the Thorn-moths of the genus *Selenia* (*Geometridae*), exhibit this phenomenon very noticeably. Amongst continental species the best-known case is that of *Araschnia levana*, a little Nymphalid butterfly closely related to the Fritillaries. In this species the upper surface of the wings, in the spring form, is brown, marked with numerous irregular black spots; in its summer form the upper side is

entirely black, except for a moderately broad, clear white band that traverses both wings. So different in appearance are these two generations that, although both were known to Linnaeus—the father of systematic zoology—in 1758, it was not until 130 years later that their proper relationship was established.

A common British Thorn-moth, *Ennomos autumnaria*.

Very rarely intermediate varieties occur, always amongst individuals of the summer brood, which indicates that this brood is less stable than the other, and, therefore, it may be inferred, of more recent development. As this also applies to the other seasonally dimorphic species of the temperate zone, and, moreover, the greater variability of the summer brood has been confirmed in some cases in the course of "temperature experiments," there seems no reason to doubt the conclusion. Several species have been experimentally exposed, at different stages of their development, to severe and often violent changes of temperature; and as a consequence it has been found possible to produce artificially from, for the sake of example, pupae that should produce the summer form, butterflies of the spring form, and *vice versa*. Curiously, the critical period, which usually occurs during the last stages of larval life, or at the moment of pupation, often varies, as between the two broods of a single species, as much as between different species. Inasmuch as these two seasonal forms seem to be related to spring (cold) and summer (hot) weather respectively, they are sometimes spoken of as temperature forms, but the term is not ideal, as it is also used to denote a much rarer type of variation that can be produced in many species artificially (as in the Painted Lady, the Red Admiral, and the Small Tortoiseshell), but occurs so rarely in nature as to be classed as aberrant.

In tropical countries, where the difference of the seasons, though often very strongly marked, is less a matter of temperature than of humidity, corresponding differences between the broods frequently occur. In these cases the different types are spoken of as " wet season " and " dry season " forms. A connection between the two groups is quite easy to demonstrate, and shows that the wet-season forms correspond with the summer broods, the " dry " forms with those of the winter. The phenomenon is of very wide occurrence, and, as would be expected, has its most remarkable exponents in those countries showing the most pronounced seasonal changes. Amongst the species of the genus *Mycalesis*, which might almost be termed Meadow-butterflies, for they are the tropical representatives of our Meadow-browns, the under surfaces of the wings in the wet season are boldly marked with pale lines and numerous prominent eye-spots. In the dry-season individuals the eye-spots are reduced to pin points, and the whole of the background generally assumes a " dead-leaf "-like appearance.

Two seasonal varieties of the African Nymphalid butterfly, *Charaxes zoolina*. The upper figure shows the dry-season form, light brown with black markings. The lower specimen is pale greenish with black borders, and occurs in the wet season.

Some of the African representatives of the genus go a step farther, in that the whole coloration changes from drab grey-brown to pale-buffish. Indeed, it is in Africa, where extremes of dry heat and wet are common, that the most remarkable seasonally dimorphic butterflies are found. The most striking example of all is the Nymphalid butterfly, *Precis sesamus*. The wet-season broods of this are bright red, with black borders and a few black spots ; the upper and under surfaces of the wings are both alike. The dry-season broods, however, are deep blue on the upper surfaces, heavily spotted with black, and have entirely different under sides of a very perfect, dark, " dead-leaf " type, quite unlike the upper side. Other species of the same genus show comparable differences, often coupled with a great development of angularity of the wings in the dry-season broods.

What is the explanation of these remarkable divergences ? We have seen that in the species inhabiting the temperate zone the spring forms are presumably the ancestral forms. In the tropical species it would appear that summer (wet season) forms are ancestral. They show greater similarities, as between the species, and less variability than the others ; and, moreover, they show none of the beautiful protective dead-leaf characters of the dry-season forms. They occur when life is most abundant (during the rains), so abundant, in fact, that there is little need for them to disguise themselves, whereas their offspring fly when everything is dried up and parched, and such insect-eating animals as are about must be hard put to it to find food enough for their needs. The dry-season forms, then, must be much more persecuted than the wet. In this lies the key to the situation. Natural Selection has secured the continued existence of the species during the dry season by giving it, for that period, protection by means of a cryptic, seasonal disguise, which renders it almost invisible when at rest, and contrasts strongly with the colours it shows when fly-ing, thereby heightening the illusion.

What factors operate the mechanism that Natural Selection has given these butterflies, at present, we do not know. The con- dition of the food of the caterpillars—succulent and fresh in the wet season, old and tough in the dry—must have something to do with it ; indeed, it is claimed by some that this is the decid-

The African members of the genus *Precis* are noted for their seasonal dimorphism. On the left is shown the red and black underside of the wet-season form of *P. antilope*, and on the right the leaf-like mottled pattern it assumes in the dry season.

ing factor ; but it has never yet been put to the test. General conditions of temperature and humidity, during critical phases of development, no doubt also play no inconsiderable part.

In certain excessively hot, arid regions, such as parts of Northern Africa, Syria, Arabia, and Southern Persia, Lepidoptera have adopted yet another device for surviving the intense heat of the summer. It has been remarked that a number of species which fly in the spring are still to be seen on the wing in the autumn, although not in evidence during the summer months. They appear, therefore, to pass through these months in a dor-mant condition, or to "aestivate," as it is called. The phenomenon is also sometimes referred to as the "summer pause." Of a like nature is the much more common habit of "hibernation," by means of which insects inhabiting the temperate zones survive the rigours of winter. Many of these habitually have to withstand temperatures that entail their being frozen "solid" for long or short spells. The egg and chrysalis stages are the least active periods of life in any butterfly and moth, and, therefore, one would naturally assume them to be those most suitable in which to hibernate. Indeed, it is in one of those stages, principally as chrysalis, that the winter is actually passed by the vast majority of species.

There are, however, numbers that hibernate as caterpillars, and not a few that do so in the adult condition. In the former category fall very many of the grass-feeding species, but also some of the stick-like looper caterpillars of the Geometer moths. An interesting development is shown by the Silver-washed Fritillary Butterfly, whose caterpillar emerges from the egg in late summer, nibbles a little of the shell it has just left, and then promptly lies up until next spring—hardly a square enough meal, one would imagine, to last it six months! Of the species that hibernate as butterflies the most familiar examples are the Tortoiseshells, the Peacock, and the Brimstone, which may at times be found asleep in thick ivy, barns and outhouses and such-like places. Hibernation is marked by a torpid condition during which no energy is expended in movement, no food is taken, and all vital functions are reduced to a minimum.

The dead-leaf-like under-side markings to which allusion has already been made are not, of course, by any means confined to the dry-season forms of the seasonally dimorphic species. Butterflies, as contrasted with Moths, normally rest with their wings folded together over the back, so that only the under surfaces are visible. And as they almost always rest amongst foliage it is not surprising that very many of them exhibit patterns on their under sides that harmonise with their surroundings ; it is more surprising, perhaps, that any do not. It is, however, not at all improbable that many of the latter kinds are, in fact, protected in some measure by their under-side patterns, not perhaps by direct resemblance to foliage, but by an effect obtained by " camouflage " methods, such as the breaking of outline by combinations of light and dark markings. Others, perhaps, secure it by means of patterns suggestive of obnoxious creatures : a large eye-spot, beak-like markings, or even " snake-head " patterns such as adorn the tips of the wings of the Wild Silk-moths (*Saturniidae*).

Of the dead-leaf type of marking the best example, and one that is displayed in many Museums, is afforded by the Indian Leaf-butterfly (*Kallima inachis*). The upper surface of the wings of this insect is orange and bright blue, so that it is very conspicuous when in flight. The moment it settles, however, nothing is visible but an under side that is veined and mottled like a dead leaf, and even has areas suggestive of mould, and tiny transparent patches suggestive of the work of leaf-puncturing insects. Similar cases occur in all tropical countries ; but there are many instances of the principle to be seen even at our own back-doors, as, for example, in the Brimstone and Comma butterflies.

Moths, as a rule, rest with the upper surface of the fore-wing alone exposed, or if they spread out the wings at all when at rest (*Geometridae*, etc.), only part of the hind-wing is visible. The under surfaces are very rarely exposed at all, and in consequence show very little pattern. The " dead-leaf " appearance, therefore, when it occurs in moths is on the upper side of the wings. It is particularly evident in species, such as the Poplar and Lime-hawk Moths, and the Lappet-moth, which habitually rest in moderately exposed positions amongst foliage, or on palings and such-like places. The pattern of most moths that rest upon exposed surfaces during the hours of daylight is, however, specialised more in the direction of a general resemblance to the surfaces, such as tree trunks, or rocks, upon which they rest, and also towards breaking the outline of the wings.

Catacola sponsa

When at rest the red and black hind-wings are covered by the fore-wings, rendering the insect very inconspicuous against the trunk of a tree or similar support.

As a general rule it may safely be said that, except perhaps in some of the cases of species that belong to mimetic associations, or are blatantly distasteful, those portions of both butterflies and moths that are exposed when the insects are at rest are definitely procryptic, that is to say, designed to hide their bearers by means of a protective resemblance to inanimate objects included in their environment.

Thecla ambrax

A butterfly from British Guiana. Note the short tails and the red eye-spots. These are considered to give the impression of a false head and so to mislead enemies. Upperside metallic blue, underside grey.

Procryptic pattern and coloration are only of importance during rest ; when active, butterflies and moths are more able to take care of themselves ; but it is a very significant fact that in many species the females only are mimetic, which shows that this sex must derive a good deal of benefit from looking like some distasteful butterfly, especially, no doubt, when engaged in egg-laying operations in situations which must necessarily often be in full view of insectivorous birds.

It has already been remarked that certain moths have mouth-parts so vestigial that they can take no food. This is, however, a comparatively rare condition. In the majority of cases the principal activity of a butterfly, or a moth, apart from reproductive functions, consists of feeding. Although some species have developed such depraved tastes as to have a preference for rotten fruit, decaying animal matter, droppings, perspiration, etc., the

K 2

real food is undoubtedly the nectar provided by flowers. The nectar, however, is not provided for nothing. In reaching down to it the head of the butterfly, or moth, is almost certain to come into contact with the anthers of the flower, and to receive pollen from them; it is also almost certain to touch the stigma of another flower, and the probability is that some of the pollen will be transferred to the stigma and result in the fertilisation of the ovules. It is, indeed, safe to say that without the aid of the Lepidoptera, and, of course, of the Bees as well, the cross-fertilisation of very many flowers would never be achieved.

Much has been written upon this subject, but we must content ourselves

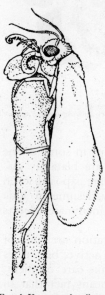

Female Yucca-moth collecting pollen from anther of Yucca. Note the remarkable development of the mouth-parts.

with brief references to one or two of the very interesting cases in which the association between plant and insect has reached such a pass that the plant could hardly dispense with the insect. Orchids are of especial interest in the adaptations they show for utilising the services of moths; so close, indeed, is this association that it enabled A. R. Wallace to foretell that in Madagascar there must exist a moth with a proboscis fully twelve inches in length, simply because only such a moth could reach the nectar of *Angraecum sesquipedale*, one of the native orchids. No such moth was known at the time, but twelve years later Wallace's opinion was confirmed by the discovery of a large hawk-moth that fulfilled the requirements and was duly, and appropriately, named *praedicta*.

More remarkable than this, however, is the association between the American Yucca-plants and the tiny, white-winged moths of the genus *Pronuba*. In these moths the portions of the mouth-parts known as the palps of the second maxillae, which are usually absent in Lepidoptera, are strongly developed in the female, and furnished with a pair of long hairy processes. By means of these the female deliberately collects pollen from the anthers of the Yucca, shaping it into the form of a ball, which she carries against the under surface of the head. She then proceeds to the stigma, upon which she deposits her ball of pollen, thus ensuring pollination. Next, she brings into operation her piercing ovipositor—a most abnormal structure amongst moths—boring a way through the tissue of the pistil to reach the neighbourhood of the ovary, and laying her eggs close to the ovules. In course of time the eggs hatch, and the young caterpillars feed upon the growing seeds that would never have developed but for the action of their parent. More remarkable, perhaps, than the actions of the moth is the instinct that prompts her, for she derives no benefit from them, being quite incapable of taking any food, either pollen or nectar, in search of which, no doubt, her remote ancestors originally acquired the Yucca-visiting habit.

True social organisations such as exist amongst the Bees, Ants, and Termites are unknown in Lepidoptera, and even the association together of any number of individuals in the adult state is rare. The migratory swarms of butterflies that are of comparatively frequent occurrence in various parts of the world afford one instance of an association; the swarms that gather at damp places to drink offer another; and the " resting groups " a third. The last-mentioned type seems to be confined almost entirely to those species that appear to be especially protected, such as the red-and-black Acraeas of Africa, and the *Heliconius* and Ithomiine butterflies of tropical America, to which reference has already been made. The Acraeas and Ithomiines are habitually more or less gregarious at all times, but the *Heliconius* butterflies seem to congregate on branches and twigs principally when going to rest for the night, the different species and varieties each forming their own clusters.

A similar habit, though with a different object, is exhibited by the migratory Monarch butterfly of North America. In the autumn, at the end of their southward flight, enormous numbers of this species sometimes mass together upon isolated trees, upon which they remain throughout the winter. The Monarch is, *par excellence*, the most confirmed wanderer of all Lepidoptera. Some forty years ago it suddenly spread over a wide area in the South Pacific, colonising a number of islands; occasionally it reaches Europe; annually in America it spreads northwards from the Gulf

Catopsilia trite

A Pierid butterfly from British Guiana. The genus *Catopsilia* in the broad sense is of world-wide distribution and contains many migratory species. Pale yellow.

States as far as Canada. The Painted Lady, which is equally persistent as a migrant, and is now almost cosmopolitan, also flies annually northwards across Europe from North Africa, usually accompanied by the Silver-Y-moth (*Plusia gamma*), the Pyralid moth, *Nomophila noctuella*, and others; but in its case no regular southward flight in the autumn has yet been observed.

In Ceylon there also occur regular migratory flights of certain species of *Pieridae* (" Whites "), usually accompanied by individuals of many other species of butterflies and of moths. The same thing occurs frequently also in Central America, and in parts of Africa. In fact, it has been shown that quite a large number of species have this migratory instinct, which is manifested either in regular annual flights in more or less definite directions, or may occur quite sporadically; but so far the factors that govern it have not been recognised. It appears probable, however, that shortage of food or water in the area whence the flights originate exerts an influence of some importance. Apart from associations of this kind there also exist those connected with sex. As a rule, quite a limited number of individuals is involved in these, but there are a few species amongst the Micro-lepidoptera that indulge in aerial dances, similar to those of the gnats. Caterpillars are much more prone to gregariousness than are the perfect insects to which they give rise.

All the interesting modifications and adaptations of butterflies and moths, to which far too brief reference has been made in the foregoing pages, serve but one great purpose : the preservation and reproduction of the species. The structure, the colours and patterns, the senses, the migrations, the variations, seasonal and mimetic, the devices for ensuring mating and so on, have all arisen in the struggle for existence. How, then, is the chain continued ?

The first obvious product of the union of the sexes is the egg. This brings to mind the extraordinarily common fallacy concerning " caterpillar's eggs." Caterpillars never lay eggs ; the adult females alone do that, and extraordinarily beautiful, too, are the eggs they lay, although it requires a powerful lens to make this obvious. They are of all shapes ; but their beauty, when seen under the microscope, lies in the delicate tracery, the sculpture and design of their shells, so reminiscent of diatoms, radiolaria, pollen grains, and other microscopic bodies. They are laid, as a rule, upon the leaves of the plant upon which the tiny caterpillar, which emerges from them, is to feed. That the female should be able to locate, amongst so much vegetation, the one kind of plant that is suitable for its offspring— for many caterpillars will die of starvation if their proper food-plant is not available—is often regarded as a very remarkable phenomenon, and so, indeed, it is ; but yet it should be remembered that the butterfly really is only the final stage of a caterpillar that itself fed upon that same kind of plant. Caterpillar and butterfly are not two individuals, but one and the same. Recognition of its own food should, therefore, not be so very difficult ; the insect still has the same brain, the same nervous system, the same, and more, senses.

After breaking its shell and crawling out, the first act of the young caterpillar, very commonly, is to consume the remains of its former home. It then settles down to its one great business in life—eating. It may live two or three weeks only, as a caterpillar, or it may drag out a period of two or three years, as do those that bore in wood ; but throughout the greater part of that time it indeed lives to eat, busily storing up the materials that are to last it throughout its chrysalis stage and also provide the wings that adorn it when it reaches maturity.

The lepidopterous larva, or caterpillar as it is usually called, is not likely to be confused with the corresponding stage of any other group of insects except, perhaps, the larvae of some of the Saw-flies—these always have more legs, however, and usually curl the tip of the body downwards beneath them. The first three segments of the body, immediately behind the head, bear the hard, chitinous " true legs," which correspond with those of the adult ; they are jointed, tapering, and provided with claws. The remaining legs are fleshy, and have the soles of the feet provided with a circlet, often incomplete, of minute hooks that almost automatically grip any surface to which they are applied. These legs vary in number according to the family to which the species belong. As a rule there are five pairs, one pair being at the extremity of the body, the other four pairs upon successive segments in an intermediate position. In the familiar " looper " cater-pillars of the Geometrid family, only the last two pairs remain, which necessitates progression in the manner implied by their name.

Caterpillars are exposed to far more dangers than are the perfect insects to which they give rise. Not only have they to escape the notice of insectivorous birds, which regard them as very great delicacies, but also they must evade those far more persistent creatures of their own class, the parasitic flies and the Ichneumon wasps. Hence we find that their protective devices are even more elaborate than those of the perfect insects. They must also have been evolved at a much earlier stage. For, whereas special adaptations of various kinds are scattered throughout the species in the adult stage, in the larvae fixed, protective devices are very often characteristic of whole families. For example, all the caterpillars of the *Geometridae* are loopers, and gain concealment by their resemblance to twigs ; most *Noctuidae* have larvae that live in conceal-ment about the surface of the ground during the day, and only come out to feed during the night ; all the species of one large section of the " Skippers " (*Hesperiidae*) live within folded leaves spun together with silk ; and

The stick-like caterpillar of the Oak Beauty moth (*Geometridae*).

the same applies to most *Pyralidae*, and to nearly all the wriggling little larvae of the *Tortricidae*. The last two families belong to the Micro-lepidoptera, which division is otherwise mainly composed of species the larvae of which actually live entirely within the tissues of leaves, tunnelling through the softer parts and forming characteristic " mines."

These general habits have, however, been so long established that there has been time for secondary modifications to arise. One of the most familiar and conspicuous caterpillars is the black, white, and orange " looper " of the Magpie-moth. It feeds openly upon euonymus, in almost any garden, disdaining the cryptic colours and habits of its relatives. Unless almost starving, birds absolutely refuse to eat it. It provides an excellent illustration of the " Warning Colour " theory advanced by A. R. Wallace, namely, that, such creatures being obviously distasteful to their natural enemies, it is an advantage to them to advertise the fact, and so save the lives that would otherwise be lost in the process of educating their enemies. The phenomenon is of widespread occurrence in many different families.

Peronea cristana (Tortricidae)

Sometimes called the Button-moth, on account of the prominent tuft of scales on the fore-wing.

Another good example is afforded by the conspicuous black-and-yellow-banded caterpillar of the Cinnabar-moth, which feeds in most obvious fashion upon the Ragwort. Distastefulness of this kind should not be confused, however, with that which some caterpillars, normally not unpalatable, acquire through feeding upon poisonous plants—a rare event, but one that has been observed on a number of occasions.

Pure protective resemblance to harmless, inanimate objects is frequently pushed to extraordinary lengths; lichens, thorns, shrivelled and twisted leaves, flowers—the caterpillars of one of the South American *Morpho* butterfly, when resting together in groups, exactly resemble an orchid—even bird-droppings and the like are all faithfully simulated. Strangest of all devices, perhaps, is that adopted by the larvae of a little South American Pyralid-moth. A number of them will live together upon the back of a single Hawk-moth caterpillar, and by resting singly in a transverse

Notocalia roborana

The wriggling larva of which is common on roses, the leaves of which it spins together.

The Oak Beauty moth, *Pachys prodromaria*.

position appear, at the first glance, to be nothing more than the connecting membrane, upon which they lie, between the segments of their host !

But the process goes a step farther, and by suggesting some creature other than a caterpillar, some living animal with a bad reputation, for example, may confer further benefits. The caterpillar of the common Puss-moth, when annoyed, assumes at once an aspect so terrifying that it has been known to scare even human beings ; the Lobster-moth caterpillar also, with its grotesque attitude, waving legs, and almost snake-like tail-end, is a most unpleasant-looking object. Many Hawk-moth cater-pillars have a device in the shape of an eye-spot on the side near the head ; and when disturbed assume an attitude that produces quite the appearance of a snake's head. And, in case these attitudes alone should prove in-efficient, many caterpillars can call formic acid to their aid, ejecting it at their enemies from a small pore just between the first pair of legs. Other protective devices are found in the irritating or "urticating" hairs with which many of the furry kinds are provided. Amongst British species these are most conspicuous in the caterpillars of the Gold-tail moth. When brought into contact with the skin they prove very irritating, and may produce a kind of rash, which is never so serious, however, as that caused by very many tropical species.

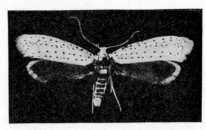

The small Ermine-moth, *Hyponomeuta padi.*

Far commoner than all these expedients, however, is the simple process adopted by most caterpillars of retiring altogether from the public gaze. Most successful in this direction are the wood-borers, and the numerous species that bore in the stems and roots of plants. Another practice that has a good many adherents is the gregarious one of forming webs or nests. Of the former a good example is furnished by *Hyponomeuta*, whose little grey and black grubs form the familiar webs on apple trees, and upon evergreen garden shrubs. Not a few species, such as the Processionary Moth of Southern Europe, and the large white African *Anaphe* moth, form quite good nests, and in Mexico there is even a species of butterfly, a Pierid (*Eucheira socialis*), that makes an amazingly tough one.

Epipyrops micromorpha
The larva of which feeds upon the waxy secretion that en-velops certain Fulgorid bugs.

The nature of the food of the larvae is not so varied in the Lepidoptera as it is in many other orders. Plants and plant refuse form the staple diet, but there are a few interesting modifications. Shortage of food will turn many species into cannibals, but a settled carnivorous habit is ex-hibited by only a few, notably certain *Lycaenidae* that feed upon green-fly, scale insects, etc. An extreme case of adaptation is shown by the *Nepenthophilus* caterpillar which inhabits the pitchers of the Pitcher plants in order to feed upon the insects that fall into it. Rubbish feeders, such as Clothes-moths, are numerous, but *Zophodiopsis* specialises upon the rubbish in the nests of the *Anaphe* moths, where alone it is to be found. *Bradypodicola* lives entirely upon the sloth, both as larva and imago. Bees' nests are not free from caterpillars, for *Galleria* larvae feed upon their wax ; but when one considers ants' nests a host of species is brought to mind that are associated, in some way or other, with ants, and are therefore termed " myrmecophiles."

Very many of the *Lycaenidae*, or " Blue "-butterflies, have upon their backs tiny pores that exude a sticky fluid much sought after by ants. This substance seems indeed to be the basis of the association between ants and caterpillars. Many species are constantly attended and " milked " by ants throughout their development. Not content with that, however, ants habitually introduce certain kinds of caterpillars into their nests. No doubt in the first instance this was a very convenient method of ensuring a constant and handy supply of the " milk," but it has often had consequences most unfortunate for the ants, for no sooner is the caterpillar settled down inside the nest than it turns to an exclusive diet of ant-grubs. This happens in the life of our British Large-blue (*Lycaena arion*) which, when fully grown, escapes from the nest and turns into a chrysalis in the ground outside. The case is different, however, with those species that pupate inside the nest, for when they emerge they have to run the gauntlet of their host's attacks before getting away. Nature has provided them with a special garment of large loose scales. These the ants seize, and, as they become thoroughly smothered and bothered with them, the butterfly escapes.

The strange habits and remarkable adaptations of caterpillars provide a subject to which far greater space could be devoted than is available in this brief account of the Lepidoptera, and one that is both instructive and entertaining. There is just as much food for thought in the behaviour of one of these creatures as there is in that of many of the higher animals. Those that have succeeded in eluding all their enemies eventually become full-grown, and turn into chrysalids, or pupae, as they are often called, in which state, being motionless, they are far more defenceless than ever. Having no need to feed, however, they can afford to retire into hiding, and to rely for their safety upon simple concealment unaided by deceptive resemblances such as they practised whilst active as caterpillars and will adopt again when they emerge as winged insects.

Just before pupation—the act of turning into a pupa or chrysalis—most caterpillars change considerably in colour, and also to some extent in shape, owing to the changes that are taking place within them. They also are apt to become restless, and to wander away from their food-plants. Very large numbers at this stage then burrow into the ground and form little earthen chambers in which to pupate. As many, possibly more, merely spin a few strands of silk about them amongst the débris upon the surface of the soil. Some remain in the leafy shelters that served them as caterpillars, but it is really only a small minority that remains exposed in any way, and these are nearly all butterflies. To these few belong, in the main, all the pupae that, in varying degrees, adopt deceptive patterns and colours ; but their ultimate protection is simply the very hard chitinous exterior that is common to them and to all other pupae.

At the moment of casting off the last larval skin, and before their new skin has hardened, caterpillars are most vulnerable ; indeed, parasitic wasps seem almost to know this, for they have been observed waiting alongside for this moment to occur, so that they can take advantage of it to lay their eggs in the soft, exposed bodies. As the caterpillar casts off its skin, so the position of the wings, legs, proboscis, and antennae can be discerned. These have been forming within the body of the caterpillar, particularly towards the end of its active life ; they will not be completely formed, however, until it is nearly time for the butterfly to emerge. It is during this short phase, when the whole body of the creature seems to be almost in a state of flux, that butterflies are particularly susceptible to those influences such as temperature, moisture, etc., that appear largely to govern the form the perfect insect shall ultimately assume, *e.g.* " wet " or " dry " season form, etc. Any severe shock is liable to result in an abnormality.

It is amongst that large body of moths (*Saturniidae, Lasiocampidae*, etc.), whose caterpillars spin cocoons within which to pupate, that the most ingenious constructional devices are to be found. The Emperor-moth provides a good example. The narrower end of its egg-shaped cocoon is loosely obscured by silk, beneath which lies a circle of stiff bristles all converging towards the apex. Thus a regular " eel-trap " is formed, preventing entrance, but allowing the moth to escape unhindered. The caterpillar of an African Eggar-moth (*Lasiocampidae*) has a trick of spinning

Malacosoma neustria
The Lackey, a common British Lasiocampid moth.

a kind of double cocoon, the upper part false and obviously empty, the lower part shallow and containing the chrysalis, which is green and harmonises with the leaf upon which it rests. But even more remarkable is another African moth (*Euproctis lanaria*, a species closely related to the Gold-tail), the cocoon of which is decorated with little white, silky balls like the tiny cocoons formed by the grubs of parasitic wasps such as attack caterpillars. Truly, Natural Selection is powerful, when it can induce in a caterpillar an instinct that gives it protection from one enemy (a bird, perhaps,) by making it appear as if it had already fallen a victim to another. The entomologist who first discovered one of these cocoons was himself completely deceived by it.

With this all too brief account of some of the interesting aspects of the life of caterpillars and of pupae, we reach the stage at which the moth emerges from its chrysalis, expands its wings, dries them, and becomes the creature dealt with in the earlier pages of this chapter.

The following brief outline of the classification of the Lepidoptera may be of some slight assistance.

Sub-order I. Micro-lepidoptera

Feet of the false legs of the larvae bearing a simple circle of hooks. Three simple, straight veins, side by side in the area of the hind-wing nearest the body. A very large group of mostly quite small moths, less specialised than the members of the other sub-order. Some of the chief families are :

(1) *Hepialidae* (*Ghost-swifts*). A very primitive group in which the two pairs of wings are structurally almost alike, and insecurely connected together by a hook-like device (jugum) on the fore-wing, which fastens on to the hind-wing. Several British species. Greatest development in Australia.

(2) *Tineidae*. Very small moths, the hind-wings of which have very long fringes of hair (cilia). Several hundred British species. The caterpillars are mainly leaf-miners.

(3) *Tortricidae*. Small moths with very square fore-wings. Very common throughout the world. Numerous British species, the best known of which is the Green Oak-beauty (*Tortrix viridana*). The very active, wriggling caterpillars live between spun-up leaves, from which they habitually drop to the ground on a silken thread when disturbed.

The next few families contain mainly larger moths that used formerly to be treated in some cases as Macro-lepidoptera.

(4) *Cossidae* (*Goat-moths*). The caterpillars are wood-borers. The

Zeuzera pyrina
The Leopard-moth (*Cossidae*).

The small Magpie-moth, *Eurrhypara urticata* (*Pyralidae*).

Goat-moth measures about three inches across the wings, and is a stout, heavy creature, of a mottled brown and black colour.

(5) *Sesiidae* (*Clearwings*), formerly regarded as related to the Hawk-moths, on account of their similar thick antennae. Seldom more than an inch across the wings. Caterpillars are stem-borers. Several British species.

(6) *Pyralidae.* These are at times excessively abundant creatures in various parts of the world. Good examples are the small Magpie-moth, and *Ephestia kuhniella*, the Meal-moth, a pest of stored grain. They are mostly rather frail, delicate insects, with long, rather spiny legs, and rather sharply triangular fore-wings. The Wax-moth represents another section in which the fore-wings are narrow and oblong ; *Crambus*, a third group in which the fore-wings are so narrow that when the insects settle on grass-stems—their usual resting place—they are almost invisible. *Crambus* is very common in meadows ; the fore-wings straw-coloured, the hind-wings grey ; rather conspicuous when flying. To this family belong the very few known moths (*Hydrocampa*, *Paraponyx*, etc.) that, as larvae,

Narasmarcha phaeodactyla
A Plume-moth.

A common European Burnet-moth, *Zygaena ephialtes.*

live aquatic lives. One of these, *Acentropus*, even goes further than this, for its wingless females never leave the water ; its males and winged females, however, fly freely. Pairing, in the case of the wingless females, takes place at the surface of the water, and sometimes results in the immersion of the male.

(7) *Pterophoridae* (*Plume-moths*). The wings are deeply cut from the margins towards the base. About an inch in expanse. Several British species, some of which are quite common.

(8) *Zygaenidae* (*Burnets*). Conspicuous, lazy, heavy creatures, common in meadows in temperate regions. Bronze-green, as a rule, with vivid red spots.

Sub-order II. *Macro-lepidoptera*

Hind-wing with only two " anal " veins. Larval false-feet with two incomplete circles of hooks, adapted for clasping leaves. The principal families are :

(9) *Lasiocampidae* (*Eggar-moths*). Large, heavy, brown moths well typified by our British Oak-eggar.

(10) *Noctuidae.* An extremely large family, consisting of the vast majority of the stout-bodied, night-flying moths.

(11) *Arctiidae (Tiger-moths)*.

(12) *Geometridae (Geometers)*. The moths have a characteristic manner of resting on tree-trunks, etc., with their wings partially expanded and pressed flat against the adjacent areas of the supporting surface. Caterpillars all "loopers."

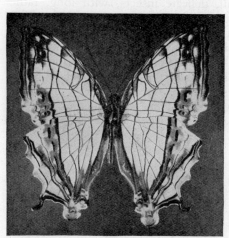

A common oriental Nymphalid butterfly, *Cyrestis thyodamas*, familiarly known as the Map Butterfly.

(13) *Bombycidae*. A small family containing the Silkworm Moth (*Bombyx mori*).

(14) *Saturniidae (Emperor-moths)*. To this family belong the Wild Silk-moths, the Luna-moth, etc. It contains most of the largest known species. They are usually brown in colour, often have transparent areas in the wings, and, very frequently, the tip of the fore-wing bears "snake-head"-like markings. Male antennae very much branched and feathery.

(15) *Sphingidae (Hawk-moths)*. The caterpillars invariably have a horn on the last segment. The moths are the most powerful fliers of all Lepidoptera, and have such a characteristic appearance that it is impossible to mistake them.

In the next families the "frenulum," an apparatus of general occurrence in moths, and consisting of a bristle on the hind-wing that fastens through a catch on the fore-wing, and serves to keep the two together, is invariably absent.

Euptychia hesione

A representative of a very large South American Satyrid genus, the New World counterpart of the genus *Mycalesis*. The eye-spots are characteristic of the whole Satyrid family.

(16) *Hesperiidae (Skippers)*. Day-flying, as a rule, with club-shaped antennae, often ending in a blunt spike. None of the wing-veins is branched; they all arise freely from the central "cell" of the wing. Several British species. They are usually treated as Butterflies, but in reality are rather widely separated from them.

The next families include the true Butterflies (*Rhopalocera*) in which the antennae are invariably club-shaped and without a sharp tip.

(17) *Pieridae (Whites)*. The Cabbage White is a good example.

(18) *Papilionidae (Swallow-tails)*.

(19) *Lycaenidae* (*Blues* and *Hairstreaks*).

(20) *Nymphalidae* (*Fritillaries*, *Tortoiseshells*, etc.). The fore-leg of the male is very minute, brush-like; that of the female very small and comb-like.

(21) *Satyridae* (*Meadow-browns*, etc.). The principal vein near the front edge of the fore-wing is always strongly inflated at its base close to the body.

Order COLEOPTERA

(*Beetles*)

By G. J. ARROW

The Beetles, or Coleoptera, form one of the largest and most easily recognised orders of insects. More than two hundred thousand different kinds have already been described and named, and it is almost certain that a million species exist in the world, many of them probably destined, as agriculture advances and primeval forests disappear, to vanish before they become known to science. Living in almost every conceivable kind of situation and exhibiting an astonishing variety of form and structure, the Coleoptera nevertheless possess certain characteristics by which they can usually be distinguished without difficulty. Their metamorphosis is complete and the larvae, which generally live in concealment, are entirely unlike the adults and pass through a quiescent pupal stage before reaching maturity. The most obvious distinctive feature of the adult beetle is found in the elytra. These are actually the anterior wings, but instead of serving for flight, have become thickened to form a pair of covers for the protection of the delicate posterior pair when not in use. These wing-covers fit closely together in a straight line along the middle of the back; and the membranous wings, except during flight, are generally folded both longitudinally and transversely beneath them. In many beetles, where the power of flight has been lost and the membranous wings are more or less atrophied, the two elytra are completely united, but the line of junction always remains. The organs of the mouth are of a rather primitive biting type, the mandibles usually very hard and strong, and sometimes of enormous size, especially in the males. The maxillae may be toothed, and serve as masticatory organs; and the labium is generally entire or not deeply divided. In spite of this biting type of mouth-structure, many beetles take no solid food during their adult life, the jaws being adapted in various ways for absorbing liquid nourishment.

The antennae of the Coleoptera assume a great variety of forms, and are their most important sense-organs; they are not merely " feelers," but the seat of the highly important olfactory sense, and perhaps, in some cases, of auditory organs as well. It is by the olfactory sense that these insects recognise other individuals of their kind, and by means of it they detect, sometimes from a considerable distance, the substances which serve as food for themselves or for their progeny. The antennae consist ordinarily of eleven joints, and are merely simple and threadlike in their simplest form ; but a greater or less number of the terminal joints may become enlarged or partially or completely united, telescoped one into another or drawn out into flat plates whose delicate sensory surfaces are protected by apposition. In a few instances (*Polyarthron, Rhipicera*) the sensory area has been increased by multiplication of the joints, which may number as many as fifty. It is usually in the males that the most remarkable developments of the antennae occur.

Two types of eye are to be found, simple and compound, but in adult beetles simple eyes, or ocelli, are known only in two families, *Staphylinidae* and *Dermestidae*. In all cases these are in addition to the compound eyes and lie between them. In the *Dermestidae* there is a single ocellus upon the top of the head in all the species except those belonging to the genus *Dermestes*. In the *Staphylinidae* a similar single eye is found in the genus *Phloeobium*, and in *Omalium* and a number of other related forms a pair of such eyes occur. Compound eyes, consisting of a cluster of facets on each side of the head, varying in number from fewer than a dozen to many hundreds, occur in all beetles except certain blind forms living underground, or in dark caves, and a few degenerate parasites. In the *Gyrinidae* and a few others the compound eyes are divided into two clusters on each side, one above and the other beneath.

Organs for producing sound are of curiously irregular occurrence, and extremely varied in situation. Wherever two hard surfaces are in contact, and can be rubbed one against the other, such organs (called stridulatory organs) are liable to be developed. They most commonly assume the form of a series of regular, microscopic ridges, set close together and capable of being plucked and caused to vibrate by a sharp edge or a series of teeth upon the opposed surface. In various families of beetles, *Erotylidae*, *Endomychidae, Hispidae*, etc., such a series of ridges occurs upon the top of the head, where it is scraped by a sharp edge just within the cavity of the thorax by rapid in-and-out movements of the head. In most of the *Cerambycidae*, of which the British Musk-beetle (*Aromia moschata*) and allied forms are examples, a similar series of fine ridges may be seen upon the mesonotum, and a squeaking note is produced by movements of the pronotum over these. In the Rhinoceros-beetles and their allies (*Oryctes*, etc.) the ridges are situated near the end of the abdomen, which the insects rub against the hinder edges of the elytra. The Dor-beetles (*Geotrupes*) employ their hind-legs for the same purpose, fine ridges upon the coxa being scraped by the edge of the cavity within which it revolves.

It is a remarkable fact that the larvae of *Geotrupes* also possess the power of stridulation, having ridged plates at the bases of the second pair of legs, against which, by movements resembling those of a fiddler, they draw the hind-legs, which are furnished with a row of sharp teeth. Still more remarkable is the apparatus found in the larvae of the family *Passalidae*. These strange grubs seem at first sight to have only four legs, for the hind-most pair are extremely small and resemble tiny hands, of which the fingers lie upon and pluck the vibratory ridges of a horny plate at the base of the second pair of legs. The adult beetles of the same family exemplify another type of stridulatory apparatus in which the wings take part. A small area in each wing is thickened and

Larvae of Lamellicorn Beetles. 1, The common Cockchafer, with three similar pairs of legs; 2, *Geotrupes*, with the third pair reduced for stridulation; 3, *Passalus*, with the third pair still more reduced and scarcely visible.

closely set with horny prominences, which lie upon and are rubbed by a hard boss with a peculiarly sculptured surface upon each side of the insect's back. Many of the Carnivorous Water-beetles (*Hydaticus, Acilius, Agabus,* etc.) produce sounds in a similar way, but the hardened spiny area is upon the upper, instead of the lower, surface of the wing and is rubbed by a specially adapted part of the wing-cover. A few instances are known in which the wings serve solely as a part of the vocal apparatus and can no longer be used for flight. The great Central American *Proculus*, belonging to the *Passalidae*, is one of these, and a curious Ceylonese insect, *Trichulus pubescens*, one of the *Erotylidae*, is another.

"Trilobite larva" (slightly reduced). These strange grubs are females and never acquire the beetle-form. The male is minute.

External differences between the two sexes of certain beetles have been already referred to. Although males and females may be identical externally, in many cases they are strikingly different. In some, as in the common Glow-worm (*Lampyris noctiluca*), the male is an active, winged creature ; while the female is entirely destitute of wings and elytra, and scarcely differs from the larva. A remarkable instance is that of the large wingless insects called " Trilobite larvae," inhabiting the Malay Peninsula and Borneo, whose real nature and systematic position was for long in dispute. It has recently been found that these strange-looking creatures, which may measure as much as $2\frac{1}{2}$ inches long, include adult females as well as larvae belonging to the family *Lycidae*, and that the males are tiny, winged insects whose bulk may be less than one-hundredth part of that of the females.

The extraordinary horns and protuberances which place some of the giant beetles of tropical regions amongst the strangest of living creatures are usually either peculiar to the males, or present only in a reduced form in the females ; but in some cases each sex has a distinctive armature of its own.

In very many beetles the antennae of the male are longer than those of the female, and in some cases (*Xenocerus, Astinomus*, etc.) many times as long. In other instances the terminal joints bearing the sensory surface are larger in the male (*Melolontha, Callirrhipis*). The legs also frequently differ in the two sexes.   In many beetles the front feet of the males are broader than those of the females, and in the water-beetle *Dytiscus* they are also furnished with peculiar suckers, but in the Indian genus *Doubledaya* and some of its

Copris draco
A West African beetle.   1, Male ; 2, Female.   The male has a long toothed horn upon the head and the female a stalked crescent.

allies those of the females are dilated. In many cases the legs of the male are longer than those of the female, and in the grotesque Harlequin beetle (*Acrocinus longimanus*) of South America and the East Indian *Euchirus longimanus* the male insect's front legs attain an extraordinary length. In other cases, as in the beautiful *Sagridae*, it is the hind-legs which reach a greater development in this sex.

Males and females may also differ in their coloration, in which case it is generally the males which show the brighter hues, probably because the females, being less active and more exposed to danger, especially when engaged in laying their eggs and providing for their progeny, need the greater protection afforded by an inconspicuous exterior.   The beautiful little *Hoplia coerulea*, found in Eastern France and Switzerland, the males of which are clothed with scales of exquisite blue and silver, has a female attired in sober brown.

The importance of the Coleoptera from the standpoint of the well-being of the human race can scarcely be over-estimated.   The depredations of some of them, like the common Cockchafer (*Melolontha vulgaris*), by which on the continent of Europe trees throughout a wide area are not infrequently stripped of their leaves in a few days, are only too familiar ; but the injury inflicted by such insects in their brief adult stage, although more apparent, is of far less importance than that occasioned by their larvae, which may spend from one to three years underground, devouring the roots of various crops. In tropical regions losses, estimated at millions of pounds annually, have been caused to sugar and other crops by root-destroying Coleoptera. Other kinds of beetles are responsible for serious losses by destroying the shoots, buds, blossoms, or fruits of important crops. Such are the Asparagus-beetle (*Crioceris asparagi*), the Apple-blossom weevil (*Anthonomus pomorum*), the Raspberry-beetle (*Byturus tomentosus*), and many more. Innumerable species belonging to several groups of beetles spend their lives burrowing in timber, some attacking only dead and decaying wood, but others damaging sound and valuable trees. These include the great family *Cerambycidae*, the *Bostrichidae*, and the *Scolytidae*. A smaller, but scarcely less injurious group, the *Anobiidae*,

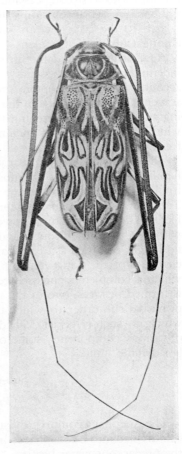

COMMON COCKCHAFER
1, Male; 2, Female. The male has the fan-like antennae longer than those of the female.

HARLEQUIN-BEETLE, male. (Reduced.)
The fore-legs, shown folded up, are nearly three times the length of the body.

includes the Furniture-beetle (*Anobium punctatum*), whose holes made in our household effects are well known everywhere, although the insects themselves are rarely seen, and the still more destructive Death-watch beetle (*Xestobium tessellatum*), by which so many ancient timber roofs, including that of Westminster Hall, have been more or less destroyed.

Another destructive series of Coleoptera are those which devour stored grain and foodstuffs of every kind, as well as manufactured goods, hides, tobacco, etc. The Rice-weevil (*Calandra oryzae*) annually destroys vast quantities of wheat and other cereals; the Pea-weevils (*Bruchus*) are scarcely less injurious to stored peas and beans; the Bacon-beetle (*Dermestes lardarius*) is a hated pest of provision stores, and a smaller species (*Anthrenus verbasci*) related to the last, devours woollen goods and sometimes works havoc amongst Museum specimens.

Against this formidable list of offences, which might be added to almost indefinitely, certain benefits must be recorded on the other side of the account. The Coleoptera perform great and important services as scavengers, removing from the surface of the soil vast quantities of putrifying substances and hastening the disintegration of dead trees and stumps, which would otherwise encumber the ground and hinder the growth of fresh vegetation.

This enormous group of insects has been divided into about a hundred families, of which only the most important can be referred to here. It was for long customary to arrange the families in sub-orders called Pentamera, Tetramera, Trimera, etc., according to the number of visible joints in the feet. The foot-structure, however, although important, varies so greatly within most of the groups, and is subject to so many exceptions, that it is no longer regarded as of primary significance. Of more importance is the character of the wing-venation, of which there are two main types, one in which a completely enclosed rectangular cell near the middle of the wing is formed between two of the principal longitudinal veins, distinguishing a primitive sub-order to which the name Adephaga is applied, the other, in which no such cell exists, called Polyphaga. The second sub-order consists of various components, some of which are well-defined, while others have less definite limits.

Sub-order *ADEPHAGA*

(*Predaceous Beetles*)

The Adephaga comprise most of the predaceous beetles and are sometimes sub-divided into Geodephaga, or predaceous land-beetles, and Hydradephaga, the predaceous water-beetles. The principal families are the following:

The *Cicindelidae*, or Tiger-beetles, are fierce and extremely active creatures which hunt and devour other insects. The majority of them, including all the British representatives, belong to the world-wide genus *Cicindela*, whose members frequent sandy places, where they are equally active on foot and upon the wing. Their larvae inhabit vertical burrows in the ground, in which they lie in wait for their victims and capture them by a sudden spring. The species of *Mantichora*, which are formidable insects measuring about two inches in length, hunt their prey upon the African veldt, and are incapable of flight. Other forms, like the Malayan *Tricondyla aptera*, are also wingless but seek their victims upon trees or shrubs instead of on the ground.

The *Carabidae* (Ground-beetles) are a much more numerous family than the *Cicindelidae*, and are found in considerable variety in every part of the world. Though swift runners, they are less active on the wing than the Tiger-beetles, and many of them have entirely lost the power of flight; nor are they so commonly diurnal in their habits, most of them lying concealed by day and emerging to hunt their prey after nightfall, although the little glittering "sun-beetles" of our gardens are exceptions in that respect. The *Carabidae* must be counted as bene-factors of mankind, many of them being voracious destroyers of harmful insects, both in their larval and adult stages. Various species of the typical genus *Carabus* are familiar inhabitants of European gardens and fields, where they perform valuable, if generally unrecog-nised, services. *Carabus violaceus* is a very common British garden insect, *Carabus nitens* is one of the most beautiful beetles found in Britain, and *C. auratus*,

Mantichora scabra
A formidable predaceous Tiger-beetle from East Africa.

although rare in Britain, is valued on the continent of Europe for its habit of feeding upon the destruc-tive Cockchafer. Various species of the genus are voracious des-troyers of snails, and this is also the habit of the members of the closely related genus *Damaster*,

CARNIVOROUS BEETLES
1, *Carabus nemoralis* ; 2, *Calosoma sycophanta*, feeding upon a Processionary Moth Caterpillar; 3, *Carabus auratus*, feeding upon a Cockchafer. On the right, the larva of *Carabus auratus*. (All reduced.)

of China and Japan. These have the anterior part of the body remarkably attenuated, enabling the beetle's head to penetrate deeply into the interior

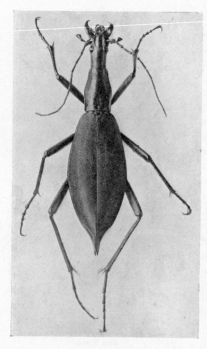

Damaster blaptoides
A Japanese beetle which feeds upon snails.

of their victims' shells. Another useful insect belonging to a nearly related genus is *Calosoma sycophanta*. This is a large and extremely beautiful species which, although it has been found in England, does not breed there and cannot be considered a British beetle. It preys upon the caterpillars and chrysalises of the devastating hosts of the Processionary Moths.

Some of the *Carabidae* have the power of protecting themselves from attack by discharging an offensive fluid from the hinder end of the body in the face of their foes. This is the case with the large and handsome African and Indian insects forming the genus *Anthia*, whose defensive discharge, if allowed to come in contact with the human skin, causes great pain. Certain others, including the British species *Brachinus crepitans*, are known as Bombardier beetles from the fact that the defensive fluid, upon its discharge, is converted into a puff of vapour to the accompaniment of a slight explosion.

Related to the *Carabidae*, although entirely unlike them in appearance, are the *Paussidae*, an exceedingly remarkable family in which the antennae, instead of being of the slender and flexible type characteristic of the *Carabidae* and *Cicindelidae*, are extremely short and thick, often consolidated into no more than two joints and of the most curious and even grotesque shapes. In some cases at least these organs seem to serve as torches, for two quite independent observers, Dr. Adam Afzelius in West Africa and Mr. Walhouse in Southern India, have reported the discovery of luminous *Paussidae*. In the first case the light was located in the antennae. Like the Bombardier beetles, these insects have also the power of discharging an explosive fluid by way of defence. They are inmates of the nests of ants and termites, and some of them show curious thoracic pits from which probably is produced a sweet secretion very agreeable to their hosts. They are fairly numerous in Tropical Africa, Asia, and Australia,

A PAUSSID
Cerapterus stali. An inmate of ants' nests, which defends itself by an explosive discharge.

but, owing to their peculiar manner of life, very little is known about them, and they would be very rarely seen were they not liable, when taking nocturnal flights, to be attracted into houses by light.

The *Dytiscidae*, or Carnivorous Water-beetles, are as voracious in ponds and streams as are the *Cicindelidae* and *Carabidae* on land. Although breathing air, like all other beetles, their entire structure is adapted to an aquatic life. A reservoir of air, into which the spiracles open, is always contained between the closely fitting wing-covers and the back, so that respiration is continuous, the supply being renewed as often as necessary by the beetle coming to the surface of the water and allowing the extremity of the body to protrude above it. This, indeed, is the usual resting attitude. All these beetles, to enable them to pass through the water with the minimum of resistance, have a perfectly even outline and oval shape. The first two pairs of legs are employed as grasping organs, the front ones in particular serving to seize and hold their prey, while the third pair are used for the sole purpose of propelling themselves through the water. For this end the tibiae and tarsi bear close fringes of stiff hairs and are so articulated that they become rigid when forced against the water in the backstroke, but bend and pass unresistingly through it when drawn forward again, the coxae forming broad immovable plates which confine the movements to the direction which ensures the maximum efficiency. So perfect is

GREAT CARNIVOROUS WATER-BEETLE
Dytiscus marginalis. 1, Male ; 2, Female.

the adaptation of these air-breathing insects for the rôle of bandits of the water that even fishes frequently fall victims to them. The Great Carnivorous Water-beetle (*Dytiscus marginalis*), common in Britain and throughout Western Europe, is a serious enemy to hatcheries of freshwater fish. A much smaller form (*Eretes sticticus*), very abundant throughout the East, is collected in great numbers for food in Burma in both its mature and immature stages.

Despite the multitude of species, of which more than two thousand are already known to inhabit the various fresh waters of the globe, there is a remarkable uniformity in the aspect and habits of the Carnivorous Water-beetles. The chief apparent difference is in size, yet the ponds and streams of England exhibit practically the entire range from the largest to the smallest.

The *Gyrinidae*, or Whirligig Beetles, form another very compact and sharply defined family of Adephaga. They all have the remarkable habit of running swiftly, generally associated in communities, over the surface of still waters, suddenly diving below for short spells, and returning to the surface to resume immediately their social dance. This curious way of life implies an even more profound modification of the primitive structure than that of the *Dytiscidae*. The surface of the body is extremely glossy, the eyes are large and, as has been already mentioned, are composed of four clusters, and the antennae are extremely short and almost rigid, so that they offer no obstacle to the sudden immersion of the insect. The fore-legs are fairly long and more completely prehensile than those of the *Dytiscidae*, but all four posterior legs are very short and broad, forming paddles with which the beetles propel themselves with great rapidity both on the surface of the water and below it. The European representatives of this peculiar family are all small and closely similar, not exceeding a quarter of an inch long.

WHIRLIGIG BEETLE

Porrhorrhynchus landaisi. The long fore-legs are for seizing its prey, and the two hinder pairs are reduced to extremely short paddles.

The largest and most striking form, attaining about an inch in length, is found in Indo-China.

Sub-order POLYPHAGA

(*Burying-beetles, etc.*)

We now leave the Adephaga, neglecting a few less important families containing only a small number of species, and proceed to the Polyphaga, of which the first great division is called the Staphylinoidea. This is distinguished by a wing-venation in which the characteristic short transverse veins forming the rectangular cell of the Adephaga wing are absent, and the so-called " median " longitudinal vein is not hooked or " recurrent," as in the other divisions of the Sub-order Polyphaga.

By far the largest family of Staphylinoidea is that of the *Staphylinidae*, of which many species are found in every part of the world. They are in general easily recognised by their long, narrow form, and the fact that the wings, when not in use, are folded into a very small compass and covered by short elytra which leave the greater part of the long abdomen exposed. They generally inhabit moist places, many of them burrowing into the soil or into rotting wood and débris of all kinds, and feeding upon various other insects to be found there. Most of the *Staphylinidae* are small and few attain any considerable size. One of the largest, *Emus hirtus*, a handsome species measuring an inch or more in length, and a rare inhabitant of Britain, preys upon the subterranean larvae of the Dor-beetles (*Geotrupes*). Closely related to *Emus hirtus* is *Ocypus olens*, a rather sinister-looking black insect, which, by the name of the Devil's Coach-horse, is a familiar inhabitant of British gardens, where it performs good service by feeding upon all sorts of harmful grubs.   A number of curious forms live only in the nests of ants or termites.   The species of *Atemeles* and *Lomechusa*, for example, are found living as favoured guests in the nests of various species of *Myrmica* and *Formica*, which, for the sake of a pleasant secretion which they lick from the bodies of the beetles, treat them with the utmost solicitude, feeding them and allowing their larvae to feed upon their own ant brood.   The species of the genus *Paederus*, which are found in most parts of the world, can exude a caustic fluid, capable of raising blisters upon the human skin.   Correlated with this means of defence is a conspicuous coloration of alternate red and blue or black bands, serving as a warning to creatures that have once experienced this unpleasant faculty to leave them un-molested in future.

DEVIL'S
COACH-HORSE

Ocypus olens.   A useful garden insect.

Allied to the *Staphylinidae* is a very interesting family of minute beetles known as *Pselaphidae*.   These also have short elytra, leaving exposed a great part of the abdomen, but the latter, instead of being long and flexible, is short and rigid, and the antennae are not simple but knobbed at the end.   Many of the *Pselaphidae* inhabit the nests of ants and termites.   The species represented here (*Claviger testaceus*) is one of the most remarkable of the British beetles.   It is about a tenth of an inch long, devoid of wings, and entirely blind, and lives only in the nests of the common Yellow Ant (*Acanthomyops flavus*) and a few other species. Like *Atemeles* and *Lomechusa*, it can exude a substance extremely agreeable to its hosts, who feed and tend it like their own brood.   The pleasant liquid is secreted from the neighbourhood of certain tufts of yellow hairs upon the back of the beetle, from which it is licked up by the ants. When hungry the little beetle intimates its need by touching a passing ant, and is then fed, applying its mouth to that of the ant, who regurgitates a drop of nourishment.   Another closely related species, *Claviger*

Claviger testaceus

Attended by ants (greatly enlarged).   One of the ants is about to feed the beetle, which puts its head into the mouth of the ant.   On the left the beetle, which is blind and wing-less, is shown rather more enlarged.

longicornis, was first discovered in Britain in 1906, in a nest of the Black Ant, *Acanthomyops niger*.   We are unfortunately quite ignorant of the manner of life of many other curious forms of *Pselaphidae* which have been found in all parts of the world.

Unlike most families of Coleoptera, which are most numerous in the warmer parts of the earth, the *Silphidae* are best represented in the temperate regions.   They are nearly all carrion-feeders, although some of the smaller forms feed upon fungi.   The typical genera, *Silpha* and *Necrophorus*, of each of which several representatives are fairly common in the British Islands, are composed of moderately large insects which feed upon carcases, to which, like vultures, they fly from afar, hunting, however, not by sight but by scent. The species of *Necrophorus* are called Burying-beetles, or Sexton-beetles, from their habit of burying the bodies of small animals, birds, mice, etc.   They are powerfully built creatures, with stout digging legs, and nearly all of them are black, with bright orange markings.   Their operations are carried on in small companies.   When a carcase has been found, the beetles creep beneath it and scrape away the soil, allowing the body gradually to sink down, the earth removed falling on top of it as the hole becomes deeper, until at last it is completely covered.   The females lay their eggs in the interred carcase, so that the larvae upon their emergence find themselves provided with abundance of food and a safe retreat.

Silpha atrata and larvae, feeding upon a dead lizard.

Apparently related to the *Silphidae* is the extraordinary family *Platypsyllidae*, consisting only of a single insect of parasitic habits, which has so far degenerated as to have lost all semblance of the ancestral beetle-form.   *Platypsyllus castoris* is a parasite of the beaver, both in Europe and North America, and was formerly considered to be related to the lice, not only from its parasitic habits, but also on account of its structure.   Eyes and wings are entirely absent, but the fact that the latter once existed is shown by the presence of a pair of very short wing-covers.   It is possible that the insects feed, not upon their host, but upon certain mites which also infest the latter.

The *Trichopterygidae* are a group of very minute beetles, which include some of the smallest of all known insects.   All their organs are well developed, but, as in certain microscopic Hymenoptera (*Mymaridae*), the wings consist of very narrow strips of membrane with broad fringes of long hairs.   The largest of these tiny beetles measure no more than a twentieth part of an inch in length, and some species of *Ptilium* and *Ptenidium* are barely visible to the naked eye, measuring only about a fiftieth of an inch long.

The *Histeridae* are a well-defined family of very compact form and hard, glossy exterior, with short legs and antennae, so constructed that they can be packed very close to the body.   They prey upon other insects, and are found in all parts of the world, many of them being valuable as destroyers of harmful pests. *Plaesius javanus* has been found a very valuable agent in preventing the undue increase of a weevil (*Cosmopolites sordidus*) terribly destructive to banana trees. Other kinds (*Tryponaeus*, etc.) prey upon wood-boring beetles and their larvae and possess a strangely elongate cylindrical shape which enables them to enter the tunnels of their prey in search of them. Others, again, belonging to the genus *Hololepta*, are of considerably larger size, reaching half an inch or more in length, but are so extremely flat as to have only the thickness of thin cardboard. This enables them to feed upon insects which harbour in the narrow space beneath the loosened bark of trees.

The remaining divisions of the Polyphagous Coleoptera are of rather unequal value. The Diversicornia consist of a large number of families of very diverse appearance and habits. The name Clavicornia is generally given to a considerable number of these families, mostly consisting of insects of very small size, usually with the last three joints of the antennae enlarged, forming a kind of club. The various families differ *inter alia* in the number of joints of which the feet consist. Many of the minute species occur in vast numbers, and not a few infest dry stores and provisions of many kinds. Some of these little beetles are amongst the most universally distributed of all insects, being carried into every corner of the world visited by human commerce. Amongst them are various species belonging to the family *Cucujidae*, *Silvanus mercator*, *Laemophloeus pusillus*, and others. An interesting member of the same family, *Coccidotrophus socialis*, was recently discovered by Professor W. M. Wheeler, living in social communities in cavities excavated by them within the leaf-petioles of a South American tree, *Tachygalia paniculata*. Each colony is founded by a single pair of the beetles, which are little creatures less than a quarter of an inch long.

Amongst the *Nitidulidae*, *Carpophilus hemipterus* is often found in large numbers in cargoes of dried figs and similar merchandise, and *Meligethes aeneus* and related species are well known throughout Europe as the tiny beetles so commonly seen upon many kinds of wild flowers. The larvae of *M. aeneus* are said to cause serious injury to crops of rape by attacking the buds and unripe seed-pods.

Many minute beetles belonging to the families *Cryptophagidae* and *Lathridiidae* feed upon fungoid growths and are found in vegetable débris, as well as in damp cellars and outhouses. The *Erotylidae* and *Endomychidae* feed upon larger fungi, and, in tropical regions, some of them attain a considerable size and exhibit striking colours and patterns, usually of black and orange or red in vivid contrasts. There is good reason for believing these to be unpalatable to birds and other insectivorous creatures and that the conspicuous patterns may be interpreted as Aposematic or Warning Coloration, serving to advertise their unpalatability and so protect them from interference. The large tropical American beetles belonging to the

L

genus *Erotylus* are black with zigzag stripes of red and orange, or bright yellow with black spots and bars. The Oriental species of the Endomychid genus *Eumorphus* are all shining black or purple, and each is decorated with four bright yellow spots. These insects possess an extremely offensive smell, they are sluggish in their movements and expose themselves freely, having evidently no need of concealment. Moreover, many species both of *Erotylus* and *Eumorphus* have the elytra curiously inflated or expanded, so increasing their conspicuousness by making their apparent size greater than their actual size. The *Erotylidae* have strong jaws and feed especially upon the hard woody fungi which grow upon decaying trees, while the *Endomychidae* confine themselves to fungi of softer substance.

Nearly related to the *Endomychidae* is a very familiar group, the Ladybirds, or *Coccinellidae*. These also are unpalatable insects and accordingly are notable for bright and conspicuous colouring and the absence of any attempt

Eumorphus marginatus
A beautiful but evil-smelling beetle which feeds upon tree-fungi in the East.

at concealment. It is on account of these characteristics that the Ladybirds are so well known and, in Europe at least, are amongst the most popular of all insects. But they have a better claim to popularity in their usefulness, the family being of incalculable value from the economic standpoint. Those representatives which are best known in Britain, the Two-spotted Ladybird (*Adalia bipunctata*) and the Seven-spotted Ladybird (*Coccinella septempunctata*), are perhaps the chief enemies of the *Aphidae*, or Greenflies, upon which they feed voraciously, both in the adult and larval states. The orange-coloured, spindle-shaped eggs are laid in clusters upon the plants infested by *Aphidae*, and the little active black Ladybird larvae on emergence fall immediately upon their prey.

As they increase in size they become of a rather more slaty colour with small red and white spots along the sides. They attain their full size after five or six weeks of greedy feeding, the posterior end of the body is then attached to the surface of a leaf, and the skin shrinks back, revealing the pupa, which after about eight days more changes to the adult insect. A second generation appears within a short time, and the winter is passed in the adult stage, the beetles congregating in large numbers beneath the bark of trees or in similar sheltered places.

Other kinds of Ladybird feed upon scale-insects (*Coccidae*) and are no less serviceable than those just mentioned. *Vedalia cardinalis* has proved of immense service to the growers of oranges and lemons. An outbreak of a previously unknown scale-insect in the plantations of these trees in California, which threatened their total destruction, was at last checked, when the pest was discovered to be a native of Australia, by the importation of this ladybird from Australia. Subsequently attacks of the same pest which occurred, with the same disastrous effect, in South Africa and in different parts of Southern Europe, were also eventually met, with equal success, by the introduction of the same useful insect into the plantations.

The species of one large Coccinellid genus, *Epilachna*, feed upon leaves, and at least one of them, *Epilachna 28-punctata*, inhabiting India, Malaya, and Australia, is responsible for serious damage to potatoes, tomatoes, and various other crops.

Certain members of the family *Dermestidae* are nearly as well known as the Ladybirds, but unfortunately have not the good repute of the latter. *Dermestes lardarius*, the Bacon-beetle, is a serious pest of provision stores, and *Dermestes vulpinus* is still more abundant, feeding upon dried animal substances of all kinds. *Attagenus pellio* is a smaller form which sometimes occurs in immense numbers where hides are stored, and also in the neigh-

GREAT BLACK WATER-BEETLE

Hydrophilus piceus. 1, Larva ; 2, Male ; 3, Female. The male is distinguished by the enlarged claws of the fore-feet. The female is grasping the floating case of silk which contains her eggs.

bourhood of poultry-houses. It feeds upon skins and feathers. *Anthrenus verbasci* is a tiny globose insect, rather prettily decorated with scales of various colours, which is the most dangerous enemy of collections of preserved insects, of which many have been reduced to dust by it. The closely similar *Anthrenus vorax* is a great destroyer of clothing and woollen goods. In all these cases the chief damage is occasioned by the larvae, which roam at large and are clothed with long stiff hairs.

The *Hydrophilidae*, with certain exceptions, are water-beetles, and their smooth, shining exterior and oval shape give many of them a deceptive resemblance to the *Dytiscidae*. Unlike those insects, they are usually not predaceous, and have much less skill in swimming, many of them only crawling upon aquatic plants or making their way along the surface of stagnant pools.

They usually carry a film of air for respiration upon the ventral surface of the body. The antennae are very short and knobbed at the end, and the maxillary palpi are unusually long—generally longer and more conspicuous than the antennae. Representatives of the family are found in all parts of the world, but there is no finer example than the British *Hydrophilus piceus*, the Great Black Water-beetle, which is nearly two inches long. The female of this species constructs a silken receptacle for her eggs, which floats at the surface of the water and has a peculiar prolongation projecting above it. The larvae, when full grown, may be three inches long. They feed upon water-snails, which are held by the insects upon their backs and there devoured. Respiration is effected through the tail. The females of other species of the group carry the egg-receptacle about beneath the body, holding it firmly with their legs, until the young emerge.

The *Parnidae* are also water-beetles, but unlike the *Hydrophilidae*, which have a marked preference for still waters, some of them are found in the most swiftly flowing streams and torrents. They have powerful claws, with which they cling to the surface of rocks and stones, their food consisting of minute vegetable growths which they scrape from these. Their larvae, like the beetles themselves, are highly specialised to adapt them to their very peculiar manner of life. They are broad and flat, with wide lateral flanges to the body, and are able to cling very closely to the water-lashed surfaces upon which they live.

DEATH-WATCH BEETLE
Xestobium tessellatum
(Much enlarged.) The great destroyer of ancient roofs.

Mention has already been made of the very serious losses due to Woodworms, the grubs of beetles belonging to the *Anobiidae*. The small round holes so often to be seen in articles of furniture or interior woodwork are the exit-holes of the common Furniture-beetle (*Anobium punctatum*) through which, the larval burrowings finished and the adult stage reached, it has eaten its way out. Previous to doing this, however, the greater part of a year has been spent in destructive burrowing in the interior in the form of a small white grub. This changes to a pupa just beneath the surface of the wood, so that only a thin layer remains to be perforated by the beetle in order to reach the exterior. The best time to destroy the insects by the application of liquid dressings is, therefore, in the early summer before the beetles emerge.

More calamitous even than the common Furniture-beetles are the related but larger Death-watch Beetles (*Xestobium tessellatum*), insects about a quarter of an inch long, which derive their popular name from the tapping noise made in signalling one to the other, to which, the cause being unknown and mysterious, ominous significance was often attached in the past, and not improbably is still where such ancient superstitions yet survive. The tapping is produced by the beetle striking its head about half a dozen times in quick succession against the surface upon which it stands, and it is answered in the same way by any other individual of the species in its neighbourhood. So far as known this habit is not shared by any other species of the family, although in South Africa certain much larger beetles of the family *Tenebrionidae*, belonging to the genus *Psammodes*, have a similar tapping habit from which they are known as "Toc-tockies." The life-history of the Death-watch Beetle is nearly the same as that of the Furniture-beetle, but the larvae feed for two years, and perhaps sometimes for three, before reaching maturity.

Not very unlike the common Furniture-beetle, and also extremely destructive to woodwork, are the Powder-post Beetles (*Lyctus linearis* and *brunneus*) which belong to a related family, the *Bostrichidae*, another group especially injurious to timber. The Powder-post Beetles do not penetrate so deeply into the wood as the Furniture-beetle, but work more on the surface, so that the mischief done is generally more apparent. Attacking layer after layer, however, they sometimes reduce panelling of walnut and other ornamental woods to dust in a very short time. *Lyctus brunneus*, the most destructive species, was regarded, not many years ago, as a rare British insect, but it has in recent years become very abundant.

Another related family, the *Ptinidae*, also includes a number of insects which, although small, are troublesome pests. *Ptinus fur* is a great enemy of dried plants, as well as of brushes and other household goods, and *Ptinus tectus*, although previously almost unknown, has since 1904 become a very serious pest, attacking all kinds of groceries and stored provisions. Nearly related to these is the Spider-beetle (*Niptus hololeucus*), a pretty little globular insect clothed with silky golden hair, which also feeds upon groceries and is commonly found in houses.

The *Cleridae* are a predaceous family which hunt other insects upon trees, flowers and foliage, etc. They are narrow-bodied, rather cylindrical insects, some so coloured as to bear the closest resemblance to the bark or lichens amongst which they lurk, and others very conspicuously orna-mented with spots and stripes of vivid colours. Some of the conspicuous forms are mimics of other insects. Various species bear a striking resemblance to the stinging wingless females of the Hymenopterous *Mutillidae*, which are found running in the same places with them. A large species of *Mutilla* inhabiting Rhodesia has the fore part of its body of a peculiar deep red hue, and the hinder part black with white spots. A Clerid beetle, *Thanasimus weissi*, which inhabits the same places, has precisely the same coloration, and the appearance of the slender waist of the *Mutilla* is produced in the beetle by means of certain marks upon the elytra. Evidently by obtaining credit in this way for a sting it does not possess the beetle avoids encounters which would often have fatal results.

The larvae of some of these insects make their way into the nests of bees and devour their brood, and others feed upon the egg-masses of locusts and grasshoppers. The *Cleridae* are abundant in most of the warm regions of the earth, but the species are not numerous in Europe. One, however, *Trichodes apiarius*, is common upon umbelliferous flowers in Southern Europe. It is a very conspicuous insect with vividly contrasted black and scarlet bands, and its larvae sometimes attack and devour the brood of the Hive Bee.

The *Telephoridae* (Soldier Beetles), unlike the last family, are particularly well represented in Europe, and many species abound in Britain, where they are familiar frequenters of wayside flowers, especially those of the *Umbelliferae*. They are fond of sunshine, active on the wing, and, like the *Cleridae*, predaceous. Perhaps the most remarkable members of the family are the species of the genus *Phengodes*, found in Mexico and the southern United States. The males of these have very voluminous wings and beautifully feathered antennae, but the females are simple wormlike creatures from one to two inches long, and almost indistinguishable from larvae. Seen in the dark, however, these rudimentary creatures are strangely beautiful, for they bear along each side of the body a row of coloured lights, some of them red and others green. This has earned them in America the name of Railway-worms.

The true Glow-worms and Fireflies constitute the family *Lampyridae*. In most of them both sexes are luminous, the light being produced by peculiar bodies situated in two or three of the abdominal segments. The lower surface of these, through which the light is emitted, has an easily recognisable opaque whitish colour. The light is not continuous, but there is generally a rhythmic pulsation while the insect is on the wing. The common Firefly of Southern Switzerland and North Italy is *Luciola italica*. The common British Glow-worm is the wingless and grub-like female of *Lampyris noctiluca*, the winged male of which is only feebly luminous. These insects feed upon snails, and the mouth organs are very peculiarly constructed to enable them to deal with these.

Nearly related to the *Telephoridae* and *Lampyridae* are the *Lycidae*, a group found abundantly in many of the warmer regions of the earth. They are flat, soft-bodied insects, narrow in front and dilating behind, sometimes to an extravagant degree. They are red, yellow, or white in colour and generally ornamented with bands or patches of black or blue. As they expose themselves freely upon flowers and foliage they are always conspicuous objects. It has also been found by experiment that they are highly distasteful to insect-eating creatures, those which have been induced to taste them invariably rejecting them with every mark of disgust. Their very distinctive exterior is therefore valuable to them as leading to ready recognition and avoidance, and it is interesting to find that they are mimicked by a great variety of other insects which have nothing in common with the unpalatable *Lycidae*, except the habit of congregating in the same places together with them.

The *Elateridae* are sometimes called Skipjacks, or Click-beetles, from their manner of springing into the air after falling upon their backs. A spinelike prolongation of the prosternum fits into a deep hollow in the mesosternum, and by almost drawing this out and then letting it spring suddenly back, the beetle bounds upwards, repeating the action until it finds a foothold again. Some of the larvae are carnivorous and others vegetarian. One of the latter is the destructive wireworm, the larva of *Agriotes lineatus*, so injurious to potatoes and many other crops. A few species belonging to the Tropical American genus *Pyrophorus* are luminous, showing greenish light from two round yellow spots on the upper side of the prothorax, and a reddish light from the lower surface. The largest of the family, the great *Tetralobus flabellicornis*, lives in its larval stage in the nests of African termites, and has often been mistaken for the termite Queen.

An African Skipjack Beetle, *Tetralobus flabellicornis*, and its larva. The latter inhabits the nests of termites and has often been mistaken for the Queen of the termites.

The *Buprestidae*, which are sometimes considered to form with the *Elateridae* a tribe Serricornia, but are really a rather isolated family, include many of the most brilliantly decorated of all the Coleoptera. Their larvae are generally wood-feeders. A strange characteristic of certain of these beetles is that of being attracted by forest-fires, flying to places over which these have just passed and burying themselves in the still-hot ashes.

We now come to a large group collectively called Heteromera from the fact that the four anterior feet have five joints, and those of the last pair of legs only four. The largest family, the *Tenebrionidae*, has representatives in every part of the world. They are generally not very active in their movements, many of them have lost the power of flight, and their food is of a miscellaneous character, but often consists of débris of all kinds. A familiar representative of the family is the common Mealworm, *Tenebrio molitor*. The adult form of this is an elongate-oval black beetle about three-quarters of an inch long.

Catoxantha bicolor
One of the largest and most brilliant of the *Buprestidae*. It inhabits India and the Malayan region.

The *Meloidae* (Oil-beetles and Blister-beetles) are another Heteromerous family, the larvae of which have remarkable parasitic habits, while the adults seem all to be protected by producing a highly irritant effect upon the skin if they are interfered with. *Lytta vesicatoria* (formerly called *Cantharis vesicatoria*) is the source of the blistering extract known as Canthari-dine. The clumsy obese blue Oil-beetles (*Meloe*) are not rare in English hedgerows in spring. The female lays an immense number of small yellow eggs just below the surface of the soil, and from these emerge a swarm of tiny and exceedingly lively little creatures which immediately climb the neighbouring plants, and, gaining the flowers, await the arrival of bees to collect the honey. Their object is to gain an entrance to the stored cells of certain solitary bees, in which alone they can develop to maturity. Seizing the first opportunity that presents itself, they grip with their prehensile claws a hair of a visiting bee and await developments. Many naturally find that their mounts are of no use to them, but a few are fortunate enough to attach themselves to female bees actually engaged in storing with honey the cells previously prepared for their progeny. Hanging on to her hairy clothing until the bee has quite finished this operation and is in the act of depositing her

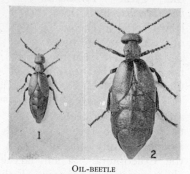

OIL-BEETLE
Meloe proscarabaeus. 1, Male; 2, Female. A degenerate parasite of bee nests, which has lost the power of flight.

egg on the top of the mass of honey, the little parasite instantly slips from her on to the egg, the bee proceeding to close the cell and begin the preparation of another. The egg is then attacked and devoured, and the parasite stands upon the empty shell, but is unable to touch the sticky mass surrounding him. The skin is now cast and the insect appears in a totally different form, as a plump grub with insignificant legs and a mouth with which it is able to absorb the honey upon which it now floats. A quiescent stage follows, and from this emerges a once more active larva which no doubt in many cases migrates to neighbouring cells and devours their contents. After this the true pupa stage is reached, and lastly the fat blue-black beetle appears. Other Meloids are carnivorous and victimise bees which store up insects of various kinds for their young, and others, again, destroy the eggs of locusts and grasshoppers ; but the means by which they gain access to the secret places in which alone they can develop to maturity is still unknown. The species of *Meloidae* are very numerous, but, although their life-histories are so varied and eventful, we are as yet ignorant of nearly all of them.

Mylabris oculata

An African Meloid believed to destroy the eggs of locusts.

Another remarkable family is that of the *Stylopidae*, which, under the name of Strepsiptera, has sometimes been regarded as forming a distinct order of insects, but their remarkable characteristics seem to be the result of degeneration induced by parasitism. They are minute insects and, although little known, are of many kinds. The males have voluminous wings but rudimentary elytra. The larvae live within the bodies of bees, wasps, and bugs, and the females are degenerate creatures, without either locomotory or sensory organs, which never leave the body of the host, but may be seen distorting its abdomen and partly protruded between the segments.

Although it is without special relationship either to the groups just mentioned or to those which follow, we may deal here with the immense tribe of the Lamellicornia, whose exact position with reference to other beetles is uncertain. They all have three or more of the terminal joints of the antennae drawn out into thin plates. They may be regarded as consisting of three families, *Lucanidae*, or Stag-beetles, *Passalidae*, and *Scarabaeidae*, or Chafers, the last vastly outnumbering the rest. The *Lucanidae*, of which about eight hundred species are known, are remarkable for the enormously enlarged mandibles common in the males. Many of the species reach a considerable size, and the Common Stag-beetle (*Lucanus cervus*) is the largest beetle found in Britain. The larvae of the *Lucanidae* feed upon decaying logs and tree-stumps.

L 2

The *Passalidae*, which also feed upon rotting wood, are a comparatively small group almost confined to the tropics. The peculiar character of the stridulatory organs in larvae and adults has been already referred to. In some at least of the species parent beetles and young seem to share the same burrows, and it is said that the young are unable to exist without their parents.

The *Scarabaeidae* include the largest and most striking of all the Coleoptera, as well as many of the most remarkable in other respects. They feed either upon vegetable tissues, living or dead, or upon excrement or carrion. To the latter class belong the ball-rolling *Scarabaei* whose strange customs have aroused attention from the earliest recorded times. The ball of dung which is pushed backwards by the beetle with its hind-legs was for ages believed to contain its egg, and it has only recently been proved that this is not the case. It is the insect's own food-supply that is treated in this way, and that intended for its young is manipulated within a chamber previously excavated in the ground. When engaged in rolling their balls the beetles are often attacked by others of their species, whose object is to secure the booty for themselves, and the struggle for possession is sometimes mistaken by observers for peaceful co-operation.

STAG-BEETLE

Chiasognathus granti (slightly reduced), from Chili. 1, Male ; 2, Female. The enormous unsymmetrical mandibles of the male, unlike the small pair possessed by the female, seem quite unsuited for practical use.

In the genus *Scarabaeus* true co-operation is not known to occur, but in the nearly related genus *Gymnopleurus* it is often the case that the ball is the joint property of two individuals, who combine in its construction and afterwards in rolling it, one pushing while the other pulls. It has been found by careful investigation of a considerable number of such couples that the one who pushes is always a female and the other always a male. Moreover, there is reason to believe that, in the event of an attack by a marauder, the latter, if successful, merely replaces the rival of its own sex and the operation proceeds as if nothing had happened. When it is necessary to reconnoitre the ground this is done by the female, while the male remains on guard, and, when the time arrives to bury and consume the ball, a suitable spot is selected by the female, the prize is conveyed there, the earth scraped away beneath it, allowing it to sink into the ground, and finally it is devoured by the harmonious couple. By a similar operation food is provided for the insects' progeny, only, instead of consuming the ball after burying it, a depression is formed in it by the female, an egg is laid in this, and the edges are brought together again, forming an air chamber in which the grub hatches, to find both shelter and a sufficiency of food prepared for him. The interior is eaten, but the outer crust is always left intact, forming a cell in which the transformations are undergone, and is only ruptured when at last the time comes for the mature beetle to emerge.

The ball-rolling is carried on in the full light of day and without any attempt at concealment, and this, so different from the custom of most terrestrial animals, which carefully avoid publicity, indicates that these beetles have nothing to fear from birds or other insectivorous creatures.

Scarabaeus sacer

The Sacred Scarab of Egypt, rolling its ball. The ball of dung is first shaped between the legs, then rolled about for a time and finally buried and devoured.

Experiments with some of these have shown that the insects are rejected with disgust, and remarkable confirmation of their unpalatability is supplied in the case of a number of species of *Gymnopleurus* inhabiting different parts of Africa. It has been found that these are mimicked by various species of the genus *Onthophagus*, which frequent the same places but are not ball-rollers. The size and colour of the *Gymnopleuri*, different in each region, are reproduced in the *Onthophagi* occurring in the same places. The imitation is so close that certain small patches of white hairs upon the abdomen in certain of the ball-rollers, which, owing to slight excisions of the edges of the wing-covers, appear as white spots upon the back, are found also in their mimics. In these, however, the white hairs, although occupying exactly the same position, are actually on the wing-covers and not on the abdomen.

The numerous species of *Scarabaeus* and *Gymnopleurus* inhabit different districts of Southern Europe, Africa, and Asia; but perhaps even more remarkable in their habits are the members of some related genera.   The species of *Copris*, for example, of which *Copris lunaris* is the British representative, form a large brood-chamber underground by the collaboration

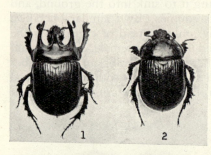

Geotrupes typhaeus

1, Male; 2, Female.   The two parents, in collaboration, excavate and provision a nest for their family.

of the male and female, the latter digging while the former carries away the excavated earth.   The male then brings the food-material and the female shapes it into balls of the proper size.   These become pear-shaped when an air-cell has been formed at the top of each containing a single egg.   The parents remain in the subterranean chamber guarding their brood during their development. The Dor-beetles (*Geotrupes*), which are familiar inhabitants of British pastures, have similar habits, the two parents labouring together at the task of storing food for their young.   In their case, however, a long shaft is first sunk and a lateral branch tunnel is dug and packed with dung for each member of the future family.   The size of the brood in these beetles is surprisingly small.

Many of the dung-beetles (sub-family *Coprinae*) as well as *Scarabaeidae* of

HERCULES-BEETLES

Dynastes hercules. (Much reduced.)   1, Male; 2, Female.   The female is not only without the immense horns of the male, but is dull brown in colour, instead of shining green and black.

other sub-families (*Dynastinae, Cetoniinae*, etc.) bear extraordinary horns or outgrowths upon the head and thorax.   These are generally confined to the male, as in the giant Hercules-beetle (*Dynastes hercules*), Atlas-beetle (*Chalcosoma atlas*), and Goliath-beetles (*Goliathus giganteus, etc.*), but they may be present in both sexes, as in the Spanish Copris (*Copris hispanus*),

RHINOCEROS-BEETLES

Oryctes boas. 1, Male; 2, Female. In spite of their formidable aspect, the horned beetles are peculiarly harmless. Most of them feed upon waste substances, but this species attacks coconut palms.

or each sex may have an armature peculiar to itself, as in the remarkable West African *Copris draco* shown on a previous page. The Hercules-beetle, measured to the tip of its horn, may reach a length of six inches, but the bulkiest of all known insects are the Elephant-beetles (*Megasoma elephas* and *actaeon*) of South America. Formidable as they appear, they are harmless insects, feeding as a rule upon decaying vegetable matter; but the Rhinoceros-beetles (*Oryctes*) are very injurious to coconut palms, burrowing into and devouring the soft wood.

The most numerous in species and in individuals of all the Lamellicornia is the Cockchafer group (sub-family *Melolonthinae*), examples of which occur in all parts of the world, the larvae feeding upon roots below the surface of the soil and the adults upon leaves. Many of them live two or three years in their subterranean stage of existence and suddenly appear on the wing in vast numbers, disappearing almost as suddenly within a very few weeks, for the adult life of these insects is short.

The *Cerambycidae*, often known as Longicorns, on account of their usually long antennae, constitute another very

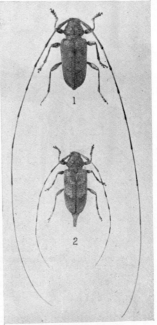

LONGICORN BEETLES

Acanthocinus aedilis. 1, Male; 2, Female. These are timber-destroying beetles found in the British Isles.

large and important group, nearly all the members of which spend their larval life tunnelling in and feeding upon timber. Most of them are long and narrow in shape, but their external aspect is extremely varied and they are particularly liable to imitate the appearance of other insects which are protected from insectivorous enemies by the possession of offensive properties of some kind. This is especially the case with those sunshine-

A Longicorn Beetle, *Nothopeus fasciatipennis* (1), which mimics the wasp, *Mygnimia aviculus* (2). These insects are found together in Borneo and in flight are almost indistinguishable.

loving kinds which frequent flowers. Those of nocturnal habits, which remain in hiding by day, usually have the colouring and markings of the bark or lichen amongst which they are accustomed to conceal themselves. Some of the diurnal forms have the elytra greatly reduced, the wings long and exposed, and the abdomen pointed and curved, so that, being similarly coloured, they bear a very close resemblance to certain wasps and stinging *Braconidae* which visit the same flowers as themselves. The European *Necydalis major*, for example, greatly resembles the hornet, and the Bornean *Nothopeus fasciatipennis* is found flying in company with a formidable wasp, *Mygnimia aviculus*, to which it bears so exact a resemblance both in aspect and movements that, except by close inspection, the two are indistinguishable. The most remarkable feature in the latter case is the reproduction by the beetle of the pattern of the wasp's wings. The occurrence of any kind of pattern in the wings of beetles is extremely unusual, but the wings of *Nothopeus fasciatipennis* are dark and ornamented with a large white patch towards the tip exactly like those of its model. The most obvious difference in bodily shape between these mimetic beetles and their models is in the broader waists of the former, but this is concealed in certain cases by a remarkable patch of white silky hairs on each side, which, leaving exposed only a narrow dark line, produces exactly the appearance of a " wasp-waist." Although normally long and narrow in shape, some of the *Cerambycidae* also mimic the flat dilated form as well as the characteristic colours and patterns of the *Lycidae*, which have been already mentioned as peculiarly unpalatable insects.

The *Chrysomelidae* are nearly related to the *Cerambycidae*, but generally feed upon foliage instead of upon wood, and larvae and adults may often be found feeding side by side. Some of them are remarkable for the fact that the young are born alive and not hatched from eggs like most insects. Many of the *Chrysomelidae* exhibit very brilliant and beautiful colouring, and many are protected by possessing more or less poisonous properties. The larvae of *Cladocera nigro-ornata*, found in the Kalahari Desert, are actually used by the natives for poisoning their arrows. The contents of the body of the grub (called N'gwa by the Bushmen) are squeezed out upon the arrow-head and produce a rapid and deadly effect upon lions and even larger animals. Many species of this family occur in great abundance and are very injurious to crops. A well-known example is the Colorado Potato-beetle (*Leptinotarsa decemlineata*), which has caused enormous losses to potato - growers in North America, and even made its appearance in Britain on more than one occasion, but fortunately it has never succeeded in establishing itself in Europe. Other serious Chrysomelid pests are the Flea-beetles belonging to the sub-family *Halticinae*. These are able to jump by

COLORADO POTATO-BEETLE
Leptinotarsa decemlineata and larvae.

means of their hind-legs, the femora of which are much enlarged, and their larvae generally live between the upper and lower membranes of leaves, devouring the soft tissue. Many species are very injurious to cabbage, turnip, and other cruciferous crops, the Turnip-flea (*Phyllotreta nemorum*) being a familiar example.

A peculiar group of *Chrysomelidae* is that of the Tortoise-beetles (*Cassidinae*), so called from their peculiar shape, the head and legs being almost concealed by expansions of the prothorax and elytra. The larvae bear a pair of tail-filaments which are carried over the back and upon which the cast skins and excrement are retained, forming a very remarkable kind of screen. Some of the Oriental and African Tortoise-beetles have in life an extremely beautiful iridescent lustre, while the Tropical American representatives are remarkable for their curious shapes and patterns.

The last great tribe of beetles is that of the Rhynchophora or Weevils, which are distinguished from those last described by the head being produced into a snout, sometimes short and sometimes extremely long and slender, at the end of which the mouth is placed. The largest family is that of the *Curculionidae*, an immense group of which there are many species in every part of the world. Many of them are clothed with minute scales, sometimes exquisitely coloured, and the arrangement of these scales produces patterns of almost infinite variety. The larvae are legless grubs, most of which live within the tissues of plants, and many are bad crop pests. The large Palm-weevils (*Rhynchophorus*) are very injurious to coconut and other palms, the larvae attacking the trees from the ground-level and hollowing out the stems. In Brazil and other regions inhabited by them these large, fat grubs are much esteemed by the natives as an article

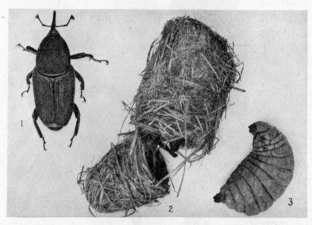

PALM-WEEVIL

Rhynchophorus. 1, Weevil; 2, Cocoon of wood-fibres; 3, Grub. These beetles are very destructive of palm trees in many parts of the world. The fat grubs are much esteemed as food by the natives of Brazil and other lands. (Reduced.)

of food. The little cosmopolitan Rice-weevil (*Calandra oryzae*), found everywhere in cargoes of grain, although very small in comparison, is closely related to the Palm-weevils.

The *Attelabinae* are a sub-family, interesting both for their curious long-necked forms and their habit of rolling leaves. These are first partly cut through by the jaws of the female beetle, causing part of the leaf to hang down, after which an egg is deposited and rolled up in the severed part, which provides food and shelter to the larva. *Attelabus curculionoides*, a bright orange-coloured insect which rolls oak-leaves and forms from them neat little barrel-shaped structures, is not uncommon in England.

A comparatively small but important family of Rhynchophora is that of the *Scolytidae*, or Shot-hole borers. These are the little beetles which make the numerous small round holes often seen in the trunks or boughs

of unhealthy trees. Many of them feed upon the layer immediately underneath the bark, causing the latter eventually to fall off. The mother beetle
perforates the bark and then drives a brood-tunnel beneath it, along which
she lays eggs at regular intervals and on each side. Each grub on emergence
burrows at right angles to the brood-tunnel, his burrow increasing in
diameter with his growth, and the whole system of burrows produces
a balanced and graceful pattern, differing according to the species. Arrived
at its full growth, each larva forms a cocoon at the end of its burrow, and
finally, as a mature beetle, bores
its way to the outside.

The members of another group
of *Scolytidae* are called Ambrosia-
beetles, from the fact that they
feed, not upon the wood of the
trees they inhabit, but upon certain
species of fungus or mildew which
they grow on the walls of their
burrows. These beetles live in
communities and are said to prepare
a special compost, in which they
plant the spores of the fungus,
introduced by them for the purpose.
When ripe the crop is gathered
and supplied to their young. In
some cases each larva lies in a
separately excavated cell, to which
the food is brought by the adults ;
in others the young are active and
are said, at a certain age, to share
in the labours of the community.
The principal genus of the first
group is *Xyleborus*, of which about
two hundred and fifty species are

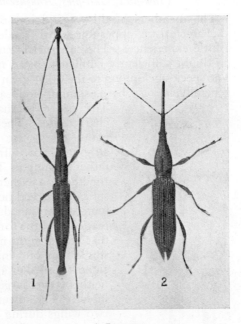

A Brenthid

Lasiorrhynchus barbicornis from New Zealand. 1, Male;
2, Female. The male is extremely attenuated.

known. The second group constitutes a distinct family, *Platypodidae*, of
very different appearance from the *Scolytidae* and without any elongation
of the head. The females of many of the *Platypodidae* are provided with
very curiously arranged bunches of long hairs upon the head. These are
said to be the receptacles in which the fungus spores are carried from the
old burrows to the new when a fresh colony is founded.

The *Brenthidae* are a peculiar group of very elongate weevils, abundant
in forest regions throughout most of the world, but with only two representatives in Europe. The extreme attenuation of many of them produces
rather a strong resemblance to some of the stick-insects (*Phasmidae*).
They are also remarkable for the usually complete difference in the form

of the head in the two sexes.   The female has a very slender snout, bearing at its tip extremely minute jaws, with which she bores into dead trees in order to deposit her eggs in the holes.   The males are larger-headed creatures with prominent jaws, and are sometimes seen fighting together.

Order HYMENOPTERA

By N. D. RILEY, F.E.S.

(Saw-flies, Gall-flies, Ichneumons, Ants, Bees, and Wasps)

The members of this most interesting and very extensive order have a characteristic appearance that renders them quite unmistakable after a little experience.   The superficial features of Ants, Bees, and Wasps are no doubt sufficiently familiar to need no further description at this point. The species belonging to the other great groups have much the same look— generally, a very hard, shining body and rather short, transparent wings.

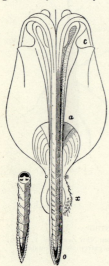

Boring apparatus of a female Giant-tailed Wasp (*Sirex gigas*).   (Much enlarged.)

The order is sharply defined and fairly easy to characterise.   The two pairs of wings (absent in many cases) are membranous, devoid of scales, although not infrequently coloured, and generally rather shining.   They are nearly always connected together on either side of the body by means of a series of curved hooks on the front edge of the hind-wing, so arranged that they fasten on to a fold in the rear edge of the fore-wing.   The linking is so effective that at first sight many species appear to have but a single pair of wings.   The hind pair is always considerably smaller and shorter than the front pair, but neither is ever large when compared with the size of the insect.   The advantages of this firm connection of the two wings during flight is very obvious.   The veins, or nervures, that run through the membrane of the wing are not numerous; frequently they are curiously curved so as to enclose a number of " cells " which are important from the point of view of classification. Towards the extremity of the front edge of the fore-wing there is usually a dark spot, known as the stigma.

The head is very freely movable.   The thorax is very well developed, as a rule, and usually has fused to it the first segment of the abdomen; the structure so formed, which is not found in any other group of insects, is sometimes called the " ali-trunk."   The " waist," due to the constriction of the next segment, or segments, of the abdomen, is one of the most conspicuous features of the order: it does not lie between thorax and abdomen, but is entirely confined to the latter.   Of the segments of the thorax the middle one (mesothorax) far surpasses the other two in development.

The antennae are generally simple or clubbed, or they may be bent in the middle, as in Bees, when the basal portion is known as the " scape," and the outer part the " flagellum." Mandibles are always present, but the other mouth-parts undergo numerous modifications in the different groups, more particularly in the Bees, in which they are often most remarkably elaborate. The three pairs of legs are always well developed, and undergo little modification except, again, in the Bees. A structure most distinctive of the females of all Hymenoptera is the ovipositor ; it is this organ that is so frequently modified to form the sting.

The general features of the Hymenoptera combine with a temperament of extreme nervous energy to give them a character for general intelligence, and a power of adapting means to an end such as are shown by no other order of Insects. The social species, such as the Ants, Bees, and Wasps, upon their own life-plane have solved social problems and industrial difficulties closely comparable with those pressing for solution in the various societies of men. Doubtless this has been achieved at the cost of a sacrifice of individuality that civilised man could not possibly tolerate. When, however, we remember that the " workers " of the ants, for example, as an accompaniment of their specialisation as workers pure and simple, have lost their sexual faculties, and that the soldiers have in some cases even lost the power of feeding themselves, we may well doubt whether such solutions of important problems are really the best, at any rate in so far as the human race is concerned.

Development is of the " complete metamorphosis " type, but as it shows certain well-marked adaptations in the different groups into which the order naturally divides, it is more conveniently dealt with when treating of those groups. The generally inactive grub, or larva, always passes through a resting pupal stage before the emergence of the adult or perfect insect.

Fossil Hymenoptera are abundant in Tertiary strata, where they are represented by species that differ very little from those now existing. In Mesozoic-beds the only known fossils are large Horntails (*Pseudosirex*), again very similar to species that still exist. Farther back still, however, in the Lower Permian, one finds fossils that are clearly ancestral to the Hymenoptera, but not actually referable to them ; and the same applies to *Sycopteron* from the Upper Carboniferous. It appears, therefore, that the order is of comparatively recent development. The only large order that is possibly, and, in fact, probably, even younger is the Lepidoptera. But of that order so very few fossils have ever been discovered that any conclusions arrived at must, in the nature of things, be largely surmise.

The Hymenoptera fall very conveniently into three main groups : Phytophaga, Parasitica, and Aculeata. The first includes the Saw-flies and Horntails, the second parasitic and gall-forming species, and the third the Ants, Bees, and Wasps.

Sub-order PHYTOPHAGA

(*Saw-flies, Horntails, etc.*)

As suggested by the name applied to this sub-order, the food of the larvae of all its members consists entirely of vegetable matter. The Horntail larvae (*Siricidae*) bore in wood, those of the Stem Saw-flies (*Cephidae*), in the stems of various plants. The caterpillars of the true Saw-flies (*Tenthredinidae*) feed upon the leaves of trees and shrubs, and, but for the greater number of their legs, might easily be mistaken for those of butterflies and moths; they are frequently strikingly coloured but rather repulsive objects, naked and shining, and commonly feed in a more or less gregarious manner. Generally they carry the last few segments curled under them, and, when disturbed, have a curious habit of quickly raising and slowly lowering this part of the body, all the members of a group moving together. The action is probably defensive. When fully grown most of the plant-feeding larvae pupate in or near the surface of the ground in a slender cocoon, after the manner of the moths. The internal feeders, however, usually pupate within the plant or tree that has served them as food and as host.

The Giant Wood-wasp, *Sirex gigas* (*Siricidae*).
(1) Male ; (2) Female.

On account of the fact that none of the Phytophaga has the first segment of the abdomen narrowed to form a waist, they are sometimes spoken of as the "Sessiliventres." The squat, waistless appearance is most in evidence in the true Saw-flies, which are rather sluggish creatures, and in the Horntails. In some of the other families, as one would suspect, there sometimes occurs a tapering of the front part of the body, but its second segment is never definitely constricted, nor is its first segment fully amalgamated with the thorax. The ovipositor in this sub-order is never used as a sting. It serves its proper function only, but, for this purpose, is very generally modified to form a kind of saw with which the female can cut into the tissues of plants (or the wood of trees in the case of the Horntails), and there deposit her eggs. In the true Saw-flies it is composed of thin, paired plates having the inner edge toothed like a saw, and the outer roughened like a file, the whole protected by a pair of sheaths. The name of the family is based upon this modification of the ovipositor.

A stem Saw-fly,
Hartigia linearis.

The phenomenon of parthenogenesis, or virgin re-production, is of very common occurrence amongst the Saw-flies, and in them has been much studied of recent years, in the hope that some light might be shed upon the mechanism of this curious development. The facts, however, are so complicated in some species that no satisfactory explanation is yet forthcoming. In about one-third of the British species the male is still unknown, the females reproduce par-thenogenetically, and give rise only to females. In some other cases, however, the unfertilised eggs give rise only to males.

There can be no doubt that the Phytophaga are the most primitive Hymenoptera now existing. The occurrence of the fossil *Pseudosirex* has already been referred to ; the other, earlier, fossils mentioned are much more closely allied to this sub-order than to either of the other two. The fact that they exhibit none of the specialisations so characteristic of the Parasitica and Aculeata also tends to con-firm a belief in their primitive nature. They are, however, not entirely devoid of transitions to-wards the development of at least the parasitic habit, for the curious and in many ways aberrant members of the small family *Oryssidae* are already actually parasitic upon wood-boring beetles, and, indeed, exhibit a few structural features more usually associated with the Parasitica. The gregarious habits of some of the Saw-fly caterpillars (already referred to), the carnivorous habit of a few of the adults, and parthenogenetic reproduction all foreshadow the much greater development of similar behaviour in the other two sub-orders.

TYPICAL SAW-FLIES
Above—*Cimbex lutea ;* below—*Pamphilius sylvaticus.*
Both species occur in the British Isles.

Sub-order *PARASITICA*

(*Ichneumon-flies, etc.*

The very large group of insects that falls under this heading can, together with the next sub-order, be readily distinguished from the Phytophaga by the " petiolate " abdomen—a waist, that is to say, is formed by the second segment of the body—and also by the reduced veining of the wings, and the worm-like larvae. The larvae are quite dissimilar to the " caterpillars " of the Saw-flies, being of the form popularly termed " grubs." From the next sub-order, with which, indeed, they have much more in common than was formerly supposed, the Parasitica can be separated by the fact that the female ovipositor is used for its normal purpose, and is never modified to form a sting, as it is in nearly all the Aculeates. The sub-order is apparently of comparatively recent development, since, with the exception of a few rather debatable forms from the Jurassic, all the known fossils are of Tertiary age.

A common British Ichneumon fly, *Ophion obscurus*, reddish in colour, which frequently comes to the light of houses in late summer and autumn.

Some 40,000 species belonging to this division of the Hymenoptera have already been described, and, as they consist very largely of most minute insects, it is certain that very many more await discovery. With the exception of the Gall-wasps (*Cynipidae*), they are almost exclusively parasitic, or at least carnivorous, in habit, attacking other insects and also to some extent such allied creatures as Centipedes.

As a whole the members of the Parasitica are to be regarded as amongst man's most valuable friends. With the aid of the parasitic Diptera (two-winged flies), they do more to keep down the numbers of plant-feeding insects than any other group of animals. The practice of " biological control," as it is called, has been developed more in connection with these small creatures than amongst any other group of insects. It is, of course, an artificially arranged control that develops, once started, upon natural lines. It consists of the use of parasitic species for the purpose of attacking and checking the work of insects harmful to crops, and frequently entails the introduction of parasites into new areas, and sometimes even the necessity of breeding them in confinement for liberation at the most suitable moment.

Some of the most romantic episodes in the development of " economic " entomology have occurred in connection with this work, and, did space permit, might well be related. When man clears virgin land he invariably disturbs the delicate balance of nature. He then further upsets it by introducing crops alien to the soil. The next thing that happens is that these crops are attacked by insects, and, indeed, very often by species that have arrived without their controlling parasites. To re-establish the biological control of these species is a slow process. First the country of origin of the pest has to be found, then its parasites (usually parasitic Hymenoptera). The latter then have to be bred, and transported, often half over the world, to the scene of their new activities. But that is not all, for careless work may result in the introduction of a hyperparasite, one that preys upon the primary parasite, or the parasite itself may run " amok " and change its habits in its new environment, so that the whole subject is one of amazing complexity, but none the less extraordinarily fascinating.

From the point of view of classification, the Parasitica fall into four somewhat unequal groups, usually termed super-families : *Ichneumonoidea* (true Ichneumons) ; *Cynipoidea* (Gall-wasps) ; *Chalcidoidea* (Chalcid wasps) ; and *Proctotrypoidea* (Proctotrypid wasps). In the last-named family the ovipositor arises from the apex of the body, whereas in the other three it arises some way before this point. The Chalcids may be recognised by their elbowed antennae ; the Ichneumons by the presence, the Gall-wasps by the absence, of a " stigma," a dark area on the front edge of the fore-wing. There is a general air of " lankiness " about all the larger members of

The Oak Gall-wasp (*Biorhiza pallida*).   Two females are shown on the galls.

the sub-order that should serve as a rough guide to distinguish them from the Aculeates ; they usually are very slender, with long legs and antennae. In the case of the small species, their size alone is generally a sufficient indication.

The Gall-wasps (*Cynipoidea*) may be conveniently dealt with first as they differ essentially in habits from the remainder of the group. They are small insects, often minute, and usually black, or very dark in colour. The female wasp lays her eggs within the tissues of the plant upon which the grub is to feed, piercing the surface by means of her ovipositor. It has commonly been thought that this act alone was sufficient to start the growth of the gall. But it now appears that this is not the case, but that the gall does not commence to form until after the grub has hatched. The precise causative agency is, however, quite unknown ; the gall swells somewhat, as the grub develops within it ; the nutritive material which serves as food is placed innermost. The shape of the gall is always characteristic of the species that forms it ; although over eighty per cent. of the known species affect the oak—a very remarkable fact—they are all distinct in appearance. Within the gall there frequently arises quite a colony of insects, forming a definite biological association. In the main these consist of the larvae of other gall-wasps, of Diptera, of Beetles, and even of Moths, all of which share the shelter and the produce provided by the original owner ; but the inevitable parasites, members of other groups of this same sub-order, also creep in.

In addition to this common practice, the Gall-wasps also exhibit certain curious features in connection with their methods of propagation that are not without interest. Very frequently the alternate generations have quite different habits and structure, one of them reproducing parthenogenetically. In many species males have never been seen at all, although thousands of females have been bred, and it seems possible that the male no longer exists. A case in point is that of the British species *Biorhiza pallida*. In that generation, which has both males and females, the eggs are laid in the roots of the oak ; these produce galls from which another generation arises in the spring, all the members of which are females. These climb up the trees and lay in the buds the eggs that subsequently give rise to the familiar " oak-apples." The common " pin-cushion " galls of rose-bushes are also produced by one of these tiny wasps, *Rhodites rosae*, in which species, however, there is no alternation of generations (known technically as heterogeny), but males are very much rarer than females. This flexibility of reproductive processes is, however, a very marked feature of all the Hymenoptera, common to all groups, and reaching its highest development in the ants and bees. No doubt it has greatly contributed to the evolution of the social organisations for which they are so well known.

The Rose Gall-wasp (*Rhodites rosae*).

The remaining Parasitica are, almost without exception, at least carnivorous, if not actually parasitic. In the vast majority of cases the female lays her eggs actually within the body of the host, after piercing the skin with her ovipositor. In many cases she merely lays them upon the surface of the victim, and in a few simply in the neighbourhood of the host. The latter phenomena are of peculiar interest, as, considered in conjunction with the more specialised method, they provide an indication of the probable lines along which the female egg-laying instinct has been evolved. Several very striking examples of this habit have quite recently been discovered, and deserve mention. Amongst the Chalcid wasps, Wheeler records finding in the nest of an ant in Texas a minute metallic-green species (*Orasema viridis*) which produces an enormous number of eggs. The minute active grubs that emerge from these—they are only 0·16 mm. long—attach themselves to the necks of the larvae and pupae of the ants. On moulting they assume the usual plump form, and eventually pupate in this situation, subsequently falling to the ground.

Another minute Chalcid wasp (*Perilampus hyalinus*) behaves in much the same way, but before attaching itself to the outside of its host and becoming worm-like its active " planidium-larva," as it is called, goes through a very remarkable performance. It has been observed crawling upon small species of caterpillar, into the body of which it subsequently bores its way. Once inside, nothing further happens unless and until another parasite of the caterpillar (a fly-maggot) appears upon the scene. When this happens the planidium descends upon and enters it in turn. Again it rests, and remains quiet until the fly-maggot has finished growing and turned into a pupa. Then it is that the planidium awakens. It bites its way out of the pupa and proceeds then to feed upon it in the same way as the *Orasema* mentioned above. In the *Perilampus*, and probably also in the *Orasema*, the eggs are laid upon foliage in situations likely to be visited by the host-caterpillars, and their enormous numbers represent an adaptation to ensure the continuance of the species, for mortality amongst them, when it is considered how few can possibly meet with all the favourable circumstances necessary to their proper development, must be extraordinarily high.

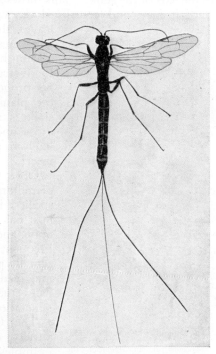

Rhyssa persuasoria. The remarkable parasite of the Giant Wood-wasp (*Sirex gigas*).

At the risk of proving monotonous, reference must be made to one other species of *Perilampus*, on account of its similarly remarkable life-history. This is *Perilampus chrysopae*, whose females lay their eggs near colonies of aphids that are being preyed upon by the larvae of Lace-wings (*Chrysopidae*). " The planidium is active immediately upon hatching, crawling rapidly about, but soon attaches itself to the leaf by means of the sucker at the tip of its abdomen, and stands out at right angles to the surface. In this position it remains for days at a time, motionless, excepting when some insect comes within its reach, when it suddenly becomes frantically active, reaching and swaying back and forth in its attempt to attach itself to the prospective host (the *Chrysopa* larva). If the latter should unfortunately come too near, the planidium attaches itself with lightning-like quickness to a hair or bristle of its host. It then leisurely crawls down the hair to the host's body and attaches itself by its mouth-hooks. Quite often the planidia are found attached to the egg-stalk of the *Chrysopa*, assuming a position at right angles to the axis of the stalk. This shows an interesting instinct in the planidium, since it may, and actually does, waylay the young *Chrysopa* larva as it

The Caterpillar of a South African Liparid Moth covered with cocoons of an *Apanteles*, the grubs of which have emerged from their host.

leaves the egg and crawls down the stalk. The prescience of the mother *Chrysopa* in placing her eggs at the end of a long egg-stalk to overcome the cannibalistic propensities of her progeny is in this case their undoing, since the planidium attached to the *Chrysopa* egg-stalk is sure to reach its proper host, while those upon the surface of a leaf are quite as likely to attach themselves to an aphid or other insect."

Once securely attached to its host, this planidium behaves just as those of the other species described. It remains quiet until its host has turned into a chrysalis, and then falls upon and devours as much of it as it needs. Frequently these minute parasites do not actually prove fatal to their host, as might be imagined. But, if this be so, on the other hand they often produce malformations, degeneration, or prevent their due development.

The Chalcid wasps exhibit a far greater variety of habit than even the foregoing examples indicate. They are, in the main, parasites of Lepidoptera, Diptera, and Bugs, and include the smallest of all known insects, namely the egg-parasites belonging to the genus *Trichogramma* and to the *Mymaridae* (Fairy-flies). Probably the smallest of all these is *Alaptus magnanimus*, which, in the adult state, only measures one-fifth of a millimetre in length. Strangely enough, quite a number of these minute forms have actually acquired the habit of swimming under water in search of the eggs of the water-bugs that they parasitise. As many as twenty individual grubs of some of these species have been known to develop within a single egg of a moderately large Swallow-tail butterfly, the North American *Papilio turnus*, in fact. In certain other egg-parasites belonging to the

Encyrtid group a very remarkable phenomenon known as polyembryony
has been developed. A single egg is laid within the egg of some other
insect, but does not prevent the larva of the latter emerging. Within it the
Encyrtid egg develops, not into a
single grub, but, by a process of
division, into a number of grubs,
often as many as one hundred individuals being formed—a device of
obvious benefit to the species, and
saving much labour to the female.

Microgaster tibialis

A member of a large genus almost entirely parasitic
on the caterpillars of butterflies and moths.
(Much enlarged.)

Some of the most curiously
specialised Chalcids are the non-
parasitic Agaonids such as *Blastophaga
psenes*, upon which the ripening of
figs depends. The males are wingless, and so modified in other respects that they bear little resemblance
to the females. The natural hosts
of this species, in the Smyrna variety
of fig, are those figs (caprifigs) whose
receptacles contain only male flowers,
which are galled by the female
Agaonids. The males emerge first,
and fertilise the females before they
leave the galls, reaching them by
boring through the surface. When fertilised the female escapes from the
gall and from the receptacle into the open, laden with pollen she has
accidentally collected upon herself in the process. She then enters other

Pimpla instigator

A very common parasite
of the caterpillars of
many species of butter-
flies and moths.

figs for the purpose of laying her eggs, and it appears
that, not being able to distinguish their sex until she
gets inside the receptacles, she frequently enters receptacles containing only female flowers, which she
therefore accidentally pollinates. Since these flowers,
however, are of different shape from the male flowers,
she is unable to deposit her eggs in them, and therefore
flies away again. If this explanation is the correct one,
and there seems now little doubt about it, the ripening of
the figs is due to the mistakes of the female *Blastophaga* !
The male never leaves the receptacle in which he
emerged from his pupal envelope.

The Ichneumons include nearly all the larger Parasitica, and also, of
course, very many minute forms as well. Some 16,000 species are at present
known. They are, on the whole, perhaps rather more catholic in their
tastes than are the Chalcid wasps, many of them being not at all particular

as to their hosts. Familiar examples are the large and rather awkward yellowish or reddish members of the genera *Ophion* and *Paniscus*, which attack many large caterpillars. These have long, curved bodies, flattened somewhat from the sides, and are typical Ichneumons. *Rhyssa persuasoria* is a remarkable species ; the female is able to bore through the bark and wood of trees by means of her ovipositor, so that she can lay her eggs alongside the larvae of the Giant Wood-wasp (*Sirex gigas*) upon which her offspring feed. *Thalessa*, a related species, has an ovipositor, used for a similar purpose, that sometimes measures as much as six inches in length. *Microgaster* is another, but much smaller species, that appears to be very partial to the "looper" caterpillars of the Geometrid moths ; its cocoons may often be observed, for example, packed like honeycomb beneath the arched and moribund body of the Magpie-moth caterpillar. And *Apanteles* is the

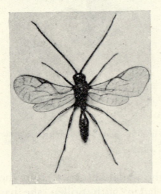

Aphidius
A parasite of the Aphid (Green-fly).
(Much enlarged.)

Cocoon of *Praon*—beneath the body of its dead
host (an aphid). (After Riley.)

common parasite of the Cabbage-white butterfly ; its grubs, on emergence from the caterpillar, spin the familiar little bright yellow cocoons in which to pupate.

All these smaller species belong to the Braconid section of the super-family. The same section also contains the valuable species of *Aphidius* and *Praon* that parasitise the Aphids (Green-fly), and whose highly beneficial work can readily be detected from the appearance of the aphids they have attacked. *Aphidius*, when full-fed, splits the underneath of the aphid's body and cements it to the leaf ; the aphid's body then assumes the colour of straw, and the *Aphidius* changes to a chrysalis inside it. *Praon*, on the other hand, forms a cocoon on the leaf, in the shape of a little pedestal surmounted by the dead body of the *Aphis*.

To the super-family *Proctotrypoidea* belong a number of minute insects with scarcely a trace of veins in the wings in many cases. Their habits are very imperfectly known. They are parasitic upon insects and spiders, and frequently upon the eggs of the former, as in the case of the two species *Teleas laeviusculus* and *T. terebrans* shown in the accompanying illustration.

Sub-order ACULEATA

(*Ants, Bees, and Wasps*)

Reference has already been made, under the Parasitica, to the characters that distinguish them from the Aculeates. There is much to be said, however, for the view that would unite the two sub-orders together under the term Clistogastra, for they are closer to one another than is either to the Saw-flies and their allies. From the biological standpoint there are many points of close contact between the two divisions. A step in the direction of the multiplicity of forms presented by the ants is visible in some of the Chalcids and Ichneumons that occur in two or more different forms; the ovipositor of the Parasitica does occasionally have a slightly paralysing effect upon the prey, in the manner so general in Aculeates; those Aculeates that are parasitic invariably lay their eggs on the surface of their prey—a practice also very common in the Parasitica—and these same Aculeates often, as adults,

EGG-WASPS

(1) *Teleas laeviusculus ;* (2) *Teleas terebrans ;* (3) eggs of a moth with a *Teleas* upon them about to pierce and lay its eggs within; (4) the same (nat. size). (All except No. 4 much enlarged.)

actually consume at times portions of the prey they are really providing for their progeny, which practice has its counterpart in the behaviour of many Parasitica that feed upon the juices exuding from the punctures they have made in the unfortunate larvae chosen to receive their eggs. Structurally also, apart from the sting, there are many points of detail, especially in the less specialised families, which clearly indicate a very close connection with the Parasitica.

A striking point about all the Aculeates is that the whole business of life is conducted by the imago ; the larva is practically helpless, and, if not actually fed by the imago, is at least provided with an ample supply of carefully gathered food which it has merely to consume. Without careful search the larvae are never seen, and the imago alone is active.

The orderly arrangement of the Aculeates in a systematic classification is a matter of very considerable difficulty ; it will be convenient to deal with them under three or four headings, each of which corresponds with some definite evolutionary trend rather than with any particular structural features.

To commence with, there are a few small wasps that may be conveniently referred to as Bethyloid wasps. They form a somewhat heterogeneous collection of creatures that have been bandied about and classed sometimes with the Parasitica, sometimes with the Aculeates proper. They exhibit all degrees of parasitism. Some are at first internal parasites, but subsequently break out of the side of the host-larva in a peculiar sack; these are the Dryinids, whose adult females have fore-legs rather like those of the Mantids, that enable them to seize and hold motionless the larva into which they insert their eggs. Others are purely external (*Rhopalosoma*) and are apparently carried about by their hosts. Others again paralyse the larva which is to form the food of their progeny, laying eggs on or near it, but without removing it from its environment. And yet another group collects, in some cavity, the larvae upon which it lays its eggs, but does not as a rule make cells. In this single group, therefore, the habits of nearly all the Vespid and Sphecid wasps, to be dealt with later, can be seen foreshadowed.

Before passing on to deal with the Ants, there is one other group, the Ruby-wasps (*Chrysididae*), to be mentioned. These form a sharply defined family of rather small but extremely brilliant insects, whose highly polished bodies glow in the hot sunshine with metallic tints of red, blue, and green. Some twenty species occur in Great Britain. They may be handled with impunity, as, although they possess a sting, it is rarely used and not supplied with poison. They prey upon the Mason-wasps, in whose cells they lay their eggs, and upon whose grubs their own feed.

Ants are sufficiently familiar to need no descriptive introduction here. They are world-wide in distribution, and are represented by some 6000 species, so far as is at present known. All the species are social, and almost all have three distinct castes, males, fertile-females (queens), and infertile females (workers). The males are winged, and have their sense and reproductive organs highly developed, the antennae relatively longer, and the head smaller than in other castes of the same species. The queen is larger than the members of either of the other castes, often attaining a great size indeed, and has well-developed mandibles and reproductive organs, with usually short antennae and stout legs; she is at first winged, but sheds her wings after pairing. In the workers the body and thorax are relatively much smaller, the head often large, the antennae, mandibles, and legs well developed. All these castes are subject to modifications, but the workers are the most variable. In some species they are of various sizes, in others of two different sizes only, without intermediates. In the latter case one of the forms is usually represented by the soldiers, which are workers with especially large heads and mandibles.

In dealing with the Termites attention was called to the fact that all the winged sexual forms from nests distributed over a wide area often emerged simultaneously, thus affording means for the intercrossing of the colonies. Precisely the same thing happens in the case of the nuptial flights of ants. The subsequent action is, however, a little different. The males die ; the impregnated female on descending to earth strips off her wings, and digs for herself a small chamber in which she lies until her eggs mature. The latter are quite minute objects, and not to be confused with the " ants' eggs " of popular conception, which are generally the cocoons of ants containing the pupae, or even the pupae and larvae themselves.

But to return to the queen ; when her eggs hatch she still has to provide the young larvae with food, and this, until they are fully grown, she supplies from her salivary glands. It has, however, been observed that she also, at times, devours some of her own eggs, and even gives them occasionally to the growing larvae. But it is not until the workers have emerged from their pupae, made their way to the surface, and commenced to fend for themselves, that the now emaciated queen can cease to rely solely upon her own efforts. From this time on, however, the workers undertake the whole management of the nest, feeding, cleaning, and tending the young, even helping them through their moults, and carrying them from place to place. They also feed the queen, and construct the nest.

The Ponerine ants, which have a world-wide distribution, and form a dominant group in Australia, are generally conceded to be the most primitive. The three castes do not differ much in size ; their nests seldom contain more than a few dozen individuals, and are usually subterranean. They are carnivorous, and include such fierce creatures as the Bull-dog ants, which are fully an inch long, and the smaller Jumping ants. They will attack almost anything, and it has probably been truthfully remarked that little is known of their economy because few observers care to run the risk of being bitten and stung to pieces by them.

Of similar carnivorous habit are the Driver and Legionary ants (*Dorylinae*). These do not construct nests, but may perhaps be said to " bivouac " from time to time in true nomadic style. From these " camps " they sally forth on dull days, or at night, in search of prey. They are extraordinarily rapacious, and travel together in columns of amazing numbers. Belt mentions that he followed a moving column of a Nicaraguan species for several hundred yards without coming to the end of it. Their foraging raids rapidly denude the areas affected of all living insects, and often of small mammals as well. Savage states that they will destroy quite large animals, if these are not free to move away, he himself having lost pigs, birds, and even monkeys in this manner. A horde of the African black Driver-ant was observed on one occasion to make a clean sweep of three dead goats in three days. Such habits may seem very objectionable ; actually they are essentially very beneficial, for scavenging is a most necessary and valuable work.

All the most specialised groups of ants have abandoned the carnivorous habit and become vegetarians. Probably the one development is a result of the other. Plant food is, on the whole, much more abundant, and obtainable with far less effort than animal food, and therefore those ants that have turned to such a diet are freed from the strain of searching for their food, and, being assured of an adequate supply, have been enabled to expand their social organisation to a much fuller extent. Undoubtedly the two developments have gone hand in hand, and it seems probable that the alteration of feeding-habit was the primary change, and enabled the secondary improvement in colonial life to take place.

It is interesting to note how this vegetarian diet has led to eventual specialisation. The first step may be regarded as that in which plant-seeds alone are utilised. In the next stage the ants have learnt to sow the seeds, and to reap the harvest. As evidence of a collateral trend may be mentioned those that have acquired the habit of storing plant-refuse and cultivating the fungus that grows upon it for their food—a practice of which an accidental beginning can easily be imagined. Finally there are those that depend not upon the plant but entirely upon its products, such as honey and the subsidiary products like the honey-dew that flows from the aphids, coccids, and other insects feeding upon the plants. All these phases are met with in the three higher divisions (sub-families) of the ants still to be mentioned.

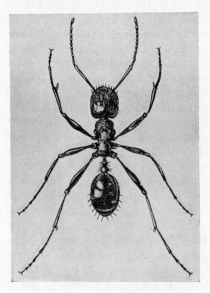

An Indian Harvester-ant, *Messor barbarus.*

To the large Myrmecine division belong the Harvester-ants and the Fungus-growers. The former gather seeds both from the ground and from the plants, remove the husks and store the grain in special granaries. The ancient naturalists, Pliny and Plutarch, observed that the ants bite off the radicle to prevent germination, an observation that has since been confirmed by modern observers. For the same purpose they also bring the seeds to the surface periodically, to dry them in the sun. The related American Harvester-ants actually grow their " ant-rice " in specially cleared areas around their nests, cultivating the soil for the purpose with great assiduity. A good example of the fungus-growers and fungus-eaters is provided by the Sauba or Parasol-ants of tropical America. The workers of this species may commonly be seen carrying on their backs small fragments of leaves, as if they were sunshades. These they store in special chambers below ground in masses on which the fungi grow. The fungi are, of course, never allowed to reach maturity, being used as food for both larvae and adults whilst still in the first stages of development. A curious association between ant and plant exists in the case of the Acacia-ants, which inhabit the very large thorns of some of these plants. The plant appears even to provide them with special food-bodies, and a sweet fluid, in return for which it secures protection from the leaf-cutting Sauba ants.

The minute, and often troublesome little brown Pharaoh's-ant (*Monomorium pharaonis*) also belongs to this group ; it frequently gets into houses, restaurants, and such places, and although rarely actually harmful, is generally a great nuisance. On the other hand, it is occasionally deliberately introduced into warehouses in India to check the ravages of the White-ants. The Tree-ants (*Cremastogaster*), which make globular nests of a papery material on the branches of trees, also belong to this group.

The Dolichoderine ants are said always to be recognisable by the peculiar odour, as of rancid butter, given out from glands at the tip of the body. They are nearly always associated with " honey-dew "-producing insects, such as aphids, and the larvae of Lycaenid ("Blue") butterflies. *Iridomyrmex* and *Leptomyrmex* are perhaps the best-

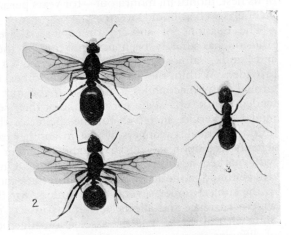

The Great Wood-ant, *Formica rufa.*
1, Male ; 2, Female ; 3, Worker. (Slightly enlarged.)

known genera, the latter being very remarkable in that no queen has ever been found in their nests, the former containing a few species that are so abundant as to be veritable pests.

In the most typical ants (*Formicinae*) social organisation reaches its zenith. The Red Tree-ant of India (*Oecophylla smaragdina*), whose queens, by the way, are green, are sometimes called Spinning-ants. The workers cannot produce silk, so they use that provided by the grubs instead. In order to make their shelters, a number of workers will hold the edges of a couple of leaves together, and then another will fasten them in this position by means of the silk spun by a larva which it holds in its jaws and moves backwards and forwards from side to side. The larvae are also used to spin protective webs as shelters over colonies of coccids that are " milked " by the ants. The remarkable Honey-pot ants of North America, South Africa, and

M

Australia also belong to this section. Their workers have a rather soft integument that is readily expanded; their food is almost entirely honey and " honey-dew." These substances they collect mainly at night, and, returning with it to the nest, regurgitate it, so that it can be swallowed again by other workers whose only function is to act as receptacles for it, and to produce it when required for feeding the colony.

Workers of this type are called " repletes "; their bodies are immensely swollen, and quite spherical; and they remain virtually immobile for months on end. As Wheeler has remarked : " Those who, in anthropomorphic mood, are wont to extol the fervid industry and extraordinary feats of muscular endurance in ants, should not overlook the beatific patience and self-sacrifice displayed by the replete Honey-ant, as it hangs from the rafters of its nest, month in, month out—for years perhaps—a reservoir of tempera-mental as well as liquid sweetness."

The relations of ants to other insects are exceedingly multifarious. Allusion has already been made to insects they tend outside their nests and " milk," almost as man tends his cows, for the honeyed secretion they provide. Within the nests numerous other creatures, comprehensively termed " myrmecophiles," are also to be met with. Many of these are tended by the ants again for the sake of their secretions; others appear to render no service in return for the shelter of the nest; others, maybe, are little more than scavengers, whilst in another category there are many that actually feed upon the ant larvae, and are either merely tolerated, or treated with marked hostility when encountered. One or two further examples will be found in the account of the Butterflies and Moths, and also references to the subject under several other orders, for the phenomenon is of very wide occurrence and affects very many insects in widely separated groups. Somewhat allied to it is the association together in the same nest of ants of different species. Sometimes these live amicably together; sometimes one species is a " social parasite " upon the other, eventually acquiring entire possession of the nest. But the most familiar form of association involves the subjugation of one species to the other, as, for example, amongst the slave-making ants of the northern hemisphere, of which the best-known species is the Red Robber-ant of Europe and West America (*Formica sanguinea*).

We have been able only to touch the fringe of the subject in this brief account of the ants. The reader who would learn more of their fascinating lives is recommended to make acquaintance with the admirable writings of Wheeler, Forel, Emery, Wasmann, and Donisthorpe.

We come now to the Wasps, a medley of families, some large, some small, some social, but mostly solitary, about whose classification there has of late been so much discussion that it is difficult to know how to group them. They are commonly arranged in two series of families, according to whether the dorsal (upper) piece of the first segment of the thorax reaches the scale-like structures (tegulae) that cover the wing-bases (Vespoid wasps), or not (Sphecoid wasps); but it should be borne in mind that the second arrangement is also characteristic of the Bees. The Sphecoid wasps, however, always have the hairs on the head and thorax simple in structure; in the Bees they are always feathery.

At the beginning of the Vespoid series are placed the Mutillid and Thynnid wasps, the latter sometimes called Flower-wasps on account of the extent to which they visit flowers, the former well known as Velvet or "Solitary-ants." In both groups there is a very remarkable difference between the sexes. The females are entirely wingless and deceptively like ants in appearance; the males are, as a rule, nearly twice as large as the females, and winged. They are handsome creatures, of moderate to small size, strikingly and conspicuously coloured in red, black, yellow, or even metallic blue. Although only three species occur in Great Britain they have a very wide distribution, particularly in warmer countries. Thynnids are very common in Australia, and Tillyard remarks

The Velvet Ant, *Mutilla europaeus*, so called on account of the ant-like appearance of the wingless female. 1, Male; 2, Female.

that: "the males fly rapidly in the sunshine; the females watch for them, and catch hold of them with their large mandibles, and are carried off for a swift nuptial flight; while pairing the female hangs head downward, attached to the abdomen of the male."

Lefroy described the pairing of an Indian Mutillid: "the male is a powerful insect . . . he finds the female, seizes her by the thorax and flies off; on some convenient spot he mates with her, clasping her firmly to him by his fore-legs and standing erect on the others . . . in the frequent intervals the male shook the female with a twisting motion as we would shake a bottle whose contents we desired to mix well." The Mutillids appear to be secondary parasites upon other ants, bees, or wasps, but the Thynnids burrow in the ground to lay their eggs upon beetle grubs, which they first paralyse.

The Australian Thynnid Wasp, *Campylothynnus flavopictus*, showing marked sexual dimorphism, in both size and structure. 1, Male; 2, Female, which is wingless.

This habit of the female Thynnid is also highly characteristic of the handsome Scoliid, or Hairy Flower-wasps, which include the largest known Vespoid wasps. In these the female is winged and generally larger than the male. Many species will lay their eggs only upon particular kinds of grubs, a fact which has been turned to considerable advantage already in waging war upon insect pests, a case in point being that of a Philippine Scoliid, which was introduced into the Hawaiian islands to deal with the *Anomala* beetle that was damaging sugar-cane. It has proved a very effective control.

The European Scoliid Wasp, *Scolia flavifrons*. A fascinating account of the habits of this handsome species was published by the celebrated observer Fabre.

The Pompilid, or Sand-wasps, have carried this predatory practice a stage further. They are not content to leave the prey selected for their offspring just where they found it. Instead, they dig little pits in which to place it, sealing them up after laying their eggs. They form a large group of extremely active insects, and, on account of the fact that their prey, without exception, consists of spiders, they are sometimes called the Spider-hunters. Some species attain a great size, three inches or more, and can even lay the giant Tarantula spider under tribute. Many accounts of their battles have been published; nearly always the wasp wins by striking from directly above and paralysing the spider.

Both solitary and social species are found in the true wasps. They are grouped under the title of Diploptera on account of their faculty of folding their wings lengthwise—a character by which they may readily be recognised. The solitary kinds (Eumenids) are generally known as Mason- or Potter-wasps or Mud-daubers, for they build little clay nests, not for their own habitation, but in which to store the paralysed caterpillars that will serve

An Indian Sand-wasp (Pompilid), *Batozonus unifasciatus*. 1, Male; 2, Female.

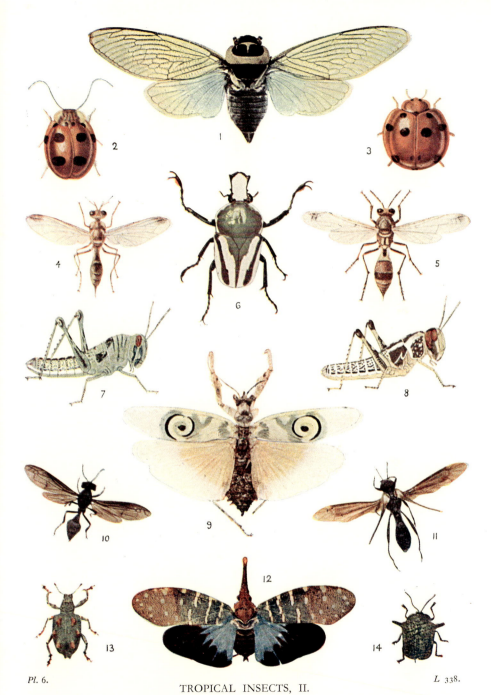

Pl. 6.   L 338.

TROPICAL INSECTS, II.

1. A Cicada from the Naga Hills, Assam (*Angamaina aetherea*).   2 and 3. Mimicry by a Cockroach (*Leis dunlopi*
fig. 2) of a Ladybird Beetle (*Prosoplecta semperi*, fig. 3).   Borneo.   (After Shelford.)   4 and 5. Mimicry of a Wasp
(*Polistes marginalis*, fig. 4) by a Fly (*Polistomimetes minax*, fig. 5).   Sikkim.   (After Study.) 6. An East African
Rose-beetle (*Ranzania bertolonii*), male.   7 and 8. Hoppers of the Desert Locust (*Schistocerca gregaria*) ; fig. 7 shows
the swarming type, fig. 8 the solitary.   9. A South African Praying Mantis (*Pseudocreobotra wahlbergi*).   10 and 11.
Mimicry of a Wasp (*Synoeca surinama*, fig. 10) by a Beetle (*Sphecomorpha chalybea*, fig. 11).   S. America. 12. A
Bornean Lantern-fly (*Fulgora intricata*).   13. A tropical American Weevil (*Rigus schuppeli*).   14. A tropical
American Tortoise-beetle (*Tauroma bicornis*).

as food for their progeny.   These nests are built in all sorts of situations. Some species utilise odd nooks and crannies in buildings, holes in the stems of plants and such-like places.   Others burrow in sandy soil and build up little towers above the orifices of their holes, only to demolish them when the burrow is fully provisioned.   But the daintiest nests are those in the form of little clay pots, or vases, built up in a hanging position

An Indian Mason-wasp, *Eumenes conica.*
The body is light reddish-brown. Female.

A British representative of
the very large and wide-
spread genus *Odynerus*—
O. parietum.

upon twigs and branches of trees.   *Odynerus* is one of the commonest genera, and has a very wide distribution, being found in countries so wide apart as England and Australia.   It contains smallish, rather stout insects, usually about half an inch in length and banded with black and orange.

The social wasps have departed very considerably, in many ways, from their close relatives the Eumenids.   A fundamental difference lies in the fact that they actually feed their off-spring.   To do this they construct nests of a spherical shape suspended from the branch of a tree, or perhaps from a rootlet if below ground (as in the common black-and-yellow species of the genus *Vespa*), of a papery sub-stance derived from weathered wood. Within the nest is a series of hori-zontal layers of cells each housing a single larva, which is provided with food by the workers, first with nectar and honey-dew, and later with the

Vespa crabro, the Hornet.

flesh of caterpillars and other insects, for they are essentially carnivorous. Males, females (queens), and workers occur in all nests, the queens being easily recognised by their much larger size.   The colonies die out in the winter, except for the queens, which go into hibernation and found fresh colonies in the spring.   A good many species are known, some of them, such as the Hornet, being of very considerable size and capable of inflicting a very nasty sting.   The black and yellow coloration of most species is very familiar; the members of the equally widespread genus *Polistes*, however, are nearly always black and more slender.

The Sphecoid wasps are all diggers, on which account they are generally spoken of as fossorial wasps, and quite devoid of social habits. The

A Chinese Wasp, *Polistes suleatus*. The *Polistes* are social wasps, usually black in colour. Their sting is very severe.

A European Sphecoid Wasp, *Sphex flavipennis*. Its interesting habits have been very attractively described by Fabre.

behaviour of the graceful and attractive species of the genus *Sphex* has been studied by numerous observers, including that inimitable entomologist and delightful writer, Fabre. They specialise upon the caterpillars of moths, and, from the fact that they sting them once in each segment of the

An Australian Sphecoid Wasp, *Bembex pectinipes*. Note the curious basket-shaped development of the fore-legs.

body, or nearly so, it has been argued that they must have an intuitive knowledge of the anatomy of their prey. The caterpillar, after being subjected to this treatment, is stored, with an egg attached, in a cell at the bottom of a vertical tunnel in the ground. *Bembex* is unique amongst these wasps in that it does not close up its cells, but continues itself to supply its growing larvae daily, almost hourly, with fresh food, usually in the form of flies (Diptera). *Philanthus* is so perverted as to prefer to feed its grubs upon Hive-bees. The bee is stung about the head, and the wasp then proceeds to squeeze its honey out of it and to feed upon this, subsequently taking the carcase to its burrow, which, it has been stated, is sometimes as much as three feet in depth. The species of *Pemphredo* and *Crabro* very generally make their nests in twigs, or the stems of plants. They are mostly rather small insects, and prey to a great extent upon small bugs, aphids, scale-insects, etc.

In the Bees the consummation is reached of the tendencies towards a vegetarian diet that have already been noticed in the social wasps and in many ants, for they are entirely dependent for their food, in all their stages, upon the nectar and pollen of plants. Honey is nectar that has been swallowed, partly digested, and then regurgitated; "bee-bread," upon which the grubs are fed, is a mixture of honey and pollen; wax, used in the construction of the nest is produced from tiny glands on the under surface of the body, and is only made by the young workers. As in the wasps, there are both " solitary " and social Bees, the former predominating. They are not, perhaps, always readily recognisable by their form, but, when this is considered in conjunction with their habits, the difficulties disappear; an indication of the structural characters that define them will be found earlier in the account of the Aculeates (p. 337).

All the species are of small or moderately large size, practically always dull in colour, black, red, and yellow predominating. The mouth-parts of the more primitive forms differ little from those of wasps, but in the " higher " forms a long tongue is developed, which is furnished at its tip with a spoon-shaped structure provided with swollen hairs, and used for collecting nectar. All except the inevitable parasitic kinds, of which even this group has its quota, are of immense benefit to man on account of their flower-visiting habits. Travelling from flower to flower, covering themselves with pollen in the process, it is impossible for them to avoid being highly effective accidental fertilisers of very many flowers. It is no exaggeration to say that the success or failure of many of man's crops depends very largely, sometimes almost entirely, upon the activities of bees.

Many plants, notably the orchids, exhibit most remarkable developments correlated with the habits of particular species of bees, and clearly evolved for the sole purpose of securing pollination. The pollen that the bees carry in this manner so beneficially from flower to flower is to them, however, largely so much adventitious matter; but they are provided with special apparatus for securing what they require for their own needs. The shins of the last pair of legs are specially adapted for the purpose. They are somewhat broadened, and flattened, and hollowed out on their inner sides, where they are also provided with several rows of short stiff bristles. By means of this apparatus the bee is enabled to brush the pollen off the hairs of its body in such a manner that it collects in the hollowed portion of the shin. The structure is known as the "pollen-basket." In some species there is also a pollen-collecting brush on the under surface of the body.

Although some 20,000 different species of Bee are known to science, distributed throughout the world, but mainly to be found in the north and south temperate zones, it has been estimated that rather less than five per cent. of them are really social. In the majority of cases each bee makes a solitary nest, preparing and provisioning one cell at a time. Transitional phases are exhibited by those in which several individuals have a common burrow, but separate cells, and by others that construct a number of cells together in the form of a nest, which they may use for the rearing of several broods. Amongst higher forms the work of such a nest becomes shared between a number of individuals. In the most highly developed the inhabitants of the nest consist of queens (fertilised females), drones (males), and the imperfectly developed females, the workers, upon whom the entire care of the establishment devolves. The nests of some of these very specialised forms persist over considerable periods of time ; the other types are usually commenced afresh each year by females that have managed to survive the winter.

Wheeler gives a most interesting account of one of the *Halictus* bees, which are so numerous in species and varied in behaviour in so far as methods of propagation are concerned. As regards its social habits, it belongs to one of the transitional types referred to above. " This bee (*Halictus malachurus*) nests in hard, clayey soil, often in congregations of more than a thousand burrows. The over-wintered females sometimes appear as early as the middle of March, and begin to clean and varnish the burrows and to visit the flowers of willows and dandelions. Although several females have been hibernating peacefully in the same burrow, their number is now reduced to three, two, or normally only one, owing to the struggles among them for possession of the burrow. The ousted individuals have to move to unoccupied nests or to dig new ones. The brood-cells are built directly off from the main gallery, provisioned and provided with eggs. If more than one female remains in the nest, these daughters of the same mother nevertheless build separate cell-clusters.

" By the middle of June the brood emerges, and consists almost exclusively of females. They are smaller than their mother and differently sculptured, and belong to a form which taxonomists have described as *H. longulus*. The first individuals to appear are unusually small. There are no *longulus* males. The mother still survives, and her *longulus* daughters remain with her and begin to construct brood-cells. This work is carried on mainly at night, as Fabre observed in *H. calceatus*. The eggs for these cells are laid by the mother, and not by the *longulus* daughters, which, however, collect the provisions consisting mainly of the pollen of *Hieracium* and *Leontodon*. The old mother remains at home and guards the nest-entrance, in the manner observed by Fabre and others. The *longulus* females forage till about the last of September, although each individual probably lives only four to six weeks. Their number increases till, in August, there are about a dozen in each nest. Females of the *malachurus* type begin to appear about the beginning of August, also from eggs laid by the old mother. They are very drowsy and lethargic, compared with the very active, bustling *longulus* females, and collect no pollen though they visit the flowers for nectar. The males, which have been appearing and increasing in numbers in the meantime, and are also the offspring of the old mother *Halictus*, pay no attention to the *longulus* females, but eagerly pair on the surface of the nest with the young *malachurus* females when they leave the burrow for the first time on some sunny day. There is, therefore, a kind of abortive marriage flight. Dissection of the *longulus* females shows that they are never fecundated. The old mother, after surviving the preceding winter and producing the summer brood of *longulus* and fall brood of *malachurus*, though much worn and with frayed wings, lives till the end of the season. Somewhat later she loses her power of flight, crawls away and dies. The *longulus* females and the males then also perish, but the young fecundated *malachurus* females go into hibernation in their mother's nest." The most fully developed type of colony, as exemplified by the Hive-bee, needs no description here, as innumerable accounts have been published, and, besides, the subject must be familiar to all.

It is quite impossible to do justice to all the Bees in the space available, but there are a few other types to which brief reference must be made. Many

The Red Mason-bee, *Osmia rufa.* 1, Male ; 2, Female. (Twice natural size.)

people must have observed from time to time that neat little sections have been cut from the leaves on their rose-bushes ; it is doubtful, however, whether many will actually have witnessed at work the Leaf-cutting bees (*Megachile*) that are responsible for the damage. In appearance these bees are much like Hive-bees, but have broader heads. They clasp the leaf between the legs and bite through it quickly with the mandibles, until a portion of the required shape has been cut out. The fragment is then transported to the nest, which is generally in the soil, or some hollow stem, and utilised for the construction of the cells. These are entirely made of portions of leaf, and are thimble-shaped, oval pieces being used for the sides and little round pieces for the lid. To this same group belong the *Osmia* or Mason-bees, whose externally rough and irregular clusters of cells are made of clay, sand, and so on, stuck together.

The largest known bees are the Xylocopid Carpenter-bees, which are handsome black or dark-blue insects with smoky and often iridescent wings, that mostly inhabit warm regions such as Africa and India. By means of

M 2

their powerful mandibles they tunnel into solid wood, sometimes to the depth of a foot or more, subsequently dividing up the burrows into cells by means of partitions formed of particles of wood.

There remain only the familiar Bumble-bees to deal with. These resemble the Wasps rather than the Hive-bee in respect of their social life, as their colonies die out every autumn and only the fertilised queens survive the winter. In the spring the queen locates a situation for her nest, which is usually underground and constructed of fine grass and such-like material. She next gathers a mass of pollen upon which she lays her eggs, covering them at the same time with a layer of wax. The grubs when they hatch are therefore literally couched upon their food; they develop rapidly and give rise to workers. As time goes on fresh pollen masses are collected, and further broods of workers raised, and the queens give up working and remain in the nest. At the

Cells of the Red Mason-bee, *Osmia rufa*, showing larva feeding on pollen masses.

A familiar British Bumble-bee, *Bombus lapidarius*. 1, Male; 2, Female; 3, Worker.

end of the season males appear, together with large females, which, when fertilised by the males, go into hibernation till the following spring. The males are short-lived, and soon die.

Some of the Bumble-bees seem to find it much less trouble to make use of their energetic relatives than to work. These are the Cuckoo-bees of the genus *Psithyrus*, which show several features of interest. Each species bears an astonishing resemblance, both in size and coloration, to the bee, always a species of *Bombus*, upon which it preys, but it always has a much tougher skin. None of the species produces workers; all of them have lost the pollen-baskets, and several other structures characteristic of the ordinary hard-working bee. The female *Psithyrus* invades the nest of the unfortunate *Bombus* upon which it is accustomed to prey, and, having killed the queen, usurps her place, takes control, lays her eggs and has her grubs fed and reared by the *Bombus* workers. The great point of interest is this : are the Cuckoo-bees, so different from the Bumble-bees in their lack of the most highly specialised features that characterise the latter, so like them in their fundamental structures, really close cousins of the Bumble-bees, or have they been evolved from some other stock not really closely related ? The latter view formerly held the field, but more recently, since it has been recognised of what little value, for the purpose

Female of the Cuckoo-bee, *Psithyrus rupestris.*

of estimating affinities, are those structures that represent the highest development of special adaptations, the former view has gained more favour. The Cuckoo-bees in this case may be nothing more than degenerate first cousins of the industrious Bumble-bees.

Order DIPTERA

(*Flies, Gnats, and Midges*)

By F. W. EDWARDS, M.A., D.Sc.

The Order Diptera includes most of the insects familiarly known as flies, gnats, and midges. Ever since the time of the Pharaohs they have been unpopular with most people, owing to the fact that some of them are too apt to force their unwelcome attentions upon us, while their size and colouring is seldom such as to excite admiration. Nevertheless, it is safe to say not only that no group of animals affords more interesting material for the student of Nature, but also that few are of greater importance to mankind in general.

Until comparatively recently the order was hardly more popular with scientists than with the general public, but although there is still a vast field open for research, the science of Dipterology has been immeasurably advanced in the last thirty years. So large is the order, and so extensive the literature dealing with it, that it will be impossible in the short space of this account to do more than give a very brief survey of the subject.

We shall, therefore, confine ourselves to a consideration of the general features and habits of flies in the different stages of their life-history, the ways in which they are adapted to their environment, and the manner in which they are related to human welfare.

CHIEF CHARACTERISTICS

The fully developed fly is characterised by the possession of a single pair of functional wings, this being the front pair, while the hind pair is replaced by a pair of small dumb-bell-shaped organs known as " halteres." This definition will nearly always serve to distinguish a member of the order from any other insect. The smaller Hymenoptera are sometimes mistaken for flies, but all of them have four wings; a few *Ephemeridae* (May-flies) have only two wings, but never have halteres. The presence of halteres being such an outstanding characteristic of Diptera, it will naturally be assumed that they are of great importance to their owners, and this is indeed the case. Experiment has shown that when the halteres are removed the insect loses its power of balancing in the air and is therefore incapable of flight; it is further believed that in many cases they act as organs of hearing, as they have a well-developed sense-organ at their base, and there is often a large rigid membrane developed at the base of the wing

A British Crane-fly, *Ctenophora ornata*, showing the vestigial hind-wings (halteres).   (Enlarged about twice.)

which may serve the purpose of an external ear, the whole apparatus having been termed " microphones of a most efficient kind."

The only Diptera in which halteres are absent are those which have also entirely lost their front wings; such creatures are not easily recognisable as " flies," and, indeed, many of them have greatly puzzled entomologists, as may be seen from the names *Aenigmatias* and *Aenigmatistes* which have been bestowed upon some of them. The loss of wings (of which some hundreds of cases are known in this order of insects) is normally associated with the adoption of some mode of life in which these organs would be useless or even disadvantageous, such as parasitism on the bodies of other animals, or living in very windy places like mountain-tops or the seashore (especially on oceanic islands, or in the stormy regions near the poles). Such conditions have resulted in winglessness in a number of different families.

Of normal winged flies the common house-fly may perhaps be taken as an average type in regard to size and form. There is, however, a very

Mydas praegrandis

From Brazil. One of the largest known flies. The mark below the left wing indicates approximately the size, with wings expanded, of the smallest known fly. (Natural size.)

great variety in both these respects ; in size, from the largest *Mydaidae* and *Pantophthalmidae*, which may measure about two inches in length of body, and over three inches in expanse of wings, to the smallest *Cecidomyiidae* or *Chironomidae*, whose bodies are hardly over half a millimetre long, and whose wing expanse may be well under two millimetres ; in form, from the most slenderly built crane-fly whose hair-like legs may be five or six times as long as its body, to the beetle-like *Celyphidae* whose wings and legs are almost hidden under the curious hemispherical expansion of the thorax. The bulkiest known fly is about a hundred thousand times the size of the least bulky, a difference comparable among mammals with that between the elephant and the pygmy-shrew.

In regard to colour, one does not usually think of flies as conspicuous or beautiful, nevertheless there are numerous examples of bright and showy wing-patterns, and few insects could be more resplendent in body than some of the Australian species of *Rutilia* and *Formosia*.

In most cases no difficulty will be experienced in recognising a fly as such merely from its general appearance, but there are not a few instances in which a deceptive resemblance is shown to bees, wasps, or other Hymenoptera, so that it may be necessary to look rather closely in order to decide to which order a specimen belongs. One such case is the familiar Drone-fly, which is strikingly like a honey-bee ; another, hardly less familiar, is that of the Bumble-bee flies (*Volucella*) which have furry bodies banded with black, yellow, and red like the bumble-bees. In tropical countries there are very many cases of extraordinarily close superficial resemblance in form and colour between Diptera and Hymenoptera.

A "Beetle-fly" from Siam, *Celyphus*. Note the tips of the wings projecting from under the hood-like thorax. (Enlarged.)

Many of these flies belong, like those mentioned above, to the Hover-fly family (*Syrphidae*), but others are to be found among the Robber-flies (*Asilidae*) and in several other families. Most of these cases are probably to be regarded as examples of what is termed "Batesian Mimicry," that is to say, imitation of a distasteful or stinging insect by a palatable or unprotected one, for the purpose of deceiving its enemies (birds or other animals) and so obtaining immunity from attack. This, however, cannot always be the explanation ; there is much to suggest that in some cases the object may be to deceive the model in order to obtain entrance to its nest for the purpose of egg-laying. But more observations are needed on the biology of many of the insects concerned before we can presume to interpret all the facts.

Some of the most beautiful examples are the African and Oriental species of the Syrphid genus *Cerioides*, each of which copies, more or less faithfully, some species of solitary wasp found in the same region, and the African Robber-flies of the genus *Hyperechia*, which closely resemble the carpenter-bees with which they are associated, and in whose burrows their larvae live. Another very remarkable instance is the Himalayan Tabanid *Melissomorpha*, which closely resembles a local honey-bee, not only in the colour of its body and wings and its general shape, but also in the peculiarly flattened legs. Unfortunately this insect, like many other mimics, is extremely rare, and nothing is known of its habits.

THEIR ACTIVITIES

Although most of the smaller Diptera have relatively feeble powers of flight, the aerial performances of the more highly developed forms are probably unsurpassed by any other insects or even by birds. Most people are familiar with the fact that some flies can keep pace with a train or motor car moving at thirty miles an hour or more ; but according to Professor C. H. T. Townsend this is nothing to the speed which can be attained by bot-flies of the genus *Cephenomyia*. He estimates that these flies can travel (at an altitude of 7000 feet) " well over 300 yards per second," that is to say, six or seven hundred miles an hour, fast enough to overtake a musket ball or the shells of Big Bertha ! We can hardly accept this estimate, but it is certain that these flies can travel extremely fast. Townsend suggests that if a flying-machine could be made on the "myiopter" principle with vibrating wings controlled from within the body and working as efficiently

MIMICRY

Three examples of mimetic flies (left) and their hymenopterous models (right). 1, A Tabanid fly, *Melissomorpha*, mimicking a Honey-bee, *Apis dorsata* (Himalayas). 2, A Syrphid fly, *Cerioides eumenoides*, mimicking a Solitary wasp, *Eumenes esuriens* (India). 3, An Asilid fly, *Hyperechia hirtipes*, mimicking a Carpenter-bee, *Xylocopa olivacea* (West Africa). (About natural size.)

and economically as the wings of *Cephenomyia* it would be possible for us to complete the " daylight-day circuit of the earth."

Many flies can not only fly with great speed, but also hover with the body motionless in mid-air. Mr. C. A. Cheetham assures the writer that he has seen a small *Pipunculus* hovering in the centre of a glass tube about a quarter of an inch in diameter and scarcely wider than the expanse of the fly's wings ; a similar observation was also made by the late Mr. G. H.

Verrall. This power of hovering is of great use to the species, especially to parasitic forms which oviposit on a living insect-host. In contrast with the above types of flight we may mention the North American Crane-fly *Bittacomorpha*, which seems to have attempted an experiment in lighter-than-air flight by developing small gas-bags in its feet.

Some flies, though fully winged, do not use their wings to a great extent, but are, on the other hand, adepts at running. This is especially true of some of the smaller flies such as the *Phoridae*, which may be seen in numbers on our window-panes in summer. Such flies usually have the femora stout and more or less flattened. The power which many flies have of walking upside down on a ceiling or climbing a smooth surface such as glass, has often been commented upon. In general this power is due to the presence of a pair of small pads on the feet, which exude a sticky substance enabling the fly to maintain its hold. Some have thought that these pads act as suckers, but that this is not the case is evident from the fact that flies can walk upside down in a vacuum. The pads (pulvilli) are not present in all flies, and many of those which do not possess them are still able to climb in a similar way. In such

An accomplished aeronaut, *Pipunculus campestris* (Britain). (Enlarged about six times.)

cases the foothold is evidently obtained through the sharp claws clinging on to the minutest irregularities of the surface.

Some flies (*e.g.* certain seashore midges) have the power of skating on the surface of water without breaking the surface film, the hairy foot-pads probably assisting them in this performance. So far as is known, only one fly possesses the power of swimming actively under water, this being a small marine midge found in coral-lagoons in Samoa; it is believed never to leave the sea, and in this respect is absolutely unique among insects; its wings have a peculiar structure and are probably the main swimming organs, although it has also been observed to swim with its legs.

Either by their own power of flight, or more frequently perhaps, " on the wings of the wind," flies are able to cover long distances. Cases are on record of swarms of salt-marsh mosquitoes being found fifty miles inland from their breeding-places, and there is a well-authenticated instance of a swarm of hover-flies occurring in Spitsbergen, to which they must have travelled across at least five hundred miles of sea. Probably this is by no means the limit of their powers of dispersal.

A few flies rely on other insects of stronger flight to carry them about, a habit to which the name " phoresy " has been given. The wingless Bee-louse (*Braula*) might be placed in this category, and it has frequently been observed that some small Borborid flies (*Limosina*) ride on the backs of dung-beetles. Other minute flies (*Desmometopa* and *Gaurax*) have been seen riding on the backs of robber-flies, and also, strange to say, of spiders. Certain midges in Sumatra and West Africa stick tight on to the wings of dragon-flies, and in order, apparently, to obtain a firmer hold they have dispensed with their claws and instead have developed their foot-pads to a remarkable extent.

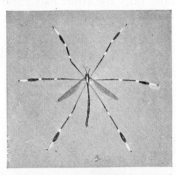

The " Phantom Crane-fly," *Bittacomorpha clavipes*. (From North America.) (Natural size.)

Some of the resting habits of flies are worthy of remark. The manner of holding the wings is often very characteristic, and provides an easy means of recognition of the species in the field ; thus the tsetse-flies can be distinguished from almost all the other *Muscidae* by holding their wings

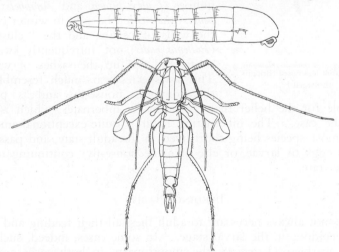

The marine Midge of Samoa, *Pontomyia natans*. Male (below) and female (above). (Much enlarged.)

flat over the back and completely overlapping. *Leptis scolopacea*, the " downlooker " of fishermen, has the habit of settling on tree-trunks with the head facing downwards. Although all flies are provided with six legs, very many only use four of them for standing upon, the remaining pair being raised when the insect is at rest.   In the mosquitoes, and a few others, it is always the hind pair which is raised ; many midges (*Chironomus*) raise only the front pair ; and a few *Mycetophilidae* (*Exechia*, etc.) hold the middle pair aloft over the back.   A number of small flies, chiefly *Tipulidae*

A large Midge, *Chironomus plumosus*, a rest with front legs raised (Britain). (Enlarged.)

and *Cecidomyiidae*, have the curious habit of resting in spiders' webs, apparently finding the delicate threads convenient supports from which to hang.   Nearly all the *Tipulidae* which have this habit (belonging to various genera, and occurring in various tropical countries) have the tarsi pure white ; possibly this renders their feet invisible to the spiders, but they need to be wary to avoid falling victims to their hosts.   The writer has noted the same strange resting habit in a British mosquito (*Theobaldia morsitans*), large numbers of the flies being seen in webs in sheltered dark corners.

For the purpose of hibernation some flies will often enter houses in large numbers, seeking shelter and protection.   Two mosquitoes (*Culex pipiens* and *Anopheles maculipennis*) may often be seen in winter covering the walls of cellars, and the " cluster-fly " (*Pollenia rudis*) not infrequently swarms in roofs, and fills up the sashes of windows. This last species bears much resemblance to the common house-fly, and is probably responsible for the belief that the house-fly hibernates, which is rarely, if ever, the case.   The hibernating habit is quite exceptional among the Diptera, most species being short-lived in the adult state, and passing the winter as eggs or larvae, or else (like the house-fly), continuing to breed at a slower rate.

FEEDING HABITS

Food is not always necessary to adult flies, all their feeding and growth having been done in the larval stage.   In some cases, indeed, such as the bots and warbles (*Oestridae*), the mouth-parts in both sexes are so far atrophied that feeding would be impossible.   Very often the male fly takes no food, and sometimes (as in the *Psychodidae*) his gut is atrophied. Usually, however, the female requires food in order to mature her eggs, and whenever the life of the adult extends to more than a few days' food is required by both sexes. Many are content with a diet of honey, pollen, fruit-juice, the liquid portions of decaying vegetable or animal matter, or the sweat of animals. Others, however, are much more specialised and have extremely varied and interesting habits.

First we may mention the predators, which suck the juices of other insects. Of these there are a great many; sometimes certain genera of a family, sometimes whole families; sometimes the female only, and sometimes both sexes. The most notable predators are the *Asilidae*, against which it has been said that " the stings

The " Cluster-fly," *Pollenia rudis* (Britain). (Enlarged.)

of Aculeates, the distasteful properties of *Danainae* and *Acraeinae* and of the odoriferous *Lagria*, the hard chitin of Coleoptera and the aggressive powers of the Odonata, are alike insufficient protection." These flies probably inject a poison into their prey to paralyse it. In contrast with the *Asilidae*, which prey upon such a variety of insects, the *Empididae* feed mainly upon Diptera; many of them (as well as other Dipterous predators) have their legs specially modified for catching and holding their prey. The *Dolichopodidae* feed on minute soft-bodied insects or worms, and instead of piercing and sucking their prey as do the *Asilidae* and *Empididae*, they envelop them in their large lips, rejecting the dried skin after absorbing the juices.

A Hover-fly, *Syrphus ribesii*, feeding at flowers of ivy. (Somewhat enlarged.)

A group of special interest is the *Ceratopogonidae*, in which we can see how the predaceous habit may lead on to blood-sucking, and so to parasitism. Some of these little midges prey on other small insects (in this case nearly always other flies of the same family or the allied *Chironomidae*). Others attack insects much larger than themselves, sucking the juices of caterpillars, the blood from the wing-veins of butterflies, moths, and Neuroptera, or the exudation from the legs of oil-beetles. One species of *Culicoides* has discovered an abundant source of food in the blood contained in the bodies of mosquitoes which have gorged themselves on mammals, and the other species of this genus (the true " midges " or " punkies ") have gone one step farther and obtain the blood directly for themselves.

The blood-sucking habit, which has had such disastrous consequences to mankind, seems to have been developed independently in several groups of flies, and the blood is obtained in two different ways. The mosquitoes (*Culicidae*), midges (*Ceratopogonidae*), " buffalo-gnats " (*Simulium*), sand-flies (*Phlebotomus*), and horse-flies (*Tabanidae*), have all retained the biting mouth-parts of the primitive Diptera. All the higher groups of flies have lost their mandibles and maxillae, and most of them feed on liquids, either directly or by regurgitating the contents of their crop on to their food, and so liquefying a further supply. Some have been able to return to the predaceous, and even to the blood-sucking habit, by develop-

The so-called Sheep-tick, *Melophagus ovinus* (Britain). (Enlarged.)

ing a special set of teeth on their lips. Among these last are the familiar stable-fly (*Stomoxys*), and tsetse (*Glossina*). It is quite probable that the blood-sucking habit in Diptera may have originated in the far-distant past, before the appearance of mammals on the earth, as some species of *Phlebotomus* and *Culex* still prefer the blood of frogs and lizards.

Three families of Diptera have taken the further step from blood-sucking (that is, temporary or intermittent parasitism) to permanent parasitism of mammals and birds, depending entirely on the blood of their hosts for food. These show most interesting adaptations to parasitic life. The wings and eyes tend to atrophy, and in many cases have entirely disappeared; the body becomes flattened, to allow free movement through the hairs or feathers; combs of strong spines (like those of many fleas) are often developed to aid in progression, and the feet and claws are highly modified for clinging. Two of these three families are exclusively attached to bats.

Apart from the three families just mentioned, few, if any, permanent parasites are known among adult Diptera. Two possible exceptions are the little wingless Phorids (*Wandolleckia*) which are found on the bodies of large African land-snails, apparently feeding on the slime, and the bee-louse (*Braula*). As already mentioned, *Braula* probably uses the bee chiefly for purposes of transport, but it also obtains food from its steed when hungry, wandering to its mouth and tickling it with its claws until it supplies a droplet of honey.

Another group of exceptional biological interest is that of the species which obtain their food from ants. The little mosquito *Harpagomyia*,

found in many parts of Africa and the East, is a good example. It sits
on the trunks of trees and waylays ants of the genus *Cremastogaster*, nipping
them between its legs, and not releasing them until they open their jaws
and supply it with a drop of food. The tongue of the mosquito is highly
modified, and bears some peculiar hairs which may possibly afford some
pleasurable sensation to the ants, but this is not known. Quite similar
habits are possessed by totally different flies of the genus *Milichia*. The
little West African Cecidomyiid *Farquharsonia* also takes food from these
ants, but in this case the fly hovers over the ants until one attempts to feed

A Fruit-bat parasite, *Cyclopodia*
greefi (West Africa). (Enlarged.)

A mosquito, *Harpagomyia splendens*, being fed by an
ant (Java). (After Jacobson.) (Enlarged.)

another, and then, without settling, steals the food. Another small fly
(*Rhynchopsilopa*, family *Ephydridae*) chases the ants from behind and takes
food from their anus; the observer (Farquharson) noted that the ants
greatly resented these attentions, apparently finding the habits of the
Rhynchopsilopa as disgusting as they seem to us. Finally we may mention
the blow-fly *Bengalia*, which robs the fierce driver-ants of their prey; and
a very extraordinary group of wingless flies (*Termitoxeniidae*) which are
found only in the nests of Termites.

MATING AND REPRODUCTION

If feeding is not an essential activity of all flies, neither is mating. There
are a small number of cases in which the female is capable of reproducing
by parthenogenesis, the male occurring but rarely, or possibly not existing
at all. Normally, however, mating is the main, if not the only, purpose of
the existence of the adult, and in connection with it many wonderful
structures and habits are developed. It is nearly always the male which
is the ornamental sex, and except in rare instances (*e.g.* the Dolichopodid,
Scellus virago) it is he who takes the active part in courtship. On the other

hand, the female not infrequently shows signs of degeneration, such as loss of wings, or reduction in antennae, the extreme case being that of the marine midge of Samoa (*Pontomyia*) in which she has lost practically all trace of appendages, and is little more than an egg-sack.

The special characters of the male may affect almost any part of the body; the eyes may be greatly enlarged, or carried out to the end of long stalks; strange horns like stags' antlers may grow out from the head; the antennae may become elaborately plumed or pectinate; scent glands may occur in the head, thorax, or abdomen; spurs, fringes, and other structures may form on any part of the legs; the wings may be altered in shape or have special patterns or distinguishing marks. Sometimes these male structures have no obvious use; the eye-stalks of *Laglaisia*, for example, may be long, short, or absent in the same species. Possibly in some cases the structures may be used for fighting off rivals; we have very little evidence at present that such fights take place, but a few cases are on record. The males of *Zygotricha* have been seen to butt one another with their big heads, and some *Micropezidae* stand upright on their long legs and push one another with their chests; males of *Empis opaca* sometimes actually fight to

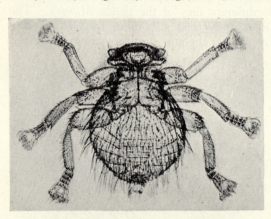

FLIES AS GUESTS OF OTHER INSECTS

Upper fig.—The Bee-louse, *Braula caeca* (Britain).　*Lower fig.*— *Termitoxema* sp. from nests of the termite, *Odontotermes obesus* (India).　(Greatly enlarged.)

the death. In nearly all cases, however, where special male organs are present, these are concerned either with capture or courtship. Enlarged eyes probably assist him in the chase; femoral spines, toothed claws, and similar structures doubtless aid in grasping; ornamentation of legs or wings is for the purpose of display in front of the female.

Mating is often a social affair among the Diptera. Every one is familiar with the dancing swarms of flies such as winter-gnats (*Trichocera*) and midges (*Chironomidae*), which sometimes attain such dimensions as to appear in the distance like clouds of smoke. These swarms nearly always consist almost exclusively of male flies, and seem to be an essential preliminary to mating ; the habit is common to a great many families of Diptera, and replaces individual courtship in those groups in which it is found ; the female simply flies into the swarm and mates with any one of its members, the pair then dropping out, or occasionally (as in a few species of the Empid genus *Hilara*) soaring away for a marriage flight. In a few cases both sexes take part in the dance in approximately equal numbers, and in still rarer cases (as in *Empis livida* and some species of *Palpomyia*) only the females dance. Some flies, especially those of strong flight like *Oestridae* and *Tabanidae* (horse-flies), congregate in numbers on high places such as mountain summits, or the tops of high buildings, and it has been suggested that these places act as landmarks to which they can go from a wide area for the purpose of meeting and mating. The snow-flies (*Chionea*), spider-like wingless crane-flies which are found at high altitudes in winter, come out on the surface of the snow to mate.

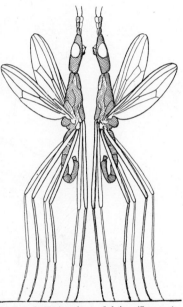

Males of *Nerius fuscus* fighting (Sumatra). (After de Meijere.) (Enlarged.)

Sound probably plays an important part in the mating of mosquitoes and midges. The loud hum produced by the swarm of dancing males doubtless attracts the females, and, on the other hand, it has been ascertained that the feathery antennae of the males respond to sound vibration and enable the swarm to hear the "trumpeting" of the female and locate the direction from which she is approaching. It has also been noted that in the case of hover-flies, robber-flies, and some other groups the courting male raises the note of his humming to a higher key, and that he is attracted by the hum of other insects such as bees.

Scent also is frequently an important influence in mating, and special organs for the production of scent are found in many groups ; these are either in the form of peculiar processes on the antennae or of eversible tubes on some part of the body. The latter type are found in the males of many moth-flies and also in the females of some species of *Empididae* and of *Palpomyia* which, as mentioned above, have the swarming habit.

Flies, especially males, are often strongly attracted by certain scents, one of the most remarkable cases of this being the powerful attraction of chloroform for kelp-flies of the genus *Fucomyia*; it has more than once been stated by doctors working in coastal towns that these flies are a great nuisance during the performance of operations. Experiments made by Howlett in India showed that male fruit-flies (*Dacus*) were strongly attracted by certain chemical odours, and while under their influence performed mating antics.

Perhaps the most interesting habits known in the Diptera are those of

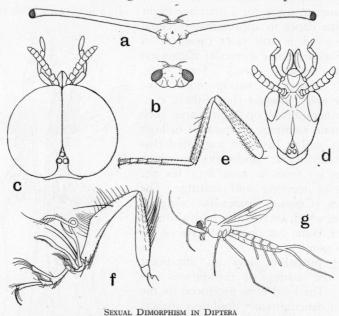

SEXUAL DIMORPHISM IN DIPTERA

a and *b*, *Laglaisa caloptera*, heads of male and female, from New Guinea; *c* and *d*, *Bibio marci*, heads of male and female as seen from above (British) [after Berlere]; *e* and *f*, *Campsicnemus magius*, front legs of female and male (British); *g*, *Palpomyia semifumosa*, female with everted scent-glands on abdomen. [After Edwards.] (All enlarged.)

the *Empididae*. In this family of predaceous flies the male often catches an insect and offers it to the female for food; not entirely, perhaps, as a love token, but probably partly to protect himself from his partner's too voracious appetite—without this bait she might turn and devour him, as the females of some predaceous midges do their husbands after mating. In the case of the *Empididae* this habit has gone through an interesting development. In the simplest cases the prey is merely caught and held, but in the genus *Hilara* it is secured by silken threads spun from special glands in the front feet of the male, and in the most highly developed species of this genus the prey may be replaced by any small object and the spinning of silk assumes greater importance than the prey, the male constructing elaborate silken " toy balloons " for his partner, which may contain the prey or other object or may be empty.

Feeding of the female by the male during mating is also practised by some other flies, as, for example, certain acalyptrate *Muscidae*. The male regurgitates a droplet of food and places it either (as in *Platystoma*) on the tip of her turned-up tongue, or (as in *Cardiacephala*) on her eye, whence she sucks it up.

Sometimes mating takes place as soon as the female emerges from the pupa, as in some *Tipulidae*, or even before, as in the New Zealand mosquito *Opifex fuscus*. The males of this last species have the extraordinary habit of skimming about on the surface of their breeding pool, hunting for a female pupa which is ready for emergence. When they find one they seize it between their powerful front legs, slit open the skin of the thorax with their strong claspers, and so assist the female to emerge, often even inserting their abdomen and mating before the female is free from the pupal skin.

After mating an interval is usually needed for the maturation of the eggs, which are generally deposited in the places where the larvae are destined to live and feed, though in some cases (as in *Bombyliidae*) they are merely dropped more or less indiscriminately while the insect is in flight. Eggs may either be laid singly or in masses ; in some species a large number of females lay their eggs on the same spot, the most remarkable instance of this being the Leptid *Atherix*, in which many hundreds of females oviposit on a branch overhanging water, and, dying on the spot, form a large ball. The number of eggs laid by one female at one time may vary from one (as in *Helicobosca*) to four thousand or more (as in some *Cyrtidae*). Aquatic flies usually lay their eggs at or just above the edge of the water, but some species of *Simulium* have actually been observed to enter water for the purpose of egg-laying, walking in to a depth of several inches.

In one mosquito (a species of *Leicesteria*) the eggs are attached to the hind-leg of the mother, apparently so that they may be inserted into small holes in the stems of bamboos, the holes containing water in which the larvae live. Many crane-flies have hard, pointed ovipositors, by aid of which the eggs are inserted into the ground, and some flies with parasitic larvae have highly developed abdominal structures enabling them to place their eggs on or in the body of their host ; a good example of the latter is *Pipunculus*, which lays its eggs on frog-hoppers while hovering over its victim, its enormous eyes doubtless helping in this. In the case of some *Conopidae* the eggs are said to be deposited on the adult bees during flight. The female of the leaf-mining *Phytomyza* cuts a slit with her ovipositor in the epidermis of the leaf, and inserts her eggs singly ; the same habit has been noted in the leaf-eating Tipulid *Cylindrotoma*. A most remarkable egg-laying habit is found in the South American bot-fly *Dermatobia*, which catches mosquitoes or other small flies, and deposits a number of eggs upon them, the eggs hatching and the larvae passing into a vertebrate host when the victimised mosquito takes a meal of blood.

Not all flies produce eggs ; in a number of cases development proceeds within the body of the mother and living larvae are produced instead. These larvae may either be newly hatched, or may be more or less fully developed, so that it is not easy to draw any hard-and-fast line between oviparous and viviparous species. A most interesting gradation in the methods of reproduction can be traced in the family *Tachinidae*, most of

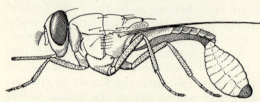

A Tsetse-fly, *Glossina palpalis*, depositing its full-grown larva. (Enlarged five times.)

whose larvae are parasitic in caterpillars. The female may deposit, (1) large numbers of very small eggs, which are placed on leaves, and subsequently eaten by the host ; (2) larger eggs, placed on or under the skin of the host ; (3) a few large eggs which immediately produce half-grown larvae ; (4) small newly hatched larvae. Blow-flies of the genus *Sarcophaga* are well known to deposit small larvae, which can creep through the gauze of a meat-safe. Two groups of flies have carried viviparity a stage farther and produce full-grown larvae which immediately transform into pupae ; these are the tsetse-flies (*Glossina*) and the parasitic louse-flies. In both these cases the female has special uterine glands which provide nourishment for the growing larvae, this form of reproduction being rendered possible by the abundant and nourishing food taken by the adult. This is the only form of " parental care " shown by any Diptera towards their offspring.

Eggs

In form the eggs of Diptera are extremely varied ; they may be round, oval, cylindrical, or of various other shapes, the eggs of *Dasyhelea*, for example, being horseshoe-shaped, and the shell may be either smooth or with a more or less complex pattern of raised ridges, sometimes with elaborate processes, flanges, or expansions. Often these forms appear to serve no definite function, though to our eyes they may be objects of great beauty. Sometimes, however, we can clearly recognise adaptation to their surroundings, as, for example, the eggs of some *Tachinidae*, which are flattened on one side for adhesion to the body of their host caterpillar, or have stalks for attachment to its hairs ; or those of some *Oestridae*, which have special flanges or stalks serving as organs of fixation to the hairs of horses or cattle ; or those of *Conopidae*, which have hooks or threads for fixation to the bodies of their host-bees ; or again those of *Ditomyia*, which are round and exactly fit into the mouths of the pores of the *Polyporus* fungus on which they are laid. The eggs of many aquatic or semi-aquatic flies—like those of some other aquatic animals—are laid in one batch and enclosed in a mass of jelly, the function of which is probably to protect them from the attacks of mould or of small predaceous enemies.

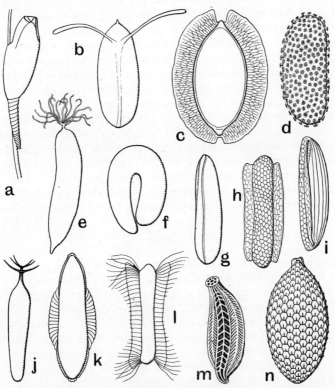

EGGS OF DIPTERA

a, Gastrophilus intestinalis, attached to hair [after Hadwen] ; *b, Drosophila melanogaster* [after Sturtevant] ; *c, Braula coeca*, Bee-louse [after Skaife] ; *d, Sciophila hirta*, a fungus-gnat ; *e, Physocephala rufipes* [after de Meijere] ; *f, Dasyhelea obscura* [after Keilin] ; *g, Musca domestica*, common house-fly [after Hewitt] ; *h, Fannia canicularis*, lesser house-fly, from beneath ; *i, F. canicularis*, from side ; *j, Mansonia humeralis* [after Dyar and Knab] ; *k, Amopheles maculipennis* ; *l, Anopheles mediopunctatus* [after Bonne] ; *m, Chagasia fajardoi* [after Silva] ; *n, Psorophora* [after Howard, Dyar and Knab]. Figs. *j–n* are all of different species of mosquitoes. (All much enlarged.)

The duration of the egg-stage varies greatly ; it may be a matter of a few days or hours, or may extend to months or even years. Probably the longest-lived eggs found among the Diptera are those of some mosquitoes of the genus *Aëdes*, which can almost certainly live for several years, perhaps

ten or more.   This power is of great use to its possessors, as it enables
them to tide over the long periods of drought in desert regions ; whenever
rain comes the eggs are washed into the pools and hatch, the development
to the adult stage proceeding rapidly.   All such eggs must be capable
of withstanding a very high degree of desiccation, and in order to enable
them to do so they are provided with very thick shells.

Even in the passive egg-stage an animal has one essential activity : it
must respire.   Among Diptera many interesting egg-structures are found
connected with respiration.   Just as the young chick has an air-chamber
within the egg, so have some Dipterous eggs a small supply of included
air, but more often the embryo has access to the external air by means of
the porous structure of the shell, this being true even of the thickest-shelled
eggs.   Some eggs which are laid on, or in, water or other liquid media,
have special arrangements for respiration.   Among mosquitoes, the eggs
of *Anopheles* are provided with special air-cells which act as floats to keep
the eggs on the surface, until the larva hatches ; in *Culex*, on the other
hand, the individual eggs have no special floats, but are glued together
in boat-shaped masses, always with the head-end downwards, so that
the escaping larvae may dive straight into the water.   The eggs of
Drosophila, which are laid in fermenting liquids, are provided with a pair
of delicate, finger-like processes which are believed to assist in respiration.

LARVAE

All Diptera pass through a larval stage, which is totally unlike the adult ;
in fact, the metamorphosis is more complete in this order than in any other
except the Hymenoptera.   The Dipterous larva, or maggot, is always
devoid of true legs, these being represented only by groups of microscopic
hairs in the positions where the legs should be.   In the majority of cases
it is also almost headless, the head comprising little more than a pair of
hook-like jaws ; the form of these jaws will serve to distinguish it from
the rather similar legless and headless maggot of some Hymenoptera.
For purposes of locomotion, pseudopodia—false feet—of various form
are often developed to replace the lost legs ; in no case are the true legs
redeveloped, this being an excellent example of the evolutionary law
which assumes that a lost organ can never be regained.   Respiration is
usually mainly, and often solely, through a pair of spiracles at the hind end
of the body.

During the course of their existence Dipterous larvae shed their skin
several times ; the number of moults has not been ascertained in all cases,
but seems to be usually, if not always, four in the case of the Nematocera,
and three in the case of the Cyclorrhapha.

The newly hatched larva, up to the time of its first moult, often differs
rather noticeably from older larvae.   One of the most noteworthy cha-

racters of the first-stage larvae is found in those which have a well-developed head—as is the case in the larvae of mosquitoes, midges, and fungus-gnats ; this is the possession of a peculiar little tooth on the back of the head, by means of which the larva breaks or slits open the egg-shell, as the young chick does with the " egg-tooth " on its beak. In a smooth transparent egg, such as that of *Mycetophila*, it is amusing to watch (under a microscope) the young larva within the egg working its head up and down until it makes an opening through which it can escape. The headless maggots, of course, have no such specialised egg-burster ; probably their mouth-hooks suffice for the purpose. In the case of *Bombyliidae, Cyrtidae*, and perhaps one or two other families, the larvae exhibit " hypermetamorphosis," the first-stage larvae possessing spines, pseudopodia, or other structures which are not present in the older larva ; they are also much more active, as they have to make their way to their hosts.

The activities of an insect in all its stages are governed by inherited instinct, and an interesting example of this is seen in the first-stage larva of the Hessian-fly. The egg of this species is laid on the blades of wheat, normally with the head end upwards. The larva, which has to make its way to the leaf-axil, has the instinct to turn round as soon as it hatches ; it does this even if the egg happens to be laid the other way round, climbing to the tip of the leaf and often dying of desiccation before it can return to the axil. Sometimes the fully formed larvae undergo a resting stage within the egg, waiting a favourable opportunity of hatching. In the case of the mosquito *Leicesteria*, whose egg-laying habits have already been mentioned, the young larvae burst off the caps of their eggs, and are all ready to pop out as soon as their heads touch water.

Dipterous larvae are found in every conceivable type of habitat, and their feeding habits are more varied than those of any other order of insects. Often there is a very great diversity, even among members of the same family, and there are many cases of wonderful adaptations to special modes of life, sometimes independently developed in unrelated forms. We may group fly larvae roughly, according to their habitat, into aquatic and terrestrial. There is no sharp distinction between these groups, the line being bridged by those which live on wet rocks, in damp moss, or in mud, while the strange habitat of the Californian *Psilopa petrolei*—pools of thick crude oil—cannot be described as either aquatic or terrestrial.

Considering first the purely aquatic larvae, we may group them into those which live in stagnant or slowly moving water, and those which live in water with a rapid current. These two groups of larvae show very different types of modification to their special needs. In the first group we find a great variety of feeding habits : vegetarians, feeding on bacteria or diatoms, on moss or other aquatic plants, either externally, or mining in leaves, stems, or roots ; scavengers, feeding on decaying vegetable matter ; carnivores, preying either on animals of different classes, or on other Diptera ; and finally—in the family *Chironomidae*—a few parasites and commensals, either on snails or on may-fly nymphs. All these larvae—except the last-mentioned—are active, free-living forms, and except in the case of the *Chironomidae*, which—partly on account of their small size—are able to respire wholly through the skin, they have to breathe atmospheric air. For this purpose most of them come at more or less frequent intervals to the surface, but others have adopted different devices. In two unrelated families—*Ptychopteridae* and *Syrphidae*—we find a telescopic air-tube on the tail of the larva which can be stretched

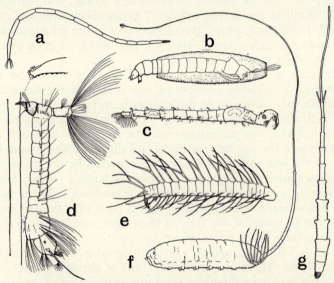

DIPTEROUS LARVAE OF STILL WATER

a, Bezzia bicolor [after Goetghebuer] ; *b, Zavreliella marmorata*, in its silken case (note hump on back which prevents it leaving the case, and blood-gills near tail end) [after Bause] ; *c, Chaoborus crystallinus* (or *Corethra plumicornis*) [after Howard, Dyar and Knab] ; *d, Mansonia richiardii*, attached to a grass root, with tip of breathing apparatus enlarged to show saw-edge [after Wesenberg-Lund] ; *e, Phalacrocera replicata* [after Alexander] ; *f, Myiatropa florea*, with everted gills and air-tube at tail extended to about a third of its full length ; *g, Ptychoptera* [after Miall]. (Various degrees of enlargement.)

up to the surface while the larva is browsing in the mud at the bottom. In *Myiatropa florea* this tube reaches a length of nine or ten inches when fully extended, that is to say, about twelve times the length of the body of the larva.

Another small biological group includes a few species of different families which are able to obtain their air by tapping the roots of water plants. The most remarkable larva in this group is the mosquito *Mansonia*, which has a wonderfully complex saw-like apparatus for piercing the roots and pumping out the air, as well as reservoirs for storing the air so obtained.

Most of these aquatic larvae have rectal or caudal gills which serve as a subsidiary means of respiration, and several genera of *Chironomidae* living in mud, where the oxygen content is very low, possess red blood and special blood-gills, this being one of the very few instances of the occurrences of haemoglobin in the insects. A few aquatic larvae—all of the family of *Chironomidae*—make themselves freely movable cases analogous to those of the caddis-flies. The green larva of the crane-fly *Phalacrocera replicata* is covered with long fleshy processes which make it very difficult to see among the water-moss on which it lives.

The aquatic predators often show remarkable modifications for this mode of life ; perhaps the most interesting is the " phantom gnat " (*Chaoborus*), which has a completely transparent body and catches its prey—

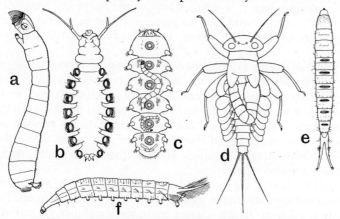

DIPTEROUS LARVAE OF RUNNING WATER

a, Simulium nölleri, from side [after Puri] ; *b, Deuterophlebia*, from beneath [after Pulikowsky] ; *c, Neocurupira nicholsoni* (family *Blepharoceridae*), with larva of the commensal midge *Orthocladius commensalis* [after Tonnoir] ; *d*, may-fly nymph with parasitic larva of *Symbiocladius equitans* attached under its wing-pads [after Claasen] ; *e, Antocha* [after Alexander] ; *f, Atherix* [after Malloch]. (Various degrees of enlargement.)

usually consisting of water-fleas—with its antennae. Several genera of mosquito larvae, and also some midges, have independently adopted a predatory life, usually devouring their nearest relatives.

Larvae living in rapid streams are not able to move about so freely, and cannot readily rise to the surface ; consequently they are compelled to breathe dissolved air, either by gills or through the skin ; running water being well-aerated, this presents no great difficulty. The main problem of such larvae is one of fixation and protection against the force of the current, and it is interesting to notice the various ways in which the problem is solved. One group (*Blepharoceridae*) has a row of suckers down the middle of the ventral surface ; another (*Deuterophlebia*) has a pair of lateral pseudopodia on each segment, the under surface of each pseudopod bearing a circlet of grappling hooks; another (*Simulium*) spins threads of silk to which it fixes itself by means of a circlet of fine hooks at the hind end of the body; others—certain genera of *Chironomidae*—spin a sort of web of silk under which they can move freely; others again—the Chironomid *Cardiocladius* and the Tipulid *Antocha*—live in fixed silken cases; still another (*Tanytarsus*) forms masses of erect tubes on the bed of the stream.

So far as is known, almost all the Dipterous larvae of rapid waters feed on the minute particles of animal or vegetable matter brought down by the stream; some of them are known to be predaceous, and only one is parasitic, this last being the Chironomid *Symbiocladius* which lives in a lump of jelly on the back of a May-fly nymph. There are also one or two interesting cases of commensalism; a small Chironomid larva in New Zealand is always found curled round the suckers of a Blepharocerid larva, and in Britain similar Chironomid larvae are found associated with *Simulium* pupae.

Every type of water is colonised by Dipterous larvae, from the seas, in which a few *Chironomidae*, *Tipulidae*, and some others are found in the littoral zones, to the small collections of water which collect in rot-holes in trees, stems of bamboo, in the leaf-axils of various plants, or in the leaves of pitcher-plants. Each of these last-named habitats has its own particular fauna, the species which breed therein seldom being found in other situations. The chief aquatic families are the mosquitoes and midges, but several others are also represented.

Terrestrial fly-larvae are even more diverse than their aquatic relatives. For convenience we may divide them into herbivores, scavengers, predators, and parasites, each of which classes includes a number of sub-divisions. Among the herbivores we may recognise (1) moss-feeders, like many *Tipulidae* and some *Chironomidae*; (2) root-eaters, a numerous class; (3) stem-borers, such as the *Chloropidae*, and some *Cecidomyiidae*, which are often very injurious to grasses, also some *Syrphidae*; (4) wood-borers, a very small group, but including representatives of at least three different families: *Tipulidae* (*Tanyptera*), *Pantophthalmidae* (*Pantophthalmus*), and *Syrphidae* (*Temnostoma*); (5) leaf-miners, including many *Agromyzidae*, some *Muscidae*, and one Tipulid; (6) leaf-eaters: only, so far as known, the Tipulid *Cylindrotoma*, and the Syrphid *Mesogramma*, which feed exposed on the leaves of flowering plants; (7) gall-makers: many *Cecidomyiidae*, some *Trypetidae*, and a few representatives of other families; (8) fruit-eaters, such as many *Trypetidae*, *Ortalidae*, and *Drosophilidae* (acalyprate Muscids); (9) seed-feeders, a few *Cecidomyiidae*; and (10) feeders on fungi and moulds: most members of the families *Mycetophilidae* and *Platypezidae*, as well as a few *Tipulidae*, *Cecidomyiidae*, and *Muscidae*. Most of the feeding habits enumerated require no special adaptations in the larvae, the two exceptions being the wood-borers and the gall-makers. It is interesting to note that the wood-boring genera each have strongly chitinised anterior and posterior extremities, for protection during boring and against the possible attacks of predators entering their burrows. The gall-makers, which produce the well-known deformations on leaves, stems or buds of plants, are a highly specialised group, each producing a more or less specific type of gall, usually on one definite host-plant, the gall, though formed by the plant, being as characteristic of the insect species as any of the morphological characters of the larva or adult. The production of the gall is believed to be due to the secretion of an irritant fluid by the larva ; often

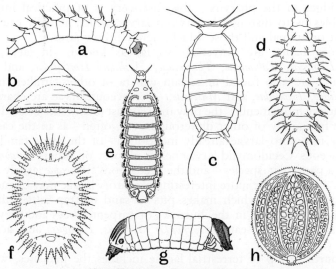

SOME TERRESTRIAL DIPTEROUS LARVAE

a, Forcipomyia palustris, which lives in moss on moist logs [after Saunders] ; *b, Phronia strenua*, under conical case formed of its own excrement ; it lives on damp barkless logs [after Steenberg] ; *c, Lonchoptera lutea*, lives under bark [after Imms] ; *d, Fannia canicularis*, lives in humus [after Hewitt] ; *e, Sycorax silacea*, lives in wet moss [after Bangerter] ; *f, Callimyia amoena*, lives exposed on bark-encrusting fungi [after de Meijere] ; *g, Pantophthalmus tabaninus*, lives in hard wood of living trees [after Austen] ; *h, Microdon*, lives in ants' nests [after Sharp]. The examples have been selected chiefly to show variety of form. All except the *Pantophthalmus*, which is South American, occur in Britain. (Fig. *g* somewhat reduced, the others enlarged.)

the digestive system of the larva is nearly functionless, food being mainly absorbed through the skin.

The scavengers (saprophagous larvae) are as numerous and hardly less various than the herbivores. Although many are general scavengers, feeding on decaying organic matter of almost any kind, others specialise more or less exclusively in a particular type of food, such as dung, leaf mould, decaying roots of annual or biennial plants, dead wood, sap running from wounds in trees, dried seaweed, birds' nests, moles' nests, or nests of ants, bees, wasps or termites, or in dead snails, or decaying flesh, or festering wounds of animals. Each of these habitats has its own special fauna, which further varies according to the state of decay of the substance. Among the most specialised larvae are those of the Syrphid genus *Microdon*, which are found in most parts of the world in ants' nests, and whose sole food consists of the dry pellets ejected by the ants from their infrabuccal pockets. The best-known scavengers in the nests of bees and wasps are the bumble-bee flies (*Volucella*). According to Keilin all saprophagous larvae, of whatever family, are distinguished from biontophagous (herbivores, carnivores, or parasites) by the possession of a set of longitudinal ridges in the pharynx; this discovery is of practical importance as it enables us to distinguish between larvae which actually cause injury to a plant or animal and those which merely follow after.

Predatory habits are universal—so far as known—in larvae of the families *Leptidae*, *Tabanidae*, *Therevidae*, *Asilidae*, *Empididae*, and *Dolichopodidae*, and are also found in certain genera of other families, including *Cecidomyiidae*, *Tipulidae*, and *Muscidae*. Predaceous larvae are characterised by their active movements; the prey may consist of any soft-bodied animals, but most frequently of other dipterous larvae, often—as in the case of the predatory mosquito larvae already mentioned—of the same family; thus the predaceous Cecidomyiid larvae nearly all prey on other *Cecidomyiidae*— often on a particular species—and the predaceous *Muscidae* largely on other *Muscidae*. Among the more interesting predatory larvae may be mentioned the Leptid *Vermileo*, which makes pits in sand to trap ants; the Asilid *Hyperechia*, which lives in the burrows of carpenter-bees and preys on the larvae; and the Aphis-eating *Syrphidae* (*Syrphus*, *Paragus*) and acalyptrate *Muscidae* (*Leucopis*).

The fourth group of terrestrial larvae includes the parasites, which are of two main types: those which, sooner or later, kill their hosts; and those which, although feeding at the expense of their hosts, cause them no serious injury. The latter are the true parasites; the former are rather "very economical predators," feeding internally instead of externally, and have been termed "parasitoids." Dealing first with the parasitoids, we may group them according to their hosts, which may be earthworms, molluscs, millipedes, spiders, adult insects, or larval insects. The parasitoids of earthworms and snails are not very numerous; they belong to the *Muscidae* and the *Sciomyzinae*. It may seem remarkable that any flies should parasitise their enemies the spiders, but members of at least three families—*Cyrtidae*, *Phoridae*, and *Chloropidae*—are known to feed upon the egg-cocoons of various spiders, and in one case (*Cyrtidae*) attack adult spiders, the young larvae entering the host at the leg-joints and making their way to its abdomen, inserting their breathing apparatus into the lung of the spider, and meanwhile feeding on its tissues.

Among adult insects, small frog-hoppers (Homoptera) are attacked by *Pipunculidae*; aphids and scale-insects by certain *Cecidomyiidae*, and by the

Agromyzid *Cryptochaetum*; bees and wasps by *Conopidae*; ants by some *Phoridae*—including *Apocephalus*, the North American ant-decapitating larva, which lives in the head of its host, causing it eventually to drop off; earwigs by the Tachinid *Bigonichaeta*; locusts by some species of *Sarcophaga*. Collectors of Lepidoptera are familiar with the attacks of the *Tachinidae* on caterpillars of all kinds; grubs of beetles, nymphs of Hemiptera, and many other insects are also destroyed by members of this family. These parasites are always enclosed—for at least a part of their life-history—in a kind of sheath formed by the host as a reaction against their presence; they respire free air either through the spiracles of the host, or through an opening they make in its body-wall. The chief enemies of bee and wasp larvae among the Diptera are the *Bombyliidae*, all of whose members are

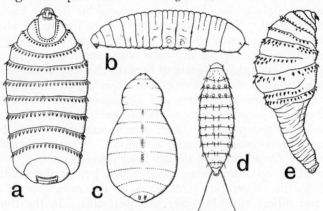

PARASITIC DIPTEROUS LARVAE

a, Gastrophilus intestinalis, horse-bot; *b, Auchmeromyia luteola*, Congo floor-maggot [after Graham-Smith]; *c, Pterodontia flavipes*, a spider-parasite, full-grown larva [after King]; *d, P. flavipes*, newly hatched larva more highly magnified [after King]; *e, Dermatobia hominis* [after Castellani and Chalmers]. (All enlarged, fig. *d* much more so.)

parasitic—though some attack other insects such as Orthoptera; ant-larvae are parasitised by some *Phoridae*. It is somewhat remarkable that Dipterous larvae seem rarely to parasitise others of the same order; among the few known instances may be mentioned the Tachinid *Bucentes*, which attacks larvae of crane-flies, and two *Bombyliidae*, which have been reared from the puparia of tsetse-flies.

The class of fly-larvae which we have referred to as true parasites is almost exclusively associated with vertebrates. These larvae again have varied modes of life, feeding either externally by sucking blood, or internally on serum or tissue. Larvae of three quite unrelated genera (*Passeromyia*, *Phormia*, and *Neottiophilum*) live in birds' nests and suck the blood of the nestlings; when numerous they may even cause the death of the young birds. The famous " Congo floor-maggot " (*Auchmeromyia*) is a nocturnal blood-sucking Muscid larva attacking man in tropical Africa, where the allied genus *Choeromyia* similarly attacks the aard-vark. Except for certain blow-flies of the genera *Sarcophaga* and *Lucilia*, which live in the stomach or under the skin of frogs, toads, and turtles, the only known Dipterous parasite of reptiles or amphibia is the Chloropid genus *Batrachomyia*, found under the skin of Australian frogs. This genus affords one of the many examples in Diptera of the great and often quite unexpected diversity of larval habits in the same family ; almost all the other *Chloropidae* whose life-history is known feed in the stems of grasses.

The internal parasites almost all belong to the family *Oestridae* and affect mammals, living either under the skin, in the nasal and frontal sinuses, in the stomach and intestine, or in the hoofs. Among the cutaneous parasites are the ox-warbles (*Hypoderma*), whose life-history has now been worked out in detail. The fly lays its eggs on the legs of the animal ; the young larvae bore their way through into the body, wandering about for some time, and eventually finding their way into the wall of the gullet, where they rest ; later they migrate to beneath the skin of the back, boring a small hole through which they can breathe. Other examples are the tropical American genera *Cuterebra* and *Dermatobia ;* the former, although they are among the largest Dipterous larvae known, attack chiefly smallish animals such as rodents ; the latter attack man, the larvae burrowing directly under the skin and forming a tumour. The remarkable method of egg-laying of *Dermatobia* has already been referred to.

The second group, comprising those which live in the cavities of the head, includes the sheep-bot (*Oestrus ovis*), the camel-bot (*Cephalomyia maculata*), and others attacking deer and elephants. In the third group, the eggs are swallowed by the host, the young larvae hatching in the stomach and fixing themselves to its walls ; the best known is the horse-bot (*Gastrophilus*), but many of the larger mammals are affected—the rhinoceros by *Gyrostigma*, and the elephant by *Cobboldia*. In this group may be seen an example of the way in which the evolution of parasites has proceeded in a parallel manner with that of their hosts, the more closely related hosts having nearly related bots. The horse-bot larva has solved the problem of respiration, just as some of the mud-living *Chironomidae* have done, by developing haemoglobin in its blood, but it has also retained its spiracles and so is able to make use of any bubbles of air which may pass. The small group of hoof-feeding larvae includes the blow-fly *Booponus*, found in the water-buffalo in the Philippines, and a larva of uncertain affinities, *Neocuterebra*, found in the sole of the foot of the African elephant, surely one of the last places in which one would expect to find an insect larva at home. The imago of *Neocuterebra* has not yet been obtained.

In addition to the *Oestridae*, certain blow-flies also attack mammals, the larvae feeding in open wounds or sores. In the genus *Chrysomyia* this habit has become fixed, and the species may be regarded as true parasites, but in tropical countries some other species whose habits are normally different may adopt the habit, like the green-bottle fly in Australia, which has become such a serious pest of sheep.

One other type of parasitism, or rather commensalism, may be mentioned. Here the fly-larva, instead of feeding on the tissues or secretions of its host, feeds only on its food. Two examples of this are known : the bee-louse (*Braula*) which lives in the cells of larval-bees, feeding on honey supplied by the workers ; and the Phorid *Metopina pachycondylae*, which is similarly fed by worker ants, the tiny fly-larva in this case clinging round the neck of the ant-larva. Another very remarkable case of commensalism, which has not yet been fully investigated, is that of certain Ephydrid larvae found living in the gill-chambers of land-crabs.

The duration of larval life is usually much longer than that of the adult, in the case of single-brooded species often extending to the greater part of the year ; in multiple-brooded species, especially in hot weather, it may be reduced to a few days ; and in the case of louse-flies and tsetse-flies the period of free larval life is a matter of hours only. Feeding and growth are normally the only functions of the larva, but there is one case in which the larva has taken on the adult function of reproduction, a phenomenon known as paedogenesis. This occurs in a small group of *Cecidomyiidae* whose larvae live under bark of various trees. The eggs develop and hatch in the body of the larva ; the young larvae break through the ovary wall and lie in the body of the mother-larva, leading a parasitic life and absorbing nutriment from the mother ; finally the skin of the larger larva bursts, and the young are set free, only to pass through a similar cycle. This method of reproduction is carried on through most of the year, but in spring some larvae pupate and produce adults.

Before pupation the larvae of some Diptera form a silken or gummy cocoon. This habit is usual among the *Simuliidae* and *Mycetophilidae*, and frequent among the *Cecidomyiidae ;* it is not so common among other families, but scattered instances occur.

Pupae

After moulting for the fourth time—or the third time in the case of the sub-order Cyclorrhapha, or the first in the case of the louse-flies—the larva becomes a pupa. The function of a pupa being development and re-organisation, its main needs are respiration and protection from enemies. As in the case of larvae, we may group Dipterous pupae into the aquatic and the terrestrial, and divide the aquatic pupae again into those living in still water and those in rapid streams.

The pupae of stagnant water seek protection either by movement, like the very active pupae of mosquitoes, in which tail-paddles have been developed as organs of locomotion ; or by remaining in the cases formed by the larvae, as do many *Chironomidae*. Respiration may be effected by the pupa rising to the surface to breathe atmospheric air, or by wriggling within the larval case, and so keeping up a current of aerated water; in the latter case respiration is either entirely cuticular or aided by a gill-like tuft of filaments, which replaces the breathing trumpets of the active

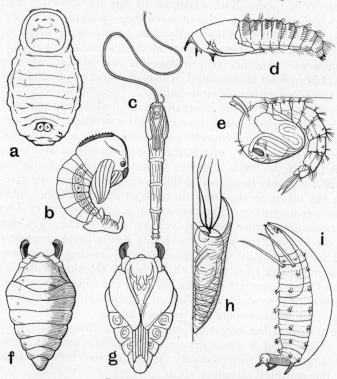

DIPTEROUS PUPAE AND PUPARIA

a, Hypoderma bovis, ox-warble, puparium showing circular cap; *b, Astomella lindeni*, a spider-parasite [after Brauer]; *c, Ptychoptera*, from still water [after Miall]; *d, Bombylius major*, bumble-bee parasite [after Russell]; *e, Culex pipiens*, common house-gnat [after Howard, Dyar and Knab]; *f* and *g, Liponeura cincrascens* (family Belphaloceridae), seen from above and below [after Hetchko]; *h, Simulium latipes* in its cocoon, from a small stony stream [after Friederichs]; *i, Phora bergenstammi*, puparium with protruding respiratory horns of pupa, from a dead snail [after Keilin]. (Various degrees of enlargement.)

Culicidae. The pupa of the mosquito *Mansonia*, like the larva, pierces the roots of water plants, and obtains air therefrom. Pupae living in rapid currents need means of attachment rather than protection; in the case of *Simulium* fixation is secured by a series of forwardly directed hooks which hold the pupa fast in the larval cocoon—this always being open in front and facing downstream; Blepharocerid pupae have the whole ventral surface flattened and closely adherent to the rocks, in addition a series of lateral sucker-like pads being developed; Chironomid and Tipulid pupae remain in the larval cases.

It is a significant fact that the pupae carry on the larval tradition as regards *methods* of respiration, fixation, or protection, even though the organs used may be different. In the case of pupae the respiratory organs are always situated on the thorax, instead of at the end of the abdomen, as is usually the case in larvae. The method of escape of the adult from the pupa in *Simulium* and *Blepharoceridae* is interesting; in both cases air obtained from passing bubbles caught and held by the respiratory organs, which are variously branched for this purpose, is accumulated within the pupal skin, and the wings of the adult are fully developed, though folded, so that when the pupal skin splits the adult is ready to rise in a bubble of air, and can take to the wing immediately on reaching the surface.

Terrestrial pupae are often provided with boring organs, such as strong chitinous processes on the head or thorax and circlets of backwardly directed spines on the abdomen, which enable the pupa to make its way to the surface of the ground or out of the larval cocoon for the emergence of the adult. Such structures are specially well developed in the *Bombyliidae*, which may need them for escape from clay cells, as well as in the wood-boring forms. The majority of terrestrial Dipterous pupae, however, are themselves soft and delicate, and find protection by remaining within the last larval skin, which becomes thickened, hard, and more or less barrel-shaped, and is known as the *puparium*.

This habit is universal in the sub-order Cyclorrhapha, and is also found in the family *Stratiomyiidae*, and in a few *Cecidomyiidae* such as the Hessian-fly. In the case of the Hessian-fly the puparium may consist of the last *two* larval skins, as it is said to be lined within with silk, which could not be done by the pupa itself. In the more primitive type of puparium—such as that of many *Syrphidae* and *Phoridae*—respiration is effected by the thoracic respiratory horns of the pupa protruding through the larval skin, but in the higher types the pupa remains entirely internal, and presumably respires air contained within the puparium; it is often much smaller than the larva. In the lower types the pupa when mature, or the adult after emergence from the pupal skin, escapes by a more or less irregular slit in the puparium, but in the higher—such as *Oestridae*—there is a definite line of suture, and a special circular cap. To effect its escape the adult in these families has a large protrusible vesicle on the front of the head which can be filled with blood and so pushes off the cap.

FLIES AND MAN

It would require a whole volume to discuss at all adequately the various ways in which the Diptera affect man; here we can do no more than offer the merest catalogue.

Firstly, let us state the ways in which flies may benefit man : (1) Flies or their larvae may be used as food, as they are occasionally by various savage races. (2) They may help to feed animals which are eaten by man, such as poultry or fish, either forming a staple food supply for the animals, or being used as bait. (3) They may assist in the pollination of fruit trees or other crops ; indeed, they probably play a greater part in this function than even the Hymenoptera. (4) Occasionally they may help in keeping down noxious weeds ; for example, *Dasyneura gibsoni* is said to have almost completely destroyed the Canadian thistle in parts of Indiana. (5) Many are of very great use in devouring or parasitising noxious insects, as, for example, the *Tachinidae* which parasitise locusts or earwigs. (6) The very numerous scavengers undoubtedly all fulfil exceedingly useful and necessary functions.

So much can be said in favour of Diptera from the human point of view. On the other hand, the ways in which they injure man or his interests are many and varied. The injury may consist of :

(1) *Damage to vegetable crops.*—The Diptera include several of the most serious corn pests, such as the Hessian-fly, gout-fly, and frit-fly, of which the first alone is said to have caused millions of pounds' worth of damage annually in North America. There are also numerous Dipterous pests of fruit, such as the pear-midge, which has rendered cultivation of pears almost impossible in parts of New Zealand ; the Mediterranean fruit-fly, and the Mexican orange-maggot. Among fodder crops, clover has often suffered severely from the attacks of the clover-midge. Root pests include a number of species directly and seriously injurious, such as the carrot-fly and the Narcissus-fly, as well as many others (such as *Bibio* and *Sciara*) which, although they may not often initiate an attack, will follow up the damage caused by other insects and fungi and render it far more serious.

(2) *Injury to domestic animals.*—The most serious are the warble-flies, which not only affect the quality of the meat, but spoil much leather by perforating the hides ; the blow-flies, which are such a scourge to sheep in Australia and New Zealand ; and the tsetse-flies, which by spreading the nagana disease have taken such an immense toll of the introduced breeds of cattle in tropical Africa. Other offenders include the horse-flies, which not only annoy stock, but in some cases spread disease, as, for example, some species of *Chrysops* which carry the disease known as surra in horses.

(3) *Damage to stored produce.*—Potato clamps may be much damaged by *Sciara ;* cheese by the well-known " skip-jacks " ; stored grapes or wines by *Drosophila.*

(4) *Annoyance or bodily injury to man himself.*—Here we may note the pestering sweat-flies, and the blood-sucking midges, horse-flies, and others which in some countries render life a trial by day, and may even—as in parts of the Canadian North-West—render tracts of country uninhabitable

by man during the summer. Of importance also are the cases where fly larvae infest wounds—as does *Chrysomyia*—or form subcutaneous boils— as *Dermatobia* in South America or *Cordylobia* in Africa—or attack the frontal sinuses, as *Oestrus ovis* occasionally does in the case of shepherds ; or get into the alimentary canal or even the bladder. Such cases as these, known by the general name of Myiasis, are usually more or less accidental, but nevertheless may cause much suffering, and even death.

(5) *Transmission of disease to man.*—This is the most serious count in the indictment against the Diptera; the death-roll due to fly-borne diseases is still a heavy one, and until the end of the last century, when the connection of flies with disease was first proved, was very much heavier. Flies may spread infection either by contamination of food, as in the case of the house-fly, which has been shown to be at least one of the agents in the spread of typhoid and infant-cholera ; by infecting wounds with patho-genic bacteria, or protozoa ; or by carrying blood-parasites of various kinds from one person to another. In the last-named category are the various forms of human malaria, carried solely by mosquitoes of the

The Yellow-fever mosquito, *Aëdes aegypti* (also known as *Aëdes argenteus* or *Stegomyia fasciata*).
(Enlarged about three times.)

genus *Anopheles ;* yellow-fever, carried by the mosquito *Aëdes aegypti* (=*Stegomyia fasciata*) ; dengue and filariasis, carried by a number of different mosquitoes ; verruga in Peru, Papataci fever in Malta, and Kala-Azar in India and China, carried by species of sand-flies (*Phlebotomus*) ; and African sleeping-sickness, carried by tsetse-flies (*Glossina palpalis* and *Glossina morsitans*).

HISTORY AND CLASSIFICATION

Although obviously one of the younger orders of insects, Diptera first arose at a rather remote period in the earth's history. Fossil flies are known from the Jurassic period, and we have reason to believe that the first ancestor of the Diptera must have lived earlier still, perhaps in Permo-Triassic times— that is to say, according to the latest computations, about two hundred million years ago. By the early Tertiary period—say fifty million years ago—they had become almost as diverse as they are at the present day, the chief advances which they have made since then being probably those made by the *Oestridae* and the louse-flies, in parasitising the mammals—which, it may

N 2

be noted, are a more recently developed group than the Diptera. When these facts are borne in mind the diversity shown by the order to-day will readily be understood.

It is probable that there are at least a quarter of a million species of Diptera now existing, but up to the present only some 53,000 have been described, of which rather over 4500 are known to occur in Britain. The classification of this large number is a matter of no little difficulty, and there is much difference of opinion as to the number and limits of the families, some authors recognising only about thirty, and others as many as ninety ; but the main divisions are fairly clearly marked and agreement concerning their relationship is becoming general. Two sub-orders are recognised, the second with two main divisions, the chief families of each being listed herewith, with the approximate number of species described from Britain and from the world.

Sub-order 1.—*NEMATOCERA*

(Adult antennae with many similar segments ; larva usually with a distinct head, or if not, with horizontally moving jaws.)

	Britain.	World.
Tipulidae, etc. (Crane-flies)	250	4500
Psychodidae (Moth-flies)	50	300
Blepharoceridae (Net-winged midges)	0	100
Simuliidae (Buffalo-gnats, black-flies)	19	300
Chironomidae, etc. (Midges)	480	2000
Culicidae (Mosquitoes, etc.)	45	1500
Bibionidae, etc. (St. Mark's fly, etc.)	45	450
Mycetophilidae (Fungus-gnats)	400	3000
Cecidomyiidae (Gall-midges and allies)	500	3000

Sub-order 2.—*BRACHYCERA*

(Adult antennae with few segments, usually fewer than ten and dissimilar ; larva with reduced head and vertically moving jaws.)

Section A.—*Orthorrhapha*

(Antennae various ; venation usually complex ; pupa usually free, rarely in a puparium ; larva with head more or less preserved, without pharyngeal skeleton.)

	Britain.	World.
Tabanidae (Horse-flies)	36	2400
Leptidae	19	650
Therevidae and *Scenopinidae*	12	650
Stratiomyiidae and allies	55	1500
Bombyliidae and allies	12	2700
Asilidae (Robber-flies)	23	3500
Empididae	330	2500
Dolichopodidae	240	2000

Section B.—*Cyclorrhapha*

(Antennae with three segments and a terminal bristle; venation reduced to a uniform type; pupa always in a puparium; larva headless, with a pharyngeal skeleton.)

	Britain.	World.
Syrphidae (Hover-flies)	220	3500
Pipunculidae (Frog-hopper parasites)	37	300
Platypezidae (Fungus-flies)	24	100
Phoridae	200	1000
Conopidae	17	500
Oestridae (Bots and warbles)	10	200
Muscidae (in the broad sense)—		
Muscidae (House-flies, etc.) . . .	370	3000
Tachinidae (Parasites)	300	5000
Acalyptrates (with numerous divisions) . .	850	7500
Hippoboscidae (Louse-flies)	7	160
Nycteribiidae and *Streblidae* (Bat-parasites) . . .	2	100

Order SIPHONAPTERA

(*Fleas*)

The fleas are a small group of insects of which about five hundred species are known, forty-six of which occur in Britain. *Pulex irritans*, the human flea, may be taken as a typical representative, and though somewhat less familiar in England now than formerly, it is still sufficiently in evidence for everyone to be acquainted with its general features and habits as an adult insect. Not everyone, however, is aware that the flea lays eggs; that these eggs hatch into tiny white legless maggots; that these maggots feed on dust in floor-cracks and under carpets; and that when they are full-fed they spin a white silken cocoon, in which they change to pupae and from which they later emerge as adult fleas. In this life-history they resemble many other insects, including flies and beetles; lengthy discussions have taken place as to whether fleas are descended from one or other of these groups of insects, but the only conclusion yet reached by entomologists is that they form an isolated group whose ancestors most probably had wings.

All known fleas are " intermittent parasites " of mammals or birds, depending for food on the blood of their hosts, but capable of a free existence for at least part of their lives. Some fleas are attached to a particular host; others may attack almost any animal which comes their way, though bird-fleas do not readily attack mammals, nor *vice versa*. Some animals, such as the mole, rat, and house-martin, may harbour a number of different species of fleas; others, such as monkeys, seals, whales, and hoofed animals —which do not make nests in which the fleas can breed—have none. A special family of fleas is connected with bats ; these are all blind, a fact which may be connected with the nocturnal habits of their hosts. Bird-fleas breed in their hosts' nests, and may often be found in numbers in deserted nests in winter.

Fleas are found in almost all parts of the world, from Novaia Zemlya to Antipodes Island, their distribution depending partly on that of their hosts, but partly also on climate. Human fleas do not occur in the Sahara, and until the arrival of the white man are said to have been absent from many Pacific Islands. Buxton remarks that " the placid natives of Aitutaki, observing that the little creatures were constantly restless and inquisitive, and even at times irritating, drew the reasonable inference that they were the souls of deceased white men."

The only fleas which differ very markedly from the usual type are the " chigoes " or " jiggers " of tropical and sub-tropical countries, the females of which attach themselves to, or even burrow into, the flesh of their hosts, while their abdomen becomes distended and globular with ingested blood and developing eggs. The South American chigoe—also introduced to and now widely spread in Africa—is a well-known pest of man, and another species attacks poultry.

As soon as a host dies its fleas leave it and seek a fresh host, and it is owing to this habit that fleas are such an important factor in the spread of plague. Plague is primarily a disease of rats, and is very fatal to them ; it is conveyed from rat to rat by the agency of fleas, and when a rat dies and no other rat is near at hand, the infected fleas may, and do, attack man and convey the disease to him. Eleven species of fleas have been shown to be capable of carrying plague from rats to man, but one in particular, the tropical rat flea known as *Xenopsylla cheopis*, is especially dangerous in this respect ; in India the distribution of plague and *Xenopsylla cheopis* almost coincide, while the disease rarely occurs in regions where the rats are infected solely with other species of flea. This is believed to be due to differences in habits between the two fleas. The larva of the common rat flea (*Ceratophyllus fasciatus*) cannot live without blood, which it obtains from the excreta of its parents ; the fleas therefore tend to remain in the nest to provide for the requirements of the larvae. On the other hand, the larvae of the plague flea (*X. cheopis*) can live on any organic refuse, such as dust in granaries ; the fleas, therefore, have no necessity to leave their hosts, and are carried about from place to place.

CHAPTER VI

Class ARACHNIDA

(Scorpions, Spiders, Harvesters, Mites, etc.)

By T. H. SAVORY, M.A.

THE Arachnida form the class which includes the Scorpions, Spiders, Harvesters, and Mites, and several other groups of less-known animals, all of which resemble one another in having simple eyes, eight legs, and two divisions to their bodies. The fore division consists of the head and breast, fused together, and called the cephalothorax; the hind division is usually called the abdomen. Breathing is carried on by " lung-books," and not by tracheae as in the insects. Trachae are present in the Araneae, but they differ entirely in structure from those of the Insecta. Only a few Arachnids live in water, the majority being land-living, generally solitary and nocturnal creatures, carnivorous in habit. The sexes are separate, and the male is usually smaller than the female, but visible differences between the two may be very slight. The young are generally hatched from eggs, and grow by a periodical casting of the skin. The development is commonly direct; but larvae are found among the mites.

The class includes two sub-classes and eleven orders, seven of which are mentioned in the following account :—

Sub-class *DELOBRANCHIATA* (Arachnida with gills, living under water).

Order XIPHOSURA, the King-crabs.

Sub-class *EMBOLOBRANCHIATA* (Arachnida with lungs or tracheae, or both).

Order SCORPIONIDEA, the Scorpions.
Order ARANEAE, the Spiders.
Order SOLIFUGAE, the False-spiders.
Order CHERNETIDEA, the False-scorpions.
Order OPILIONES, the Harvesters.
Order ACARINA, the Mites.

Sub-class *DELOBRANCHIATA*

Order XIPHOSURA

(King-crabs)

Near the Atlantic coast of America, and in the shallow waters of Japan, India, and the Malay Peninsula, there may be found about half a dozen species of primitive Arachnida of a very remarkable type. These form the genus, originally known as *Limulus*, of the King-crabs.

The fore-part of the King-crab consists of a huge, semicircular, dome-shaped shell; the abdomen is a broad hexagon, which fits into the hinder-border of the shell, and is prolonged backwards in the form of a strong, hinged, tail-spine. The colour of the shell is dark green, or black, and it presents a clean, polished appearance. All the creature's limbs are hidden beneath its body, the only features visible from above being the eyes, of which there are four.

Most of the life of *Limulus* is spent burrowing in the sand, in water less than ten fathoms deep. This is a region comparatively free from formidable opponents, and it is probably this absence of competition that has enabled *Limulus* to persist in its relatively primitive form ever since the remote Silurian days. It can travel through the sand with surprising speed, by pushing the front edge of its carapace downwards and forwards, while the sharp spine is thrust into the sand behind. At the same time it shovels away sand from beneath by means of extensible fan-like organs borne on its hindmost legs. Occasionally it leaves the sand and swims with the help of its gills, and the tail-spine which it uses as a lever. Thus it progresses partly by hopping and partly by swimming. It feeds on shell-less molluscs and marine-worms, which it seizes in its jaws, or chelicerae, and holds them beneath its mouth in such a position that the characteristic projections from the legs can shred them to pieces, small enough to drift into its mouth.

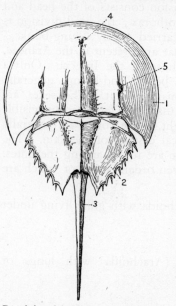

Dorsal view of the King-crab, *Limulus poly-phemus*. 1, Carapace covering pro-soma; 2, Meso- and meta-soma; 3, Telson; 4, Median eye; 5, Lateral eye.

The eggs are laid during the summer in shallow water, close to the land. The male grasps the hinder edge of the carapace of the female, and the two proceed together, stopping for a few moments at intervals. At each stopping place a nest of eggs may be found, buried under about two inches of sand. It thus seems probable that the female thrusts her genital plate into the sand before discharging the eggs, and that fertilisation follows their laying. Each nest contains about a thousand eggs. Some species of King-crab carry their eggs about with them, in the same way as do lobsters.

Each egg has a shell of a leathery consistency. The creature that hatches from it is known as a trilobite-larva, because of a superficial resemblance to that fossil. It is very active and swims and burrows like its parents. But this stage is soon followed by a moult, whereupon the abdomen becomes more close-set and the tail-spine appears. It continues to grow in this way, the old cuticle splitting along the lower side of the front edge of the carapace, and the legs and body being thrust out through the split. The growth after each successive moult is rapid, and continues for about eight years, when the shell attains a diameter of nine or ten inches.

Sub-class *EMBOLOBRANCHIATA*

Order SCORPIONIDEA

(*Scorpions*)

Scorpions are the largest of the land-living Arachnida, and are essentially lovers of hot countries. The separation between the head and the thorax is evident, since the former alone is unsegmented and bears a conspicuous pair of powerful chelicerae, or claws, resembling those of a crab. The abdomen consists of six ring-like segments, the last of which ends in a fine, curved point, traversed by a poison-duct. This " sting " is usually carried point downwards, but in attack or defence the tail is raised over the back, so that the sting points forwards.

Scorpions generally hide during the day, concealed under logs of wood, or under stones or in holes in the sand, which the creature digs for itself with its four middle legs. They hunt their prey, which consists almost entirely of insects and spiders, at night, although their powers of vision are feeble ; they seem to be quite deaf. They are apparently helped by a pair of curious comb-like organs, called the " pectines," borne by the middle portion of the body, which seem to be used continuously to feel the ground over which the scorpion is walking.

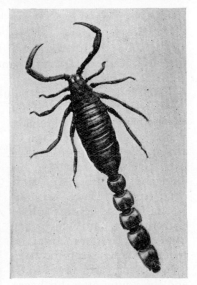

A Scorpion from Egypt.

When a scorpion finds a victim, it is promptly seized and torn in pieces with the chelicerae, though, if it is strong enough to offer resistance, it is paralysed by the sting, and is then slowly eaten. Scorpions, like spiders, are slow feeders, and may often spend an hour or more in the consumption of a single beetle. The poison they secrete is much more powerful than that of spiders, and is instantaneously fatal to insects and centipedes. It is not without effect on man, but a scorpion is quite immune from its own poison. This is of interest, since it disposes of the legend that scorpions in danger from fire commit suicide. A scorpion's food seems to provide its body with all the moisture it needs, for these creatures never drink. In this respect they are well adapted to the dry localities in which they are generally found, and, like other Arachnids, they can survive prolonged fasts.

Tail of a Scorpion, *Buthus bicolor*, showing the poison gland and sting.

The ferocity of scorpions has been much exaggerated. They will not use their sting unless considerably provoked; indeed, when they are discovered they show a much more marked desire to avoid notice than to attack. To their own kind, however, they are always hostile. They generally lead solitary lives, and if two are found together, one is either courting or eating the other.

Like spiders, scorpions indulge in a form of courtship before mating. They raise their tails and entwine them in a preliminary dance, after the conclusion of which the male grasps the chelicerae of the female in his own and leads her to a suitable spot. Here, without letting her go, he digs a hole with his feet, into which they both retire. After mating, the female sometimes eats the male.

Scorpions are viviparous, and the young after birth are carried on their mother's back, during which time they do not

Buthus cristatus. A Scorpion.

feed. In this they resemble young Wolf-spiders. After their first moult, they leave the mother and lead an independent life, which may extend to as much as five years. The largest species attain to a length of over eight inches; the smallest scarcely measure a quarter of an inch. About three hundred species of scorpions have been described.

Order ARANEAE

(*Spiders*)

Spiders are in many ways the dominant order of the Arachnida; in their world-wide distribution—some fourteen thousand different kinds are known—and in their diverse ways of achieving success in the battle of life, they are challenged only by the mites.

The spider's body, like that of other Arachnida, is divided into two parts. The fore-part, the cephalothorax, bears the eyes, of which there are usually eight, and the eight legs. At the tip of the abdomen are the spinnerets through which the silk is extruded; and almost the whole of the life-history of spiders is governed by their silk-producing ability. From the day when the young spiders emerge from the egg into the silk cocoon containing them, during their migrations in their quest for food, and through their winter sleep, spiders make a continuous use of this invaluable material. Few other creatures can produce it, and none uses it to the same extent.

A newly hatched spider possesses two instinctive habits which distinguish it from the adults. It does not shun the light, and it shows for a time a tendency to climb upwards. Soon after it is free from the cocoon, it escapes from the unwelcome crowd of its brethren by climbing as high as possible on the plants or other objects about it. Arrived at the top, it turns its head to the breeze, raises the abdomen and exudes a drop of liquid silk. The slightest wind draws out this drop into a long thread

A spider, *Cteniza californica*, showing eyes, chelicerae, two palpi, eight legs and spinnerets.

of silk, which at last begins to exert a pull on the tiny feet, when their grip is at once relaxed, and the body is carried upwards by the breeze. In this way are produced the long threads of " gossamer " which have attracted the notice of naturalists and poets from time immemorial. In spring and autumn the long threads may often be seen streaming away from the trees and palings under suitable weather conditions, and in certain parts of America the gossamer shower is recognised as an annual occurrence. Accompanying the true migration-threads there are often a number of rags or flakes of silk, due to threads spun by the active spiders on the ground, which get entangled together and are carried away by the current of hot air that rises from the ground.

A remarkable feature of this strange aerial migration is the swiftness of the preparation operations. When described, it sounds as though it were a matter of slow climbing, turning, and spinning followed by a period of waiting, whereas these actions are often all but simultaneous. A little spider may run up one's finger and apparently straight on into the air. Its journey may be yards, or it may be miles. Gossamer has descended on

ships two hundred miles from land ; and oceanic islands, like South Trinidad, have received most of their spider population as migrants that have travelled very great distances. It is not to be supposed that there is one species or even one genus of "Gossamer-spiders." The young of most of the spiders that spin webs, or hunt in the sunshine, disperse in this way, but those that burrow and hide under stones in the daytime are not well represented among the aerial migrants.

Heteropoda venatoria
A hunting-spider, often imported into England in crates of bananas.

As soon as a spider has established itself after its voyage, it must begin the everlasting quest for food. There is, of course, a large number of spiders that do not spin webs, and these are simple huntsmen, more or less assisted by different specialised habits. Many of the more primitive spiders are wanderers with no permanent home. During the day they are hidden beneath any chance shelter, and at dusk they come out to roam in search of food. A common British brown-and-black spider, *Scotophoeus blackwallii*, often traps itself in a bath or basin when so occupied, and we find it in the morning.

Xysticus cristatus
A Crab-spider common in England.

Wolf - spiders (*Lycosidae*) are extremely plentiful from spring to autumn in meadows and fields—small brown species, which scatter hastily at our approach. These are rapid, active huntsmen that are enabled to catch their prey through their own fleetness of foot.

More subtle than either of these are the Crab-spiders and the Jumping-spiders. Crab-spiders (*Thomisidae*) lurk among fallen leaves, and dart suddenly upon their unsuspecting victims. They owe their name to their habit of running sideways, or backwards. Some of them hide in flowers, matching the colour of the petals so that they may be overlooked by visiting insects. A common British species that well illustrates this habit is *Misumena vatia*, which may be yellow when on yellow flowers, or white when on white ones. It has the power of changing its colour to match its surroundings, and if transferred from one background to the other may complete its change in a couple of days. Many of the foreign species of this family are of remarkable beauty, and one of the most interesting is *Phrynarachne*, which protects itself in a remarkable way. These spiders occur in Malaya, Ceylon, and other parts of the East, where there are butterflies accustomed to alight on the droppings of birds. Upon leaves *Phrynarachne* spins a small, irregular, white web, which exactly resembles the outline of a dropping, and stations itself in the middle. In this situation its black and white markings complete so perfectly the setting it has already made that not only butterflies but even butterfly-collectors are deceived.

The Zebra-spider, *Salticus scenicus*.

Jumping-spiders belong to a very large family (*Salticidae*) characterised by their large eyes and keen eyesight. One small member of the family, the Zebra-spider, *Salticus scenicus*, is common in most parts of England, where it may be found hunting on palings and brick walls. These spiders creep about their chosen hunting-ground, stopping now and then, straightening the fore-legs, and carefully surveying the neighbourhood in anticipation of a meal. As soon as an insect is marked down they approach it with almost imperceptible movements, until near enough to jump upon the victim unawares. Their aim is very seldom at fault, and their victims are quickly killed and eaten. They guard against a false step by laying behind them, as they move, a silk thread bound down at frequent intervals. Like the mountaineer's rope this prevents a slip from developing into anything more than a moment's swaying at its end.

This drag-line habit, which is common to nearly all spiders, suggests the probable origin of the web by means of which the majority of spiders obtain their food. A spider accustomed to shelter in a particular place, returning after each hunting expedition, would soon form in the neighbourhood of its shelter a large number of " drag-lines " radiating from a common centre. As soon as it acquired the habit of responding to the shaking of these lines, by running out to seize the cause of the disturbance, the more primitive type of web, such as is spun by many spiders to-day, came into being. The bluish, rough-looking webs so common in shed windows, and seen diverging from cracks in wooden palings and keyholes in gates, are of this type.

The common cobweb of our houses is a development of this, one edge of the fringe which lines the retreat being enlarged and spread out as a sheet, supported by numerous threads above and below. The advantage of a big sheet is obvious, and the superstructure of supporting threads delays passing insects and throws them down on to the sheet. When such a web is spun out-of-doors, among the bushes, the tube in which the spider lives is a conspicuous object, and so we find that many spiders have abandoned it and live upside down on the under side of the sheet. Others again have abandoned both tube and sheet, and retain only the tangle of threads which originally supported the latter; webs of both these types are very common on hedges and bushes in summer and autumn.

The commonest of all House-spiders, *Tegenaria derhamii*.

It is clear that the circular or orb-webs which form such beautiful and familiar objects must represent a considerable advance from either of these conditions. It seems probable that the web has arisen first out of an economy of silk, since it is better to make a flat web than a solid one, and secondly out of a simplification of the spider's own movements. The finished orb-web possesses such striking beauty that it is hard at first to believe that it is the result of less complex activities, but this seems none the less to be the truth. The fact is that simplicity of construction has a value in the struggle for existence, while its beauty is an accidental accompaniment.

All spiders' webs spun on bushes have the disadvantage that the owner is bound to spend a long time in exposed positions. In temperate regions the risks attendant on such exposure are less serious than in the tropics, where some remarkable protective devices are to be found. Sometimes the spider spins a central shield, or a band, and rests behind it; sometimes she adds a zigzag or an irregular band of silk round her resting-place so that the eye of the observer is caught by it, and attention directed away from herself; sometimes she hangs up in the web a row of cocoons, or a row of pellets made of the remnants of her captures, and these additions so closely resemble herself that it is very difficult, even for man, to distinguish the spider from the pellets. Some spiders add decoys to their webs. They make two or three heaps of débris which they surround with threads like those in the centre of the web, so that the web seems to contain three or four spiders. The real spider has then a good chance of escaping the attacks of its enemies.

Whatever may be the form that the web may take, it is always used in the same way. The spider, either in the web, or in a retreat close by, feels

The common Garden-spider, *Epeira diademata*. Left—male ; right—female.

the vibration of the threads produced by the impact of an insect, rushes out to the spot and seizes the victim. Often, by shaking the web, the prey is caused to struggle and so to entangle itself further ; frequently the captive is tied up in bands of silk before being carried away to be eaten. The common Garden-spider, *Epeira diademata*, is often seen to treat her captives in this way.

All spiders possess in the front of their bodies glands which secrete a poison that exudes from the tips of the fangs. This poison generally quietens an insect in a second or so, and many of the larger spiders are even able to deal successfully with such opponents as fish, mice, and humming-birds. The stories of the Tarantula's bite will not bear investigation, nor is any British spider able to produce more than local irritation by biting a human being, but a certain number of tropical species are more dangerous. The genus *Latrodectus* contains species found in many parts of the world, whose bites are known to be dangerous to man, to camels, and to horses, and the Argentine *Glyptocranium* has also a bad reputation.

Spiders are able to consume a relatively large amount of food, and to store it in the tubes which open out of their intestines. Thus they are able to tide over long-enforced fasts by living on their reserves. Cases have been known of spiders surviving a fast of thirty months. However, when they are well fed, their characteristic method of growth may be seen. The supporting skeleton of a spider's body is entirely on the outside, so that growth within causes this coat to become tighter and tighter. When it has become too small the outer shell is cast, or " moulted." The creature suspends itself upside down, its feet close together, and its abdomen supported by a thread from its spinnerets. By bending its legs it causes the outer shell or cuticle of the abdomen to split along the middle of the back, the split extending round the sides of the cephalothorax. The cuticle soon shrivels off the abdomen, and the carapace falls away easily ; the most tedious part of the business is the extraction of the legs. These are gradually pulled out from their old skins by a series of heaving movements, and as many as six hundred pulls may be necessary. After the moult the spider is paler in colour than usual, and its cuticle is soft. It is considerably exhausted and remains motionless for some time, after which it carefully combs itself all over before the new cuticle hardens. This probably sets its hairs and spines in the right directions.

The Black Widow, *Latrodectus* ; one of the dangerously poisonous spiders.

At such a moult legs that may previously have been lost are renewed. It is well known that spiders, like most other Arachnids, escape if they are caught by one leg, by casting the limb in exchange for their freedom. The limb grows again beneath the cuticle, and appears when the latter is moulted. It often happens that a leg is lost too soon before the moult to enable the new leg to be completed. The spider then appears with a shorter leg, and this explains the occurrence of spiders with an asymmetrical set of legs. About eight or nine moults seem to be usual before the spider is mature, but some species, which live more than a year, apparently undergo an annual moult even though they are full-grown.

Like all other animals, spiders run an unceasing risk from attack by enemies, which include birds and all insect-eating animals ; ichneumon-flies, which lay their eggs either in their cocoons or on their bodies ; and wasps, which store them in cells as food for their grubs. Like other animals they avoid these risks by their coloration ; by protective resemblance to their surroundings ; by mimicry ; and by special habits.

The colours of spiders are seldom conspicuous, and bright tints are found only in species that live among flowers. There is generally some degree of resemblance between the colour of a spider and that of its normal environment, but cases of close protective coloration are rare, except when considered together with the spider's shape. In this matter of shape, spiders present some extraordinary forms. In some of these we can recognise a protective resemblance or mimicry ; in the spiked forms we can see a discouragement to tender mouths ; but in many we can see no apparent reason, until the habits are more fully investigated.

Spiders which resemble their own cocoons, or heaps of rubbish in their webs, have already been mentioned. There are many such. An African spider, *Cladomelea akermani*, is a good example, since it fixes its egg-cocoons to the grass, binding several blades together to make a firm support, and then rests among them. The spider is almost indistinguishable from the cocoons, and the whole conspicuous group closely resembles the fruit of a plant. Another African spider is even better protected. Its abdomen has a curious camel-like hump, to which it owes its name, *Menneus camelus*. In life it sits close against a twig, its legs stretched out before and behind, and its hump looking exactly like a thorn or a broken stem. So close is this resemblance that its discoverer, for a time, believed that the spider dropped from its web in the day and lived at the bottom of the bush. It was only by minutely searching each branch that the spider was found, and a resemblance which can thus deceive even the eyes of men who know what they are seeking is indeed remarkable.

A few spiders are protected by warning-colours, in the form of streaks of yellow and black which seem to be Nature's recognised danger signals ; and a few show the interesting phenomenon of flash-colours. Such spiders, as they run, are bright and conspicuous ; then, of a sudden, they stop and, crouching, cover up the bright areas. The eye of the observer has gone on, and when it is brought back the spider is invisible against its surroundings. It seems to have melted into the air.

The phenomenon of mimicry is widespread among spiders, which do not, like butterflies, mimic each other, but other animals, such as caterpillars, snails, beetles, and ants. The snail-mimics cling to the under sides of leaves, where, with legs drawn in, they look like small molluscs ; they remain unmoved if the leaf is plucked, behaving as a snail would. The beetles mimicked are chiefly of the lady-bird group, which possess an unpleasant taste and flaunt vivid colours. Ant-mimicry is the commonest and closest. Nearly all families of spiders possess examples of this type, and there are whole genera thus protected. The general outline of an ant's body is very different from that of a typical spider, so that considerable modifications are necessary to produce a likeness, and yet in many instances this is achieved with amazing success. Again, men familiar with both ants and spiders, and aware that there are spiders among the ants they are observing, have time after time picked up the wrong creature, or picked it up in confessed ignorance of whether it were ant or spider. The deceptive appearance is enhanced by the fact that the spiders also mimic the ants' habits. They adopt their busy bustling gait, and hold their fore-legs outstretched in front, imitating antennae.

It must not be forgotten that these wonderful adaptations are shown only by the minority. The rank and file are not protected in these ways, and have to rely more on their special and often remarkable habits. It is a matter of common knowledge that the Garden-spider, when disturbed, shakes its web, a habit which must confuse and startle the onlooker. By vigorous contractions of its legs the web is made to vibrate rapidly, and the spider itself appears as a mere blur.

The commonest of the protective habits, and one which is shared by nearly all spiders, is that usually described as " shamming-dead." A sudden disturbance in its neighbourhood usually causes the spider to draw in its legs and remain motionless. If it is a web-spider it falls from its web on a silk thread, either to the ground or to the shelter of a leaf below. Spiders huddled up in this condition are difficult to detect among vegetable débris and herein lies their protection. They do not look like dead spiders, which are rarities in Nature, and are easily recognised. Again, all spiders share the capacity, already referred to, of being able to shake off a leg if they are caught by one. In this action the leg is always shed from the second joint, and bleeding automatically stops, but if a spider is chloroformed it may be picked up by a leg, swung about and generally subjected to treatment which would normally cause it to cast its leg.

By these various methods young spiders escape the dangers that beset them, and a proportion reach maturity, when they seek a mate. Jumping-spiders, whose sense of sight is keenest, exhibit the most elaborate courtship activities. Many of their males are decorated with tufts of hair, or with black or coloured patches on their bodies or legs, and when a male sees a female he displays these ornaments in a sort of dance in front of her. He raises his front legs, or he waves them about, or he holds out the adorned legs of one side and walks round in a circle, or he raises his abdomen. Whatever he does, his dance is peculiar to his species. Yet always it displays his charms as well as possible, and always the female watches him intently as he circles around her, perhaps as many as a hundred times. Sometimes she ends the dance by joining in, the two then whirling round together.

Wolf-spiders also possess good eyes, and their courtship is similar to that of the Jumping-spiders but less elaborate. Legs or palpi, or both, are waved before the female, or stretched out towards her, sometimes quivering, sometimes gracefully and gently raised and lowered. Crab-spiders cannot see well. The male climbs upon the female's back, and if she tries to escape, seizes her by the leg. The only form of courtship is the stimulation she receives from his feet, with which he tickles her back as he crawls about.

With spiders that spin webs, courtship is of a different nature, since they cannot see well, and most of their actions are governed by their very delicate sense of touch. If a male House-spider, for example, is dropped on the web of a female, he drums vigorously with his palpi upon the sheet of the web. The female, waiting in the tubular part of the web, behaves as if she could distinguish between the disturbance he has provoked and that produced by a captured fly. She waits expectantly and lets the vibrations play round her; the male gradually approaches until he can touch her with outstretched fore-leg. The female of one common species, *Agelena labyrinthica*, appears to fall into a kind of trance as a result of this courtship. The male picks her up by one leg and carries her about, nor does she awake till the mating is over.

In many other web-spinners the two sexes seem to signal to one another. The male pulls upon the threads, and the female replies, so that a real exchange of sentiments is occurring between the two, but of a purely tactile nature. Sometimes the males hang about the outskirts of the web for days, until the female is prepared to receive them; sometimes the female takes the lead in courtship and is the more ardent in plucking the

A British spider commonly found on gorse bushes, *Agelena labyrinthica*.

threads. It is evident that there is a language of touch, and that many spiders can speak it well.

The popular belief that female spiders habitually eat the males after mating is not justified by the facts. Such things do occur, no doubt, but they are mainly accidental, some species being more inclined to cannibalism than others, but in reality male spiders during courtship are comparatively safe, and after mating they have a fair chance of escape. These chances lessen as the season advances, when the female is probably more hungry and the male less active. It often happens that the male and female live together in the web or the nest for a longer or shorter time, and a sort of common life is possible. They have even been observed to share the same fly.

It would not be easy to find elsewhere in biology a more beautiful instance of the complementary nature of the male and female characters than is shown by the sexes of spiders. Maturity in the male impels it to abandon its web, to take to a wandering life, and when the opportunity occurs, to carry out the elaborate activity of courtship; whereas maturity in the female impels it in due course to perform in the correct order all the complicated actions necessary for making a cocoon.

When the eggs within her are matured, the female spider, whether mated or not, lays them in a cocoon. Spiders' cocoons take all sorts of shapes, from simple spherical sacs to elaborate and beautiful structures in which leaves and grass and other substances play their part, as well as silk. The spinning of the cocoon is a lengthy process, which often occupies more than a day, and it is one in which the general methods of procedure are much the same for all species. First, the spider spins a small sheet of closely woven silk, no longer than herself. Sometimes this sheet is contained in a silk-chamber of its own, and the making of this special nursery occupies the female for a day before the sheet is placed in it ; sometimes the sheet is spun on the ground or is suspended close to the web.

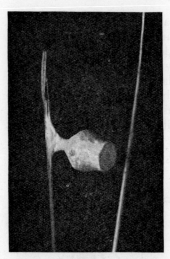

Cocoon of *Agroeca brunnea*, coated with mud and attached to a stick.

Sometimes the eggs are laid straight upon this sheet, sometimes a soft cushion of flocculent silk is placed on it to receive them. This silk is produced by special glands and is often coloured yellow or brown. A second layer may cover the eggs, and over all yet another sheet is woven. The first sheet is then picked up and the cocoon rounded off. Finally, there may be a characteristic addition of a coating of mud-plaster, or a layer of gritty particles, which help to make the cocoon inconspicuous and to protect it from the attacks of ichneumon-flies. Many spiders, having spun the first sheet of the cocoon, attach the eggs to its under surface.

The Water-spider, *Argyroneta aquatica* ; male.

The finished cocoon is, in the majority of cases, now fixed to a wall, fence, or tree, and left to hatch next spring, by which time its maker will be dead. Some spiders, however, remain on guard over their cocoons, readily attacking any insect that approaches. In a few species this care lasts until the young emerge, and the mother spider may tear open the cocoon to help them to struggle out. Other spiders, again, take the greatest care both of their cocoons and of their young. One of the most remarkable examples of this is the curious long-legged species, *Pholcus phalangioides*, common indoors in the south of England. This creature carries her cocoon in her jaws, and only frees herself from it, with some difficulty, on occasions when she feeds or cleans herself.

Wolf-spiders show the greatest tenacity in guarding their cocoons, which they carry attached to their spinnerets; so burdened, they are a familiar sight in fields and gardens in summer. If the cocoon is forcibly taken away, the spider seems to be dazed; she moves slowly with none of her usual speed and precision. If she encounters it again and touches it (she cannot recognise its appearance), she at once refixes it and regains her former manner. These actions are automatic rather than affectionate —she will accept any cocoon, a pith-ball, or even a pellet of cotton-wool.

These Wolf-spiders give their young more attention than do most spiders. As soon as they are hatched, the young ones climb upon their mother's back and there maintain a precarious foothold until old enough to fend for themselves. The mother presents a very remarkable appearance with her numerous family running all over her, hiding every part save her legs and eyes. If one of them ventures so far forward as to cover an eye, his mother gently sweeps him off with her leg. If any are scattered by accident, as sometimes occurs, they will readily continue their journey

The Water-spider, *Argyroneta aquatica*, in its air-filled diving-bell, spun among plants under water.

upon any other spider they may be lucky enough to meet. It has been observed that two or even three whole families may crowd upon one spider, although the young do not, as a rule, descend voluntarily. They have been seen, however, when the mother is drinking, to come down and refresh themselves.

The young of many web-spiders live for a short time in the parents' web; and among the family *Theridiidae*, that spin irregularly tangled webs, a sort of family life has been witnessed. If a fly is caught in the web, the mother kills it, and bites it in several places. The young then approach and feed themselves at the wounds the mother has made. A more remarkable fact is that they have been seen to collect round their mother and apply their mouths to hers, evidently being fed by her in this extraordinary way.

The young spider that first breaks through the outer coat of its egg is a curious and incomplete little creature. It is not a larva, and equally it is not a perfect spider. Its little body is usually transparent, and the yolk within its alimentary tract is quite visible under a microscope. Often it has no eyes, and its mouth is seldom complete. It cannot spin, and continuously it keeps up a steady movement of its legs as if to promote the circulation of body-fluids within. After a certain time it moults, and its eyes and spinnerets appear. Only at this stage is it ready to take its first great step into the world, when, by escaping from the cocoon, it begins on its own account the life that has already been described.

It is dangerously easy, in one's first admiration of the spider's wonderful webs and cocoons, and in surprise at its courtship and its maternal care, to attribute to it a degree of intelligence, and to its actions a degree of conscious striving, that is certainly not justified. In fact, the truth lies towards the other extreme. Whereas it is very difficult to explain the behaviour of some insects if we do not admit that they show intelligence, it is equally difficult to find in spiders any indisputable evidence of intelligent behaviour. The actions of spiders are mostly " reflexes " and " tropisms," rising at times to the level of the complex tropisms that we call instincts. A few examples will make this clear.

It has been seen how the frightened spider drops motionless in a trance-like condition. This is a reflex action, comparable to our own involuntary coughing when our throat is irritated. Such actions depend on close connection between certain nerves and certain muscles ; they are controlled by a part of the nervous system that is not concerned in volition and are performed without any " stopping to think." The reflex which produces the trance-like condition in spiders is called forth by a sharp tap on the box in which a spider is kept. Experiment has shown that the action is carried out perfectly by the legs of a spider whose abdomen has just been cut off, and moreover, if the cephalothorax is again bisected, so that each half carries two pairs of legs, the same response is shown, if more slowly.

Tropisms differ from compound reflexes in that they involve movements of the whole body rather than of a part, and they are often due to an adjustment of the body so that the stimulus falls equally on its two sides. The familiar example is the flight of a moth to the lamp. Tropisms govern the majority of the spider's activities. Early in life the young spider is impelled to climb, preparatory to its gossamer-flight. It is responding to a tropism which turns it away from the force of gravity, it is negatively geotropic. Many spiders are negatively heliotropic, that is to say, they avoid the light of day, being active only at night. Web-spiders respond to the shaking of their webs by flies or by tuning-forks, and this vibrotropism causes them to catch their food. Stereotropism makes spiders, and many other animals, bring as large an area as possible of their bodies into contact with the solids, hence they secrete themselves in crevices.

It is characteristic of tropisms that they are modified, destroyed, or reversed by changes of either internal or external conditions. Thus Wolf-spiders in dull cool weather are stereotropic, and lie hidden ; when the sun shines they are heliotropic and negatively stereotropic, coming out to hunt their prey, and it is a well-known fact that the temporary passage of a cloud over the sun causes Wolf-spiders to disappear in an almost incredible way as the stereotropism reasserts itself. It is interesting to note that motion in the sunshine is one of the most risky habits any creature could adopt, wherefore we find in Wolf-spiders a maternal care for eggs and young, which presumably is enough to ensure the necessary rate of survival.

Complex tropisms develop into instinctive actions and chain-instincts like web-spinning and courtship. Spiders illustrate very well the tyranny with which an instinct drives a creature through a set series of actions with the minimum ability to adapt itself to changed conditions. For example, in a most illuminating experiment, half of the spiral thread of an orb-web was removed as soon as it was spun. The spider, on its return to the web, began again where it had left off and laid down the second half of the spiral. It could not readapt itself, go back on its tracks, or start again. In these blind actions, unmodified by circumstances, uninfluenced by experience, incapable of improving with practice, there is no evidence that the spider is behaving in a conscious way. The instinct is called forth by a certain circumstance and the spider responds. It spins a web in a sealed box, or in a box in which the smell of a female lingers will go through its courtship antics. Some stimulus pulls the trigger and the spider acts—irresistibly, irrationally.

There are at least fourteen thousand species of spiders already known, and their classification has presented difficulties of which the solution is only now beginning to appear. The group is divided into nearly sixty families, arranged in three sub-orders.

Sub-order *LIPHISTIOMORPHAE*

(*Primitive Spiders*)

The first sub-order, the Liphistiomorphae, includes a small number of primitive spiders found in India, Japan, and the Malay States. They possess the remarkable character of having a segmented abdomen, which bears about twelve plates of chitin on its upper surface. This recalls the presumably segmented abdomen of the spiders' general ancestor, and, indeed, the nearest relatives of these Liphistiid spiders are certain fossil spiders of the Carboniferous age.

Sub-order M*YGALOMORPHAE*

(*Trap-door Spiders and Bird-eating Spiders*)

The second sub-order, the Mygalomorphae, includes the Trap-door spiders, the so-called " Tarantulas," and the Bird-eating spiders of the

Two aspects of *Eurypelma hentzii*, a Trap-door spider whose body is two inches long.

tropics. These spiders have four lungs instead of two, generally four spinnerets instead of six, their jaws work vertically instead of sideways, and there are other minor structural differences which separate them

The Trap-door of *Eurypelma hentzii* shut and open.

clearly from other spiders. They have themselves evolved along different paths, associated with different habits. Some have perfected the art of burrowing. In these the jaws are provided with a special row of teeth with which they dig; their burrows are lined with a silk tube and closed with a trap-door made of layers of silk and earth. The outside of this door is coated with moss or with whatever grows in its neighbourhood, and wonderful concealment is obtained. The inside often shows two small holes into which the spider fixes its feet so as to hold the door tight when danger threatens it from without. Some of the burrows have branches and some have a second trap-door as a way of escape.

The other spiders of this sub-order have become hunters, instead of diggers. Their bodies have a thick coat of protective hair and their jaws have no rake. This group includes the largest known spiders, the very biggest, *Theraphosa leblondi*, having a body three and a half inches long. Some of them are consequently able to overcome humming-birds, and have earned the popular name of Bird-eating spiders, but insects are their usual food. These large spiders are often popularly called " Tarantulas," but they are far removed from the true Tarantula of Italy, a much smaller insignificant Wolf-spider. There is but one member of this sub-order that occurs at all frequently in England; this is *Atypus affinis*. It does not make a trap-door ; its home is a silk tube, the lower part underground, the upper suspended among the grass and plants in its neighbourhood.

Sub-order *ARACHNOMORPHAE*

(*Crab-spiders, Wolf-spiders, etc.*)

The rest of the British spiders belong to the biggest of the three sub-orders, the Arachno-morphae. The simplest of these spiders, the *Dysderidae*, spin a lining tube to their retreat, producing the lining into a bell-like fringe round the mouth. Then there is a large group of comparatively primitive spiders, which are not web-spinners but hunters. Some of these, the families *Clubionidae* and *Drassidae*, are merely nocturnal wanderers ; more advanced families of the group are the Crab-spiders, *Thomisidae*, that lurk and pounce sideways, and the Jumping-spiders, *Salticidae*, that have specialised in leaping. All the spiders of these families have two claws. It is a general rule (certain exceptions apart) in both the chief sub-orders that web-spiders have three claws and hunters two.

Pisaura mirabilis, a common British hunting-spider, carrying her cocoon.

The next group of web-spiders includes the *Amaurobiidae*, whose silk is bluish in appearance due to its having been carded by a special comb on their hind-legs, and the *Agelenidae*, which includes the common house-spiders. The Wolf-spiders, *Lycosidae* and *Pisauridae*, are a specialised offshoot of this tribe ; they are three-clawed huntsmen.

The last group includes the largest families of spiders. The *Linyphiidae* spin the sheet-webs so common in blackberry bushes, the *Theridiidae* are the makers of the irregular tangles often seen in holly, and, finally, the *Epeiridae* and the *Uloboridae* are the makers of the familiar orb-webs.

Order SOLIFUGAE

(*False-spiders*)

Solifugae, like scorpions, are inhabitants of hot countries ; about two hundred species are known to occur in Spain, Greece, South Russia, and the tropical parts of Asia, Africa, and America. In appearance, they some-what resemble hairy spiders, but their thorax consists of three separate

Galeodes arabs, dorsal aspect.

Galeodes arabs, ventral surface, showing sense-organs on fourth pair of legs.

segments and their chelicerae are well-developed, formidable weapons. The large muscles that work these organs produce a swelling which gives the creature the appearance of having a big head, on which the two eyes are situated.

Most Solifugae are nocturnal, but a few are lovers of sunshine. They are extremely rapid in their movements, so that they are difficult to catch, and hold the first pair of legs before them as organs of touch. It is generally believed that they are venomous, but, as a matter of fact, they produce no poison. The strength of their chelicerae is sufficient to produce very serious wounds in the bodies of the insects which form their prey. They also fight with each other with extreme ferocity.

Order CHERNETIDEA

(*False-scorpions*)

False-scorpions form an interesting order of the smaller Arachnida, found throughout the habitable world. Yet because of their small size— the largest is a quarter of an inch long and most are less than a tenth— and their retiring habits, they are seldom found and little known. Many hide under stones, among moss, and under the bark of trees. The " Book-scorpion " is an example which lives indoors, and in stables and sheds they often occur, hiding in cracks in the woodwork and under heaps of

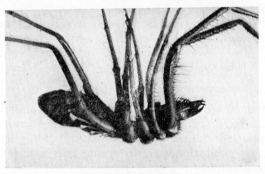

Galeodes arabs
The Egyptian " Sun-spider."

A False-scorpion,
Chalifer latreillii.

hay or straw. Some are partial to heaps of manure and a few are found on the shore, even below the tide-mark.

Their slight outward resemblance to scorpions is due to a large pair of palpi, their weapons of attack. Their segmented abdomen is rounded behind, and there is no sting. The chelicerae are small and produce silk which the creature uses for making nests.

They are carnivorous, their food consisting of insects and mites smaller even than themselves. The silk nests which they form are used for wintering, or for protection during the casting of the skin, or as brood-nests for their young. They are rounded in shape and are just large enough to contain the animal in comfort without undue cramping ; the silk is white, of tissue-paper-like consistency, usually coated on the outer side with tiny particles of earth or vegetable matter, the collection of which is the

O

first step in making the nest. The creature carries them to the chosen spot and arranges them in a circle, and then builds them up, one upon another, fixing them by brushing silk upon them from its chelicerae. At first, when the circular rampart is quite low, the particles can be picked up by merely stretching out the long palpi, but later the spinner has to climb over the wall and back again with each load. The solid matter is never overspun from the outside, and the silk hardens so rapidly that the frequent climbing in and out does not seem to injure the wall. In this way the cell gradually grows round the maker within, and when it is quite closed in, the creature continues energetically to brush silk against the inside of the walls.

In spring about thirty eggs are laid in a brood-pouch which, at first, remains attached to the mother. In the abdomen of the female are certain glands which evidently pass nutritive matter to the egg-sac during the attachment. When the eggs hatch, the newly born young develop a sucking organ with which they imbibe fluid from the centre of the sac, until the first moult. After a second moult the mother bites a hole through the cell and the brood escapes.

Twenty-four species of False-scorpions are known in England and rather less than a hundred in Europe.

Order OPILIONES

(*Harvesters*)

Harvesters, or Harvest-spiders, are of common occurrence throughout the world, and many of the foreign species are very remarkable creatures. Their compact bodies, supported on their characteristically long legs, are never brightly coloured, but in all species are so wonderfully sculptured that they are well worth examination.

The cephalothorax carries two large eyes placed back to back on a tubercle, which is usually decorated with spines. Close to this are the orifices of two odoriferous glands. It is supposed that Harvesters are able to escape from their enemies by the emission of an odour, but it seems to be very difficult for human nostrils to detect it. A number of spines are symmetrically placed about the creature's body and the segments of the abdomen are marked by transverse rows of tubercles.

The long legs, which serve also as sensitive organs of touch, do not look as though they were adapted to rapid and precise movements, but Harvesters can nevertheless move with a fair turn of speed. Often a Harvester may be seen on the trunk of a tree with its legs outstretched as if sunning itself, and a slight touch on one leg causes it at once to drop to the ground. The legs are very readily cast off if they are seized, and to catch a Harvester it is necessary to grasp two or three legs at once.

The jaws of Harvesters are weak and do not look as if they were very

efficient, yet the creatures are carnivorous and eat mites, insects, caterpillars, and spiders, as well as each other. Occasionally they eat the bodies

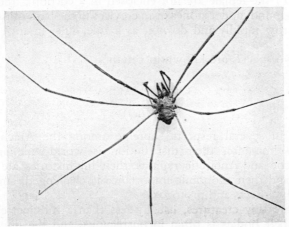

A Harvester, showing conspicuous chelicerae of male.

of dead animals, but refuse them if they are not fresh, and sometimes they
eat the softest parts of plants. This is probably for the sake of moisture,

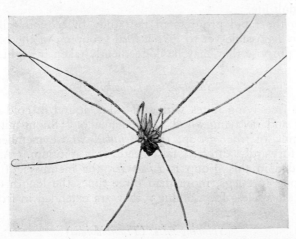

A Harvester.

as they are thirsty animals and may sometimes be seen drinking drops of
dew.

Male Harvesters are a little smaller in the body and longer in the leg than
females ; their spines are sometimes longer and their colours a little brighter,

but there are no other visible differences.   The males fight fiercely with one another during the mating season.

The eggs of the female are not enclosed in a cocoon ; they are laid in holes in the ground, under stones or in crevices in the bark of trees.   Young Harvesters grow rapidly and do not, as a rule, differ in any essential from the adults.

Twenty-two species are known in Britain.

Order ACARINA

(*Mites*)

Mites are in several respects supreme among the Arachnida.   Their numbers are immense, their distribution is world-wide and embraces both the Arctic and Antarctic regions, their life-histories are various and remarkable, and their economic importance is challenged, among invertebrates, only by insects and protozoa.

Yet they are tiny creatures, usually less than a millimetre long.   The division of their bodies is often inconspicuous, and the number of their eyes is variable, many being blind.   Their mouth-parts are diverse, according to their mode of life, and their legs are variously terminated by suckers, claws, or simple bristles.   Mites hatch from the egg as larvae which possess only six legs, and in some cases a nymph stage exists between larval and adult life.

Owing to the rapid progress of the study of economically important mites, it is not possible yet to give a final grouping of the order, but for our present purpose they may be conveniently taken in eight divisions.

Snout-mites (*Eupodoidea*)

These are free-living mites with soft skins, found in cold damp places under moss and decaying wood.   The name of " Snout-mite " is given to one family of the group, the *Bdellidae*, whose members possess a prominent forwardly directed false-head or capitulum.   A remarkable genus included in this group is *Linopodes*, the members of which have extremely long fore-legs, more than three times the length of the body.   Such limbs are useless for walking ; they are extended in front and used as feelers.

Spinning-mites (*Trombidoidea*)

These mites are all distinctly coloured, and are characterised by an ability to produce silk.   Their silk glands open into the mouth, from which the silk issues, and are probably modified salivary glands.   The notorious " red-spider," *Tetranychus telarius*, belongs to this group.   It is a common inhabitant of our gardens, where in small numbers it does little damage. Occasionally, however, whole bushes are covered with masses of their webs, under which the females lay their eggs. These mites are vegetable feeders ; they suck the sap of plants and give the leaves a blistered appearance, and when present in large numbers may be a serious pest.

The so-called Harvest-bugs, which often attack the arms and hands of labourers working in the fields in autumn, are probably the larvae of several species of the genus *Trombidium*. They attack other mammals and are often to be found on rabbits or moles. They force their mouth-parts into the skin, which then hardens round the pharynx, forming the so-called proboscis. The trouble they cause varies in different people ; at its worst there is a rash and a slight degree of fever, but no disease is known to be conveyed by these mites.

Among the more remarkable genera belonging to this group is *Syringo-philus*, widespread as a parasite within the quills of birds' feathers. The family *Cheyletinae* is also curious on account of the enormous jaws of its members and their acquisition of a faculty for hopping instead of crawling.

Water-mites (*Hydrachnoidea*)

Two families of mites live habitually in water. The *Halacaridae* are for the most part found in salt water, although sometimes occurring inland. They have hard bodies and crawl upon or burrow in the sand. They do not swim. The large family of freshwater mites, however, the *Hydracaridae*, swim rapidly with their hairy legs. They are the most beautiful of the mites, being richly coloured and diversely shaped. In habit they are carnivorous, occasionally even parasitic.

Ticks (*Ixodoidea*)

The Ticks are the largest of the mites, and, economically, the most important. They are all parasites which suck the blood of their hosts, and are capable of enormously distending their otherwise flattened bodies. Their jaws are cutting organs, used to pierce the host's skin, and between them is a hypostome, provided with barbs, which affords a firm hold.

Ticks may be troublesome for two reasons. Their bites may permit the entry of microbes, producing sores, or, more important, there may be protozoa parasitic within the tick which enter the host attacked and produce diseases. The extraordinary feature of these protozoa is that they can remain alive in the body of the tick, even if the latter is unfed, for months or even years ; moreover, they may find their way into the ova and so be transmitted to a second generation.

The life-history of a tick is one of the most complex stories provided by Arachnida. The eggs, some thousands in number, are laid in the earth, and hatch into larvae which resemble their parents but have only six legs. The larvae climb up the grass and wait in patience until an animal passes. At its approach, they exhibit great activity and, if possible,

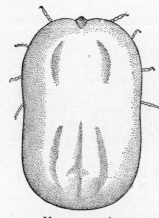

attach themselves to it by the animal's hair. Once in position the larva plunges its rostrum into its host and gorges itself. When fully fed, it drops to the ground, hides itself and rests until its huge meal is digested. It then casts its skin, becoming a nymph with eight legs, which climbs up the grass again and repeats the actions of the larva. The second moult produces a mature male or female tick, which in the same way seeks a third host. Pairing takes place on the body of this host, and the fertilised female drops to the ground to lay her eggs. The ability to undergo prolonged fasts is, no doubt, a special adaptation in connection with this extraordinary life-history.

Margaropus annulatus
The Cattle-tick; distended female.
× 5. (After Salmon and Stiles.)

The common Sheep-tick of this country, *Ixodes ricinus*, which is often picked up by dogs from pasture land, is comparatively harmless, but a large number of the ticks of foreign lands are known or suspected to convey disease. Redwater fever in cattle and heartwater in sheep are examples of tick-borne diseases, but reptiles, birds, and man are also included among their victims.

Gamasoidea

These are pale-coloured carnivorous mites, both free-living and parasitic. They may be found on bats and on beetles, and in even more surprising situations, as, for example, in the bronchial passages of seals and the lungs of monkeys. The genera that live on beetles are not parasites, but use the insect merely as a conveyance.

Gamasus coleoptratorum (magnified). A mite frequently seen upon beetles. (After Berlese.)

Beetle-mites (Oribatoidea)

These mites owe their popular name to their hard cuticle, upon which many of them fix particles of grit and dirt, quite concealing their true shapes. They are free-living, and are found under bark, in dead wood, and in lichen or moss. They are blind, but react to a bright light by moving away from it.

Itch-mites (Sarcoptoidea)

Some of the most familiar and some of the smallest mites belong to this group. The typical genus, *Sarcoptes*, includes *Sarcoptes scalei*, popularly known as the Itch-mites. These are tiny squat creatures like diminutive tortoises. After pairing, the female burrows in the skin of her host, laying eggs behind her, until after two or three months she has laid perhaps a hundred eggs. She is then unable either to turn round or to withdraw,

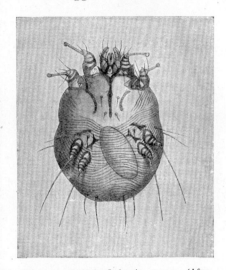

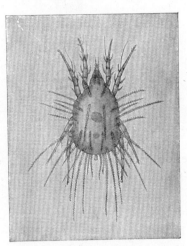

Sarcoptes scabiei, the Itch-mite, × 100. (After Canestrini.)

House-mite, *Glycyphagus domesticus*, × 50. (After Michael.)

and dies within the host. The eggs hatch after a week and the young mature within a month, so that infection spreads rapidly, and the parasites may be transferred by contact to other persons or to animals.

To this group belong also the familiar Cheese-mites of the genus *Tyroglyphus*, and the microscopic *Tarsonemus woodi* which lives in the tracheal tubes of the honey-bee and is the cause of Isle of Wight disease.

Gall-mites (Demodicoidea)

One family of this group includes the genus *Demodex*, mites which are microscopic skin parasites. They live in the hair follicles of man and other mammals and cause mange. They are elongated in sheep, with a tapering abdomen and very short legs. The other family, *Eriophyidae*, are vegetable feeders only, and are the cause of very many of the galls that grow on the leaves and buds of plants. *Eriophyes ribis*, which feeds on black-currant buds, is a familiar example, and sometimes becomes a

Demodex caninus
Ventral view of female.
Greatly magnified.
(After Canestrini.)

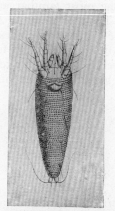

Ventral view of a Gall-
mite, *Eriophyes sil-
vicola*, × 135. (After
Canestrini.)

serious pest. These mites are unique in possessing only two pairs of legs.

PART II

SUB-KINGDOM VERTEBRATA

SECTION X

Phylum CHORDATA

By M. Burton, M.Sc.

The Coming of the Vertebrates

Between the two great sections of the Animal Kingdom, the Invertebrates and the Vertebrates, there is a clear division, and the gulf between them is but imperfectly bridged by certain remarkable and unfamiliar types such as *Phoronis*, the Tunicates or Sea-squirts, and the worm-like *Balanoglossus*, which form a transitional series showing how the Vertebrates may conceivably have arisen from an Invertebrate stock. That the two big sections of the Animal Kingdom had a common origin there is good reason to believe, but it is impossible, at present, to fill in the details of the early history of the Vertebrates.

Perhaps the most striking illustration of this transition is that furnished by the Tunicates, which, in their adult stages, bear not the slightest resemblance to a Vertebrate. Some, to be found in rock-pools during the summer months, look like bags of jelly, often brightly coloured. But in their larval stages, to be presently described, they are obviously Vertebrates, recalling in many of their features the tadpoles of frogs and toads.

Phoronis and *Balanoglossus* are not so easily interpreted, but a probable place in the Vertebrate descent can be demonstrated.

The true position of these strange types will become apparent as this section progresses, and especially so if the essential differences between the Invertebrates and the Vertebrates are first clearly grasped.

In the lowliest types of Invertebrates we find neither nervous tissue nor blood-vessels. But in the higher Invertebrates where these appear the central nerve-cord runs along the ventral wall of the body, while the main blood-vessel is dorsal, as in the earthworm, for example. Some only of the Invertebrates possess limbs, and these have an external, instead of an internal, skeleton.

The Vertebrates are all fashioned on a common foundation. In its simplest, most primitive form the body is elongated, and supported by a long, elastic rod running from one end of the body to the other. Above this rod runs the central nerve-cord, starting with a concentration of the nervous tissue, in the head, to form the brain; and beneath runs the main artery of the body. In the lowliest of the Vertebrates there is no true head or brain, and the dorsal blood-vessel gives rise in the throat to a complex branching system of fine blood-vessels, supported on arches of gristle, or cartilage, to form the breathing organs, or gills, for the oxygenation of the blood. Slits in the sides of the throat provide exit for the water taken in by the mouth and passed over the gills, which in its passage gives up oxygen to the blood, and receives from it carbon-dioxide, a waste product of the blood. There are no limbs in these primitive types, such as Amphioxus. These appear later in the fishes in the form of fins, and as we trace the evolution of the Vertebrates we find these fins replaced by limbs capable of supporting the body on land, as in the Amphibia.

The supporting rod which forms the earliest foundation of the skeleton of the Vertebrates is known as the notochord, and this persists even in the highest members of the group, though in them only as a passing phase, being replaced later by a series of bony cylinders joined to one another by fibrous tissue, and forming the vertebral column. These vertebrae come into being, as will be shown, by calcification of rings of tissue round the notochord, breaking it up into the segments.

The study of the various groups of the Phylum Chordata reveals the possible manner in which the notochord, the forerunner of the backbone, came into being. In *Balanoglossus* and its relatives, shortly to be discussed, the only sign of a notochord is a hollow outgrowth from the front end of the alimentary canal, and this, as such, persists throughout the life of the animal. In the Tunicates a notochord persists throughout the larval period, but disappears in the adult. In the lancelets (Amphioxus) it arises in the embryo, as in the Tunicates, as an outgrowth from the upper wall of the alimentary canal, to extend in the larval stage from tip to tip of the body as a stiff skeletal rod. In the lampreys, the notochord persists throughout life, and is strengthened by a stout envelope of membranous tissue. It seems clear, therefore, that the vertebral column first arose as an outgrowth from the wall of the gut, but in the course of time, and as a result of changes brought about by calcification, it grew into an organ very different in appearance, function, and texture from the organ from which it originated. This same sequence of events can be traced in the embryo of any of the higher Vertebrates, each individual recapitulating the history of its race.

The evolution of a backbone has been accompanied by other profoundly important developments, such as the formation of solid walls around the brain ; of jaws for feeding purposes ; and limbs for locomotion. But these additions have been of slow growth.

The survival of these extremely primitive types has given us the key to many otherwise insoluble problems in regard to the evolution of the Vertebrates, or Chordata, which we now divide into two distinct groups, the Protochordata, or Acraniates, those with a notochord or the rudiments thereof, but without a cranium ; and the Craniata, in which the brain is protected by a solid wall of bone or cartilage, known as the cranium. Protochordata is a collective term which includes the sub-phyla Hemi-, Uro- and Cephalochordata, and the Phoronidea.

Group PROTOCHORDATA

(The Primitive Vertebrates : Phoronis, Balanoglossus, Lancelets, and Sea-squirts)

The first of these bridging or annectant types, to which reference has just been made, constitute the Sub-phylum Phoronidea, with the single genus *Phoronis*, whose members are distributed throughout the seas of the world. In appearance *Phoronis* is very like a typical polypide of the Polyzoa, with a worm-like body measuring from a quarter of an inch to six inches long, contained within a tubular sheath, and bearing at the head end a large lobe crowned with numerous tentacles.

In its mode of living, and method of development, it is very like the Polyzoa ; but here the resemblance ceases, its internal anatomy being built on a plan resembling that of the Vertebrates. At the front end of the digestive tract there is a short diverticulum which, from a general consideration of its position, structure, and development is universally regarded as the rudiment of a notochord.

The next Sub-phylum, the Hemichordata, contains a number of animals differing widely among themselves but agreeing in this, that they are built up of a blend of vertebrate and invertebrate characters. *Rhabdopleura* and *Cephalodiscus*, both marine animals, found in almost every sea throughout the world, have considerable external resemblance to *Phoronis*, and through it to the Polyzoa, but their anatomy approaches even more to that of the Vertebrates. Both multiply by budding, to form colonies invested in a tough, horny covering, thus resembling the colonies of Polyzoa and Hydrozoa; while the larval form of both, called a Tornaria, is extremely like that of the Star-fishes and Sea-urchins.

The next in this series of links is a curious worm-like animal, *Balanoglossus*, which burrows in the mud at the bottom of the sea, passing the mud through its body, extracting such animal matter as it contains, and ejecting the purely inorganic matter in the form of casts, much in the same way as an earthworm. The strong resemblance it bears to the true worms, together with the fact that its larva closely resembles that of the Echinoderms, caused it to be regarded, when first discovered, as a worm. When its internal anatomy came to be investigated, however, it was found that the resemblance was only superficial. Inwardly, it is built decidedly on the Vertebrate plan, with internal gills opening to the exterior by gill-slits, very like those of an embryonic fish; a vertebrate system of nerves and muscles; and the rudiments of a notochord. *Balanoglossus*, in fact, makes a very close approach to the Lancelet, which we shall examine later on, and through it to the Lampreys.

Before dealing with the two last-named, the concluding links in a chain of evidence which enable us to see how the great Vertebrate group has been evolved from Invertebrate ancestors, we must turn to another group of animals which, while contributing also to the same chain of evidence, have developed in a somewhat unusual manner. This group constitutes the Tunicates (Sub-phylum Tunicata), already referred to. One section of them, found in the rounded, jelly-like masses growing on the rocks of the seashore at low tide, has been given the apt name of Sea-squirts.

The tribe, as a whole, are extremely interesting creatures, since they are living witnesses to the truth that evolution does not necessarily signify progression. In the larval state they present all the characteristics of a primitive vertebrate, namely, a dorsal nervous system, well-developed sense-organs, a notochord, a ventral heart, and a powerful tail for swimming purposes. In fact, at this stage, they closely resemble a larval fish, or the tadpole of a frog. Following the normal course of events, we should expect such larvae to develop into adults very like fishes, or frogs. But at the end of their larval life, when such a change should take place, the reverse happens. A process of degeneration sets in in most cases and the promise of the larva remains unfulfilled, for it fixes itself at the bottom of the sea head downwards. At the same time, the tail is gradually lost, being partly absorbed by the body, partly disintegrated and cast off; the notochord disappears, and the elaborate nervous system is reduced to a small knot of nerve-cells with a few small branches radiating from it.

Other changes follow, during which the animal is enveloped in a large, thick-coated bag, with one hole at the top and another at the side, and acquires a well-developed gill-chamber, a weak intestinal tract, and a system of very fine blood-vessels. It has now lost all power of locomotion, and has to depend entirely for its food on the small organisms brought in by the current of water drawn in through the gill-chambers. This current is maintained by the action of countless cilia on the gills, and enters by the hole in the top of the body, bringing with it food and oxygen, and leaves by the second aperture, carrying with it the products of excretion. A noteworthy feature in the economy of the Sea-squirt lies in the fact that at regular intervals the flow of the blood is reversed.

The thick-coated bag referred to which encloses the body of the Tunicates is spoken of as the tunic, and the substance of which it is composed as tunicin, hence the name. These animals are divided into three orders.

The first, the Larvaceae, are peculiar in that they do not undergo the degeneration which accompanies maturity in the Sea-squirts, but preserve

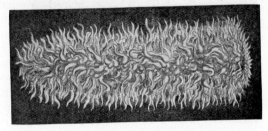

A colony of *Pyrosoma*.

Each finger-shaped outgrowth of the surface marks the position of a single individual embedded in the common body of the colony.

Botryllus

A small colony of the gelatinous Golden-star Ascidian growing on seaweed.

throughout their life the characters of the tailed larva. They are all free-swimming, haunting the surface, and but rarely occurring at depths greater than a hundred fathoms. They are for the most part transparent, and almost invisible in the sea ; but many develop an orange, or violet pigment, so that when present in vast numbers they will colour large tracts of the sea's surface.

Oikopleura, a typical member of the Larvaceae, has a more or less oval body, internal organs closely resembling those of the Sea-squirt, a long tail, with a notochord running down its centre, and a tubular nerve-cord. The body temporarily secretes a thick coat of tunicin which is, however, shed after a short while. The purpose of this temporary sheath is not fully understood.

The Ascidiacea, or Ascidians, the next order, includes the Sea-squirts, which have a common general resemblance. Most of them are sedentary, some lead an entirely independent existence, some form colonies by repeated budding, each individual being attached to its fellows only by a short stalk, or stolon, while others form massive colonies in which the various individuals are surrounded by a common gelatinous coat. A good example of the latter is the Golden-star Ascidian, *Botryllus*, found on rocks and seaweeds at low tide on our coasts. In this, the individuals are of a golden-yellow colour and are arranged in radiating groups like many-pointed stars. On the other hand, the beautiful, phosphorescent *Pyrosoma* of tropical seas is free-swimming, and consists of a hollow gelatinous cylinder, closed at one end, in which the individuals are embedded. Such a colony may be from a few inches to several feet in length.

The Thaliacea, or Salps, are again all free-swimming, and more or less barrel-shaped Tunicates, with essentially the same characters as the Sea-squirts, except that the two openings are at either end of the body. Their transparent bodies reveal a number of muscular bands, arranged rather like the hoops on a barrel, which by their contraction not only drive water through the body, supplying it with food and oxygen, but also serve to drive the animal through the water. Salps frequently appear in swarms round our coasts, and may be taken in hundreds with a tow-net. This fecundity is due to their method of reproduction. A long, backwardly directed stolon is produced which becomes covered with buds, each bud developing into a new salp and eventually breaking free to lead an independent existence. In this way their numbers may be increased a hundredfold in a very short time.

Solitary Salps are commonly found swimming at or near the surface of the sea, but are so transparent that they escape observation. The example given also shows the conspicuous hoops of muscle.

We now come to what is perhaps the most interesting and most convincing link between the Vertebrates and the Invertebrates, a small group of fish-like creatures, from one to three inches long, which live in the sand in shallow waters almost the world over. They form the Sub-phylum Cephalochordata, or Acraniata; the former name signifies that the notochord, instead of ending just behind the brain, as in all the higher Vertebrates, is continued forward almost to the front end of the body; the latter refers to the absence of a cranium.

Of the sixteen species known, one, *Branchiostoma lanceolatum*, or Amphioxus, as it is more familiarly called, is found round the British coasts. Although an active swimmer during its larval life, it is found when adult lying buried in the sand, with the head protruding above the surface. The slender body, pointed at each end with a glistening surface, bears a delicate fin, running along the back and around the tail. Near the front end of the body, on the under surface, is a large circular orifice, fringed with delicate tentacles, leading into a bowl-shaped vestibule, at the centre of which is the mouth. The sides of the body are marked with the contours of a series of chevron-shaped muscles. A slight bulge on the lower half of the body, extending from behind the mouth to about three-quarters the length of the body, denotes the position of the atrial cavity, containing the enormous throat, or pharynx, perforated on either side with about a hundred pairs of slitted gill-openings.

In addition, the atrial cavity contains the liver, a simple outgrowth of the gut, richly supplied with blood-vessels, and, during the breeding season, the reproductive organs. The gills are clothed with lines of cilia, whose action causes a current of water to flow in at the mouth and out through a pore at the hinder end of the atrial cavity. Food brought in by the current of water is trapped on its way through the gill-slits, and passed down to a groove, the endostyle, running along the bottom of the pharynx, where it becomes entangled in a layer of mucus. Thence it is steadily passed backwards along the endostyle to the stomach.

The blood-vessels around the gills are arranged in a network, comparable with that of the Tuni-cates, but the rest of the circulatory system, although as simple as that of an earthworm, is built on the same fundamental plan as that of a fish, except that

THE LANCELET (*Amphioxus*)
Amphioxus is common in the sand-banks around British shores. It is very active and not easy to capture.

there is no heart. The excretory organs are paired nephridia, small coiled tubes, recalling those of the Chaetopod worms.

Apart from the notochord there is practically no skeleton. Certain of the more delicate parts are strengthened by layers of connective tissue, but there is no bone, or cartilage. There are no ears, or organs of sight, but numerous pigment spots scattered along the upper surface of the spinal chord, which runs almost the length of the body and is situated just above the notochord, are probably sensitive to light. The sense of smell is probably located in a small pit, opening on the top of the head and communicating with the brain.

During the breeding season, the reproductive organs swell up and shed their contents, spermatozoa in the males and ova in the females, and these pass out into the sea, by way of a small pore, where the eggs are fertilised. This usually occurs in the evening, and by the morning the larva is fully formed. The embryonic stages leading up to the formation of the larva are very similar to the corresponding stages in most bony fishes, and in the Amphibia. The larva itself is very similar to the adult.

The characters already discussed, together with numerous details of structure and development, which it is impossible to discuss in so limited space, show the Cephalochordata to be very lowly animals, with most of the essential characters of a true Vertebrate. Hence we may be reasonably justified in regarding them as close representatives of the ancestral stock of the Vertebrates. More particularly is this so, since, as we shall see later on, the larval form of the lampreys, themselves true craniate Vertebrates, is extremely like Amphioxus, both in its external form and in its anatomy.

Class MARSIPOBRANCHII
(*Lampreys and Hag-fishes*)

The Cyclostomata, for a long time considered to be primitive fishes, are now regarded as a separate class of the Craniata. Their slender, eel-like proportions, and the two rows of gill-openings on the sides of the body immediately behind the head, give them the appearance of fishes, which is increased by their aquatic habits. On closer examination, however, we find a number of marked differences. There is a centrally placed fin running around the hindermost part of the body, but it contains no fin-rays and there are no paired fins. The skin is entirely scaleless, and is coated with a layer of slime, the product of numerous slime-secreting glands in the skin.

Buccal-funnel of a Lamprey, showing the horny teeth lining the inner wall. The mouth is situated at the bottom of the funnel.

The mouth is situated at the bottom of a large, suctorial, funnel-shaped buccal-cavity. This large circular sucker at the front of the body, beset on its inner surface with numerous small horny teeth, is one of the most striking and characteristic features, and the one from which the name of the group " Cyclostomata " is derived. The tongue is muscular and protrusile, armed with horny plates, and moving with a piston-like action. With it the animal rasps off the flesh of the fish on which it feeds.

The internal anatomy, in addition, differs in a number of striking features from that of the fishes. The skeleton is entirely cartilaginous, the spinal column being little more than a notochord surrounded by a membranous sheath, and the cranium no more than a crude, cartilaginous box housing the brain. Since there are no paired fins there are, naturally, no limb-girdles. Ribs are absent also. On the other hand, the front end of the body-cavity is supported by an elaborate cartilaginous framework, known as the branchial-basket, in which the gill-chambers are contained. In the head-region, too, the simple cranium is surrounded by a complex system of cartilages for supporting the large buccal-funnel.

The respiratory system shows certain peculiarities which are largely due to the habit of the Cyclostomata of attaching themselves to other bodies by the buccal-funnel. The row of gill-openings on either side of the body lead into short tubes, and thence into the spherical gill-chambers. Respiratory currents of water are pumped in and out of the chambers directly through the lateral gill-openings.

The Cyclostomata are world-wide in their distribution, and are represented in the British Isles by four species, three lampreys and the Hag-fish. The largest of these, the Sea Lamprey, exceeds three feet in length, and spends most of its time in the sea, only ascending the rivers to spawn. It is found throughout the North Atlantic and Mediterranean. The Lampern, or Freshwater Lamprey, the better known of the British Cyclostomata, is only about sixteen inches long. This generally spends most of its time

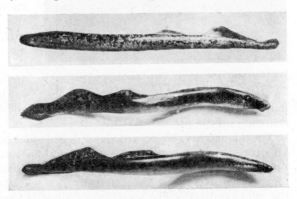

SEA LAMPREY (top). FRESHWATER LAMPREY. BROOK LAMPREY.
Illustrating the slight difference in form between the various species.

in the sea. The Brook Lamprey, seldom more than twelve inches long, is a permanently freshwater species.

The Lampern was at one time sufficiently abundant in the rivers of Britain to form a marketable commodity, and as such figures conspicuously in the earlier annals of this country. The Brook Lamprey is occasionally used for bait. Against this small economic value, one has to set the heavy toll they levy on the fish of the neighbourhood, whereby they have become anathema to the fishermen.

Spawning takes place in the spring and summer; and during the winter those lampreys which spend part of their time in the sea migrate to the rivers, making their way by fixing themselves with their suctorial mouths to fishes or the bottoms of boats, or by swimming with easy, eel-like movements. Arrived at a suitable spot, they pair off, each pair making a nest in the form of a groove on the river-bottom, which they then surround with a palisade of stones transported, one at a time, by the aid of the mouth-sucker. When the eggs are laid, they are partially covered over with sand or mud. This period of spawning evidently saps their vitality, for by the end of the breeding season they are exhausted, and drift downstream in a moribund condition.　It is doubtful, indeed, whether many survive to reach the sea again.

The young lampreys, known as Ammocoete-larvae, or " Prides," are worm-like, blind, and toothless, and spend the first two or three years of their lives burrowing in the mud.　They are so unlike their parents that they were regarded, for a long time, as belonging to an entirely different species.

The fourth British representative of the Cyclostomata, the Hag-fish, is entirely marine and lives preferably in deep water.　It causes considerable annoyance to fishermen by its habit of boring into fish, and in a surprisingly short space of time eating away the flesh and leaving only the skin and bones.　Possessing a ravenous appetite, and, in places, extremely numerous, it inflicts great damage on the fishing grounds by entering the nets and fastening on the fish.

The suggested appearance of *Cephalaspis* in life, based on its fossil remains.

The Hags may be regarded as degenerate lampreys.　They have the same eel-like body, and the same general anatomical features.　The large suctorial funnel is absent, and the mouth is surrounded by a number of sensory barbels, while there is only one gill-opening which supplies all the gill-chambers.　The secretion of slime is even more highly developed than in the lampreys, and large quantities can be emitted without apparently impairing the vitality of the animal.

The Cephalaspidae, a group of animals characterised by a large head-shield, whose fossil remains are found in the Silurian and Devonian rocks, have recently been shown to be primitive lampreys.　A similar, though much-reduced, head-shield can be demonstrated in the modern lamprey, although it cannot be seen with the naked eye.

CLASSES SELACHII, PISCES

By J. R. NORMAN, F.L.S.

INTRODUCTION

THE term "fish" is frequently erroneously applied to any animal which lives in the water, but the zoologist restricts the name to certain aquatic members of the great group of Vertebrates. We may generally define a fish as a vertebrate adapted to a purely aquatic life, breathing by means of oxygen obtained from the water by the use of internal gills, and propelling and balancing itself by means of fins. The fishes may be readily distinguished from the Lampreys by the presence of jaws, and by the paired and lateral nasal sacs, each of which is generally provided with two external nostrils. The form of the fins and the structure of the gills are other features separating the two groups.

Thus defined, fishes present an extraordinary diversity in shape and size, their bodies being modified in a multitude of different ways to accommodate them to the varying conditions under which they live. The open sea, the depths of the ocean, the rocky or sandy stretch of shore, the majestic river, swiftly running brook, the mountain torrent and placid lake or pond, each provides its peculiar forms of fish-life variously modified according to circumstances. To describe in any detail the many parts which go to make up a fish's body would be outside the scope of this work; it must suffice to survey briefly the more important and characteristic external features, and to touch upon one or two internal organs, the form or function of which is of special importance. The remainder of the internal organs, including the skeleton or supporting framework, must be almost entirely omitted, as it will be seldom necessary to mention them in the succeeding pages.

If we examine a typical, swiftly moving fish such as a salmon or a mackerel we observe that the body is fusiform, or spindle-shaped. This is a shape calculated to reduce friction with the surrounding water to a minimum, and the one best suited for progression in that medium. This practical end is furthered by the absence of any projections on the body liable to hinder forward movement. The shape realises to perfection the mechanical conditions which human ingenuity has evolved in the form of the submarine. All fishes do not, of course, possess this ideal streamline form, but any radical departure from it must inevitably lead to a loss in the swimming efficiency; indeed, it is only where rapid mobility ceases to be of importance to the life of the species, and is replaced by some compensating factor, such as heavy armour, or protective coloration, that the more specialised and often bizarre forms are able to escape extermination in the ruthless struggle for existence continually being waged in the sea.

Three regions of the body may be recognised: head, trunk, and tail. There is no neck as in the land animals, the gill-opening alone marking the boundary between head and trunk. In a similar manner, the trunk merges insensibly into the tail, the dividing line being denoted by the vent. The relative proportions of these parts vary greatly in different fishes.

The head probably presents more diversity in external appearance than any other region of the body. It may be naked or covered with scales; the covering skin may be thick, or so thin that the patterns of the underlying bones are clearly visible ; it may be roughened, or provided with powerful spines, giving the fish a truly formidable appearance. The part of the head situated in front of the eyes, which are typically lateral in position, is called the snout, and bears the nostrils on each side ; the part behind the eyes is known as the postorbital region ; that between them as the interorbital region. The eyes, although modified for aquatic vision as shown by the spherical lens, are, nevertheless, built on the same general plan as those of land vertebrates ; the sight, however, seems to be much more limited. The nostrils serve solely as organs of smell, and are scarcely ever used for breathing.

As far as food goes, fishes are either predatory, plankton-feeders (feeding on minute organisms near the surface of the water), or vegetable-feeders ; and the normal diet is nearly always reflected in the form of the mouth

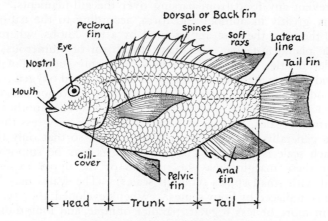

EXTERNAL FEATURES OF A TYPICAL FISH
Showing the relative positions of the fins and different regions of the body.

and teeth. Predatory forms like the pike possess large and powerful jaws ; non-predatory forms a comparatively small mouth. The mouth may be at the end of the snout (terminal) or on its under surface (inferior). It is bordered on either side by an upper and lower jaw, and may sometimes be more or less protractile, that is, the bones of the upper jaw can slide on certain bones of the skull, so that the mouth can be protruded or retracted at will. There is no movable tongue, as in higher verte-brates, and the sense of taste seems to be poorly developed.

The teeth present an extraordinary diversity in form, size, number, and situation, and often provide a useful character for distinguishing genera and species. They are developed not only in the jaws, but may be present on the roof of the mouth, in the throat (pharyngeal teeth), and on the tongue. As in the case of the jaws, the character of the dentition is intimately associated with the usual diet of the species; herbivorous fishes like the carp and its allies have quite toothless jaws, plankton-feeders of the herring type have more or less minute, needle-like teeth, while a predatory fish such as a shark is provided with strong, sharply pointed, and sometimes saw-edged teeth.

Respiration is accomplished in fishes by means of internal gills. Water is taken in through the mouth, drawn through the clefts which lie on either side in the walls of the pharynx, and, after being passed over the gill-filaments, is finally expelled through the gill-opening or openings. Between the clefts are the gill-arches, jointed skeletal structures, bearing on their outer edges a double row of fine, red gill-filaments, while their inner margins are provided with some stiff appendages known as gill-rakers. These project across the clefts, and serve to strain the water and to prevent any food from passing over the gill-filaments. The gill-rakers vary greatly in number and form, according to the nature of the food; in the pike they are represented by a few knobs, whereas in the herring, a plankton-feeder, they have the form of numerous, close-set and slender bristles. The gill-filaments are richly supplied with blood-vessels, and as the water passes over them the contained oxygen is absorbed by the blood and any impurities are given off from the blood into the water.

In addition to the skin, most fishes are provided with another covering in the form of scales, which, in order to facilitate progress through the water, are generally arranged like tiles on a roof, so that only the hinder part of each scale is visible. The hinder edges may be smooth (cycloid scales), or these margins may be toothed or the upper exposed parts roughened with small spines (ctenoid scales). The scales may be absent altogether or replaced by bony scutes. When developed, they are generally arranged in more or less regular, parallel, oblique, and longitudinal rows. The lateral line, which forms a continuation of the muciferous channels present on the head in fishes, is a conspicuous feature, and appears as a lengthwise row of tube-bearing scales running along the middle of each side of the body from behind the head to the base of the caudal fin. In some fishes the lateral line is incomplete, or even absent; in others there is more than one lateral line on each side. Each of the modified scales communicates with an underlying channel containing a series of sense-organs. The function of these organs is not yet perfectly understood, but is probably connected with the perception of movements in the water, enabling the fish to avoid obstacles and providing a hint as to the presence of food or enemies.

It is sometimes of importance to ascertain the age of a particular fish, and this can be effected, in some forms at least, by what is known as " scale-reading." Examined under a lens, or microscope, each scale is seen to consist of a number of concentric rings representing stages in the growth of the scale; the distance between the consecutive rings is intimately connected with the rate of growth, which in turn depends on the amount of food taken by the fish during a certain period. In winter time, when food is comparatively scarce, the rings tend to be crowded together and to form a more or less definite " zone," indicating that growth has been slight during this season ; by counting the number of these zones on a given scale the approximate age of the fish may be determined.

The fins, which are composed of rays joined together by a thin membrane, are supported by special parts of the internal skeleton. We may recognise two kinds of fins : median or unpaired, and paired. The median fins comprise a dorsal, in the middle line of the back ; a caudal, at the hinder end of the fish ; and an anal, on the lower edge of the body behind the vent. The paired fins are of two kinds only, the pectorals and pelvics, corresponding respectively to the fore and hind limbs of land vertebrates. The pectorals are always placed close behind the head, but the position of the pelvics varies in different fishes. The latter may lie in the middle of the abdomen (abdominal), below or a little behind the level of the pectorals (thoracic), or in front of the pectorals (jugular) : in the last instance we have a fish in which the " legs " actually lie *in front of* the " arms." The form and position of all the fins present considerable diversity, and are of some importance in classification. In the more primitive fishes the rays are simple, articulated, flexible rods, but in the more specialised groups the anterior rays of the dorsal and anal, the outer rays of the pelvics, and sometimes of the pectorals also, have been converted

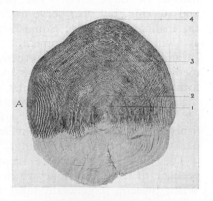

SCALES OF SALMON

A. A four-years-old fish—two years in the river and two years in the sea. B. A six-years-old fish.

into stiff pointed spines ; these may be very strong and provide useful weapons for defence or offence, especially when they are associated with poison glands hidden under the skin. The spinous portion of the dorsal may be separated off as a distinct fin, and the soft part may be broken up into two or more sections ; occasionally, both dorsal and anal fins are joined to the caudal.

The actual propulsion of the fish's body through the water is effected normally by lateral flexions of the muscular tail, aided by movements of the caudal fin. That is to say, the tail is lashed vigorously from side to side in order to drive the body forward. The dorsal and anal fins act primarily as keels, and are concerned with giving stability to the fish, but in some species relatively slow progress is accomplished by means of wave-like movements of these fins alone. The pelvics assist the median fins in keeping the body from rolling over, and seem to function after the manner of bilge keels. The pectorals are generally used for balancing and steering, but also serve to check the forward movement, acting after the manner of brakes ; some fishes, however, actually employ these fins as swimming organs, sometimes using them in the same way as oars. In addition to carrying out these normal functions, one or more of the median or paired fins may be specially modified to take part in the per-formance of tasks which at first sight would hardly appear to be among their duties : some of these modifications will be described in the suc-ceeding pages. There is yet another method sometimes employed by fishes to produce forward movements, namely by squirting jets of water backward from the gill-openings.

The air-bladder may be mentioned here, as it represents an organ peculiar to fishes, and one which is of some importance in classification. When present, it generally takes the form of a long cylindrical bag com-posed of silvery membrane and filled with a mixture of gases. In many fishes a narrow tube connects the bladder with the gullet, in others no such connection exists. The function of the air-bladder is a hydrostatic one : by the absorption or secretion of gas the fish is able to accommodate itself to the changes of pressure at different depths. In a few forms the air-bladder acts as an accessory breathing organ, functioning exactly like a true lung.

Finally, a few words concerning the colours of fishes. The prevailing impression that fishes cannot challenge comparison in this respect with the birds, for example, is totally erroneous, and is largely due to the difficulty of observing fishes in the living condition, and to the fact that the natural tints fade with great rapidity after death. Further, with few exceptions the fishes of our own rivers and seas are rather soberly coloured, and it is among the denizens of tropical seas, and especially among those fishes living in the neighbourhood of coral reefs, that the really vivid and often bizarre combinations of colour are encountered. Sober or vivid, however, the colours of fishes have a meaning, and for the most part represent an adaptation to the surroundings—an effort, so to speak, on the part of the fishes to resemble as near as possible their immediate habitat.

Still more remarkable than the colours themselves is the power possessed by many species of rapidly changing their colours or markings. The leopard cannot change its spots, nor the bird the pattern of its feathers (except as the result of a moult), but many tropical fishes can change in

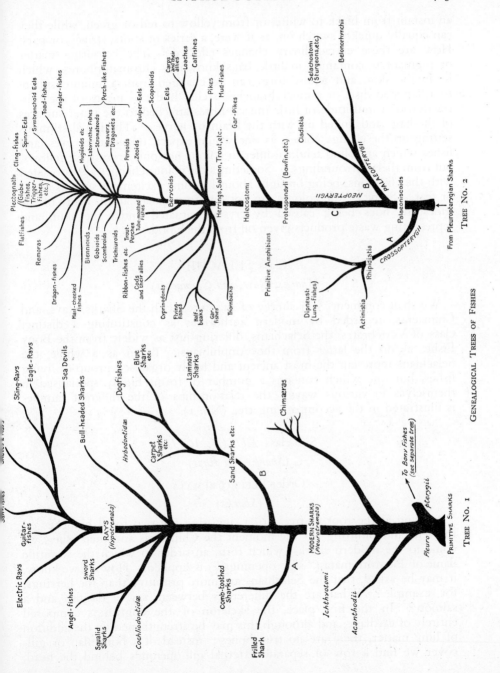

GENEALOGICAL TREES OF FISHES

an instant from black to white, or from yellow to red or green, while they can equally quickly switch on, as it were, a series of spots, stripes, or bars. How are these extraordinary changes effected? The colouring matter or pigment is contained in little bags known as chromatophores, which lie in the skin, and whose form can be changed from a minute sphere to a flattened disc, or a much-branched stellar body, by means of the contraction of a multitude of little muscle fibres attached to the outer surfaces of the bags and linked up with the brain by nerves. The initial stimulus setting up the change comes, as one would expect, through the eyes, and fishes which are blind tend to differ in colour not only from their fellows, but from their surroundings. Sometimes the colour changes are associated with the emotions, being brought about by some excitement such as anger or fear. Some of the colours are not due to pigment at all, many of the iridescent hues being caused by crystals situated under the skin, and representing waste products given off from the blood.

Class SELACHII
(*Sharks, Rays, and Chimaeras*)

We shall commence our survey of the fishes with the Sharks, Rays, and Chimaeras, regarded by modern authorities as constituting a distinct class of Vertebrates, the Selachians, differing just as widely from the Bony Fishes as do the latter from the Amphibians. Taken as a whole, the Selachians represent the most ancient and lowly organised group of living fishes, but one which contains a number of forms highly specialised in themselves in various ways; the relationships of the different families is illustrated in the accompanying tree (No. 1).

Sub-class *EUSELACHII*
(*Sharks and Rays*)

Order PLEUROTREMATA
(*Sharks*)

Starting at the root of tree No. 1, ignoring the two fossil branches on the left, and omitting for the moment the Chimaeras and their allies, we come to the modern sharks, which form an order to which the scientific name of Pleurotremata (" side openings ") is applied. How do we know, it may be asked, that the Selachians are more primitive than the herrings, for example? What are the differences between, say, a dogfish and a salmon? In the first place, the skeleton of the dogfish is composed entirely of cartilage, and although this may be strengthened by the addition of limy matter, there are no true bones; instead of a bony flap or gill-cover we find a row of separate external gill-openings behind the head, varying in number from five to seven; a single nostril is present on each side instead of two; there is no air-bladder; and, finally, instead of being clothed with thin overlapping scales, the body is covered with numerous closely-set bony nodules, embedded in the skin, and each provided with a small spine covered with enamel. These dermal denticles, as they are called, provide the well-known shagreen used extensively by cabinet-makers for polishing wood. They are especially interesting in that they provide us with an explanation of the origin of the teeth, not only of the sharks themselves, but of all fishes and higher Vertebrates. Examined closely the denticles are found to be essentially similar in structure to the teeth, and the dentition of the jaws must have arisen in the first place by the fusion, or the great enlargement, of individual denticles lying in the skin lining the edges of the mouth.

Another important character common to all living Selachians is the presence in adult males of specialised organs known as " claspers," developed as modifications of the hinder portions of the pelvic fins. Unlike the generality of fishes, the eggs are fertilised internally as the result of

FRILLED SHARK
Unique among living sharks in the elongate body and terminal mouth.

copulation between the sexes, and these remarkable organs have been evolved to assist this function.

Turning to the branch marked A in the tree, we find two interesting families of sharks which present several primitive features, among which may be mentioned the possession of six or seven gill-openings instead of five as in nearly all other forms, the curious comb-like teeth, each with many cusps or processes along the cutting edge, the simple spinal column, and the single dorsal fin. The comparatively rare Frilled Shark is unique in its eel-like body and wide mouth, which is almost terminal in position. In all other sharks the mouth is placed under the head, and the pushing forward of the pointed snout above the jaws, forming an efficient cut-water, is a modification which clearly accompanied increased speed.

In branch B we may notice the Lamnoid or Mackerel Sharks, a family containing not only the most active and most ferocious of the tribe, but also the largest, and some of the most sluggish. The terrible Great White Shark, or Man-eater, attains a length of more than forty feet, and its huge jaws are armed with powerful, triangular, knife-like teeth with saw-edged margins. The normal diet of this shark consists of other fishes, but it has been known to devour men. The Basking Shark is equally large, but quite harmless, the mouth being provided merely with numerous, small knob-like teeth. It feeds entirely on small marine creatures which it strains from the water by means of the long, slender, and closely set gill-rakers.

The Carpet Sharks are curious, thick-set fishes, with relatively large

BLACK-FINNED SHARK
A swift pelagic shark of the open sea. A member of the family of Blue Sharks.

heads. Instead of roving about in active search of prey, they rely on patience and cunning to obtain a meal. The beautiful carpet-like pattern of the skin, which gives them their name, enables them to conceal themselves in their natural surroundings, the general appearance of the fish when lying motionless on the bottom being that of a weed-covered rock. This

HAMMER-HEADED SHARK
Unique among fishes in having the head produced on each side into a great outgrowth bearing the eye at its extremity. It is a relative of the Blue Sharks.

deception is made more perfect by the presence of little fleshy tags on the head and round the mouth, which resemble pieces of seaweed.

In the last two families of this branch we have sharks of entirely different habitat. The Blue Sharks and their allies are speedy, voracious, pelagic forms, coloured for the most part in drab and uniform hues of bluish, or greyish above, and white below. Perhaps nine-tenths of the sharks we read about in books of travel belong to this group. One or two species penetrate for some distance up the larger rivers, and one lives entirely in fresh water. The dried fins of these sharks form an important article of trade in India and China, where they are used for making gelatin, and their skins provide a handsome and durable leather. The truly remarkable Hammer-headed Shark belongs to this family ; the relation of this unique

LESSER-SPOTTED DOGFISH

A small littoral shark. This is a common British species, often a great nuisance to fishermen, whose baits it destroys.

configuration of the head to the economy of the fish has never been explained.

The Dogfishes, or Rousettes, are sharks of small or moderate size, living either close to the shore or in the depths of the ocean. Unlike the pelagic sharks, most of the littoral species exhibit striking colour patterns made up of dark spots, or bars on a light ground. Most pelagic sharks bring forth their young alive, but the majority of the shore forms, including the Dog-

PORT JACKSON SHARK

A member of the family of Bull-headed Sharks, all of which inhabit the Pacific.

fishes, produce eggs which are enclosed in oblong, horny protective cases, nearly always provided with a long tendril at each corner, which serves to anchor the case to weed or rock. Empty cases are frequently thrown up on the beach after a storm, and are popularly known as " purses." These fishes are eaten at certain seasons by the poorer classes of the population, and provide a wholesome and nutritious food.

Passing farther up the main trunk of our tree, we come to a group of five branches, two of which have left no living representatives, and all of which seem to have evolved along their own lines from a common ancestor. The Bull-headed Sharks of the Pacific include the well-known Port Jackson Shark, with its curious arrangement of teeth designed to grind up the shells of the molluscs on which it feeds. The family, which for want of a better name we have called the Squalid Sharks, comprises a number of genera and species varying greatly in form and habits, of which the best known is perhaps the Spur-dog, or Picked-dog. Unlike the true Dog-fishes already mentioned, this fish has a strong spine in front of each of the two dorsal fins; the spines are provided with glands secreting a virulent poison, and are capable of inflicting painful wounds. The Spur-dogs are found in shoals, and are the *bête noire* of our fishermen, whose nets and catches are ravaged by these " scavengers of the sea." The Angel-fish, or Monk-fish, is the sole representative of a family of modified Squalid Sharks,

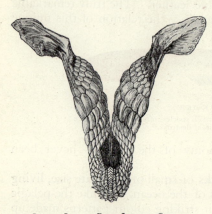

LOWER JAW OF PORT JACKSON SHARK
These curious teeth are specially adapted for crushing and grinding the shellfish which form the shark's principal food.

which in their broad, flat heads and enlarged pectorals bear a superficial resemblance to the rays. In habits this fish is more ray-like than shark-like, being a voracious ground-feeder, subsisting on flat-fishes, molluscs, and crustaceans. It produces its young alive, and as many as twenty at a birth have been recorded.

Order HYPOTREMATA
(*Rays*)

The second order, the Hypotremata (" under openings "), which includes the skates and rays, is a specialised offshoot from the early sharks, all the members of which have become more or less modified for a life on the sea-bottom, with a diet consisting for the most part of molluscs, crustaceans, and other creatures less active than fish. They may be readily distinguished from the sharks by the position of the gill-openings, which lie on the under side of the head; this change in position has been brought about by the great enlargement and forward extension of the pectoral fins, which are more or less attached to the sides of the head. Attention may be drawn to a pair of large openings on top of the head, lying immediately behind the eyes : these are known as the spiracles, and were once functional gill-clefts.

The rays use the spiracles for taking in water for breathing purposes, and in this way avoid the danger of clogging the delicate gills with sand, as might happen if the mouth were used as in other fishes. As in most bottom-living creatures, the colour of the upper surface is similar to the ground on which the fish lies, thus assisting concealment; the under side is usually a dead white. Very few members of the order descend to any depth in the sea, but the Saw-fishes ascend rivers, and some of the Sting Rays live permanently in fresh water.

The Guitar-fishes, a group which includes the Halavi Ray illustrated here, although possessing all the characteristics of the rays proper, have retained the elongate form of the sharks; the body is only moderately flattened, and the muscular tail

HALAVI RAY
Also known as the Fiddler-fish.

is still the sole organ of locomotion. The body is covered with a uniform shagreen, and the skin provides a tough leather. The Saw-fishes are Guitar-fishes in which the snout has been drawn out into a long, flat blade, armed on either edge with a row of sharp teeth set in sockets. The teeth in the jaws, as befits a ray, are blunt and placed close together in pave-

SAW-FISH
Some of the Saw-fishes ascend rivers well beyond the influence of the tides. They grow to a large size; "saws" six feet in length are by no means rare.

ment form. Saw-fishes may attain a length of more than twenty feet, and by means of side-to-side sweeps of the saw they are able to create havoc among the shoals of fishes on which they feed.

The true Skates and Rays have enormously enlarged pectoral fins, which appear as huge fleshy lobes on either side of the body. The head, body, and pectorals together form a flattened, circular, or rhomboid disc, sharply marked off from the much-reduced tail with its tiny dorsal and caudal fins. These fishes swim by means of gentle undulating movements of the pectoral fins, and the tail acts merely as a rudder. Owing to the small size, and the position of the mouth, a ray cannot at once seize its prey, and resorts to stealth to secure its dinner. Quietly approaching its victim, which may be a crustacean, or small fish, it darts suddenly over it and

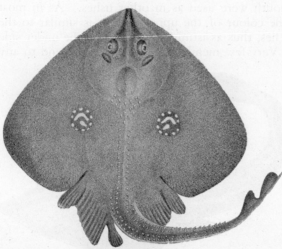

CUCKOO RAY

Note the enormously enlarged pectoral fins, joined to the sides of the head and body. The tail and dorsal fins are much reduced in size.

smothers it with its body. Instead of shagreen, the skin is smooth or variously armed with a number of larger or smaller spines or bucklers. As food they are little esteemed, the flesh being considered coarse ; it is much improved, however, by the addition of hot butter—the *raie au beurre noire* of the epicure ; but even when simply boiled the flesh of some species, at any rate, is delicious.

The Sting Rays are even more specialised. The caudal and dorsal fins have entirely disappeared, and the slender, whip-like tail is armed with one or sometimes more long saw-edged spines. The " sting " may be as much as eight to fifteen inches long, and may inflict an unpleasant jagged wound, which rarely heals without danger of blood-poisoning.

INDIAN STING RAY

The serrated spines on the tail are replaced from time to time by new ones growing up from behind. Two or more spines may be in use at the same time.

Their cousins, the Eagle Rays, feed almost exclusively on shell-fish, and their diet is reflected in the form of the teeth, which take the form of large, flat molars, arranged like paving stones on the floor, and in the roof, of the mouth. With their extremely powerful jaws these fishes are able to deal successfully with huge clams, to crush which a force of nearly a thousand pounds must be required. The Sea Devils, so-called on account of the projecting horn-like lobes of the pectoral fins, are the mightiest of the rays, probably reaching a weight of twelve hundred pounds. Some of them possess the remarkable habit of leaping clean out of the sea, to which they return with a noise rivalling the discharge of a cannon. Finally, there are the Torpedoes or Electric Rays, with smooth naked skin and electric organs of complicated pattern, capable of giving severe " shocks."

Sub-class *HOLOCEPHALI*
(*Chimaeras*)

We may return now to the Chimaeras, which, although specialised in their essential characteristics, are in many respects more primitive than any other Selachians, and represent a group of great antiquity. They agree with the sharks in many points of their internal anatomy, and in their large eggs provided with horny protective cases, but approach the Bony Fishes in having four gill-arches, crowded together in the hinder part of the head, a single gill-opening on each side, and a movable flap or gill-cover. The jaws are armed with large, flat plates, studded with hardened points or " tritors," which take the place of the ordinary teeth. In spite of this specialised dentition, however, the diet is a very varied one, ranging from seaweeds to other fishes. Another curious feature, which has been

RABBIT-FISH OR CHIMAERA

These remarkable fishes agree with the Sharks in having an entirely gristly skeleton, and in a number of other characters ; they approach the Bony Fishes in having a single external gill-opening on each side of the head.

evolved within the group, is. the possession of accessory clasping organs in the male. These are situated on top of the head, and in front of the pelvic fins, and are additional to the usual claspers already described.

The Arctic Chimaera, or Rabbit-fish, occurs in the Atlantic and Mediterranean, and is not uncommon in our own waters. Its habit of pursuing shoals of herrings has earned for this fish the nickname of " King of the Herrings." In the related Elephant-fish of the Antarctic and South Pacific the snout is produced and provided with a curious fleshy appendage at the tip, said to function as an organ of touch.

P

Class PISCES
(*Bony Fishes*)

Sub-class *PALAEOPTERYGII*
(*Palaeoniscoids, Bichirs, Sturgeons, Spoonbill, etc.*)

The great class of Bony Fishes (Pisces) must have originated from very primitive Selachians far back in the Silurian epoch. The chief features distinguishing a bony fish from a shark have been already mentioned, and little need be added here. The internal skeleton may be composed of cartilage, or bone, but there are always a number of more superficial " membrane bones," as they are called, which have developed in the deeper layers of the skin. A new set of bony jaws bearing the teeth have replaced the old cartilaginous jaws of their ancestors. The gill-clefts, instead of opening separately to the exterior, open into a special branchial chamber with a single aperture behind ; the chamber is protected on the outside by a movable bony flap known as the gill-cover.

We may recognise three main sub-classes, which bear the rather terrifying scientific names of Palaeopterygii (" ancient fins "), Neopterygii (" young fins "), and Crossopterygii (" fringe fins "). The relationship of these main groups, and of the various orders of which they are composed, is illustrated in tree No. 2. The differences between them are of a technical nature, involving the form of the skeleton and scales, and the structure of the fins.

It may be noted that as far as the living representatives are concerned, the three groups present immense diversity in size : the first and the last together comprise some ten genera with about thirty species, while the Neopterygian sub-class contains numerous genera and probably at least fifteen thousand species, as compared with a few hundred in the Selachians. Nevertheless, the few living forms of the other groups are worthy of our special attention, representing, as they do, highly interesting survivals of ancient and lowly organised types, and providing us with clues, not only as to how a bony fish was originally evolved from a cartilaginous one, but also as to the manner in which a land animal has been derived from a fish.

Omitting for the moment the branch marked A at the base of the tree, we may start with the Palaeoniscoids, a group of fishes which were predominant in late Palaeozoic times, and died out at the end of the Jurassic period. The typical members of this group were active, predaceous fishes, whose bodies were covered with rhomboid plates packed closely together ; these plates were coated externally with a glistening enamel-like substance known as *ganoine,* and the surfaces were often beautifully sculptured.

Passing up the stem marked B, we may notice the group of fishes known as Cladistia, of which the Bichirs of the Nile and other parts of tropical Africa, and the curious eel-like Reed-fish of West Africa, are the sole living representatives. They have retained the primitive covering of thick, dense, ganoid scales ; the caudal fin forms a symmetrical fringe round the end of the body (a very primitive type of fin), the dorsal is broken up into a series of finlets, and the pectoral is formed of a scaly basal lobe, around which are arranged the fin-rays in the form of a fringe. The air-bladder is composed of two lobes, which open into the floor of the throat

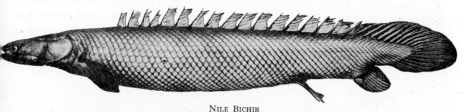

NILE BICHIR

Note the series of separate finlets along the back and the peculiar form of the pectoral fins.

by a common duct ; these bear a strong resemblance to the lungs of land animals and are, in fact, sometimes used as such, the Bichirs having the habit of coming to the surface and gulping air. These fishes are, in the main, lethargic, bottom-living creatures, subsisting chiefly on small fish which are swallowed whole. The young are provided with large, feathery external gills, somewhat similar to those of a tadpole ; they are later replaced by the more efficiently protected internal gills.

The Sturgeons of to-day, although the descendants of an ancient and

AMERICAN LAKE STURGEON

Attains to a length of six feet and a weight of 100 lbs.

primitive group of fishes, are themselves highly specialised, and not a little degenerated. With the exception of a small patch on the upturned part of the tail, the ganoid scales have been lost, but the body is armed with five rows of bony scutes, or bucklers, each with a sharp spine. The snout, which is produced into a shovel-like beak, is provided with a row of four feelers, or barbels, on its lower surface ; the mouth is on the under side of the head, can be protruded like a funnel, and is devoid of teeth except in the very young.

The Sturgeons mostly seek their living in the sea, but enter the larger rivers to spawn. Their food consists almost entirely of small invertebrate creatures, which are stirred out of the sand or mud by the fish's snout, and detected by means of the barbels. In addition to the flesh, which is esteemed as food, the roe of the Sturgeon provides caviare, and the lining of the air-bladder is the basis of isinglass. The Spoonbill, or Paddle-fish, a member of a related family, which inhabits some of the rivers of the United States, has an entirely naked body, and the snout takes the form of a spoon-like beak, with flexible edges. This remarkable structure is used for stirring up the mud, the agitated material being gulped down and strained by the gill-rakers.

Sub-class *NEOPTERYGII*

Orders Ginglymodi, Protospondyli

(*Gar Pikes, Bow-fin*)

The Gar Pikes, although confined to-day to the fresh waters of North America, were at one time much more widely distributed, their fossil remains occurring in various parts of Europe. They are slender, cylindrical fishes, with a complete armour of thick, ganoid scales (similar in appearance to those of the Bichirs, but of a different structure), and with long crocodile-like jaws armed with strong teeth. The small dorsal and anal fins are placed at the hinder end of the body, and the structure of the backbone is unique among fishes in that the vertebrae are joined together by ball-and-socket joints. Their food consists almost entirely of small fishes, and the Alligator Gar, which attains a length of more than twenty feet, is not only extremely destructive to certain food-fishes, but causes great damage to the nets of fishermen. As

Long-nosed Gar Pike

The thick ganoid scales are similar in appearance to those of the Bichirs, but are of a different structure. This species grows to a length of about five feet.

food, the Gar Pikes are unfit even for dogs, the flesh being rank and tough.

The Bow-fin is the sole living representative of the next order. In this fish the shining ganoid scales have been replaced by thin, overlapping cycloid scales, and the dorsal fin is long and low, occupying nearly two-thirds of the length of the back. Its general distribution is similar to that of the Gar Pikes, and remains of its extinct relatives are similarly found in Europe. The male is smaller than the female, and may be readily recognised by the round black spot, bordered with orange, at the base of the caudal fin. The female deposits the eggs in a crude, circular nest placed among reeds or other aquatic vegetation. The nest is constructed exclusively by the male, who mounts guard over the eggs until the young are hatched. The Bow-fin is extremely voracious, feeding on fishes, crustaceans, and insects ; its flesh is ill-flavoured and seldom used as food. It can live for some considerable time out of water, and in its natural haunts, where the water may be foul or muddy, frequently comes to the surface to take gulps of air. This species goes under various names in different parts of America, among which may be mentioned " Dogfish, " " Mud-fish," " John A. Grindle," and " Lawyer " ; the last-named title is said to be applied because " it will bite at anything, and is good for nothing when caught ! "

Order ISOSPONDYLI
(*Herrings, Salmonid Fishes, Wide-mouths, etc.*)

Having disposed of the more primitive living Neopterygian fishes, we may pass farther up the main stem of the tree. The order known as Halecostomi (" Herring-mouths "), a group of extinct plankton-feeding fishes, like the herrings, whose place they occupied in Triassic and Jurassic times, may be briefly noticed, as these finally gave rise to the earliest members of the order Isospondyli (" equal vertebrae "), a group comprising a vast assemblage of genera and species, which for convenience we may term Soft-finned Fishes. All agree in having the air-bladder connected with the gullet by a pneumatic duct, and in having the pelvic fins abdominal in position.

The Ten-pounder and its allies, widely distributed in warm seas, are handsome, silvery fishes, generally herring-like in form and structure, and almost exactly similar to the early offshoots from the Halecostomi. The presence of a bony gular-plate between the lower jaws is a mark of their lowly origin, a character in which they resemble the Bow-fin already mentioned. These fishes are of little value as food, although eaten raw by the Hawaiians and Japanese. The Tarpons resemble the true Herrings in form and coloration, and may be regarded as the ancestors of those fishes. They may be readily distinguished by the relatively huge scales, which are in great demand for ornamental work, and by the form of the dorsal fin, in which the last ray is drawn out into a long filament. The Common Tarpon, an inhabitant of the tropical parts of the Atlantic, is particularly abundant off the south-eastern coasts of North America, where it is the favourite game fish of the sea-anglers. Growing to a length of six feet or more, and a weight of 110 pounds, the Tarpon may leap clean out of the water when hooked, and its fighting spirit makes its capture a matter of considerable strength and skill, and not a little patience. Although strictly a sea fish, it frequently ascends rivers in pursuit of schools of fry of other fishes, which form its chief food. A much smaller species, the Ox-eyed Herring, inhabits the seas of India, and unlike its larger relative provides excellent eating.

The Lady-fishes, close relatives found in most warm seas, possess blunt, rounded teeth, used for crushing the shellfish on which they feed. The larvae are quite unlike the adults, being transparent and ribbon-shaped, and recalling the Leptocephali of the Eel to be described in due course. Other allied forms worthy of mention are the large, brilliantly silvery Milk-fishes of the tropical Pacific, in which the jaws are devoid of teeth ; and the Moon-eyes of the rivers in the central parts of the United States and Canada, shad-like fishes with strong, sharp teeth in the jaws and on the tongue. None of these is of any value as food, the flesh being tasteless and full of small bones.

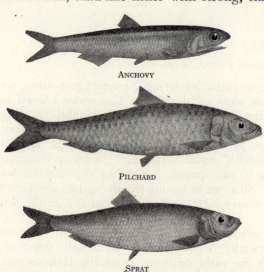

ANCHOVY

PILCHARD

SPRAT

The Anchovy is readily recognised by the pointed snout overhanging the mouth. The Sprat is very closely related to the Herring, but may be distinguished by the more backward position of the dorsal fin.

The Herrings form a large family comprising some two hundred species, and may be distinguished from their nearest relatives by the absence of the lateral line and adipose dorsal fin. In many of the genera the belly is saw-edged, and the scales are thin, fragile, and easily removed. They occur in large numbers in all tropical and temperate seas, but rarely at any great distance from the shore ; many, like the Shads, enter the rivers for the purpose of spawning, while others reside permanently in rivers or lakes. Nearly all are plankton-feeders, with small, feeble teeth and numerous, slender, closely set gill-rakers.

The Common Herring is one of the most important commercial fishes of our islands, and in the dried, salted, or smoked state is eaten throughout the greater part of the civilised world. In one year nearly 462,000 tons of Herring were landed by fishing vessels in Great Britain alone, representing a value of more than four and a half million pounds sterling. So important is this fish to the welfare of nations, that its spawning and feeding grounds have determined the location of cities, and its annual migrations have been the subject of many years of patient investigation by scientists of Europe. Man is not the sole " enemy " with which the Herring has to contend, the shoals being constantly decimated by sea birds, other fishes, whales, and porpoises. In spite of the huge toll levied on its numbers, however, the Herring is believed to be on the increase. The young fry of the Herring, together with those of its near relative the Sprat, form the basis of the commercial " whitebait." The Pilchard, a member of a more southerly distributed genus (*Sardina*), is another important economic species, forming the basis of the Sardine industries of France and Portugal (the Sardine is nothing more than a young Pilchard), and of the once important Pilchard fisheries of Cornwall. The Japanese regard their Pilchard as the most important food-fish.

While the eggs of the Herring are firmly attached to rocks or stones on the sea-bottom, those of the Pilchard and Sprat float at the surface ; the larvae are all long, slender, and transparent. The Anchovies, sometimes regarded as a distinct family, may be recognised by the conical snout, which overhangs a deeply cleft mouth.

Mention may be made of the Smooth-heads, curious deep-sea fishes of wide distribution. Nothing is known of their habits or food.

The Salmonid Fishes are an especially interesting group. They provide fascinating problems of distribution and evolution to the naturalist ;

BLACK SMOOTH-HEAD

About forty species of Smooth-heads are known, curious deep-sea fishes related to the Herrings and Salmonids.

their size, beauty, and " gameness " make them a favourite with the sportsman ; and their flesh provides a rich, nutritious food. In form and appearance they are not unlike some of the herrings, but may be distinguished by the presence of a small fleshy flap, or " adipose fin," on the hinder part of the back. Widely distributed in the Arctic and temperate parts of the Northern Hemisphere, they have recently been successfully introduced into Australia, New Zealand, and other parts of the globe where conditions are suitable. Contrary to the general opinion, they are not really freshwater fishes, but represent marine fishes which are gradually establishing themselves in fresh water. Many of the species are anadromous (*i.e.* ascending rivers for spawning purposes), while others never go to the sea, and it is of interest to note that we find both migratory and non-migratory forms within the limits of the same species (*e.g.* the Trout).

The common Atlantic Salmon enters all suitable rivers on both sides of the Atlantic to spawn, although modern pollution has rendered several once famous salmon rivers no longer inhabitable for the species. The fry, or alevins, remain in fresh water for two years after hatching, during which period they are known as " parr " ; they then assume a silvery livery and migrate to the open sea as " smolts " ; after a year or more in the sea, where they feed largely on herrings, mackerel, etc., and grow at a rapid rate, they return once more to the rivers to spawn. Salmon which have just spawned are known as "kelts," and are recognisable by their large heads, leanness, and general enfeebled condition. The well-known Trout has a similar distribution in the sea to the Salmon, but is absent in America, and the presence of freshwater forms in the countries to the north of the Mediterranean, and in North Africa, Corsica and Sardinia,

SALMON

This fish was caught in the River Awe and weighed 56 lbs.

indicates that Sea Trout, although now extending southwards only as far as the Bay of Biscay, must have ranged much farther south in comparatively recent times.

In form and coloration the European Trout is one of the most variable of fishes, and a number of different names have been given to British forms which are now regarded as pertaining to a single species. Thus, although the silvery, black-spotted Sea Trout, and the variously coloured Brown Trout differ greatly in appearance, there are no actual structural differences, and the young are exactly similar. The rate of growth, dependent to a great extent on the nature of the habitat and food, varies enormously in different localities, the small Trout of some of the

SEA TROUT

The Sea Trout is not a distinct species from the Brown Trout, although in some mountain streams the latter does not weigh more than 3 or 4 ozs. when adult, whereas the Sea Trout attains a weight of several pounds.

Welsh mountain streams averaging little more than a few ounces in weight, while some of the lordly fish of the large rivers and lakes will attain a weight of fifty pounds.

The Salmon and Trout of the North Pacific form a distinct group (*Oncorhynchus*), which includes the famous Quinnat, and Sock-eye Salmon, and the well-known Rainbow Trout which is introduced into our own waters. Many of these fishes are of great economic importance, and form the basis of the "tinned salmon" industry. Unlike our own Salmon, none of the individuals return to the sea after spawning, but die as soon as the reproductive functions have been completed.

The Char, an allied genus including both migratory and non-migratory forms, are more Arctic and Alpine fishes than the Salmon and Trout. The species which reside permanently in lakes are found in the British Isles in Scotland, the Lake District, North Wales, and in Ireland, preferring deep cold stretches of water. The pretty little Brook Trout of Canada and the

WIDE-MOUTH

A representative of a large and varied group of oceanic fishes, some of which live at considerable depths. The teeth of some are comparatively feeble, but many of the species are provided with powerful " fangs."

northern United States, which has been introduced into several English streams, is really a Char.

To conclude the Salmonid family, mention may be made of the White-fishes, inhabiting the northern parts of Europe, Asia, and America, and including among the British species the Vendaces, Pollan, Powan, and Gwyniad ; and the handsome Grayling, with its long dorsal fin.

BEAKED MORMYRID

A member of a large family of curious fishes found only in the rivers and streams of Africa.

Of the remaining members of the order Isospondyli, space will not permit more than the mention of some of the more interesting forms. The group of " Wide-mouths " includes a vast number of deep-sea genera and species, concerning the habits of which we know next to nothing. Nearly all have elongate bodies, and are deep black in colour ; and many of them are provided with rows of " lamps " or luminous organs, which may serve as recognition marks or to light up the surrounding water.

Some of the genera have powerful fang-like teeth, while others have a relatively feeble dentition.

The Osteoglossids are freshwater fishes found only in Australia, Africa, and America, and are characterised mainly by the large, dense scales. The Arapaima of Brazil and the Guianas attains a length of fifteen feet, and is probably the largest freshwater fish known. The Feather-backs of the fresh and brackish waters of West Africa and the Oriental Region are curious fishes in which the long anal fin is united with the caudal, and the dorsal is small or altogether wanting. The largest species attains a length of four feet. The Mormyrids are strange fishes, very variable in the form of the head, body, and fins, and found only in the rivers of tropical Africa. They are remarkable for the relatively huge size of the brain, and for the possession of electrical organs on each side of the tail. Some of the Nile species were reverenced by the ancient Egyptians, and are represented in their mural frescoes. The grotesque Beaked Mormyrid, illustrated on the preceding page, uses the appendage on the chin to obtain small animals hidden under stones or in the mud.

Order HAPLOMI

(*Pikes, Mud-fishes, etc.*)

The Pikes, with their allies the Mud Minnows and Black-fishes, form a small order, the Haplomi, distinguished mainly by peculiarities of the internal skeleton. The Common Pike, found in many parts of Europe, Asia, and America, is too well known to require description. It is abundant throughout the British Isles, where it is esteemed by the angler but strongly disliked by others on account of its destructiveness to more valuable fish.

PIKE

One of the most voracious of all freshwater fishes. In addition to other fishes the Pike sometimes feed on frogs, voles and even water-birds.

The jaws of the Pike fairly bristle with teeth, those on the roof of the mouth being movable and directed backwards. Fishes form the main item in its diet, and many are the stories of its unexampled ferocity and greediness ; cases of cannibalism are common enough, and when driven by hunger it will attack even man himself. The record British Pike seems to have scaled more than seventy pounds, but the famous Muskallunge of America reaches an even greater size. The little Black-fish of Siberia and Alaska is renowned for its vitality, remaining frozen for weeks at a time and thawing out as lively as ever.

Order OSTARIOPHYSI
(*Characins, Cyprinids, Loaches, Cat-fishes*)

We now encounter a very large order, the Ostariophysi, one which includes the majority of the freshwater fishes of the world. A comparatively modern group, geologically speaking, these fishes have originated from early herring-like forms, and have undergone considerable changes in structure, some being highly specialised, others variously degenerate. They all agree in having a chain of little bones connecting the air-bladder with the internal ear ; this apparatus is probably designed to assist the fishes to perceive changes in pressure as well as sounds or movements in the water, the air-bladder actually acting as an extra " ear." Two well-defined sub-orders may be recognised : the Cyprinoids, with a naked head, and with the body generally covered with overlapping, cycloid scales, and the Siluroids, or Cat-fishes, with the body naked or variously armoured with bony scutes, or plates.

Sub-order CYPRINOIDEA
(*Characins, Carps, Loaches*)

The Characins, the most generalised members of the first group, include a vast assemblage of genera and species, extremely diverse in form and habits, and confined to the rivers and lakes of Africa and Central and South America. They are, for the most part, carnivorous, feeding on smaller fishes or invertebrates. The Tiger-fish, known to the Arabs of the Nile district as " Dog of the Water," is probably one of the most formidable. It attains a length of about four feet, is remarkably pike-like in appearance, and the jaws are armed with savage, pointed teeth. The notorious Piraya, or Caribe, of South America, with its deep body, saw-edged belly, and triangular, razor-like teeth, is renowned for its extreme ferocity and fear-lessness.

PIRAYA or CARIBE

A Characin fish renowned for its fearlessness and ferocity.

Any animal unlucky enough to fall into water inhabited by these pests may be assailed in an instant and reduced to a skeleton in an incredibly short space of time, the smell of blood attracting these " ravening wolves " in their hundreds. The handsome Dorado, of the Plate River, is known to the Spaniards as Salmon, and bears a superficial resemblance to that fish. It feeds on shoals of smaller fish, which it pursues with vigour, and is a great favourite with the angler. Among the non-carnivorous forms may be mentioned the Moon-fish of the Nile, with small mouth and extremely feeble teeth, feeding entirely on vegetable matter. This fish is frequently represented on the monuments of the ancient Egyptians.

Closely allied to the Characins are the South American Gymnotids ("bare backs"), with long eel-like bodies, very lengthy anal fins, and no dorsal fin. Other features in which they resemble the true eels are the complete absence of the pelvic fins and the small gill-openings; these characters, however, have been acquired as the result of peculiar habits and mode of life similar to those of the eels, and do not indicate actual relationship. A still more remarkable feature of these fishes is the position

DORADO

A well-known sporting fish of the Rio Plata of South America. A member of the large and varied family of Characins.

of the vent, which, instead of lying in the middle or hinder part of the body, is in, or near, *the throat*. The Electric Eel is perhaps the best-known species. This fish grows to a length of six feet, or even more, and the tail is provided with batteries capable of giving a shock of sufficient strength to paralyse the strongest man.

The Carps, or Cyprinids, comprise a greater number of species than any other family of fishes: nearly 1500 species are known, including such well-known fish as the Carp, Roach, Chub, Minnow, Tench, and Bream. The original home of the family seems to have been in India and South-East Asia, whence they spread over the greater part of Asia, Africa, Europe, and North America. In Australia, a country which was split off from Asia at

ELECTRIC EEL

This species grows to a length of six feet. It inhabits marshes and shallow rivers and is much dreaded on account of its "electric shocks."

an early period of the earth's history, Cyprinids are entirely absent, and although living side by side with the Characins in Africa, none have penetrated into South America. The chief characteristic of these fishes is that they carry their teeth, not in the mouth, which is entirely toothless, but in the throat. These pharyngeal, or throat teeth, are arranged in two or three rows on each side of the gullet, and may be hooked at the tips in those species feeding on other fish; are molar-like in shellfish-feeders; and with hollow grinding surfaces in those which subsist on a diet of mud.

For the most part, the Cyprinids are small, feeble fishes, providing the principal food of predatory river fishes. They owe their success in competition with their more powerful neighbours to their great fecundity and insignificance. Certain species, however, grow to a large size, and the famous game-fish of India, the Mahseer, a single scale of which is as large as the palm of the hand, reaches a length of six feet. As food the members of this family are of little value, the flesh being generally coarse and tasteless. The Common Carp has been successfully introduced from the East into all parts of Europe, and into America, where it grows to a large size, and may, under favourable circumstances, attain a great age. The

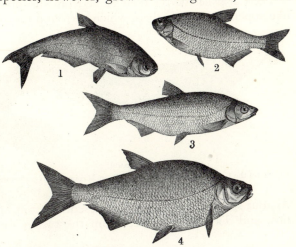

1. ZOPE. 2. WHITE BREAM. 3. ZARTHE. 4. COMMON BREAM.

Members of the large and widely distributed family of Cyprinid fishes. The White Bream and Common Bream are British species, but the Zope and Zarthe occur in Central Europe.

Mirror Carp, with its few enlarged scales, and the Leather Carp, with its thick skin totally devoid of scales, are domesticated varieties which have been produced by fish culturists on the continent. The popular little Gold-fish is a near relative, which in its native waters of Eastern Asia is coloured like any other Carp. It is only the domestic varieties, of which several monstrous forms have been bred by the Chinese and Japanese, which lose the black and brown pigment and exhibit the familiar gold or silver colours.

TENCH

Sometimes known as the " Doctor-fish " on account of the healing power attributed to the thick slime covering the body, which is said to act as a sort of balsam. This idea is now discredited.

The Loaches form a separate family, and are essentially fishes adapted for life in hill streams. When the water in which they live becomes excessively foul, these fishes are able to use their intestines as accessory breathing organs, swallowing air by the mouth and expelling it through the vent. They are very susceptible to changes of atmospheric pressure, and one species is known in Germany as the " weather fish."

Sub-order *Siluroidea*
(*Cat-fishes*)

The Cat-fishes derive their name from the presence of several tentacle-like appendages, or barbels, which surround the mouth, some of which may

GIANT LOACH
Known on the Continent as " Weather-fish " on account of its susceptibility to changes of atmospheric pressure.

be even longer than the fish itself. They are nearly all carnivorous, bottom-feeding fishes, and these " feelers " aid them in seeking for food in very muddy water where eyes would be of little use. Indeed, the eyes are often very much reduced.

A stout spine is nearly always present in front of the dorsal and pectoral fins, and has been derived from the fusion or modification of certain

ELECTRIC CAT-FISH
Found in the rivers of Africa. If kept in an aquarium with other fishes it soon kills its companions.

soft fin-rays. These spines are often formidable weapons with saw-like edges, and are capable of inflicting painful and jagged wounds. No true scales are ever developed.

Although no Cat-fishes occur in our own country, and only two in Europe, as many as 1600 species are known, distributed over almost every other part of the world. Unlike the Cyprinoids, they are not exclusively f r e s h w a t e r

MAILED CAT-FISH (Male)
Found in the rivers of South America.

fishes, a few having returned to the river estuaries and to the sea. The oriental Sac-gilled Cat-fishes are provided with a complicated accessory breathing apparatus, enabling them to live for long periods away from water. The European Wels, or Glanis, is the largest strictly freshwater fish of that continent, reaching a weight of four hundred pounds. It is a voracious fish, inhabiting the rivers east of the Rhine. One or two African Cat-fishes of the genus known as Synodonts have the truly remarkable habit of floating or swimming in a leisurely manner *upside down*. This habit has had a curious result, in that the normal coloration has been completely reversed, the back of the fish being silvery-white and the belly dark brown or black. The Electric Cat-fish, another native of Africa, is completely enveloped by its " batteries," which have been evolved from the skin.

MAILED CAT-FISH (Female)
Note the covering of bony plates which distinguishes the members of this family from the other Cat-fishes.

The curious Mailed Cat-fishes of South America have the body armoured all over with bony plates. They are inhabitants of swift-running streams, or brooks, and are able to cling to stones by means of the strong, sucker-like mouth which is placed on the under side of the head. While thus attached, water is inhaled for breathing purposes through the gill-opening, and expelled again through the same aperture. Their food consists of minute invertebrates and more or less putrified matter ; as a consequence of this diet, the teeth are slender, close-set, and bristle-like, and the intestine very long and coiled round and round like a watch-spring.

Orders APODES, INIOMI, LYOMERI, AND HETEROMI
(*Eels, Scopeloids, Gulper Eels, Thornbacks*)

The True Eels form an important order, the Apodes (" without feet "), characterised by the serpent-like body, which is either quite naked or provided with vestigial scales embedded in the skin ; the small gill-openings ; and by the absence of the pelvic fins, and of a separate caudal fin.

The Eels provide an admirable object lesson in the effect of adaptation to a specialised mode of life, their smooth,

CONGER AND COMMON EEL
In classical times the flesh of the Conger Eel was esteemed as a great delicacy.

elongate bodies being peculiarly fitted for burrowing in the mud for purposes of concealment, or for creeping in and out of holes and crevices in rock or coral. Their swimming movements are of necessity different from those of the generality of fishes, forward progression being effected by undulating side-to-side wriggles of the whole body and tail, sometimes aided by gentle movements of the long, flexible dorsal and anal fins. Eels are found in all tropical and temperate parts of the world, and the great majority of the species live in the sea.

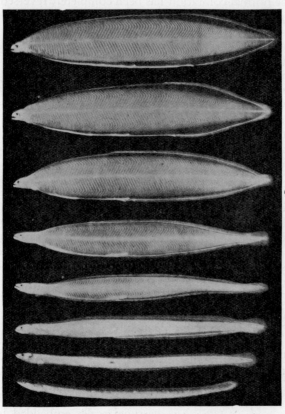

METAMORPHOSIS OF THE COMMON EEL

This photograph shows the remarkable changes undergone by the *Leptocephalus* larva in the course of its transformation into the Elver.

The Freshwater Eels differ from most other members of the order in that they spend the whole of their adult life in fresh water, only returning to their original home in the ocean for the purpose of propagating their kind; this done, they die, for no Eel ever returns thence ! The Common Eel, familiar to us all, has a remarkably wide distribution, being found on the coasts and in the rivers of Western Europe, and in the countries bordering the Mediterranean, extending as far eastwards as Palestine. In its feeding habits the Eel is a regular glutton, and something of a scavenger beside, its varied diet including voles, waterbirds, frogs, small fishes, fish spawn, crustaceans, and worms. It is owl-like in its habits, committing many of its depredations at night.

Thirty years ago practically nothing was known of the breeding habits of the species, and the elucidation of this mystery provided one of the most fascinating biological discoveries of recent years. Towards the autumn a number of adult fishes cease to feed, lose their normal greenish or yellow colour, and assume a silvery livery ; at the same time the eyes become larger, and other changes occur, involving the form of the snout and pectoral fin. The call to the sea seems to be all-powerful, for individuals living in remote ponds will wriggle across stretches of grassland, on damp nights, in order to reach the nearest sea-going river. Once in the sea, they make their way to the spawning grounds, situated two or three thousand miles away in the Western Atlantic, south-east of Bermuda, and having deposited and fertilised the eggs, the parents die. Next spring the larvae hatch out—curious, transparent creatures, with flattened, leaf-like bodies, small heads, and jaws provided with a few long, needle-like teeth. These larvae feed on minute organisms at or near the surface of the ocean, and gradually swim or drift eastwards across the Atlantic, finally approaching the coasts of Europe when a little more than two years old.

Having attained an average length of three inches, they now cease to feed, undergo a gradual reduction in size, and, at the same time, a remarkable transformation, ending up as tiny cylindrical elvers, or glass-eels, about $2\frac{1}{2}$ inches in length. They are now ready to enter fresh water, and run up the larger rivers literally in their millions. In our own country the ascent of elvers occurs in late winter or spring. Few obstacles seem to be too great to be overcome in this ascent, and our elvers at last find a suitable resting-place in river, pond,

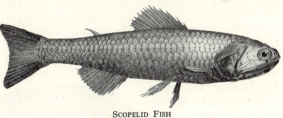

SCOPELID FISH

Note the regularly arranged miniature " lamps " on the sides of the body.

or stream, where they will remain until they themselves are old enough to set out on the great journey which will end their lives.

Among the marine forms we may mention the Congers and the Morays, or Painted Eels. The Common Conger of our coasts reaches a considerable size, provides good sport for the sea-angler, and is wholesome eating. The Conger is a voracious fish, and when hungry will not hesitate to devour the weaker members of its own kind. The Morays are remarkable for their brilliant coloration, generally mottled in pattern. They are usually to be found in the neighbourhood of coral reefs, where their striking livery, instead of being conspicuous, harmonises with the background of corals and associated animal life. The Mediterranean Murry, known to the Romans as *Muraena*, was much esteemed by them as food, and was bred in specially constructed reservoirs, occasionally being fed on the corpses of slaves.

The order of Scopeloids (Iniomi) includes a number of remarkable fishes, of whose habits we know next to nothing, but which are of great interest in presenting some extraordinary adaptations to life in the depths of the ocean—the region of perpetual night. In the truly abyssal forms we find that the eyes are either of enormous size, very much reduced, or altogether wanting. Where the eyes have disappeared, special organs of touch are sometimes developed to compensate for the loss of sight. Nearly all the Scopeloids have soft, fragile bodies, black or silvery over black colour, and many oceanic forms are provided with luminous organs of some sort which serve to light up the abysmal depths.

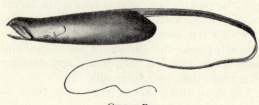

GULPER EEL

A deep-sea fish related to the Scopeloids. The throat and stomach are capable of great distension.

In the Lantern-fishes, these phosphorescent organs take the form of groups or rows of miniature lanterns on the sides of the body, reminding one of the costermonger's pearlies. Some have larger organs known as sternchasers on the upper part of the tail, while others are provided with a large head-lamp on the front of the head. They are small, feeble fishes, swimming near the surface at night and descending to unknown depths by day, and providing food for various oceanic fishes, whales, and porpoises. The Lizard-fishes, on the other hand, live fairly close to the shore, and, unlike their oceanic relatives, are brightly coloured. The Indian Bummalow, which enters the estuaries and rivers of Bengal and Burma, provides, when dried and salted, the well-known "Bombay Duck," a relish much appreciated in curries.

The Gulper Eels, and Spiny Eels, or Thornbacks, each form a

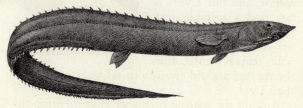

THORNBACK or SPINY EEL

These are not true eels but deep-sea fishes of uncertain relationships. Little is known of their habits.

distinct order (Lyomeri and Heteromi), the former being in all probability degenerate relatives of the Scopeloids. The Gulper Eels are black, scaleless fishes, living at great depths in the ocean, and remarkable for the huge size of the mouth, which has a cavity larger than the rest of the body, and for the enormously distensible stomach, enabling them to swallow fishes several times their own weight. The relationships of the Thornbacks are uncertain, and as they are also deep-sea forms, little is known about their habits.

Orders Microcyprini and Synentognathi
(Cyprinodonts, Gar-fishes, Half-beaks, Flying-fishes, etc.)

The Cyprinodonts, or Killifishes, recognisable by their flat heads, protractile mouths, usually large scales, and by the absence of a distinct lateral line, are confined to brackish and fresh waters of tropical America, Southern Europe, Asia, and Africa. They are all small fishes, some species being less than an inch in length when full-grown, while few attain a length of a foot. The teeth are small, and vary in form according to the diet, some species being carnivorous, others vegetarian. Their habit of voraciously devouring insect larvae, and particularly the larvae of mosquitoes, makes certain species valuable allies to man in his war against the dread malaria, a disease which is carried by the mosquito. The introduction of the little " Millions-fish " of Barbados into fever-stricken districts has proved most efficacious in checking the scourge.

In many Cyprinodonts the two sexes present striking differences, the males being smaller and more brightly coloured. The form of the fins may be different also, as in the well-known Sword-tailed Minnow of Mexico, in which the male has the lower lobe of the tail produced into a long and pointed process. Many males indulge in elaborate courtship before mating, a feature which makes these fishes great favourites with aquarium lovers, especially

FOUR-EYED FISH (Male and Female)

The upper part of the eye is constructed for vision in the air, the lower part for vision under the water. A member of the order of Cyprinodonts.

as they breed freely in captivity. Among the larger members of the order we may mention the Four-eyed Fishes of South America, so-called because each eye is divided into two parts by a dark horizontal partition—a lower part adapted for vision under water, and an upper for vision in the air. Thus equipped, a fish swimming at the surface is able to observe its food in the water, and at the same time to detect insects skimming above the surface.

The famous Kentucky Blind-fish is a member of a small family of Cyprinodonts found mostly in caves and subterranean streams in the United States. As the result of living in perpetual darkness, the eyes of these fishes have been reduced to mere functionless vestiges, although better developed in the young. Furthermore, the absence of light has led to the body becoming quite bleached. To compensate for the loss of vision, the head and body have developed ridges of little papillae, which are highly sensitive, and enable

BALAO or HALF-BEAK
In this curious fish only the lower jaw is produced instead of both as in the Skippers and Gar-fishes.

their possessor to perceive the slightest movements in the surrounding water. So effective are these sensory organs, that the fishes are able to obtain the

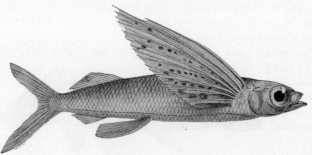

FLYING-FISH (side view)

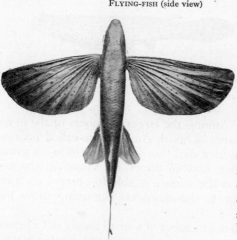

FLYING-FISH (top view)
The greatly enlarged pectoral fins function merely as parachutes and are not actually flapped as in birds.

small creatures on which they feed with as much ease as if they possessed normal sight, and it is to this adaptation, coupled with the absence of large predaceous fishes in caves and underground streams, that they owe their survival in the struggle for existence.

The next order (Synentognathi) comprises a number of interesting forms which exhibit many resemblances in structure to the Cyprinodonts. The dorsal and anal fins are both placed far back on the body, the scales are thin and cycloid, and a distinct lateral line is present. The Gar-fishes, or Needle-fishes, with the jaws drawn out into a slender " beak " armed with sharp, unequal teeth, bear a superficial resemblance to the Gar Pikes already described, but the groups have nothing else in common. They are voracious fishes, capturing their prey while skimming along at the surface of the sea, and some of the larger species, five or six feet in length, may be dangerous to man.   As food they are wholesome and tasty, in spite of the curious bright green colour of the bones which remains even after cooking.   The Sauries, or Skippers, are closely related forms, differing in possessing a number of little detached finlets behind the dorsal and anal fins.   The Balaos, or Half-beaks, are vegetarians, subsisting almost entirely on green seaweed, and have the lower jaw only produced.

We may note here that in all these long-jawed fishes the young are provided with short jaws, which are equal in length ; in the young Gar-fish the lower jaw grows out much more quickly than the upper, so that at one period of its life it is exactly like a Half-beak.   Many of the above-mentioned fishes frequently make spasmodic skips or leaps from the water, and this tendency has culminated in the Flying-fishes which are able to make more or less lengthy flights by means of their enormously enlarged pectoral fins. It must be pointed out, however, that the fins are not flapped like the wings of birds, but merely used as parachutes, the fish supplying the motive power by a strong flick of the tail as it leaves the water.   Generally the flights, which may be more than 150 yards in length, are close to the water, but in breezy or stormy weather the fishes are frequently carried on to the decks of ships.   They are always found in shoals, and feed at or near the surface on crustaceans or little fishes.

Orders ANACANTHINI AND ALLOTRIOGNATHI
(Cods and their allies, Opah, Ribbon-fishes, etc.)

The Order Anacanthini (" without spines ") includes fishes in which the fin-rays are all jointed and flexible, but which differ in several respects from the soft-rayed fishes already described.   The air-bladder does not communicate with the gullet, and the pelvic fins are placed far forward on the body, being sometimes actually in front of the pectorals ; a true caudal fin is either absent, or very much reduced, the so-called tail-fin of the cods being composed largely of rays belonging to the dorsal and anal fins.

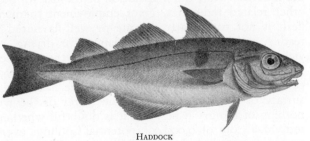

HADDOCK

Distinguished from the other members of the Cod family of Great Britain by the large black blotch on the side. One of our most important food fishes.

In the Cod family the body is longish and covered with small cycloid scales. The mouth is rather large, provided with relatively strong teeth, and situated near the end of the head ; there is often a short barbel below the chin, which probably functions as a sensory " feeler." The members of this family are soberly coloured fishes, nearly all marine, and mostly inhabiting the frigid and temperate seas of the Northern Hemisphere ; some have become accustomed to living at great depths, and these abyssal forms, on account of the low temperature of the water, generally extend much farther southwards. About 120 species are known, including the Cod, Whiting, Coalfish, Haddock, Pollack, Hake, and Ling, to mention only the better-known food-fishes of our own waters. The Burbot of Europe, Siberia, and North America holds the distinction of being the only truly fresh-water species. We select for special mention the Common Cod, which will serve to typify the family.

The Cod, which is nearly always caught on long lines, each with a row of baited hooks, is, next to the Herring, the most sought-after fish in the world, and the fishery has for many years been highly lucrative to fishermen of many nations. The great fishery of the Newfoundland Bank has been immortalised by Kipling in his novel, " Captains Courageous," whilst the

GRENADIER or RAT-TAIL
A deep-sea fish from the South Pacific Ocean.   Related to the Cods and their allies.

French industry has been accurately and vividly described by Pierre Loti in his book, " An Iceland Fisherman." In their pursuit of the Cod the French fishermen were led farther and farther into the Atlantic, and this resulted eventually in the discovery of Canada. It has been estimated that no fewer than 300 to 400 millions of Cod are caught annually in the Atlantic ; about 200,000 men take part in the fisheries, while the preparation of the fish for the market, together with other related industries, gives employment to many more people. The flesh is not particularly delicate or well-flavoured, but it takes salt very readily, and is peculiarly well adapted for drying. In addition, the liver yields the valuable medicinal oil used in the treatment of wasting diseases.

The Cod is extremely prolific, as many as 9,000,000 eggs having been counted in a single fish of medium size. The eggs and fry float at the surface of the sea, and are at the mercy of the wind and waves, to say nothing of hungry fishes, and it is doubtful whether more than five or six individuals out of 9,000,000 potential Codlings ever reach maturity. The varied diet of this species includes other fishes, crustaceans, molluscs, and worms, and we read of a fish caught in 1676 whose stomach contained " a work in three treatises "—a truly highbrow meal !

The Grenadiers, or Rat-tails, form a distinct family distinguished by the long, tapering tail, which ends in a filament, and by the more backward position of the pelvic fins. The mouth, which is frequently toothless, may be protrusible and funnel-like, and placed on the under side of the head. These fishes are found chiefly at considerable depths in the Atlantic and Pacific, and little is known of their habits.

The members of the next order, which includes the Opah and the Ribbon-fishes, are all distinguished by the peculiar structure of the mouth, which is protractile and actuated by a mechanism different from that of all other fishes. The Opah, or Moon-fish, a large oceanic species inhabiting the warmer parts of the Atlantic and Pacific Oceans, is remarkable for its form and vivid coloration. It is a large fish, attaining a weight of more than five hundred pounds, with a plump, smooth body, oval in shape, and nearly as deep as long. It is steely blue above, bluish with golden and purple reflections on the sides, and rosy red beneath; the whole body is covered with round, silvery spots, while the jaws and fins are bright vermilion. It rarely descends to any depth, and feeds largely on young fishes, cuttle-fishes, and crustaceans. It provides excellent eating, the flesh being tender, oily, and almost unsurpassed in delicacy of flavour.

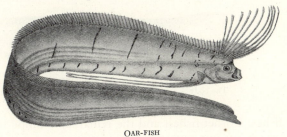

OAR-FISH

Large Oar-fishes seen swimming at the surface have been described as "Sea-serpents." This species is sometimes called "King of the Herrings," from an idea that it accompanies shoals of these fishes.

The Ribbon-fishes derive their name from the form of their bodies, which are long, very much flattened, extremely fragile, and covered with shining silvery skin. The food is similar to that of the Opah, and the mouth is consequently small, and either toothless or provided with some feeble teeth. These fishes live in the open sea, rarely at depths greater than three hundred fathoms, and many of the species are distinctly rare, being known only from occasional specimens cast ashore during storms. The Deal-fishes are remarkable for the curious arrangement of the tail-fin, the lower lobe of which disappears in the adult, and the upper is turned upwards nearly at right angles to the body. In the young Deal-fish some of the fin-rays are prolonged into long and delicate filaments, which may be many times the length of the body.

The Oar-fish derives its name from the presence of two long pelvic fins which are dilated at the tips something like the blade of an oar. The body is long and thin, sometimes reaching a length of twenty feet, and they differ from the Deal-fishes in the absence of a caudal fin. The front rays of the dorsal fin are very long, each terminating in a red flap, and when seen swimming with undulating movements at the surface of the sea, it is not surprising to find the Oar-fish described as a sea-serpent " having a horse's head with a flaming red mane." The order also includes the very rare and singular oceanic fish known as *Stylophorus*, about a foot long, with telescopic eyes, and with a small, toothless mouth, appearing when protruded at the end of a long funnel-shaped pouch.

Order SOLENICHTHYES
(*Tube-mouthed Fishes*)

These fishes, although including a number of diverse and curious-looking forms, all agree in having the snout drawn out into a more or less lengthy tube, at the end of which is placed the tiny and generally toothless mouth. The tube often acts as a kind of syringe, the food being sucked in with the water. These fishes abound in all tropical and temperate seas, living for the most part close to the shore, and sometimes entering rivers. In addition to the forms described below, the order includes the Trumpet-

SHRIMP-FISH
The body is completely encased in a thin bony cuirass with a knife-like lower edge.
Note the tail fin, which points downwards.

fishes, Cornet-fishes, and the remarkable Snipe-fishes, of which one species occurs on our own coasts.

The Shrimp-fishes (*Centriscus*) are perhaps the most extraordinary of all living fishes. The body is much flattened, with a knife-like lower edge, and is for the greater part enclosed in a transparent bony cuirass, which terminates behind in a long strong spine. The median fins are all crowded together at the hinder end of the body, the tail actually pointing downwards. These grotesque creatures, which are generally found in small shoals,

BANDED PIPE-FISH
This photograph shows the male carrying the eggs on the under surface of the body. They are contained in a groove, and attached to the body by a sticky secretion.

can apparently move equally well in a horizontal or vertical position, and have even been observed swimming *on their heads* !

The Pipe-fishes and Sea Horses, sometimes grouped together as " Tuft-gilled fishes " on account of the fact that the gills are reduced to small lobate tufts, may be recognised by their complete external armour, which takes the form of a delicate bony framework composed of a series of rings round the body. They are all small, defenceless creatures, depending for protection mainly on their resemblance to surrounding objects. The Pipe-fishes, for example, with their peculiar form and swaying movements, bear a close resemblance to the fronds of seaweed among which they live, and the concealment is rendered more perfect by the power which they possess of rapidly changing their colours to suit the surroundings. The Sea Dragons of Australia carry this mimetic resemblance even farther, the body being provided with long, leaf-like appendages of skin, which, when streaming out in the water, give a truly remarkable imitation of a piece of weed.

SEA DRAGON

A relative of the Sea Horses from Australia. It bears an almost perfect resemblance to the seaweed among which it lives, the skinny processes with which the head and body are adorned imitating the fronds of the weed.

The swimming movements of these fishes are unusual, the dorsal fin being the principal organ of locomotion, aided, in the case of the Pipe-fishes, by wriggling movements of the whole body. The Sea Horses, which habitually swim in an upright position, using the dorsal fin as a kind of propeller, are unique in making use of the tail as a prehensile organ to anchor them to a piece of weed or floating timber. In nearly all the members of this family the care of the eggs and young is undertaken by the father, who carries them about with him tucked away in a pouch situated on the under side of his body or tail.

SPINY-RAYED BONY FISHES

Orders BERYCOMORPHI AND ZEOMORPHI

(*Berycoids and Zeoids*)

With the order of Berycoids we return to the main stem of the tree and commence our survey of the spiny-rayed fishes, in which the rays of the front part of the dorsal and anal fins are modified into stiff, sharply pointed s p i n e s, the spinous part of the dorsal sometimes being separated off as a distinct fin. The pelvic fins are always placed far forward on the body, and the outermost

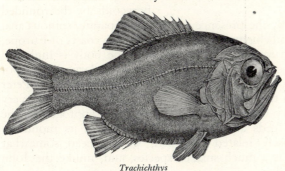

Trachichthys

A New Zealand member of the order of Berycoids.

ray of each is spinous. These spines are generally employed as defensive weapons, but may be used also for attack.

The Berycoids, distinguished by the large number of rays in the pelvic fins, and by the forked tail-fin, are generally regarded as being the most primitive of all spiny-rayed fishes. They are certainly the most archaic, a profusion of forms being abundant in Cretaceous times, while relatively few genera exist to-day.

Beryx, known in Spain as Alfonsino, is a large, handsome fish, with a deep body, very large eye, and bright scarlet coloration. It is found in deep water in the warmer parts of the Atlantic, and is becoming increasingly commoner in our fish-markets. The Soldier-fishes, so-called on account of the strong armoury of spines, are inhabitants of coral reefs. Their livery is frequently brilliant, the ground colour being scarlet or crimson, and often with golden, silvery, or blackish stripes. The remarkable little Pine-cone Fish of Japan has the body enclosed in a kind of bony box formed of strong plates which have the appearance of being roughly put together. Another extraordinary form known as *Anomalops*, which occurs in the depths of the sea, is provided with a powerful "lamp" placed on a movable flap below the eye.

JOHN DORY

Common on the Western and South Western coasts of the British Isles, and landed in large quantities by trawlers. The flesh is much esteemed by connoisseurs.

The Zeoids are readily distinguished from the Berycoids by the rounded or square-cut tail-fin, and by the presence of a small, separate, spinous anal fin. The John Dory, found chiefly in shallow bays on the coasts of Europe, is perhaps the best-known member of this order. The body is high and very much flattened, and on the middle of each side is a large black spot ringed with yellow, said to be the mark made by the thumb of Saint Peter when he took a coin from the fish's mouth. The mouth is large and very protrusible, the John Dory being in the habit of quietly approaching the small fishes on which it feeds and suddenly shooting out its mouth to seize the prey. The closely related Boar-fish, with a head somewhat resembling that of a pig, is a much smaller species, and, unlike the John Dory, is of no value as food.

Order PERCOMORPHI
(Perch-like Fishes)

Sub-order *PERCOIDEA*
(Percoids)

This important order includes a huge assemblage of forms which may be generally distinguished from the Berycoids by the smaller number of rays in the pelvic fins. This great group may be further sub-divided into a number of sub-orders, which are indicated in the tree by a series of short radiating branches. We shall outline the main characteristics of these sub-orders here, but of the large number of families, genera, and species which they contain it will be possible to mention only a comparatively small proportion; we shall select for mention those which present features of more particular interest.

The sub-order of Percoids includes the more typical families of the order, all of which agree in having the pelvic fins composed of a spine and five soft rays, and situated below the pectorals; the spinous part of the dorsal fin is generally well developed, and formed of stiff, sharp spines; the scales are nearly always of the "ctenoid" kind. The range of the group is almost cosmopolitan, and, although there are three important freshwater families, most of the Percoids are marine, being abundant on the coasts in tropical and sub-

BANDED SEA PERCH or GROUPER
A tropical species widely distributed in the Indian Ocean. These fishes are capable of almost instantaneous colour changes.

tropical seas, and becoming rather scarce in the colder parts of the world.

The Bass, which ranges from the Mediterranean to our southern coasts, will serve as a typical representative of the large and varied family of Sea Perches. Bass occur in large shoals near the coast, and frequently enter rivers in pursuit of small fishes and crustaceans on which they feed. Reaching a length of three feet, and a weight of nearly thirty pounds, this fish has long been a favourite with the angler on account of its sporting qualities, and it has been greatly esteemed for the table since the time of the Romans, who kept the fish in freshwater ponds to improve its flavour. The Jew-fish, the prize of the Californian angler, is one of the largest of the Sea Perches, sometimes scaling as much as five hundred pounds.

The tropical Sea Perches, variously known as Groupers, Rock-fishes,

Hinds, and Merous, abound in nearly all warm seas. Their handsome liveries and remarkable power of instantaneously changing their colours and markings has earned for these fishes the name of " Chamaeleons of the Sea." So rapid are some of these colour changes, that a Grouper has been observed to enter a clump of coral coloured brown, or yellow, and to leave it a few seconds later with white or scarlet livery. As we pointed out in the introduction, these changes are generally related to the colours of the rocks, corals, and weeds among which the fish is swimming ; sometimes, however, they are associated with excitement, or emotion of some kind, and such familiar expressions as " scarlet with rage " or " white with fear " assume a literal meaning when applied to these quick-change artists.

The Snappers, a family which includes some important food-fishes, are scarcely less numerous and varied than the Sea Perches. All are carnivorous, and some, like the Red Snapper of the Gulf of Mexico, reach a considerable size. The Grunts, which derive their name from the sounds made by the fishes when taken from the water, are smaller fishes, often beautifully marked with undulating stripes of blue and yellow. The inside of the mouth is generally coloured a vivid scarlet. The Nile Perch, or *Lates*, a member of another family, is a large carnivorous fish which was much reverenced by the ancient Egyptians, who frequently mummified its body. It reaches a length of six feet or more, and is found in the Nile, Senegal, Niger, and Congo. The silvery Robalos of tropical America belong to the same tribe.

RED MULLET

This is a British species, visiting our shores in the summer months. Note the pair of barbels below the chin ; these are highly sensitive, and are used for stirring up the sand in search of food.

The Red Mullets, inhabitants of most warm seas, are chiefly remarkable for the pair of long barbels attached to the chin. These fishes swim about in shallow water, using the barbels as feelers to aid them in the search for the small worms and shellfish on which they feed. The Surmullet of Europe was much esteemed by the Romans both for its colour and for the quality of its flesh. The colours of this fish appear to be brightest during the time intervening between its capture and death, and the wealthy Romans had it brought alive to their tables in order to watch the display of colour occasioned by its death agonies.

The Sea Breams are a large and varied tribe, the members of which are distinguished from one another chiefly by differences in the dentition. The Common Sea Bream, for example, feeding mainly on crabs and shellfish, is provided with stout, blunt, crushing teeth at the sides of the jaws; the Black Sea Bream, on the other hand, subsists almost entirely on sea-weed, and has bands of small teeth in each jaw, with a row of cutting teeth on the outside. The Sheepshead, with chisel-like incisor teeth in front and molar teeth at the sides, lives on a diet of clams and oysters, and is one of the important food-fishes of the Atlantic coast of North America. The Schnapper of Australia, and the Gilt-head of the Mediterranean, a silvery fish with a golden band between the eyes, are other species which are of some economic importance; the latter was highly esteemed by the Romans. The famous Red Tai of Japan has

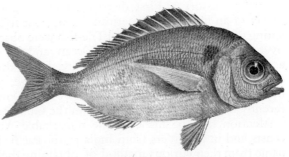

COMMON SEA BREAM

An important food-fish. It lives in the deeper waters of the Atlantic Ocean, entering the Channel and North Sea every summer.

even become a sort of national emblem, and in prints and images is always associated with the fish-god Ebisu.

The fishes variously termed Drums, Croakers, or Roncadors derive their names from the sounds made by many of the members of this family. The noise is produced by means of a special muscle attached to the air-bladder, which is itself of a complicated nature and acts as a resonator. The drumming noise is said to occur chiefly at the breeding season, and is a signal for the assembling of the shoals. The Squeteagues, with a wide mouth and strong canine teeth, are predaceous fishes which swim near the surface of the sea, but the majority of the Drums have small mouths and comparatively feeble teeth, and feed on the

SPOTTED FIRM-FIN

A member of the family of Cirrhitids. Note the unbranched and thickened lower rays of the pectoral fin.

bottom on worms, crustaceans, molluscs, etc. The Maigre (or Meagre) is the only British species, and reaches a length of nearly six feet; the same fish is known in South Africa as " Salmon."

The fishes known as Cirrhitids have the lower rays of the pectoral fins unbranched, thickened and free at the tips; these modified rays, which may be drawn out into fine filaments, probably function as organs of touch. Some are small, handsomely coloured fishes of the coral reefs, but others, like the Trumpeter of Australia, which reaches a weight of eighty pounds, are important food-fishes.

The Tile-fish, a member of a family of fishes known as Blanquillos, has a curious history.   First discovered in 1879, this fish soon became the object of an important American fishery, but following a heavy gale in the spring of 1882, millions of dead Tile-fish were observed floating at the surface over a huge area of the Atlantic Ocean, and for many years afterwards not a single fish was caught.   It is believed that this appalling decimation of the species was due to some climatic change, perhaps the sudden influx of cold water.   It is not extinct, however, as originally supposed, but has recently appeared in its old haunts in the Gulf Stream.

Mention may be made of the remarkable Archer-fishes, found on the coasts and in the rivers from India to the Pacific Islands, which derive their name from their curious method of obtaining their food.   The Archer-fish

TILE-FISH

The back and sides are bluish or purplish with golden spots, the head rosy, while the fins are spotted with yellow.   Note the large fleshy crest on top of the head.

is a slow swimmer, and quietly approaches its prey, an insect hovering over the water or settled on a leaf; it then takes careful aim, and shoots one or more drops of water from its mouth, devouring the insect as it falls into the water.   This interesting habit is even continued in captivity.

The small, deep-bodied Chaetodonts, or Butterfly-fishes, are abundant in the neighbourhood of coral reefs.   Each of the jaws is provided with a brush of slender teeth, and the relatively tiny mouth is often placed at the end of a tube-like snout, which is used for poking into holes and crevices in the coral in search of the small worms and shrimps on which they feed.   Most of these fishes are brilliantly coloured, yellow and black predominating, and almost every species exhibits a different arrangement of bars, stripes, spots, or blotches.   These vivid liveries are by no means as conspicuous as one might suppose, the markings tending to break up the outline and to obscure the form against a background which may be as bright as the fishes themselves.   They are further protected by their excessive quickness of movement, while their deep bodies and spinous fins make them difficult for a larger fish to swallow.

The Pomacentrids, also inhabitants of coral reefs, vie with the Chaetodonts in brilliance of coloration, but are more normal in form.   Some of

Pl. 7.

CORAL REEF FISHES FROM THE PHILIPPINE ISLANDS.

1, 2, and 3. Butterfly-fishes.   4. Moorish Idol.   5 and 6. Surgeon-fishes.   7. Siganid.
8, 9, and 10. Goat-fishes.

the members of the genus *Amphiprion* are particularly brilliant, the ground colour being red, chocolate, or orange, with broad cross-bands of pale creamy blue. When alarmed these little fishes will take shelter in holes in the coral, and some will even take refuge within the larger sea-anemones. This curious habit is perhaps for the mutual benefit of both animals, as the *Amphiprion* is said to attract the attention of some carnivorous fish, and to lure it within reach of the anemone's tentacles before darting into the interior; landlord and tenant then share the spoils.

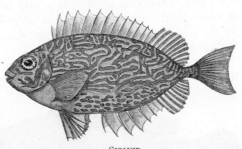

SIGANID

The Siganids are related to the Surgeon-fishes, but lack the spine on each side of the tail.

The Surgeon-fishes, or Tangs, derive their name from the presence of a sharp, knife-like, movable spine on either side of the tail. When at rest this spine is hidden in a sheath, but when turned outwards it forms an effective weapon as the fish lashes its tail. Many of them are small, brightly coloured fishes, inhabiting coral reefs, but some of the species grow to a large size and are valued as food. Like their relations the Siganids, they are mainly vegetarians, the small mouth being provided with a single row of cutting teeth.

The Carangids form a large family, which includes a number of diverse types of which we may select for mention the Horse Mackerel, Dolphin, Yellow-tail, and Pilot-fish. The Horse Mackerel, or Scad, a species which occurs on our own coasts, swims in large shoals at the surface of the sea, feeding on the fry of herrings, pilchards, and other fishes. Like nearly all the Carangids, which are essentially pelagic fishes, the Scad is bright silvery on the sides, with

PILOT-FISH

A Carangid fish known to the ancients as Pompilus or " Dolphin's Louse." It is a rare visitor to British waters.

metallic blue on the back, and it is specially characterised by having a row of keeled shields along the lateral line on each side of the body. The Dolphin is a large, swift, pelagic fish, growing to a length of six feet, and much valued as food. It pursues the shoals of flying fishes, who leap out of the water to escape its attentions. Its brilliant blue coloration, with golden reflections and deep blue spots, fades with great rapidity after death.

The deep head, with a sharp, almost vertical cutting edge in front, and the long body tapering behind, give the Dolphin a curious appearance.

The Yellow-tail is another large species, and is much sought after by sea anglers on account of its activity and sporting qualities. The Pilot-fish is of smaller size, blue in colour, with six dark bands across the body. It is widely distributed, and sometimes appears on our coasts in company with large sharks or ships. It is said to accompany sharks and pilot them to their food; in return for this service it enjoys the protection afforded by the close proximity of its formidable companions, as well as a share of their banquets.

We may briefly notice the Blue-fish, a near ally of the Carangids, a species which inhabits the warmer parts of the Atlantic. It reaches a weight of twelve to twenty pounds, has a strong mouth and sharp teeth, and enjoys the reputation of being the most voracious and destructive of all fishes. On the Atlantic coast of the United States it is regarded as a table-fish of high quality. Large shoals of Blue-fishes move about like a pack of hungry wolves, in pursuit of fishes which may be nearly as large as themselves, destroying anything before them and leaving behind them

CUCKOO WRASSE (Male and Female)
In many of these fishes the two sexes have a totally different coloration. This is a common British species frequently taken by sea-anglers.

a trail marked by blood and pieces of fish. They seem to be absolutely insatiable, the young decimating the shoals of fry, while their parents turn their attention to larger game. As an example of the damage wrought by these butchers, it has been estimated that the Blue-fishes inhabiting a stretch of the coast of New England alone destroy no fewer than 10,000,000,000 fish in a single day!

The Wrasses, another large and varied tribe, are not unlike the Sea Perches in general appearance. The small mouth, with thick lips, is armed with rather strong, conical teeth; the throat teeth are well developed, rounded or lozenge-shaped, those on the floor of the gullet being borne on a special triangular bony plate. This apparatus is designed to crush up the crabs, shellfish, etc., on which these fishes feed. Wrasses are found in all tropical seas, as well as in more temperate regions on both sides of the North

Atlantic, and about half a dozen species occur on our coasts. Most of them inhabit shallow water, living among rocks and weeds. Many of the tropical forms exhibit brilliant and specialised colour patterns, and, indeed, our own species are brightly liveried, especially at the breeding season. The two sexes are frequently quite different in colour, and unite in building a crude nest formed of seaweed and pieces of broken shell.

The Parrot-fishes have a truly remarkable dentition, rows and rows of small teeth being soldered together to form sharp-edged plates, a structure recalling the beak of a parrot. They are herbivorous fishes, biting off pieces of weed with their " beaks," and chewing them between the upper and lower plates of throat teeth, which form flat pavements. Many of the species attain a fair size and are valued as food. The *Scarus* of the Mediterranean was especially esteemed by the ancient Greeks and Romans for the delicacy of its flesh, and much was written about its habits by classical authors. Pliny describes it as the best of all fish : " *Nunc Scaro datus principatus.*"

JAWS OF A PARROT-FISH

The numerous teeth are soldered together to form sharp-edged plates.

The Perch, one of the best known and most handsome fishes of our own lakes and rivers, will serve as a typical example of the first of the three important freshwater families of Percoids. The Perch is a bold, predaceous fish, attaining a maximum weight of four or five pounds, and is found throughout the greater part of Europe and Asia. In America it is represented by a closely allied species, the Yellow Perch. In the spring shoals of Perch migrate to the reedy shallows, in which they breed ; the eggs are joined together by membrane, and are laid in long strings or ribbons, which float in the water with one end attached to

COMMON PERCH

This is mainly a freshwater fish, but sometimes occurs in brackish waters, as in the Baltic.

a water-plant. This family also includes the little Pope, or Ruffe, the *bête noire* of the English angler ; the graceful little Darters of the rivers of the United States, many of which are remarkable for their brilliant coloration ; and the larger Pike Perches, some of which attain

Q

a length of four feet, active predaceous fishes with pike-like heads and strong teeth.

The family of Centrarchids includes about thirty species of freshwater fishes from North America. The Small-mouthed Black Bass is a celebrated sporting fish, and, with its cousin the Large-mouthed Black Bass, has been introduced with fair success into some of our English rivers. They feed on fishes of all kinds, and will also devour frogs, snakes, and even rats. The Sun-fishes are smaller, generally deeper-bodied forms, whose pretty colours and interesting breeding habits make them great favourites for the aquarium. The Common Sun-fish, or Pumpkinseed, and the Long-eared Sun-fish, are perhaps the best known ; the latter is so-named because the gill-cover is produced into a long, black skinny flap, with a deep blue or red border.

The last freshwater family is represented by the Cichlids, which replace the Perches in Africa and Central and South America. Nearly six hundred species are known, more than half of these being found in Africa. In Lake Tanganyika, for example, there are about one hundred different kinds which are found nowhere else, and the other great lakes all have their quota of peculiar forms. The Cichlids vary greatly in form and in dentition ;

CHROMID

A member of the freshwater family of Cichlids, which replace the Perches in Africa and in Central and South America. This family contains nearly 600 species.

some being vegetarians, others carnivorous. In some species the male develops a large hump on the head in the breeding season, which disappears afterwards. The eggs and fry are frequently cared for by the parents, the female often carrying them about in her mouth until they are hatched, and for some time afterwards. The Chromid of the Lake of Galilee is said to have formed part of the miraculous draught of fishes recorded in the Gospels, and a black spot on its side is said to commemorate the touch of St. Peter. The Brazilian Angel-fish, with its almost circular, strongly compressed body, is a familiar sight in aquaria. The body is crossed by several deep black bars, which harmonise with the stems of the reeds among which the fish rests suspended in the water.

We may now notice a comparatively small group of fishes which differ from the Percoids in having the pelvic fins far forward below the throat. The Weevers, of which two species are found in shallow water on the

British coasts, have the gill-cover armed with a strong spine which is grooved for the passage of a virulent poison ; the stout spines of the dorsal fin are grooved for the same purpose. Their habit of resting almost completely buried in the sand, while lying in wait for the small fishes and shrimps on which they feed, render these fishes liable to be stepped upon by unwary bathers, with painful and occasionally even dangerous results. When disturbed they will actively manoeuvre the head in order to bring the spine into play, and they are a great nuisance to shrimpers, who fre-quently catch them in their nets. The Star-gazers, so named because the eyes are placed on top of the head and directed upwards, also habitually bury them-selves in sand, and resort to stealth to obtain a meal. One species is said to protrude a little red filament from its mouth, and to wriggle this about just like a tiny worm, thus luring inquisitive little fishes to destruction.

MALE DRAGONET

The differences between the sexes in these fishes is very pronounced, and an elaborate courtship is indulged in prior to mating.

The Dragonets, with one common, and another rarer, British species, are chiefly remarkable for the extraordinary differences exhibited by the two sexes. The male is generally much more brightly coloured, and has larger fins. His colours are accentuated in the breeding season, when the suitor is " showing off " before the lady of his choice, and a most elaborate courtship is indulged in before pairing takes place. Unlike most other fishes with courting habits, the Dragonets take no heed or care of the eggs once they are laid, and simply leave them to float about in the sea.

Sub-orders STROMATEOIDEA AND ANABANTOIDEA
(Stromateoids and Labyrinthic Fishes)

The fifty odd species comprising the sub-order of Stromateoids all agree in having a small mouth, with a single row of feeble teeth, and a pouch-like gullet with thick muscular walls covered on the inside with little horny teeth. They feed on crustaceans, little medusae, and the fry of other fish, and are found in the open sea, some living at the surface, others at considerable depths. Some of the species have a wide distribution, and the Black-fish and two species of Rudder-fish occur at rare intervals on the British coast. The Rudder-fish has the curious habit of following any floating object such as a spar, log, or barrel, for the sake of the barnacles and other creatures adherent to wreckage of this sort.   The young of many Stromateoids habitually shelter under jelly-fishes, whose stinging tentacles serve to protect them from other fishes.   These little fishes often enjoy complete immunity themselves, although fishes of other kinds are often caught and eaten.   The Butter-fishes, found on both coasts of North America, and the Trevally of Australia and New Zealand, are food-fishes of excellent flavour.

The Labyrinthic Fishes derive their name from the possession of a special accessory breathing organ, more or less rosette-like in form, which lies in a special chamber above the gills.   This organ, which reaches its highest development in the Climbing Perch, enables these fishes to live out of water for comparatively lengthy periods.   They are all confined to the fresh waters of tropical Asia and Africa.   The Climbing Perch is not only able to leave the water and to crawl about on land, but can ascend low trees, the means of locomotion being supplied by the spines on the edges of the gill-covers, aided by the anal spines.   This fish is valued by the natives as food, and the ease with which it can be carried in jars without water makes it a simple matter to ensure a constant supply of fresh fish.

The Gourami, reaching a weight of more than twenty pounds, is also valued for the table, and has been successfully introduced by the French into several of their tropical colonies.   Though largely a vegetarian, it will also take flesh, fish, frogs, insects, or worms.   The much smaller Paradise-fish is renowned for the beauty of its form and coloration, and breeds freely in captivity.   Its interesting nesting habits make it a popular favourite for the aquarium.   The Fighting-fish of Siam, scarcely four inches in length, is another beautiful species.   The males have larger fins and brighter liveries than the females, and indulge in extensive displays and elaborate courtship, not unmixed with a certain amount of bullying, when selecting a mate.   The fierce fights which take place between the males in the breeding season have led to these fishes being cultivated by the Siamese and Malays, who match the fish against each other, like fighting cocks, and stake large sums of money on the result of the combat.

The Snake-heads, carnivorous fishes of Africa and Southern Asia, have a comparatively simple type of breathing organ, but are able, nevertheless, to migrate overland by means of wriggling movements, aided by the pectoral and caudal fins.   During prolonged droughts they will burrow deeply into the mud, and remain in a torpid condition until the rain once more fills the ponds and streams.

Sub-orders *MUGILOIDEA AND POLYNEMOIDEA*
(*Mugiloids and Thread-fins*)

The Grey Mullets, Atherines, and Barracudas, comprise the sub-order of Mugiloids, differing from the Percoids in having the pelvic fins

situated well behind the pectorals.   The Grey Mullets, quite unrelated
to the Red Mullets already mentioned, are stoutly built fishes with
blunt heads, bluish silvery in colour, often with dark stripes along the
rows of scales.   The mouth is feeble, and the teeth are represented merely
by a fringe of bristles.   They are found in all tropical and temperate seas,
three species occur-
ring on our own
coasts, and frequent
shallow bays and
estuaries, sometimes
entering fresh water.
Their food consists
almost entirely of the
decomposed animal
and vegetable matter
contained in the mud.

SPOTTED GREY MULLET

The food of these fishes consists largely of decomposed animal and vegetable
matter contained in mud.   The species figured occurs in Indian seas.

Most of the Grey Mullets grow to a foot or two in length, and all are
good eating.

The Atherines, known also as Sand Smelts, or Silversides, are for the
most part small, slender fishes, bluish in colour, with a broad silvery
band or " stole " along the side.   Carnivorous fishes in their diet, they
frequent inlets and mouths of
rivers, and frequently enter fresh
water.   In such countries as
Madagascar, Australia, New
Guinea, and Mexico, where true
freshwater fishes are scarce, we
find a number of peculiar species
of Atherines which have established themselves permanently in
rivers and lakes.   The " Pescados
blancos " of the Valley of Mexico
grow to a length of fifteen inches,
and are the most important food-
fishes of the markets of that
region.

JAWS OF THE BARRACUDA

These ferocious fishes, which may grow to a large size, do
not hesitate to attack bathers and may inflict dangerous,
if not fatal, wounds.

The Barracudas are found in
all warm seas, where they feed
voraciously on fishes of all kinds.   They are long, slender fishes, rapid swimmers, with pike-like heads and strong jaws, armed with long, sharp-edged
teeth.   Some of the species attain a length of eight feet, and are renowned for
their extreme boldness and ferocity, a fact which makes them more feared
than sharks in some countries.   They will not hesitate to attack bathers,
frequently with dangerous or even fatal results.   Their flesh is delicate

and well flavoured, but is reported to be poisonous in the case of certain species, at least at some seasons.

THREAD-FIN

The Thread-fins are most nearly related to the Grey Mullets.

The Thread-fins (Polynemoidea), so named because the lower rays of the pectoral fins are drawn out into long filaments which act as feelers, have a blunt snout projecting beyond the mouth, which is provided with small teeth. Some of the species grow to a large size, and are of considerable economic value; the flesh is valued as food, and the air-bladder, or "sound," as it is called in the trade, provides a good isinglass.

Sub-orders TRICHIUROIDEA AND SCOMBROIDEA
(*Trichiuroids and Scombroids*)

The Trichiuroids (" Hair-tails ") are all more or less elongate in form, with the body generally strongly compressed, the snout beak-like, and the large mouth armed with formidable, sharp-edged teeth. They are active and voracious fishes, living for the most part in the open seas ; the surface swimmers are silvery in colour, while those living in comparatively deep water are violet-brown or black. In the Scabbard-fishes and Cutlass-fishes the caudal fin, although sometimes reduced in size, is normal and forked, but in the true Hair-tails, very long silvery fishes of tropical seas, this fin is altogether wanting and the tail tapers to a fine point. The Scabbard-fish is said to be extremely susceptible to cold, and in New Zealand, where it is known as the " Frost-fish," hundreds of individuals sometimes drift ashore on cold nights apparently in a state of temporary coma.

The famous South African Snoek, known in Australia as Barracouta, and the prickly Escolar, or Ruvetto, of the Atlantic, are important food-fishes, being caught on hook and line. The Snoek reaches a length of four feet, the Ruvetto being even larger. Finally, mention must be made of the truly remarkable " Great Swallower " of the depths of the Atlantic. This is a small black fish, with long, needle-like and depressible teeth, and an extremely distensible bag-like stomach, which enables it to " get outside " another fish many times its own size. This fish is perhaps more nearly related to some of the Percoids, but its true position has not been settled.

The Scombroids, readily recognised by the conical or much prolonged snout, and the deeply forked tail set on a narrow base, are essentially adapted for rapid movement. Nearly all are inhabitants of the open seas, and, as might be expected with such powerful swimmers, many of the species are very widely distributed. Our own Mackerel will serve as the type of a large tribe, which also includes the Tunnies, Albacores, Bonitos, etc. It is in the Mackerel that we find the ideal streamline form mentioned in our introduction realised almost to perfection, every line in the contour of this beautiful fish being suggestive of swift and easy motion. The head pointed like a bullet, with the two jaws fitting so closely together that it would be difficult to insert a knife-blade between them, the spindle-shaped body, tapering towards the tail and covered with small smooth scales offering practically no resistance to the water, are all features clearly designed for speed. The spinous dorsal fin, set in the middle of the back, can be received into a groove like the blade of a penknife, and the pectoral and pelvic fins can likewise be fitted into lateral depressions ; the slender part of the tail, carrying the powerful crescent-shaped caudal fin, gives this fin great freedom of movement. The spinous dorsal is followed by a series of finlets, each composed of a single branched ray, and acting as a tiny rudder with independent movements of its own. The shoals of

SHORT-FINNED TUNNY

A powerful and rapid swimmer. Note the strong crescent-shaped tail and the streamline form.

Mackerel swim at or near the surface of the sea, and feed on all kinds of shrimp-like creatures as well as on the fry of many other fishes. It is much valued as food, a grilled Mackerel being considered one of our great table delicacies ; as with all the members of this family, the flesh is rich and oily.

The Tunny, found all over the warmer seas of the world, reaches a length of ten feet, and a weight of fifteen hundred pounds. The extensive migrations undertaken by these fishes are as yet imperfectly understood, but are almost certainly dependent on the movements of the shoals of Mackerel, Pilchard, and other small fishes on which they feed. In the Mediterranean, where they appear in huge numbers in early summer, Tunnies are perhaps the most important food-fishes, and have been the object of extensive fisheries from time immemorial. They are canned in large quantities by the French and Italians, but were eaten fresh, or salted, by the ancient Greeks and Romans, portions of the flesh from the belly forming the *pièce de résistance* at many a classical feast. The Tunny is also a favourite with the anglers, the members of the world-famous " Tuna

Club " at Avalon, California, devoting themselves almost exclusively to catching this monster on rod and line.

The Sword-fish, the most rapid swimmer of all the fishes, is not unlike a gigantic Mackerel in which the snout has been drawn out to form a long, flat, sharp-edged sword.   It grows to a length of about twenty feet, and is reputed to use the sword, not only for splitting such large fishes as Bonitos, but also for striking with side-to-side movements among a shoal of smaller fishes, before feeding on the stunned and wounded victims.   There appears to be little authentic evidence of these habits, however, and some authorities are inclined to doubt whether the sword

SWORD-FISH
One of the swiftest oceanic fishes known.

really serves as an offensive weapon at all.   True, broken swords have been discovered from time to time embedded in the bottoms of ships, but whether as the result of premeditated attacks, similar to those which these fishes are said to make on whales, or to inadvertent collisions when travelling at high speed, it is impossible to say.   On the Atlantic coast of the United States there is an extensive Sword-fish fishery, individual specimens being chased and harpooned like whales.   The Spear-fishes and Sail-fishes differ in having a rounded spear instead of a sword.   When at rest, the huge dorsal fin of the Sail-fish projects from the water, but when under way this fin, as well as the long pelvics, is folded away into a deep groove in the body.

Sub-orders GOBIOIDEA AND BLENNIOIDEA
(*Gobies and their allies ; Blennioids*)

The Gobies and their allies, comprising the sub-order of Gobioids, are all carnivorous fishes of small or moderate size, the giants of the group reaching a length of two or three feet, while a species from the Philippines measures scarcely half an inch when full grown.   They are found in all tropical and temperate parts of the world, generally on the coast and nearly always in shallow water ; but they occur also in lakes, swamps, and rivers.

The Guavina of the rivers of Central America and the West Indies, a large species much valued as food, will serve as the type of a family in which the pelvic fins are placed close together, but remain quite separate. In the true Gobies these fins are united to form a disc, or cup, which serves as a sucker, and enables the fish to hold on to rocks and stones and thus withstand the motion of the waves. The species are excessively numerous and diverse, many having interesting habits in the breeding season, but space will permit mention of no more than two or three which present features of special interest. The White Goby, one of the several species common on our own coasts, differs from nearly all its relatives in swimming in the open sea; it is chiefly remarkable for the fact that its whole life's course is run in a single year. It is a small transparent fish, about two inches long, and is netted in huge numbers in the Mediterranean, and either fried like whitebait or stewed in milk.

The curious Mud-skipper of the coasts of tropical Africa, Asia, and Australia frequents mangrove swamps and mud-flats uncovered by the tide, where it may be observed scrambling about, or skipping over the mud in search of food. Correlated with this habit, we find that the pectoral fins are each attached to a sort of arm which can be moved backwards and forwards, the anal fin is low, and the lower rays of the caudal are thickened, whilst the eyes are placed close together on top of the head, and are capable of being turned in every direction. The Blind Goby of California lives fastened to the underside of rocks, or crawls about in the crevices, like a little slug. It is pale pink in colour, and is covered all over with a smooth, naked skin. In the young the eyes are small but functional, but the absence of light soon leads to their reduction, and they are represented by mere vestiges in the adult fish.

With the Blennioid Fishes, a large and varied sub-order, differing from the Percoids in having the pelvic fins, when present, placed close together below the throat, or even farther forward, and the soft rays of these fins reduced in number, we conclude our survey of the great order of Perch-like fishes. This group includes such diverse types as the Wolf-fishes, Blennies, Cusk Eels, Gunnels, and Brotulids.

The Wolf-fishes of northern seas are the giants of the sub-order, reaching a length of five feet, or more, and are remarkable for their powerful dentition. This consists of large conical teeth in the front of the mouth, and strong, crushing molars at the sides and on the middle of the roof; it is designed to bite and crush the shellfish, crustaceans, and other armoured creatures on which they feed. The Common Wolf-fish, or Sea Cat, is quite plentiful in deeper water round our own coasts, moving closer inshore during the breeding season, when these fishes become particularly pugnacious, and may make savage and unprovoked attacks on persons bathing or wading among the rocks. It provides excellent and nutritious food, although it is often despised on account of its unprepossessing appearance.

The Blennies, a large and varied tribe, which includes some five hundred species, are mostly small, active fishes, found near the coast in tropical and temperate seas, a few entering brackish, or even fresh water. Each of the jaws is provided with a single row of slender teeth set close together like the teeth of a comb, behind which there is usually a pair of long fang-like teeth. Blennies are generally found between tide-marks, sheltering among rocks and weeds, feeding on worms, molluscs, and various sorts of crustaceans. Several species occur in abundance on our own coasts, and form the best-known tenants of small rock-pools. The Shanny, reaching a length of about six inches, and remarkable for the variability of its coloration, is perhaps the commonest. This fish attaches its eggs to the roof of a crevice in the rock, and they are assiduously guarded by the pugnacious male. The handsome Butterfly Blenny has a skinny tassel above each eye, and the high dorsal fin is provided with a large black spot margined with white.

BUTTERFLY BLENNY
A British species distinguished by the large black spot margined with white on the dorsal fin.

The Rock-skippers, with tiny, movable teeth set loosely in the gums, are vegetarians. About one hundred species are known, from tropical parts of the world, all of them of rather small size, and many of them with bright liveries or distinctive markings. At low tide these active little fishes may be seen moving about on the shore, or skipping from rock to rock by means of a series of leaps produced by strokes of the tail. In many respects they recall the Mud-skippers, but their pectoral fins are not constructed to enable them to move about on land. The Gunnel, or Butter-fish, of our own shores, will serve as an example of a family found only in Arctic and northern seas. This is a longish, flattened fish, about ten inches in length, and yellowish-brown in colour, with a row of eye-spots along the back. The female, sometimes assisted by the male, deposits the eggs generally in a hole made by a boring mollusc, and then fashions them into a ball by coiling herself round them. The Viviparous Blenny, or Eel Pout, as its name implies, brings forth its young alive, the little fishes being about two inches long when they are born. It is eel-like in form, and reaches a length of one or two feet ; it frequents bays and estuaries on the coast of Europe, from Scandinavia to the eastern end of the English Channel, living among rocks and stones.

The family of Brotulids includes a number of deep-sea forms, concerning the habits of which little is known. In certain underground caves and streams of Cuba are found a few degenerate relatives of the Brotulids, the only freshwater members of the family. Like other fishes which have been deprived of light, the eyes of the Cuban Blind-fishes are vestigial, but are well formed and movable in the young. The fish vary in colour from dark blue to pinkish white, and as a compensation for the loss of sight are provided with minute barbels on the head, which function as organs of sense, and perhaps aid them in securing the blind shrimps on which they are said to feed.

Finally, we may notice the little eel-like fishes without pelvic fins, belonging to a genus known as *Fierasfer*. They possess the curious habit of sheltering inside the bodies of the echinoderms known as Sea Cucumbers, popping in and out of their host at will. Sometimes the shells of mussels and oysters serve them as a temporary home, and cases are on record in which the intruder has come to a sad end, being imprisoned by the mollusc and permanently entombed in a layer of mother-of-pearl.

Order SCLEROPAREI
(*Mail-cheeked Fishes*)

The important order of Mail-cheeked Fishes includes a large assemblage of different forms, all of which agree in having a bony " stay," or backwardly directed process, running from one of the bones below the eye towards the gill-cover. They are mostly carnivorous, with pointed teeth, living for the most part in the sea and fairly close to the shore. The most primitive members of the order, the Rock Perches, or Scorpion-fishes, bear a strong resemblance to some of the Sea Perches, from which they have clearly been derived. The spines on the head are generally strongly developed, giving these fishes a formidable appearance. Another characteristic feature is the presence of little membranous processes all over the head and body. They provide an excellent example of what is known as mimetic resemblance, their form and coloration copying closely the rocks among which they live, while the little skinny flaps, gently waving about in the water, simulate weeds. One little fish of the genus *Minous* found in India is always clothed with a living colony of polyps. This association brings protection to the fish, and at the same time helps the polyps, which are carried about to fresh feeding-grounds.

Some of the Rock Perches reach a fair size, and are important food-fishes. A viviparous species, known as the Norway Haddock, is sometimes taken off our northern coasts. The striking Lion-fishes of the tropical Pacific possess very long, needle-like dorsal spines, relatively huge pectoral fins, and a banded, zebra-like coloration. These fishes, some of which grow to a foot in length, lurk in crevices in the rock, and are dreaded by fishermen on account of their poisonous spines. The Poison-fishes are still more monstrous, with large, ugly, and irregularly shaped heads, and with the dorsal spines transmitting a venom of a deadly nature. Most of them have a drab and uniform coloration, and when hiding in crevices in a reef can scarcely be distinguished from the rock itself. If the dorsal fin be cut off as soon as the fish is caught they provide quite good eating, and may often be seen in the markets of India and Japan.

The Gurnards have the head protected with strong bony plates, and may be readily recognised by the form of the pectoral fin, in which the three lowest rays are detached to form finger-like appendages. These are freely movable, and are used, not only for creeping about on the sea-bottom, but also for turning over the sand in search of food. Several species occur on our own coasts, most of them being valued as food. The closely related Sea Robins have the body enclosed in a complete coat of mail, and have two feelers attached to the pectoral fin instead of three.

The small, active Greenlings of the North Pacific, remarkable for the possession of several lateral lines on each side of the body; the curious Horse-fishes found only on the coasts of Chile, South Africa, and Australia, unique among fishes in being able to shed their skin and replace it by a new one; and the Flat-heads, a large and numerous tribe, many of the members of which grow to a considerable size and are valued for the table, are other interesting members of this order.

RED GURNARD

Note the form of the pectoral fin, in which the three lowest rays are detached and thickened, forming finger-like appendages used for walking about on the sea bottom.

The little Bullhead, or Miller's Thumb, so familiar an inhabitant of the rivers and streams of England and Wales, will serve as the type of the family of Bullheads or Sculpins, which includes a great variety of species found in northern seas, as well as a few which have established themselves in fresh water. This fish, which rarely exceeds a length of four inches, frequents sandy or gravelly shallows, and feeds mostly on small fishes and crustaceans. Its normal coloration is brownish or yellowish, spotted or marbled with brown or black, but it is able rapidly to change its colours to harmonise with the ground on which it is lying. The strong, sharp spines on the gill-covers and head, as well as those of the dorsal fin, provide an efficient protection against predaceous fishes and even birds. The Father-lasher, a well-known inhabitant of the rock-pools on our coasts, is a closely related species. The Armoured Bullheads, a family which includes the British species known as the Pogge, have the body enclosed in a series of bony plates.

The Lump-sucker is a plump, deep-bodied fish, with a thick skin studded with bony tubercles of varying sizes, and with the pelvic fins joined together to form a sucking disc, which is used for clinging to rocks and stones.

The common species, sometimes known by the curious name of " Cock and Hen Paddle," is found on both sides of the Atlantic, and is not rare on our own coasts. It may reach a length of two feet and a weight of fifteen pounds, but such individuals are exceptional. The male, which assumes a particularly bright livery in the breeding season, mounts guard over the mass of reddish eggs, which are deposited in a cleft in the rocks. The Sea Snails, remarkable little fishes, not unlike tadpoles in general appearance, are closely related ; two species occur in British waters.

The Flying Gurnards, by no means closely related to the true Gurnards, have the pectoral fins greatly enlarged, and, like the Flying-fishes, are able to leave the water and glide through the air for some distance. They are frequently brilliantly coloured, the " wings " being beautifully marked with black, red, and blue.

LUMP-SUCKER

The body is covered with bony tubercles, some of which are enlarged and form regular longitudinal series.

The Sticklebacks may be mentioned here, since most modern authorities regard them as being related to the Mail-cheeked fishes. They are found in the seas and fresh waters of the Arctic and temperate regions of the Northern Hemisphere, being widely distributed in Europe, Northern Asia, and North America. In spite of their insignificant size, these fishes are of great interest, not only because of their remarkable habits, but also on account of the extreme variability exhibited by individuals of the same species.

The ubiquitous little Three-spined Stickleback, or Tittlebat, the " Tiddler " of the juvenile angler with his bent pin, is too well known to

STICKLEBACKS (3-spined)

require description here. There are very few ponds, streams, or ditches in our islands which do not contain examples of this species, and they are equally at home in estuaries, or in the sea itself. It is of interest to note that individuals living in inland waters have the body nearly naked, the bony plates on the sides being reduced to a few lying behind the head, whereas marine forms are nearly always fully armoured. So different are the two types that they were originally regarded as distinct species.

Sticklebacks are renowned for their pugnacity and voracity, which is truly remarkable when we consider their small size. They feed on shrimps, insects, worms, etc., but are also especially destructive to the eggs and fry of other fishes, employing the greatest industry, sagacity, and greediness in seeking them out, and destroying them in huge numbers. In the breeding season the male assumes a special livery—the lower parts of the body turning to a brilliant red—and sets about the building of an elaborate nest, composed of sticks and weeds, cemented together by mucous threads secreted by his kidneys. The nest being completed, he then goes a-wooing and, having captivated the lady of his choice, leads her to his nest, where the eggs are deposited and fertilised. Among Sticklebacks morality appears to be of

STICKLEBACK (15-spined)

a lax order, for no sooner has the first love taken her departure than he introduces another to the nest, and so on, wife after wife, until it is filled with eggs. The father then mounts guard over the nest, defending it with untiring vigilance, not only until the eggs are hatched, but for a further period until the young are able to take care of themselves. The Ten-spined Stickleback is another British freshwater species, while the Fifteen-spined Stickleback, distinguished by the tube-like snout and large number of dorsal spines, is a form found exclusively in the sea.

Orders HYPOSTOMIDES AND DISCOCEPHALI
(*Dragon-fishes and Remoras*)

The Dragon-fishes, small, grotesque creatures found in tropical seas, are perhaps remotely related to the Mail-cheeked fishes, but their true position in the system is somewhat obscure. The body is enclosed in a kind of box, composed of a series of bony plates, and the large pectoral fins enable them to skim over the surface of the water like the true Fly-ing-fishes.

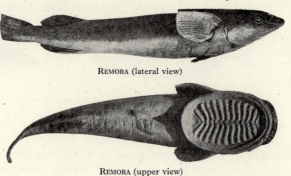

REMORA (lateral view)

REMORA (upper view)

The remarkable sucker on top of the head represents a modified dorsal fin, each of the lamellae being a fin-ray.

The Remoras, or Sucking-fishes, comprising the order Discocephali (" disc heads "), are distinguished by the presence of a flat, oval sucker, of complicated structure, situated on the broad and flat upper surface of the head. This curious apparatus is of great interest in itself, but its evolutionary history is even more remarkable, for we know that it is nothing more than a much modified dorsal fin. Each of the transverse plates with free hinder margins, with which the disc is provided, represents a fin-spine, which has been split into two and the halves bent outwards. These plates, or lamellae, are normally recumbent, but when the disc is applied to a flat surface they are slightly raised, thus creating a series of vacuum chambers.

All the Remoras are pelagic fishes, widely distributed in warm seas, the larger species reaching a length of three or four feet. They appear to be of a lazy nature, and habitually attach themselves by means of their suckers to the bodies of sharks, cetaceans, turtles, or even ships, thus obtaining a free ride to fresh feeding-grounds. Once among a shoal of small fish, they leave go and swim actively in pursuit of the prey, returning once more to their " anchorage " to complete the digestion of the meal. The natives of various countries make use of captive Remoras for catching turtles, dugongs, etc. Knowing that they will stick to the carapace of a turtle with extraordinary tenacity, they launch them into the water, held by a line attached to a metal ring round the tail, and as soon as the line is taut the fish can be drawn to the surface still firmly glued to the " catch."

Order HETEROSOMATA

(*Flat-fishes*)

There can be few fish with which we are more familiar than the Flat-fishes, an order which includes such important food-fishes as the Halibut, Plaice, Turbot, and Sole. Yet it is probable that comparatively few people have any conception of the evolutionary history of this remarkable group, or of the wonderful course of events which leads to what we may describe as the " flat-fish " shape. The members of this order differ from all other fishes in having both the eyes on the same side of the head, the two sides being generally referred to as the " eyed-side " and the " blind-side." Unlike the Rays, another group of fishes which have adapted themselves to a life on the sea bottom, the two sides of a flat-fish do not represent the dorsal and ventral aspects of the animal : that is to say, they

METAMORPHOSIS OF THE PLAICE

The young larva is quite symmetrical and swims at the surface, but the eye of the left side soon commences to move round the head to the opposite side, and the little fish sinks to the bottom.

are not the back and the belly, but the right and left sides. A flat-fish swims by means of undulating movements of the whole body, progressing by means of wave-like movements passing from the head to the tail, assisted by similar movements of the long, fringing dorsal and anal fins. It does not swim, as is often supposed, in a vertical position, but retains the same attitude that it holds when at rest on the sea-floor—the eyed, or coloured, side being uppermost.

It is a well-known fact that in many animals the various phases of development repeat, to some extent, the history of the race ; and the Flat-fishes provide us with an excellent example of this recapitulation, as it is called. When first hatched, the little fish is quite symmetrical, has an eye on either side of the head, and such pigment as is present is equally developed on both sides. It then swims at the surface of the sea, but after a time one eye moves round the top of the head on to the other side, the young fish sinks, and thereafter lies, or swims, at or near the bottom with the eyed-side uppermost. As growth proceeds the whole head becomes twisted and distorted, and the colour disappears entirely from the blind-side, except in certain individuals known as "ambicolorates," in which, for some unknown reason, the lower surface is partly or entirely pigmented like the upper side even in the adult.

Psettodes

A primitive Flat-fish from tropical seas. Note the upper eye on the top of the head, and the dorsal fin commencing well behind the eye.

On the coasts of West Africa, India, and China we find a primitive type of Flat-fish known as *Psettodes*, which will repay careful study. In general appearance, in the large mouth and strong teeth, and in the form of the paired fins, it bears a marked resemblance to some of the Sea Perches, and differs from all the other Flat-fishes in that the eye of the blind side comes to the top of the head only, while the dorsal fin does not extend forward on to the head. Moreover, the anterior part of this fin is formed of slender spines, and the pelvic fins each contain a spine and five soft-rays, just as in the Perch. *Psettodes* does not appear to have succeeded in making up its mind whether to have the eyes on the right or the left side, for, whereas in other Flat-fishes a species is definitely dextral or sinistral (with the exception of certain " reversed " examples in some species), in *Psettodes* we find that individuals with the eyes on one side are as common as those with eyes on the other. Some of the Sea Perches are known to have the habit of lying on their sides when at rest, and there is little doubt that the Flat-fishes originated from some Sea Perch which lengthened its resting periods, remaining on its side when waiting for its prey and then darting out in active pursuit, as does *Psettodes* to-day.

The coloured upper surface of a Flat-fish generally bears a marked resemblance to the ground on which it lies ; and these fishes possess a remarkable power of rapidly changing their colour to harmonise with the surroundings, the stimulus bringing about the change being received through the eyes. A Turbot, for example, is of a uniform brownish-grey when resting on sand, but quickly develops a series of yellow spots separated by a dark network if it moves on to a patch of gravel. A Mediterranean species was placed by a zoologist on a black-and-white background, resembling a chess-board, and the fish was induced to do its best to simulate this pattern. This it succeeded in doing remarkably well, although taking half an hour to change its colour instead of a second or two, the pattern being an unaccustomed one.

FLOUNDER

Unlike other British Flat-fishes, the Flounder enters rivers, and usually ascends as far as the first falls which bar its progress.

We may recognise two main groups of Flat-fishes, which may be roughly termed Flounders and Soles, and each of these sub-orders may be further

ZEBRA SOLE

An Indian species remarkable for its banded coloration. The dorsal, anal, and caudal fins are united to form one continuous fringing fin.

sub-divided into two families distinguished by the position of the eyes. In the Flounder group the Halibut, Plaice, Flounder, Dab, Lemon Sole (in no way related to the true Sole), and many other species, have the eyes on the right side ; while of the members of the sinistral family we may mention the Turbot, Brill, Megrim, and Scald-fish. The Halibut is the largest of all Flat-fishes, reaching a length of nine or ten feet, and a weight of four hundred pounds. The mouth is large, equally developed on both sides, and provided with strong teeth suited to a diet composed of other fishes. In the Plaice and its allies, less active fishes, living and feeding on the bottom instead of actively swimming in pursuit of prey, the mouth is smaller, the teeth being blunter and better developed on the blind side of the head. The Sole group, with rounded snout projecting above the mouth, and with small teeth confined almost exclusively to the blind side, is divided into two families : the true Soles, with the eyes on the right side, and the elongated Tongue Soles of tropical seas and estuaries, in which the eyes are on the opposite side.

Order PLECTOGNATHI

(*Trigger-fishes*, *Globe-fishes*, *Trunk-fishes*, *etc.*)

The Plectognathi ("joined jaws"), an order of fishes related to the Perches, but distinguished by a number of well-marked anatomical characters, includes a large assemblage of strange and diverse types. This is one of the few groups of fishes the members of which are not only of very little economic value, but are actually dangerous to eat. They have nearly all acquired a curious form of self-protection by the development of poisonous alkaloids in the flesh, which may produce a violent disease known as ciguatera, often terminating fatally in a short time.

The Three-spined Fishes, the most primitive members of the order, are

smallish species, silvery in colour, with bluish backs, inhabiting the Indo-Pacific region. They feed exclusively on shellfish, and each jaw is provided with two rows of teeth—strong incisor teeth outside, and blunt crushing teeth within. The Trigger-fishes have each of the jaws armed with eight powerful cutting teeth, and are also mollusc-eaters. They

TRIGGER-FISH

The species illustrated here is a rare visitor to our South-Western Coast.

do great damage to the pearl-fisheries, boring holes in the shells and eating the pearl-oysters. The spinous dorsal fin has a curious structure : there are three spines, the first being stout, and hollowed out behind to receive a bony knob at the base of the second, which is much smaller ; this mechanism keeps the first spine immovably erect unless the second one is pressed down like the trigger of a gun. About fifty species are known from warm seas, one occurring occasionally on our southern coast. Many of them are very brightly coloured, and among those inhabiting the neighbourhood of coral reefs we find species with most fantastic and often bizarre markings.

The File-fishes, or Leather-jackets, are closely related, but, instead of having the body armed with large rough scales, have the skin covered with little spines set so close together that they give it the appearance of velvet. The single dorsal spine is frequently provided with rows of barbs, and forms a most effective weapon. They are generally of smaller size than the Trigger-fishes, and are usually more or less soberly coloured. They frequent rocks and reefs, in fairly shallow water, living for the most part on a herbivorous diet.

The grotesque Trunk-fishes provide a good example of animals which have sacrificed swimming power, and rapid mobility, for heavy armour. The head and body are enclosed in a hard box, formed by the union of hexagonal, bony plates, only the

TRUNK-FISH

A common species from the tropical Indo-Pacific region.

small mouth, fins, and tail projecting, or being capable of movement. The box may be three-, four-, or five-sided, and is often armed with spines. One species, known as the Cow-fish, or Cuckold, has a pair of strong spines projecting forward from the forehead like horns. About twenty species occur in tropical seas, ranging in size from about four inches to a little more than a foot.

In the Globe-fishes, or Puffers, the teeth are united to form strong, sharp-edged plates, one on either side in both jaws, the whole biting apparatus recalling the beak of a parrot. As in the Trunk-fishes, the spinous dorsal and the pelvic fins have completely disap-

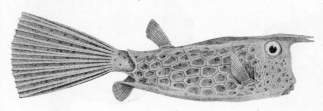

HORNED TRUNK-FISH

An Indian species with a pair of horns projecting from the forehead.

peared, while the soft dorsal and anal are short and feeble. These fishes derive their name from their habit of swallowing either air or water until the body is blown out like a balloon ; when thus inflated the little spines with which the skin is covered stand erect, giving the fish an alarming appearance, and one calculated to scare off any advancing enemy. When removed from the water a Puffer will generally swell up immediately, but the process can be hastened by a gentle tickling. Many species are found in the warm seas of the world, and a few have established themselves in rivers in tropical countries. Those which swim freely in the open sea seem to have a silvery

coloration, with greenish or bluish black, but the remainder are variously striped, spotted, or marbled to harmonise with the rocks, corals, and weeds among which they live. The Porcupine- or Burr-fishes with similar habits are closely related, but the spines in the skin are fewer in number and very much stronger, as a general rule, while the stouter tooth-plates are well suited to crushing the corals and shellfish on which they feed.

PUFFER or GLOBE-FISH

The Puffers are capable of inflating themselves with air, a protective device intended to scare away any enemies.

The Sun-fishes, not to be confused with the little freshwater fishes of North America which bear the same name, are huge oceanic fishes, of wide distribution in tropical and temperate seas. The Round-tailed Sun-fish, perhaps the commonest species, has a truly extraordinary shape, the deep and oval body being extremely abbreviated behind, so that the

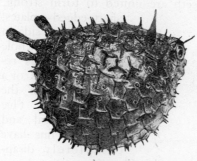

PORCUPINE-FISH

When inflated and almost circular in form these fishes will float passively near the surface of the sea. The roots of the spines spread out and are in contact with one another, forming a more or less complete coat of mail.

SUN-FISH

Note the short and high dorsal and anal fins and the abbreviated tail with its somewhat wavy caudal fin.

dorsal, anal, and caudal fins have the appearance of being attached to the posterior end *of the head!* The dorsal and anal fins are very high, and immediately behind them the curious rounded tail-fin, with wavy outline, fringes the hinder end of the body. This remarkable modification is very difficult to explain, but is probably connected with the peculiar diving habits of the creature. This species, which may weigh more than a ton when fully grown, is fairly common in the Atlantic, and is a frequent visitor to our coasts in the summer months. It is generally observed basking at the surface of the sea, but fishes taken from the stomachs of captured Sun-fishes show that they sometimes descend to considerable depths. The Oblong Sun-fish is a much smaller species, rarely exceeding a length of two feet. Sun-fishes undergo remarkable changes during growth, and the young are so different from the adults that they have been described as distinct genera.

Orders Xenopterygii, Opisthomi, and Symbranchii
(*Cling-fishes, Spiny Eels, Symbranchoid Eels*)

We now come to three comparatively small orders of fishes, which, although of some importance to the student, present few points of interest to the general reader, and may, therefore, briefly be dismissed. The Cling-fishes are curious little creatures, rarely exceeding a length of three inches, and usually of a bright red colour. The lower surface of the body is quite flat, and is provided with a sucking disc of complicated structure, formed in part by the pelvic fins. These fishes are nearly always found between tide-marks, clinging to loose stones or shells, and feeding on small crustaceans, worms, etc. Three or four species occur on our shores. The carnivorous Spiny Eels, of rather small size and no economic importance, inhabit the fresh waters of Southern Asia and Africa. They have a more or less eel-shaped body, but seem to be actually related to the perches. Some of the species are fairly common, but little is known of their habits.

The so-called Symbranchoid Eels, although they are eel-like in form and general appearance, have nothing in common with that group of fishes, and have probably been derived from the Blennioids. Few species are known, all that have been found occurring in rivers and swamps of tropical Asia, Australia, and Tasmania, and in Central and South America. The famous Cuchia of India is remarkable for the possession of a pair of special lung-like accessory breathing organs, which enable it to live for lengthy periods away from water, the fish frequently being found coiled up in the grass at the edge of a pond after the manner of a snake.

Orders Haplodoci and Pediculati
(*Toad-fishes and Angler-fishes*)

The Toad-fishes, now recognised as constituting a distinct order, have a broad, flattened head, and an elongate body, which is either naked or covered with small scales. The comparatively small number of species are all inhabitants of tropical and temperate seas, the majority occurring on the coasts of America. They live for the most part among rocks and weeds in comparatively shallow water, where their mottled coloration tends to render them inconspicuous to their prey, which consists of small fishes, molluscs, and crustaceans. They will lie patiently waiting for a meal for hours on end, but display remarkable activity when a shoal of small fishes approaches, and their voracity is very great. They possess a reputation for producing musical sounds, made entirely by the vibration of the air-bladder, and a Californian species, appropriately named the Singing-fish, is particularly gifted in this respect. The Poison Toad-fishes of tropical

ANGLER or FISHING FROG

The first ray of the dorsal fin is modified to form a lure, which is used to attract smaller fishes within reach of the Angler's jaws.

America have the spines of the dorsal fin and of the gill-cover hollowed to transmit a virulent venom, which is contained in an elaborate series of little poison-bags connected with the spines by ducts.

The curious and interesting Angler-fishes constitute the last order of Neopterygian fishes. They form a large and varied group, distinguished from all other fishes in having the first ray of the dorsal fin placed on top of the head and modified to function as a line and bait. In other characters they are not unlike the Toad-fishes, to which they are clearly related. The first sub-order includes all those Angler-fishes which live on the bottom of the sea in shallow or moderately deep water, and whose coloration is of mottled variety, and generally bears a marked resemblance to the ground on which they lurk, or the rocks and weeds among which

they lie. Thus concealed, they " angle " for their prey by waving the
" line and bait " in the water, attracting the attention of some unlucky
little fish,. and luring it to destruction. The line, which is nothing more
than the drawn-out first dorsal ray, varies considerably in length, and the
bait is generally represented by a
skinny flap or tassel.

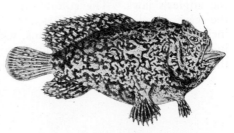

The Angler, or Fishing Frog, of
the North Atlantic, has a huge,
flattened head, and a colossal mouth,
armed with rows of sharp teeth,
which may be readily depressed
inwards and thus facilitate the entrance of the victim ; once erected
again, however, they effectively bar
any chance of escape. This ugly-
looking creature, which grows to a

FROG-FISH
Note the frog-like mouth and the short line and bait.
(After Cuvier and Valenciennes.)

length of five feet or more, feeds gluttonously on fishes of all kinds, which
it attracts within reach of its jaws by means of the line and bait. Lying
motionless on the bottom, in comparatively shallow water, and generally
among rocks and weeds, the Angler looks for all the world like a weed-
covered rock, a deception which is made more complete by the presence
of little skinny flaps which cover the skin and fringe the mouth. At times,
when this patient angling
appears to be devoid of
results, the Angler will go
in active search of a meal,
and not infrequently rises
from below to seize and
devour water-birds swim-
ming at the surface of the
sea.

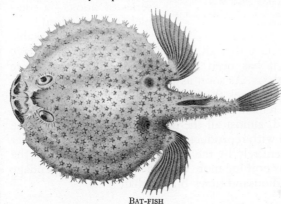

The smaller Frog-fishes
and Sea Toads differ in
having the body com-
pressed instead of flattened,
and the smaller mouth is

BAT-FISH
The muscular limb-like pectoral and pelvic fins are used for creeping
about on the sea bottom. (After Richardson.)

oblique, or nearly vertical.
Many species are known,
those inhabiting coral reefs being brightly coloured and handsomely marked.
The truly grotesque Bat-fishes, with relatively tiny mouth and greatly
reduced line and bait, have the body flattened and covered all over with
bony warts. They creep about on the sea floor, using the pelvic fins (which
are in advance of the pectorals) as fore-legs, and the arm-like pectoral fins
themselves as hind-limbs.

The Ceratioids, forming another sub-order, inhabit the open ocean, at depths ranging from 250 to 1000 fathoms. In this region of total darkness the bait has become a luminous bulb, often of a complicated structure, used as a gleaming lure to attract little fishes within reach of the angler's jaws. The coloration of most of the species, as is usually the case in deep-water fishes, is uniformly blackish. The sub-order includes about fifty different forms, which exhibit great diversity, not only in the form of the body, but in the size and shape of the mouth, and in the structure of the lure. The luminous bulb is placed directly on the head itself in some species, while in others it is at the end of a line which is several times as long as the fish itself. In one remarkable species, of which only a single specimen has ever been caught, the flexible line is placed at the end of a stiff, bony rod, and is itself produced beyond the bait and ends in a series of hooks—a complete angler indeed!

FEMALE CERATIOID ANGLER-FISH (with attached Male)
The specimen illustrated was more than three feet in length and the male about four inches.

The most remarkable feature of these fishes is the fact that all free-swimming individuals have proved to be females, and it has been shown that the males are mere dwarfs, parasitic on the females. As soon as they are hatched, the males, at that time relatively numerous, seek the females and, seizing hold of them by any part of their bodies, remain attached for life. The mouth, jaws, teeth, fins, and gills—indeed, almost all the organs of the male with the exception of those connected with reproduction—degenerate, and thereafter the little fish is nourished entirely by the blood of his spouse after the manner of an embryo. He is nothing more than an insignificant appendage of the female, who may be a thousand times bigger than he is.

Sub-class CROSSOPTERYGII
(Lung-fishes and their allies)

Returning to the branch marked A at the extreme base of the tree, we may conclude our survey of the great class of Bony Fishes by a brief account of the sub-class known by the scientific name of Crossopterygii (" fringe-fins "). The most primitive members of this ancient group flourished in the Devonian and Carboniferous epochs of the geologist, but have left no living representatives. These early forms seem to have afterwards diverged along three main lines, as indicated in the tree. One of these died out in Cretaceous times, and need not concern us here; the second led to the Lung-fishes, of which a few survivors remain alive to-day; while the last gave rise to creatures which were progressively less and less truly aquatic, or dependent on their gills for breathing purposes, and eventually became the first of the Amphibians, the vanguard of that great army of marine creatures which later conquered the dry land and spread over the earth's surface.

Space will not permit us to discuss in detail this wonderful transformation of a truly aquatic fish into an air-breathing, four-footed land vertebrate; it must suffice to point out that a study of the Lung-fishes surviving to-day gives us some idea as to how this transformation may have taken place in the course of countless generations, as well as a clue to the type of environment which must have been necessary to bring about the change.

The Lung-fishes belong to an order known as Dipnoi, or Dipneusti (" double-breathers "), a name which refers to the fact that these fishes

AFRICAN MUD-FISH

The Mud-fishes include only three species, which have a wide distribution over the tropical parts of Africa. They are most often found in marshes in the neighbourhood of rivers, where, during the dry season, they remain dormant in the mud.

have adapted themselves to breathing atmospheric air by means of the air-bladder which has become a lung (in four of the five living species it is actually divided into two lobes), as well as air dissolved in water by means of gills. At times, owing to periods of drought or excessive foulness of the water, the " lung " entirely replaces the gills as a respiratory organ. The paired fins are lobate—that is, with a thick central part supported by a jointed axis; the scales are cycloid, and sometimes overlapping; and the dentition consists of large crushing plates, not unlike the tooth-plates of the Chimaeras. Judging by the fossil remains, these fishes seem to have been widely distributed at an early period of geological history; but to-day only five species remain, belonging to three well-marked genera. One of these occurs only in the freshwater portions of the Burnett and Mary Rivers of Queensland, Australia; another in the Amazon and its tributaries, and in the swamps of the Chaco country; while the last genus, with three species, is found in the rivers and swamps of tropical Africa.

The Barramundi, or Queensland Lung-fish, easily distinguished by its large scales and paddle-shaped paired fins, grows to a length of about four feet and is known to the local inhabitants as " Salmon." In spite of measures which have been taken to protect this zoological rarity, it seems to be in great danger of early extinction. The Barramundi has the habit of frequently rising to the surface and gulping air, and when the water becomes foul during the hot season the power of lung-breathing becomes a real asset to the fish. The Mud-fishes of Africa, and the *Lepidosiren* of South America, differ in having eel-like bodies covered with small scales embedded in the skin, and tapering, whip-like paired fins. The young of all these species breathe by means of feathery external gills, which are later replaced by the more adequately protected internal gills.

The Mud-fishes are remarkable for the manner in which they are able to survive a prolonged drought. When the dry season approaches, and the marshes commence to dry up, these fishes bury themselves in the mud, and a quantity of slime emitted from their bodies mixes with the mud to form hard cocoons in which they lie dormant until the next rains, breathing air through a narrow passage leading from the cocoon to the exterior. The American form also retires into the mud in times of drought, the mouth of its burrow being closed by a porous lid through which the air can filter. The male *Lepidosiren* develops in the breeding season a number of filaments, richly supplied with blood, which are connected with the pelvic fins ; the function of these appendages is not properly understood, but they probably serve as accessory breathing organs, enabling their possessor to remain near the eggs without rising to the surface.

SECTION XII

CLASS AMPHIBIA

By H. W. PARKER, B.A.

GENERAL CHARACTERISTICS

MANY creatures are equally at home in water or on land, and are consequently spoken of as amphibious. Crocodiles, otters, climbing perch, penguins, and frogs are all amphibious, but only the last-named are true Amphibians in the scientific sense of the word. One of the most obvious differences in the lives of these various animals is that the frog commences its life as a thoroughly aquatic tadpole, without legs or lungs, and breathing at first by means of gills, but subsequently undergoes a drastic change to become a four-legged, land-living animal breathing by lungs. This division of their lives into two phases is found in the great majority of the Amphibia, though some specialised forms have found it convenient to dispense with either one phase or the other. Other characters which distinguish this group of animals are cold blood, a naked skin without visible scales or other external covering, no true fins, no special membranes (amnion and allantois) round the developing embryo, and the skull articulated with the backbone by two knobs (condyles). No single one of these characters will at once distinguish an Amphibian, but the combination of all of them is quite definitive of the group.

Closely allied to the frogs and included with them in the Amphibia are the newts, a group of rare, worm-like, burrowing creatures, the Coecilians, and an extinct group known as Stegocephalians.

Order STEGOCEPHALIA

These animals (unfortunately they have no name in common speech) are known only from the fossil remains of their skeletons, which are found in the rocks of the Coal Age (Carboniferous and Permian) and from a few footprints in some still earlier rocks (Devonian). No other back-boned animals, except fish, are known from any rocks of this early period, and it thus seems fairly safe to assume that the Stegocephalians were the first back-boned animals which ever walked on the surface of the earth. They did not survive long, however, for in the strata above those of the Coal Measures their remains disappear entirely, their place being taken by reptiles which had begun to make their appearance, probably as an offshoot from the Stegocephalia themselves, late in the Carboniferous period.

It has been possible to recognise among the fossil remains at least two hundred different forms, which show considerable differences, but they are all of the same general type. The skull is triangular in outline when

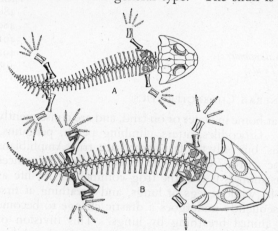

SKELETONS OF STEGOCEPHALIANS
A, *Protriton*; B, *Pelosaurus* (from Credner, enlarged).

seen from above, flat, and built up of massive, sculptured bones like those of a crocodile, and completely roofed in except for the openings for the nostrils, eyes, and the pineal eye. The latter was an unpaired eye-like structure on the top of the head, behind the paired eyes, and traces of it persist in many modern reptiles, though it is entirely absent in all present-day amphibians. The brain-cavity of the skull is small, but the mouth is huge and, as a rule, beset with numerous, simple, conical teeth, though in one group, *Labyrinthodontia*, as the name implies, each tooth has a complex pattern due to foldings of its crown. There is no definite neck, the limbs are short and weak, with four fingers and five toes which are generally without claws, the tail is short and tapering, and there are overlapping fish-like scales on the lower surfaces at least. The picture this description conjures up is that of a sluggish, not over-intelligent, crocodile-like beast. Associated with some of the skeletons, however, remains have been found of what appear to have been aquatic larvae, for they show distinct impressions of gills, though in general structure they are not at all fish-like. The inference, therefore, seems to be that the Stegocephalians started life as aquatic larvae, like the modern newts, and this feature would necessitate periodical visits to water for egg-laying and probably a normal existence not far from that element.

Such were the Stegocephalians, the ancestral stock from which have sprung the myriad vertebrate forms which have since peopled the earth.

Of their origin we know nothing, but it is only reasonable to search for it among their only back-boned predecessors, the fish. To make the transition from a life in water to one on land an animal would need to acquire two important features, a means of breathing air, and a new method of locomotion ; but both of these are at least foreshadowed in some fishes, to wit the Lung-fishes, which existed long before the Amphibia came into being. They can breathe air by means of a modified swim-bladder, serving as a lung, and the bones of the two pairs of rod-like fins, which correspond with the walking legs of a land animal, suggest the bony axis of a simple digit-bearing limb. On this foundation it is not difficult to imagine how, if the pools and swamps inhabited by a race of Lung-fish were very, very slowly dried up, such fins might gradually become transformed into limbs. As the animals became more and more terrestrial, they would lose the now useless gills.

Order APODA

(Coecilians)

To most people Coecilians are known, if at all, only by name, but to the naturalist they are creatures of supreme interest and mystery ; for not only are they rare, but their habits render observations of the living animal extraordinarily difficult. They are almost all burrowing creatures, superficially resembling large, bluey-grey earthworms. There are no limbs, or tail, the head is small and pointed, and the body cylindrical, with ring-like folds which give it the appearance of being divided into segments ; nevertheless they have a backbone and skull, a mouth beset with sharply pointed teeth, nostrils, sometimes a pair of tiny eyes hidden beneath the skin, and a small tentacle lying between the nostril and the eye.

The Coecilian *Ichthyophis* and its eggs, removed from an underground nest.

The whole organisation of these peculiar creatures bespeaks extreme specialisation to a burrowing existence, but there is little doubt that they are more closely related to the newts than to any other living animals. In only a few instances is anything of the life-history known, but in some, how-ever, we find that fundamental division of the life-cycle into two parts, one aquatic and one terrestrial, which characterises the Amphibia. In *Ichthyophis*, a common form in South-East Asia, the female constructs a burrow leading from a pond or stream to a small chamber, in which she lays her eggs, spherical, gelatinous, semi-transparent bodies strung together like beads on a rosary. Around these she coils herself for the purpose of protection, and in each egg there develops a tiny eel-like creature, with three pairs of feathery, blood-red gills on either side of the neck. These " external " gills are, however, lost before the eggs hatch. When this happens the little creatures take to the water, and breathe by means of " internal " gills, which lie in slits leading from the mouth, like those of a fish. After a free-swimming larval period lungs are developed, the gills are lost, and the little creatures enter upon a terrestrial existence like their parents. Though most Coecilians are burrowing creatures, living chiefly upon earthworms, a few in Brazil have returned to a life in the water. Some have the same developmental history as *Ichthyophis*, but a few pass through the entire larval stage within the egg, emerging as fully metamorphosed individuals like their parents ; in these cases the eggs may be laid, or they may be retained within the body of the mother until the young are ready to hatch.

Although so modified for a special type of life, Coecilians are in some ways more closely allied to the Stegocephalians than to any modern amphibian ; this is shown by peculiarities of the skull, which contains bones present in the Stegocephalians but lost in newts and frogs, and by the presence, in some species, of scales embedded in the skin, a character not found in the other living groups.

Order CAUDATA

(*Newts and Salamanders*)

There is no essential difference between these two terms, " salamander " being usually applied to the larger species and " newt " or " eft " to the smaller. The order to which they belong contains all the tailed amphibians,

CRESTED NEWT
Male (above) and female in nuptial dress.

and their appearance is sufficiently familiar to most people to make any introduction superfluous. Nevertheless we may briefly consider the Common Newt as an example of the general type of Caudate. It is a small lizard-like animal, barely three inches long, with short limbs, bearing four clawless fingers and five similar toes. The skin is perfectly smooth, and in colour is yellowish or olive above, with black spots, which, in females, may form a definite stripe along each side ; the lower surface is yellow, with an orange or vermilion stripe along the tail and some black spots, these being larger in males than in females. They spend the summer months in cool, damp localities, feeding on small insects, spiders, and so on, but towards autumn they withdraw into some hollow beneath a log or stone for hibernation. At the first call of spring they wake up and repair immediately to the water, the male having during the winter assumed his "nuptial dress," constituted by a high, festooned crest extending from the head along the back to the tip of the tail, and a blue, crimson-bordered stripe along the lower surface of the tail.

Thus gaily attired, the courtship begins. First he swims round in short, swift rushes looking for a mate, and, having found her, swims up to her until their noses are almost touching. There he remains quite motionless for a short time;
then, bending his tail forwards along his flank, he commences to lash himself, first on one side, then on the other. Suddenly he butts her violently, and if she, resentful, moves away, heads her off and again begins his gentle self-casti-gation. After a longer or shorter period of this amorous play the male deposits a sper-matophore, which the female picks up, and subsequently the eggs are laid, either singly or in bunches of two or three, attached to the leaves of water-plants whose edges are folded over and stuck to-

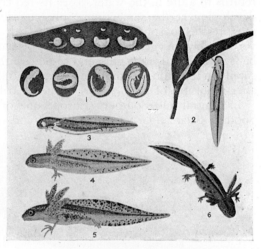

Stages in the development of a Newt.
(1 and 2 enlarged.)

gether by the gummy secretion which surrounds the eggs. About a fortnight later the young emerge as limbless, tadpole-like creatures, with three pairs of tufted external gills. They attach themselves to water-plants by means of a pair of thread-like projections from the upper jaw, and there remain for some days. Later they take up an active existence in the water, feeding on small crustaceans, insects, and other small organisms. Slowly limbs are developed, the fore-pair first; lungs also develop and late in the summer the larvae "metamorphose," losing their gills and the fin-like membrane of the tail, developing eyelids, and leaving the water.

Though this type of life-history is by no means of universal occurrence it is the common course in the more unspecialised families, such as the *Salamandridae*, which contains most of the European forms and some North American species.

Family Salamandridae

In addition to the Common Newt there are in Britain two others, the Crested Newt, a larger animal with a warty skin and a crest along the back throughout the year in the male, and the Palmate Newt, distinguishable by its smaller size and the presence of webbing between the digits at all seasons. Both these forms have life-histories similar to the Common Newt, but in North America the Red-eft (*Triturus viridescens*) often has a third stage in its life-history. The larvae are quite similar to those we have described, and these become transformed into a reddish-coloured terrestrial adult. After about a year's sojourn on land, however, this animal returns to a life in the water, loses its red colouring and becomes greenish, developing at the same time "pharyngeal respiration." All amphibians can breathe to some extent through their skin, but, unless the water is very highly oxygenated, this will not alone suffice. But the Red-eft, be it noted, has lost its gills, and to replace them has developed a rich blood supply in the lining-membrane of the mouth, so that, by taking in mouthful after mouthful of fresh water, oxygen can be absorbed by the blood.

In Central and Southern Europe one of the commonest species is the Spotted Salamander, a shiny, black-and-yellow-coloured animal, which

EUROPEAN SPOTTED SALAMANDER

reaches a length of about nine or ten inches and lives in cool, damp localities, feeding on small invertebrates. Its vivid pattern suggests a warning-coloration, and, indeed, this animal is poisonous, but only if eaten. The skin of all amphibians contains glands of two kinds, the one secreting mucus, which keeps the skin moist, but which is also slightly poisonous, and the other secreting a milky fluid which, if swallowed, produces violent vomiting and profuse salivation. In the Spotted Salamander the glands of the latter type are grouped together above each shoulder and produce a swelling, the so-called "parotoid" gland. In this species, too, there is some modification of the breeding habits, for pairing takes place on land, the males never entering the water, and the eggs are retained inside the body of the mother until they have hatched and limbs have been developed ; at this stage the larvae are born, the female, though a bad swimmer, entering the water for the purpose of parturition. After a free-swimming stage of about three months the larvae assume the adult form.

This process has been carried even farther in the Black Salamander, a species which inhabits the higher regions of the Alps, for here, although many eggs are formed, only two develop (the remainder breaking up to serve as food for the developing embryos), which actually complete their metamorphosis inside the parent's body, so that there is no free-swimming stage.

Another modification found in this family, and one of very common occurrence throughout the Caudates, is the reduction of lungs in forms which live in and about mountain brooks. In torrential streams lungs, which make the animal buoyant, would be a drawback, since they would increase the chances of it being carried away, and since the water is always very highly aerated the skin alone will suffice for respiration. Under these conditions lungs are greatly reduced in size and sometimes completely lost. The larvae, again, in this turbulent environment have to rely more on crawling than on swimming for locomotion, and consequently usually lose the fin-like crests of the tail. *Chioglossa*, in the mountains of the Iberian Peninsula, *Euproctus* in Corsica, Sardinia, and the Pyrenees, and *Salamandrina* in the Apennine Mountains, have all followed this evolutionary path.

Family Hynobiidae

The *Hynobiidae* are a family found in North-East China and Japan, and are very similar to the typical salamanders. *Hynobius*, the commonest form, has undergone some modification of its life-history, the eggs being laid in two, spindle-shaped, jelly-like sacs, whilst *Onychodactylus*, an inhabitant of the mountain streams of Japan, has followed the common road of such forms and, in addition, has developed claws on its fingers and toes, perhaps to give it a better grip for crawling against the rush of the water.

Family Ambystomidae

The *Ambystomidae* are a group of North American forms which are very similar in their general life-history to the Salamandrids. But one form, the Axolotl, has a remarkable history and is of the greatest interest. These animals, so familiar to aquarists, are large, black, blunt-headed creatures like giant larval newts, with great tufts of gills on each side of the head, and are only found in a wild state in some lakes near the City of Mexico. They never leave the water, but reach sexual maturity in their gilled state, producing larvae just like themselves, and for many years they were regarded as forming part of a separate group of newts, the Perennibranchiates, that is to say, "permanently gilled." But in 1864 a number were sent to the Zoological Gardens in Paris, where they bred for several generations. Suddenly, however, it was noticed that the young of one brood had *lost their gills* and the crest on the tail, had developed eyelids, and acquired a different coloration. They had, in fact, metamorphosed to the well-known North American "Tiger Salamander" (*Ambystoma tigrinum*)! It at once became clear that the Axolotls were merely a race of "permanent

R

larvae," though why such a race should have been evolved in just the one locality is still a mystery. Permanent or " neotenic " larvae occur also abnormally in some other groups of salamanders, and this strange phenomenon furnished an explanation of the true position of many other so-called " Perennibranchiates."

Family Plethodontidae

The *Plethodontidae*, chiefly North American salamanders, are all lungless, and though many are now dwellers in the lowlands and frequent sluggish rivers and ponds, it is believed that the whole group were originally dwellers in brawling mountain brooks, and that those which have changed their habitat were unable to redevelop their lost lungs.

The most remarkable form is a blind, colourless creature with spindly legs, which is only found in some underground streams in Texas. This animal, *Typhlomolge* by name, is, like the Axolotl, a neotenic-larva, but it has progressed farther and appears to have lost the ability to metamorphose. What its terrestrial stage would be like we cannot tell, but, from the larval organisation, it is believed that it would be some kind of Plethodont.

The breeding habits of members of this family show some modifications. The eggs, which are in strings, bunches, or single, may be laid on the banks

ITALIAN NEWT (*Hydromantes fuscus*) with the chamaeleon-like tongue extruded.

of streams or in water. In the latter instance the young which emerge are limbless " tadpoles," but if the eggs are laid on land development proceeds until the limbs are formed before the eggs hatch, and the larvae can wriggle into their proper element. In one or two cases the eggs are retained by the mother until the young have completed their metamorphosis. To this category belongs the little *Hydromantes fuscus* of the Maritime Alps and the mountains of Northern Italy. This newt, some three or four inches long, is a cave-dweller, which seeks its food climbing about the almost vertical rocks by which it is surrounded. It feeds on insects and small spiders, which are captured by means of an enormously extensible, chamaeleon-like tongue. When not in use this organ is mushroom-shaped, the " stalk " being composed of very elastic fibres which are kept in a state of compression. But when the restraint is removed, out shoots the heavy tip to a distance of fully an inch, about one-third the animal's entire length, and, as it is thickly coated with a sticky saliva, the prey adheres to its surface and is carried into the mouth.

The remaining Caudates are all of the " Perennibranchiate " type ; that is to say, they are permanent larvae which have entirely lost the power of transforming, but since they do not closely resemble the larvae of any of the known terrestrial forms, they are grouped into separate families. The Olm (*Proteus anguinus*), of the subterranean streams of Carniola, is one of these creatures, and, like most dwellers in a perpetual night, is blind and colourless. It has a flattened, wedge-shaped snout, weak limbs, with only three fingers and two toes, rudimentary eyes entirely under the skin, and three pairs of tufted, blood-red gills, con-trasting vividly with the dead-white of the rest of the body. The eggs are laid singly, attached to stones, and hatch out into miniature replicas of the parents. The food consists principally of freshwater shrimps.

THE OLM (*Proteus*).

Allied to the Olm is the " Mud Puppy," common in the rivers and ponds of eastern North America. This, however, is a more robust-looking animal, with strong five-fingered limbs, functional eyes, and a grey-brown, black - blotched coloration. Another North American form is the Mud-eel (*Siren*), found in the swamps and ditches of the southern United States. It is specially adapted to a life spent burrowing in mud and weeds, and has a long, eel-like body with only a single pair of very short limbs (the fore pair), three pairs of external gills, and both the upper and lower jaws covered by a horny, beak-like sheath.

THE MUD-EEL (*Siren*).

Similar in appearance to the Mud-eel is the Blind-eel (*Amphiuma*), an inhabitant of the Mississippi and its tributaries. This, however, has two pairs of limbs, though both are very short and only equipped with two or three fingers and toes. It is not quite so " larval " as some of the preceding animals, for the external gills are lost, while the internal gills are rudimentary, lungs being the principal organs of respiration. Similar to *Amphiuma* in this respect are the " Hell-bender " of the southern U.S.A., and the Giant Salamander (*Megalobatrachus*) of China and Japan. Both these, however, have well-developed limbs, and a typical salamandrine appearance.

The last-named is the largest living Caudate, a living specimen in Lord Rothschild's possession measuring about five feet in length.   In its native haunts it lives in holes in the rocks of mountain streams, and is much sought for as an article of food.   Perhaps the most interesting feature of its life-history is that it exhibits one of the earliest types of parental care for the young. The eggs, which are about as big as grapes and strung together like beads, are laid in cavities under stones.   After they

THE BLIND-EEL (*Amphiuma*).

have been laid the male drives away the mother and remains on guard until they hatch ; as, however, he eats large quantities both of eggs and young his " care " may not be so disinterested as would appear at first sight.

Order SALIENTIA

(*Frogs and Toads*)

This, the only remaining order of amphibians, is also numerically the largest, and though there is not such profound structural modification here as in the Caudates, there is, nevertheless, great adaptation to the widely different environmental conditions under which its members live. The terms " frog " and " toad " are not applicable to sharply defined groups of related forms ; but the former is usually applied to the slenderer, smooth-skinned species and the latter to those of squat appearance and warty skins.   They are all tailless, and the Common English Grass-frog may be taken as an example of the normal structure and commoner habits of the whole group.

Its most striking features, as compared with the newts, are the relatively short, stout body, very short neck, exceedingly long hind-limbs, and the absence of a tail; the snout is long and rather pointed, the eyes large and prominent, and just behind each of them is a sharply defined, circular patch of skin which indicates the position of the ear ; the fore-limbs are short, with only four fingers, of which the third is by far the longest, whilst the hind-legs are very long and powerful, with five long toes connected by webbing.   The skin is smooth and moist, and when closely examined will be seen to be covered with small pits, the openings of innumerable mucus and poison glands, such as we have already encountered in the salamanders.   The mouth is very large, with small closely set teeth in the upper jaw, and two small patches of teeth (the vomerine teeth) on the forward part of the palate, but, as in most of the group, the lower jaw is toothless. The tongue is large, covering almost the whole of the floor of the mouth, and attached *in front* only, so that the tip, which is deeply cleft, is turned towards the throat.

Throughout the summer the frog lives in damp, cool localities, usually among grass, through which it progresses normally by leaps. It feeds chiefly on flies, caterpillars, spiders, and earthworms, which are captured either by a quick snap of the mouth, or, if sufficiently small, by means of the tongue. This is accomplished by flicking the free end of the tongue forwards so that, hinging at its point of attachment, it describes a semi-circle, and the tips, folding over the unfortunate insect, help to hold it whilst the tongue is withdrawn. The food is never chewed, but swallowed whole by convulsive movements, during which the eyes are forced right down into the head, and if the prey is large and unwieldy, the hands are used in an almost human manner to assist in stuffing it into the mouth. Breathing is accomplished, not by movements of the ribs, as in most vertebrates, since these are absent, but by movements of the floor of the mouth whereby air is first drawn in through the nostrils and then, with the nostrils closed, forced into the lungs.

Towards the approach of winter the animals withdraw into the mud at the bottoms of ponds and ditches and there pass into a state of torpor or hibernation, remaining until the approach of spring. Then, earlier or later, according to the season or the latitude, they awake and immediately congregate in the water, the males developing a tendency to " sing." The sound, in this species a feeble " grouk-grouk," may be produced either in air or under water, the mechanism being the passage of air backwards and forwards over the vocal chords between the lungs and a pair of " vocal sacs," or pouches of the lining of the floor of the mouth on each side of the tongue. These sacs are visible externally when full of air, forming a pair of small, rounded swellings beneath the throat. After much fighting among the males for the possession of mates, the small black eggs, numbering perhaps four thousand in a clutch, are laid, each being surrounded by a thick layer of transparent protective jelly, and the whole mass floats on the surface of the water. The adults, after spawning, leave the water to resume their more or less terrestrial existence, and the males lose, to a greater or less extent, their disposition to croak.

After a period varying from a few days to a week, or more, according to the temperature of the water, the eggs hatch, the emerging, very imperfect, black tadpoles, which have tufted external gills, remaining quite passive in the water, crowded together, and attached by the tips of their snouts to any convenient object. A few days later the external gills are lost, their function being assumed by the internal, fish-like gills, which lie in slits connecting the mouth with the exterior. At this stage the head and body form one rounded mass propelled by a long tail. In the body may be seen a pair of eyes with a metallic sheen, a small mouth, and halfway up on the left-hand side of the head is a short, backwardly directed tube from which a constant stream of water emerges. This opening, the spiraculum, leads into a chamber lying beneath the fore-part of the body into which the gill-slits open, and the stream of water which emerges from it is the water taken in at the mouth and passed over the gills. The mouth is equipped with a pair of horny, beak-like jaws, used for cutting and biting, and the lips surrounding it are beset with regular rows of minute horny teeth whose function is to act like the teeth of a file in rasping away dead vegetable matter or the green slime which grows on stones.

Growth is rapid ; soon rudiments of hind-limbs appear, and shortly afterwards the tadpole will be seen to make periodical visits to the surface of the water, apparently to breathe ; the lungs are developing. Towards May or June the fore-limbs appear suddenly, the left first, thrust through the spiraculum, the right shortly afterwards breaking through the skin of the spiracular cavity in which they have hitherto been concealed. At this period feeding ceases, for the adult mouth is now developing within the larval one, and the horny jaws and teeth fall off. Slowly the animal begins to assume the familiar frog-like shape, and though to all intents and purposes it is fasting, nourishment is supplied by the now functionless tail. Before it is completely absorbed, however, the animal, now a miniature frog, leaves the water to begin its terrestrial career. Such, briefly, is the life-story of the Common Frog, and, with modifications in details only, the life-history of many of its allies.

The whole group is divided, roughly, into two great series ; one comprising those which, like the Common Frog, have the halves of the shoulder-girdle (the girdle of bones which serves for the articulation of the fore-limbs) fused together in the middle line in front ; the other, those which, like the Common Toad, have the two halves simply overlapping in front. These two types are again sub-divisible into groups of related forms, or families.

Family Ranidae (Frogs)

To the first group, *Firmisternia*, belong a number of forms related to the Common Frog of the family *Ranidae*, which are distributed through Europe, Asia, Africa, and North America. They show great diversity of habits and habitats ; some are entirely aquatic, others entirely terrestrial, not even going to the water to breed ; some live in the plains and breed in quiet waters, whilst others live among mountains and lay their eggs in rushing streams ; some are burrowers, and others tree-climbers. For each type of habitat there is modification in a definite direction which is not, as we shall see, characteristic of only this one group of frogs.

Terrestrial species with the common type of tadpole, adapted for life in quiet waters, are widely distributed. Among them we may mention the Edible Frog (*Rana esculenta*), common throughout Europe, and extending eastwards to China. It is a larger species than the Common Frog, and, apart from its edible qualities, chiefly remarkable for the vocal powers of the males. Here the vocal-sacs are greatly developed, and appear, when inflated, as two spherical bladders as big as marbles on each side of the neck. The voice, admirably rendered by Aristophanes in his famous chorus as "Brekeke-kex," when heard in concert, may be perfectly deafening. There are in Europe and North America a number of species similar in size and general appearance to our Common Frog; but there are some species which claim attention on account of their size. Of these we may mention the American Bull-frog (*R. cates-biana*), whose cry is playfully

EDIBLE FROG (*Rana esculenta*).
Male, with vocal sacs distended.

transliterated as "more rum, more rum"; the Indian Bull-frog (*R. tigrina*); and, largest of all frogs, the giant Goliath-frog (*R. goliath*) of the Cameroons, which is as big as a medium-sized terrier and can eat a full-grown rat.

Terrestrial species which breed in mountain torrents usually have a specialised type of tadpole, which does not hatch from the egg until it has reached a more advanced stage of development. Here the body is depressed, to enable it to wriggle beneath stones, and the tail is long and powerful, but with a much narrower membranous crest than in the familiar type already described. The more specialised species have even, like some fish in similar environments, developed suckers by which they can cling to rocks and stones in the face of the current. Of species with this type of tadpole we may mention the famous Hairy-frog (*Trichobatrachus*) from the Cameroons, which is remarkable as

THE HAIRY-FROG (*Trichobatrachus*).

the only amphibian with "hair." Structurally, however, this growth, which is profusely developed over the sides and the backs of the thighs of the male only, is not true hair, but simply elongate filaments of the skin, and, despite many suggestions, its function, if it has one, is still unknown.

Perhaps the most remarkable type of adaptation is found in the East Indian and Polynesian frogs *Cornufer*, and *Rana opisthodon* of the Solomon Islands. These animals, in accordance with their strictly terrestrial life, have the webbing between the toes greatly reduced, and, to avoid the necessity of returning to the water for breeding, the eggs are very large and provided with a very tough shell, within which the tadpole completes its development; that is to say, the tadpole stage is passed within the eggs, so that there emerges therefrom, not a larva, but a fully developed froglet.

Burrowing forms are not numerous in this family, but the general trend of modification for this type of existence, a stout body and short, powerful hind-limbs equipped with a large " shovel " on the heel, is shown by such forms as the African *Rana delalandii*. Thoroughly aquatic forms, such as *Rana hexadactyla* and *Oxyglossus*, have depressed bodies, long, fully-webbed toes, and, as a rule, a much-reduced tongue. Arboreal species, however, such as the various forms of *Rhacophorus* in the Indo-Malayan region and *Chiromantis* in Africa, are of the ordinary slim, long-legged terrestrial type, but the tips of the fingers and toes are dilated to form large discs. These, being kept permanently moist, adhere, after the manner of a schoolboy's sucker, when they are pressed against any smooth surface, and so enable the frogs to climb vertical trunks with ease.

Many of these arboreal species have also a peculiar breeding habit. Whilst the eggs are being laid, an act which does not take place in water but close to its edge, or on a branch overhanging it, the female paddles the jelly-like mass into a froth by movements of the hind-limbs, and the outside of this frothy mass soon hardens to form a meringue-like crust; inside this " nest " the eggs develop, but as they do so, the jelly inside liquefies, and slowly dissolves away the outer crust, so that the tadpoles when released either slide or are precipitated into the water. One of these arboreal frogs, *Rhacophorus pardalis*, of the Malayan region, is famous as Wallace's Flying-frog. The great naturalist assured us that this species, by spreading out its fully webbed hands and feet to act as planes, could glide from a tree to the ground; unfortunately, in working out the area exposed by the spread-out hands and feet he made a very serious error and, when this was detected, the story was rather discredited. But within the last year or two it has been shown, experimentally, that various other tree-frogs, with much less fully webbed hands and feet than Wallace's frog, can fall from considerable heights and land in safety on their feet.

Family Brevicipitidae (*Pug-toads*)

This family is closely allied to the preceding, but its members are more restricted in their distribution, being confined to the three great southerly directed land masses of the globe, and are not adapted to so many different types of habitat. There are no truly arboreal, aquatic or torrential stream dwellers, and the typical members, from which the family takes its name, are burrowing forms which have become specialised for feeding on white ants. The huge colonies of these insects which abound in tropical countries have attracted the attention of many widely different groups of animals besides frogs, and all these have, in various ways, become specialised for this type of diet only. The Pug-toads, which have become ant-eaters, have all undergone precisely similar changes, so

SIAMESE PUG-TOAD (*Glyphoglossus*).

that, among others, *Glyphoglossus* of Siam, *Rhombophryne* of Madagascar, and *Breviceps* of Africa have acquired a superficial similarity. They are obese-looking creatures, with small heads, tiny eyes, a narrow mouth and long tongue, weak fore-limbs, and powerful digging-shovels on their heels. They burrow into ants' nests, and, ensconced in some hole near a gallery along which the ants pass and re-pass, lead what has been aptly described as a " colourless if gastronomically satisfying existence."

SOUTH AFRICAN PUG-TOAD (*Breviceps gibbosus*).

Embryo of Papuan Toad, removed from its egg-membranes to show the respiratory tail.

Other members of the family are more frog-like in appearance and habits, but the tadpoles all lack the horny beak and teeth common in the other families. Some species of the Malayan genus *Microhyla*, however, have the mouth produced into a large membranous funnel by means of which they are able to suck in the accumulations of animal and vegetable detritus which float close to the surface film of the water. Others, particularly in New Guinea, have succeeded in escaping from the necessity of going to the water to breed by laying a few large eggs. The increased amount of yolk thus gained enables the tadpole to undergo its whole development within the egg. Although during this development the tadpole is not active it must breathe, and gills of the ordinary type would be of little use in such a situation ; their function, however, is taken over by the tail, which loses its muscular tissue, becomes large and leaf-like, and acquires a network of blood-vessels, so that, as it lies close under the egg-membrane, it exposes a large surface just where there is the greatest supply of oxygen.

Family Leptodactylidae

The remaining families of frogs are almost, but not quite, all characterised by a toad-like shoulder-girdle ; technically they are known as *Arcifera* and are divided into several families, of which the first, the *Leptodactylidae*, greatly resembles the Firmisternal Ranids ; it is confined to South America and Australia, with one or two species in South Africa. In South America there are a number of forms, *e.g. Leptodactylus*, which greatly resemble our Common Frogs, but some of them show peculiar " nesting habits." The male digs mud from the bottom of the pond, or stream, in shallow water, and constructs a circular wall which rises just above the surface of the water. In this crater-like nursery the eggs are laid, and here they hatch. The tadpoles are protected during their earlier stages by this wall, but have to wait for a freshet or storm before they can leave it for regions in which there is a more plentiful food supply. Many of the Australian species, being dwellers in a dry region, are burrowers, and have the usual digging-shovels on their heels. Some have the life-history modified to suit the climate. The eggs are large, and laid on land, the tadpole developing until the limbs are beginning to appear.

Tadpoles of the Paradoxical Frog (*Pseudis paradoxa*).

Then there is a halt, and in this condition they remain until a storm of rain releases them from the egg-capsule and carries them down to some pool, often very transitory, in which they rapidly undergo the remainder of their development.

Several thoroughly aquatic species are present in South America, among them the famous Paradoxical Frog (*Pseudis paradoxa*). The adults are of the normal, depressed form with long, fully webbed toes ; but the paradox lies in the tadpole, which, before metamorphosis begins, is considerably larger than the adult frog. A full-grown tadpole may be ten and a half inches long, whereas the newly metamorphosed froglet measures only about an inch and a half !

Arboreal species in this family are legion ; most of them belong to the genus *Hylodes*, and all are equipped with adhesive discs on their fingers and toes. They all display the phenomenon of " direct development," *i.e.* the tadpole metamorphoses within the egg, which is laid on land, and here again, as in the Pug-toads, the function of breathing is assumed by an expanded leaf-like tail. There are other remarkable breeding habits, and among them special mention must be made of Darwin's frog (*Rhinoderma*), which frequents the forests of South Chili. Here the vocal-sacs of the male serve as nurseries for the young. How the eggs are put into these sacs has never been observed, but as many as seventeen tadpoles have been found there, the sacs being tre-

SOUTH AMERICAN POISON-FROGS (*Dendrobates trivittatus*).

mendously enlarged and extending backwards between the muscular wall of the abdomen and the skin. Inside this astonishing brood - chamber they undergo their full development, and then escape as froglets through their father's mouth.

Allied to this family, but sometimes placed in a separate group, are the Poison - frogs (*Dendrobates*), brilliantly coloured little creatures with contrasting patches of vivid green, or red, or yellow, on a black background. The secretion of the skin is extremely venomous, and is used by some tribes of Indians in the preparation of their poisoned arrows. These frogs lay their eggs on land ; the tadpoles which emerge therefrom attach themselves by their mouths to their father, who has remained near the eggs, and he carries them to some pool where they drop off to commence a normal aquatic life.

Several Leptodactylids are extremely bizarre ; the Horned-frogs (*Ceratophrys*), for example, have huge bony heads nearly as big as the rest of the body and often have the eyelids drawn out into curious horn-like prominences. They attain obscurity amid the undergrowth of the forests which they frequent by a geometrical " camouflage " pattern of green and yellow and rusty-red.

Family Bufonidae (*True Toads*)

These animals, though scarcely anatomically distinguishable from some members of the preceding group, are, as a rule, so alike that the veriest

amateur would have no difficulty in recognising them as toads. They are
of world-wide distribution, and two of them, the Common Toad and the
Natterjack, occur in Britain.   The former is a squat, warty creature
characterised, like most toads, by a pair of large glandular swellings above
each shoulder.   Contrary to general belief the skin is not slimy, but quite
dry.   When this skin is shed, as it is periodically, it is not cast off like

the skin of a snake ; it splits
along the middle of the back,
is pulled downwards and forwards by the hind limbs, and
finally thrust into the mouth
by the fore limbs and swallowed.

This creature is unfor-
tunately the subject of many
silly superstitions and is un-
deservedly maligned in consequence.   It cannot squirt
venom, though in extreme
agony it may exude a milky
poison from its paratoid

COMMON EUROPEAN TOAD, in expectant attitude.

glands ; neither can it drink milk, nor suck cow's udders ; in fact, it is an
extremely unobtrusive, harmless creature which, by reason of the number
of noxious insects it destroys, ought to be regarded as the gardeners'
and farmers' best friend.   The Natterjack is similar to the Common Toad
but smaller, rather local in its distribution, given to running like a mouse
rather than crawling, and distinguished by a narrow light stripe running
from the tip of the snout along the middle of the back.   The habits of the
two species, and of most other toads, are very similar.   Many species have
voices, some quite musical, and that of the Natterjack is a rather
powerful " krac-krac-krac."   The breeding habits are similar to those of
the Common Frog, but the eggs, instead of forming a shapeless mass, are
laid in two long, distinct strings.

Some exotic toads have specialised breeding habits.   The Southern
Asiatic *Bufo penangensis*, for instance, has a tadpole modified for a life in
torrential streams.   This is especially apparent in the enlarged, downwardly
directed mouth, which acts as a sucker.   The most remarkable habits,
however, are shown by two West African genera.   In the one the eggs
are laid on land, are " brooded " by the mother, and the tadpoles metamorphose within them ; in the other they are retained within the body
of the mother, and the young are actually born fully developed, the only
known instance of the kind among the Salientia.

Family Hylidae (Tree-frogs)

The true Tree-frogs are most common in America and the Australian region, but with one or two species in temperate Asia and Europe. They are not adapted in the adult stage to so many different modes of life as are some of the previous families, but they show very great diversity in their breeding habits. There are one or two species which are almost entirely terrestrial and one even fossorial (*Pterno-hyla*). The majority, however, are tree-dwellers, with adhesive discs on the tips of their fingers and toes. Many, like the common European Tree-frog (*Hyla arborea*), are of a brilliant green, but others show varied colour-patterns, often with stripes and bars, whilst all have considerable powers of colour-change.

The more unspecialised forms have breeding habits similar to the Common Frog; but we find, again, particularly in South America, in different environments, pond-breeders with typical tadpoles; tadpoles adapted for life in torrential streams, and nursery-builders like some Leptodactylids; some which glue their eggs to leaves overhanging water, though here without forming the meringue-like froth of *Rhacophorus*, and others again which have a direct development. The tadpoles of this last type, however, differ from those we have already encountered in their respiratory mechanism, for instead of the tail assuming

A Toad Tadpole adapted for life in torrential streams.

this function it is performed by the external gills. Lost at an early stage in other tadpoles, these are here retained, and modified to form huge, thin, mushroom-like structures which almost entirely enfold the developing larva. In many of these forms we also find parental care for the young.

Female *Hyla evansi*, carrying clutch of eggs.

In the simpler forms the large eggs, each in its tough, transparent capsule, just adhere to the back of the mother, who carries them about until they hatch; but in the more advanced cases we find the gradual development of a horseshoe-shaped fold of skin on the parent's back, which protects the eggs. This structure has its culminating point in forms like *Gastrotheca*, where there is a definite pocket on the female's back, opening by a small aperture just above the vent. How the eggs find their way into this pouch we do not know, but within it they undergo at least part of their development. In some species the tadpoles hatch within the pouch and leave the mother for a free-swimming stage, but in others they actually metamorphose within the brood-chamber.

A very peculiar feature of a few Hylids is the conversion of the skin of the head into bone so that there is a hard bony shield all over the top of the head. The possessors of this peculiar structure live, to a large extent, in holes and hollow trees, and the head is then used like a snail's operculum; it is bent downwards and thrust into the opening of the lair to form a very efficient stopper.

Family Pelobatidae (*Spade-foot Toads*)

These acquire their name from the fact that the European *Pelobates* and the North American *Scaphiopus* are burrowers, with well-developed shovels on their heels. By vigorous backward scratching movements of

THE EUROPEAN MUD-DIVER (*Pelodytes*).

the hind-limb this shovel scoops up loose soil, and the animals thus work their way backwards into the earth. In the burrows so constructed they remain hidden throughout the day and only venture out at night. The other European form, the Mud-diver (*Pelodytes*), and the South Asiatic members of the family, however, lack the shovel. The Mud-diver is quite frog-like in appearance though nocturnal in habits. It frequents the banks of streams, into which it plunges when alarmed to hide in the mud. Most of the South Asiatic species, however, are rather toad- than frog-like, and some are of considerable size. *Megophrys cornuta* is remarkable for the horn-like prominences into which the upper eyelid is produced.

The breeding habits of all are of the simple type found in the Common Frog, but the tadpoles of some species of *Megophrys* have the toothless mouth and the expanded, surface-feeding funnel which we have encountered in the Pug-toads.

Family Discoglossidae (*Bell-toads*)

For the most part these are aquatic, and as in most aquatic frogs the tongue is reduced in size and cannot be protruded. In addition to the agile, frog-like *Discoglossus* found in the Iberian Peninsula, North Africa, and on some of the Mediterranean Islands, there are two other semi-aquatic European species, the Fire-bellied Toads. These are both small, warty creatures, obscurely coloured above, but the lower surfaces have vivid red (*Bombina bombina*) or yellow (*Bombina variegata*) spots on a black background. The secretion of the skin is very poisonous, and of course when the animal is swimming its warning colours are visible to its most likely enemies, fish and water tortoises. When it is on land this vivid coloration is hidden, and it is consequently extraordinarily interesting to find that, if alarmed under these conditions, it either rolls over on its back or lifts up its hands and feet to expose their brightly coloured lower surfaces.

MALE MIDWIFE-TOAD (*Alytes*), with eggs.

These aquatic species all have normal breeding habits. The Midwife-toads, how- ever, of South-West Europe, are more terrestrial, and accordingly have developed a special method of egg-laying. Pairing takes place on land, and the eggs are laid in two convoluted strings, through the loops of which the male pushes his hind- legs ; with this precious burden he retires beneath a stone, or into a hole. For about three weeks he carries these eggs about with him, and if the weather be dry, he will emerge at night and plunge into the water to make good any loss of moisture which the eggs may have suffered ; when, at the end of this period, the larvae have lost their external gills and assumed the typical tadpole form, the male migrates to some suitable pond and there relieves himself of his burden. The young hatch out imme- diately afterwards to enter upon a free-swimming existence until the tadpole stage is completed.

Family Pipidae (Plat-handers, etc.)

This, the single remaining group of frogs, is a highly specialised one, containing only a few forms in Africa and tropical South America. They are all exclusively aquatic, and are distinguished, in addition to internal specialisations, by the complete absence of a tongue. The African Plat-handers (*Xenopus*) have sharply pointed, tactile fingers and long, fully webbed toes, the three inner being provided with claws ; they frequent ponds and sluggish rivers, feeding on worms and aquatic insects. The eggs, which are laid singly, attached to stones or water-plants, hatch out into a peculiar fish-like tadpole with a long tail, broad, flat head and a huge, gaping, toothless mouth, which has a long tentacle at each corner. These tadpoles feed on minute particles of organic matter floating in the water, which are strained out of the stream passing over the gills.

The Surinam-toad (*Pipa*) is, like its African relatives, thoroughly aquatic, with long, webbed toes and a very depressed bodily form, but it differs in having the tips of the fingers terminating in sensory, star-shaped discs. Its most interesting feature, however, and one which has rendered it famous, is its extraordinary method of rearing its young. The eggs as they are laid are passed upwards on to the back of the mother, where they adhere and gradually sink down, each into a little pit in the skin of the parent's back. These pits are formed in response to the stimulus set up by contact with the egg, the skin of the back at this time being specially thickened to receive the eggs, which are at last quite concealed. The opening then acquires a little lid, and thus ensconced the tadpoles pass through their whole larval history, to emerge as fully formed froglets.

SECTION XIII

CLASS REPTILIA

By H. W. PARKER, B.A.

GENERAL CHARACTERISTICS

LITERALLY the word " reptile " means a " crawler," but this is hardly a sufficient, nor yet even a moderately accurate, definition of the group. As we know them to-day, reptiles may be defined as cold-blooded vertebrates, with horny scales, and without gills at any stage of their lives. These few characters serve to differentiate them at once from any other living animals, but when fossil forms are taken into consideration accurate definition becomes almost impossible. There is little doubt that reptiles themselves arose from the Amphibia, which were the only terrestrial back-boned animals in existence before them, and reptiles were the ancestral stock from which birds and mammals were derived. There is no reason for believing that any group of animals arose suddenly, and completely differentiated from its immediate predecessors, since, where a fossil record of any group exists, it is always found that the earlier members of the series approach more and more closely to the ancestral stock. Probably, therefore, if the whole story were fully known it would be found that each new group arose by such gradual stages as to render it impossible to draw any save the most arbitrary line dividing the two.

Fossil Reptiles

The earliest-known reptilian remains have been found in the later beds of the Coal Measures, but, since in the beds immediately overlying these strata at least five different reptilian orders are known, it is clear that the group must have had quite a long evolutionary history prior to that period, and it is generally believed that the first true reptiles must have separated from their amphibian ancestors early in the Coal Age. What conditions favoured the origin of these animals, or what forces were at work to produce them we can, of course, only surmise. Nevertheless, it is clear that a reptile which relies entirely on its lungs for breathing and, through the development of protective membranes (amnion and allantois), round its developing embryos, is not under the necessity of returning to the water to lay its eggs, is a much more efficient terrestrial animal than an amphibian.

This conclusion is reflected in the story which the rocks tell us. During the periods which followed the Carboniferous epoch—the Permian and Triassic—reptiles increased and multiplied, not only in numbers but in diversity of forms adapted to different environmental conditions, and became the dominant group of terrestrial animals, whilst the amphibia, previously the lords of the earth, dwindled into insignificance. This period has been aptly called the " Age of Reptiles " ; for, whilst the " higher " forms, Birds and Mammals, made their appearance during its course, they never seriously challenged the reptiles in any of the varied environments which they had conquered.

Plesiosaurs and Ichthyosaurs

The primitive reptiles were doubtless short-legged creatures, not vastly different in appearance from their amphibian progenitors, and from such a central stock arose such a wealth of arboreal, terrestrial, aquatic, flying, and burrowing forms that it will be possible to mention here only a few

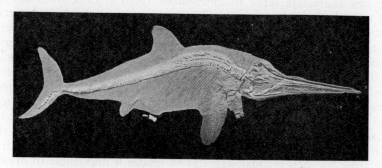

Remains of an Ichthyosaur, showing the outline of the body and limbs.

of the more important. Aquatic forms are well represented among fossils, and one group, the Crocodiles, persists to the present day. A return to life in the water was a retrograde step for terrestrial animals, so far as habitat was concerned. But, since no animals are definitely known to have redeveloped structures which they have once completely lost, it necessitated considerable structural changes to fit them for it.

The highest degree of specialisation for a purely aquatic life is exhibited by the Plesiosaurs and Ichthyosaurs. Plesiosaurs had a broad body, much-shortened tail, four short paddle-like limbs, and a long neck. They may be regarded as the reptilian equivalents of the seals and sea-lions. Ichthyosaurs, on the other hand, are comparable with whales ; here the neck was shortened, and was not distinct from the body, the head elongate, the limbs small and fin-like, and the powerful tail with a pair of flukes formed the principal organ of propulsion. The flukes of the tail, however, were vertical as in the fishes, and not horizontal like those of the whales. The largest known were about thirty feet in length.

Pterodactyls

Though there are flying reptiles at the present day, none are comparable with the Pterodactyls, or Flying Dragons, which were the first vertebrates to conquer the air. Their efficiency as flying organisms cannot be doubted, and was probably as great as that of the majority of birds and bats, though, like many another highly specialised reptile, they died out,
leaving their domain to their
competitors. Though Pterodactyls, birds, and bats have
all achieved the same end by
approximately the same means
—the modification of the fore-
limb into a flapping wing—

Restoration of a Long-tailed Pterodactyl.

the three groups cannot be regarded as at all nearly related, and a closer examination of the flying mechanism reveals fundamental differences in its structure.

In birds the fingers are reduced to three, and of these the first and third are extremely reduced in size. The wing-surface, formed of feathers, is attached to the greatly elongate fore-arm and the bones of the palm of the hand and fingers. In bats the wing-surface is provided by a fold of leathery skin which is stretched between the fore-limb and the body and is supported by four greatly elongate fingers, the thumb being free. Ptero-dactyls, like bats, had a membranous wing stretched between the fore-limb and the sides of the body ; but here the fifth finger is lost and the first three are free, whilst the fourth, supporting the wing, is so tremendously lengthened that it is longer than the whole of the rest of the arm together. Apart from the structure of the wing, however, Pterodactyls resemble birds rather than bats, and the two groups have had a very similar evolutionary history.

The earlier Pterodactyls, like the earliest-known bird, the famous *Archaeopteryx*, had an elongate head with teeth in both jaws, and a long tail, but their descendants, like the modern birds, had the tail reduced to

a mere stump, and many had a beak-like, toothless mouth. Of their habits we, of course, know nothing, but it seems probable that they were quite comparable with birds, though the flight may have been more laboured and clumsy ; the smallest known are scarcely larger than a sparrow, but the biggest, with a wing-span of twenty-five feet, far surpassed in size any other flying creatures.

Skeleton of a Short-tailed Pterodactyl.

Dinosaurs

The terrestrial reptiles of the past were legion, and they show adaptations to all the varied environments which their successors, the mammals, have occupied. The smallest were probably no bigger than many present-day lizards, but the opposite extreme was reached by such creatures as the dinosaur *Branchiosaurus*, whose length has been estimated as one hundred and twenty feet, and which probably weighed about forty tons ! The largest and most important group, the Dinosaurs, contains a most amazing variety of forms, some herbivorous, some predaceous, some adapted for running over hard ground, and some marsh-dwellers ; some apparently were defenceless, and others possessed an array of bony armour such as has never been developed elsewhere in Nature.

Purely herbivorous and strictly terrestrial were the Bird-footed Dinosaurs such as *Iguanodon*, a bulky creature about thirty-four feet long, with a comparatively short tail and neck, short fore-limbs, and long powerful hind-limbs, with but three toes. These animals probably walked on their hind-limbs only, using the short fore-limbs to steady themselves when browsing on the leaves of trees. Also herbivorous, but probably marsh-dwellers, were the Sauropods, the group which contains all the largest reptiles such as *Branchiosaurus*, *Brontosaurus*, and *Diplodocus*. These were all quadrupedal in gait, and most of them had very long tails and necks, the latter enabling them to wade about in comparatively deep water, possibly to escape from the fierce carnivores of the land.

The carnivores do not approach the huge herbivores in size, but, even so, many of them were colossal, and must have been terrible creatures.

The culminating form of this series is aptly named *Tyrannosaurus rex*, the King of the Tyrant-saurians. This creature reached a length of forty-seven feet and was as massive as an elephant, with a huge head and gaping mouth armed with tremendous, dagger-like teeth, three to six inches long, with short, grasping fore-limbs and long, powerful hind-limbs. Such a tremendously powerful creature seems to have been well fitted to prey upon the huge but relatively defenceless herbivores, but its very size may often have proved its undoing ; its bulk precluded agility, and its ponderous charge may have often terminated in its impalement on the horns of one of the armoured dinosaurs.

Like the Sauropods and Bird-footed Dinosaurs, the armoured Dinosaurs were herbivorous ; but all of them developed a heavy armature of bony plates, probably as a defence against those predaceous animals just referred to. All were terrestrial, and many must have been extraordinarily grotesque ; *Stegosaurus*, for example, was compressed from side to side, with an arched back ornamented with a double row of huge, triangular bony plates along its crest, and the end of the tail armed with fearful horn-like spikes two feet or more in length. The North

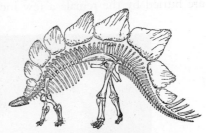

Restored Skeleton of the Armoured Dinosaur (*Stegosaurus*).

American Horned-dinosaurs were rhinoceros-like animals with the skull produced backwards into a saddle-shaped frill protecting the neck and often with three long, bony horns on the head, one above each eye and one on the tip of the snout.

Such, in brief, were the Dinosaurs, at one time undisputed kings of the earth. Whether their feeble reptilian brains were outwitted by the more intelligent mammals, or whether they became extinct through racial decay, or were unable to adapt themselves to changing climatic conditions, we shall never be able to discover ; but before the end of the Cretaceous period they were all extinct, and the earth and air were given over to the rising tide of mammals and birds. A few branches of the reptilian tree, however, survived, and their descendants still hold their own in the struggle for existence.

Order RHYNCHOCEPHALIA

(*Tuatera*)

To this order belongs the famous Tuatera of the islands of Cook Strait, New Zealand, the only living representative of the group, and the most archaic of modern reptiles. This remarkable animal is often spoken of as a "living fossil," since, not only is it structurally the most primitive of modern forms, but species closely related to it roamed the earth during the Great Age of Reptiles.   Externally there is little to indicate the anatomical features which render this animal so interesting to zoologists. The head is large, with rather prominent ridges above the eyebrows, the body compressed, covered with granular scales interspersed with larger tubercles, the limbs relatively short and the tail compressed, with a saw-like crest.   The coloration is of a uniform dull brown.   Its general appearance, in short, is that of a moderate-sized lizard, or a small crocodile.

These animals, now becoming increasingly scarce, are sluggish in disposition, and live in short burrows which they dig and which they often share with petrels, birds common on the islands to which the Tuatera is now confined.   Reproduction is by means of leathery-shelled eggs, which are buried by the female a few inches beneath the surface, and there is no

THE TUATERA.

evidence of any parental care, the eggs being left to hatch by the heat of the sun.   The young, which emerge about thirteen months later, have to fend for themselves from the beginning.

Anatomically the interest of these creatures is centred in the structure of the skull, which more resembles that of the crocodiles than the lizards, in the backbone, and ribs, and in the presence of a rudimentary third, or pineal, eye.   This organ, situated on the top of the head, shows, in the Tuatera, the typical structure of a rather primitive eye, which was probably an important sense-organ in some of the earlier reptiles, but which has changed its function in their descendants.   It is still visible externally in the majority of lizards, but only persists as a small lobe of the brain in other modern reptiles ;   in mammals it is represented by the " pineal organ," one of those ductless glands whose secretion is poured into the blood-stream and plays such an important part in the development and growth of the body.

Order LORICATA or CROCODILIA

(*Crocodiles and Alligators*)

Crocodiles, Alligators, and Caimans are, like the Tuatera, of ancient lineage and are the few survivors of a formerly much more numerous group; their fossil ancestors can be traced back to the times of the Dinosaurs, and it is not improbable that the two groups arose from a common stem. They are not a flourishing group, for they show comparatively little structural diversity in adaptation to different environmental conditions. All are semi-aquatic, feeding and passing most of their lives in water, but frequently coming ashore to bask, and capable of making long migrations overland in search of water in times of drought. Adaptation to their essentially aquatic life has brought about some extremely interesting structural modifications. Thus, for example, the nostrils are produced into a sort of dome projecting above the top of the snout, and the internal nostrils have shifted backwards so as to open at the extreme hinder end of the palate, well into the throat. In this way a continuous passage is formed from the nostrils to the wind-pipe, an arrangement which enables a crocodile to drown its prey whilst still able to breathe itself. Furthermore, the eyes are situated on the top of the head, so that the animal can lie in the water with only the nostrils and eyes exposed and thus take its victims by surprise. The side-to-side flattening of the tail, which forms the chief organ of propulsion, and the relatively weak limbs, are also adaptations to an aquatic life. The close-fitting armature of horny scales, beneath which are bony plates, must be regarded as a protection during internecine battles.

These animals have within their ranks the largest living reptiles, though some are quite small; one of the South American Caimans (*Caiman palpebrosus*), for example, scarcely attains a length of four feet. The largest species is undoubtedly the Salt-water Crocodile (*Crocodilus porosus*), but the maximum size to which this species may grow is difficult to determine accurately, on account of the exaggerated stories which have obtained currency. Specimens of thirty feet have been reported, but it is doubtful whether any of this size now exist, since firearms are too well distributed for many very old individuals to survive.

The Gharial, and False Gharial, are almost exclusively fish-eaters, with long, slender snouts and numerous sharp, interlocking teeth specially adapted for fish-catching. The remainder, whether crocodiles or alligators, may be described as omni-carnivorous, for though fish form their staple diet they will also eat anything they can overpower. Lying quietly in the water, with only the nostrils, eyes, and perhaps part of the back showing, they look like floating logs, and any unwary bird or beast approaching within range of the powerful jaws is seized, dragged under the water, and eaten. There are undoubtedly occasional man-eaters, but, as a rule, they recognise man as the arch-enemy, and in his presence become wary and difficult to approach.

One of the commonest questions asked concerning these animals is, "how can one tell the difference between a crocodile and an alligator?" Actually, there is very little external difference, and the two terms are

often misapplied. Crocodiles have the fourth tooth of the lower jaw, the first enlarged one, fitting into a *notch* in the side of the upper jaw, whereas alligators, including Caimans, have it concealed in a pit.

None of them is gregarious, though large numbers may be present in restricted areas which are specially suited to their requirements. During the pairing season the sexes are enabled to find each other by hearing and by smell. The males during this period develop considerable vocal powers, the call usually being an intermit-

The first enlarged tooth of the lower jaw fits into a notch of the Crocodile's upper jaw (top), but into a definite pit in an Alligator's.

tent bellow, which may be audible half a mile away. As a further aid both sexes possess two pairs of scent-glands, one pair at the sides of the throat close to the angles of the lower jaw, and the other just within the vent. Both pairs are close to the soil when the animal is at rest, and the strong, musky secretion which they produce leaves a trail which can be followed by individuals seeking a mate.

Reproduction is always by means of eggs, which are elongately oval in shape, about twice as big as a hen's egg, and covered with a hard shell. The number in a clutch varies with the size of the individual from about twenty to ninety. They are always deposited on land, in a nest the site and type of which differs slightly in the different species ; they are never incubated by either parent. The Nile Crocodile (*C. niloticus*) deposits its eggs in a hole eighteen inches to two feet deep, excavated in a sandy spot, the eggs being arranged in two layers with a layer of sand between. Many other species, however, including the Long-snouted Crocodile (*C. cataphractus*) of West Africa, and the North American Alligator (*A. mississipiensis*), sweep together a mound of vegetable débris in the middle of which the eggs are laid. Incubation is effected chiefly by the heat of the sun, though in the case of the mound-builders the heat generated by the fermentation of the decaying vegetable matter probably assists. The mother remains in the vicinity of the nest, visiting it from time to time, and ultimately, warned by the hiccough-like cries of the young ones when they are ready to leave the eggs, scratches away the covering of the nest and conducts her brood to the water. The young, which are two or three times as long as the eggs from which they emerge, are able to break their way through the stout egg-shell by means of a special " egg-tooth " which develops on the tip of the snout, but which is lost soon after hatching.

THE NILE CROCODILE (*Crocodilus niloticus*).

They are able to feed as soon as they leave the egg, and usually show the same vicious, snappy temperament as the adults. Growth is fairly rapid, about a foot a year under favourable conditions, for the first five or six years, but becomes slower with increasing age, although it probably never completely ceases.

They are undoubtedly more at home in the water—where they swim by means of the long, powerful tail, with the limbs folded close against the body—than on land, where their normal gait is merely a crawl, with the belly and tail dragging along the ground ; nevertheless they spend much of their time basking in the sun on shore, or on sand-banks, and when excited can run at a considerable pace with the body held well off the ground. Many species in cooler climates hibernate, buried in the mud throughout the winter, and some tropical species may " aestivate " in a similar manner through the dry season, when the rivers and pools dry up.

The Salt-water, or Estuarine, Crocodile is the most widely distributed species and is the only one which enters the sea. It is found from Bengal to Southern China, Northern Australia, and the Fiji Islands, and is often encountered well out at sea. The others frequent only fresh waters, and their range is consequently more limited. Some of the better-known crocodiles are the Mugger, or Marsh Crocodile, in India, the Nile Crocodile, which, though now rare in Egypt, is still fairly common from the Sudan to Rhodesia, the Central American Crocodile, which is also fairly common

THE SPECTACLED CAIMAN.

throughout the West Indies, and the Orinoco Crocodile of northern South America. True alligators occur only in the Mississippi basin (*A. missis-sipiensis*) and in Southern China (*A. sinensis*), but their near relatives the Caimans, which include the Brazilian Jacarè tinga (*C. trigonatus*), and the Jacarè àssu (*C. niger*), are confined to tropical South America.

Order CHELONIA

(*Tortoises and Turtles*)

These animals, scientifically termed Chelonians, are, like those of the two preceding orders, the survivors of a formerly much more numerous group, and can be traced back to the bygone ages when reptiles were the dominant animals, without showing any great simplification of structure. They display considerable powers of adaptation to environmental conditions, and hence it is that a great number of forms (some 225 species are known) have been able to survive in the struggle for existence. Structurally they are one of the most remarkable groups of living vertebrates. Their most obvious characteristic, the shell, has necessarily imposed a severe handicap on their powers of adaptation, for none of them has been able to dispense with it, and its nature precludes any very great diversity of bodily form.

The shell proper is a bony structure composed of two halves, an upper carapace and a lower plastron, the two being more or less firmly united at the sides, but widely separated in front and behind to accommodate the head, tail, and limbs. The bones composing both carapace and plastron are normally firmly united with each other by sutures, and their number and arrangement are fairly constant throughout the whole group. The union of the upper and lower halves of the shell may be bony and quite rigid, or cartilaginous and flexible, and in some forms transverse hinges may be developed across either carapace or plastron. A shell of this kind is almost unique among the vertebrates. It is, however, not a new structure, but is of the same nature as the bony dermal armour found in many other groups of reptiles. In the Chelonians the bony plates have been reduced in number but greatly increased in size, and have become fused to the ribs and backbone. Correlated with this development

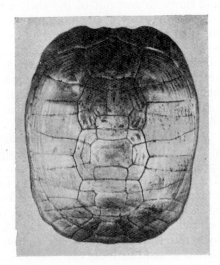

Shell of a Tortoise, with (left) and without (right) the horny plates.

and the bodily rigidity which it imposes, the great muscles of the back are entirely lost.

In most Chelonians the bony shell is overlaid by horny plates, which have the same general arrangement as the bones, but do not correspond with them. The plates are of exactly the same nature as the horny scales which cover the exposed soft parts, but instead of being shed periodically as these are, the older growth remains attached, so that each " shield " (as the plates of the shell are called) is not only growing in area to correspond with the growth of the animal, but is continually increasing in thickness. In colder climates the animals sleep through the winter, and during this period growth practically ceases, so that the increase in size of the shields progresses by a series of jumps which are visible as a series of concentric lines, each of which represents one growing period. But with increasing age the rate of growth diminishes, so that the lines are scarcely distinguishable, and at the same time the boundary of the original shield which the tortoise had on hatching becomes obliterated through wear.

The presence of a shell, which renders the ribs immovable, has necessitated the development of a rather different method of breathing as compared with other reptiles, where air is drawn into, and driven out of, the lungs by outward and inward movements of the ribs. As in the Amphibia, which also have no movable ribs, air is pumped in and out of the lungs by movements of a system of bones and cartilages (the " hyoid apparatus "), which dilate and compress the throat and floor of the mouth, and this action is assisted, to some extent, by the piston-like movements of the head and limbs in and out of the shell when the animal moves. Some water-tortoises have evolved additional mechanisms which enable them to utilise the air dissolved in the water, and so do not need to come to the surface so frequently to breathe. In some, the hinder part of the intestine is dilated to form two large sacs which have a rich blood supply, and these are continually filled with water and emptied through the vent. Others, like some salamanders, have special recesses of the mouth and throat— again, with a rich blood supply—and these are filled and emptied through the mouth.

No modern tortoise or turtle has teeth, but the jaws are covered with a horny beak which usually has sharp cutting edges. Most terrestrial species are strict vegetarians, but aquatic forms are usually carnivorous. The voice is not well developed in females, which as a rule can only hiss. But males, at least during the pairing season, emit cries which in small species may be only a feeble piping, but in larger tortoises may be a hoarse bellow. Reproduction is always by eggs, which are spherical and covered by a tough, membranous, or sometimes a hard, brittle shell. They are buried in sand or loose earth, and usually hatch in a few months ; in some northern countries, though, the young may not cmerge until the following spring.

The general form and the limbs show modifications corresponding with the conditions under which the animals live. Terrestrial species have a relatively larger, high, domed shell, into which the head and limbs can be withdrawn, and the limbs are club-shaped. Aquatic species, on the other hand, have low, flat shells which are often far too small to accommodate the head and limbs, and the fingers and toes remain distinct, though connected by webbing. Intermediate conditions may be found in those species which are amphibious, while the limbs of the marine turtles are transformed into definite " flippers," or paddles, recalling those of whales and penguins, or of the old Sea-dragons.

Of Chelonians existing at the present day there are three great groups : (1) The Snake-necked Tortoises (Cryptodeira), which almost all have the shell covered with horny shields, and retract the neck by a vertical S-shaped bend. (2) The Side-necked Tortoises (Pleurodira), similar to the preceding group, but drawing back the head by a simple lateral bend of the neck. (3) The true Mud-turtles (known in America as tortoises) (Trionychoidea), which have the bony shell much reduced and covered with soft skin.

Sub-order *Cryptodeira*

(*Snake-necked Tortoises*)

Family Chelydridae

The first of these groups contains by far the largest number of species and all the typical tortoises. It is divided into several families, the first of which (*Chelydridae*) contains only a few North and Central American freshwater species, the best known being the Common Snapper (*Chelydra serpentina*) of the eastern United States and the Alligator-snapper (*Macrochelys temminckii*) of the Mississippi and Missouri basins. They are both large,

powerful animals, characterised by relatively huge heads, with tremendously powerful jaws, small, rough shells, long, alligator-like tails, and numerous, soft, projecting folds of skin on the neck and soft parts. They are both fish-eaters, and on account of their vicious nature and the ter

N. American Alligator-snapper (*Macrochelys temminckii*).

rible bites they can inflict are greatly disliked and feared by bathers and fishermen.

The method of capturing the prey adopted by the Alligator-snapper is remarkable. Lying quietly on the bottom, with the mouth agape, the rough shell and waving, frond-like appendages of the neck and limbs give the whole creature a remarkable resemblance to a weed-covered log or stone. Inside the mouth, however, are two white, writhing, worm-like projections, which by their similarity to a maggot, or similar grub, are believed to attract unwary fish literally into the jaws of death.

Family Kinosternidae

The Musk-turtles (*Kinosternidae*) are a group of small, freshwater Chelonians of North and Central America ; they rarely exceed a foot in length, and have derived their popular name from the rather offensive odour which many of them emit from a pair of glands, situated just in front of the hind-limbs, whose function is probably the same as that of the musk-glands of crocodiles. In many species hinges develop across the plastron, or breast-shield, so that when the limbs are withdrawn the shell can be closed by drawing up the projecting front and hind lobes until they touch the carapace. The Stink-pot Terrapin (*Sternotherus odoratus*), which ranges throughout eastern North America from Canada to Texas, is the commonest and best-known species.

Family Testudinidae

The True Tortoises (*Testudinidae*) are world-wide in their distribution, except for Australia and those northern and southern latitudes where the winter is too severe. Some are entirely aquatic, and others so strictly terrestrial that they are soon drowned if they fall into water. Nevertheless, there are all intergradations between these two extremes. As examples of aquatic species we may mention the " Slider-terrapins " of North America, this being the term under which a variety of edible freshwater terrapins are sold, to distinguish them from the brackish-water Diamond-backed Terrapins. The " sliders " include the beautiful Painted-terrapin, so familiar to aquarists, and a variety of similar forms which inhabit the fresh waters of the eastern United States, and which, though edible, are not to be compared in delicacy of flavour with the Diamond-backs. The latter inhabit brackish

PAINTED-TERRAPIN (*Chrysemys picta*).

creeks and estuaries, feeding on shrimps, periwinkles, and such-like marine creatures. They are so much sought after that they are now becoming extremely rare. To supply the demand "Turtle Farms " have been established, where they are bred and reared until they reach a marketable size.

Less aquatic than these are the Wood-terrapins (*Clemmys in-sculpta*) of North America and the Leprous-terrapins (*C. leprosa*) of Southern Europe and North Africa. Corresponding with the change of habitat the web between the fingers and toes is reduced. Less aquatic still are the European Pond-tortoises

EUROPEAN POND-TORTOISE (*Emys orbicularis*).

(*Emys orbicularis*), pretty little creatures frequenting rivers and marshes throughout Central Europe. These animals are often kept in captivity, and offered scraps of bread and lettuce by their kind-hearted owners. Unfortunately for the tortoises they are strictly carnivorous, feeding on aquatic insects, tadpoles, frogs, and fish, which are deliberately stalked and seized with a quick, sideways snap of the head.   They are very shy, and often the only indication one can get of their presence is a slight " plop," and rings of ever-widening circles on the water.

Structurally water-tortoises, but in habits terrestrial, are the North American Box-turtles (*Terrapene*), which have such a very highly developed hinge across the plastron that they can withdraw into their shells and close both openings entirely.   They have, however, departed from the rather flattened form of the majority of aquatic Chelonians, and have the high, domed shell of such typically terrestrial forms as are included in the genus *Testudo*.

This genus is an assemblage of terrestrial tortoises, and contains, among others, the well-known, but now, alas, almost extinct, Giant-tortoises, some of which develop a shell-length of over four feet and may weigh six hundred pounds.   There are, or rather were, three groups of these animals, one confined to the Galapagos Islands, where every small island had its own race and the largest several races.   Another is peculiar to the Mascerene Islands (Bourbon, Mauritius, and Rodriguez), and a third to the Seychelles and Aldabra.   Structurally they do not differ appreciably from other members of the same genus, though the bones of the shell are greatly

MARION'S TORTOISE (*Testudo sumeirei*), photographed about 1890.

reduced in thickness.   This reduction became possible because they lived under ideal conditions, with no enemies, and therefore no need of a heavy shell.   With an inexhaustible supply of food, they increased to almost incredible numbers.   Then fell an unfortunate day, the invasion of their retreats by Man, who speedily discovered that not only were they excellent eating, but that, on account of their ability to live for months without food, they formed ideal provisions for sailing-ships, where fresh meat was always desired but rarely obtainable.

In consequence of the raids which followed this discovery their numbers were rapidly decimated. At the present time a few, probably, survive in a wild state on the Galapagos Islands and on South Aldabra, whilst a number of domesticated specimens exist in the Seychelles. They have been the subject of much idle speculation as to the age to which tortoises can live. Reliable records are scanty, but one of the best authenticated is that furnished by the famous Marion's Tortoise, which in 1766 was taken from the Seychelles to Mauritius ; when the British took possession of the island in 1810 this specimen was taken over too, and was said, at that time, to have attained its full size. From then onwards it lived in the Artillery Barracks, but about 1918, blind through age, it fell down a well and was killed. It must consequently have been well over one hundred and fifty years old at the time of its death.

Approaching the Giant-tortoises in size are the Spurred-tortoises of Africa, but most of the other species of *Testudo* are relatively small. In Europe there are two land tortoises, the Margined-tortoise (*T. marginata*) of Greece and the Spur-tailed Tortoise (*T. hermanni*) of the other Mediterranean countries, whilst the tortoise so commonly imported into England, the so-called Greek-tortoise (*T. graeca*), is a native of North Africa and Asia Minor. All these are similar in habits and appearance ; they feed on vegetables and fruit, and hibernate in holes which they dig in loose earth. The round, hard-shelled eggs are laid in a shallow hole, the earth replaced and stamped flat, by allowing the body to drop on it repeatedly, and the eggs are then left to their fate. The young, which hatch late in the autumn, when they are about as big as a florin, retire almost immediately into hibernation.

TORNIER'S TORTOISE (*Testudo tornieri*), with flattened, flexible shell.

Some tortoises are burrowers ; the North American Gopher-tortoises (*T. polyphemus*), for example, are inhabitants of dry, sandy districts and construct their own burrows, often several yards in length. But Tornier's Tortoise (*T. tornieri*), of East Africa, is an inhabitant of rocky localities, and, unable to burrow, hides in clefts and crannies of the rocks. In adaptation to this mode of life the shell has become remarkably flattened, and the bones reduced so much in thickness that the whole animal is distinctly soft.

Family Chelonidae

The True Turtles (*Chelonidae*) are represented by only three important species—the Hawksbill, the Green-turtle and the Loggerhead. They are all marine, frequenting tropical and sub-tropical seas, and only coming ashore for egg-laying. For this purpose unfrequented, sandy beaches are chosen, and the females laboriously wade out of the sea, usually at night, dig pits in which the round, leathery-shelled eggs are deposited, fill up the hole, and return again immediately to the sea. The Hawksbill, which may be recognised by its hooked beak and the fact that the shields of the back overlap, is the smallest species, and the source of the true " tortoise-shell." The horny shields of the shell are stripped off by immersion in boiling

EDIBLE GREEN-TURTLE (*Chelone mydas*).

water, and the plates, when heated in steam, can be welded together to form slabs thick enough for commercial purposes.

The Green-turtle, the species so much in demand for the supply of turtle soup, derives its name from the greenish tinge of the fat. It is a larger species than the Hawksbill, reaching a length of four feet, and, like the Loggerhead, has the shields of the carapace meeting edge to edge. It may be distinguished from the latter by its smaller head and the presence of only four pairs of large shields on each side of the central row. Its general habits are similar to those of the Hawksbill, but it differs from any of the other marine turtles in being largely herbivorous, its principal food consisting of the marine grass, *Zostera*. The Loggerhead is very similar to the preceding, but may be distinguished by the presence of five or more paired plates on either side of the middle series. It is of little commercial value, though its eggs are eaten.

Family Dermochelyidae

The next family contains but a single, present-day species, the Luth, an animal very similar in habits and general appearance to the True Turtles, but distinguished from them by the absence of horny plates on the back. It furthermore differs from all other modern Chelonians in the construction of its shell, since the bony carapace and plastron are built up of a number of irregularly disposed, polygonal, interlocking plates, of which only one or two can be recognised as corresponding to the bony plates of other tortoises and turtles. It is the largest living species, reaching a total length of eight feet and a weight of nearly a ton.

THE LUTH or LEATHERY-TURTLE (*Dermochelys*).

Sub-order *PLEURODIRA*

(*Side-necked Tortoises*)

The next great group of the order, the Side-necked Tortoises (*Pleurodira*), are all aquatic and are sub-divided into three families, one (*Carettochelydidae*) characterised by the absence of horny plates on the shell and the possession of flippers, another (*Pelomedusidae*) by the presence of horny shields and a shell large enough to accommodate the head and limbs, and the third

THE MATAMATA (*Chelys fimbriata*).

(*Chelydidae*) similar to the preceding, but with such long necks that the head cannot be withdrawn into the shell. Of the first family there is but a single, imperfectly known species, from New Guinea. The other two contain most of the aquatic tortoises of Australia, Africa, and South America. They all have the typical, depressed shells and webbed feet of freshwater dwellers, and many are superficially very similar. *Podocnemis* of the

Amazon basin may be mentioned as one of the few aquatic tortoises which is herbivorous. It frequents shallow backwaters, feeding on the fruit and leaves which fall into the water. Formerly it was so numerous that the collection of its eggs, for the sake of the oil they contain, formed a regular local industry. Another well-known South American species is the grotesque-looking Matamata (*Chelys fimbriata*), which superficially resembles the Alligator-snapper. It has a small, rough shell, and the neck and soft parts are decorated with soft, fimbriated projections and lobes of skin which, when the creature is at rest, give it the appearance of a rough, weed-covered log, an effective piece of camouflage as it lies in wait for victims. Unlike the Alligator-snapper, however, the jaws are weak, and the fish which form its principal food are swallowed whole.

Sub-order *TRIONYCHOIDEA*
(*Mud-turtles*)

The Mud-turtles (*Trionychidae*), the only family of the last great group of Chelonians, are all dwellers in the mud of slow-running rivers and pools in Africa, Asia, and North America. They are all carnivorous. The bony carapace and plastron are much reduced in size, and the whole creature is very flat, almost circular in outline, and entirely covered with soft skin. The feet and hands are broadly webbed, with only three claws on each, whilst the jaws are concealed by fleshy lips, and the snout is produced into a short, soft proboscis which carries the nostrils at its tip. Little is known of their habits, but they all seem to feed on fish or molluscs, the jaws being modified in accordance with the diet. Fish-eaters have sharp, cutting edges to the jaws, but the mollusc-feeders have broad crushing pads.

N. AMERICAN MUD-TURTLE (*Trionyx ferox*).

Order SQUAMATA
Sub-order *LACERTILIA*
(*Lizards*)

Lizards, of which about 2500 species are known, are one of the dominant groups of reptiles of the present day. They are an ancient group, for their ancestry can be traced back to the days of the Dinosaurs, but, unlike the equally ancient crocodiles and Chelonians, they have retained that plasticity which has enabled them to fill so many environmental niches and compete successfully in the struggle for existence. It has been said, and probably with truth, that if mammals were suddenly blotted out the lizards would people the earth with as many and as diverse forms as ever existed in the Great Age of Reptiles.

Typically they are four-limbed reptiles distinguished from Chelonians by the absence of a shell, and from crocodiles and the Tuatera by the presence of only a single bony arch across the temporal region of the skull. But though usually distinguished from their close relatives, the snakes, by the presence of limbs, there are limbless lizards which resemble snakes in so many respects that no single external character, or group of simple characters, will serve to distinguish the two. The only absolute differences between them are the persistence, in lizards, of some of the bones which normally support the fore-limbs, and the

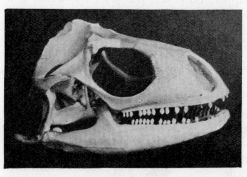

Skull of an Iguana.

complete closure of the front end of the brain-case in snakes. As a general rule, though, it may be said that if the tail is long, those with a single row of transversely enlarged plates beneath the belly are snakes, and those without, lizards ; but if the tail is short and stumpy, snakes have hard, overlapping scales, and lizards a soft skin divided into rectangular segments.

As has already been mentioned, lizards are a plastic group and have become modified in correlation with the different conditions under which they live. There are flying, aquatic, burrowing, and terrestrial forms, and the latter are found in every different type of terrain from the humid tropical forests to deserts, steppes, and high mountains. Like all other groups of cold-blooded, air-breathing creatures their extreme northern and southern range is limited by climatic conditions, no species being able to exist in those regions where the sub-soil remains frozen throughout the year ; the greatest profusion of individuals and species occurs in the tropics.

In conjunction with habits or habitats they exhibit great diversity of structure, the organs showing the greatest modification being, as might be expected, those that come directly or indirectly in contact with the environment. How these are affected may be briefly mentioned first and exemplified later, when we come to consider the different groups. The skin is normally covered with a layer of horny scales, which is shed periodically, and the scales themselves may be small and granular, hard and overlapping, irregularly enlarged to form a defensive armour of tubercles or spines, or almost entirely absent; they are, also, often underlain by bony plates (osteoderms). The general bodily shape varies greatly; terrestrial species are, as a rule, rather depressed, arboreal and aquatic forms are compressed from side to side, and burrowing or cryptozoic animals long, cylindrical, and rather snake-like. The latter type of bodily form is also usually coupled with a greater or less reduction of the limbs, which sometimes may be entirely absent, and, in different groups, show all stages of degeneration. The digits are also modified; for they may be bound together into opposable bundles, be equipped with adhesive pads in climbing forms, or be webbed, or have comb-like fringes of long scales in desert-dwellers.

Tails are sometimes long, whip-like defensive weapons, or short globose storehouses of reserve nutriment, but most often they serve for purposes of defence by their extreme fragility. This seems paradoxical, but is nevertheless true, for the tail, which has definite " cleavage planes " passing through the middle of the vertebrae, is so fragile that it can almost be cast off at will; the lost member retains its muscular irritability, and its wriggling movements may distract the pursuer's attention for the short time necessary to enable the lizard to gain a place of safety. A new tail is regenerated from the stump of the old one, and, should the old tail be damaged but not completely lost, a new one often grows out from the wound, thus producing one of those double, or sometimes triple, tails which are occasionally found.

The sense-organs which show the greatest modification are the ears, eyes, and tongue. Ears, which are entirely exposed in many terrestrial forms, are concealed by overlapping scales, or completely covered, in burrowing or desert-dwelling lizards, which also exhibit all stages in the development of a transparent window in the lower eyelid. The tongue is usually flattened and only slightly notched in front, but in some it is quite snake-like, bifid, rounded, and retractile into a basal sheath. Teeth vary according to the diet. The majority of lizards feed on insects, and such forms have, as a rule, all the teeth alike, simple, sharply pointed cones adapted to seizing and holding the small hard-shelled prey; more rarely, in conjunction with flesh or vegetable food, they may be flattened to form cutting organs, serrated, or enlarged to form flat crushers.

Many lizards lay eggs which are buried in sand or humus and left to be hatched by the heat of the sun. In different families, however, the practice of retaining the eggs within the body of the mother until the young are ready to be hatched has been developed. In this method (ovoviviparity) the developing embryos receive all their nourishment from the yolk stored up in the egg ; but in a few skinks the eggshell is entirely lost, the amount of yolk reduced, and the developing young are nourished by the direct transmission of food from the maternal blood stream to that of the embryo (viviparity).

The Lizards, like all other series of animals, may be sub-divided into a number of families whose members are closely allied, the indications of relationship being centred chiefly in characters of the skull and skeleton. It scarcely seems necessary to mention these features, fundamental though their importance is to the zoologist, but it is hoped that the few external characters mentioned under each heading will be sufficient for the recognition of the more important families.

Family Gekkonidae (*Geckoes*)

Geckoes are small, soft-skinned lizards with the eye covered by a transparent, watchglass-like covering ; the digits are frequently expanded and furnished with adhesive pads underneath.   This group occurs everywhere in warmer climates, even on the remotest oceanic islands, and its members are adapted to very diverse habitats.   As a rule they have a short, stout body, a large head and weak limbs, and all are insect-eaters.

The pads of the feet and hands, so characteristic of most geckoes, consist of transverse plates beset with numerous tiny, hair-like processes which give the whole surface a velvety appearance ; this velvety pile accommodates itself to any irregularity of the surface, and pressure forces out the air from between the hairs until the whole pad is so closely applied that it adheres after the manner of a schoolboy's " sucker," but without the intervention of a film of moisture.   Adhesive lamellae are not, or are only feebly, developed in ground-living species, but these often show other digital modifications.   The wraith-like *Palmatogecko*, of the deserts of South-West Africa, for example, has the fingers and toes webbed to their tips to enable the animal to walk over, and burrow in, loose sand.

A MEDITERRANEAN GECKO
(*Tarentola mauritanica*).

All geckoes have extremely fragile tails, and this organ often assumes the most bizarre forms.   It may be relatively long and slender, short and globose, fusiform, leaf-like, or ornamented with rows of tubercles or thorn-like spines, excrescences which are not uncommon on the backs of many species.   The voice, absent in most lizards, is developed to a certain extent in this family, the call usually being a feeble click or chirp which is roughly imitated by the name, Géc-ko. All the species, so far as is known, reproduce by means of eggs, which have a hard, calcareous shell.

Family Uroplatidae

This family contains only a few, very gecko-like animals in Madagascar, the best known being the species *Uroplates fimbriatus*. This is a relatively large animal (reaching a length of about fourteen inches) in which the body is much depressed, and is bordered by a serrated fold which also fringes the limbs ; the tail, too, is flattened and leaf-like. The colouring closely resembles that of a patch of lichen, so that, when the animal is at rest on a tree-trunk, its broken outline and cryptic colouring render it very inconspicuous.

Family Scincidae (Skinks)

Skinks are the commonest lizards in the world. Their distribution is cosmopolitan, and though the family is not well represented in America, the tropical parts of the Old World possess a perfectly bewildering array of species. They are clothed with an armour of large, hard, slippery, over-lapping scales, beneath each of which is a bony plate. None is very large, the largest species being the Australian Blue-tongued Lizard (*Tiliqua scincoides*), which reaches a length of about two feet, and, though many have well-developed limbs, a very large number of the smaller species have adopted cryptozoic or burrowing habits, and show all stages in the loss of digits and

THE SKINK (*Scincus scincus*).

the reduction of the limbs. In some the fore-limbs show greater reduction than the hinder pair, but in others the converse is true.

The genus *Lygosoma*, a world-wide group containing over a hundred species, shows this degeneration to the greatest extent, a few of its species being quite limbless. It also shows progressive reduction of the eyes and concealment of the ears in burrowing forms, and the development of a transparent disc in the lower eyelid in those inhabiting sandy terrain. Commencing as a few enlarged, semi-transparent scales, in the more advanced forms the whole lower eyelid has lost its scaly character and become quite transparent. The culminating point of this development is, however, reached in such forms as *Cryptoblepharus*, where the lower eyelid is quite transparent and fused to the upper, thus superficially resembling the transparent eye-covering of geckoes and snakes. Within the genus *Lygosoma* there can also be found every stage from egg-laying to true viviparity. The majority of these lizards retain their eggs within the body until they are ready to hatch, but a few, including the common Blue-tailed Skink (*L. cyanurum*), which abounds on almost every Pacific island from Tahiti to New Guinea, lay membranous-shelled eggs ; on the

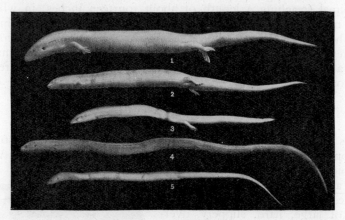

Five Skinks of the same genus, showing progressive stages in reduction of the limbs.
(1) *Chalcides ocellatus* ; (2) *C. mionecton* ; (3) *C. delislii* ; (4) *C. tridactylus* ; (5) *C. guentheri*.

other hand, one or two South Australian species are known to be truly viviparous.

The Skink, which has given its name to the whole family, is a small North African and Syrian species (*Scincus scincus*), adapted for life in desert regions. It has a wedge-shaped head, small eyes, and short, paddle-like limbs ; the fingers and toes are fringed by broad projecting scales which greatly increase their area, so that it can dive into, and literally swim through, loose sand at such a pace that if a specimen is dropped it will be a foot underground by the time one can make any attempt to recapture it.

Another genus which shows various stages of limb reduction and the development of a transparent disc in the lower eyelid is *Chalcides* of South Europe, North Africa, and Western Asia ; one species (*C. tridactylus*) is, like some *Lygosomas*, truly viviparous.

Family Lacertidae

This family is confined to the Old World (though absent from Madagascar and the Australian region) and contains the majority of European lizards.

Pl. 8. WALL LIZARDS (*Lacerta muralis*).

Its members all have well-developed, five-fingered limbs, long fragile
tails, and, as a rule, the scales of the back are small and granular. The
head, however, is covered by large, regularly arranged plates, beneath
which are osteoderms. The European species almost all belong to the
genus *Lacerta*, of which two species, the Common Lizard (*L. vivipara*)
and the Sand-lizard (*L. agilis*) occur in Britain. The former of these is
the smaller (rarely exceeding a length of five or six inches), and is fairly
common throughout Great Britain and Northern Europe. It is brown
or olive in colour, with darker streaks and round lighter spots on the
flanks, and the lower surfaces of males may be yellowish or orange. As
its name implies, it normally produces its young fully developed, but there
are records of specimens which have laid eggs. Like most other Lacertids

EUROPEAN GREEN-LIZARD (*Lacerta viridis*).

it feeds chiefly on insects and small spiders. The other British species,
the Sand-lizard, is a larger animal, and, though plentiful on the continent,
is rare in England, where it is confined to a few isolated localities in
Lancashire and the south. Females are brownish, with rows of darker
and lighter spots and patches, but the males are a beautiful emerald green,
with an irregular dark stripe down the middle of the back and small white
spots. Unlike the Common Lizard, this species lays eggs.

Two common South European species are the Green-lizard, a much
larger form, usually of a vivid green colour, more or less speckled with
black, which ranges northwards to the Channel Islands, and the Wall-
lizard, with a similar distribution. The latter occurs in thousands on
every wall and bank through Central and Southern Europe, and is so
extremely variable in its colour pattern that it would need a large book to
describe all the known forms. On the islands of the Mediterranean
almost every tiny islet has its own colour variety, often endowed with the
rank of a distinct species, and on the mainland too, the colour varieties
are almost endless. Here, however, intergradations from one form to
the next are known, and it is almost impossible to tell whether we have to
do with a number of distinct, but closely allied, forms which interbreed
where they meet, or with one or two very variable ones which, in different

S 2

regions, are beginning to take on the semblance of new species. The most beautiful South European form is the Eyed-lizard (*L. ocellata*), which reaches a length of eighteen to twenty inches and is coloured a brilliant greenish-yellow, with rows of blue, black-bordered, eye-like spots along the flanks.

Other interesting Lacertids which may be mentioned are *Acanthodactylus*, of South-West Europe and North Africa, which, in correlation with life in sandy districts, has the superficial area of the fingers and toes increased by a fringe of elongate scales along their outer edges ; *Cabrita*, in India, has a transparent disc in the lower eyelid; and *Ophisops*, another dweller in sandy places, has the transparent lower eyelid fused to the upper.

Italian variety of the European Wall-lizard (*Lacerta muralis brüggemanni*).

Family Teiidae

This American family superficially resembles the Old World Lacertids, but is distinguishable by the tongue, which is always narrow, deeply bifid, and often retractile into a basal sheath, like that of a snake. Though not a wide-ranging group (it is almost confined to South America, with only a few forms extending northwards into the southern United States) this is one of the most diversified. The largest species is the Teju or Teguexin, which reaches a length of three or four feet, and in appearance and habits resembles the Old World Monitors.

Another large form is *Dracaena*, of the Amazon basin, which is herbivorous and, in connection with this diet, has the cheek teeth converted into large, oval crushers.

THE TEGUEXIN.

More like the typical lizards are the Race-runners (*Cnemidophorus*), inhabiting the tropical parts of South America and extending northwards into the United States. Usually characterised by a number of narrow, yellow stripes on a dark background, these animals live in dry, sandy regions and have acquired their name from the amazing speed at which they run when disturbed. Similar to them are the Ameivas, found throughout the West Indies and tropical South America, which show almost as great local variability as the European Wall-lizards.

The smaller Teiids show progressive elongation of the body, coupled with limb reduction and the development of a window in the lower eyelid. These modifications are, as in other families, developed in conjunction with burrowing habits or life in sandy districts. The extreme development of the lower eyelid is shown by such forms as *Gymnophthalmus*, where it is entirely transparent and fused to the upper eyelid, and the greatest degree of limb reduction is found in *Scolecosaurus* and *Bachia*. The former of these is a small worm-like creature which lives in rotten wood and feeds on white ants. It still retains three or four clawed fingers and toes ; but *Bachia* is more degraded. Here the fingers are reduced to clawless tubercles, and the hind-limb is sometimes represented by but an undivided stylet ; the body is worm-like, the head scarcely perceptible, the eyes minute, and the scales are reduced to squarish plates arranged in regular longitudinal and transverse rows.

Family Amphisbaenidae

These animals are so named (*amphi*, both ; *baino*, go) from the similarity of the head and tail and their ability to move either head first, or tail first. They are burrowing, worm-like creatures, without visible eyes or ears, with small heads, short, bluntly rounded tails, and a soft skin divided into rectangular segments which are arranged in regular transverse and longitudinal rows. They live in damp, sandy regions, constructing subterranean galleries, and seldom or never appear on the surface. Their food consists of earthworms, white ants, and similar creatures.

A blind, limbless, burrowing Lizard (*Amphisbaena*).

Only one genus (*Chirotes*) has external rudiments of limbs ; in these animals, inhabitants of Mexico and Lower California, the fore-limbs alone persist, in the form of short paddles with five, four or three clawed fingers. The other members of the family are found in South America, Africa, and some of the European countries round the Mediterranean.

Family Varanidae (Monitors)

The Monitors, or " Goannas," are large lizards of the Old World, with small, closely set scales and a long, protrusible, snake-like tongue. The

largest is the comparatively recently discovered "Dragon" of the East
Indian islands of Komodo, Rintja, and Flores (*Varanus komodoensis*), which,
though only reaching a total length of about ten feet, is nevertheless a
very heavy powerful animal. Like all the other members of this group
it is carnivorous, and in its native haunts feeds largely on small wild pigs,

A Monitor (*Varanus salvator*).

though no meat, whether freshly killed or not, comes amiss to this voracious
creature. The other species, widely distributed through South Asia,
Africa, and Australia, differ from the "Dragon" in being much more
slimly built, and in having relatively long, whip-like tails ; in habits, however, they are all very similar.

In many districts, particularly India, where the Kabara Goya (*V. salvator*)
and Bis-cobra (*V. bengalensis*) are fairly common, these animals are
erroneously regarded as poisonous. Although the animals do bite, the
wounds so inflicted are not dangerous, since these lizards have no venom
glands. More often the long, whip-like tail is used for defence, and,
though, again, in no way venomous, it forms a very efficient weapon. One
species, the West African Monitor (*V. exanthematicus*), often seeks to escape
danger by "shamming dead" ; assuming a ridiculous pose on its back,
it places one hind-foot in its mouth, and so remains until the supposed
danger is passed. The whole group is very uniform in general appearance
and in colour pattern, the latter usually consisting of a grey, brown, or
black ground colour, with dull yellow markings in the form of transverse
bars or round, yellow, eye-like spots.

Family Pygopodidae

These snake-like lizards (found in Australia, Tasmania, and New Guinea)
have very long, fragile tails, no fore-limbs, and the hind-limbs reduced
to a flap on either side of the vent, while the large eyes are protected by an
immovable transparent covering. These degenerate creatures, sometimes
called "Slow-worms," are not burrowers, but are "cryptozoic," living
in thick grass or similar herbage, and hiding beneath stones. This type
of habitat, as we have seen in other groups, is often correlated with a
greater or less reduction of the limbs, and it seems reasonable to suppose

that, if movement can be achieved in any other way, limbs or any other projecting organs are more of a hindrance than a help under these conditions. Actually, movement is produced by a series of side-to-side undulations of the body, which pass backwards from the head to the tail as a series of waves; each of these waves, in its passage, presses against the surrounding medium, in this instance thick grass, and forces the animal forwards. One of the commonest of these Australian " Slow-worms," *Pygopus*, reaches a length of nearly two feet, of which about sixteen inches belong to the tail.

AUSTRALIAN " SLOW-WORM " (*Pygopus*), showing the rudimentary hind-limbs.

Family Helodermatidae (*Gila Monsters, etc.*)

The Gila Monsters and Beaded-lizards of Texas, Arizona, and Mexico (*Heloderma horridum* and *H. suspectum*) are *the only two known poisonous lizards*. They are obese-looking, sluggish creatures with short stumpy tails, a covering of small bead-like scales, a broad tongue, and a warning coloration of alternating rings of black and either yellow or pinkish-orange. The teeth are hooked and each has a groove from its base to its tip, which acts as the channel whereby the poison, secreted by a row of glands along the inside of the lower lip (contrast with snakes, where the poison apparatus is always in the upper jaw), is introduced into the blood of the victim. They are desert-dwellers, feeding chiefly on small lizards on which the venom acts rapidly, producing paralysis; but the bite is not, as a rule, dangerous to man.

Family Anguidae (*Glass-snake, Slow-worm, etc.*)

The few lizards of this family resemble the skinks in the possession of large, smooth, overlapping scales with bony plates beneath them, but they are distinguished by the possession of a long protrusible tongue. Most of the species are American and have well-developed, five-fingered limbs, but one genus, *Ophisaurus*, has only a pair of style-like rudiments of the hinder pair. The Scheltopusik, or Glass-snake of South Europe and Morocco, is one of the species of this genus and is a relatively large beast, reaching a length of nearly four feet, with a long, extremely fragile tail. It is the fragility of this appendage, which literally cracks apart into fragments if the animal is roughly handled, which has given the name

Glass-snake, not only to the European species (*O. apus*), but to its North American relative (*O. ventralis*).

The species known in England as the Slow-worm, or Blind-worm (the

latter very inapt, as the animal has quite well-developed eyes), also belongs to this family and lacks all external rudiments of limbs. This is a shy creature, frequenting grassy banks and ditches, and is a beautiful silvery colour with narrow, brown, longitudinal stripes. It is remarkable as one of the few reptiles which preys almost exclusively on slugs. Like the Common Lizard it is ovoviviparous, the young, usually some six to twelve in a litter, being born in August.

EUROPEAN " SLOW-WORM " (*Anguis*), with new-born young escaping from the egg-membrane.

Family Zonuridae (*Girdled-lizards*)

The Girdled-lizards of Africa and Madagascar which represent this family have an armour of large, rough scales, regular plates on the head, and a short, thick tongue.

The larger members of this family often have whorls of tremendously enlarged spiny scutes on the tail, which thus becomes a very effective weapon for defence, and have well - developed, pentadactyle limbs. But some of the smaller spe-

SOUTH AFRICAN GIRDLED-LIZARD (*Zonurus giganteus*).

cies, for instance those of the genus *Chamaesaura*, are cryptozoic and show that reduction of the limbs which we have already noticed in correlation with this habitat; the most degenerate species has only undivided remnants of the hinder pair.

Family Iguanidae (*Iguanas*)

Iguanas, in the broader sense of the word, are lizards clad with small scales—even on the head—thick, non-protrusible tongues, and teeth fused to the inner slope of the jaw-bones ; this latter characteristic is almost the only absolute difference between this family and the next, the Agamas. Iguanas are, however, with the exception of three genera—one in the Fiji Islands and two in Madagascar—entirely American, whereas the Agamids are an exclusively Old World family. They show considerable differentiation in accordance with aquatic, arboreal, and terrestrial habits, but none have taken to burrowing, and consequently there are no species with reduced limbs.

Arboreal species almost always have the body compressed from side to side, a crest of elongate, blade-like scales running from the nape of the neck along the middle of the back, and very long tails. The Common Iguana, found throughout tropical South and Central America, is an arboreal species of this type, and, like many other arboreal lizards, its colour is greenish with irregular, wavy bands of brown. It reaches a length of about six feet and is usually found in trees overhanging streams and rivers, into which it unhesitatingly plunges if alarmed. The food consists largely of tender leaves and fruits, but small birds and mammals are not despised.

Another genus of arboreal lizards are the Basilisks (*Basiliscus*), not to be confused with the wholly mythical Basilisks of the Egyptians and Romans, which frequent the same regions, but which exhibit some curious modifications. The hinder part of the head is produced into a flat lobe, like a cock's comb, the toes have a wide fringe of elongate scales, and the males have an enormously developed crest along the back and tail. This crest, at its maximum development, is as deep as the body, supported by rays, and covered with a layer of very delicate scales. The fringes of the toes are not, as in those other lizards where we have already encountered this character, an adaptation to enable the animal to run over soft sand, but over the surface of water ! This, almost unique, power is best shown in younger animals which will, if disturbed, scutter across the surface of water on their hind-limbs. The allied Cuban *Deiroptyx*, however, not only runs over the surface, but, on reaching some quiet corner, deliberately dives to the bottom to seek safety.

Usually arboreal, and not at all aquatic, are the Anoles, sometimes known as American Chamaeleons, which, like some Geckoes, are adapted for climbing by the development of adhesive lamellae beneath the toes. They are small animals, which have earned the sobriquet of "Chamaeleon" by their extraordinary powers of changing colour, and possess remarkably highly developed "dewlaps." This organ is a pouch of very distensible skin beneath the throat, and can be expanded by a special development of the hyoid apparatus, but what its function may be is unknown. From the fact that it is often brightly coloured and more developed in males than in females, it would appear to be in the same category as the brilliantly coloured secondary sexual characters of many mammals and birds.

The best-known aquatic Iguanids are the famous Marine-lizards

(*Amblyrhynchus*) of the Galapagos Islands, the only lizards which are known regularly to enter salt water. They live on the shores, often in herds of thousands, feeding on the seaweeds which are exposed at low tide, and are often entirely immersed in the swells of the restless Pacific.

The strictly terrestrial Iguanids are, as a rule, depressed rather than compressed, the tail is shorter, and the crest along the back always relatively low. Depressed bodily form is carried to an extreme in the so-called " Horned-toads " (*Phrynosoma*) of the deserts of the southern United States

MEXICAN HORNED-LIZARD (*Phrynosoma*).

and Mexico. They are squat, short-legged creatures which, like many other desert-dwellers, have a veritable armour of thorn-like spines. These reach their greatest development on the back of the head, and, in addition to forming a defensive armour, break up the outline of the body to such an extent that, in conjunction with a colouring which strongly resembles the background, the animals are almost invisible in their natural surroundings. A unique characteristic of the Horned-toads is their ability, when frightened, to squirt a fine jet of blood from the eye, sometimes to a distance of five feet. Whether this extraordinary performance really has any defensive value, or is merely an uncontrollable reflex action caused by fright, has never been discovered.

Family Agamidae

The Agamids are the Old World counterpart of the Iguanas, but are distinguished from them by the fusion of the teeth to the crests of the jaw-bones, and not to their inner surfaces. The general appearance of these lizards varies with their habitats in almost exactly the same way as in the preceding group, but there are none analogous with the Anoles in the possession of climbing-pads under the digits.

AUSTRALIAN THORNY-DEVIL (*Moloch*).

Corresponding with the Horned-toads are the Australian Moloch-lizards, or Thorny-devils, desert-dwellers, with very depressed bodies, short tails, and an armour of huge, irregular spines, of which the largest are situated above the eyes. Spines are also developed, but to a less extent, in the African and Asiatic Agamas, also inhabitants of dry regions, and in the Mastigures (*Uromastix*) of Northern Africa and South-West Asia. The latter animals are almost entirely herbivorous, and, correlated with this diet, their front teeth are modified to form cutting blades. They dig burrows, to which they retire at night, and, as their spines are confined to the tail where they form regular whorls, they lie with the tail towards the opening of the burrow ; in this position the tail is most favourably situated for the repulsion of any would-be invader.

Another terrestrial form of the normal, depressed type is the Australian Jew, or Bearded-lizard (*Amphibolurus barbatus*), so-called from the numerous long narrow spines beneath the throat and fringing the head behind the ears. The famous Australian Frilled-lizards (*Chlamydosaurus*), though terrestrial, have, however, adopted rather different habits, and their bodily form is more like that of an arboreal species. The body is circular in section, rather than depressed, the tail very long, the fore-limbs comparatively weak, and around the neck is a frill-like fold of skin, supported by cartilaginous rods like the ribs of an umbrella. When the animal is at rest this frill is

MALE " FRILLED-LIZARD " (*Chlamydosaurus*) at bay.

folded, cape-like, about the shoulders. If, however, it is disturbed, it first seeks safety in flight, running swiftly on the hind-legs, with the body inclined forwards, the fore-limbs folded against the sides, and the long tail raised as a counterpoise. But it soon tires and stops to face its pursuers, with widely opened mouth and the frill erected so that it stands out like a ruff at right angles to the neck. This attitude, with the saffron-yellow of the mouth contrasting with greenish-yellow, red-splashed frill, is certainly impressive, and dogs which will not hesitate to attack larger lizards, such as a monitor, have been known to halt and retire discomfited before it.

As examples of normal arboreal species we may mention the Blood-suckers, and their allies, from the Indo-Burmese area. They are all compressed lizards, with long tails, often with a crest of blade-like spines running from the nape of the neck along the back, and usually there is a dewlap such as we have already encountered in the Anoles. Almost all of them are capable of a considerable amount of colour change, but these changes are produced more by physical conditions—warmth, sunshine, etc.—and by mental disturbances rather than as a direct response to the colour of the background; the Blood-sucker has, in fact, gained its name from the blood-red head and neck which it acquires under the influence of excitement.

A FLYING-LIZARD (*Draco*), with " wings " expanded.

By far the most remarkable of all the Agamids are the Flying-lizards (*Draco*) of the Malayan region, the only lizards with any pretensions to ability to fly. The flying, or really gliding, mechanism is, as in the Flying Squirrels and Lemurs, a greatly developed fold of skin along the sides of the body. But it is here supported by five or six enormously elongate ribs, and, when not in use, is folded against the sides of the body. These little lizards—the largest is barely fifteen inches long—are arboreal in habits, and the body and upper surfaces of the wings, the only parts visible when they are folded, are usually rather dull shades of brown or grey to harmonise with the branches among which the animals live. When, however, they take to the air, which they do in little gliding flights from branch to branch, or soaring against the wind, the lower surfaces of the wings are exposed, and these are often so brilliantly coloured in reds, oranges, and blues, with black markings, that the animals resemble gaily coloured butterflies. At the conclusion of the flight, the wings are folded, and the transition from conspicuous gay colours to unobtrusive shades, harmonising with the background, is so abrupt and deceptive that the animals seem to vanish.

Family Chamaeleontidae (*Chamaeleons*)

Chamaeleons are lizards highly specialised for arboreal life, and are characterised by the modification of the feet into grasping organs by the fusion of the digits into opposable bundles (the two outer fingers being opposed to the three inner, and *vice versa* for the toes), a prehensile tail, an extremely protrusible tongue, and independently movable eyes. Indeed, they have so many obvious peculiarities that they are sometimes regarded as forming a separate group, distinct from, but allied to, the remaining lizards. They are found throughout Africa, Madagascar, Arabia, Southern India, and Ceylon, but Central Africa and Madagascar are the regions where the greatest number and most diverse forms occur. The tongue is a truly remarkable organ and is the mechanism whereby the prey—flies and other insects—is captured. It is club-shaped and provided with a sticky secretion at its tip, whilst the narrow basal portion is composed of very elastic fibres. When not in use this basal portion is telescoped over a bony style, and is in a state of compression. The prey is deliberately stalked until it is within range, when out shoots the tongue with lightning speed and unerring precision, and the victim is withdrawn adhering to its sticky tip.

The mechanism by which the tongue is shot out to such a remarkable distance—seven or eight inches in a fully-grown Common Chamaeleon (*Chamaeleon chamaeleon*)—is partly its own elasticity and partly the forcing of blood into hollow spaces within it. As has already been pointed out, when not in use the elastic basal portion is under compression, and when the restraint is removed the tongue shoots forward, assisted by the pressure of the blood inside it. The momentum of the heavy tip carries it forwards until the basal piece is under tension—this tension and the action of certain muscles effect its withdrawal. The peculiarities of the eyes are probably connected with the method of feeding, since a nice appreciation of distances is essential for the successful use of the

A THREE-HORNED CHAMAELEON (*Chamaeleon oweni*).

tongue, and such an ability to judge distances accurately is only possible with binocular vision. The eyes of a chamaeleon are large and prominent (though the eyelids, which are fused into a large circular covering, only leave a small opening), and are independently movable, so that they can both be focussed upon the same spot in front of the animal.

The ability of these animals to change colour has made their name proverbial, but their powers in this direction are almost always greatly exaggerated and are quite equalled by those of some iguanas and agamids. The mechanism of colour change consists of a number of cells (chromatophores), lying in the lower layers of the skin, which have a number of branches extending towards the surface. Each of these cells has pigment granules which may be either black, yellow, or red, and the flow of one or more kinds of pigment towards the surface, and the withdrawal of others, produces the predominant colour of the moment. The flow of these pigments is partly voluntary and partly involuntary. Changes in the intensity of the light, change of temperature and emotion, produce marked and characteristic responses, but there is little direct response to the colour of the environment.

The normal colour of a Common Chamaeleon is a greyish-green, with numerous small dark specks and rows of pale brown patches on the sides of the body. In the dark, at ordinary temperatures, the colour fades to cream, with irregular yellow spots, but exposure to hot sunlight produces a uniform darkening until the whole animal may be dull black. High temperatures in the shade result in greens, and low temperatures dull greys ; excitement or fright bring paler shades, with brown patches and yellow spots, and anger causes the light regions to darken. Blues and reds do not appear to be within the range of this particular species, though others can compass them, but the combinations and various shades of green, yellow, brown, black, and white seem almost endless.

As in other groups of lizards most species lay eggs, but in a few the eggs are retained within the body of the mother until they are ready to be hatched. Another feature, also found in other groups but perhaps more pronounced here, is a tendency towards the production of bizarre ornamentations. Many species have the head produced upwards into a pointed casque, and the edge of this may have a pair of movable fleshy flaps which are erected when emotions hold sway. Others have a fin-like crest along the back, and many have horns on the head. These may be simply a single or bifid prolongation of the tip of the snout or be a flexible fleshy proboscis. In others, however, there may be a further pair of horns situated above each eye, and, as a rule, these are better developed in males than in females.

Sub-order OPHIDIA

(*Snakes*)

Like their allies, the Lizards, snakes are one of the dominant groups of present-day reptiles, and some two thousand or more forms are at present known. Of their ancestry we know little, for very few fossils have been found, but it seems fairly certain that they were derived from a lizard-like ancestor, and, as we have already had occasion to point out, the two groups are even now only separated by a few, relatively trivial, differences.

The salient external features of a typical snake are the absence of limbs, except perhaps rudiments of the hinder pair, no movable eyelids or visible external ears, a forked slender tongue which can be withdrawn into a sheath at its base, pointed, recurved teeth, and a series of transversely enlarged plates beneath the belly. Internal characters which are of importance are the complete absence of any of the bones connected with the fore-limbs, the closure of the brain case in front, the union of the two halves of the lower jaw by an elastic ligament instead of by fusion, and the great development of one lung at the expense of the other.

Many of these characters we have already encountered in lizards, particularly in those modified for a burrowing or semi-burrowing existence, and it seems not improbable that snakes originally arose as a group modified for such a life, but that subsequently many of the species invaded other environments. A serpent moves, not as the conventional representations would imply, by a series of vertical waves, but like a limbless lizard, by a series of side-to-side undulations. Where an animal is surrounded by a relatively dense medium, there is sufficient resistance to the backward passage of the waves to drive the animal forwards ; but the majority of snakes have acquired an additional mechanism—the transversely enlarged plates of the lower surface. Each of these plates is overlapped in front by its predecessor, but its hinder edge is quite free, and to each is attached a pair of movable ribs. When the ribs are moved forwards the scute, with

Skull of a Python.

its leading edge hidden by the one in front, slips easily over the surface, but when the ribs are moved backwards the free hinder edge of the plate catches on the slightest projection, or irregularity of the ground, and thus gains the " foothold " necessary to enable the snake to push itself forwards. As there are often more than two hundred of these shields, progress becomes possible over any surface which is not absolutely smooth.

The development of a hard transparent covering to protect the eye is another feature found in many lizards, but whereas in the latter this covering is usually a modified lower eyelid, in snakes it probably represents the " third eyelid " (nyctitating membrane). The covering over of the ear, too, is a character found in many burrowing lizards, but in snakes it is probable that hearing is of a different nature from that of most other animals. There is no ear-drum, and the bone which usually transmits vibrations from the ear-drum to the sensitive mechanism of the inner ear rests with its outer end against the bone which supports the lower jaw. Any movement of the jaw would consequently be expected to produce a sensation of appalling din, but snakes seem to be able to hear to some extent, and it is possible that the ear is attuned, not to air-borne vibrations, but to those transmitted through the earth. The sense of smell is well developed ; but snakes have another very important sense-organ—the tongue. The constant play of this organ, when one of these animals is excited, or is investigating something, makes it evident that great reliance is placed on the sensations which it receives, though what these really are we have no means of telling. It seems not unlikely that we have to deal with some sense allied to that of smell, for an egg-eating snake can readily differentiate between a good egg and an addled one!

Whatever may be the function of the tongue, one thing it certainly is never used for, and that is to lick the prey all over to cover it with slime before it is swallowed. All snakes are carnivorous, the food consisting of birds, small mammals, lizards, other snakes, frogs, toads, or fish in the larger species, and insects, earthworms, and so on in the smaller. The victim may be killed by constriction, or poison, or actually eaten alive; but it is always closely investigated by the tongue before being swallowed. Snakes do not chew their food, but swallow it whole, and to permit the swallowing of meals which are often of greater diameter than the diner there are several adaptations. Apart from a general elasticity of all the tissues in the region of the neck, the bones supporting the lower jaw are movable, permitting of a tremendous gape, and the two halves of the lower jaw can be pushed widely apart to enlarge the mouth aperture.

The actual mechanism whereby the food is forced into the mouth is centred in the hooked teeth, and the laborious swallowing process proceeds as follows. First the victim is worked round until its head is in the snake's mouth, and then the teeth of either side are worked alternately forwards. Their hooked shape allows them to be pushed forwards, but not easily drawn back, so that, when those of one side are engaged, the opposite side of the head can be worked forwards a short distance, and so on alternately, until the snake has literally drawn itself over the carcase. During this operation the snake would be in danger of suffocation were it not for a special provision which enables it to push the end of the wind-pipe (the glottis) out of the mouth between the separated halves of the lower jaw, and so continue breathing however long the swallowing process may continue. A further disadvantage of this type of feeding is the likelihood of teeth being broken off by the victim's struggles. Actually this is by no means infrequent, but the loss is countered by the provision of several series of reserve teeth in different stages of development within a special fold of the lining of the mouth—the *vagina dentis*. Immediately one of the functional series is lost the next in succession moves into its place and becomes fused to the jaw-bone.

In addition to their primary duties as feeding organs some of the teeth of poisonous snakes are modified to form " fangs." These are always situated in the upper jaw, either at the front or hind end, and the passage for the venom is either a simple longitudinal groove, or a groove whose edges have met and so produced an enclosed channel opening at the base and tip of the fang. The venom itself is a pale, straw-coloured liquid manufactured by a special gland situated behind the angle of the mouth, and is conveyed to the fangs by a duct which opens near their bases. It owes its poisonous properties to various proteins, the two most important being one which attacks the blood corpuscles and tissues, and one which acts directly on the nerves, producing paralysis. The preponderance of one or other of these two agents determines the nature of the consequences of snake-bite. If the nerve poison predominates, paralysis, general prostration, and difficulty in breathing are the most dangerous symptoms ; but if the victim survives this stage, recovery is usually rapid and complete.

If, on the other hand, the blood toxin is present in excess, there is little or no paralysis, though there may be general prostration ; even if the patient recovers from this, however, there will be severe local symptoms at the site of the bite, with much swelling, and possibly gangrene, which may cause death even months afterwards. The venom is destroyed by

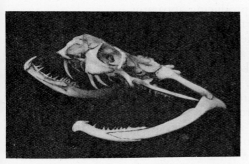 

Skull of a proteroglyphous Snake ; the poison fangs are situated at the front of the upper jaw.

Skull of an opisthoglyphous Snake ; the poison fangs are at the hinder end of the upper jaw.

such substances as potassium permanganate and bleaching powder (but not by carbolic and similar disinfectants), and this property, together with attempts to prevent the absorption of the poison into the system, should form the basis of first-aid treatment. Apply a tourniquet above the fang punctures ; make a free incision into the wound, and, if possible, wash them out with a solution of permanganate or bleaching powder. The tourniquet should not be kept on for more than half an hour, but should be released for a few seconds, from time to time, to restore the circulation. Large doses of stimulants are useless, but small doses may be useful in cases of collapse. Finally, get the patient under competent medical supervision as quickly as possible.

Despite a widespread belief in the efficacy of " snake-stones " and various so-called " cures," there is only one known reliable treatment for snake-bite, and that is by means of " anti-venines." These are now manufactured in almost all countries where dangerous snakes are common, their method of preparation being the immunisation of horses against a particular venom by increasing regulated doses of the poison. The blood serum of the horses is then drawn off in small quantities, sterilised, and made up ready for inoculation. It has not, however, yet been found possible to make an anti-venine which is efficacious against more than one or two kinds of venom, so that, to ensure correct treatment, an effort should be made to identify the snake responsible for the accident.

In general habits snakes are secretive and timid rather than aggressive, though there are occasional instances of apparently unprovoked attacks. They are not confined to any one type of terrain, but, like the lizards, have become adapted to many different environmental conditions. They are cosmopolitan, except for some islands such as New Zealand and Ireland, and those northern and southern countries where the winter is too severe to enable them to hibernate out of reach of the frosts. None has a true voice, though they can all hiss, and a few, for instance the Rattlesnakes, have a special sound-producing apparatus.

Like that of most other reptiles, the skin is covered by a layer of horny scales which is shed periodically, the operation being termed "sloughing." Sloughing commences at the lips, and by vigorous rubbing the old skin is turned back on itself and the snake gradually works its way out, turning the cast skin inside out in doing so.

Most snakes lay eggs, which are elliptical in shape and have a soft parchment-like covering. They are laid in places exposed to moist heat (the English Grass-snake prefers a manure heap to almost any other situation), and are generally left to their fate. A few, however, exhibit some degree of parental care, and in some the eggs are retained within the body of the mother until they are ready to hatch.

A blind, burrowing Snake, *Typhlops punctatus*.

Some of the more important groups, or families, may be considered briefly to try to give an idea of the great amount of adaptation which these seemingly so similar creatures have really undergone.

Family Typhlopidae

Blind Snakes: small, harmless, burrowing creatures with a general worm-like appearance, a bluntly rounded head in which the eyes have sunk beneath the scales, a very short, blunt tail, smooth shiny scales which are not enlarged on the belly, and teeth only in the upper jaw. They inhabit almost all tropical countries, and are entirely subterranean in habits, feeding on worms, insects, and so on. Usually they are pinkish in colour, but some are irregularly marked with black and yellow.

Family Leptotyphlopidae

Another family of Blind Snakes very similar to the preceding, but having teeth in the lower and not in the upper jaw. One member of this family, the Common South American Blind Snake (*Leptotyphlops albifrons*), is interesting on account of its colour. The body is uniformly brown, but the head and tail both have a white spot which enhance their similarity to such an extent that it needs very careful examination to distinguish the two. This type of colouring has been called " directive mark," and is designed, apparently, to confuse any would-be attacker as to which of the two extremities should be seized.

Family Ilysiidae

Harmless, burrowing snakes, larger than most of those of the preceding families, with tapering heads and tails, teeth in both jaws, slightly enlarged scales on the belly, and a pair of claw-like rudiments of hind-limbs. They inhabit swampy regions and feed principally on other snakes and fish. The South American *Ilysia* is frequently regarded as a mimic of the venomous Coral-snakes, which it superficially resembles, and *Cylindrophis* of Burma and the Malayan regions also exhibits what appears to be mimicry. In the latter snake the upper surfaces are brown, or black, with light cross-bars ; the belly is white, with transverse black bands,

THE MALAYAN EARTH-SNAKE (*Cylindrophis rufus*).

and the lower surface of the tail vermilion. When the animal is brought above ground the tail is bent upwards to exhibit the brilliant colour of its lower surface, and, if the animal is annoyed, the tail snaps round as if it were a striking head ! Though sufficiently remarkable in itself, this behaviour appears scarcely credible when it is realised that the highly venomous, burrowing *Doliophis* of the same regions has a similar colouring and exactly the same reactions.

Family Boidae

Boas and Pythons. These are non-poisonous, often large, snakes with claw-like rudiments of hind-limbs, enlarged scales beneath the belly, and teeth in both jaws. The two groups cannot be readily distinguished by any external character, but Pythons are most numerous in the Old World and the Boas have their headquarters in the New. The latter are almost all arboreal, or semi-arboreal, and the tail is usually more or less prehensile.

THE ANACONDA (*Eunectes*).

They all kill their prey, small mammals and birds, as a rule, by constriction, that is, by throwing one or two coils round it and then tightening them up until the victim is crushed. All snakes are extremely muscular, and the pressure of the coils of even a small one may be sufficient to paralyse a man's arm, but it is very doubtful whether there is any foundation in fact for the many travellers' tales of large Boas and Pythons killing and eating men, cattle, and horses. The prey *must* be swallowed whole, and, wonderfully distensible though a snake's mouth is, it is probable that even a thirty-foot snake would be unable to accommodate anything much bulkier than a small pig. The length of the meal is, of course, quite a different matter, and records of snakes which have swallowed one of their fellows as long as themselves are by no means uncommon.

Almost any large constricting snake is liable to be called a Boa Constrictor, but actually the name is only strictly applicable to a single South American species (*Constrictor constrictor*), which seldom reaches a length of more than eleven feet. The largest true Boa is the Anaconda (*Eunectes murinus*), a half-aquatic, half-arboreal species which frequents the forests of the Amazon basin; it is reported to attain

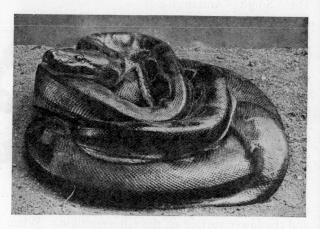

A PYTHON,
showing the claw-like rudiment of a hind-limb at the base of the tail.

a length of over thirty feet, but specimens of twenty-five feet seem to be rare. The colour is dark green, with rows of sharply defined, circular, black spots, and the skin of a healthy specimen has a beautiful iridescent bloom. In contrast with these may be mentioned the small, sand-loving species of the genus *Eryx* from Northern Africa, South-East Europe, and South-West Asia, which all have short tails, drab colours, and small heads merging imperceptibly into their bodies.

The majority of Boas retain their eggs within the body until the young are fully developed, but the true Pythons almost all lay leathery-shelled eggs. The latter group, however, exhibits some degree of parental care ; the female often coils herself about the clutch of eggs, which may number over a hundred, and it has been found that when doing so her temperature rises above that of the air around her, and there is thus true incubation. Like Boas, Pythons are semi-arboreal, and often have prehensile tails, and all of them are fond of water, in which they will lie and soak for days on end. The largest species is the Reticulated Python, of the Indo-Chinese and Malayan Regions, which reaches a length of close on thirty feet, but almost all of them are relatively large. They occur throughout Africa (*e.g.* Rock Python and Royal Python), South Asia (*e.g.* Indian Python), and Australia (*e.g.* the Carpet-snake), and all exhibit the same type of colour pattern.

Family Colubridae

This family contains the vast majority of snakes, and its members may usually be recognised by the following combination of characters : limbs are entirely absent, enlarged plates are present across the belly except in some aquatic forms, the poison fangs, if present, are not movable, and the head is usually covered by enlarged scales. They are distributed throughout the temperate and tropical regions of the world and every different kind of terrain is inhabited. So similar are the modifications which different species have undergone, in conjunction with the same habits, that it is possible to form an accurate conclusion as to a snake's mode of life simply from its appearance. Burrowing forms are all small with short tails, small heads gradually merging into the body, and tiny eyes.

Desert-dwellers are rough-scaled with sombre colours. Terrestrial species in well-watered regions are " normal," that is to say, they have moderately long tails, a cylindrical body, a head well differentiated from the neck, and well-developed eyes. Tree-dwellers are very elongate, with long slender tails, long pointed snouts, and, usually, very large eyes, whilst thoroughly aquatic forms have the nostrils situated on the top of the snout and fitted with valves so that they may be closed when the animal is under water, and, as a rule, the enlarged scutes of the belly are greatly reduced or entirely absent.

Three series of Colubrids may be recognised : those without poison fangs (*Aglypha*), those with poison fangs at the hinder end of the upper jaw and preceded by smaller solid teeth (*Opisthoglypha*), and those with poison fangs at the front of the mouth (*Proteroglypha*) ; each of these divisions can be further sub-divided into sub-families.

Considering first the entirely harmless *Aglypha*, one group differs from all the others in the absence of a groove beneath the chin. This groove is merely a part of the mechanism which enables the two halves of the lower jaw to be pushed apart, and its absence in this group (the *Dipsadinae*) is connected with a change in feeding habits. All the Dipsads, which inhabit South-East Asia, the Malay Archipelago, and Central and South America, are tree-dwellers and feed exclusively upon slugs, a diet which is sufficiently soft and compressible to be swallowed without any excessive stretching of the mouth.

Another small group of harmless snakes are the heavy-bodied, ugly, freshwater and estuarine forms (*Acrochordinae*) of South-East Asia and

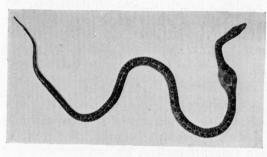

AN EGG-EATING SNAKE (*Dasypeltis*)
with an unbroken egg in its gullet.

Central America which conform to the general aquatic type. They feed largely on fish, and the more thoroughly aquatic species have lost the ventral plates and have the body compressed from side to side with a fold along the lower surface which simulates a median fin. Forms such as these are quite helpless out of water, but the less specialised have a cylindrical body, with enlarged scales on the belly, and are still capable of fairly rapid movement on land.

A few species in tropical and South Africa, the Egg-eating Snakes (*Dasypeltis*), are possibly the most remarkably modified members of the whole group. They have only a few tiny teeth in the jaws, but some of the vertebrae of the neck have downwardly directed projections which actually penetrate the gullet. As their name implies, these snakes feed on eggs—birds' eggs of almost any kind—and the mouth is so remarkably distensible that an egg can be swallowed whole. In the gullet, however, its progress is arrested by the bony projections from the vertebrae. Then the snake, by compressing the muscles of the neck and by backward and forward rocking movements, saws through the egg-shell ; the whole egg promptly collapses, the liquid contents run down into the stomach, and the empty shell is vomited as a small elliptical pellet.

The remainder of the non-poisonous snakes are united into one group (the *Colubrinae*), which occurs commonly throughout the world, except in the Australian region, where it is only scantily represented. Its members may be more or less aquatic, arboreal, terrestrial, or semi-burrowing, and they show considerable specialisations to their different environments.

Perhaps the most thoroughly aquatic species is one which inhabits Lake Tanganyika (*Glypholycus*), which super-ficially resembles some of the Acrochordine snakes, but the Common English Grass-snake and its allies are all water-loving.

The Grass-snake (*Natrix natrix*) is widely distributed through Northern Europe and is very variable in its colour pattern. Commonly it is greyish-green, with some

THE EUROPEAN GRASS-SNAKE (*Natrix natrix*).

black markings on the back, and with at least traces of a yellow or orange collar round the neck, though this is usually interrupted at the back, and is chequered black and white beneath. It frequents damp or marshy localities, is an expert swimmer, and feeds almost entirely on frogs. Its southern relative, the Viperine-snake (*N. viperinus*), very common in Spain and Southern Europe, is more aquatic and feeds almost exclusively on fish, habits which are shared by the Indian Keel-backs (*N. piscator*) and North American Moccasins (*N. fasciatus*) and Garter-snakes (*Thamnophis*). Many of these snakes have a peculiar method of defence, an exceedingly offensive smelling secretion produced by a pair of glands just inside the vent;

A Grass-snake with its slough.

if the animal is captured it twines itself about its aggressor and covers him with this disgustingly smelling secretion and with excrement.

The strictly terrestrial forms, such as the Rat-snakes of Europe and North America (*Coluber*), the Chicken-snakes (*Elaphe*), and the Indian Rat-snakes, feed chiefly on small birds, mammals, toads, and lizards, and either kill their prey by constriction or eat it alive. Some have specialised feeding habits, the English Smooth-snake (*Coronella austriaca*), for example, feeding almost exclusively on Sand-lizards, and being only found in England in those localities where this lizard also occurs. This particular species

is often confused with the Adder, but may be recognised by its smooth scales, the enlarged plates on its head, and its round pupil. The North American Kingsnakes (*Lampropeltis*) also have a special diet, for they feed entirely on other snakes, venomous or otherwise, which they kill by constriction. Another peculiar protective device is found in the American Hog-nose Snakes (*Heterodon*), which in their broad, flat heads

KING-SNAKE (*Lampropeltis*)
A non-venomous, snake-eating species.

and stout bodies externally resemble some vipers. If annoyed they puff themselves up and hiss vigorously, but if this display of " frightfulness " fails to impress the enemy they roll over on their backs and " sham dead." There is one flaw in their acting, though, for if turned the right way up they promptly roll over again !

Turning now to the Back-fanged Snakes (*Opisthoglypha*) we have to deal with a group which, technically speaking, is poisonous. The fangs, however, are situated at the back of the mouth so that, unless the object bitten is very small, or the snake particularly large, they are not brought into play. Consequently, so far as man is concerned these snakes cannot normally be considered dangerous. Some of the larger species, such as the Boomslang, may nevertheless be able to inflict a poisoned bite, and then the consequences may be serious, for the venom resembles that of the vipers, and its principal poisonous constituent is of the blood-destroying type which we have already mentioned. The group is sub-divisible into three sub-families which, strangely enough, exactly correspond with the last three sub-families of the non-venomous snakes which we have just considered.

First there is a group of freshwater snakes (*Homalopsinae*) corresponding to the Acrochordines. They are stout-bodied creatures, found in South-East Asia, Papuasia, and North Australia, with valvular nostrils on the top of the snout, and often with the large scales of the belly greatly reduced. As in most aquatic snakes, the young are born alive.

Next, there is a single Egg-eating Snake from Bengal, which, like the

African egg-eaters, has a reduced number of teeth, though still retaining its poison fangs, and has the same saw-like projections from the backbone penetrating the gullet. Lastly, there is a group (*Boiginae*) corresponding with the *Colubrinae* and, like it, cosmopolitan in distribution and adapted to the same kinds of environment.

The majority, however, are tree-snakes, and possess that slender bodily form which is so characteristic of this type of habitat. Many of them are brilliantly green to harmonise with foliage, others brown to match the branches, but some exhibit brilliant colour patterns which, though conspicuous enough when removed from their natural surroundings, are scarcely noticeable in the dappled light and shade of the bushes the animals frequent. To this latter category belongs the Indian Flying-snake, which is often black, with yellow dots on each scale, and a row of yellow, four-petaled, red-centred " flowers " along the middle of the back. Even more remarkable than its colouring, though, is the faculty which has given it its name, an ability to " glide " to a limited extent. If one of these creatures is frightened when in its native haunts, it will literally fling itself into the air, and, with the body held rigid, make a comparatively gentle descent to the earth and possible safety. There is no special mechanism, as in the Flying-lizards, but, by pushing the ribs outwards to their full extent and drawing in the belly, a large concave surface is produced which checks the fall considerably and converts it into a rapid glide.

Some members of this group, for instance the South African Boomslang, have the power of spreading a " hood " as a threatening gesture. The flattening of the neck, however, is vertical, not horizontal like that of the Cobras, and is produced by the inflation of the windpipe and not by movements of the ribs. In snakes the cartilaginous rings, which are always present in the windpipe to prevent it from collapsing, are not quite complete along the side nearest the backbone, and between their free ends there is a strip of very elastic tissue. When air is forced from the lungs into the windpipe, with the mouth and nostrils closed, this strip of tissue stretches, and the whole of the animal's neck is blown up like a balloon. But, as the ribs offer some resistance to any sideways inflation, the greatest diameter of the swelling is from back to front.

Of the terrestrial members of this group we may mention *Coelopeltis*, common in Southern Europe (and one of the largest snakes of the continent), and the tropical American False Coral-snake, *Erythrolamprus aesculapii*. The latter is one of the most variable snakes in the world, and its numerous colour varieties, with alternating rings of brilliant crimson and black, mimic the much more venomous true Coral-snakes. South America also possesses, in common with Africa, a number of small burrowing forms which conform to the general type of burrowing snake. Some of them, notably *Apostolepsis* in South America and *Parkerophis* in South Africa, also show that " directive mark " coloration which we have already encountered in the Blind Snakes.   The body is yellow, sometimes with longitudinal black stripes, and the head and stumpy tail are both black with white dots, so that the similarity of the two is truly remarkable.

The remaining Colubrine snakes are all characterised by the possession of poison fangs at the front of the mouth, and this group (*Proteroglypha*) contains many of those which are so justly dreaded.   There are two groups of them, the one terrestrial, containing the Cobras and their allies, and the other marine ; both must be regarded as dangerous, though the Sea-snakes are often so docile that they can be handled with impunity. The venom of almost all of them is characterised by the predominance of nerve poisons, and consequently it is extremely rapid in its action. The great danger lies in its paralysing influence, and this stage of the poisoning, with general prostration and the possibility of complete paralysis of the breathing mechanism, usually occurs within a few hours of the injection of the venom.

THE INDIAN COBRA (*Naja naja*).

The best-known members of the group are probably the Cobras, widely distributed through Southern Asia and Africa.   They are all characterised by their ability to spread a horizontal " hood," by pushing outwards the long ribs of the necks.   The action is a warning gesture, comparable with the various threatening actions in which so many other animals indulge. There are several different species, the better-known ones being the Indian Cobra (*Naja naja*), the Hooded or Egyptian Cobra (*N. haje*) and the Black-necked Cobra (*N. nigricollis*), but all are similar in their general habits and behaviour.   They feed chiefly on small rodents, and it is the prevalence of these creatures in and around human habitations which attracts the snakes to regions where they are most liable to come into contact with mankind.

The King Cobra or Hamadryad (*N. hannah*), however, although very closely allied to the others, is almost entirely a snake-eater, and is the only one of the group which exhibits any signs of parental care.   A rude, but definite, nest is made of dried leaves, and in it the eggs are deposited, whilst the parents remain on guard in the vicinity of the nest until the young have been hatched.   Many cobras have an additional defensive mechanism, besides their fangs, and this is also found in the allied South African Ringhals (*Sepedon haemachaetes*).   The venom can be " spat " for a considerable distance, often several yards, and should the venom so discharged enter a person's eyes, intense irritation is set up which results in temporary, or sometimes permanent, blindness. Although the action is called " spitting " the mechanism is really rather different ; by compression of the poison glands a trickle of venom is forced out through the fangs, and at the same time a blast of air is exhaled which carries the liquid forward as a fine, spreading spray.

Allied to the Cobras are the dreaded African Mambas, of which two varieties, a black and green, are commonly recognised. Actually, however, no very small black ones (in reality they are

THE HAMADRYAD (*Naja hannah*).
A venomous snake-eating species.

more of a dark olive colour) have ever been found, whereas the green ones are almost always smaller than the black, and it seems very probable that the two colour varieties are really growth stages of the same species. When young the mamba is green, and almost entirely arboreal in habits, but with increasing age it becomes more and more terrestrial and its colour gradually darkens.

In the Indian region another group of large, dangerous forms are the Kraits (*Bungarus*), and in Australia there are many dangerous species. In fact, the majority of the Australian snakes belong to this group. Some of the best-known are the Black-snakes (*Pseudechis*), which reach a length of six feet and can erect a small cobra-like hood ; the Tiger-snakes (*Notechis*) ; and the Death-adders (*Acanthophis*). The last-named are rather unfortunately so styled, since Adder means Viper, but the mis-application of the word is understandable, as this particular snake has a broad, flat head, without the large shields of most other Colubrids, and a thick-set body which gives it a very viperine appearance.

In the New World the only representatives of the group are the true Coral-snakes, small, burrowing or semi-burrowing snakes with a brilliant " warning coloration " of crimson and yellow and black bands. Another burrowing form with a warning coloration is the Malayan *Doliophis*, which we have already met when considering the *Ilysiidae* ; apart from its habits this animal is remarkable for the enormous development of the poison glands which, instead of being confined to the head, extend backwards over the first third of the body and even displace the heart !

The other great group of front-fanged snakes, the Sea-snakes, are highly specialised for life in water. They have valvular nostrils on the top of the snout, and the tail is flattened from side to side to produce a paddle-like swimming organ. All of them produce fully developed young, and many have the scales of the belly so much reduced that they are absolutely

T

helpless on land. They are found throughout the tropical parts of the Indian and Pacific Oceans, but the majority frequent inshore waters and are most numerous around the coasts of the Indian and Malayan regions and along the chain of islands to North Australia. All known sea-

A common Sea-snake (*Pelamis*).

snakes are venomous. Though seldom exceeding four feet in length a few reach eight feet or more, and these are often of great girth, the greatest diameter being in the hinder half of the body. They feed on fish, particularly eels.

Family Viperidae

Vipers and Rattlesnakes are characterised by the possession of a movable upper jaw which allows the poison fangs to be folded down flat on the palate when the mouth is closed. They are usually stoutly built animals, with large, flat heads, which, as a rule, are covered with small scales similar to those of the body. All the species are poisonous, and all the larger ones dangerous to man. The venom is characterised by the predominance of blood- and tissue-destroying agents, and typical symptoms of viper bite are pain at the site of the wound, followed, within a few hours, by vomiting, profuse salivation, bleeding of the nose and intestine, and complete prostration. These primary symptoms may not prove fatal, but they are always followed by secondary symptoms, in the form of painful swelling of the bitten parts, which may become dangerous even weeks afterwards.

There are two groups of these animals, the True Vipers and the Pit-vipers and Rattlesnakes. The first of these (*Viperinae*) have no pit between the nostril and the eye and are confined to the Old World. They almost all produce fully developed young and are chiefly terrestrial in habits, though a few are modified for other environments. The African Night-adders (*Causus*), for example, are small, semi-burrowing creatures and are characterised by the presence of enlarged scales on their heads like the Colubrids, and the tropical African *Atheris* is a tree-dweller equipped with a prehensile tail. The latter is usually green, or olive, in colour, to harmonise with its surroundings, but terrestrial species living in dry localities are usually coloured in shades of grey, brown, or black.

This type of coloration is well illustrated by the African Puff-adder (*Bitis arietans*), a large (four to five feet), sluggish, heavily built creature common throughout the drier areas of Africa ; it is coloured pale brown, with regular, chevron-shaped, darker cross-bars, and harmonises so well with the soil that many accidents occur through people failing to notice the animal until they actually tread upon it. In contrast with this, the closely allied Gaboon Viper (*Bitis gabonica*), which is an inhabitant of the damp forests of tropical Africa, attains obscurity by means of a geometrical " camouflage " pattern of bright blues, reds, and yellows. Many vipers, particularly desert-dwelling forms, have developed horns or spines on the head. The Horned Puff-adder has a pair of horn-like scales on the tip of the snout, and the Egyptian Horned Viper (*Cerastes cornutus*) has a prominent, thorn-like spine above each eye. Desert life usually implies a pallid coloration, and often necessitates burrowing abilities in order that the animals may escape both from the excessive heat of the middle of the day and the chill of the night. Both these characteristics are found

in such vipers as *Cerastes* and *Echis*, Northern African and South-West Asiatic forms. They bury themselves by means of the scales of their sides which, having a pronounced, serrated " keel," act, through shovelling movements of the sides of the body, as scoops to dig up the loose sand and throw it on to the animals' backs.

THE EGYPTIAN HORNED VIPER (*Cerastes cornutus*).

The family is represented in Europe by a number of species of which the Adder (*Vipera berus*), common in England and the northern countries, is one of the best known. It is the only poisonous British snake and may be distinguished from the other serpents of these islands by the absence of enlarged plates on its head, and by its vertically elliptical pupil. It is extremely variable in colour, grey, brown, reddish, or entirely black specimens occurring in the same localities, and the zigzag band down the back, which is so often given as a diagnostic character, is too often absent or indistinct to be of value. Its bite is painful and gives rise to severe symptoms, but is not often fatal to averagely healthy adults. Allied to the Adder is the Indian Daboia, or Tic Polonga (*V. russelli*), a species which reaches a length of five feet, and is readily recognised by its distinctive colour pattern of three rows of large reddish, black- and white-edged spots on a pale brown background.

The Pit-vipers and Rattlesnakes (*Crotalinae*) of America and South-East Asia are distinguished from the true vipers by the presence of a deep pit between the eye and the nostril. This cavity is lined by scales similar to those of the rest of the head, and, although it has a very rich nerve supply, its function, if it has one, is quite unknown. They show greater adaptations to different environments than the true vipers, there being aquatic as well as terrestrial and arboreal forms. The North American Copper-heads (*Agkistrodon mokasen*) and Cotton-mouths (*A. piscivorus*), with large plates on their heads like Colubrids, are swamp- and stream-dwellers, which feed chiefly on fish and frogs. Arboreal forms are well represented in South-East Asia by the various species of *Trimeresurus*,

THE COPPER-HEAD.
A North American Pit-viper.

which all have a prehensile tail; the commonest species (*T. gramineus*) is usually bright green in colour with a yellow stripe along the flanks, and a red tail. Terrestrial forms are best represented in America, where the dreaded Bushmaster (*Lachesis mutus*), which sometimes attains a length of twelve feet, the Fer-de-Lance (*Bothrops atrox*), the Jararaca, and the Jararacussu are by far the most dangerous poisonous snakes.

The Rattlesnakes are chiefly North American, and it has been suggested that their peculiarity, the rattle on the tip of the tail, has arisen in response to the peculiar conditions of life on the prairies. These great open spaces were formerly the abodes of huge herds of large-hoofed mammals, like the bison, and it is easy to see that any snake which was in the track of one of these herds would have a very poor chance of escaping from such a multitude of heavy feet. Though it might, by its venom, kill one or two individuals, of what avail would that be if it were itself crushed out of existence? Some warning, audible at a distance, would be far more advantageous by preventing encounters so disastrous for both sides.

The rattle is developed from the single horny scale which covers the tip of the tail and which, instead of being conical, as in other snakes, here has two ring-like constrictions, and so resembles three bulbs connected with each other. Newly born Rattlesnakes have no rattle, but when sloughing occurs the old horny covering of the tip of the tail cannot be shed because its forward constriction fits into the hinder constriction of the new one. In this way a new joint is added to the rattle with each successive moult; but the size of the rattle is no true indication of age, firstly because sloughing is not a regular periodical occurrence, but varies in its frequency according to the individual and conditions, and secondly, because the older joints gradually wear away. The noise is produced by a rapid vibration of the tail which shakes the loosely fitting horny shells, and is a shrill sound sometimes audible twenty yards away.

The largest and most dangerous species is the Diamond-back Rattler (*Crotalus adamanteus*), confined to the South-East United States, which reaches a length of about eight feet. Other well-known forms are the Prairie-rattler, which occurs all over the Great Plains from Canada to Texas,

A DIAMOND-BACK RATTLESNAKE.

and *C. terrificus*, which ranges from Texas to the Argentine. The Side-winder (*C. cerastes*) is a small, desert-dwelling form from the south-western United States, and, like some of its Viperine allies in the deserts of the Old World, it has developed a horn-like process above each eye.

SECTION XIV

CLASS AVES

By W. P. Pycraft, F.L.S.

CHAPTER I

CHAPTER II

CHAPTER III

CHAPTER IV

CHAPTER V

CHAPTER VI

CHAPTER VII

CHAPTER VIII

CHAPTER IX

CHAPTER X

CHAPTER I

ESSENTIAL FEATURES

THOUGH the number of those who find in birds a source of constant delight be legion, there are few who possess for them more than an aesthetic interest. That interest will become a never-failing source of wonderment and inspiration as soon as any attempt is made to penetrate the mystery of their being. A field will then be entered which can never be fully explored.

Even to answer the simple question, " What is a bird ? " we have to make rapid mental comparisons, more or less unconsciously, with other creatures which are *not* birds, in order to frame an answer, which would probably be " a creature covered with feathers, having two legs and two wings." Carry the examination a little farther, and the answer will be not only much more complete, but much more provocative of further questions, for an interest will be stimulated which will be as a consuming, unquenchable fire.

The enlarged definition will include a character which is found elsewhere only in the reptiles—a single knob, or " condyle," for the articulation of the head with the body. And the search for this will have brought out the fact that between the birds and the reptiles there is a blood relationship, which is found most emphasised in the structure of the skeleton and of many of the internal organs.

The realisation of this relationship must form the foundation of all our cogitations on birds, whether we study them in the field or the Museum. We must get all the information we can, from both sources, if we are to obtain a real grasp of the why and the wherefore of their being ; if we want to understand their emotions, and the causes which have moulded the almost bewildering variety of form and colour which they present. Not the least fascinating of these varied themes is that which concerns the powers of adjustment they display to the conditions of their external environment : adaptations made in " the shifts for a living " which all animals and plants have to make. Water-birds and land-birds, seed- and insect-eaters, and the carnivorous types are, all alike, results of this " adjustment."

For the sake of convenience, as well as for the sake of expressing the results of this adjustment, some sort of classification has been found necessary. The older workers depended alone on superficial likenesses. To-day we realise that these are deceptive, that no classification is of value unless it expresses blood relationship.

The accompanying " Tree of Descent " will give perhaps the readiest means of grasping the essential features of this descent, and of the basis of the classification of to-day ; and it should be consulted from time to time, as these pages are perused, since it will be best to examine the several

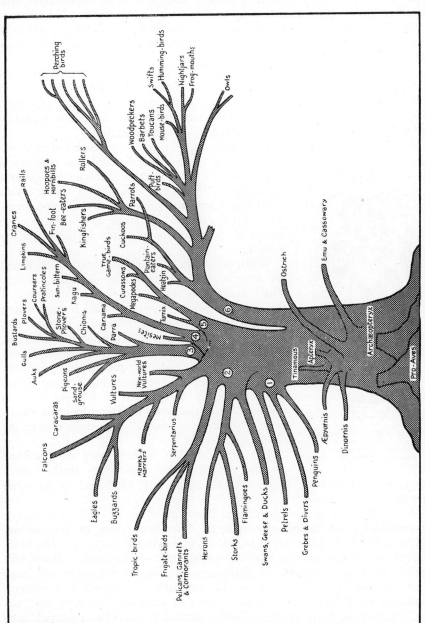

Tree of descent, showing the six main groups of " Neognathine " Birds, and the relative position of the " Palaeognathae " or Ostrich-tribe.

Perching birds

Humming-birds
Swifts
Nightjars
Frog-mouths
Owls

Woodpeckers
Barbets
Toucans
Mouse-birds

Hoopoes & Hornbills
Bee-eaters
Rollers

Fin-foot
Kingfishers
Puff-birds
Parrots

Rails
Cranes
Limpkins
True Game-birds
Cuckoos
Plantain-eaters
Hoatzin

Bustards
Plovers
Coursers
Pratincoles
Stone-Plovers
Kagu
Curassows
Megapodes

Gulls
Chionis
Cariama
Turnix

Auks
Parra
Mesites

Pigeons
New-world Vultures

Sand-grouse
Vultures
Caracaras

Falcons

Eagles

Buzzards

Hawks & Harriers

Serpentarius

Tropic-birds

Frigate-birds

Pelicans, Gannets & Cormorants

Herons

Storks

Flamingoes

Swans, Geese & Ducks

Petrels

Grebes & Divers

Penguins

Æpyornis

Dinornis

Tinamus

Apteryx

Ostrich

Emu & Cassowary

Archæopteryx

Pro-Aves

6
5
4
3
2
1

types of birds in their systematic order.   But it is to be remembered that classification is only a means to an end, not an end in itself.   We are concerned here rather with the problems of how birds live and move and have their being, and of the changes of form they have undergone, rather than with their classification.

This problem embraces a very wide range of subjects, such as nests and eggs ; the condition of the young at birth ; the form of the body in relation to its external environment ; and the coloration of the plumage. These will be discussed not as a connected theme, but as they are found in the several groups of birds as defined by our classification.

As touching this matter of classification it must be remarked that the scheme used here is based mainly on anatomical characters of too technical a character for general discussion.   But the dissecting table also furnishes us, in addition to material for pedigrees, with most valuable evidence as to the precise nature of the adjustments made in the shifts for a living.

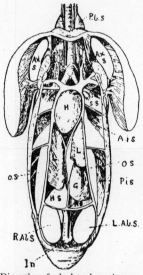

Dissection of a duck to show air-sacs.
P.b.s.,   Pre-bronchial ;   *A.i.s.*, Anterior intermediate ;   *P.i.s.*, Posterior intermediate ; *L.Ab.s.*, Left Abdominal sac.

When we speak of the " evolution " of birds, we refer to the results of the different ways in which birds have responded to the conditions of their environment, responses which have often brought about profound differences in structure, giving rise to new types.   Contrast, for example, the Ostrich, the Penguin, the Eagle, and the Woodpeckers.   These various and widely different forms could never have arisen but for the ability of their tissues to respond in different ways to the demands of the exterior environment, demands largely governed by that all-important matter, the food-supply.

The possession of feathers may be described as the " hall-mark " of the bird.   Such structures, and they are of wonderful complexity, are found in no other animal.

In that they have a four-chambered heart and warm blood, birds resemble the mammals, but the blood corpuscles differ from those of mammalian, and agree with those of reptilian, blood in having a nucleus.   The brain of birds is much more like that of reptiles than of mammals.   Birds, like reptiles, have no partition, or diaphragm, cutting off the lungs and heart from the rest of the viscera.   In all mammals this partition is present. Finally, in birds alone do we find a series of air-filled chambers, or " airsacs," within the body-cavity.   Their function, it has been suggested, is to lighten the body during flight.   This view, however, is now discarded.

They probably serve to maintain an adequate supply of air to the lungs during the strenuous movements of flight.

Birds are remarkable for the fact that they have no sweat-glands. Indeed, their only external gland is the " oil-gland," whose function has yet to be discovered, though it is always said to be used for dressing the feathers. No less characteristic is the foot, though it presents many modifications or adjustments to special needs. Even in the earliest known bird, Archaeopteryx, it is a typical avian foot, with the hind-toe long, and directed backwards. It has, indeed, acquired all the characteristics of a true perching foot hardly distinguishable from that of, say, a rook. But in many other arboreal birds, e.g. parrots, cuckoos, woodpeckers, the outer toe is turned backwards to lie side by side with the hind-toe. Many birds which spend their lives entirely on the ground have lost the hind-toe; the Ostrich retains only the third and fourth. In water-birds like ducks and gulls the front toes are joined by a web, while in the grebes and coots they have broad lobes in place of webs.

The external differences which we perceive between different species, and different individuals of the same species, are to be regarded in part as characters, which, having started, are free to go on increasing in intensity unless, and until, checked by Natural Selection ; or in other words, until they become harmful to the individual; and in part as adjustments due to use, or in some cases disuse.

Keep these things in mind, and the study of birds will afford an insight into the problems of Life impossible to those who are content with superficial, external appearances.

The Class AVES comprises two main divisions, or Sub-classes, the Archaeornithes, or Lizard-tailed Birds, and the Neornithes : the latter including every other known bird, whether fossil or living, after the first known bird, the Archaeopteryx.

Sub-class *ARCHAEORNITHES*

(*Archaeopteryx*)

Under the somewhat formidable title, Archaeornithes, we lay the foundation of our study of birds. Those who so often clamour for " missing links " will find one in Archaeopteryx. For though clad, after the manner of birds, with feathers it yet retains many very unmistakable reptilian characters, the most conspicuous of which are teeth in its jaws, a long, lizard-like tail, and claws at the tips of its fingers. This last character is one on which great stress must be laid, and more said hereafter.

This profoundly important link in the ancestry of birds was discovered in the Solenhofen, or Lithographic limestone of Bavaria, in 1861, and is now in the British Museum of Natural History. Sixteen years later a second specimen, belonging to a distinct species, was found in the same quarry. This was in a much more perfect state of preservation, and is now in the Berlin Museum. Let us begin its study with an examination of its tail.

The lizard-like tail of Archaeopteryx.

This was long, and tapering, and made up, like that of a lizard, of a number of vertebrae, each of which, from the point where the tail left the body, bore a pair of well-developed tail-feathers ; apparently there were about twelve pairs in all, thus forming a tail very unlike that of modern birds, which appears to be fashioned on a very different model. And this because, as may be seen in the accompanying figure, all the feathers are ranged fan-wise about a short, flat blade of bone known as the " pygostyle." If, however, this be examined in an embryo it will be found to be made up of a number of separate pieces, answering to incipient vertebrae—the remnants of the once lizard-like appendage. If you could " telescope " the tail-skeleton of Archaeopteryx you would get the tail of the modern bird, for all the feathers by this process would be brought to the common base seen in birds of to-day.

The wing, as in modern birds, contained but three fingers, each of which, however, bore at its tip a large claw, a distinctly reptilian character. Birds of to-day still retain vestiges of the first and second claws, but the third is found only occasionally in embryos of the African Ostrich. In modern birds what answer to the " palm-bones "—the metacarpals—are all welded together ; that of the first digit, or thumb, has become reduced to a mere excrescence at the base of the second finger with which the third finger has also been welded. Beyond the metacarpals are a varying number of small " finger-bones "—two for the thumb, three for the

Tail of an Eagle to show tail-quills and " pygostyle."

second finger, and one for the third. But the nestlings of living birds display a wing-skeleton much more like that of Archaeopteryx. For here we have a separate semilunar mass, answering to a number of fused wrist-bones, closely applied to the bases of the fingers, but not welded there-with. This was the condition of the hand in Archaeopteryx throughout its whole life. The two free wrist-bones—the radiale and the ulnare—are just as in their ancient ancestor.

Restoration of Archaeopteryx.

The feathers of the wing are structures of tremendous importance in deciding what we may call the plane, or level, of evolution to which Archaeopteryx had attained ; for it is claimed by some authorities that this wonderful reptilian bird had not yet acquired the power of true flight. That it was incapable of long, sustained journeys in mid-air is probable enough ; but make note of the fact that these feathers answer exactly to the hand and arm-quills, or primaries and secondaries of living birds, and they possessed the same amazing complexity of structure. Now, it is in the last degree improbable that structures so intricately complex, so exactly like those of living birds, could have come into being save as reactions to the strains and stresses peculiar to flight. All our experience of anatomy shows that the form and structure of any organ reflects the uses to which that organ is put. When swimming becomes the only mode of locomotion the fore-limb becomes transformed into a " flipper " as in the penguins, whales and dugongs, and the hind-limb may disappear.

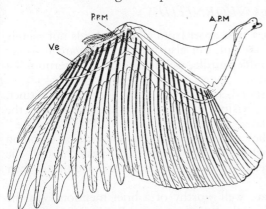

Wing of a Rook, showing disposition of the Primaries and Secondaries. *A.p.m.* Anterior and *P.p.m.* Posterior patagium. *V.e.* Elastic " vinculum."

The conspicuous length of the second and third fingers, which, it will be noted, project beyond the wing-feathers, is not to be interpreted as merely a heritage or survival of a reptilian fore-limb. The digit is altogether too long to have served as a walking-foot. Its length is a response to its function as an essential part of the wing, and this is true also of the protruding claws, for we may take it that they annually played a rôle of profound importance, and that was during the annual moult, when, as in some modern birds like the ducks and geese, all the quill- or flight-feathers were shed at once. The retention by these birds of this ancient habit is possible because during this time they can escape their enemies by retreating to the water and hiding among the reeds. All other birds, to-day, moult their wing-feathers in pairs, so that flight is at no time hampered. Archaeopteryx, it is to be remembered, was an arboreal bird ; and during the time that its wings were rendered impotent for the purposes of flight it used them as hands, for climbing purposes when the long second finger and the claw on the third finger would serve as valuable aids.

The nestling Hoatzin presents a stage in the development of its wing exactly comparable with the wing of the moulting Archaeopteryx.

No one seems to have realised how much is to be gleaned by a little thoughtful study of the foot of Archaeopteryx. It not only bears no likeness whatever to that of a reptile, but it is practically indistinguishable from that of, say, a crow. It could have assumed this transformation from a reptilian type of foot only by long and intensive use of the foot for grasping the boughs of trees. Inasmuch as the foot had to be used more than the wing its advance in the avian direction took place at a greater speed than the wing.

Sub-class *NEORNITHES*

Archaeopteryx stands out as a type apart from all other birds not merely on account of its long, lizard-like tail, but also because in regard to other parts of its skeleton—the shoulder-girdle, pelvic-girdle, and sternum—it was far more reptilian than avian.

The Neornithes which, as stated, include all birds, living and extinct, other than Archaeopteryx are divisible into two groups by reason of the structure of the bones of the palate. We divide them into " Palaeognathae " and " Neognathae." That they are divergent branches of a common stock is shown by the fact that all the " Neognathae " pass through the " Palaeognathine " stage in regard to the palate, before acquiring their more characteristic differences.

These two types of palate are well worthy of a brief mention. In the " Palaeognathae "—that is to say, the " ancient-jawed "—the bone running down the middle of the roof of the palate, known as the vomer, forms a long, flat beam, pointed in front, and cleft behind into two narrow plates which run down to embrace the " pterygoids," which in turn articulate with the quadrate by which the lower jaw is attached to the skull. This type is found in its most primitive condition in the Emu, and in process of change in the Rhea and Tinamou. The Neognathine type of palate came about by reduction in the size of the vomer, and a gradual movement inwards, towards the middle line, of the palatines. These bones, it should be remarked, connect the vomero-pterygoid bar with the maxilla, or base of the upper jaw. In the South American Ostrich, Rhea, and in the Tinamou, this inward movement of the palatine has already begun. Seen in its final form, and without evidence of intermediate stages, the derivation of the Neognathine from the Palaeognathine palate would have seemed impossible.

The Penguins afford the most complete transitional stages between these two types of palate to be found among the Neognathae. In the nestling Penguin the vomer, still very long, has been laterally compressed to form a " knife-blade," while its divergent hinder ends run backwards and touch the pterygoids, which terminate in sharp points embraced by the palatines. As development proceeds the pterygoid becomes, as it were, fractured at the point where it first meets the end of the palatine. The small triangular splint, hitherto closely adherent to the palatine, now fuses therewith, and a beautiful cup-and-ball joint is formed at the point of fracture. Owing to this change, the vomer now appears as if it were attached to the palatine, and had no relation with the pterygoid, which, indeed, in this process of transformation, it will be seen it just fails to meet. As we pass on to examine the palates of other types of this group we find the vomer growing smaller and smaller, till, in Game-birds, it is reduced to a mere splinter of bone, and in the Falcons to a tiny nodule, or it may be wanting altogether. In the Barbets the vomer is large, and still attached to the pterygoid, which does *not* " fracture."

CHAPTER II

Division PALAEOGNATHAE

(*Suture-palates*)

Order STRUTHIONES

(*Ostrich, Emu, Cassowary, etc.*)

WE come now to the Palaeognathae, which may be more simply called the " Ostrich tribe." Great as is their range of differences in size, form, and coloration, with the exception of the Tinamous they all agree in having lost the power of flight, and their wings present a most interesting series of gradation in degeneration, growing smaller and smaller, until, as in some of the Moas, it not only vanishes altogether, but the shoulder-girdle, which afforded it support, vanishes also !

With the loss of flight went the keel of the breast-bone, hence this group, in many books, is referred to as the " Ratitae," or raft-breasted, a bad designation since other birds, not in the least related, have also, becoming flightless, lost this keel.

In the matter of their feathers the Ostrich tribe are again peculiar. But here, once more, we are faced with the results of degeneration due to the loss of flight which has resulted in the loss of the " hooklets " which hold together the web, or vane of the feather, so that it no longer forms a continuous elastic whole. All but the African Ostrich and the Tinamou have lost the tail-feathers.

Not having before considered them, some may be inclined to regard these structural features as mere " anatomical details " that might well have been omitted. But the moment they are sympathetically reviewed they assume a new and fascinating aspect, for they prove to be guide-posts along the track of evolution, records of the results of use and disuse, and the transformations which ensue with such changes. And this will become more and more evident as the various members of this ancient group of birds are passed in review. There are six in all living to-day, and two extinct forms of quite exceptional interest—the Moas, and the Roc, or Aepyornis, of which mention must be made, The living members are the Emu, Cassowary, Rhea, Ostrich, Apteryx, and Tinamou.

Family Casuariidae

(Emus and Cassowaries)

One speaks of " *the* Emu and *the* Cassowary " when referring to these birds in a general sense, as types, but as a matter of fact, each of the Struthious types of which mention has been made is represented by more than one species, though these differ one from another, for the most part, only in unessential details.

Of the Emus, only two species are now living, *Dromaeus novae-hollandiae*, now confined to the interior of Eastern Australia, though at one time ranging into Tasmania and the islands of Bass's Straits ; and *D. irroratus*, of West and South Australia. They are large birds, standing about five feet high. A third species, *D. ater*, till comparatively recent times lived on Kangaroo Island off the south of Australia. Only a stuffed skin and a few bones have been preserved. It was a much smaller bird than the living species. Three fossil species have also been described.

The drab tone of their coloration, and the fact that the sexes show no appreciable differences in this regard, may be taken as evidence of their primitive character, and this is supported by the structure of the palate already referred to. They are, in fact, the lowliest members of the Struthious birds. The extreme reduction which the wing has undergone bears further witness to their ancient lineage. For the hand is reduced to the merest vestige, while the arm and fore-arm are extremely short. Of " flight-feathers " and tail-feathers there are none. Another witness to their primitive character is seen in their " pterylosis," that is to say, of the distribution of the feathers. In the higher types the feathers are not evenly distributed over the body, as are the hairs of a mammal, but are restricted to sharply defined areas, or " pterylae," divided from one another by well-defined spaces.

The feathers of the Emu, and also of the Cassowary, present yet another and very important character. Each consists of two shafts of equal length, one lying above the other. The lower one is called the " after-shaft," or *hyporhachis*. In the non-struthious birds, or Neognathae, the after-shaft is always reduced to a downy or semiplumous state, standing in sharp contrast with the main shaft which always presents a well-defined elastic vane, or web. Moreover, in the Neognathae the size of this after-shaft varies greatly : it may be absent altogether.

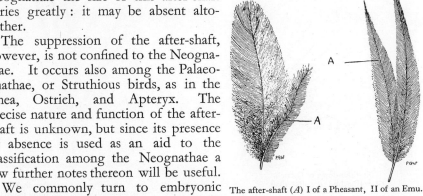

The after-shaft (*A*) I of a Pheasant, II of an Emu.

The suppression of the after-shaft, however, is not confined to the Neognathae. It occurs also among the Palaeognathae, or Struthious birds, as in the Rhea, Ostrich, and Apteryx. The precise nature and function of the after-shaft is unknown, but since its presence or absence is used as an aid to the classification among the Neognathae a few further notes thereon will be useful.

We commonly turn to embryonic and early post-embryonic stages in the development of bodies, or organs, to find evidence of ancestral characters, since these are repeated more or less faithfully in the course of development of all living bodies, be they plant or animal. But the early history of the after-shaft, as seen in nestling Struthious birds, is puzzling. It is but barely traceable in the nestling Emu and Cassowary, wherein the adult feathers have the after-shaft as long as the main shaft—a relation we should not expect. But it can be explained on the assumption that the after-shaft of the adult Emu is a secondary modification. In the nestling-down of the Rhea and Ostrich there is a relatively large after-shaft—though by no means as long as the main shaft—while in the adult it is generally wanting. Finally, in the Tinamous, the after-shaft in the nestling-down is as long as the main-shaft, and in the Martineta Tinamou it is almost as complex in structure as the main shaft, which is more like that of the typical " definitive " or adult feather in structure than in any other known bird. We have, indeed, in this nestling the most highly developed of all nestling-down feathers, a feature of more importance than has as yet been realised. Nevertheless, in the adult Tinamou, the after-shaft is absent.

Finally, before dismissing this theme of the nestling-down something must be said of its coloration.

In the Emu it presents, in a very strongly marked degree, the primitive longitudinally striped pattern, alternate black and white stripes covering the whole body. In the Rheas, the neck is hardly, or not at all, striped. In the Ostrich the neck is striped, and so also is the body, but here that pattern is discerned only with difficulty, owing to the fact that the down-feathers have assumed a very specialised structure, the rami of the feathers

Nestling-down of Ostrich.
r.r. = Rhachis ; *a* = after-shaft.

Nestling-down of Tinamou.
rh = Rhachis ; *a* = after-shaft ;
h = hyporhachis ; *t.f.* = terminal plaments.

forming hard, flattened, and curled rods, thus completely breaking up the continuity of the stripes.

Let us revert to our survey of the adult Emu. Its haunts are sandy plains and open forests, where it feeds upon fruit, roots, and herbage ; it is fond of bathing ; it can, indeed, swim, and will cross even broad rivers. The early morning and the evening are its chosen times for feeding. Keen-sighted and swift of foot, it contrives to escape its enemies by outracing them, but when brought to bay it will kick backwards. Though monogamous, it wanders during most of the year in small parties.

Normally a silent bird, in the breeding season it develops considerable sound-producing powers ; and this by means of a singular modification of the windpipe. Near the middle of the neck this is pierced by a long slit, and its lining membrane bulges out, so to speak, to form a large inflatable sac immediately under the skin. When " courting " this can be filled with air, which apparently by its violent expulsion produces a loud booming sound. At other seasons of the year no more than a hissing noise is ever produced.

The eggs, from seven to thirteen in number, are of a verdigris green colour, and have the surface curiously granulated, giving the effect of shagreen. The duties of incubation, which extend over eight weeks, it is to be noted, are performed by the male, and this seems to be true of all the Struthious birds.

NESTLING EMU (showing longitudinal stripes).

Unless steps be taken for its protection in some reservation, this most interesting type is doomed to extinction in the not distant future, since its presence clashes with the interest of the sheep-farmers. By the erection of fences cutting them off from their migrations in search of water, thousands are killed during periods of drought, within the short space of a week or two, by thirst.

ADULT EMU (*Dromaeus novae-hollandiae*).

That the Cassowaries are very closely related to the Emus admits of no question ; but they have attained to a more advanced stage of evolution, since the adults display a very striking coloration whose range is enlarged by the fact that it differs with every species, and there are many.

The layman is often mystified by the facts advanced by the Man of Science as evidence of evolution ; and generally because the facts are such as cannot readily be grasped by those who are unfamiliar with anatomy. But here, in these Cassowaries, we have a very simple illustration of the gradual rise and development of new characters resulting in profound transformation.

After the nestling-down stage is passed a plumage of a uniform chestnut brown is assumed, and a large bare horny plate appears on the crown of the head. As the months pass the neck-feathering becomes so scanty as to expose the skin, which has a blue tinge, like that of the adult Emu, while the horny plate on the head begins to rise up into a " mound." The " quill-feathers " of the wing, absent in the Emu, are here represented by some five or six long, bare, tubular shafts, with a slender " vane " at the tip. This is the juvenile plumage. The assumption of the adult dress marks a great change, for the body is now clothed with a plumage of glossy black, the " vanes " have been worn off from the " quill-feathers," which now become thick solid shafts, and, so far as we can see, are neither useful nor ornamental, while the mound on the head has become a huge crest, or casque, formed of a delicate filagree-work of bone with a thin covering-sheath of horn. But this is not all. The neck is now bare of

CASSOWARY (*Casuarius rogersi*).

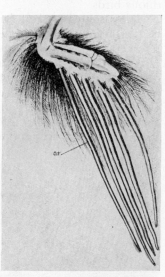

Hypertrophied wing-quills of adult Cassowary.

feathers, and the skin has flashed into a blaze of colour—scarlet, yellow, violet, blue, in varying proportions, according to the species. But besides this it has developed long paired lappets of skin, or sometimes of a single median lappet.

Here, then, we can study the evolution of resplendent plumage, which follows the same lines in every group of birds.

There is yet another peculiarity about the Cassowaries, and that is their method of fighting. This they do by striking forwards and downwards with the foot, the inner toe of which is armed with a specially developed, long, spike-like nail, quite unlike that found in any other bird.

About twenty species and sub-species were described in a great Monograph some years ago by Lord Rothschild. Their temper, he tells us, is sullen and treacherous, and they are extremely pugnacious ; even the different sexes will fight with but little provocation at any time. In other birds, this pugnacity is confined to the breeding season.

Unlike the Emu, the Cassowary frequents forests, feeding on vegetable matter and fruits, as well as insects and any small vertebrates which come its way. The rather surprising number of species may be attributed to the fact that they are spread over a number of islands, and, being in consequence isolated, new tendencies to variation are not swamped by intercrossing. Only one species is found in the mainland of Australia, the rest are distributed over New Guinea and the neighbouring islands.

Family Rheidae
(*Rheas*)

The Rheas of South America, though indubitable " Ostriches," yet present striking differences from the African Ostrich on the one hand, and the Emus and Cassowaries on the other. Having regard to the fact that

they are New World types this is not surprising. When they split off from the common ancestral stock, and from what centre, we have no means of knowing ; but they have developed along independent lines and present many structural features found in no other birds. One of these, the palate, has already been discussed. Another concerns the hip-girdle, which is unique, for that portion of the vertebral column enclosed between the " innominate bones " —that is to say, the pair of beams which form the upper part of the hip-girdle—have completely degenerated, so that the vertebral column is discontinuous, the terminal tail vertebrae being cut off from the lumbar vertebrae.

Though smaller than the African Ostrich or the Emu, the Common

RHEA and young (*Rhea americana*).

Rhea (*Rhea americana*) is still one of the world's largest birds. But Darwin's Rhea, named from a skin brought back by Darwin from the voyage of the " Beagle," is much smaller, and differs not merely in its coloration, but also in having the tarsus for the most part feathered. They both have relatively large wings—though quite useless for flight—and no tails.

Whether roaming over the treeless flats of the Argentine Pampas, the scrub-covered plains of Patagonia, or the dry, open Sertoes of Brazil, their habits are much the same, for they roam in flocks of from three to seven during most of the year, but number as many as twenty or thirty after the breeding season, when the immature birds accompany their parents. And as the African Ostrich displays a predilection for the society of zebra and antelopes, so these birds associate themselves with herds of deer or guanacos. When alarmed they can run with surprising speed, raising sometimes one wing, sometimes the other, as if for steering purposes.

Family Struthionidae
(*African Ostriches*)

The African Ostrich, represented by at least four species, is the largest living member of its tribe, standing about eight feet high and weighing about three hundred pounds. In this bird the wings are still relatively large, and the " quill-feathers " of considerable length, though now functionless, but they, with the tail-feathers, have always been highly prized by men as ornaments, and to-day these birds are bred in large numbers for the sake of these feathers.

AFRICAN OSTRICH (*Struthio camelus*).

If the wing has become degenerate from lack of use, the leg, or rather the foot, in response to what we might almost call excessive use has undergone a very material change. Of the original five toes of the reptilian foot, but four now remain in birds, though vestiges of the fifth are to be found in the embryo. These four surviving toes present many and interesting changes of form and function in different groups of birds. In some the hind-toe has become obsolete, or is even wanting altogether. The Ostrich has gone further still, reducing the number of toes to two, one very large, which bears all the strains of locomotion, while the other is greatly reduced in size. This foot, indeed, seems to be drifting towards the condition found in the horse—that is to say, to a single toe.

Now, this condition is to be studied in connection with the haunts of the bird. Note that it lives on vast sandy plains, consorting with herds of zebras and antelopes ; its foot has responded, in a precisely similar way to that of its ungulate companions, because it is put to a like use—running on hard, hot sand. The wings, when running, are spread out like sails, to lift the body, if ever so little, and increase the speed.

In coloration there is a striking difference between the sexes. The cock has the head and neck almost bare, and the body-plumage of a glossy jet-black relieved by the magnificent white plumes answering to the flight-feathers of the wing, and the tail-feathers. The hen, on the contrary, has the body-plumage of dull, greyish-brown. But this plumage must be regarded, in some measure, at any rate, as a " protective coloration," for in the breeding season the hen sits by day, when she harmonises well with her sandy surroundings, while the male sits by night.

His splendours are best seen when in an amorous mood he starts to court the female. Then, Mr. Cronright-Schreiner tells us, he will run slowly and daintily on the points of his toes towards her, with the neck slightly inflated, upright and rigid, the tail half drooped, and all his body-feathers set on end. The wings are raised and opened out, so that the two form a great fan behind the head. This is the first stage of his " wooing." He next starts to " roll." Dropping suddenly on to his hocks, he starts a strange play with his wings ; opening them to their full extent, and turning them so that the hinder edge, bearing the great white plumes, stands vertically upwards, he waves them backwards and forwards alternately and slowly, one wing coming forwards as the other turns backwards. Meanwhile the long neck is curved to bring the head near to the body, and inflated with air. Every now and then some of this air is suddenly expelled, producing a sound like a sharp " click."

The period of courting over, the females presently start laying their eggs, depositing them in a shallow depression scraped by the cock, while his female stands round him, the sand removed being used as a " rampart " round the nest. Each nest will contain about fifteen eggs—weighing about three pounds apiece—and these are laid on alternate days. Hatching takes place in about six weeks.

Family Apterygidae
(Kiwis)

Though generally we speak of " *the* Kiwi" or " *the* Apteryx," there are, as a matter of fact, several species of this remarkable type, though they differ one from another only in the matter of their coloration and size. There is very great difference in this last character, but the largest species is but a mere pigmy compared with the other members of the Ostrich tribe whether recent or fossil. About the precise relationship with regard to the Kiwis even the highest authorities differ somewhat widely. They stand, a race apart, but with leanings towards the extinct Moas ; and it is significant that they occupy the same territory—New Zealand.

MANTELL'S APTERYX (*Apteryx mantello*).

Inhabiting thick scrub, and nocturnal in their habits, they feed upon worms, which are discovered largely by scent. As if to facilitate this means of hunting, the nostrils have moved forward along the beak, which is of considerable length, till they open at its very tip, a position found in no other birds. But grubs, beetles, and berries are also eaten. The eyes are extremely small, and, apparently by way of compensation, tactile vibrissae, in the form of long, hair-like feathers, have been developed around the head. The wing, in regard to its skeleton, is even more reduced than in the Emu or Cassowary, only the merest vestige of the hand remaining. But it presents yet another feature which seems to have been quite overlooked. And this concerns the length of the upper arm bone or humerus, which, in proportion to the fore-arm, is extremely long, slender, and curved. If we infer, as we may justly do, that the wing has shrunk at the same rate in all its segments, we must conclude that originally this was a wing with a very short hand and a very long humerus, as in, say, the Albatross, or the Rhea. The wing of the Emu and the Cassowary, on the other hand, has a very short humerus, and, judging the other segments by this standard, we may take it that originally the wing in all its segments was short, like that

Wing of Apteryx, showing inflated shafts of " flight-feathers." *cl.*=claw ; *h.*=humerus ; *md.r.*= primaries.

of the Game-birds of to-day.

The few degenerate quill-feathers which yet remain are remarkable for the fact that the part answering to the " rhachis," which bears a small, degenerate vane, remains as hollow as the quill, and has free edges turning inwards. In birds with functional quills this rhachis is filled with a mass of pith-like cells. But this is not all. These quills, retaining the vane throughout life, are exactly similar in structure to those of the immature Cassowary, wherein, as has already been pointed out, the vane is shed when the mature plumage is assumed and the hollow quill becomes solid.

As with the species already described, the males alone incubate. The eggs, generally two in number, laid in a nest-chamber at the end of a burrow, are of enormous size, relatively to the size of the bird, a fact which gave rise to the schoolboy " howler " that the Apteryx is " a bird which lays eggs bigger than itself " !

When fighting they thrust the foot forwards and downwards with great force, after the fashion of the Cassowary. The Maories hunted them for food with muzzled dogs, thereby beginning the work of extermination which has been speeded up by the white settlers, so that their final disappearance from the list of living species is at hand.

Family Dinornithidae
(Moas)

The Moas of New Zealand, though now extinct, at one time roamed over the North and South Islands in great numbers and were finally exterminated by the Maories, who hunted them for food. Some species were of gigantic size, standing nearly nine feet high, some were little bigger than a Common Turkey, but of more massive build. In common with the other members of the Ostrich tribe, they were flightless. Some, indeed, were not only wingless, but had lost even the shoulder-girdle which supports the wing.

It would seem, however, that some other agency besides the ravages of man contributed to their destruction, for in one great morass, abounding in springs, their bones have been found in enormous numbers, layer upon layer, as if the birds had been driven thither by some unusually prolonged drought where even the springs gradually dried up. The birds flocked thither to scramble for the last possible moisture for their parched throats, and there died. Skeletons, and mummified parts of the head and neck and feet, parts of the windpipe, and a few feathers are all that are left to us. The feathers, it is to be noted, had a long after-shaft as in the Emus and Cassowaries.

In Madagascar lived another giant bird (*Aepyornis*), sometimes called the Roc. This also was one of the Ostrich tribe and flightless, and probably exceeded the largest Moas in height, while it resembled the Rheas, Moas, and Tinamous, rather than the Emus and Cassowaries, in regard to its structure. Its egg exceeds in size that of any other known bird, having a capacity of about two gallons. They are sometimes washed out of the sand bordering lakes during stormy weather, and are found by the natives floating on the water. The biggest measures three feet in its largest circumference by two feet six inches in girth.

Family Tinamidae
(*Tinamous*)

Though possessing a curious external likeness to the Game-birds, their internal structure, and especially the bones of the palate, show Tinamous to be really " Struthious," or Ostrich-like types, from which, however, they differ in one very striking feature, to wit, they are none of them flightless. On the wing, indeed, the flight of some species is described as very fast, though noisy, but they soon settle. But, it is to be noted, they are great

MARTINETA TINAMOU (*Calopezus elegans*).

runners, and difficult to " flush," hence the experiment of introducing the Rufescent Tinamou into England as an additional " Game-bird " was not a success. Its solitary habits were also against it, from the sportsman's point of view.

Their eggs are remarkable for the extraordinary beauty of their colour—vinous, reddish-chocolate, purple, blue, sage-green, and primrose—and the singular glossiness of the surface, so that they look more like highly glazed porcelain than egg-shells.

Some possess the very peculiar kind of feathers known as " Powder-down " so extensively developed by the Heron tribe ; while the nestling-down, which has already been described, is of quite exceptional interest.

Though between sixty and seventy species have been described, none of them displays any beauty of coloration comparable with some of our Game-birds. Their favourite haunts are the undergrowth of forests, grassy flats interspersed with bushes, and open pampas of Central and South America. The nest is a hole, scraped in the ground, under the shelter of some bush or tuft of grass, lined with dry herbage and leaves, and the task of incubation is left to the male.

Unlike the rest of the Struthious birds, and the " Game-birds," they utter, at times, a mellow whistle of several notes, varying in tone in different species. Curiously enough, some have a small hind-toe—like the Apteryx —while others have lost it. And this character is used in their classification, those without the toe being included in a section by themselves. The Martineta Tinamou (*Calopezus elegans*) is one of these. It is also one of the handsomest of its tribe, the male being adorned with a long black crest.

CHAPTER III

Division NEOGNATHAE

(*Jointed-palates*)

THAT the Palaeognathae, with the exception of the Tinamous, are all flightless is due, not to the fact that they never attained to the power of flight, but that they have lost it. And there are many others, belonging to the Neognathae, now to be discussed, which are in like case. For flightlessness is the inevitable fate of all birds finding themselves in an equable climate, with an abundance of food always at hand, and no enemies to speak of. And this because they have then no incentive to fly, and in the course of time, it may be hundreds of years, they lose the ability to fly, so that the wings, growing smaller and smaller in succeeding genera-tions, finally vanish altogether as in some of the Moas already described.

It is not merely that the condition of the palate enables us to divide living birds into these two main groups ; there are other anatomical characters which are associated with this change of palate. These, however, will be found discussed at length where anatomy holds the dominant place. Let us, then, proceed to the discussion of the types which constitute the Neognathae, which sub-division includes the remain-ing living species.

In the first place, all the Neognathae, for example, have the feathers massed together to form sharply defined tracts, or pterylae, but presenting in each of the larger groups a characteristic arrangement peculiar to that group. In many, especially the aquatic types, a thick coating of " down-feathers," forming a sort of " under-fur," invests the whole body ; in others, as in the Game-birds, down is absent, leaving the skin between the tracts quite bare.

The immature, or " nestling stages " present a wide range of differences, which can be broadly ranged under two types—Nidifugae and Nidicolae. In the former, the more primitive, the young are hatched with a thick covering of down-feathers, and are able to run and accompany the parents in search of food within an hour or two of leaving the egg. They are never fed by the parents. In the latter they are hatched blind and helpless. Many, at hatching, are quite naked, but soon become down-clad, as in the young Garnet; some remain naked till the feathers appear.

Though the character of this nestling-down has already been referred to, one or two further points may profitably be considered here, though briefly. There seems good reason to regard the nestling-down as a degenerate survival of an ancestral, adult plumage; and very strong evidence of this is furnished by the nestling Martineta Tinamou on the one hand, and by the nestling tawny-owl on the other. In the Tinamous the feathers have a loose, semiplumous, or " downy " appearance; but when carefully examined they are found to possess a long main shaft and a well-marked " vane " through its barbs and barbules, which, however, do not interlock to form the firm, resilient web of typical adult feathers. The Game-birds and the Anserine birds show a further stage of degeneration. In nearly all the other birds this degeneration has proceeded even further, till, by the gradual shortening and ultimate loss of the shaft, all the barbs arise from a common base.

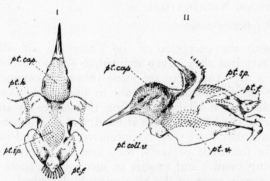

The Rifleman bird, showing the form of the feather-tracts. *Pt.cap.*, Head-tract; *Pt.sp.*, Spinal tract; *Pt.f.*, Femoral tract; *Pt.h.*, Humeral tract; *Pt.coll.v.*, Neck tract; *Pt.v.*, Ventral tract.

In nidifugous birds the nestling-down forms an ample covering for the body. This is true also of many nidicolous types, such as in the Hawk tribe, for example; but among the Picarian and Passerine types it has become greatly reduced in quantity, so that the skin is barely covered. In many, as in young Woodpeckers, or young Crows, it has vanished altogether.

These nestling-down feathers arise from the same feather germ as the later " definitive " feathers, and hence are called " pre-pennae "; but in some birds, as in young Cormorants, the downy investment is only in part made up of pre-pennae, the rest being formed of down-feathers which are later followed by the adult down-feathers, which not merely cover the *apteria*, or spaces between the feather-tracts, but also invade the tracts themselves. These down-feathers are hence called " pre-plumulae." In examining and describing nestling birds note should always be made as to whether the down-feathers answer to pre-pennae, or pre-plumulae, or both.

Legion COLYMBOMORPHAE

(*Divers, Penguins, Petrels, etc.*)

Order COLYMBIFORMES

(*Divers and Grebes*)

Family Colymbi

From the " Tree of Descent " it will be seen that the *Colymbi*, with the Penguins (*Sphenisci*) and the Petrels (*Tubinares*), are to be regarded as sharing a common ancestry at the base of the first of the six main branches of the Neognathine section of the tree.

Their ancient lineage is attested by the remains of that remarkable bird *Hesperornis* (placed by some authorities in a Sub-class Odontolcae), which became extinct in Cretaceous times. In all the essential features of the skeleton it is an indubitable diver. But its jaws were armed with teeth, as they were in the still older Archaeopteryx. They were, however, already beginning to foreshadow the evolution of the " horny beak " of modern birds, since only the hinder half of the upper jaw bore teeth, the rest was ensheathed in horn.

We shall probably be right in assuming, on the evidence of these teeth, that the *Colymbi* began to " take shape " in Jurassic times. In support of this view is the fact that not only was *Hesperornis* flightless, but its wing had become reduced to a mere rod of bone answering only to the upper arm, or humerus. But, having lost its wing, it is not surprising to find that it had lost the keel of the breast-bone also.

Skeleton of *Hesperornis*.

Though the Grebes and Divers of to-day display skeletal characters somewhat different from the skeleton of *Hesperornis* this is not to be wondered at ; for it must have taken long ages to attain to the nicely adjusted balance between structure and environment that these birds display : and " adjustment " implies changes. We have here a witness as to the effects of an intensively aquatic life and the pursuit of swiftly moving prey under water.

The most obvious of these adjustments is the position and form of the hind-legs. In both Grebes and Divers by the shortening of the thigh-bone the leg has been brought far back, so that, in the living bird, it emerges at the extreme hinder end of the body, thereby serving more efficiently to propel it through the water. *Hesperornis* presented this peculiarity, and both *Hesperornis* and modern Divers share another peculiarity which is found at the upper end of the " shin-bone," or tibia. This is produced into a long spike rising far above the level of the thigh-bone ; and furthermore the base of this spike is hollowed out to receive the end of the femur at the knee-joint. As a consequence the leg can never be straightened out, but is always flexed. This accounts for the fact that the Divers cannot walk. They come ashore only to breed, and then must lie on their breasts and push themselves along by the feet. The Grebes are not so much hampered in this respect, and can walk. But in these birds the spike at the top of the tibia is smaller, while the leverage required by the thigh muscles is afforded by a very

RED-THROATED DIVER (*Colymbus septentrionalis*) in nuptial plumage.

long, spike-shaped knee-cap, which, being movable, gives more play at the knee-joint, even though it is anchored by ligament to the tibial spike.

The Divers, inhabitants of the Arctic and sub-Arctic waters of the northern hemisphere, number no more than five species. The Red-throated Diver is a well-known British bird, fairly often seen at sea during the autumn and winter months. It breeds in Northern Ireland and Scotland ; and for this purpose forsakes the sea and takes up its quarters inland by the side of lochs, · laying two dark-brown-coloured eggs in a mere apology for a nest.

BLACK-THROATED DIVER (*Colymbus arcticus*) in nuptial plumage.

At the breeding season it undergoes a striking change of coloration, the most conspicuous feature of which is a large patch of deep rust-red on the fore-part of the throat—hence the name " Red-throated Diver."

The Black-throated Diver is another species breeding round the lochs of the North and West of Scotland. In the matter of its nest and eggs it differs but little from the Red-throated species.

Here, again, a resplendent dress is worn during the breeding season, and, again, the coloration of the neck—a black, oblong patch—gives the name to the species. Black and white, beautifully contrasting in broad masses, colour the rest of the upper parts, save the head and nape which are of an ashy-grey, while the sides of the neck are beautifully striped with black and white.

The Great Northern Diver, a much larger bird than the two foregoing species, only visits our waters in the winter.

THE GREBES

That the Grebes and Divers are closely related there can be no doubt ; but they present some extremely interesting points of difference in the matter of their skeletons. Having regard to the fact that they lead a similar mode of life these differences are more marked than one would have expected, for both are almost exclusively aquatic, coming ashore only to breed, and then nesting either at the water's edge as with the Divers, or *on* the water, the nest being anchored to reeds ; and both obtain their food by diving for it.

In both Divers and Grebes the pelvis is laterally compressed to an extent met with only in the Apteryx among the Struthious birds, but the likeness is no more than superficial. These two types differ, again, markedly in the form of the breast-bone, for it is extremely long and rather narrow, in the Divers, and emphatically short and wide in the Grebes. The bare statement of these anatomical peculiarities is doubtless, in itself, uninteresting to the general reader, but the moment they are thoughtfully examined they become invested with a new significance, for they draw attention to the different responses which living bodies make to the same moulding forces of the external environment. In this case these " moulding forces " are found in the medium in which they live. Fresh water is less buoyant than salt water—the Grebes enter the sea only when driven by long frosts, which drive them from their chosen haunts ; the Divers come to fresh water only to breed. The differences in the skeletons of the two types, we may suppose, are due to the relative differences in the density of fresh, or salt water.

Again, both the Grebes and the Divers have the bones of the foot, the so-called " tarsus," laterally compressed, to form a sort of blade with knife-like edges, thus offering less resistance to the water in swimming. In the Divers the toes are fully webbed, after the manner of aquatic birds, while in the Grebes they are, instead, provided with broad lobes of skin, as in the Coots and Phalaropes. In yet another particular the Grebes differ from the Divers, and this consists in the absence of perceptible tail-feathers, but they can be found, mere vestiges, if carefully sought for.

Neither Divers nor Grebes spend much time on the wing, but the shape of the wing is very different in the two types. Long and relatively narrow in the Divers, it is broad and much curved in the Grebes; and there is one species which has lost the power of flight completely. This lives on Lake Titicaca, Bolivia, at an elevation of 12,644 feet. Here, again, is an illustration of the results of isolation and life where there is no necessity for travelling long distances for food.

The Divers are exclusively carnivorous, feeding on fish and crustacea; the Grebes have a more varied diet, including a certain amount of vegetable matter. Most birds swallow small stones, which are stored in a hard, muscular gizzard for the purpose of grinding up the food. This is especially true of seed-eating birds. The Divers are no exception to this rule, small stones and pieces of shell being used for triturating purposes. But the Grebes alone among birds swallow, not stones, but their own breast-feathers.

SLAVONIAN GREBE (*Podicipes auritus*) in nuptial plumage.

In the matter of coloration the Grebes display a surprising range of variety, and often great beauty, and in all the breast-feathers have a remarkable satin-like sheen. This fact brought our own Great-crested Grebe to the verge of extermination owing to the ruthless demands of the milliners.

The young in down are strikingly different from those of the Divers, inasmuch as in the latter they are of a uniform greyish, or brownish-grey, while young Grebes are longitudinally striped from the head downwards; and this coloration is very sharply defined in the Great-crested Grebe. Furthermore these youngsters at this stage present a heart-shaped patch of bare skin, of a vivid vermilion red, on the crown of the head. No explanation of this seems to be forthcoming, but it may, possibly, serve as a recognition mark to the parents when seeking members of their family, generally five in number, which have strayed away among the maze of reeds around the nest.

An analysis of the coloration of the Grebes, as presented by the different species, would prove a fascinating theme could each be illustrated by coloured plates, and were space not to be considered. It must suffice to comment on the fact that in these birds resplendent plumage is confined to the head and neck, and takes the form of richly coloured frills and lappets. Our own Great-crested Grebe may well serve as an example of this type of coloration. Herein the head is set about with a great " Elizabethan " frill, which can be opened and closed at will. When fully spread it presents a beautiful gradation of colour, passing from a rich chestnut, at its base, into a deep blackish-brown at the margin of the frill, and the effectiveness is further enhanced by the white face and the rich dark brown of the feathers of the crown, which are produced backwards into a pair of long, erectile " ears."

The Slavonian Grebe presents a modification of this frill, which starts from the base of the beak and spreads backwards, upwards, and forwards, on each side of the head, to terminate above the eye. The coloration of the frill, and of the crown, is of a rich dark brown with a metallic-blue, contrasting with which is a broad band of golden yellow running from the base of the beak, over the eye, backwards, to terminate in a projecting flabella. In the Eared Grebe the elongated and somewhat loosely constructed feathers covering the aperture of the ear are greatly extended, forming a broad, spreading patch of golden-yellow. Both sexes, in each of these cases, are ornamented alike.

Order SPHENISCIFORMES

(*Penguins*)

Family Spheniscidae

The Penguins are a supremely interesting group, and the striking peculiarities which they display leap to the eyes when they are compared with the Divers. The wings are no longer wings, but " flippers," and this because, instead of the legs, the ancestral Penguins used the wings as swimming organs, just as do the Auks and Guillemots to be described in due course.

In birds which fly the wings can be " folded up " ; that is to say, the forearm and hand can be drawn up so as to lie under one another. In the Penguins this is no longer possible ; there is practically no movement either at the elbow or the wrist ; the arm, fore-arm, and hand are permanently extended ; movement is possible only between the arm and the body, or, to be more precise, between the arm and the shoulder-girdle, which, by the way, is remarkable for the singularly broad, scimitar-like blade-bone, seen in no other bird. But besides this lack of flexibility the bones have all become greatly flattened, while there are no flight-feathers. All the feathers of the body, indeed, are peculiar in their structure, the horny shaft being very broad, and the elastic vane very small, hence they are often, but erroneously, described as " scale-like."

The legs, though extremely short and web-footed, are never used in

U

swimming, and they have preserved considerable freedom of movement, so that walking is performed with comparative ease, and they can even climb up slopes. This ability to walk has been retained because, since these birds nest in vast colonies spread over a wide area, it is essential that they should be able to pass readily from the nest to the sea for food. The Divers and Grebes do not nest in large colonies, and have, therefore, no need to walk; they can build their nursery either *on* the water or at its very edge.

Some of the Penguins, it is to be noted, feed on fish, some on small crustacea, yet all have a very remarkable tongue, whose surface is covered with long, conical papillae, set in parallel rows; the precise function of these yet remains to be discovered. They build no more than a mere apology for a nest—just a few stones and shells, lining a hollow in the ground—and lay no more than two white-shelled eggs.

The nestlings, which for a long time remain helpless in the nursery, like nestling Divers, are covered with long, dull, brown-coloured down-feathers, which are later borne out upon the tips of the true-feathers, and finally break up. In size the adults show a considerable difference; the great Emperor Penguin standing as much as three feet high, while the pigmy of the tribe, the little Blue Penguin (*Eudyptala*), is no bigger than a Puffin.

Curiously enough, these birds have never passed north of the equator, but they range from Dassen Island in South Africa to the farthest limits of the Antarctic. The best-known species is the well-known " Jackass," or Cape Penguin (*Spheniscus demersus*). It breeds there in vast hordes on Dassen Island, and is protected for the sake of its eggs, which are used as food, and the guano which accumulates to a great thickness all over the breeding ground. These birds, however, have to share the island—about a mile square—with hordes of Cormorants and Ibises; the Penguins and the Cormorants annexing separate territory. The Penguin colony is estimated to number about nine millions !

Having grown enormously fat they come ashore to moult, and here they remain, fasting, for about a month. They then put to sea again, returning in about a month, once more loaded with fat, and commence to breed. Shallow pits are dug with the feet, the bird lying on its belly and kicking out the sand in showers; a few stones serve for a lining and the nest is complete. The female incubates the eggs, and the male generally stands close beside her, occasionally going to sea to find food for himself and her.

The largest living member of the tribe is the Emperor Penguin (*Aptenodytes forsteri*), standing some three feet high, and weighing from eighty to ninety pounds, yet a pigmy compared with the extinct Eocene species which stood seven feet high. Its near relation, the King Penguin, is only slightly smaller, and very similar in coloration, though in this respect the nestling is markedly different.

Pl. 9.

EMPEROR PENGUIN (*Aptenodytes forsteri*).

The Emperor Penguin has a very restricted range, its breeding colonies being found only on Cape Crozet in the far Antarctic. These were discovered in 1911 by Lieuts. Royds and Skelton, during Captain Sir Robert Scott's first Antarctic Expedition, after a most terrible journey and hardships almost incredible. The late Dr. Edward Wilson, who, with his chief, sleeps under the snows of the South Pole, later visited the colony, and gave a most wonderful and vivid description of the singular life-history of this extraordinary bird.

That it should have established itself in a region so desolate, and in conditions so rigorous, is nothing short of marvellous. Not once in its whole life does it ever rest on dry land, for when it comes " ashore " to breed it has to accept the sheet of ice fringing the great land-mass for *terra firma*.

ADULT KING PENGUINS
(*Aptenodytes patagonica*).

As a consequence of the terrible conditions under which they must perform the duties of incubating—a temperature of 78° F.—the egg must be specially protected to prevent its precious contents from freezing. This is done by placing it on the back of the feet as soon as it is laid, and covering it over with the feathers of the abdomen. To permit of this the skin, in this region, can be thrown into an overlapping fold, forming a sort of pouch, opening downwards.

The male and female share this onerous task. With the arrival of the nestling the difficulties of the parents are immensely increased, and these account for the terrible infant mortality which Dr. Wilson estimated to be as high as seventy-seven per cent. Much of this is due to the fact that birds which have lost their own young yearn still for something to nurse, and so, when the time comes for successful parents to change guard, the bereaved ones crowd round and scramble for the precious infant, which, in the struggle, is sometimes torn to pieces, or falls down into a crevice and is speedily frozen to death !

The coloration of the nestling is remarkable, and totally unlike that of any other penguin, even the King Penguin, the adults of which, in size and coloration, closely resemble the Emperor ; for the nestling-down of the King Penguin is of the typical, clove-brown hue, while the young Emperor is clothed in a pale, smoke-grey down with a black head, and a large white patch covering the whole side of the face, a coloration so far inexplicable. This down is exchanged for feathers at the end of four months; while the young King Penguin retains the down for no fewer than *ten* months !

With the breaking up of the ice during the "summer" the breeding colonies are borne seawards on an ice-raft, the parents at the time being in full moult, and the young in down, so that neither can enter the water. But this fasting period is soon passed.

The Adeliae Penguin contrives to thrive in conditions only a little

YOUNG KING PENGUIN, with down-feathers still on the head and neck.

less rigorous, its breeding stations being Cape Adare and other neighbouring areas of South Victoria Land. But while the Emperor chooses the darkest, coldest, and more tempestuous time for reproduction, the month of August—to give its young the full benefit of the "summer" months— the Adeliae chooses the summer months, the young appearing in December. Nevertheless this "summer" is somewhat trying, since their "rookeries" are generally found in the most wind-swept regions of the Antarctic. The choice of such sites seems forced upon them, as only on wind-swept places kept bare of snow can solid ground and pebbles be found for nesting purposes.

It has already been remarked in these pages that the Penguins are very capable pedestrians. They have to be; for, breeding in vast colonies, there is no accommodation for all at the edge of the sea. And so it comes about that journeys up precipitous slopes, to a height even up to one thousand feet, are cheerfully made for the purpose of securing peace and quiet, even though this choice commits them to long and weary journeys to the sea and back for food. But they evidently enjoy climbing, for, as Dr. Murray Levick tells us, in his wonderful book on "Antarctic Penguins," these birds will spend hours in climbing up floating bergs to a height of one hundred feet and more, and slithering down will start again to climb. Having regard to the fact that they have no hands, and such extremely short legs, these are wonderful performances.

No useful purpose would be served by describing in these pages the characteristics whereby each of the seventeen species of Penguins known to science may be distinguished, for except occasionally they are rarely ever seen alive save by those who have the good fortune to explore the isolated corners of the world where these birds live. Of their life-histories we know little save of the Antarctic species, and of the " Rock-hoppers," described by Moseley in his " Voyage of the ' Challenger '."

His notes on the nesting habits of the Magellan " Jackass Penguin " (*Spheniscus magellanicus*), for example, are especially noteworthy, since these Magellan birds, so closely akin to the African " Jackass " (*S. demersus*), nest in large and deep burrows in the peat-banks on the seashore, and have a curious habit of laying out pebbles round the mouths of the burrows, and even on the ground between the burrows. Since these pebbles are of different colours, Moseley suggests they are placed here to satisfy their aesthetic feelings ! This, however, is probably only a part of the interpretation. Dr. Levick has shown that the Adeliae Penguins like coloured pebbles, especially if they be red, and use them for the purpose of nest-building. Is the pebble-collecting of the Magellan-penguin a survival from the days when they built nests of pebbles on the bare ground ?

Most of the Penguins are fish-eaters, and this being so one would have supposed that they would have the same type of beak as that seen in the Grebes and Divers. It is, however, in no case so " dagger-like " and pointed. In the King and Emperor Penguins it is long and decurved ; in the genus *Catarrhactes*, thick and heavy, and coloured red. In the Adeliae Penguin, which lives entirely on the free-swimming crustacea known as *Euphausiae*, it is extremely short, and would seem to be ill-adapted for its purpose. But this shows how cautious one must be in drawing deductions of this kind.

In all the upper parts the plumage is of some shade of bluish-grey, the under parts white ; but in the King Penguins the coloration is enlivened by a brilliant patch of golden-yellow on each side of the neck ; a similar patch, but much smaller, is seen in the Emperor Penguin. The " Rock-hopper " (*Catarrhactes chrysocome*)—so-called from its habit of jumping from one rock-boulder to another with both feet together—has a long pair of crests, one on each side of the head, and these are also golden-yellow.

Order PROCELLARIFORMES
(*Petrels and Albatrosses*)
Family Procellaridae

By the older naturalists the Petrels were regarded as near allies of the Gulls, to which some species certainly present a superficial resemblance. As a matter of fact, they are more nearly allied to the Divers and Penguins.

All are marine, and they display a wide difference in point of size, ranging from the lordly Albatrosses with a wing-span of twelve feet to the little Storm-petrel, or " Mother Carey's Chicken."

Those who do not desire to appeal to anatomical characters may always readily distinguish between a Petrel and a Gull by the fact that in the former the beak-sheath is hooked at the tip, and composed of a number of separate pieces, of which a median arched plate covers the nostrils, hence the term " tube-nosed " often applied to them.

There are a large number of species, divisible into well-marked groups, and displaying most interesting modifications of form and structure, in accordance with their mode of life. Some, like the Shearwaters, dive for their food; some, like the Albatrosses, rarely touch the water. The young remain long in the nest in a helpless condition, and are clothed in a thick, woolly down.

In surveying the " Tubinares " it will be best to begin with the more primitive, that is to say, the least specialised types, thereby a standard of comparison will be obtained as between the Albatrosses on the one hand and the Diving-petrels, or Shearwaters, on the other. These lowlier types, in short, will afford us an insight into the nature of the process of transformation.

STORM-PETREL (*Hydrobates pelagicus*).

The little Mother Carey's Chicken, or " Storm-petrel," is a small bird and sooty-black save for a large white patch at the base of the tail. It feeds upon small crustacea and small fish, which seem to be snatched from the water as the bird skims its surface on the wing, though, as they have been seen to alight on the surface and close their wings, some food is doubtless taken at this time. Its habit of pattering with its feet on the water as it flies is familiar to mariners, who, in consequence, likened its action to that of the Apostle Peter, who, we are told, walked upon the water, and hence the name Petrel (Peter-elle).

It lays its single white egg at the end of a burrow, or in the crevices of rocks, on the bare soil, or a few bits of grass. These burrows have a strong odour of musk, and the bird itself, like all the Petrels, has a characteristic and strong odour, which, however, is not musk-like. The Storm-petrel, in common with all other Petrels, has the unpleasing peculiarity of vomiting oil whenever it is handled. This ability to distil oil in such profuse quantities seems to be peculiar to these birds.

Like most of the Petrel tribe, the Storm-petrel, during its residence ashore for breeding purposes, is nocturnal, though non-brooding birds may be seen abroad during the day.

The Fulmar-petrel stands in strong contrast with the Storm-petrel in that it is content with a slight cave in the side of a cliff for its nursery, a hole so slight as to do no more than half-conceal the sitting-bird ; but quite as commonly it will nest on open, exposed ledges, like the Guillemots.

Its stronghold, so far as Great Britain is concerned, is St. Kilda, where the Petrels nest in tens of thousands. But in recent years its range has spread to various parts of the coast of Northern Scotland, and to Ireland. Save during the few weeks of the nesting season it never comes to land, even in the stormiest of weather.

It is a comparatively large bird, having a yellow beak, a back of pale pearl-grey, and the rest of the plumage white.

FULMAR-PETREL (*Fulmarus glacialis*).

This is the " typical " plumage ; but the Fulmar is what is known as a " dimorphic " species, that is to say, it appears under two very distinct forms. In the second, or " grey " phase, the coloration is of an ash-brown hue, darkest on the back and wings. It feeds largely on floating molluscs, cephalopods, and small crustacea.

Another remarkable species is the Pintado-petrel, or " Cape-pigeon " (*Daption capensis*), well known to those who travel in big South African liners for its habit of following the ships for the sake of the scraps thrown overboard. It has once occurred in Yorkshire, once in Sussex.

The Snowy-petrel of the icy regions of the Far South must find mention here on account of its snow-white plumage, wherein it contrasts with all the other Petrels.

BROAD-BILLED BLUE-PETREL (*Prion ariel*).

Another remarkable species is the Broad-billed Blue-petrel (*Prion ariel*), wherein the beak is, as its name implies, extremely broad, and is fringed with long lamellae like those of a duck. Doubtless this stands in intimate relation to its feeding habits, of which, however, we have no detailed account.

The Giant-Petrel, or " Nelly," of the Southern Seas, is the largest of the true Petrels, rivalling the Albatross in size. As with the Fulmar, it presents a dark and a light phase, some individuals being entirely white, and these are commonest in the extreme limits of its Antarctic range. Unlike the other Petrels they are carrion-eaters, preying also on young birds.

THE SHEARWATERS AND THE DIVING-PETREL

All the Petrels so far considered are " Gull-like " in shape, that is to say, when on land the poise of the body is horizontal with the legs well under the middle of the body, and at right angles to its long axis. We may gather from this that, though they swim, this is relatively but an occasional mode of motion with them. With the Shearwaters matters are certainly otherwise, even though they are more often seen on the wing than afloat. Their flight is strikingly reminiscent of the Swift, the long wings being kept almost motionless as they glide over the surface of the water, up the crest of one wave and down into the hollow to climb the next, tilting the body so that now one wing is almost touching the water and now the other, but with scarcely a wingbeat throughout their course. When they fold their wings it is apparently only to sleep, or to feed. And they feed under water. This much was well attested in the case of a Manx Shearwater which seized a baited hook deep down in the water and was brought struggling to the surface.

MANX SHEARWATER (*Puffinus puffinus*).

Though we may claim as " British birds " several species of Shearwater, only one, the Manx Shearwater, is resident and breeding on our coasts. Yet even this is so seldom seen, and then well out at sea, that most people are unaware of its existence. Nevertheless, its numbers amount to an enormous total. As many as 150,000 are estimated to breed on one small island of the Scillies alone ! They are so rarely seen because, in the first place, they come ashore only to breed, and in the second, they enter and leave their burrows only during the night when the male and female change places, the one going out to feed, the other returning to brood.

This habit has apparently been evolved to enable them to escape the persecution of the Great Black-backed Gulls, which is merciless. These birds wait at the entrance to the burrows and pounce upon any which have the temerity to attempt to leave during daylight. One may spend a whole day in the midst of one of these bird-warrens without seeing the slightest sign of any of the occupants; but about ten o'clock at night a wild and almost deafening chorus of birds is set up—*cock-a-thrordon, cock-a-thrordon, cock-a-thrordon,* with an accent on the middle of the last syllable. Then, like ghosts they leave, and like ghosts they return.

GARNOT'S DIVING-PETREL (*Pelecanoides garnoti*).

The habits of the Shearwaters, of which there are many species, are all alike. They feed chiefly on floating molluscs, crustacea, and cephalopods.

There are, further, the little Diving-petrels (*Pelecanoides*) of Australia and New Zealand and the far South Atlantic. There are three species in all, and differing from one another chiefly in coloration. They are singularly interesting little birds because they have undergone a very intensive adaptation to the physical demands of diving for food. Thereby the skeleton has come to assume a somewhat close likeness to that of the Auk tribe, and more especially to the Little Auk. In the Shearwater, it was remarked, the legs have shifted backwards so that the body assumes an upward tilt when on land, but in the Diving-petrels it is held almost vertical, as in the Auks.

THE ALBATROSSES

The Albatrosses are the largest members of the Petrel tribe. About fifteen species are known, grouped into three genera. The largest species is the Wandering Albatross, measuring up to twelve feet across the expanded wings. It breeds on some of the islands in the Southern Ocean in colonies of thousands, and in the matter of its nesting habits differs profoundly from all the other Petrels, building a tall mound of mud and grass with a hollow at the top for the egg. The Petrels, it will be remembered, with the exception of the Fulmar, breed in burrows; and it may be that this habit has been enforced to enable them to escape their numerous enemies. The Albatrosses, partly on account of their great size, and partly from their breeding on islands remote from the mainland, have no need to resort to burrows.

The young Albatross, thickly covered with a woolly down, rapidly becomes enormously fat, and as soon as this stage is attained the parents depart on their wanderings, leaving the youngster to complete its nestling stage of development in solitude and fasting. By the time they return the youngsters are fully fledged, and are driven off the nest now required for another generation.

The flight of the Albatross is remarkable for the surprising distances which can be traversed without flapping the wings : a peculiarity it shares with the Shearwaters. But the wing of the Albatross differs from that of all the other Petrels in its enormous length and the shortness of the quills, or " flight-feathers," which gives the wing a curiously ribbon-like form. The skeleton of the wing is also peculiar, having an extremely long humerus, or upper arm-bone, and a very short hand.

A Black-browed Albatross was captured in Cambridgeshire in 1897, and on this account it is to be reckoned as a " British bird " ; but it is also to be noted that fossilised bones of the Albatross have been found in the Red Crag of Suffolk, which suggests that at one time the Albatross was once a more frequent visitor to our shores, and may even have bred here.

Legion *PELARGOMORPHAE*

(*Storks, Swans, Geese, Birds of Prey, etc.*)

Order CICONIIFORMES

(*Gannets, Cormorants, Pelicans, etc.*)

Sub-order *STEGANOPODES*

The relationship between the Divers, Penguins, and Petrels on the one hand and birds like the Gannets and Cormorants on the other is not one that leaps to the eyes. It is, however, incontrovertible, but since it rests on complex anatomical characters it would be out of place to discuss it in these pages.

Family Phalacrocoracidae

The birds which form the group Steganopodes, though differing profoundly in external form, all share one very singular character in common —all the toes are included within one web. In all other web-footed birds the hind-toe is free : it may even be wanting altogether.

Again, all these steganopodous birds are fish-eaters, and the diversity of form which they display is to be interpreted as the result of their different modes of fishing. Many breed together in colonies of hundreds of thousands, while others, more restricted in their geographical range, are far less numerous and do not breed in colonies.

The Gannets, represented by many species, are all birds with long,

pointed wings and of powerful flight, obtaining their food by diving.
The Common Gannet (*Sula bassana*), which breeds in vast numbers on Ailsa Craig, St. Kilda, the Bass Rock, and a few other stations in Great Britain, is the best-known member of its tribe. When fishing it mounts high in the air, then descends, like a bolt from the blue, with closed wings, to plunge far below the surface to secure its prey. As with all the other Gannets, between the skin and the body is interposed a mass of air-cells, which apparently serve as a cushion to break the force of the impetuous descent.

COMMON GANNET (*Sula bassana*).

The adults are pure white, save the wing-quills, which are black, and the head and neck, which, in the breeding season, is suffused with a rich buff hue; but the immature birds are black, with white spots. Curiously enough, the nestling looks like a mass of white swansdown. This development of black pigment by the immature birds, and its disappearance in the adult, is a phenomenon demanding further investigation.

In this connection it is worth noting that the Brown Gannet, or Booby, which has a wide geographical distribution, is of a uniform sooty-brown, while there are other species which have more or less brown in their plumage. These, then, are to be regarded as more primitive types, the white species as the more specialised, and latest evolved.

WHITE-BREASTED CORMORANT
(*Phalacrocorax albiventer*).

The Cormorants and Darters, though closely related to the Gannets, are birds of a very different build. Their powers of flight are limited, and this by lack of use, for most of their life is spent on, or under, the water; one species, indeed, Harris' Cormorant, has lost the power of flight and the keel of the breast-bone

completely.   They differ again from the Gannets in the form of the beak,
which, in the Gannets, is long, pointed and dagger-shaped, with a finely
serrated edge, while in the Cormorants it ends in a sharp hook.   But
Gannets, Cormorants, Darters, and Pelicans all agree in one singular feature
—they have no external nostrils, though vestiges of these are found in
the embryo.   The closure of the nostrils is quite inexplicable, since they
remain open in all other diving birds.

The Cormorant and the Shag differ but little one from another save
in size.   But the Cormorant in the breeding season develops a white
patch over the thigh, often said to be composed of those curious
feathers known as filo-plumes, the long, hair-like feathers, so conspicuous
in a plucked fowl ; while the Shag,
at this season, wears a crest.

DARTER (*Plotus anhinga*).

Both Cormorant and Shag are of
a uniform bottle-green colour, but
are brown in their immature stages,
while the nestlings, which remain
long helpless in the nest, constructed
of seaweed, are clothed in a dark
brown down.   About forty species
of Cormorant are known, and some
of these have white breasts, with
caruncles of yellow skin on the face.
But these two species, so alike in
general appearance, differ in one
important particular.   The Shag is
exclusively a dweller by the sea ; the
Cormorant will make its way inland
to found colonies on lakes, often
building nests on trees.   Though mostly fish-eaters, some species live
mainly on crabs and other crustacea.

The tropical and sub-tropical Darters, or " Snake-birds " (*Plotus*), may
be described as river Cormorants, deriving their name " Snake-birds "
from the curious " kink " in the neck, forming a spring-like mechanism
by which the neck can be suddenly " shot-out " with lightning speed,
when the scurrying victim is transfixed on the spear-like point of the beak,
and brought to the surface to be swallowed.   The Cormorant holds his
prey with the hook of the beak.

The cutting-edges of the Darter's beak, by the way, differ markedly
from the Cormorant's in that they are beset with long, needle-like points.
The striking differences in the form and use of the beak in these two types
may be explained by the fact that the Darters strike only at small fish ;
the Cormorant, on the other hand, will seize surprisingly large fish, and has
a correspondingly capacious gullet.   Nevertheless the Darter's jaws and

gullet are sufficiently distensible to enable it to swallow very young alligators and young terrapins, as well as water-snakes and newts.

Family Pelecanidae

The general appearance of the Pelican tribe is too well known to need description, but in spite of their unwieldy bulk on land they are birds of powerful flight. The most striking feature of their external anatomy is the huge pouch depending from the lower jaw, which is really only an exaggerated development of the area of loose, bare skin found in the Cormorant and Gannet. Its evolution has come about in response to a different mode of fishing, for these birds commonly plunge their heads down among shoals of fishes and scoop up their victims by the pouchful. They can, however, and do, when occasion demands, dive from the air like a Gannet, though never to the same depth.

ROUGH-BILLED PELICAN (*Pelecanus erythrorhynchus*).

As touching its manner and power of flight, it should be noted that though it arises from the water somewhat laboriously, with outstretched neck, as soon as it is fairly on the way the neck is doubled up till the head rests between the shoulders, as with the Heron. With an expanse of wing as much as ten feet, the bulky body is easily supported. It will soar in majestic circles in the teeth of the strongest gale, and in fine weather will mount, with its fellows, to prodigious heights to wheel about in the sky for the pure joy of movement, descending like a winged meteor with the roar of the air rushing through its stiff pinions.

About nine species of Pelicans are known, which inhabit the tropical and sub-tropical regions of the world, and one of these, the White-pelican, was once a native of Great Britain.

Finally, mention must be made of the remarkable North American Rough-billed Pelican (*Pelecanus erythrorhynchus*), which, in the breeding season, develops on the ridge of the middle of the beak a large, nearly quadrate, crest of horn. At the end of the season this is shed. This is to be regarded as a secondary sexual character, of the same nature as the ornamental plumage developed by other birds at this time.

Family Phaethontidae

There is something suggestive of a Gannet in miniature about the Tropic-birds (*Phaethontidae*), but the beak is more sharply pointed, while in the matter of size it does not exceed that of a small gull. In all but six species are known, and they are confined to tropical and sub-tropical seas. Large numbers breed in the Bermudas and the West Indies, and they are no less numerous in the Indian and Pacific Oceans.

They are remarkable for the satin-like gloss of the plumage, which is mostly white, and, in the Yellow-billed Tropic-bird, the breast may be suffused with a beautiful rose-pink. The largest and most striking species is the Red-billed Tropic-bird (*P. rubicauda*), of the Indian and Pacific Oceans, wherein the elongated, almost spine-like central tail-feathers are of a bright crimson red, and the beak is also red, while the whole plumage is suffused with a roseate tinge.

These birds dive, like the Gannet, from a great height, in pursuit of their prey, which consists of small fish and squids ; but though in the descent the wings are closed, after the manner of the Gannet, the flight is very different and more nearly resembles that of the Pigeon in the rapidity of the wing-beat. On land they walk with difficulty, owing to the short-ness of their legs, which have degenerated from lack of use even more than in the Gannets and Cormorants.

No nest is made, and the choice of a site for the egg varies considerably : caves, ledges of rocks, under bushes, and on trees, according to the con-ditions of the breeding-ground. The egg—for, like the Gannet, they lay but one—is remarkable for the richness of its coloration, being commonly of a mottled purplish-brown, but there is a considerable variation in this matter. Stress is laid on this coloration because it is so strikingly different from what obtains in the Cormorants and Gannets, wherein it is of a pale blue, overlaid by a thick, white, chalky incrustation.

The young, clothed in a thick, white down, remain for a long time in the nest, perfectly helpless, and are fed, as with all the steganopodous birds, by regurgitation, the young thrusting the head down the parent's throat and withdrawing semi-digested food.

Family Fregatidae

The Frigate-birds are the most highly specialised of all the steganopodous birds, the whole energies of the body having been concentrated on flight. Hence the legs are extremely short, little more than the feet being visible in the living bird, a condition recalling that seen in the Swifts, but the toes are surprisingly long, though only webbed half way. In the general appearance of the birds the relatively enormous length of the wings and the long, forked tail are the most marked features. The beak is long, and hooked like an exaggerated Cormorant's beak.

Their mode of life is as unlike that of their congeners as is their bodily conformation, since they live almost entirely by chasing and causing other sea-birds to disgorge their newly swallowed food, which they catch in mid-air as it falls. But besides this they will also kill and eat the young, not only of other birds, but, when occasion offers, even of their own species.

This is not all, however, for their courtship behaviour is also remarkable. At this time a dozen or more males may be seen sitting side by side on the bare bough of a tree projecting from a cliff over the sea, each with a great scarlet air-filled pouch suspended from the lower jaw and extended on to the neck—answering to the pouch of the pelican—but here modified to contain air. When fully inflated this pouch rivals the rest of the body in size. When a female approaches, these gaily decked swains set up a strange chorus—" wow-wow-wow-wow-wow-wow "—and clatter their beaks like castanets. When they take to flight the air is slowly forced from the pouch, leaving but a patch of bare skin.

CHAPTER IV

Order CICONIIFORMES

Sub-order CICONIAE

(*Herons, Storks, and Ibises*)

THE short-legged, web-footed Gannets, Cormorants, and Pelicans seem to have little in common with the long-legged, long-necked Storks and Herons. Yet anatomically they can be shown to be but divergent branches of a common stock.

Like the steganopodous birds they have what is known as a " desmognathous " palate, and their skeletons when closely examined are found to present the same underlying structural characters, but modified to suit the demands made upon them. This relationship will be the more easily grasped when the members of the two main types are surveyed as a whole.

Family Ardeidae

The Common Heron (*Ardea cinerea*) of this family may, happily, still be seen standing among the reeds of some quiet river-bank, or stalking majestically over a mud-flat in search of eels and other fish, which are struck with lightning speed by the dagger-like beak, whose edges are serrated the better to hold such slippery prey.

This is its normal environment, and in the pursuit of this mode of life the long legs, long neck, and long beak have developed. In all the herons the hind-toe is long, and placed low down, at the same level as the front toes, and this is associated with its habit of perching on trees, wherein commonly the nest is built. The foot presents yet another peculiarity, inasmuch as the inner edge of the middle claw is serrated, that is to say, has a comb-like edge, but as to the use of this comb nothing is known.

Nor is any explanation forthcoming as to the origin or function of certain strangely modified feathers known as " powder-downs," which form two large mat-like patches on the breast, and a large patch over each thigh. In appearance they look like wool, but when touched leave on the fingers an excessively fine powder recalling Fuller's-earth. " Powder-down " feathers are found in various types of birds, but nowhere in such luxuriant tufts. In the Tinamous, for example, they occur, but scattered over the body. They give the feathers a curious " bloom " comparable with the waxy bloom of a grape.

SNOWY EGRET (*Ardea candidissima*).

In flight the Heron doubles up the neck till the head rests on the back between the shoulders, as, it will be remembered, do the pelicans. Herein the herons differ from the storks, which fly with outstretched necks like swans.

The nest is little more than a platform of sticks, though a very substantial one. The eggs are of a beautiful greenish-blue, save in some of the bitterns, where they are white, or yellowish-brown. The nestlings remain long helpless in the nest, and have but a scanty covering of hair-like down.

No useful end would be gained by describing the plumage of all the known species of herons, for there are many, but the more important types which have emerged in the course of the evolution of the tribe must find a place here. Undoubtedly the most beautiful are the snow-white Egrets, whose long and extraordinarily beautiful plumes are so coveted by the milliners, who sell them under the name of " Ospreys." It should be remembered that the collection of such plumes involves a hideous amount of cruelty, since these feathers are only worn during the breeding season, and are only to be obtained by the slaughter of the birds whose young, in consequence, are left to die of slow starvation.

Though we have no evidence of such a relationship, yet one is tempted to regard the complete de-pigmentation seen in the Egrets as the final sequel to an inherent tendency shared by several nearly related forms. For the Reef-herons, of the genus *Demiegretta*, and the Blue-heron (*Florida coerulea*) present two phases, one in which the plumage is bluish-grey, the other white, and both types may be found in the same nest; while in the Reddish-egret (*Dichromanassa rufa*) one is rufous, the other white.

In the handsome Purple-heron (*Phoyx purpurea*), a very rare British bird, the plumage presents rich contrasts of chestnut red, grey, black, and buff.

Since the herons, in the course of their evolution, have developed some extremely specialised types, they should, perhaps, be regarded as a later development of, or offshoot from, the storks, to be considered presently. They are taken first here because being more familiar birds the story of the evolution of the whole group will be the more easily grasped.

What is meant by this specialisation can best be illustrated by the case of that remarkable bird, the Shoe-bill (*Balaeniceps rex*), a bird found only in the swamps of the White Nile. It is a much bigger bird than the Common Heron, which it resembles in coloration. But it stands alone in the enormous size of the beak, whose form can better be realised from the accompanying picture than by description. No adequate interpretation of the building up of such a beak can yet be made, but it may perhaps be

SHOE-BILLED HERON (*Balaeniceps rex*).

associated with the nature of its food, since it seems to feed largely on that strange fish the *Polypterus*, whose body is armed with great bony enamelled scales. To seize and hold prey with such an armour-plated surface may well require a beak of special shape. The form of the foot and the presence of powder-down patches show that *Balaeniceps* is a true Heron.

We have a parallel in the matter of the beak in one of the South American Boat-billed Night-herons (*Cancroma*), a bird which lives by rivers winding through the Great Brazilian forests.

The typical Night-heron, represented by many species, one of which is a rare straggler to the British Islands, is very like *Cancroma* in its general

appearance, save for the beak, which is dagger-like, as in the herons and
bitterns.

In the great swamps of the Valley of the Danube, the Night-heron
(*Nycticorax griseus*) breeds in vast colonies in common with herons, egrets,
bitterns, and spoonbills. The ornithologist Seebohm gives a lurid picture
of one of the colonies. The nestlings he describes as little fiends, tearing
one another to pieces with savage ferocity, while the parents look on
unmoved " as if fratricide were the proper moral pastime for the young.'

Here is an aspect of the struggle for
existence, and the survival of the
fittest, worth taking note of.

The Bitterns have a world-wide
distribution, being absent, however,
from the Far North. Yet not more
than about twenty-five species are
known. The plumage is generally
streaked and vermiculated with black
on a buff background. The back of
the neck in these birds is merely
down-covered, but is amply protected
by the feathers running down the
sides of the neck which are very long,
and can be drawn round to protect
this somewhat ill-covered area. They
frequent swamps and morasses in
the seclusion of which they hide by
day. They feed on fish, frogs, water-
voles, aquatic insects, and vegetable
matter.

Time was when the Common
Bittern. (*Botaurus stellaris*) was a
common British bird, but it was
almost exterminated by drainage, and

BOAT-BILLED NIGHT-HERON (*Cancroma cochlearia*).

collectors. Having been afforded adequate protection, however, on some
of the Norfolk Broads, a few pairs now breed there annually.

The Bitterns furnish some very striking examples of protective coloration. When alarmed their custom is not to seek safety by flight, but to
keep absolutely motionless, tilting the body backwards, and thrusting
the head and neck vertically upwards, keeping the breast and fore-part
of the neck and throat towards the source of danger. The dark streaks
on the throat and breast then come to blend with the dark intervals between
the reed-stems, while the buff tints of the plumage harmonise perfectly
with the dead reed-leaves and stems, and other vegetation. Only by the
merest accident will the bird be discovered while thus posed.

The Common Bittern has long been famous for the remarkable resonant noise it makes during the breeding season, a sound which is made without the aid of any special mechanism.

Family Scopidae

The very remarkable bird known as the Hammer-head, which constitutes the above family in itself, is a native of Africa and Madagascar, and forms a most interesting connecting link between the herons and the storks, presenting features found in both, as well as some peculiar to itself.

It is heron-like in the form of its feet, having a long hind-toe on the same level as the three front toes, and in some of its internal anatomy. It differs from the herons in the absence of powder-down patches above the thigh, and in the absence of a pectinated claw; while in the matter of its flight it is intermediate between the herons and the storks in that the neck is only slightly curved.

HAMMER-HEAD (*Scopus umbretta*).

The beak is like neither that of the heron nor the stork, being blunt-pointed and laterally compressed. The coloration of the plumage, again, is peculiar, being of a uniform clove-brown, with a purplish gloss, while the head bears a huge crest and a tuft of long feathers on the cheeks. Finally, in regard to its appearance, it is a relatively small bird, of about the size, say, of the Black-backed Gull.

Its haunts are wooded districts in the neighbourhood of water. But the strong individuality of this bird is shown in a very striking way in the manner of its nest-building, which is utterly unlike that of any other heron, or of any of the storks. For it builds in either the fork of a tree or on some rocky ledge, a huge mass of sticks forming a nest with a roof like that of a Magpie, and lines the chamber thus formed with roots, grass, and rushes, or clay, a choice of materials which recalls that of the storks. The eggs, from three to five, are white.

Family Ciconiidae

Though anatomically there is no difficulty in distinguishing a stork from a heron, those who are not well versed in ornithology may well find some difficulty in distinguishing the one from the other when seen, say, at the Zoo.   But when the two types come to be compared it will be noticed that the herons are of a more slender build, with relatively longer and thinner necks, and a more slender, dagger-like bill.   The foot, however, will set all doubts at rest, for in the Storks (*Ciconiidae*) the toes are shorter, and the hind-toe is relatively short, and set above the level of the front toes.   Moreover, the storks have no serrated claw.   The nestlings, again, differ from those of the heron's, being entirely down-clad.

Of the more superficial anatomical characters it may be mentioned that the storks have no powder-down patches, and a very small triangular tongue —in the herons this is long and slender.   The storks, again, are voiceless birds.   The herons croak—the Common Heron, it will be recalled, often utters a harsh note while on the wing, which sounds like " Frank-Frank," on which account they are often called " Franks " in Norfolk.   When the stork does desire to make audible sounds it does so by an excessively rapid snapping of the beak, the bird at the same time bending the head till the beak points earthwards, and slowly raising the head through a half-circle till it comes to rest on the back.   A pair commonly do this in unison, producing a weird effect.

The structural distinctions between herons and storks are reflected in the differences in the matter of haunts and habits which the two types display ; for the storks, though never found far from water, seek much of their food on the adjacent marsh.   Frogs and water-voles, grasshoppers, and lizards, as well as fish and aquatic insects, form the main diet.

One of the handsomest of the tribe is the White Stork, wherein the plumage is white, set off by black quill-feathers and red legs and beak. It is an occasional visitor to Great Britain, but in some parts of the continent, as in Holland and Germany, it is very common, displaying a great liking for homesteads, and building its nest of sticks on the roofs of houses.   It is considered, indeed, a piece of good fortune to have a pair of these birds nesting about the place, and so to attract them a special platform, commonly an old cart-wheel, is erected on the roof to support the nest.

The Black Stork, also a rare visitor to Great Britain, is a smaller bird than the White Stork, and, as its name implies, is mostly black in its colora-tion, which is relieved by a wonderful purplish metallic gloss ; but the under parts are white, while the beak and legs are of a carmine red.   It is found in Central and Southern Europe, all over Africa, and ranging east-wards into China, and, in winter, India.   Unlike its white relative it shuns human habitations, seeking the solitudes of swamps, and nesting in trees, lining the nest with moss.

The White-bellied Stork (*Abdimia sphenorhyncha*) recalls the Black Stork in its general appearance, though considerably smaller. In some respects, as in the bill and some internal anatomical characters, it recalls the herons ; but it displays a greater vividness of colour than the Black Stork, the bare space round the eye being blue, that on the throat red, while the beak is greenish, with a red tip, and there is a bright red band round the ankle-joint. From the Sudan nearly to East Africa it is to be found in vast numbers, and during the breeding season it frequents the villages, where as many as thirty nests may be built in a single tree. In the Sudan this bird is as much venerated as is its white cousin in Holland.

The giants of the Stork tribe are the " Adjutants," or " Marabouts" (*Leptoptilus*), of Africa and India, represented by several species. The military title is bestowed on account of their stately movements in walking, while the name " Marabout " is derived from the loose and voluminous under tail-coverts which form the much-prized " Marabout " feathers of milliners.

These birds display marvellous power on the wing, soaring to enormous heights like vultures ; and with the vultures they will dispute over the same carcase, for they have a marked taste for carrion. In India they are, on this account, rigorously protected, forming, as they do, most efficient scavengers. There is something rather disreputable about the appearance of these birds, for the head and neck are bare, save for an untidy straggling mass of hair-like feathers, while

ADJUTANT STORK (*Leptoptilus dubius*).

from the throat hangs a loose fold of pinkish, scurf-covered skin, which, at will, can be suddenly inflated to form a pendulous bag of considerable length, and as suddenly the air will be expelled. Small birds, frogs, and fish are also eaten. But they are sociable birds, herding in great flocks, save when in towns, where they are solitary and welcomed as scavengers. They also breed in colonies, building great nests of sticks on the precipitous ledges of cliffs, and sometimes in trees.

Africa has yet another giant species, the Saddle-billed Stork (*Xenorhynchus senegalensis*), so named from a triangular outgrowth of yellow, waxy-looking skin at the base of the beak, which has a slight upward curve. It is found both on the White and Blue Nile, and is a singularly handsome bird ; the beak is crimson with a black median band, while the legs are black with toes of carmine red. The plumage is for the most part black, with metallic purple and green reflections, the under parts dazzling white. The South American Jabiru is a nearly allied species, differing conspicuously, however, in having a featherless head and neck, the bare skin being black, with a scarlet inflatable pouch, though this is not pendulous as in the Marabout. The plumage is white.

One of the most remarkable of the Storks is the " Open-bill " (*Anastomus*), so-called from the fact that the upper and lower jaws are curved so as to leave a large gap between their cutting-edges which meet

OPEN-BILLED STORK (*Anastomus oscitans*).   WOOD-IBIS (*Pseudotantalus ibis*) in immature plumage.

only at the base and the tip of the beak ; in young birds the beak has the normal form. The use of this singular modification is not apparent, but it is probably intimately associated with the bird's habit of feeding on molluscs, whose shells are forced open by the beak. One species is found in India, another (*A. lamelligerus*) in Africa. This last is further note-worthy from the fact that the shafts of the feathers of the fore-neck and under parts are spread out into shining horny plates.

The Wood-storks (*Tantalus*), known also as Wood-ibises, have in so far as the form of the beak is concerned a likeness to the true ibises, to be considered presently. They may, indeed, be regarded as connecting links between these and the storks. In size they are not greatly inferior to the White Stork ; but they differ from all the rest of the Stork tribe in that the immature birds differ in their coloration from the adults. The handsomest of the five species is the African (*Pseudotantalus ibis*), wherein the plumage is white, with a rose-tinge on the back, a yellow beak, and red legs and feet. The young are of an ashy-grey colour. These birds are found in Africa, India, and America. All alike seem to feed upon fish and reptiles.

Family Ibidae

Whether the Ibises and the Spoonbills now to be passed in review are really to be derived, as some hold, from the Wood-ibises or not they, at any rate, serve in no uncertain way to bring home what we may call the " virility " of certain stocks, which seem to be endowed with a peculiar potentiality to branch again and again, giving rise to new types seemingly adjusted to almost identical conditions of the physical environment.

Of the ibises there are so many species that it would be wearisome to describe them all ; but however widely they differ in their coloration, which is often of great splendour, they all share one character in common, and that is the long, rather slender and much decurved beak, whose sides are marked by a deep groove. Like the herons some have a serrated claw in the middle-toe ; and like the storks they have only the vestige of a tongue. But they are not all silent as storks, for the Black-headed Ibis has a " booming call," the Indian *Inocotes* a melancholy scream.

The handsome Glossy-ibis is an accidental visitor to the British Islands. The upper parts of the plumage are brownish-black, glazed with metallic green and purple, the under parts of a rich reddish-brown. Another dark-coloured species is the Indian " Warty-headed Ibis " (*Geronticus papillosus*), which has a triangular patch of red " warts " on the top of its head. The general coloration of the plumage is black, with a steel-blue gloss on the wings and tail. It is a very common bird in India, and further remarkable for the fact that, unlike its congeners, it lives in open country far from water, feeding largely on insects.

One of the most famous species is the Sacred-ibis, wherein the head and neck are quite bare and inky-black, while the plumage is snow-white, relieved by long drooping plumes of black. The Ancient Egyptians used this bird as the emblem of Thoth, the secretary of Osiris, holding it in great veneration, as is shown by the vast number of mummified bodies which have been found by Egyptologists. This bird is now extinct in Egypt, but still breeds plentifully on the Upper Nile and in the Sudan. One of the most singular species is the Crested-ibis (*Lophotibis cristata*) of Madagascar; reddish chestnut is the prevailing coloration, with white wings and an enormous crest. Certainly the most beautiful is the small

Scarlet-ibis of tropical America, the whole body being of a flaming scarlet hue.

The Spoonbills (*Platalea*), though nearly related to the ibises, are to be distinguished therefrom at a glance by the strange shape of the beak, which is flattened out as though it had been placed in a press, and terminates in a broad, spoon-shaped expansion. Organs of singular forms are generally found to be the outcome of adaptation to some special function. But it is difficult to apply this interpretation to the beak of the spoonbill, which feeds on small fish, frogs, shell-fish, crustacea, and aquatic insects —practically the same diet as the ibises. When, however, its habits and mode of feeding come to be intensively studied the key to this singular beak may be found.

One species, the White Spoonbill (*Platalea leucorodia*), at one time used to breed annually in the British Islands ; it is now only a casual spring migrant. Its coloration is pure white with a yellow tinge on the crest and fore-neck, while the beak is yellow at the tip, the rest black, barred with yellow. In winter the occipital crest is absent. The Roseate Spoonbill of tropical America is of a rose-pink colour, with a white neck, back, and breast, and carmine wing and tail-coverts ; the bald head is yellowish-green, the throat orange, the beak greenish-blue, and the feet crimson, while a curly pink tuft is carried on the fore-neck during the breeding season.

Family Phoenicopteridae

Tracing out the pedigrees of the various types of birds is always a fascinating task. For evidence we have no written records, but must turn to that furnished by bones and muscles and viscera. The pedigree of the Stork tribe can be traced with a fair amount of certainty owing to the many interesting connecting links which have survived. The Hammer-head (*Scopus*) links up the herons with the storks ; the Wood-ibises form the connecting link between the ibises and the spoonbills. And we come to the still more interesting link furnished by the Flamingoes (*Phoenicopteridae*), which seem to show very clearly a relationship between the Stork tribe as a whole, on the one hand, and the Anseres on the other.

These birds are stork-like in their long legs and necks, and the condition of the newly hatched young, and Anserine in the thick fleshy tongue and lamellae which fringe the inner side of the upper jaw. Into the deeper-seated anatomical characters on which this matter of affinity is finally settled there is no need to enter here.

The most arresting feature of these birds is the beak, which is unlike that of any other bird, the upper jaw being flat and bent at a sharp angle upon itself, across the middle, while the lower jaw forms a deep trough, its sides modelled to fit the shape of the upper jaw. When feeding the bird wades through the water—wherefrom alone it can obtain its food

—with the head inverted and held almost between the legs, so that the lower jaw is uppermost.   Though frogs, crustacea, and molluscs form part of its diet, much of it is obtained by rapidly passing water through the mouth and filtering it by means of the fleshy tongue and lamellae, whereby minute organisms are sifted from the water and swallowed.   The skin covering the beak is thin and smooth, as in the Anserine birds; whereas in the Stork tribe it is invested in a horny sheath.   The singular form of this beak is apparently a late acquirement, since in the fossil *Palelodidae* it was straight, as it is in the nestling flamingoes.   The toes are fully webbed, as in the Anserines, and these birds swim well.

Flamingoes build, in colonies, remarkable nests of mud, forming high mounds, hollowed at the top for the eggs.   Two eggs form the " clutch," and they are of a delicate greenish-blue, though this colour is entirely hidden by a white chalky incrustation, as in many steganopodous birds.

IMMATURE ROSY FLAMINGO (*Phoenicopterus roseus*).

There are many species of flamingoes, and one, the Rosy Flamingo (*Phoenicopterus roseus*), is an occasional straggler to the British Islands.   In the Rhone delta and in the South of Spain they breed in large numbers.

CHAPTER V

Order ANSERIFORMES

(*Screamers, Swans, Geese, and Ducks*)

THE Swans, Geese, and Ducks would seem to have little enough in common with the Stork tribe; nevertheless a study of their anatomy shows that the two types are really blood-relations.   But whatever may have been their ancestry it is clear that they have become moulded to meet the requirements of an intensively aquatic life.   The Stork tribe are essentially waders, hence their long legs and necks, though they can swim at need.

By seeking their food out on the open water, instead of inshore, the Anserine birds were enabled to take new kinds of food, neglected by other animals, and thereby escape competition. As a sequel the beak has assumed the form we see to-day, while the legs are shortened, and a web has developed between the toes.

The young are of the nidifugous type, accompanying their parents in the search for food, and feeding themselves, thus differing conspicuously from the Ciconiiform birds wherein the nestlings are fed by regurgitation. The nestling-down is far less degenerate than in the Stork tribe, the feathers presenting a well-defined shaft and rami. The under-coat of down is not developed in the nestling. Finally, they develop the body-feathers long in advance of the wing-feathers, and this because they seek safety, when danger threatens, not by flight, but by swimming.

Family Palamedidae

There are probably few, save specialists, who have ever seen or heard of " The Screamers," who belong to the above family, and yet they are birds of profound importance. They furnish the link already referred to between the Stork tribe on the one hand and the typical Anseriform birds on the other ; though, seen in the flesh, at the Zoo, for example, they look like neither.

As large almost as a swan, with rather longer legs, the beak is like that of a game-bird, not merely in shape, but in the absence of lamellae on its inner surface, while the feet are reminiscent of those of the water-hen, the toes being very long and having no webs. Like the gannets, between the body and the skin is interposed a mass of air-cells, whose function has yet to be discovered. But more than this, the wing is armed with a pair of formidable spurs, which must prove terrible weapons in a fight. Finally, unlike all other birds, the ribs have no " uncinate processes," that is to say, short bony spurs, projecting back from one rib on to the next behind it.

HORNED-SCREAMER (*Palamedia cornuta*).

There are two genera and three species of Screamers. The Horned-screamer (*Palamedia cornuta*), ranging from Guiana and Amazonia to

Ecuador and East Peru, is easily recognised by the long, slender, horn-like outgrowth which projects from the forehead, curving upwards and forwards for a distance of five or six inches. Its coloration is of a dark brown with a metallic, green gloss on the inner secondaries and wing-coverts. The feathers of the crown of the head and fore-breast are of a silver-grey, the latter broadly tipped with black, while the abdomen is pure white. The iris is orange-yellow.

The second genus, *Chauna*, has no horn, but a crest of feathers, and is represented by the Crested-screamer, or Chaja (*C. cristata*), and the Derbian-screamer (*C. derbiana*). The Crested-screamer is of a dark grey coloration with a black ring round the neck, while the Derbian-screamer is of a glossy slate-black, with a grey head and crest, and red neck and legs.

CRESTED-SCREAMER (*Chauna cristata*).

They are all swamp-dwellers, and swim with ease. The flight is slow, but powerful. They will often, indeed, mount in spiral circles to an immense height. At such times, the Crested-screamer is said to make a melodious "song." On the ground, at certain times of the year, this species will congregate in thousands and sing in concert, the effect being almost awe-inspiring in its grandeur. The volume of sound is considerable and can be heard over a distance of two miles.

The nest is a massive structure of reeds and rushes, some two feet thick, with its foundations in the water—or it may actually be floating. In a slight hollow the four or five buffish-white eggs are laid, but, it should be noted, no down is used as a covering for the eggs, as in the true Anserine birds.

Sub-order ANSERES
(*Swans, Geese, and Ducks*)

Family Anatidae

The Swans, Geese, and Ducks present some extremely interesting modifications of structure which have come into being in response to the conditions imposed by their chosen environment.

The breast-bone is very long, with a low keel, and in some of the swans this keel is strangely modified to serve as a chamber for a long loop of the windpipe. In this matter of the breast-bone they differ conspicuously from the storks, wherein it is short and wide. The humerus, or upper arm, in the swans is very long, but is relatively much shorter in the ducks. The Anserine birds, again, fly with great speed, but they never soar as do the storks. On a long journey they travel in a characteristic <-shaped formation, with the neck straight out.

For the most part they feed on small aquatic organisms and vegetable matter ; but some are fish-eaters, and some live upon shellfish.

In response to the nature of their food, and its capture, the tongue is thick and fleshy, fringed along each side with lamellae and terminating in a horny tip, while the sides of the beak are also fringed by lamellae to form a sifting apparatus for separating small organisms from the water which is passed rapidly through the mouth, a method of feeding recalling that of the " Whale-bone whales." The beak has only a covering of soft skin, instead of a horny sheath, as in other birds, and it terminates in a hard " nail."

The nest of these birds is remarkable for the fact that it is always thickly lined with down-feathers plucked by the female from her breast.

THE SWANS

The discovery of Australia brought to light many marvels, among them the Kangaroo and a *Black* Swan—till then a thing incredible. But now we know of yet another species with a snow-white body and

BLACK SWAN (*Chenopis atrata*).

a black neck. These exceptions apart, all other swans are white. They are all large birds, and are represented by no more than a few species.

The extreme length of the neck is a direct adjustment to their feeding habits. They cannot dive, but obtain much of their food—freshwater mollusca, worms, aquatic insects, and roots and leaves of water-plants—by thrusting the head and neck down to the bottom of the water.

Three species of swan visit the British Islands, and one of these, the Mute, or Polish-swan, is kept in large numbers on our ornamental waters. It is the only species which swims with the wings raised, arch-wise, over the back, giving the bird a singularly graceful appearance. The male is further distinguished by a large, tumid, black excrescence at the base of the beak.

The smaller Bewick's Swan, like the North American Trumpeter-swan and our Whooper-swan, are remarkable for the fact that the windpipe grows to an inordinate length, so that part of it has to be received within a chamber formed by a thrusting apart of the outer walls of the keel of the breast-bone. The effect of this elongation of the windpipe is to produce a deep trumpet-like note, which is especially loud in the Trumpeter-swan.

The Black Swan, so often seen on ornamental waters, was discovered by the Dutch navigator, Willem de Vlaming, in 1697, on what is now known, in consequence, as the Swan River of Western Australia.

The Black-necked Swan was discovered by the Navigator Narborough in August, 1670, in the Straits of Magellan. The light red knob at the base of the beak and the black neck make a fine contrast with the white body.

Finally we have the Coscoroba-swan, the smallest species, and serving as a connecting link between the swans and the geese. The plumage is pure white in colour save for the black tip to the primaries, while the beak and feet are red.

The Geese

Though there would be no difficulty in distinguishing between a typical swan and a typical goose, or between a goose and a typical duck, it is impossible to draw a hard-and-fast line between these three types. And this because of the intermediate types which blend the boundary line.

The Coscoroba-swan might pass for a goose ; and some of the geese might well pass for ducks ! But speaking broadly, the geese have a characteristic beak, sloping steeply from the base, while its cutting edges are provided with horny, sharp-edged, conical processes simulating teeth, structures which are intimately associated with their more vegetarian diet. Though aquatic, they feed on land much more than either swans or ducks.

MAGPIE-GOOSE (*Anseranus semipalmata*).

One of the most interesting of these " intermediate links " is the " Magpie-goose," or Semipalmated Goose (*Anseranus semipalmata*), of Australia and Tasmania. It has a swan-like beak, and unusually long, yellow legs, and a long hind-toe, while the front toes are only partially webbed. The head and neck and the wings are black, the rest of the plumage white. But this bird presents yet another strange feature, in that the windpipe, having grown too long for the neck, is thrown into a series of coils between the skin and the body, an arrangement which is found in a number of different birds in no way related one to another.

As a rule, there is no difference in the coloration of the sexes among geese, but the genus *Cloephaga* furnishes two striking exceptions in the Upland-goose (*C. magellanica*) and the Kelp-goose (*C. antarctica*), wherein the males are almost entirely white, while the females are soberly clad in chestnut and greyish-brown, with flanks barred with black. These species may well have been derived from some ancestral form like the Ashy-headed goose (*C. poliocephala*), wherein both sexes wear a dark livery of chestnut and black.

But it is not merely in its coloration that this genus, which contains six species, is notable ; for in all the beak is conspicuously short, in this recalling the Cape Barren Goose of South-East Australia and Tasmania, wherein the beak is still shorter. This is a large and powerful bird, greyish-brown in colour and spotted with black. It is evidently nearly related to the still larger, extinct, flightless goose of New Zealand.

Of the more typical geese mention must be made of the Grey-lag (*Anser cinereus*), the species from which our domesticated goose was derived. It is the only species which breeds with us, though as a breeding-bird it is now rare. But rather more than one hundred years ago it bred abundantly in the English Fen-country, where the young were caught in large numbers and kept with the vast flocks of tame geese that at one time formed so valuable a property to the dwellers in the Fens. The Bean, Pink-footed, and White-fronted, are the other allied species, all winter visitors to Great Britain.

The Brent and the Barnacle-geese (*Branta*) visit us often in large numbers in the winter. The latter was believed by the ancients to be hatched from barnacles ! This myth gained currency owing to the fact that no one had ever succeeded in finding its breeding-places, which, indeed, were not discovered until a few years ago to be Spitzbergen, North-East Greenland, and North-West Siberia.

As nearly related to the Brent-goose we must regard the Red-breasted Goose (*Branta ruficollis*), the most vividly coloured of all the geese. Its general coloration is of a bluish-black, but the sides of the head and neck and the fore-part of the breast are of a rich chestnut red relieved by a large white spot at the base of the beak, and a broad white ring surrounding the region of the ear and continued down the neck as a conspicuous white stripe, while a white band, barred with black, runs along the flanks.

The Chinese-goose (*Cygnopsis cygnoides*) of Eastern Siberia and Mongolia is a species which has proved amenable to domestication, and is regarded by some as the stock from which the domestic geese of many Eastern countries have sprung. It may frequently be seen on ornamental ponds in public parks. It is the largest living goose, and walks with a strange upright carriage. The peculiar swelling at the base of the beak is said to be present only in domesticated birds. A conspicuous dark brown band down the back of the neck is another of its many strik-ing features.

COTTON-TEAL (*Nettopus coromandelianus*).

Whiteness is rare among the geese. But Ross's Snow-goose (*Chen rossi*) of Arctic America, and the "Wavy" of North-East Asia and North America, are white. Ross's Goose is a rare visitor to the British Islands. The parent species is probably *Chen coerulescens* of North America, a grey-brown bird with a white head and bluish rump. The food of these birds, it is to be noted, consists of rushes, berries, and insects—that is to say, they are losing their aquatic habits.

We must pass now to a number of species which serve, in various degrees, as links between the geese and the ducks. The little Pigmy-geese, or Cotton-teal, not larger than a bantam fowl, unlike all other geese, dive for their food. There are several species, ranging from Africa to the Indian region, and beyond through Celebes and New Guinea to Australia.

COMB-DUCK (*Sarcidiornis melanonota*).

There are four types, represented by the genera *Plectropterus*, *Sarcidiornis*, *Cairina*, and *Chenalopex*, of which it is hard to say whether they are really ducks or geese. As one sees them alive, say in a Zoo, *Chenalopex* is a goose, while *Cairina* is a duck. But appearances are deceptive.

The African Spur-winged geese (*Plectropterus*), of which there are two species, are distinguished, as their name implies, by the presence of a spur on the wing, which is of formidable size, and is borne on the wrist-joint. The beak is much more like that of a swan than a goose, being very long and surmounted at the base by a horny knob, while the face is bare, and the base of the beak is ornamented by a cluster of fleshy caruncles ; finally, the legs have large scutes down the front, again unlike the geese. They are large black-and-white birds, and haunt swamps.

In *Cairina*, the Muscovy-duck of tropical America, the caruncles of the face are still more in evidence, and of a vivid red colour. Its general appearance is that of a rather clumsily built duck.

In the Comb-ducks (*Sarcidiornis*), represented by an African, an Indian, and a tropical American species, the wing, as in *Plectropterus*, is armed with a spur ; while the beak is surmounted at its base, in the males, by a fleshy, laterally compressed protuberance or " comb." They are large, goose-like birds, of glossy black plumage. Their relationship to the true ducks is indicated by two quite independent characters. In the first place, the syrinx has the curiously inflated form, so characteristic of the ducks ; and in the second, the wing has a " speculum," whose definition it is convenient to defer for the moment.

MANDARIN-DUCK (*Aex galericulata*) (Male).

The sub-family *Plectropterinae* contains some strangely contrasted types. For at one end we have the relatively huge Spur-winged Goose, and the " Comb-duck " or " Knobbed-goose " (*Sarcidiornis*), and at the other the tiny Summer-duck and Mandarin-duck (*A e x*). T h e Summer-duck is an American species of considerable beauty. Even more so is the eccentric-looking Chinese Mandarin-duck, wherein the wings of the male develop a pair of upstanding, shield-like feathers, triangular in shape, and of a rich golden-brown colour, while a great crest of the same hue surmounts the head. The female, as with the female Summer-duck, is quite soberly clad.

The Egyptian-goose (*Chenalopex*) is goose-like in the matter of size and shape, but here also the wing has a speculum, and the windpipe a duck-like syrinx. Moreover, the coloration is more in keeping with the ducks. Its most conspicuous feature, apart from the wing, is the large chestnut-red patch surrounding the eye.

Probably the nearest allies of the genus *Chenalopex* are the Sheldrakes (*Tadorna*), among which our own bird is by far the most vividly coloured. And here, too, both male and female are alike, save that in the latter the protuberance at the base of the coral-like beak is wanting. This protuberance recalls the similar but much more conspicuous development seen in *Plectropterus* and *Sarcidiornis*. The name " Burrow-duck," by which it is sometimes known, is bestowed on account of the fact that it breeds in burrows, preferably those deserted by rabbits, failing which it will dig for itself.

The singular Tree-ducks (*Dendrocygna*) are birds of moderate size, but with conspicuously long legs, and with a very long hind-toe. They have the habit of perching much in trees, where they build, generally on a stump or in a hollow trunk. The White-faced Tree-duck is a good example of the group. Failing trees, they will build in long grass; they are inter-tropical and range round the world.

What may be called the " typical ducks " include so large a number of species that it would be impossible to enumerate and describe them here, even briefly. But this is of no great matter, for they are mostly known to all of us. They include a considerable number of British species like the Wild-duck, Teal, Pintail, Shoveller, Wigeon, Garganey, and Gadwall.

They all agree in having a globular, thin-walled chamber at the base of the windpipe, at any rate in the males, serving, one would suppose, to increase the resonance of the voice. But since the loud, raucous " quack, quack " of the Wild-duck is produced by the female, who has no " sound-box," one must suppose that the low, sibilant note of the Mallard is produced by this structure, and that what obtains here obtains in all cases when this sound-box is present. We can only assume that the aberrant species, goose-like in some characters, duck-like in others, which possess this sound-box, have inherited this peculiarity from a common ancestor. In further support of this view we have the " mirror " or speculum of the wing, which

WHITE-FACED TREE-DUCK
(*Dendrocygna viduata*).

in the typical " surface-swimming " ducks attains to highest development. Herein it is formed by a patch of metallic-blue, or green, oblong in shape, which runs across the middle of the outermost secondaries, and is banded above by a white bar formed of the tips of the major-coverts.

These birds are called " surface-swimming " to distinguish them from the diving-ducks. The first-named are all of freshwater species, though, at times, they will resort to the sea. When swimming in shallow water much of their food is obtained from the bottom by submerging the head and neck and fore-part of the body, thus enabling the beak to reach the mud. They can, on occasion, completely submerge the body, but they never really " dive."

x

A great deal of their food consists of minute floating animals and vegetable organisms, which are obtained by passing water rapidly through the mouth and straining it of its floating particles by means of the lamellae fringing the beak. In the Shoveller these lamellae attain to a great length, and are conspicuous even when the beak is closed. The latter, by the way, is also greatly expanded towards the tip, hence the name Shoveller.

The Diving-ducks comprise the Scaups, Pochards, Tufted-ducks, Golden-eye, Long-tailed, and Harlequin-ducks, Scoters, Eider-duck, the " Stiff-tailed ducks " (*Erismatura*), Torrent-ducks, and Mergansers. Many of these are exclusively marine, and all dive for their food. The males, alone, have a resplendent dress, the females being of varying shades of dark brown or grey ; while, as with the surface-feeding ducks, the males

KING-EIDER (*Somateria spectabilis*) (Male and Female).

go into " eclipse " after the young are hatched. At this time, and for a few weeks, they wear a dress closely resembling that of the female, and at this " eclipse " moult all the quills of the wing are shed at once, which is true also of the swans and geese. Being able to escape from their enemies by swimming, they are enabled to moult after this fashion. Non-aquatic birds moult their quills in pairs, and so always retain the power of flight.

The Scoters and Eiders feed entirely on mollusca, crustacea, and echinoderms. But though their habits are so similar their differences in the matter of coloration are profound. The Scoters are velvety black ; the Eider combines cream and white, with a patch of delicate sea-green on the head, while the under parts are black, a very unusual type of coloration, the under parts being almost always white, or paler than the upper. Again, though the food in the two types is so similar the beaks are very different in shape. In the Scoters it is short, and much inflated at the base ; while in the Eider-duck it is conspicuously long.

Related apparently to the Scoters is the strange " Steamer-duck " (*Tachyeres*). It is a large, heavy bird, ash-grey in colour, and remarkable for the fact that it loses the power of flight after its first moult.

STEAMER-DUCK (*Tachyeres cinerea*).

The " Stiff-tailed " ducks, so-called because of the long, narrow, and almost spike-like tail-feathers, often carried erect when the bird is swimming, contain one remarkable species in the " Musk-duck " (*Biziura*), which bears a singular and leathery pouch beneath the lower jaw, this being inflated through an opening under the tongue.

Between the Stiff - tailed ducks on the one hand and the Mergansers on the other, come the " Torrent-ducks." The Chilian-merganser, or Torrent-duck (*Merganetta*), frequents the high mountain torrents of the Andes. It is remarkable for the fact that the wing is armed with a strong spur, while the edges of the jaws have no " teeth." The New Zealand Soft-billed duck is another strange form wherein the upper jaw is provided on each side with a soft dependent membrane, an adaptation to its diet of insect-larvae on which it chiefly feeds. The extremely restricted geographical range and their peculiar modes of life make them birds of exceptional interest from the evolutionary point of view.

MUSK-DUCK (*Biziura lobata*) with inflated pouch.

The Mergansers, or " Saw-billed " ducks, are fish-eaters, and hence they have come to differ from all the other ducks by reason of the adaptation of the beak to this purpose. Herein it has become long and narrow, hooked at the tip, and furnished at the sides with horny " teeth," forming an admirable pair of forceps for holding slippery prey. Though largely fish-eaters they also eat crustacea, and, in the summer, insect-larvae and earthworms, obtained in the neighbourhood of the nest.

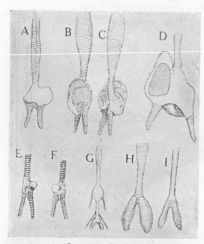

SYRINX OF DUCKS

A, Mallard; *B*, *C*, Pochard; *D*, Goosander; *E*, *F* Steller's Eider; *G*, Velvet Scoter; *H*, *I*, Common Scoter. (Male left, Female right.)

The characteristic "bulb" at the end of the windpipe found in the majority of the ducks is here greatly enlarged, but its walls are fenestrated, the apertures being closed by a very delicate, tense membrane. In the male Goosander the middle of the windpipe develops two enlargements. In the male Merganser there is but one such swelling.

The breast of the male Goosander, in the breeding season, displays a wonderful salmon-pink, but this fades after death with extreme rapidity.

CHAPTER VI

Order FALCONIFORMES

(*Birds of Prey, or Accipitrines*)

BY the older ornithologists the "hawks and owls" were regarded as forming a separate and well-defined group of birds readily distinguishable from all others by reason of their formidable beaks and talons and their rapacious habits. The "hawks"—which included Eagles and Falcons, Kites and Buzzards—constituted the "Diurnal," the Owls the "Nocturnal," birds of prey.

But a more exact study of their anatomy has shown that this supposed relationship has no existence in fact. Here, as in groups already discussed, we have certain "annectant links" by which the line of ancestry can be traced. These show us that the Falconiformes are unquestionably related to the Ciconiiformes, for they reveal, in their deeper structural anatomy, characters which link them with the Steganopodes on the one hand and the storks on the other : two groups which have already been shown to be derivatives of a common stock.

The Falconiformes, generally speaking, may be described as arboreal birds, which have become profoundly modified as a consequence of their rapacious habits. The beak has assumed a hook-shape for tearing up flesh and has its base covered by a swollen area of soft skin, generally yellow, called the " cere," and pierced by the nostrils. The feet have developed long, lithe toes, and large, curved, sharp claws for seizing and holding prey; to facilitate this function the under surface of the toes commonly develop bulbous pads, or " tylari." All, of necessity, are swift of wing and all have a characteristic upright carriage. The sight is keen.

The lower part of the gullet is enlarged to form a crop, where the hastily taken meal can be stored and slowly passed down to the stomach, which has a soft interior; the fur or feathers of the victims serve the part of the " gizzard-stones," swallowed by other birds, for the breaking-up of the food received.

The young are hatched in a helpless condition, and are clad in a thick, downy coat, composed both of pre-pennae and pre-plumulae; and the females may be distinguished by their larger size. In many of the " hawk tribe," indeed, as with the Sparrow-hawk, the female is conspicuously larger than the male, while in others this difference is but slight.

Though all are carnivorous, insects form the larger part of the diet with some.

Sub-order CATHARTES
(*New-World Vultures*)

The term " Vulture " usually connotes those birds of gruesome habits associated with battlefields, and dead and dying camels which have died in the desert from thirst. But these are the " Old-World Vultures," to be described presently. The Vultures of the New World are birds of a very different type. In their deeper-seated, anatomical characters they share many features with the Steganopodes and the storks.

Externally the " New-" can be distinguished from the " Old-World " Vultures by the fact that the nostrils are " pervious," that is to say, they form a conspicuous aperture, or " window," when seen against the light, while in all the other birds of prey they are separated by a median bony partition. The claws on the toes are comparatively small and blunt, and this because, being carrion-eaters, they do not have to hold struggling prey.

The gigantic Condor (*Sarcorhamphus gryphus*) of the Peruvian and Chilean Andes is one of the largest living birds retaining the power of flight, and is a bird of very remarkable appearance : the head, in the male, being surmounted by a fleshy comb, the neck being bare and lead-coloured, while its base is encircled by a " ruff " of white, downy feathers. The nest, which consists of no more than a few sticks, is placed on the ledge of some precipitous cliff, and never contains more than two white eggs. The young take nearly a year to acquire full powers of flight.

Nearly a hundred years ago, that delightful old naturalist, Charles Waterton, strove valiantly to prove that the " Turkey-buzzard " discovered its food by scent, not by sight. Many years after, Darwin made experiments on captive Condors, to show that it was by sight, not by scent, that they lived, and later researches have confirmed his conclusions. And what is true of the American, is true also of the Old-World Vultures.

Very different in appearance is the King-vulture. Much smaller than the Condor, it is an undoubtedly handsome bird. The base of the beak, in the male, is hidden by large fleshy caruncles of a bright vermilion, and a pair of lappets of the same hue at the base. The eye is no less remarkable, for the iris is white, while the cornea has a vermilion border. As in the Condor the head and neck are bare, but the skin glows with vivid shades of orange, purple, and crimson. The plumage harmonises well with these colours, the upper parts being of a rich cream colour, save the greater wing-

HEAD OF CONDOR (*Sarcorhamphus gryphus*).   HEAD OF KING-VULTURE (*Gypagus papa*).

coverts and quills, and tail-feathers, which are black. Round the neck is a downy frill of dark grey. The under parts are white, with a tinge of cream, while the feet are slate-coloured. The female has the whole of the upper parts dark grey.

Its geographical range extends from Brazil to Mexico, Texas, and Florida. Primaeval forests up to an elevation of five thousand feet, or well-wooded plains, are its haunts. It is by no means a common bird, and but little is known of its habits.

The striking coloration of the King-vulture is in itself remarkable for a bird of prey, but it becomes still more so in the light of the fact that all the other members of the group have a plumage of funereal black.

The Black-vulture (*Catharistes*) and the Turkey-vulture (*Rhinogryphus*) are very much alike in their general appearance, but with a very different distribution. The first-named ranges from Patagonia to North Carolina and Texas, while the Turkey-vulture, on the other hand, has the widest distribution of the whole group, ranging over nearly the whole of

temperate and tropical America, including the West Indies.   There are
three other species of the
genus *Rhinogryphus*, all of
which are confined to
South America.   So far
as records go these birds
differ but little in their
habits, hence the fact
that one species should
have so wide a range
and the remaining three
be confined to different
regions of South America
is in need of explanation.

BLACK-VULTURE (*Catharistes urubu*)

The nesting habits of
the Black- and Turkey-
vultures are worth
noting, for the Black-
vulture lays its two eggs
in an apology for a nest on the ground, sometimes in the open, sometimes under the shelter of bushes or rocks,
and in small colonies.   The Turkey-vulture
similarly makes its nest on the ground,
but commonly it is placed in caverns and
crevices of rocks, or in hollow trees, while
occasionally the deserted nest of a heron is
used.

TURKEY-VULTURE (*Catharistes aura*).

While the Black- and Turkey-vultures are
common in the streets of small towns and
in the villages, where they perform the work
of scavengers, the Great Californian-vulture,
which rivals the Condor in size, is restricted
to the Pacific coast-region of the United
States, from Oregon to Lower California.
At one time numerous, its members were
rapidly reduced by the use of poisoned meat
laid down by the stockmen for the destruction of carnivorous mammals.   Fortunately,
however, this fine bird still has a stronghold in the barren and almost inaccessible
mountains.

Its funereal black plumage is relieved by
a white band across the wing, and, unlike
the Black- and Turkey-vultures, it has a ruff round the neck.

Its flight is described as majestic. Of its breeding habits little is known, save that, unlike the species just described, it builds a huge nest, placed either on rocks or in trees. The two eggs are of a greenish-white, without the blotches of red and chocolate which distinguish the eggs of the preceding genera.

Sub-order GYPOGERANIDAE

(*Secretary Birds*)

The Secretary Birds, of which there are two species, one (*Serpentarius secretarius*) confined to the southern and eastern part of Africa, the other (*S. gambiensis*) ranging from Senegambia to South Abyssinia, are, without question, " accipitrine " birds, but structurally they stand apart from all the other members of this group. They are to be regarded, in short, as standing on its outer fringe. In regard to the external features the most

SECRETARY BIRD (*Serpentarius secretarius*).

striking is the great length of the legs, recalling those of the storks, or cranes ; while the foot, though of the accipitrine type, differs from that of the eagles and hawks in the shortness of the toes and the smallness of the claws. But these are characters which are intimately associated with their functions, which here are to serve the requirements of locomotion rather than seizing and holding living prey. For, though these birds can fly well, they spend most of their time walking about. Eagles and hawks walk but seldom, and after a laborious fashion. The beak, again, though of an accipitrine type, is not sharply hooked like that of the hawks and eagles.

In regard to its plumage the most striking features are the long feathers which stand out from the head—suggesting a bunch of quills borne above each ear by an unusually zealous secretary !—and the great length of the central tail-feathers.

They feed largely on snakes and lizards, and on this account are protected by law, at least in South Africa. In attacking these creatures the feet alone are used, the bird striking forwards and downwards with great force. In the case of snakes, venomous or otherwise, the wings are outspread and used as a shield, so that if the blow fails and the snake bites, it expends its venom fruitlessly on the quill-feathers. Occasionally, it is said, lizards are killed by being carried aloft and dropped. Small mammals and birds are also among their victims.

The nest is of great size, and apparently used during several successive years.   Usually placed in a bush or tree, it is composed of sticks and clay, with a lining of wool and hair.   Two rust-spotted white eggs are laid, and the young remain in the nest about four months.   They are covered in white down.

Sub-order *ACCIPITRES*

(*Vultures, Harriers, Buzzards, Eagles, Hawks, Kites, and Falcons*)

The masterful and the merciless in Nature have always prospered, and the history of the " Birds of Prey " may be cited as a witness to this assertion. It is shown by the superb attainments in the matter of flight which they display, their intense and restless vitality, and the perfection of their organisations for the work of slaughter.   To avoid undue competition they have, by adaptation to the pursuit of special kinds of prey, come to break up into a number of more or less distinct types, too numerous to be reviewed here in detail.   Some have become adapted to a diet of carrion, some to a reptilian, and some to an insect diet.

The Accipitrines are here divided into three families : (1) Vultures ; (2) Harriers, Buzzards, Eagles, Hawks, and Kites ; and (3) the Falcons.

Family Vulturidae

The Old-World Vultures, if they had long legs and longer necks, would not, externally, be much unlike the Secretary Bird.   The kinship between them is indisputable.   But each type has developed along its own line in response to its mode of life.

There are many genera and species of Vultures, and it would serve no useful purpose to describe them, even briefly, since in their habits they are all essentially alike.

What, again, is worth pondering over, is the origin and development of their taste for carrion, and the consequent physiological changes which accompanied it, for the ingestion of putrescent meat entails fatal consequences in many animals ; but when the ancestral vulture contrived to adjust itself to such food the foundation was laid for the enlargement of his race, since a new source of food was thereby tapped.

One of the most noteworthy of the accompaniments of the Vulture's life has been the sharpening of his powers of vision.   For these birds find the carcases they seek, not, as was at one time believed, by scent, but by sight. From an altitude of one thousand feet or more, a hungry bird will survey the country, and, finding a body, at once descends ; another, a mile or so off, noting its action, swiftly hurries after it.   And so, for miles round, each bird noting the action of his nearest neighbour receives his summons to the feast.   Thus, in an incredibly short space of time a host assembles, where an hour before not one was to be seen.

Of the Vultures, the least specialised, structurally, is the giant Lammergeier, or Bearded-vulture (*Gypaetus barbatus*), a bird which at one time could have been seen any day in the wilder ranges of the Swiss Alps, but man, in his march of "progress," leaves a trail of wanton destruction behind him, including the ruins of his own creation. He has made vacant places on the earth which once were inhabited by creatures the world could ill spare, among them the Lammergeier, for never again will this bird be seen here. Happily, however, there are parts of Spain, as well as in the Italian Alps, the Caucasus, and the Himalayas, where its wondrous flight can still be watched. Another species (*G. ossifragus*) represents it in North-East and South Africa.

It is a fierce, morose-looking bird, with a curious tuft of bristles hanging from the lower jaw, hence the name "Bearded-vulture." The general colour of the plumage is greyish-black streaked with white, as to the upper parts ; tawny on the neck and under parts. The iris is orange-coloured, set off by a circle of vermilion.

Solitary by nature it breeds only on the faces of the most inaccessible cliffs, building a great nest of sticks, lined with wool and hair, wherein is laid one egg of a pale orange colour, marked by darker spots and blotches. Though dead animals provide its chief food, small mammals are also occasionally killed. The larger bones of its victims are said to be carried to a height and dropped, to smash them.

That curious and rather singular-looking black-and-white species known as the "Vulturine Sea-eagle" (*Gypoheirax angolensis*) of West Africa affords a most interesting link in the evolution of the Vultures. Its correct position among the hawk tribe has always been a puzzle to the systematist, who had no knowledge of internal structure. Hence by some it was placed with the Sea-eagles, because fish form no small part of its diet. Its favourite haunts are the mangrove swamps, as well as the sea-coasts. Like the Sea-eagles it also eats garbage. Its flight and its external appearance is vulture-like ; and its relationship to these birds is proved by its anatomy.

In the European Cinereus- and Griffon-vultures we find the emergence of the typical vulture, wherein the head and neck are bare, or sparsely covered with short down, and there is a large ruff of downy feathers encircling the base of the neck.

The Black- or Cinereus-vulture may be described as a Mediterranean species, displaying a preference for wooded districts. Though somewhat repulsive in appearance and sluggish in its habits, when on the wing it is a fine performer.

The development of anything like "ornament" in birds of this type seems incongruous. Yet we find it in the Indian Pondicherry-vulture. Herein the naked skin of the base of the head is produced into a pair of large membranous flaps, pinkish in colour like the rest of the head. Another species of the genus is found in North-East and South Africa.

The Egyptian-vulture (*Neophron percnopterus*) might well be described as the most vulturine of all its tribe, since it seems to prefer its food in a far more putrescent state than any other vultures, and ordure above all else. It is a small species, white in plumage, and with the bare area of the head and neck yellow. It differs from all other vultures in having long, slit-like nostrils. This species is commonly represented in the Egyptian hieroglyphics and sculptures. In Leviticus it is referred to as the " Geier-eagle."

EGYPTIAN-VULTURE (*Neophron percnopterus*).

Repulsive though the habits of the vulture tribe may appear to be, it is not to be forgotten that they render valuable service to man in hot countries, where they play the part of scavengers.

Before passing to review the various types of Harriers, Eagles, Buzzards, Hawks, and Kites, it would be well to remark that, including the vultures, more than five hundred species of " Birds of Prey " are known to science. As one would suppose, many differ only in details of coloration. It will afford, then, a far more helpful grasp of the nature of these birds to select only such as are of outstanding importance ; they are the " expression points " of the evolutionary phases which the group has undergone.

Family Buteonidae

The nearest allies of the vultures are the moderately large forms known as " Harrier-eagles," represented in the adjoining figure by that most remarkable bird the African " Bateleur-eagle " (*Helotarsus*). It is a bird of striking appearance, for the face and legs are of a vivid crimson, while the plumage is of a rich mahogany-red, set off by black scapulars, flight-feathers, and tail. The latter is extremely short, giving to the bird a curious appearance while on the wing. It is mainly a snake-eater. The nearly related " Serpent-eagles " (*Spilornis*), as the name implies, affect a like diet, snakes and lizards, varied by small mammals.

These birds display a singular coloration, varying in detail in the different species. It is well illustrated by the Bacha Serpent-eagle (*S. bacha*), wherein the breast is of a light chestnut, relieved by numerous, conspicuous, sharply defined, round white spots. The head has a crest of white feathers, each terminating in a large dark-brown spot. The upper part of the plumage is dark brown, with white spots on the wings.

Better known is the Short-toed-eagle (*Circaetus gallicus*) of Southern and Central Europe and Palestine and India. A large, dark-coloured species haunting the plains, sluggish in habit, quartering the ground with slow, heavy flight, or poising itself aloft on motionless wings, seeking for snakes, frogs, and even fish from the shallows, while small mammals, birds, lizards, crabs, and insects are also eaten.

Not very distant allies of these are the long-legged harrier tribe, of which, perhaps, the most primitive is the curious Banded Gymnogene (*Polyboroides typicus*) which feeds almost entirely on frogs and lizards. Like the true Harriers, it nests on the ground, and lays white eggs. Our own Marsh, Hen, and Montagu's Harriers furnish good examples of these birds, which present a curious disc-like disposition of the feathers of the face, recalling that of the owls. These, again, are largely frog- and lizard-eaters, though small mammals and birds are also eaten.

BATELEUR-EAGLE (*Helotarsus ecaudatus*).

A very different type is now to be considered, to wit the Giant Harpy- and Hawk-eagles, which seem to have descended from the same common stock as the Short-toed eagles (*Circaetus*). The Giant Harpy-eagle (*Thrasaetus harpyia*) is one of the fiercest and most powerful of all the birds of prey, ranging from Mexico to Texas, where it is known as the " Winged Wolf," or Lobo Volante. This name is apparently justified, since it feeds on fawns, monkeys, and foxes. Another terror to monkeys is the Great Monkey-eating eagle (*Pithecophaga*) of the Philippines. Of the Hawk-eagles mention must be made of the handsome Crowned Hawk-eagles (*Spizaetus* and *Spizastur*). Of the four species of these two genera undoubtedly the finest is the tropical African Crowned-eagle (*S. coronatus*).

BANDED GYMNOGENE (*Polyboroides typicus*).

Of what are known as the " True Eagles " we may take as the type our own Golden-eagle (*Aquila chrysaetos*), which may still be seen any day in the Highlands of Scotland, thanks to generous protection. The feet in all the species of this group are always feathered to the toes. When immature the Golden-eagle has a white base to the tail, on which account it is often mistaken for the Erne, or White-tailed eagle, to which it is in no way related.

The Birdnesting eagle (*Ictinaeus malayensis*), of the Indo-Malay countries, is an ally of the true eagles. It spends most of its time on the wing, hunting for birds' nests, and chiefly feeding on the eggs and young found therein.

The typical Buzzards (*Buteo*), though somewhat resembling small eagles, and often associated therewith by systematists, are more nearly related to the Rough-legged buzzards. They are certainly somewhat eagle-like in their flight. In their habits they hardly sustain the dignity of eagles, since though they prey on rabbits they will also stoop to rats and mice, as well as fish, reptiles, and insects. While they seize their prey on the ground they rarely take birds, and hence our own " Common Buzzard " (*Buteo buteo*) should be regarded by the farmer and gamekeeper as an ally rather than an enemy. In some parts of England this bird is still fairly common.

HARPY-EAGLE (*Thrasaëtus harpyia*).

What we may call the typical " hawks " are allied to the Buzzards, but are of a much more active type. They are long-legged birds, have relatively short wings and long tails, and the breast transversely barred.

The British Sparrow-hawk may serve as an example. Herein the differences between the sexes in the matter of size is extremely marked, the male being much smaller than the female. The male Sparrow-hawk, again, has brighter and more sharply differentiated barring on the breast than the female, and has the upper parts more purely coloured. The flight of this group is terribly swift, and their prey mostly small birds. On this account the Sparrow-hawk, in olden times, was used by falconers to take partridges. The smallest member of the genus is the Little Sparrow-hawk (*Accipiter minimus*) of South Africa, and the largest is Cooper's-hawk (*A. cooperi*) from temperate North America.

The Goshawks (*Astur*) are allies of the Sparrow-hawks. Our British Goshawk, now very rare, looks very like a huge Sparrow-hawk. Immature birds have the breast longitudinally striped ; the adults transversely barred.

It is still greatly valued where falconry survives with us, for the pursuit of hares and rabbits.　One of the most remarkable is the pure white Australian species (*Astur novae-hollandiae*).　Since this bird does not hunt in the snow its white plumage is somewhat of a puzzle.

More or less nearly related to the Goshawks are five species of the African genus *Melierax*.　These are, indeed, singular birds, for they possess, what is surprising in a bird of prey, the power of emitting a low, sweet whistling, or piping song, hence they are known as " singing hawks " or " chanting goshawks."　They have but one rival, also an African species, and this is the not distantly related " Buzzard-eagle " (*Asturinula*).　The function of this song, said to be extremely pleasing and melodious, calls for investigation.

GOSHAWK (*Astur palumbarius*).
(*Left*, Immature ; *Right*, Adult.)

No careful records have yet been made as to the occasions when it is uttered.

The Singing-hawks have an ash-coloured plumage, with black quill and tail-feathers, and a barred breast. Bold and rapid in flight, their prey consists of small mammals, birds, reptiles, and locusts. They haunt rocky places or bush-country, and nest in trees.

The Sea-eagles (*Haliaetus* and *Haliastur*), of which five species are known, are more nearly related to the Kites and Honey-buzzards than to the true Eagles (*Aquila*). The three types are apparently divergent branches of a common stock.

The White-tailed Sea-eagle, or " Erne " (*Haliaetus albicilla*), was once a resident breeding species in Great Britain.　Scotland was its last stronghold. Though essentially a maritime species, and feeding upon fish, both mammals and birds as well as carrion were included in its bill of fare.　The " American Eagle " is the White-headed or Bald Sea-eagle (*H. leucocephalus*).

The Kites and Honey-buzzards come next.　The Common Kite (*Milvus ictinus*) was once one of our commonest, as it is now one of our rarest, resident birds of prey.　Three or four hundred years ago foreigners were struck with its abundance in the streets of London, where, as in other large towns, it played the very useful part of scavenger.　Its soaring flight would be a joy to watch, if the two or three pairs yet breeding with us should happily increase in number.　But the egg-collector is their most deadly foe.　In olden days kings esteemed it as quarry for their falcons.　Its red coloration and forked tail make it easily recognisable.

The Black-kite (*Milvus migrans*) and the Black-shouldered kite (*Elanus coeruleus*) are two other species doubtfully included in the British list.

Most people probably regard a deeply forked tail as the hall-mark of the kites. Our own Kite has a very conspicuous and rather shallow fork ; but in the beautiful American Swallow-tailed Kite (*Elanoides*), which is black, with a pure white head, neck, and under parts, the tail, which is extremely long, has an excessively deep fork. Its skill on the wing is wonderful. It will catch bees or other insects with one of its feet as it dashes along, and eat them in mid-air, or will snatch up a lizard, snake, or frog with a lightning swoop. Flocks are often seen; and should one of their number be wounded, they will hover around it after the fashion of Terns in like circumstances.

CRESTED-BAZA (*Baza subcristata*).

In the so-called "Cuckoo-falcons" of the genus *Baza*, aberrant kites, the tail is rounded. But the really conspicuous feature of these birds is not so much the form of the tail as the singular coloration of the plumage, which differs from that of all other birds of prey in that, in some species, as in the Australian Crested-baza (*B. subcristata*), the breast is marked by broad transverse bands of chestnut-red on a white ground. These are forest-haunting birds of which little is known save that they feed on chamaeleons, grasshoppers, and other insects. Another species with a rounded tail is the Brahminy-kite (*Haliastur*), a most conspicuously handsome bird, pure white save the wings and back, which are of a rich chestnut-red.

SWAINSON'S KITE (*Gampsonyx swainsoni*).

Mention, too, must be made of the diminutive Swainson's Kite (*Gampsonyx*), scarcely larger than a Blackbird. It ranges from Guiana westwards through Brazil to Peru, and eastwards to Trinidad. What interpretation is to be placed on this vast difference in size as between this pigmy and the rest of the kites ?

Two most remarkable members of the Kite tribe now remain to be considered. The first of these is the Awl-billed or Everglade-kite (*Rostrhamus sociabilis*), ranging from Florida to Bolivia and Argentina. Its coloration is slaty-black, with white bases and tips to the feathers of the forked tail, orange cere and feet, and a crimson iris. But the really singular feature of the bird is the beak, which is conspicuously slender, with a long terminal hook. This, in itself, proclaims some peculiarity of diet, and it is found in the fact that it feeds exclusively upon molluscs of the genus *Ampullaria*, the hook of the bill serving to extract them from their shells, while the long legs and sharp talons serve to drag these molluscs from the muddy swamps in which they live. This, however, is not all. This bird, unlike the usual custom of the Hawk tribe, is gregarious, slowly beating over the marshes in small companies. Nor are they less sociable when breeding, twenty or thirty nests being commonly built close together; each nest a slight platform of twigs or plant stems with a lining of aquatic herbage, whereon two or three whitish eggs blotched with yellowish-brown and grey are laid.

The second of these two is represented by three species of the genus *Machaerhamphus*. All three are remarkable for the shortness of their beaks and enormously wide mouth, recalling that of the Night-jars. Now the African *M. anderssoni* of Damaraland, the Cameroons, and Madagascar is known to be crepuscular and to feed on bats. Hence we may infer that the other two have the same habits.

From the Kites we pass to the Honey-buzzards, one species of which, *Pernis apivorus*, still occasionally breeds in Great Britain. There are several genera and species of these birds, distinguished by the short, closely set feathers on the " lores," the space in front of the eye, which in all the other birds of prey is bare. Little is known of the habits of most of these, but our own woodland species hunts on the ground, feeding largely upon bees, wasps, and grubs—though not on the honeycomb, which has to be broken up; but small mammals, birds, and even worms are also eaten.

Family Pandionidae

The Ospreys have always been an ornithological stumbling-block. The earlier authorities regarded them as forming a link between the " diurnal " and the " nocturnal " birds of prey, on account of the fact that the outer toe is opposable to the rest, and that the feathers, as in the Owls, have no after-shaft.

The belief that the Ospreys—there is but one genus and three species—are related to the Owls is now everywhere discarded, but their precise affinities are by no means easy to determine. They seem to be with the Kites, the Cuckoo-falcons, and the Honey-buzzards, or rather with the stock from which these were derived. A fact of some significance, but hitherto not taken into consideration, is that the downy young are marked by conspicuous, dark, longitudinal stripes on a light background, wherein they differ from all other birds of prey.

They may be described as almost exclusively fish-eaters, though frogs and water-snakes are also eaten, and when pressed by hunger even beetles will serve. The better to grip their slippery prey the soles of the feet are studded with large, horny, cone-shaped spikes.

At the present day the Osprey is only a migrant to Great Britain, since, owing to the ruthless slaughter waged against birds of prey of all kinds, by those who should know better, our own breeding birds have become exterminated. It used to breed on Ullswater and on several Scottish lochs. If only the spring passage-migrants were left unmolested the now obsolete breeding places would probably again be tenanted, and we might once more watch the thrilling sight of the Osprey's plunge.

On Gardener's Island, near Long Island, New York, the Osprey breeds in colonies. Here as many as two hundred nests may be seen. Only when the supply of food is practically constant and inexhaustible do birds ever breed in colonies. Hence the Hawk tribe as a rule not only breed in isolation, but permit no other members of their kind within the breeding territory.

The nest, placed in a tree or on the ground, as circumstances determine, has a foundation of rough sticks, into which are worked clay, cow-dung, leaves, and seaweed and moss. These nests seem to be used year after year, new materials being added each season. As a consequence they attain to a huge

OSPREY (*Pandion haliaetus*).

size, up to, it is said, half a ton in weight! So large are they that small birds, and even night-herons, build their own nests within the fabric of these huge structures ; while field-mice construct their nests beneath such as are placed on the ground.

THE CARACARAS AND FALCONS

The survey of the accipitrine birds ends with the curious Caracaras, or " carrion-hawks," of America, and the Falcons. Superficially they are not much alike, the Caracaras being long-legged " ground birds," the Falcons the swiftest birds that fly ; nevertheless anatomy shows that they share a common ancestry.

The Caracaras at one time were regarded as allied to the Secretary Birds ; later they were associated with the Harriers. This uncertainty one can now interpret, owing to what has been discovered concerning their anatomy.

The Brown-milvago, of the genus *Milvago*, might well be likened to a short-necked, short-legged Secretary Bird, while in the genus *Polyborus*, in its heavier, laterally compressed beak, it is reminiscent of the eagles.   From the very fact that they seem to partake of characters of different types of the same great group we may infer their early isolation.   The shortness of their toes and the relatively feeble development of the claws we may attribute, in part, to this ancient derivation, and in part to the fact that they live largely on the ground.   They feed on dead carcases, but they are by no means exclusively carrion-eaters.

Altogether seven genera are recognised, differing in coloration rather than in their habits.   They differ from all other birds of prey, externally, in having a slight web stretched between the bases of the front toes.   The brightly coloured, naked skin of the cheeks and throat, which waxes and wanes in intensity in response to emotional stimuli, gives them a vulturine appearance, and there may be said, indeed, to be a " taint " of vulturine blood in their veins, since they are types which broke away from the rest of the accipitres in common with the Old-World Vultures, before either had assumed its present form.   This, too, will account for their carrion-

CARACARA (*Polyborus tharus*).

eating habits, though they supplement this diet by frogs, reptiles, and birds whenever opportunity offers.   Furthermore, they are more or less gregarious, hunting in families or small parties, and roosting in company.

Though most of the species are South American, one, *Polyborus cheriway*, ranges to Florida and Lower California.   The nest is always made with sticks, lined with grass, hair, and wool ; while the eggs, two to five in number, are cream-coloured with reddish blotches.   Generally the nest is placed in trees.

THE FALCONS

Though we commonly speak of the sub-family of the Falcons as if they were a crisply defined group, this is by no means the case.   We have to come at them by way of a number of intermediate forms—" falcons in the making."

It would seem that the Falcons and the Carrion-hawks (*Polyborus*) are to be regarded as divergent branches of a common stem.   The Serpent-eagles would also seem to have a share in this ancestry, since both *Micrastur* and the " Chanting-hawk " (*Herpetotheres*)—the latter sometimes included in the *Falconidae* and sometimes among the Serpent-eagles—reveal anatomical characters which are shared also by the Falcons.

The Chanting-hawk (*Herpetotheres*) is a New-World species, ranging from South Mexico to Paraguay, and generally regarded as a near relation of the Short-toed Eagles, or " Harrier-hawks," and feeding, like them, on snakes and lizards. It is a crested bird, of a dark brown colour above and creamy-buff below. The name " Chanting-hawk " is bestowed on account of its habit of sitting aloft, bobbing its head while uttering a gruff " ha-ha."

But be this as it may, we have in the diminutive " Falconets " *Microheirax* and *Polioheirax* a much more definite foreshadowing of the Falcons, the aristocrats of the Hawk tribe. These two types, commonly called " Finch-falcons," for the smallest species are hardly bigger than finches, inhabit the Indo-Malayan region. One species of *Polioheirax*, somewhat larger than the rest, is found in Africa. In spite of their small size they are birds of fiery spirit and dashing flight, as befits falcons, though they capture little beyond insects. Mice, however, and small birds, are eaten when occasion offers.

What we may call the " true Falcons " are distinguished by their stout, hooked beak, which is marked along the upper cutting edge, near the tip, with a deep notch, and the long wings and tail. They are all birds of great powers of flight, and some are of considerable size.

SINGING-HAWK (*Melierax canorus*)
(see p. 636).

The commonest of the British Falcons is the Kestrel (*Falco tinnunculus*), whose hovering flight affords us such pleasure during the summer. The male is but slightly smaller than the female, but is distinguished by having a light bluish-grey head, neck, and tail, the latter with a subterminal bar of black bounded by a white border ; while the back and wings are of a pale cinnamon-chestnut, with small black spots. In the female the upper parts are rufous, barred black, and the tail has several narrow black bands. Immature birds resemble the females.

Though, till recently at any rate, shot at sight by the gamekeepers as " vermin," this bird really lives almost entirely on mice and large beetles ; only when these are not to be had will they turn to small birds. It is always easy to discover the food of this, and every other member of the

Hawk tribe, by collecting and examining the "pellets" thrown up at their breeding or roosting places. These pellets, or "castings," consist of the hair, crushed bones, and hard parts of beetles, thrown up from the stomach after all the soft parts have been dissolved.

No nest is built, the eggs being laid in old and flattened nests of crows, the sparrow-hawk, or buzzard, or an old squirrel-drey ; or in a hollow scratched out on the ledge of a cliff, in hollow trees, or even on the ground. The eggs, four to five in number, are white, washed or blotched with dark red-brown, so much so as often to extinguish the white ground.

The habit of the Kestrel, to hang high up, suspended by rapidly vibrating wings (hence it is often called the "Wind-hover"), without moving from the spot being surveyed, shows almost incredible powers of sight ; for the mid-air halt is made for the purpose of scanning the ground below for mice and beetles, which must be largely obscured by grass and other herbage.

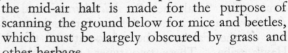

The Merlin (*Falco aesalon*) is the smallest British Falcon, the upper parts of the male being slate-blue in colour and with a broad, black tail-band ; it does not greatly exceed a blackbird in size. The female is dark brown above and white below, with streaks of dark brown on the breast. It is to be found during the breeding season— when not too mercilessly shot down—on moors and heathy areas along sea cliffs ; at other times it resorts to the open country. The flight of this bird is very different from that of the Kestrel, being pursued close to the ground and at great speed. It feeds on small birds and insects. The nest is generally placed on the ground, and con-sists of no more than a few heather stalks, or grass-bents, placed in a slight hollow scratched for their reception.

PEREGRINE-FALCON (*Falco pere-grinus*).

Where unmolested the Hobby (*Falco subbuteo*) still breeds with us. This handsome bird, somewhat larger than the Merlin, looks rather like a Peregrine in miniature, but the breast is longitudinally striped, not barred as in the Peregrine. Its wings are extremely long, and the flight is extraordinarily swift, so much so that it can seize the swallow, and even the swift, on the wing. Its food, however, is furnished mainly by dragon-flies, beetles, and the larger grasshoppers. It is essentially a woodland species, building no nest, but using the deserted nests of crows, rooks, sometimes of the heron, and sometimes of squirrels.

The largest and finest of our resident Falcons is the Peregrine (*Falco peregrinus*). It is, indeed, *the* Falcon, for it was this bird which was so highly prized in the olden days, when falconry was considered the highest form of sport. Almong falconers the male is known as a Tiercel, or "Tassel," the term "Falcon" being reserved for the larger female.

Of a blue-grey colour above, with indistinct darker markings, and white below, streaked on the base of the neck, and barred on the breast and thighs with black, it is easily distinguished. Further points of note are the dark "moustachial" patches, like those of the Hobby, and the brown iris. This last feature is characteristic of all the falcons, wherein they differ from the hawks, *e.g.* the Sparrow-hawk, where the iris is yellow. The "cere" and feet of the Peregrine are also yellow, as in most of the birds of prey.

It is a bird of extremely powerful flight, preying upon ducks, waders, sea-fowl, pigeons, grouse, partridges, lapwings, crows, small birds, and even of the smaller species of its own tribe—the kestrel, merlin, and hobby. When really hungry it will even eat frogs and beetles.

As an exponent of speed on the wing this bird has few rivals ; its pursuit is deadly ; its headlong "stoop" from a height is incredibly swift, and has well been described as accompanied by a rushing, mighty sound. The victim is struck and killed by the forward thrust of the great claws of the hind-toes. The elongated bulbs, or "tylari," on the under surfaces of the toes are strongly developed.

As a British breeding-bird this fine species is now, unfortunately, confined to precipitous cliffs by the sea and the wilder mountain districts. No nest is made, the

GREENLAND-FALCON (*Hierofalco candicans*).

eggs being laid in a hollow scratched in the scanty turf growing on some ledge on an inaccessible cliff. On the Continent it will use old nests of crows and other birds in trees.

Finally we come to the great Greenland- and Iceland-falcons, which on rare occasions visit the British Islands. They are large birds, the females measuring nearly two feet from the crown of the head to the tip of the tail.

The Greenland-falcon is white, with blackish streaks and markings on the back and wings, and white below. It is, however, a curiously variable species, some individuals being nearly white, others more or less conspicuously marked with streaks and bars of black, and this is not merely due to age. Very dark immature individuals make very dark adults.

The home of this bird is within the Arctic Circle, and here it breeds. Of necessity it is a cliff-breeder, since it lives beyond the limit of trees. It builds no real nest, but, resorting to the same site year after year, the pellets thrown up from the mouth, and its hardened excrement, form a substantial " eyrie "—a truly remarkable " nest." The eggs have a ground colour of orange-red, with darker mottlings ; there may be as many as four in a " clutch." It feeds upon lemmings, the Arctic-hare, and ptarmigan ; and when breeding near the sea, guillemots and turnstones. Such as wander to our shores prey on rabbits, voles, pigeons, gulls, and wading-birds.

This, and the darker Iceland-falcons, which were known as " Ger-falcons," were held high in esteem in the Middle Ages by falconers, though more, perhaps, on account of their rarity than their prowess, for they are not so fiery in their dash as the Peregrine. In those days hawking was pursued also to provide delicacies for the table. The Prince and the Baron alone were allowed to use " the falcon-gentle " ; to the yeoman and the burghers were allotted the goshawk ; the plebeian might use the sparrow-hawk ; the serf was permitted only the kestrel.

CHAPTER VII

Legion *ALECTOROMORPHAE*
(*Game-birds, Crane tribe and Plover tribe*)

Order GALLIFORMES
(*Game-birds*)

THE lowermost bough of the three great branches of the right-hand side of the Tree of Descent has now to be taken in hand. It is the branch which gave rise to the Galliformes, a sharply defined group of birds, yet without doubt furnishing the " sap " for the development of the Cranes and Rails, and the Plover tribe.

The Game-birds are divided into two groups—the Peristeropodes and the Alectoropodes. The first-named contains the Megapodes, or Mound-builders, and the Curassows and Guans, wherein the hind-toe is placed on the level of the front toes, while in the Alectoropodes the hind-toe is placed higher up, above the level of the front toes. They are all arboreal types, though many now spend most of their time on the ground in their search for food. Some, like the partridges, never ascend trees.

All are essentially grain- and seed-eaters, though many largely feed on insects. The beak is short and arched, and the lower jaw fits well into the upper.   Hard grain and seed, since it cannot be broken up in the mouth, must be softened before being passed on to the stomach, hence it is stored in a bag-like dilatation of the gullet known as the " crop " ;   thence it is slowly passed down to the stomach, or " gizzard," whose walls are formed of great masses of muscular tissue, while the lining of its cavity has become thickened to form a pair of horny pads.   The grain passed into the cavity is crushed by the muscular action of the gizzard walls, aided by small stones stored in the cavity for this purpose.   In other words, the horny pads and the sharp edges of the stones act like a pair of millstones.   The blind-gut, or caecum, is always of great length.

The feather-tracts are sharply defined, and the feathers have a large after-shaft.   There are no down-feathers, but " filo-plumes " are scattered all over the body, growing from the feather-sheath of every feather.   These are the hair-like structures which have to be singed off in a plucked fowl.

Save the migratory quails, they are not birds which take extended flights ; though some, like pheasant and grouse, are capable of terrific speed over short distances.   The wings when extended have a characteristic shape, being short, wide, and much arched ;   and when folded they do not cross over the back as in long-winged birds.

In the skull the vomer, so large in the Palaeognathae, is here much reduced.   The breast-bone is remarkable for the deep notches which mark its hinder portion, and these attain to their maximum in the division known as the Alectoropodes.

The sexes often differ in a very striking way in the matter of coloration and ornament, as in the case of the peacock and the pheasant, for example. In many species the legs are armed with formidable spurs.

The young are of the nidifugous type, being down-clad, and able to run with the parents in search of food almost as soon as hatched, feeding themselves under the guidance of the parent.   The downy plumage is longitudinally striped, often conspicuously so, and the flight-feathers appear long before the down of the rest of the body is shed, since it is necessary to acquire flight at the earliest possible moment.   In the ducks and geese and swans the body-feathers precede the wing-feathers, for here escape from enemies is made, not by flight, but by retreating to the water.

Sub-order *PERISTEROPODES*

(*Brush-turkeys, Curassows, etc.*)

The first sub-order of the Game-birds includes two families—the Megapodes, or Brush-turkeys, and the Curassows, Penelopes and Guans.   They are distinguished by having the hind-toe (hallux) on the same level as the other toes, and the inner notch of the sternum less than half the length of the entire breast-bone.

Family Megapodidae

The Megapodes, or Brush-turkeys, are among the most remarkable of living birds, and this on account of their breeding habits, to be described presently. There are many species distributed among half a dozen genera, and ranging in size from that of a turkey to that of a large pigeon. The sexes are alike, and some species make some approach to splendour in the matter of their coloration.

Though mainly confined to the Australian region they extend eastwards to Samoa, westwards to the Nicobars, and northward to the Philippines and Ladrones. Their haunts are the hill-valleys, among thickets, and near the sea. Having, apparently, become adjusted to a diet which is sufficient for their needs only so long as they are able to seek it far and wide, and incessantly, they are unable to fulfil the usual parental duties of incubation and the care of offspring. As a consequence, they lay eggs of enormous

CUMING'S MEGAPODE (*Megapodius cumingi*).

size, so that the chicks are enabled to pass, within the egg, what answers to the "nestling stage" in other birds, being nourished by the great store of food-yolk. The formation of such eggs is, of necessity, a lengthy process, and this makes an additional need for the prolonged pre-natal life of the chicks. Accordingly the eggs are buried and left to hatch by themselves, either by the heat engendered by decaying vegetation or of the sun. When the young escape from the shell they force their way out of the surrounding soil full-feathered and able to fly, and quite capable of fending for themselves. Neither parent nor offspring know anything of each other.

As a consequence of the laborious work of digging, the feet of the Megapodes are, relatively, of enormous size—hence the name of the group, though some are known as " Mound-builders."

Cuming's Megapode (*Megapodius cumingi*) may well serve as an example of the Mound-builders. A pair of these birds, with their feet, will heap up soil and dead vegetable matter by kicking it backwards towards a common centre, till a large mound twenty feet in diameter is formed. In this, at intervals, at a depth of from one to three feet, the eggs are laid. As the same mound is used year after year, it may attain to huge proportions. One was measured which had a circumference of one hundred and fifty feet. The eggs are placed in the heap with the narrow end downwards, and they are hatched by the heat generated by the decomposing débris, which may attain to 93° Fahr.

Though this species has a wide range—from the Philippines to Palawan, the small islands of the north of Borneo, the Sula Islands, and Celebes and Tujian Islands—the form of the mound is the same. Wallace's Megapode (*Eulipoa wallacii*), of the Malay Islands, instead of building a mound buries its eggs in a burrow on the beach. The burrows are driven at night into the sand, sloping obliquely to a depth of three or four feet. The Maleo of Celebes (*Megacephalon maleo*) also buries its eggs on the beach, but in holes in the coarse black volcanic sand at a depth of one or two feet. But for the looseness of the soil, burrows instead of mere holes would probably be made. And, apparently, because of this looseness of the material to be excavated, the feet and claws are smaller than in the other species.

The Maleo is rather a handsome bird, having a curious, almost spherical, horny " helmet " on the back of the head, and the naked skin round the eye flesh-coloured. The upper parts of the plumage are glossy black, and the breast of a beautiful salmon-pink.

Catheturus, the Australian " Brush-turkey," has the head and neck bare, a bright yellow wattle at the base of the neck, and the rest of the bare area reddish, while the plumage is blackish-brown.

Not much seems to be known of their food. Macgillivray's Megapode (*Megapodius macgillivragi*), of the Louisiade Archipelago, feeds on insects and their larvae, small snails, seeds, and fruits. The Ocellated Megapode (*Lipoa ocellata*) of South and West Australia is interesting from the fact that white ants live on the decaying vegetation of the mounds formed by the birds; and on the ant larvae the young Megapode feed on their emergence from the shell.

Family Cracidae

The Curassows and the Guans in this family, though undoubtedly nearly related to the Megapodes, differ very widely in their habits, being essentially arboreal, and feeding on fruits obtained high up in the trees. During the middle of the day they commonly descend to the ground to scrape about among the fallen leaves for insects. Ranging over the greater part of South America one species extends as far north as Texas.

They differ, too, in their nesting habits, building a nest of sticks, grass, and moss, of considerable size, on the horizontal branch of a tree, though sometimes on the ground. The eggs are white, and have a granulated shell.

One of the largest and handsomest species, attaining to a length of three feet, is the Crested-curassow (*Crax alector*) of the northern parts of South America. It is glossy black in colour, and with a large crest of curled feathers. Some nearly allied species, like the Wattled-curassow (*Crax carunculata*), differ in having a large, swollen, brightly coloured knob at the base of the beak and wattles on the throat. They are domesticated by the natives, and used as food.

In Gray's Curassow (*Crax grayi*), of which the male is unknown, the head has a crest of buff feathers, a glossy black head and neck, and the back and tail heavily barred with black on a buff ground, while the breast is of a chestnut colour. The Razor-bill Curassow (*Mitua mitu*) has the beak moulded to form a sharp ridge or crest. The traveller-naturalist Bates, when in Rio Tapajos, found one of these birds kept as a pet in the house, and it seemed to regard itself as one of the family, attending at all meals and begging for tit-bits from various members of the family.

WATTLED-CURASSOW (*Crax carunculata*).

It showed a special fondness for a little girl, following her about wherever she went. The Black-penelope (*Penelopina nigra*), which, as its name implies, has a black plumage, enlivened, it may be remarked, by a large red wattle on the neck, is chiefly remarkable for the fact that when making a rapid descent with outstretched wings, it gives forth a crashing noise like that made by a falling tree.

The Guans are very similar in appearance to the Penelopes, and display an extraordinary aptitude for domestication, becoming embarrassingly familiar. In some species the windpipe is of great length, being stowed away in coils between the skin and the muscles of the breast, at any rate in the males.

PIPING-GUAN (*Pipile jacutinga*).

Sub-order *ALECTOROPODES*

(*The True Game-birds*)

This group includes the Turkeys, Pheasants, Partridges, and Grouse ; characterised by having the hind-toe (hallux) raised above the level of the front toes, and by having the inner notch of the breast-bone extended forwards to beyond its middle, the width of the notch reducing the sternal plate to a mere ledge on each side of the keel. All normally nest on the ground.

The group may conveniently be divided into two families—*Phasianidae* and *Tetraonidae*. The *Phasianidae* includes three sub-families—the *Meleagrinae*, or Turkeys, confined to the southern parts of North America and Central America ; the *Numidinae*, or Guinea-fowls, of Africa ; and the *Phasianinae* of Asia. The *Tetraonidae* is not further sub-divided, and is spread over the whole of the northern areas of the Old and New Worlds.

Birds of the highest economic importance are here included ; some, like the Turkeys and Guinea-fowls, and the Jungle-fowls, having furnished us with our domesticated poultry.

HONDURAS-TURKEY (*Meleagris ocellata*).

Family Phasianidae

In this family the nostrils are covered by an over-arching " operculum " ; the legs are scale-covered, and are commonly armed with one or more pairs of spurs. In the Snow-partridges the legs are partially feathered. In the sub-family *Meleagrinae* (Turkeys) there are but two wild species, one of which, ranging from Southern Canada to Mexico and the eastern and south-western States, is so like our own domesticated bird as to need no description as to its general appearance. It haunts wooded country and feeds upon seeds, nuts, fruits, lizards, and insects. It is a polygamous species, and in the Spring the males fight viciously and strut about before their mates after the fashion of our domesticated bird.

Very different in appearance is the Honduras-turkey, which is confined to Yucatan, British Honduras, and Guatemala. Its plumage glows with metallic reflexions of brassy-green and greenish-copper, passing into steel-blue on the rump, while the tail-feathers are marked with brilliant ocelli of metallic green-blue and copper. The head and the caruncle, which hangs over the beak, are blue, while red, berry-like excrescences are scattered over the neck.   The curious tuft of bristles so conspicuous in the common turkey is wanting in this bird.   It is one of the wildest and shyest of birds, and of great speed on the wing.   During the breeding season the male makes a sonorous, drumming noise, and then utters his peculiar " song " which recalls the rapid pecking of a distant woodpecker or the song of the great Bull-toad.

The sub-family *Numidinae* comprises the Guinea-fowls.   The general form of these birds, of which there are many species, is like that of our domesticated bird, the extremely short tail, turned downwards, giving the body the peculiar rounded shape familiar to us all.   They are divisible into two groups—the Crested and the Helmeted ; the former having a crest of black feathers, the latter a horny casque on the crown.

CURLY-CRESTED GUINEA-FOWL (*Guttera cristata*).

Our domesticated bird seems to have been derived from the common Guinea-fowl of West Africa (*Numida meleagris*), and to have been introduced early in the sixteenth century ; though some say it was known to the Romans.

The handsomest of all is the Vulturine Guinea-fowl (*Acryllum vulturinum*) of East Africa, wherein the feathers of the neck are produced into long, white hackles with blue margins ; the back and chest are similarly coloured ; the breast and belly are cobalt-blue, while the rest of the plumage is black, minutely spotted with white.   The naked parts of the head and neck are also coloured cobalt-blue.   Though discovered so long ago as 1834, practically nothing is known of its habits.   Specimens are always to be seen in the Zoological Gardens in London.

The sub-family *Phasianinae*, includes the Peacocks, Pheasants, Partridges, and Quails.   The Peacock is too well known to need description, but it should almost be called *the* Peacock, because there are really two species differing from one another in no uncertain way, yet few people, even on seeing the two side by side at the Zoo, appear to realise their distinctive features.   But in what we may call the Common Peacock (*Pavo cristatus*), so often kept to give added splendour to large gardens, the crest-feathers of the crown have bare shafts and a vane at the tip, and long, rather loose feathers on the neck, so that individual feathers are indistinguishable ; while in the much more rare Burmese Peacock the crest-feathers have the vane running the whole length of the shaft, while the neck-feathers seem to form great overlapping, sharply defined scales. In the Common Peacock the naked skin of the face is livid white, while in the Burmese bird it is bluish-green round the eyes and chrome-yellow on the cheeks.

Another point about these supremely beautiful birds which is worth bearing in mind concerns what is usually called the " tail." These wonderful feathers are really glorified *tail coverts ;* the true tail is behind them, as anyone can see who will watch a peacock in display. In a wild state these two birds haunt dense forests. The Common Peacock is widely spread throughout India, and extends into Ceylon and Assam, from sea-

ARGUS-PHEASANT (at rest).   ARGUS-PHEASANT (*Argusianus argus*) (in display).

level up to three thousand feet, or even higher. In places it is extremely abundant. The Burmese species (*Pavo muticus*) is a native of the Indo-Chinese countries, extending north to Chittagong, and east through Siam to Cochin-China, and southwards through the Malay Peninsula. It is also found in Java. Nowhere is it numerous, and always it shuns human settlements.

THE ARGUS-PHEASANT

While the Peacock in his pride seems to have been fashioned out of burnished metal, possessing an iridescence indescribably beautiful, the

Argus-pheasant (*Argusianus argus*), in like mood, seems rather to be arrayed in the softest painted velvet, displaying intricacies of pattern and subtleties of colour such as defy description.

The dominating feature of this bird is the enormous length of the secondary wing-feathers, and these bear a series of " ocelli " which, when the wing is spread during the " love display," have, as Darwin was the first to point out, the appearance of balls lying within a socket and lighted from above. External to these eye-spots the broad vane is marked by oblique wavy bars. A further singular feature is presented by the primary quills, which seldom display any very special ornamentation. But here, in the beauty of the coloration, they surpass the achievement of any other known bird.

PEACOCK-PHEASANT (*Polyplectron chinquis*) (in display).

When in display these gorgeous wings are spread to form a huge circular screen, topped by an enormously long and beautifully tinted pair of tail-feathers. The rest of the bird is entirely hidden.

The Argus-pheasant ranges from Siam to Sumatra, and everywhere it seeks the most secluded parts of the forests. Here, in the breeding season, the male chooses a level spot shut in by cane-brakes, and clears it of all dead leaves and weeds for a space of six or eight yards square, and here he displays before his mate. A smaller species, Gray's, is found in Borneo. A second genus, Rheinhardt's Crested-argus (*Rheinhardtius*), one of the rarest of all Game-birds, is found in Tonkin. But in this the wing-feathers are quite normal, through the tail is extremely long. Nothing is known of its habits.

THE PEACOCK-PHEASANTS

That there are ties of blood between the Peacocks, Argus-pheasants, and Peacock-pheasants seems to be shown by the tendency of all these groups to develop ocelli-bearing feathers. In the Peacock-pheasants these ocelli are distributed over the whole of the plumage on the upper surface, save the head and neck. These birds, five species in all, are natives of dense jungles and hill forests of the Indo-Malayan countries, and the islands of Sumatra, Borneo, and Palawan. The legs of the male are armed with two, three, or even four spurs, the number commonly differing on the two legs.

The females are less resplendent, and the Grey Peacock-pheasant (*Polyplectron chinquis*), at any rate, has a curious habit, when followed by her chicks, of carrying her tail widely spread to form a shelter for the brood. They run forward when she calls, to pick up food, and having eaten it immediately return to their shelter.

The Jungle-fowl (*Gallus*) in themselves form an interesting group, and become still more so from the fact that it is from the Red Jungle-fowl (*G. bankiva*) that our domesticated cocks and hens have been derived. At least four distinct species are known to inhabit the dense jungles of the Indian Peninsula, Indo-Malayan countries, and adjacent islands. The Javan Jungle-fowl (*G. varius*) differs from the rest in that the upper edge of the comb is not serrated and in having but a single throat-wattle.

It should be noted that the males at the June moult replace the neck-hackles and tail-feathers by short feathers like those of the female. At the second, September moult, these resplendent feathers are resumed. Here we have a phase in the evolution of a resplendent dress, which begins

JAVAN JUNGLE-FOWL (*Gallus varius*).

with a " seasonal " breeding dress, worn only for a few weeks, as in many of the plover tribe. In the ducks it is worn during the greater part of the year, and exchanged for the " eclipse dress " worn after the breeding season for a few weeks. In many of the Game-birds—Jungle-fowl, Black Grouse, English Partridge—only traces of this " eclipse dress " remain, confined either to the head and neck, or the head, neck, and tail-feathers, as in the Jungle-fowl.

THE PHEASANTS

The Pheasants present a most striking and, to the evolutionist, a most suggestive range of differences in the matter of size, form, and coloration. No useful end would be obtained by describing all the known genera and species, for without the aid of a large number of coloured plates such descriptions would make but tiresome reading. Resplendent colour and ornament are the dominant features of the Pheasant tribe.

The Golden-pheasant and Amherst Pheasant well illustrate a neglected aspect of bird-life—the concentration of their physiological activities in the development of colour and ornament, which is confined, be it noted, in these birds to the male, save in cases where by disease of the ovaries, or other disturbance of the reproductive activities, they are assumed by the females.

This brief survey must begin with the Golden-pheasant (*Chrysolophus pictus*) of Southern and Western China. Herein the head is surmounted by a great crest of golden-yellow feathers, while the neck bears a semi-circular, erectile ruff, or frill, of golden-orange barred with black. At the base of the neck is a great patch of metallic green feathers, while the back and rump are again golden-yellow, with long crimson hackles covering the base of the tail, which is of extraordinary length and exquisitely mottled with buff and black. The whole of the under parts are of a crimson-scarlet.

MIKADO PHEASANT (*Calophasis mikado*).

Scarcely less beautiful, yet standing in the strongest contrast with this bird, is Lady Amherst's Pheasant. Herein the head bears a crest of blood-red, while the neck-frill is white, barred with black, having a steel-blue gloss ; the shoulders, mantle, and chest are dark green, with a metallic sheen, contrasting with the rest of the under parts, which are white. The long, middle pair of tail-feathers—concealing the rest folded under them as in the Golden-pheasant—are white, barred, and vermiculated with black. The females in these two species are closely alike and quite soberly clad. The Amherst Pheasant is a native of West China and East Thibet.

Both these birds, when courting the female, adopt the same method of displaying their splendour, the neck-frill being spread and twisted sideways towards her, apparently so that she may lose nothing of their beauty.

The species of the genus *Phasianus* are too well known to need a long description. Several have been introduced to our coverts during recent years, but the experiments proved failures. The " Common Pheasant " of to-day is a more or less pure-bred example of the Chinese Ring-necked Pheasant, ranging from the Lower Ansor, Manchuria, Corea, and East Mongolia into China. This was introduced many years ago, and has now almost replaced the " old English pheasant " (*P. colchicus*) with which it freely interbred. Whether this last is an indigenous species or not is uncertain. There is no record of its introduction, and we find mention of it in Anglo-Saxon bills of fare.

The Barred-backed Pheasants (*Calophasis*), though represented by no more than two species, are striking-looking birds, with a very characteristic coloration. This much may be seen, even without the aid of colour, in the beautiful Mikado Pheasant.

The " Silver-pheasants " of the genus *Gennaeus* are an interesting group, and an extremely puzzling one, on account of the freedom with which the Indo-Burmese species interbreed, making it a matter of considerable difficulty to define the precise number of species occupying this area.

The White-crested *G. albocristatus*, of the Western Himalayas, as its name implies, has a white crest; the upper parts black with a purple and blue metallic sheen, and whitish under parts. *G. nyctherimus*, the Silver-pheasant of South China, embroidered as a badge on Mandarins' dresses in the days of the Emperors, has the plumage for the most part white, relieved by irregular lines of black, a purplish-black crown, crest, and under surface. They frequent thin forests.

The Fire-backed Pheasants of the genus *Acomus*, natives of the dense damp forests of Indo-Malayan countries, Sumatra, and Borneo, number in all six species. They are mostly black in plumage, having a patch of fiery bronze-red on the lower part of the back, hence their name. These birds are further interesting for the fact that the females, which are entirely black, have the legs armed with a pair of spurs as large as those of the male.

The Great " Eared-pheasants " (*Crossoptilon*) of the high forest regions of Thibet and China, where they ascend to a height of twelve thousand feet above sea-level, stand in strong contrast with the Fire-backs in having the plumage *white* or slaty-grey. All have a tuft of long, white feathers projecting backwards from the side of the face, hence the name " eared." This genus is further singular in that both sexes are coloured alike. As with the preceding genus, little is known of these birds in a wild state.

The remarkable Bulwer's Wattled-pheasant (*Lobiophasis*) is related to the Eared-pheasants. It has the whole head naked, the skin being of a bright blue, and produced into a pair of upturned, " horn-like " ornaments and a pair of throat-wattles. The plumage is black, set off by the dark crimson colour of the neck and chest, and the enormous, sickle-shaped, white tail. It is a native of Sarawak and North Borneo.

The Himalayas and West China have produced some remarkable pheasants, and none more so than the magnificent Moonals (*Lophophorus*). Of the four species perhaps the most beautiful is the so-called Common-moonal (*L. refulgens*), or " Impeyan Pheasant," of the Himalayas. This bird looks as though it had been wrought in burnished metal—a black-bronze, glowing with indescribably beautiful hues of golden-green, purplish-blue, and reddish-copper. The head is surmounted by a crest of spade-shaped feathers of a dark metallic green, shot with purplish-blue. Until recent years, be it said to our shame, there was a hideous and persistent slaughter of these birds for millinery purposes. "There are few sights more striking," wrote the late Dr. Hodgson, "than that of a grand old cock . . . glittering and flashing in the golden sunlight, a gigantic rainbow-tinted gem." The call of this bird, it is somewhat surprising to note, is a loud, plaintive whistle.

Mention must be made of the splendid Tragopans, or Horned-pheasants (*Tragopan*), of the higher ranges of the Himalayas and China. They derive their name from the presence of a pair of blue and fleshy caruncles above the eyes, and these, with an orange-coloured fleshy wattle at the throat, become tinged with blood and vastly increased in size during times of sexual excitement. At other times they are quite inconspicuous. The greater part of the plumage may be described as of an orange-carmine colour, relieved by round white spots. The Tragopans, of which there are five species, are all strictly forest birds.

IMPEYAN PHEASANT (*Lophophorus refulgens*).

The Partridge-like Game-birds form the sub-family *Perdicinae*. The term "partridge-like" is somewhat of a misnomer, for it is employed to include birds which are by no means "partridge-like" in their general appearance, but agree in having a wing wherein the first flight-feathers are longer than or equal to the tenth, and a short tail. But this purely arbitrary and most unsatisfactory system must be tolerated only until someone undertakes a thorough anatomical study, including all the known Game-birds—the work of a life-time. The most important members of this sub-family are the Partridges, Quails, Wood-partridges, Red-legged Partridges, Francolins, and the Snow-partridge and Snow-cocks.

Our Common Partridge, *Perdix cinerea*, needs no description, but the distinction between male and female may well be pointed out. This is to be found in the pattern of the wing-coverts, which in the females are transversely barred with buff.

Of the seven species of Quails, mention must be made of the Common Quail (*Coturnix*), which, years ago, bred with us annually, but now does so no longer, partly owing to the insensate netting of these birds on the shores of the Mediterranean in the spring, where they are taken in tens of thousands to supply the great restaurants of London and the Continent with luxuries that could well be dispensed with.

The smallest of all the Game-birds are the four species Painted-quails (*Excalfactoria*). The best-known is the Indo-Chinese (*E. chinensis*), measuring five inches long. It breeds freely in captivity, and the young, when but a week old and no bigger than walnuts, are fully able to fly.

The Crested Wood-partridge is remarkable for the huge crest of almost hair-like feathers which surmounts the crown, contrasting with the rest of the plumage, which is black, with metallic reflections of steel-blue and purplish-blue. It ranges from Siam to the Malay Peninsula.

The Red-legged Partridge (*Caccabis*), though common in some parts of England, as in Norfolk, is an introduced species from South-West Europe. Though a very handsome bird, it is not a favourite with sportsmen—who introduced it— owing to its habit of taking to its legs rather than to its wings to escape the guns. Its immature dress displays none of the splendours of colour of the adult stage.

The Francolins are a numerous tribe, which may be described as African, since of nearly fifty species only five are Asiatic. Though the coloration is rich and varied, as compared with some of the

BARE-THROATED FRANCOLIN (*Pternistes afer*).

Game-birds, it presents no very striking features. For the most part the plumage is black, relieved by markings of chestnut, buff, and white. In some species spurs are wanting, or they are worn only by the males, while a few are found in both sexes. For the most part they rarely perch ; some, however, especially in South Africa, habitually do so. One of the largest and best known is the Cape-francolin, or " Cape-pheasant " (*Francolinus capensis*). They run with great speed, and the flight though heavy is swift.

The Snow-partridge (*Lerwa*) and the Snow-cocks (*Tetraogallus*) are Alpine birds. The former is met with at elevations of from ten to fifteen thousand feet, while the Thibetan Snow-cock ascends to nineteen thousand feet above sea-level.

The Snow-partridge, a Himalayan species, is about the size of a Red-grouse, black above, barred with whitish, and rich chestnut below. The Snow-cocks, represented by five species, are large birds approaching the Capercaillie in size, and presenting no great differences in coloration, which is generally of a dark grey above, heavily streaked with white on the wings and lower back, and below with narrow longitudinal streaks of dark grey. The beak and feet of the Thibetan Snow-cock are of an orange-red colour.

The American Tooth-billed Partridges (*Odontophorinae*) have the beak in some species relatively thick, while the tip of the lower jaw is notched, and the legs have no spurs. They are somewhat quail-like in form, though one or two species have long tails.

The Scaly-partridge (*Calipepla*) of the high, barren plateaux of Mexico has the feathers edged with black, giving to the plumage a scaly appearance. Of much more striking appearance is the Californian-quail (*Lophortyx*) of the brush-covered hills and cañons of the Western States of North America and California, up to an elevation of nine thousand feet. The crown is surmounted by a long, black crest of two feathers, turned forwards. The general coloration is of a smoke-grey, relieved by a black throat and a gorget of white, while the flanks are striped with white.

Even more striking, perhaps, is the Plumed-partridge (*Oreortyx*) of the Sierras of the Western States of North America. Here, as in the Californian-quail, the crown bears a long crest of two feathers, and the general coloration is smoke-grey. But the throat is chestnut-red with a curved white band on each side, while the flanks are barred with black, red, and white after a fashion recalling our " French-partridge."

Of the Thick-billed Partridges (*Odontophorus*) of the forests of Central and South America, more than a dozen species are known. They seldom fly, and take to the trees when alarmed.

Family *Tetraonidae*

The Grouse differ from the Pheasants, Partridges, and Quails in having the nostrils entirely hidden by feathers; the legs are either partially feathered, as in the Hazel-hens and Ruffed-grouse, or completely feathered as in Capercaillie, or Black-grouse and Ptarmigan, and these are never armed with spurs. The toes are either scale-covered, and with a series of horny comb-like fringes on each side, as in Capercaillie and Black-grouse, or completely feathered as in the Red-grouse, Willow-grouse, and Ptarmigan; in the last-named even the soles of the feet are feathered. In some species, as in the Willow-grouse and Ptarmigan, there are striking seasonal changes of plumage, governed by climatic conditions rather than seasonal—an important point.

One of the best-known of this group is the Red-grouse (*Lagopus scoticus*), which is indigenous to Great Britain; it is found, indeed, nowhere else, ranging from the Yorkshire moors to the extreme north of Scotland. It is also a native of Ireland. This bird, seen in the poulterers' shops, is just a " Red-grouse," and nothing more. The expert ornithologist, however, has shown that it displays numerous colour phases, due largely to climatic conditions and complex seasonal changes which it shares in common with the Willow-grouse and Ptarmigan. These changes are of too technical a character to be discussed here.

WILLOW-GROUSE (*Lagopus albus*) (Summer).

The nest is a slight hollow in the ground, sheltered by heather, and lined with moss and grass. The eggs, from seven to ten in a clutch, have a ground colour of buff, heavily spotted and blotched with dark reddish-brown.

The Willow-grouse in its summer dress differs from our Red-grouse chiefly in having the quill-feathers and under parts *white*. It is a circumpolar species, and differs yet again from the Red-grouse in that it turns white in winter. In their habits the Willow-grouse very closely resemble the Red-grouse, though their haunts are different, since they are found among birch and willow-trees, and, unlike the Red-grouse, are fond of perching in trees and prefer to roost in them.

WILLOW-GROUSE (*Lagopus albus*) (Winter).

The Ptarmigan (*Lagopus*) are represented by four closely allied species, with similar haunts among the high stony tablelands above the limits of tree-growth and heather.

Our own species, *L. mutous*, is confined to the highlands of Scotland, and has been more intensively studied than any of the others. It is remarkable for the fact that it develops three distinct plumages during the year. In its summer dress, worn from May to July, the male is mottled and barred with grey and must-colour, on a dark brown background; the female with rufous buff, on a black background. In the autumn dress, from August to October, the prevailing hue is grey, freely mottled with black.　From November till April they wear a pure white livery, save that all but the middle tail-feathers are black, and there is in the male a black bar in front of the eye, whereby it may be distinguished from the Willow-grouse in its winter dress.

The white plumage of the Willow-grouse and Ptarmigan is a protective coloration, concealing them from their enemies—Arctic foxes, Snowy-owls, and Greenland-falcons.

The Capercaillies (*Tetrao*), of which four species are known, are among the giants of the family.　The species best known is *Tetrao urogallus*, a bird of the pine forests of Europe and North and Central Asia.　As a British bird it is confined to the eastern counties of Scotland.　In the month of April the male resorts to some particular pine tree, known as the " laking-place," and here, at dawn and sunset, with outstretched neck, drooping wings, and tail spread like a fan, he gives utterance to his pent-up emotions, accompanied by his " love-song " or " spel "—three notes several times repeated.　Towards the end of his song he has worked himself up to such a blind state of excitement that he is oblivious to all around him.　Continental " sportsmen " take advantage of these moments to get within shooting range—and the song is soon over.

The Black-grouse (*Lyrurus*), whose beautiful curled tail is used as a regimental badge, needs no detailed description.　By some authorities this bird is said to range, in suitable localities, over the greater part of Europe and Northern and Central Asia.　By others these continental birds are regarded as distinct sub-species, so that *the* Black-grouse becomes confined to the British Islands, where its headquarters must be regarded as Scotland, though it is to be found in fair numbers in Devon and Somerset, parts of Wales, the English border counties, and the Midlands.　The hen, known as the " Grey-hen," is totally unlike the male in plumage, being of a rufous colour, barred with glossy black, and having a forked tail.

Pine and birch forests are the true home of this bird, but it will wander out on to the moors and into the stubble-fields in search of food, generally in early morning and evening.　In April the males, which are polygamous, engage in strange dances performed in some chosen spot.　With drooping wings and outspread tail, a number of males will strut about, each challenging his neighbour, and from time to time one or other will leap into the air in its excitement ; every now and then two birds will come to blows, sometimes inflicting on one another no uncertain evidence of the seriousness of the encounter.

Two or three very remarkable American species of Grouse must be mentioned here.　One of these is the Prairie-hen (*Tympanuchus*) of the Mississippi Valley and Canada.　Though possessing no brilliancy of coloration, the plumage being barred with rufous and black on a whitish background, it displays two conspicuously ornamental features.　The first of these is a frill, or ruff, of long erectile feathers ; and the second a couple of inflatable sacs on each side of the neck, visible only when distended, when they form two large orange-coloured bulbs. They are displayed only during their " courtship " dances, when the males gather together to fight mimic battles. At this time the long feathers of the ruff are thrown forwards over the head till they look like two horns, the orange-coloured sacs bulging out behind them ; at the same time the wings are drooped and the tail spread, while the back feathers are set on end, as in a turkey-cock. They face one another like fight-ing-cocks, and strut about in various strange attitudes, at times leaping into the air, and these antics are ac-companied by curious booming sounds audible at a great distance.

The Sage-hen (*Centrocercus*) of the Rocky Mountain Plateau is the largest of the American Grouse. Grey in coloration, with a long tail, and a curious " frill " round the neck, formed of feathers which are produced into long thread-like stalks, it also has inflatable and brightly coloured neck-sacs, which can be inflated till the head is almost hidden. The gizzard, it should be noted, unlike that of any

PRAIRIE-HEN (*Tympanuchus americanus*).

other Game-bird, has soft walls, a condition associated with the fact that this bird feeds mainly on the leaves of the sage.

Finally we come to the Hazel-hens (*Tetrastes*), or Gelinottes, which are Old-World forms. The Common Hazel-hen (*T. bonasia*), of Europe and Central Asia, haunts the pine forests and birch woods of mountainous areas. Its flesh is highly esteemed, and large numbers are sent, frozen, to the London markets from Scandinavia and Russia. In its general coloration it is, as to the upper parts, of a greyish or rufous hue, barred with black ; the breast-feathers are black, margined with white ; while in size it is but little larger than a partridge.

CHAPTER VIII

Order GRUIFORMES

(*Cranes and Rails*)

THE Cranes and Rails comprise birds of very different forms and habits, yet all sharing in varying degrees of intensity the same general conditions of life. That is to say, they have become adjusted in various ways to life in fens and marshes, though in no case shall we meet with transformations so radical as will be found when the Plover tribe come to be surveyed.

But before what may be called the typical Gruiformes can be discussed, certain other extremely interesting, though at the same time extremely puzzling, forms must be examined. To the systematist, who is seeking for convenient modes of classification—that is to say, of marshalling the various families and genera into crisply defined groups—these " nondescript " types are anathema ; they cripple where they do not spoil his definitions and orderly sequences. To the evolutionist they are precious links, though often he is left in despair as to the correctness of his inferences. Let us, without more ado, dispose of the only " thorn in the flesh " so far as the Cranes and Rails are concerned.

Family Mesitidae

Mesites is an extremely rare bird, hence it has no name in common speech. It is a native of Madagascar, and is known only to the specialists. On this account it might be urged that it scarcely calls for mention in these pages. But the purpose of this book is to help those who have a love for Natural History to gain an insight into the many and interesting problems this subject presents.

In shape it suggests, more perhaps than anything else, some sort of Rail of a reddish-brown coloration. But how vague are its characteristics may be gathered from the fact that by some authorities it is held to belong to the Game-birds, by others to the Rails. Geoffroy Saint Hilaire, a great French naturalist, regarded it as a Pigeon ; while others have included it with the Ardeine, or Heron tribe, and it has even been assigned a relationship to the Passeres !

Taking all the evidence into consideration it would seem to be most nearly related to the Rails. Among its more striking features must be noted the presence of no fewer than five well-defined patches of powder-down feathers—hence its association with the Heron tribe ; but these peculiar feathers are found also in the Crane tribe, as well as in some other groups. The keel of the breast-bone is but feebly developed, and the furculum, or " merry-thought," is reduced to a vestigial condition, showing that the powers of flight are extremely limited. The beak is long and slender, and the nostrils form long slits ; these are Rail-like characters. The plumage is of so loose and fragile a character that the feathers of the back curl up soon after death. Hardly anything is known of its habits, but it is said to nest on the ground.

Family Rallidae

The Rail tribe are an exceedingly interesting group, all adapted to a life in swamps, by reedy pools, and the banks of rivers. But some species, be it noted, like our Land-rail, have become adjusted to drier ground, and haunt long grass and cornfields.

The better to glide about stealthily through the mazes of reed-stems and similar cover, the body has become, as it were, laterally compressed; so much so that the body of the sternum has become reduced to a mere ridge along each side of the keel of the breast-bone, and the hip-girdle, or pelvis, is also extremely narrow. The wings and tail are short, and the power of flight is comparatively feeble, though it must be borne in mind that some, like our Land-rail, are capable of extensive migrations, for this bird leaves us in the autumn for Africa and returns in the spring. All those whose haunts are near water swim well, though the toes, which are often conspicuously long, are never webbed.

Our Water-rail (*Rallus aquaticus*), a bird seldom seen but still fairly common in suitable localities, may be described as a typical Rail. Though sombre in its coloration it is yet rather a handsome bird, having a long, dull-red bill, dark-brown upper parts, and slate-grey under parts, barred with white on the flanks.

WATER-RAIL (*Rallus aquaticus*).

The Land-rail, or Corn-crake (*Crex crex*), is decreasing in numbers with us every year, but its strange, ventriloquial cry — *crake-crake-crake* — still heard in favoured localities, contributes to the music of our summer days. It is from this cry, so commonly heard while the musician is hidden among the corn, that the name "Corn-crake" is derived. The Little-crake (*Zapornia*), the Spotted-crake (*Porzana*), and Baillon's-crake (*P. bailloni*) are nearly related to the Corn-crake, and are also to be numbered among our British birds; but they are rare. In all these, as in the Corn-crake, the beak is short.

The Wood-hens, or Weka-rails (*Ocydroma*), of New Zealand, of which there are several species, are large, tawny-coloured, flightless birds, haunting dry woods and ravines, and living in burrows, from which they emerge at dusk. The Kelp-hen (*O. fusca*) has taken to a life on the seashore, feeding on molluscs and the small crustacea found among the stranded seaweeds. But the inland species will eat young birds and lizards, as well as caterpillars and other insects, worms, and berries.

Mention must be made of the large, handsome Rails of Central and South America of the genus *Aramides*, of which *A. ypecaha* may be taken as the type. The coloration above is olive-green, with a chestnut nape and a black rump and tail; while the under parts are greyish, save the throat which is white, and the belly which has a vinous tinge. The beak is yellow, the legs scarlet. These birds, perhaps on account of their large size, have a decidedly aggressive disposition, for near homesteads they will attack poultry. In its native wilds it struts about in stately fashion, sometimes on the ground, sometimes on the larger boughs of trees. It also displays the very un-rail-like characteristic of rising from the ground when alarmed with a whirring flight like that of a partridge.

WEKA-RAIL (*Ocydromus australis*).

Our Coot (*Fulica*) and Water-hen (*Gallinula*) represent another type of the Rails—to be distinguished at once by the "frontal-shield," a bare area of soft skin, red in the Water-hen, white in the Coot. Both these birds swim and dive well, but the Water-hen has long, slender toes, and no web between them, while the Coots, curiously enough, have broad, rounded lobes along the sides of the toes. Why should these have developed in the one and not in the other? In their haunts and habits they seem to differ only in that the Coot is gregarious.

The "Purple-gallinules," some dozen in number, might almost be described as large Water-hens, but with vastly larger beaks, red frontal-shield, and red legs. The coloration, as the name implies, is mostly some shade of purplish-blue. They are found in Africa and Madagascar, and from the Mediterranean to South China and Polynesia. The now extinct flightless *Notornis mantelli* was one of this group, but less gorgeously coloured, having but a tinge of blue over an olive-green background.

PURPLE-GALLINULE (*Porphyrio caeruleus*).

In the matter of size the Rails show a considerable range; the smallest is about the size of a skylark, the largest, *Megacrex*, of New Guinea, may attain to a length of twenty-one inches. But this is a mere pigmy compared to some of the fossil rails, as, for example, *Leguatia gigantea*, of Rodriguez, which stood six feet high.

In their nesting habits the Rail tribe show striking differences. Some, like our Coot and Water-hen, construct the nest of dead leaves, grass, and sedge, at the edge of the water—though the Water-hen will sometimes build in trees or bushes, or will use the old nests of Wood-pigeons or Rooks. At least two species of the genus *Creciscus*, allied to our Spotted-crake (*Porzana*)—ranging from the United States to Paraguay—are known to build a spherical nest, with an entrance at the side, and one is said to make a sort of ladder to reach a platform before its porch.

The nestlings of all so far examined are black, but in the Coot and Water-hen alone have the young been described from living specimens, and these display some interesting features. In the young Coot the head is studded with vermilion-red papillae, exactly like those which cover the red wattles of the pheasants ; and distributed among these papillae are numerous long, yellow, hair-like feathers, producing a very striking effect, contrasting strangely with the head of the adult, wherein the only ornamental feature is the white frontal-shield. The young Water-hen is no less singular, inasmuch as it assumes temporarily, if imperfectly, the coloration of the adult, the beak being red, and there is an incipient red frontal-shield. But in the fledgling the red colour vanishes, and is succeeded by a dull olive-green, which in due time again gives place to red.

Family Aramidae

The curious birds, the Courlans, seem to hold an intermediate place between the Rails and the Cranes. In general appearance, indeed, they may be likened to large Rails, and we may well regard them as standing at the parting of the ways between the two types. The beak, which is long and grooved, is markedly laterally compressed, and

LIMPKIN (*Aramus scolopaceus*).

the legs and toes are also long. Like the Rails, and unlike the Cranes, they lay numerous eggs, from ten to twelve, as large as those of a turkey. They are, however, white, not spotted as in the Rails. Haunting swamps and the banks of shallow streams, they feed largely on molluscs, the shells of which are easily broken by the powerful beak. Small reptiles, insects, and worms are also eaten.

There are but two species : one, the " Clucking-hen," or Limpkin, of Central America and South Florida, is of a chocolate-brown colour, flecked with white, and with purple-bronze reflections over the upper parts ; the other, ranging from Guiana to Argentina, is known as the " Lamenting-bird," or " Crazy-widow," from its weird cries.

Family Psophiidae

Though the Trumpeters, anatomically, are nearly related to the Courlans, they do not in the slightest degree resemble them externally, neither do they present any likeness to the Cranes. Rather they have the appearance of some long-legged Gallinaceous bird, especially so in regard to the beak.

GREY-WINGED TRUMPETER (*Psophia crepitans*).

The tail is so short as to seem wanting, and this gives the body a rounded appearance recalling that of the Tinamous or the Guinea-fowls.

There are six species in all inhabiting the vast forests of tropical South America, sometimes forming flocks of as many as three hundred individuals. They perch, but seldom fly, and run swiftly. At need they will take to the water. They have a very deep-toned, ventriloquistic voice, produced apparently by the aid of a long windpipe which, instead of entering the chamber formed within the keel of the sternum, as in the Cranes, coils itself between the skin and the breast-muscles. They are easily tamed, and the natives of Brazil keep them to protect their poultry. So tame do they become that they will follow their owners about like a dog.

The Grey-winged Trumpeter (*Psophia crepitans*), one of the best-known species, is black, with velvety plumage on the head and neck, and curiously loose grey feathers on the lower back. There are no very striking differences of coloration between the different species.

Family Gruidae

One can readily understand the difficulty which most people find in distinguishing Cranes from Storks ; for there is, indeed, a superficial likeness between them; large size, long necks and legs, are common to both. In the Cranes, of the family *Gruidae*, however, it will be noticed that the beak is often short, but when elongated it is cylindrical rather than cone-shaped, and is more or less conspicuously grooved. Furthermore, in many species the inner secondaries are greatly elongated, falling down on either side in long, graceful plumes.

They have a wide geographical range, but are not found in the Malay Islands, Papuasia, and Polynesia. Their headquarters are in North-East Asia. America possesses only three species, Australia but one. Their haunts are swamps and fens, and the margins of lakes. But, unlike the Storks, they do not enter the water; and they differ, again, in their diet, being largely vegetarian, eating grain when in the neighbourhood of cultivated areas, and acorns, bulbs, tubers, and the like in waste places. Yet lizards and frogs and insects are also eaten. Though often found in openings of forests, where there is swampy ground, they never perch upon trees, nor build their nests therein.

They are gregarious after the breeding season, and often congregate in immense flocks. All the northern species migrate south for the winter. In the spring they often perform strange " courting dances," meeting one another with nodding heads, outstretched necks, and wings widely spread; after which they will bow towards the ground, then spring into the air after a fashion which to those privileged to watch the performance savours of the ridiculous.

" KAFFIR " CROWNED-CRANE
(*Balearica chrysopelargus*).

The nest is commonly a large pile of reeds and rushes, with a depression in which the eggs, two in number, are placed. Some species, however, make no more preparation for the eggs than a mere hollow scraped in the ground, or among standing corn or long grass.

The Common-crane (*Grus communis*) now rarely visits the British Islands, but it was, long ago, a fairly common bird, and even nested here, in suitable localities, up to the end of the sixteenth century. It is a large bird, ashy-grey in colour, with a red, warty patch on the crown, white cheeks, and long, trailing, bluish-black inner secondaries.

While grey of various shades is the prevailing colour among the cranes, there are several species wherein by a " watering down " of the pigment a white plumage has resulted. The white Japanese-crane still retains some of the dark pigmentation, the throat and part of the neck being greyish-black. The Whooping-crane of the United States and Mexico, and the Asiatic

White-crane, are entirely white, save the flight-feathers, which are black. In many of the cranes the red papillae, confined to the crown in the Common-crane, extends over the side of the face and throat.

The African Crowned-crane (*Balearica pavonina*) forms a striking contrast with its congeners, having the head surmounted by a great tuft of spirally twisted yellow and white bristles, tipped with black ; a patch of velvety-black and very short feathers rises from the forehead ; the cheeks are bare and white, the skin being very smooth and with a swollen appearance ; on the throat is a conspicuous red wattle. The smaller wing-coverts are white, the secondaries chestnut-red, forming conspicuous patches of colour when the wing is closed. The "Kaffir" Crowned-crane (*B. chrysopelargus*) differs chiefly in having a larger throat-wattle.

Unlike most of the Cranes the windpipe does not form a coil within the keel of the sternum, a peculiarity already described in some of the Swans.

Family Cariamidae

In regard to the relationship of the Cariamas, or Seriemas, there have been many opinions. Some authorities have held that they are nearly related to the Secretary Birds, to which they bear a superficial resemblance ; but it is now generally conceded that the evidence derived from a study of their anatomy shows that their relationship is unquestionably with the Crane tribe. The young are thickly down-clad, and are of the nidifugous type. Here, again, the Cariamas agree with the Crane tribe and differ from Serpentarius and the rest of the Accipitres.

BRAZILIAN CARIAMA (*Cariama cristata*).

There are two species. The Cariama (*C. cristata*), ranging from Pernambuco to Paraguay, is ochreous-grey, marked above with zigzag lines of umber, while the under surface is whitish, with brown stripes. A large crest surmounts the base of the beak. The second, smaller species, Burmeister's Cariama (*Chunga*), of Argentina, has but a small crest, is darker in coloration, and has shorter legs, which are black instead of red as in the Seriema.

Family Rhinochetidae

The Kagu (*Rhinochetus jubatus*), of New Caledonia, is a rare and extremely interesting species, a primitive and aberrant member of the Crane tribe, nearly allied to the Sun-bittern, presently to be described. Among its many peculiarities is the presence of powder-down feathers, which are distributed over the whole body instead of in concentrated patches as in the Herons. When at rest, with its head resting between the shoulders, it has a general resemblance to a night-heron ; the form of the beak adds not a little to this likeness. The plumage is of a slaty-grey colour, and the head is surrounded by a long, pendent, but erectile crest.

KAGU (*Rhinochetus jubatus*) in " courting " attitude.

But its whole appearance is changed during moments of excitement. Watch two of these birds at the Zoo. Every now and then they will stop, and suddenly facing one another will droop their wings and throw the great crest forwards, while the beak is bent towards the neck. The change is surprising. But when courting they are seen in a still more striking light. The body is tilted up, the beak just touching the ground, and the wings are widely spread, displaying broad bands of rufous, black, and white, as if to make the most of its unsuspected splendours. It feeds on molluscs, worms, and insects.

Family Eurypygidae

The Cranes and Rails are to be regarded as the most recently evolved of the Gruine types. From the base of the stem from which they started there radiated a number of other branches, some of which survive to-day as isolated forms, like the Courlan, the Cariama, and the Sun-bittern, now to be reviewed. The Sun-bittern, of the *Eurypygidae*, and the Fin-foots, presently to be described, are the last of these relics.

The name Sun-bittern is certainly a misnomer, for the birds bear not the slightest likeness to any of the bitterns ; nor are they very specially given to basking in the sun. It cannot, indeed, be very well compared with any other bird. Of about the size of a Curlew, the beak is long and somewhat slender, but " crane-like " ; the neck is conspicuously slender, while the body and tail seem to be too long for the somewhat short legs. The toes are rail-like. In coloration *Eurypyga helias*, the smallest and handsomest of the two species, presents a subdued but indescribable beauty. The head is black, with a white stripe over the eye and another beneath it, and a white throat. The rest of the plumage is variegated with black, brown, chestnut, bay, buff, grey, and white, so mottled, belted, or specked with wavy or zigzag lines as to resemble the coloration of some moths.

SUN-BITTERN (*Eurypyga helias*) in display.

In its courtship display the wings are widely spread and thrust forwards towards the ground, the tips of the primaries almost touching it, forming a great oval shield, displaying bars and bands and patches of chestnut-red, white, and grey, composing a colour scheme of rare beauty, but beyond words to describe adequately.

It is a native of Guiana and the interior of Brazil; but in Colombia and Central America occurs a larger and somewhat differently coloured species which is found on the large rivers where the banks are wooded and swampy; it feeds on small fish and insects, which are speared by the long beak with great dexterity.

Family Heliornithidae

The Fin-foots are singular birds, of which there are three species. They were regarded at one time as nearly related to the Grebes and Divers, to which, indeed, they bear some sort of resemblance; but their long tails, and the fact that they walk easily with the legs well under the body, should have given pause to those who were inclined to ascribe their relationship to the Colymbiformes. They are undoubtedly Gruiform types, though this can be established only by reference to anatomical characters.

FIN-FOOT (*Heliornis fulica*).

There are three species, each placed in a genus by itself. *Heliornis* occurs from Guatemala to Paraguay; *Podica* in West Africa; *Heliopaias* ranges from Assam to

Sumatra—a very interesting geographical distribution. The head is small, the beak rail-like and stout, the neck thin, while the toes are lobed, much after the fashion of the coot's foot. The wings are long.

They haunt swamps and rocky streams of inland woods, and swim and dive well. They feed on fish, small crustacea, and insects.

Heliornis fulica barks like a dog and has a red beak and yellow feet spotted with black ; *Podica* has red feet ; while *Heliopaias* has an orange beak and green feet.

The superficial likeness which these birds present to the Grebes and Divers, and their still closer likeness to the Coots, has come about through their intensively aquatic habits ; they furnish another to the many instances already cited in these pages of the transformation effected in the course of adjustment to intensive and restricted movements.

CHAPTER IX

Order CHARADRIIFORMES

THE Plover tribe, perhaps more than any other group, serves peculiarly well to illustrate the plasticity of birds which expresses itself in so many forms. Plovers and Gulls and Guillemots are types well known to all ; and they gain an immensely greater interest when it is realised that the three types are all descendants of a common stock, each developing along a line of its own, in accordance with its mode of life and the stage of evolution which had been attained when the new trend of development began.

Here, as in the previous groups, we find isolated types, which, having started off along a definite line, lacked impetus to proceed further, or, what is perhaps nearer the truth, entered on a line of development which by harmony with its environment became stabilised.

All are types adapted to a life in open country, and generally near water. Some, like the Ringed-plovers, Dunlin, Turnstone, and Purple-sandpiper, are essentially shore birds, haunting sandy beaches and estuaries. Some, like the Curlews, are moorland birds. These, however, may be called the new arrivals, the latest " expression points " of evolution. Some of the older types have become adapted to desert conditions.

The Gulls and the Auk tribe are types of remarkable interest ; and no less so are the Sand-grouse and Pigeons, which at first sight hardly seem capable of being brought within the scope of " Plovers." The evidence on which this assertion of relationship is based is to be found in a study of their anatomy, and it admits of no dispute.

No one of the great groups yet discussed stands sharply defined from all the other groups. This is inevitable, for large groups stand to one another in the same relation as allied species—they are branches of a common stem. Types which have branched off low down the stem will, of necessity, retain more of the characters appertaining to the stock as it existed at the time when it began to break away from the group to which it is nearest allied. The Cranes and Rails and the Plover tribe represent some of these great happenings in Nature, and hence it is that some of the Gruiformes present types reminiscent of the Charadriiformes. So nicely balanced are they in this regard that it is difficult to give a " casting vote " as to which of the two groups they belong.

In the evolution of the Charadriiformes, certain fairly well-defined types have come into being which may be grouped in six sub-orders : the Otides (Bustards), Limicolae (Plovers), Lari (Gulls), Alcae (Auks), Pterocles (Sand-grouse), and Columbae (Pigeons).

Sub-order *OTIDES*
(*Bustards*)
Family Otidae

The Bustards (*Otidae*) well illustrate this matter of what we may call indeterminate, or intermediate, types. By some authorities they are

GREAT-BUSTARD (*Otis tarda*).

regarded as belonging to the Cranes ; but the evidence, on the whole, seems to show that their affinities are rather with the Plovers than with the Gruiformes.

The Bustards are birds of heavy build, the largest species approaching the smaller Ostriches in size. The legs are long and stout, and the hind-toe is absent. All are inhabitants of plains and deserts, hence the absence of the hind-toe and the shortness of the front toes, for the feet are never used for perching.

The Great-bustard (*Otis tarda*) must be sought now in parts of Germany and Spain, the Khirgis Steppes, and Siberia ; but time was when it was common on the great heaths of Norfolk and Suffolk, and Cambridgeshire, the Wolds of Lincolnshire and Yorkshire, the downs of Sussex, and on

Salisbury Plain. They were often hunted with greyhounds; but they were swept away, with much else that was beautiful, by the " march of civilisa-tion," which creates only that which is fleeting and destroys that which was inherently permanent. It is, indeed, a handsome bird, and of great size, males having a wing-span of eight feet and weighing thirty pounds or more.

The adult male bears a tuft of white, bristle-like feathers on each side of the lower jaw, which adds not a little to his majestic appearance. The head is bluish-grey, the upper surface chiefly ochreous-yellow, barred with black, the wings white, save the primary quills which are brownish; the breast is banded with rich chestnut and grey, and the rest of the under parts are white.

The food is mainly vegetable, corn and peas where they are to be had, and small mammals, lizards, insects, and worms.

During the courting season this bird behaves in a most extraordinary manner. It draws the neck down on to the back and inflates it to a great size, by means of a large air-sac opening under the tongue, then droops the wings, twisting the second-aries upwards, and turning the tail for-wards over the back till the white under tail-coverts are displayed, forming a billowy mass, blending with the upturned white quills, and giving a quite grotesque effect, which is emphasised by strutting about while uttering guttural sounds like *oak-oak-oak.* This posturing serves to arouse the latent amorous feelings of his mate, who at last yields.

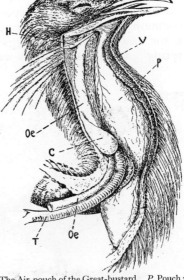

The Air-pouch of the Great-bustard. *P*, Pouch; *H*, Hyoid; *Oe*, Gullet; *C*, Crop; *T*, Windpipe; *V*, Vascular tissue.

The Little-bustard (*Tetrax tetrax*) and Macqueen's-bustard (*Houbara macqueeni*) are two other species which occasionally visit Britain during the colder months of the year.

The largest of all is the African Paauw (*Eupodotus kori*), called also by the Boers " Gom-paauw," in allusion to its fondness for mimosa gum. It has a totally different display, the male throwing its head up stiffly, with straight, upstanding neck, and inflating the gullet and crop till the latter descends like a feathered tube nearly to the ground. At the same time the throat is inflated and the tail upturned, while the wings are drooped.

Sub-order *Limicolae*

(*Plovers, Sheath-bills, Pratincoles, Seed-snipes, Jacanas, etc.*)

The term " Plovers " includes not only the typical and familiar Ringed-, Golden-, Grey-, and Green-plovers of the sub-family *Charadrinae*, but also the Sandpipers, Snipe, and Woodcocks, and these constitute a formidable array of species, so that only the more striking forms can be surveyed here.

Family Charadriidae

We may well begin with the Green-plover, or Lapwing (*Vanellus vanellus*), since this is probably the species most generally known from its all too common appearance in the poulterer's shop ; while even more deplorable is the vast number of its eggs collected to provide table delicacies in the spring. On account of this wanton destruction to provide luxuries which

Golden-plover (*Charadrius apricarius*) (Summer).   Golden-plover (Winter).

can well be dispensed with, this bird is rapidly diminishing in numbers, and it is one of the most valuable allies of the farmer.

The Golden-plover (*Charadrius apricarius*) has a very striking " breeding plumage," wherein the upper parts are spangled with black and gamboge-yellow, with a white band crossing the forehead and continued backwards above and below the eye and down the neck to the flanks ; while the sides of the head, neck, and breast are black, bordered by a broad band of white along the flanks. The abdomen is white. Towards the end of July a complete moult takes place, after which the golden-yellow of the upper parts is more pronounced, but the black areas are replaced by white. Both sexes assume the breeding dress.

This bird breeds on the moorlands of Devon and Somerset, Wales, North-East Yorkshire, and all over Scotland and its islands, as well as in the mountain areas of Ireland and the bogs of Connaught. The nest is a slight depression scraped in the soil and scantily lined with lichens.

The nearly allied Grey-plover (*Squatarola squatarola*), which is only a winter visitant to Great Britain, similarly assumes a black neck and breast in the breeding season ; but the upper parts are then spangled with black and white. In the winter dress the upper parts are of an ashy-grey colour, the under parts white. The Grey-plover can always be distinguished from the Golden-plover, apart from its somewhat large size, by the black axillaries and the presence of a vestigial hind-toe and claw.

The true Dotterel (*Eudromias morinellus*) was once a fairly common British breeding species, but it is now confined to the Lake District and Scotland. Of an ash-brown above, enlivened by a white band from the eye backwards down the neck, and a black crown, a white gorget, chestnut-red breast, and black belly, it is a conspicuously handsome bird. And it is to be noted that this resplendent dress is worn all the year round, and by both sexes ; the female, indeed, is occasionally more vividly coloured than the male.

Of the Ringed-plovers, commonly but wrongly called " Dotterel " (*Aegialitis*), one species, *A. hiaticola,* breeds in some numbers along our sandy beaches. The nearly related Kentish-plover, distinguished from the Ringed-plover by having black instead of yellow legs and a small black patch on each side of the fore-breast instead of a broad band, is remarkable for the fact that it breeds only on the shingle beaches of Kent.

One of the most remarkable of living birds is the New Zealand Wry-bill plover (*Anarhynchus*), a small species, not unlike the Kentish-plover, but having a more pointed beak which is always conspicuously bent towards the right, apparently to enable it the more readily to pick up small crustacea from under stones.

There are several species of plovers perhaps nearly related to our Green-plover, which have the face in front of the eyes ornamented with fleshy wattles, brightly coloured, and projecting downwards on each side below the beak ; some of them, furthermore, have the wing armed with a long, sharp spur. One of these, the Spur-winged lapwing of Egypt—which, by the way, has no face wattles—is said to attack birds on the wing with its spurs.

The Turnstone (*Arenaria*), one of our common shore-birds, is so-called because of its habit of turning over stones with its beak to obtain the small sand-hoppers and insects hiding there. Its orange-coloured legs and tortoiseshell coloration make it easily recognisable.

Another of our shore-birds, and nearly related to the Turnstone, is the Oyster-catcher (*Haematopus ostralegus*) of the sub-family *Haematopodinae*.

It can be recognised at once by its black-and-white plumage, long, orange-red beak, and thick, pink legs. Large flocks often congregate on shingle-banks and mud-flats, when its loud call, *klee-eep, klee-eep*, draws attention to its presence even before it is seen. It is especially fond of limpets, but other " shell-fish "—except oysters !—are also eaten. It is worth noting that some species, like *H. unicolor* of Australia and New Zealand, is black and has brick-red legs. *H. ater* of Peru and Patagonia is also black, and has an upturned beak.

Here must be mentioned that singular bird the " Ibis-billed curlew " (*Ibidorhynchus*), which has the coloration of a gull rather than of a plover,

STILT (*Himantopus himantopus*).

AVOCET (*Avocetta recurvirostra*).

the upper part of the plumage being pearl-grey, and a long, curved, red beak, and greenish-grey legs and toes. It ranges through Turkestan and China to the Himalayas.

The Plover tribe furnishes striking examples of adaptability to various environmental conditions. A good illustration is presented by the remark-able Stilts (*Himantopus*), whose legs in proportion to their bodies are of enormous length and great slenderness. The beak is also long and very slender. They obtain their food—small crustacea and aquatic insects —by wading. One species, the Black-winged Stilt, occasionally ranges to the British Islands. The New Zealand Stilt (*H. melas*) is uniformly black.

The nearly related Avocets are noteworthy on account of the long, slender, upturned beak. These birds are also long-legged, and when wading feed by swinging the head from side to side so as to sweep the surface film of the water with its strange jaws. One species (*Avocetta recurvirostra*) used to breed with us in large numbers, but raids on their eggs for marketing exterminated them.

The Phalaropes, Sandpipers, Godwits, and Curlews, of the sub-family *Tringinae*, comprise all the remaining types which are, in common speech, known collectively as the " Waders," and they present a wide range in size, form, and coloration. When they are seen arrayed on the shelves of a museum the profoundly interesting problems which this variety of form presents is entirely missed, unless they are reflectively contemplated. There is a " meaning " behind these differences of form and coloration, seasonal and sexual. A general survey of the more outstanding types is all that can profitably be given here.

The Phalaropes, with which this series begins, are extremely interesting types, and two species are to be reckoned among our British birds. One of their most striking peculi- arities is the fact that their toes are fringed with broad lobes, like those of the Coots and Grebes ; another is that the females are slightly larger and more brightly coloured than the males. Where this is the case it is generally found that the female courts the male, who undertakes the sole duties of incubation and the care of the young. The Phalaropes are no exception to this rule.

DUNLIN (*Erolia alpina*) (Summer).

The Grey-phalarope, which visits us in winter, breeds in Northern Europe. In its breeding dress the crown is black, and the back variegated with cinnamon-buff and chestnut-red, with a white patch on the face and white wing-bar ; but in the winter the upper parts are grey, with a black nuchal patch, and white below.

The smaller Red-necked Phalarope, which still breeds with us, but in numbers greatly reduced by the raids of egg-collectors, is dark slate-grey above, relieved by streaks of pinkish-buff and a white wing-bar. The throat is white, and below it is a patch of rich chestnut-red running up the side of the neck behind the throat-patch. In winter the chestnut throat-patch is lost, the upper parts assume a light slate-grey colour, with loops and streaks of white. It breeds in swamps and, after the manner of its tribe, swims well.

The Dunlin (*Erolia alpina*), known to the " shore-shooter " as the " Stint," is one of a considerable number of species of small wading-birds presenting well-marked differences of coloration and size, but all having the same general form—long, or rather long and rather flexible beaks, and long legs. Nearly allied are the Sandpipers. The summer dress of the Dunlin exhibits a blend of rufous, grey, and black above, and a large, black breast-patch below. In the winter ash-grey replaces the mottling of rufous and black, and the breast is entirely white.

The Curlew-sandpiper (*Erolia ferruginea*) in its winter dress is very like a Dunlin, but in its breeding plumage it differs in a very striking manner, the under parts being of a rich chestnut and the white rump barred with black. Of its nesting habits little is known, for it breeds in the far north of Asia. The Pectoral-sandpiper (*Tringa maculata*), of Alaska and Hudson's Bay, is remarkable for the fact that the male when courting mounts into the air above his mate, with the gullet inflated with air after the manner of a pigeon, and uttering a booming note. The Purple-sandpiper comes to us

RUFF (*Machetes pugnax*).

in the winter, chiefly to our rocky coasts, where it feeds among the seaweed close to the water's edge. Though often washed off by the swell, it swims well. It is easily recognised by its short, yellow legs and purplish-black colour, relieved by a white patch on the secondaries. It breeds in the Arctic regions.

The Knot (*Canutus canutus*) is another common "shore-bird" with us, which breeds in the Arctic regions. Grey above and white below in its winter dress, its breeding plumage is conspicuously different, the head and neck being reddish, and the rest of the upper parts variegated with black, cinnamon, and white, while the under parts are of a lively chestnut. The Spoon-bill Sandpiper (*Eurhynorhynchus pygmaeus*) is another singular type, the beak being expanded at the tip to form a broad "shovel." Nothing seems to be known of its nest or eggs, for it breeds in the far north; nor can any explanation at present be given for this strange beak.

The genus *Totanus* contains a large number of species of which the best known is the Redshank (*Totanus calidris*). This is one of our native birds whose habits on its breeding grounds are such a delight to watch. The Greenshank (*Glottis nebularius*) is another, whose breeding haunts are the hill districts of Scotland. In this bird the beak is slightly upturned, and the legs are green—hence its name.

One of the most interesting of all, a relative of our Common-sandpiper, is the Ruff (*Machetes pugnax*), and this on account of the unique range it displays in the coloration of the great Elizabethan ruff, and the upstanding " ears " which it develops at the courting season. Though a hundred birds be examined no two will be found alike ; and these differences are emphatic. The ruff, for example, may be uni-coloured, barred, or streaked ; it may be white, or buff, or black ; glossed with purple or chestnut ; and the " ears " differ as widely in their coloration. But more than this. At this season the feathers around the beak, as far back as the eyes, are replaced by fleshy and brightly coloured papillae. Finally, the plumage of the rest of the body differs quite as much, individually, as does the ruff. For the student of evolution and of the " behaviour " of animals, these birds are of surpassing interest and value ; nevertheless, they are being slowly exterminated, for they, unfortunately, furnish *delicatessen* to the gourmet. In days long past these birds bred in numbers in our fens ; to-day an occasional pair, under vigorous and most zealous guardianship, may succeed in rearing their young. Our supplies now come from Holland. How long will they last ?

The Godwits form the small but very distinct genus *Limosa*, very hand-some birds, with long legs and long beaks. The Black-tailed Godwit, nearly as large as a Whimbrel, up to 1847 nested annually in our fens. But our breeding stock was exterminated partly by drainage and partly on account of relentless netting for table luxuries. Only during the spring and autumn migrations do they visit us now. For some inexplicable reason this bird never succeeds in perfecting its breeding dress, the brightly coloured feathers of this plumage being intermixed with those of the grey winter dress. The smaller Bar-tailed Godwit, in its breeding dress, has the head, neck, and under parts of a chestnut-red ; the upper parts are variegated with wood-brown and black, while the tail is barred with dark brown.

The Curlews and Whimbrels, though represented by many species, do not differ widely in appearance from our Common-curlew : a large bird with a long, decurved beak, long legs, and a plumage striated with dark brown. It is one of our commonest shore-birds, and may easily be dis-tinguished by its curious cry, " Courlie ! " On the moors and pastures, where Curlews breed, they feed on berries, worms, snails, spiders, and insects; by the shore on crustacea and molluscs. This change of diet is interesting when it comes to be correlated with the shape of the beak. The Whimbrel (*Numenius phaeopus*) is smaller, and distinguished by the pale stripe along the crown. It breeds in the Orkneys and Shetlands and the Outer Hebrides.

The Snipes and Woodcocks of the sub-family *Scolopacinae*, though represented by a considerable number of species, present a general uniformity in the matter of their coloration. In all, the beak is not only long, but from the fact that it is always used for probing into the ground, the conforma-tion of the bones of the skull has been materially modified, so much so as to bring the aperture of the ear downwards and forwards, so that it occupies a position below, and, in the Woodcocks, in front of the eye. But there is another point concerning the beak which is worthy of note. These birds feed, not upon " suction " as some suppose, but mainly upon worms. To obtain these the beak has to be thrust down into the soil closed. This being so it would be impossible to thrust away the closely embracing soil, but for the fact that the tip of the upper jaw can be forced away from the lower jaw far enough to enable a worm to be seized and withdrawn. The ability to effect this movement is due to the skeletal framework of the beak, which, however, is of too complicated a character to be profitably explained here. The Dunlin possesses similar powers.

The Snipes have a characteristic type of plumage whose significance is seldom appreciated. Briefly, the upper parts are longitudinally striped with pale wood-brown on a dark background, to harmonise with the coarse grass amid which the bird crouches when alarmed ; not until almost trodden on, as a rule, will it take to flight, and even then by means of a curious zig-zag course it endeavours to baffle its enemy.

The Common-snipe (*Gallinago coelestis*) has a very remarkable flight when courting. Mounting to a great height it descends at speed, at the same time spreading the outermost pair of tail-feathers, which are specially stiffened, till they stand quite apart from the rest. As a consequence, in the rushing, downward dive they give forth a note singularly like the bleating of a goat. The smaller Jack-snipe, which does not breed with us, makes a noise while courting like that of a galloping horse, and also during flight. In the Pin-tailed Snipe the six outer tail-feathers are reduced almost to spines, but they do not seem to give out any musical note during flight. This bird breeds from the Yenesei to the Pacific.

The Woodcocks have a different type of coloration, but this can be explained by the nature of their haunts, since they frequent moist places in woods. Our native Woodcock (*Scolopax rusticola*) may well serve as a type of this coloration. Herein the head is marked by four broad, transverse, black bands, while the rest of the upper parts are of a rich reddish-brown vermiculated with black. The under parts are transversely barred. No mere description, however, will convey the highly protective value of this coloration, which makes the bird invisible amid its surroundings, so long as it remains perfectly still. The courting habits of the Woodcock are very different from those of the Common-snipe, though they also take the form of a " love flight," known as " roding," and performed in the rides of the woods and adjacent open spaces, at about thirty feet from the ground. The flight during this performance is by a slow, flapping, and rather owl-like action, and it is accompanied by curious croaking noises like " guroo-guroo," and a sharp " ittic-ittic." It also barks and buzzes when the young are in danger.

The American-woodcock (*Philohela minor*) differs from our bird in having two silvery-grey streaks along the back, and rufous under parts without bars, though there is an incipient gorget of black feathers at the base of the neck.

Finally, mention must be made of those rather singular birds the " Painted-snipes " (*Rostratula*) ; one species, *R. capensis*, ranges over Africa and India, while another, *R. australis*, is confined to Australia, and two are South American.   In their colora-tion, and also in the form of the beak, they are more like Sandpipers than Snipe, and it is probably to these birds, rather than to the Snipes, that they are most nearly allied.   The coloration of *R. capensis* is of an almost uniform greenish-brown, relieved by black frecklings, and with golden-buff ocelli and streaks on the upper parts.   There is a chestnut patch on the cheeks and a white ring round the eye, while the under parts are white. In the Old-World species, as with

PAINTED-SNIPE (*Rostratula capensis*).

the phalaropes, the female is more brightly coloured than the male, and in her the windpipe forms a coil between the skin and the breast-muscles, which is not the case in the male.

Family Chionididae

Those singular and extremely interesting birds, the Sheath-bills, are unknown save to those well versed in ornithology.   There are but two species, and they seem to form a link between the plovers and the gulls.   The most conspicuous feature about them is the peculiar saddle-shaped horny sheaths at the base of the beak, and the bare face beset, in the Sheath-bill (*Chionis alba*), with white papillae.   The wings have a blunt carpal-spur, and the plumage is white.   They inhabit the islands around the southern end of South America and in the South Atlantic Ocean.

SHEATH-BILL (*Chionis alba*).

They feed chiefly on mussels, the shells of which they break with ease, crustacea, seaweeds, and the eggs of other birds.   Both species are often found far out at sea. In their gait and flight they are said to resemble ptarmigan, and in their courting displays they recall the pigeons. They build a nest of rough plant stems in a hollow among the rocks, or in a deserted petrel's burrow.

Family Glareolidae

The Pratincoles, Coursers, and Crab-plovers of this family include some extremely interesting birds, which are to be regarded as " outliers " from the main stem of the Plover line.

The Pratincoles do not in the least resemble plovers, externally. In their long wings they recall the terns, while in the form of the beak, which is very short, and the wide gape, they resemble the swallows, with which, indeed, they were placed by Linnaeus. The Common-pratincole (*Glareola pratincola*) presents a further resemblance to the swallows in that it has a long, deeply-forked tail. But the application of the test of anatomical characters reveals its true relationship. As with the rest of its tribe the claw of the middle-toe has a pectinated edge.

COMMON-PRATINCOLE (*Glareola pratincola*).

The Common-pratincole occasionally visits the British Islands. It breeds as near to us as Western France, and all over Southern Europe and North Africa. Its coloration is subdued : brown above, with white tips to the secondaries, and white below, save the throat which is buff, bordered by a black line, and the fore part of the breast which is brownish.

There are many species, and all have a swallow-like flight, while like swallows they feed on insects captured in mid-air. But like the plovers they can run very fast, a feat impossible to a swallow. They haunt sand-banks, lagoons, and bare plains, or coast-lands.

The Coursers are comparable with long-legged plovers, but the beak is slender and decurved ; the hind-toe is absent, but, as in the Pratincoles, the middle-toe has a comb-like or pectinated edge. One species, the Cream-coloured Courser, is an occasional visitant to Great Britain. Its coloration is what is known as "isabelline," that is to say, of a rather dark-cream colour, to harmonise with the sandy wastes on which it lives. It feeds on insects, chiefly grasshoppers, and small molluscs. Crouching on the sand when alarmed, and trusting to its concealing coloration, it will, at last, jump up and run with great speed ; only as a last resort will it take to flight.   The South African Courser (*Cursorius bicinctus*) has a very different coloration, being mottled with brown above, and with the buff under parts crossed by two black pectoral bands, while there is much chestnut on the wing-coverts.

The so-called Egyptian-plover (*Pluvianus aegyptius*) is really one of the Coursers.   It is also known as the "Crocodile-bird," from its habit of entering the open mouths of crocodiles in its search for the leeches adhering to the creatures' teeth.   But it is much more active on the wing, being frequently seen skimming over the surface of the water.

The Crab-plover (*Dromas*) is another of these un-plover-like plovers, found only on the seashore, from the Red Sea to Natal, and through the Indian Ocean and the Bay of Bengal.   White in plumage, with black wings, it has a large, black, compressed, and very solid beak, long legs, and webbed toes,

CRAB-PLOVER (*Dromas ardeola*).

the claw of the middle-toe having its inner edge serrated.   It nests in colonies, in burrows in the sand, like many of the petrels, and lays but a single, large, white egg.   As touching its food, it would seem to feed largely on crustacea, but the form and size of the beak seems to suggest that molluscs with heavy shells are also eaten.

Family Thinocorhidae

The Seed-snipes represent further ornithological puzzles.   On rare occasions specimens are to be seen at the Zoo, but, like the immediately preceding species, these are birds known only to the student of ornithology. It is, therefore, all the more necessary to draw attention to their existence here.

In general appearance they resemble the partridge, from which, however, they differ conspicuously in their long wings and short legs.   Natives of South America, they range from Peru to

GAY'S SEED-SNIPE (*Attagis gayi*).

the Falkland Islands, frequenting hill country and feeding on seeds. They run with great speed, but seek escape from enemies by crouching close to the ground, their grey coloration rendering them invisible from their stony surroundings. But when flushed they rise suddenly and make off with a twisting flight like that of the Snipe.

Family Oedicnemidae

The Stone-curlews have always been a puzzle to systematists. Some regard them as closely allied to the Bustards, and though this relationship has been called in question there seems to be some ground for the association. The long legs and short toes, of which only three are present, are very suggestive of the Bustard. But the beak is plover-like, though rather heavy, and the eyes, which are conspicuously large, are yellow.

About fifteen species are known, and one of these, the " Norfolk-plover " (*Oedicnemus oedicnemus*), is a resident British bird. Like its congeners it haunts heaths and downs, feeding on snails and insects, especially the larger beetles and grasshoppers. Frogs and mice are also eaten.

STONE-CURLEW or THICK-KNEE (*Oedicnemus oedicnemus*).

It is largely crepuscular in habits, hence the large eyes ; and it generally escapes notice during the day by the likeness of its mottled grey-and-brown plumage to its surroundings. It runs with short, quick steps, with head lowered. In flight it shows conspicuous white patches on the wings and tail, and a dark band across the wings. No nest is made, its two or three eggs, light-stone-coloured, blotched and streaked with sepia-brown, being deposited in a slight hollow in the ground. The nestlings have a short, sandy-coloured down marked by longitudinal black lines. When danger threatens, like the parents they stretch themselves at full length on the ground, the head and neck included, and lie perfectly still ; and so long as they remain thus detection is almost impossible.

Family Parridae

The Jacanas and Water-pheasants are an extremely interesting group. For in the first place it is clear that they broke away from the main stem of the Plover tribe long ago. This explains the strong superficial likeness they display to the Rails, as may be seen, for example, in the Madagascar Jacana. For a long time, indeed, they were supposed to be Rails ; but a study of their anatomy has shown that they are, in fact, aberrant Plovers. But further than this, they illustrate, in no uncertain way, that reciprocity which exists between living organisms and the physical conditions imposed by the external environment.

These pages teem with such instances, but they are not always so palpable as in these birds. The evidence in this case is furnished by the extreme length of the toes and claws ; no other birds have such claws, and no other birds, be it noted, have the same mode of life. The typical Plovers always live in the neighbourhood of water, in marshes, or by streams, or on the sea-shore. They can swim at need, but they do not enter the water, as do Rails such as the Water-hen and the Coot. The Jacanas can and do enter the water, but for the most part they live *on* it ; for their haunts are sluggish streams and lakes, whose surface is more or less completely covered with huge water-lily leaves and other floating vegetation, over which these birds walk, as on land. It is to this habitat that we must attribute the enormous length and straightness of the claws, which give the foot a vastly greater area of support when walking over the treacherous surface of floating weeds.

MADAGASCAR JACANA (*Metopidius allinucha*).

These birds are further remarkable for the brilliancy of their plumage, which in some species displays seasonal changes of alternating splendour, and a proneness to develop vividly coloured fleshy membranes, or wattles, round the head ; in this recalling some of the Spur-winged Plovers, like *Chettusia* and *Hoplopterus*. A further likeness to these types is found in the presence of wing-spurs. It may, indeed, be found, after a more intensive study of these types, that they are related ; that is to say, that the Spur-winged Plovers and the Jacanas have descended from a common stock.

The Jacanas have a wide distribution, extending over the tropical and sub-tropical areas of both hemispheres. One of the most striking species, the Indian Jacana (*Hydrophasianus chirurgus*), is of a bronze-brown above and purplish-black below. The head is white, with a black occiput ; the neck golden behind and white in front, with a dividing line of black. The wings are mainly white, and the primaries are produced into long filaments, while the tail in its great length reminds one of that of a pheasant. The South American *Parra jacana* has a red frontal lappet, falling below the beak into lobes, an orange beak, olive legs, and a large, yellow wing-spur. The plumage is chestnut, with greenish-black head and neck and under parts, and maroon flanks, with yellow, black-tipped quills.

Metopidius indicus has a large, blue, frontal-shield ; a beak tinted with blue, green, and pink ; slate-coloured legs ; and small, blunt wing-spurs. The plumage of the back is coloured bronze and maroon, while the head and neck are greenish-black to purple. There are a considerable number of species, presenting a wondrously varied coloration, as is clear from the examples just cited. The immature birds are commonly less resplendent. Their food consists of insects, molluscs, and seeds. Some build a small cup-shaped nest, others a large one of aquatic herbage placed near the water's edge, or on floating vegetation. The eggs, after the rule among the Plover tribe, do not exceed four, and are pear-shaped, with glossy shells of buff, olive-green, or brown, thickly covered with fantastic scrawls, and occasionally black blotches. The nestlings are of the nidicolous type.

Sub-order *LARI*

(*Gulls and Terns*)

In their external appearance the Gulls and Terns present no likeness to the Plover tribe. Nor, indeed, is there, so far as the evidence of outward appearance goes, any sort of reason for supposing that there exists any relationship between the Gulls and the Auks. Here, again, then, we find the necessity of an appeal to the evidence furnished by anatomy in our search for blood relationship. And this evidence at the same time reveals most important facts concerning the moulding influences imposed by the physical conditions of the external environment. These factors are not so much left out of account as unrealised by those who are content to see in birds nothing more than so many different " species," which " somehow " have come into existence.

Huxley was the first to show that the Gulls and the Plovers were blood relations, and this by a study of their skeletons. Later the oologists confirmed this relationship, urging the strong likeness in the coloration of the eggs in the two types.

Family Laridae

Gulls have such an outstanding individuality that there is no need to enlarge upon their general form, save a remark that they have escaped any marked specialisation, being able to walk with great freedom and to be equally at home on the water, while their powers of flight are superb. There is a superficial likeness between Gulls and Petrels, but the latter may always be distinguished by the composition of the beak-sheath which, as has already been pointed out, is made up of several distinct pieces.

In the matter of food they are omnivorous, and though for the most part marine, some species make their way inland for considerable distances during the winter months.

THE SKUAS

Without doubt the most ancient members of the group are the Skuas, which differ from the more typical gulls in having a fairly well-marked " cere " at the base of the beak. In their mode of life they may well be described as semi-parasitic, since they live almost entirely by chasing gulls, and even gannets, until these disgorge the food they have recently swallowed, which is caught before it reaches the water ! This is a habit also followed by the Frigate-bird of tropical seas. The largest species is the Great-skua, or Bonxie of the Shetlands, where on Unst and on Foula it is jealously

GREAT-SKUA (*Megalestris catarrhactes*).

guarded from the raids of egg-collectors. It is a large and powerful bird, of a dark-brown colour, more or less distinctly mottled with chestnut and dull white. This coloration should be borne in mind, since it may be regarded as of ancient character, reproduced, with modifications, in the immature stages of many species of gulls, *e.g.* the Black-backed and Herring-gulls.

The Great-skua not only robs gulls, but it also eats them. The smaller Kittiwake is its principal victim, but it will also slay the Herring-gull which is its superior in size. The Antarctic MacCormick's-skua is a nearly related species which levies a heavy toll on nestling penguins.

Of the four British species of Skua, two, the Great-skua and the Arctic- or Richardson's-skua, breed in the Shetlands, the last-named also in the Orkneys, the Hebrides, and on the mainland in Sutherland and Caithness. It presents two forms, one of an entirely sooty coloration, and the other with light under parts. The adult has the central tail-feathers greatly elongated, a feature also of the Long-tailed or Buffon's-skua, a circumpolar species, and a more or less frequent migrant to our shores. In this bird the upper parts are of a dark brown, the belly white, and there is a tinge of buffish-yellow on the cheeks and neck. The Pomatorhine-skua has also elongated central tail-feathers, but instead of being long and pointed they are conspicuously broad, and so twisted that the " blade " is turned vertically instead of horizontally like the rest of the tail-feathers.

The Gulls and Terns

The Gulls differ from the Terns, or " Sea-swallows," in one important particular : they have an immature plumage markedly different from that of the adult, so much so that at one time the grey-brown young of the Greater and Lesser Black-backed Gulls and Herring-gulls were collectively regarded as representing a distinct species—the " Grey-gull." And it is to be noted that even the expert ornithologist can distinguish between them only after most careful examination, though in their adult plumage they are markedly different. These birds, in this respect, furnish most interesting data as to the significance of immature plumage and the evolution of species, since they share a common likeness for at least three years before they fully reveal their specific differences. The smaller gulls assume the adult dress at the end of their first year.

HERRING-GULL (*Larus argentatus*).
Immature.   Adult.

The prevailing hue of the Gulls is pearl-grey and white, the grey hue being confined to the back and wings. But in some, like our Great and Lesser Black-backed Gulls, the pigmentation of the back has become intensified to a slate-black, darkest in the larger species. Both species, like the Herring-gull, when adult, have the beak of a bright lemon-yellow, with a vermilion patch on the conspicuous angle near the tip of the lower jaw. Further distinguishing features are found in the coloration of the legs, which in the Herring-gull are of a flesh-pink, in the Lesser Black-backed bright yellow, and in the Great Black-backed flesh-coloured. In all the iris is of a lemon-yellow, when adult.

There is a decided tendency among the *Laridae* to develop a black crown, and the further extension of this in a number of species to form a hood, investing the whole head. In the Pomatorhine- and Buffon's-skua the crown, nape, and fore-part of the face are black ; in the Black-headed Gull, so common inland in the winter, the hood is complete, but is of a sooty-brown rather than black. In the Mediterranean Black-headed Gull, Sabine's-gull, the Little-gull, the Great Black-headed Gull (*Larus ichthyaetus*), all rare British species, and the Great Pacific Black-headed Gull (*Gabianus pacificus*), it is jet-black. In the last-named the tail has a subterminal black bar, an interesting feature, since this in other species, like our Black-headed

Gull, is a sign of immaturity. Since the Herring-gull and Great and Lesser Black-backed Gulls have the head and nape streaked with brown in their winter dress, it would seem that they once had, but have now lost, a black head.

It is worth noting that *L. crassirostris*, of the Chinese and Japanese seas, and *L. belcheri*, of Peru, have, like the Pacific-gull, a black, sub-terminal tail-bar in the adult, and an irregularly striated head in the immature stages. *Larus fulginosus* of the Galapagos is particularly worth notice in this connection, since it has a black hood, and the whole of the upper parts of a deep lead colour, while the under parts are grey. Bleach the grey and white by the dilution and final extinction of the pigments, and reduce the hood to

striation, and we have the Black-backed Gulls in winter dress. Most of the Black-headed Gulls have red beaks and legs, but these in Sabine's-gull are black, and the tail, furthermore, is forked as in the terns. As already remarked, this " hood " is worn only during the breeding season.

SABINE'S-GULL (*Xema sabinii*).

In all the Gulls, save the Kittiwake, the juvenile plumage conspicuously differs from that of the adult. In some the change from the one to the other is very gradual, taking as long as three years in the Black-backed and Herring-gulls, wherein the coloration at each successive moult becomes paler. In others, as in the Black-headed Gull, the change is rapid. The juvenile dress, which is mottled brown and buff, and white below, with a buff tinge on the flanks, is worn only for a few weeks. It is succeeded by a plumage like that of the adult, save that there is a broad band of brown feathers formed by the lesser wing-coverts, and a black subterminal bar across the tail. The adult dress is assumed at the end of the first year. In the Kittiwake the juvenile plumage differs from that of the adult only in having the lesser wing-coverts black, and a black tail-bar.

THE TERNS

The Terns may be described as Gulls in miniature, but they differ in their much longer wings and deeply forked tails, hence the name Sea-swallows, and in their much shorter legs. The beak is also more often slender, and the webs of the toes are less developed. They differ also in their feeding habits, for the Gulls are largely scavengers, and the larger species, like the Black-backed Gulls, lay a heavy toll on the eggs of Guillemots and other cliff-breeding species. The Terns feed entirely on small fish and crustacea, which they seize by a downward plunge from mid-air, though they do not dive and swim under water as the Kittiwake is said occasionally to do.

For the most part the plumage is grey above, save the head and neck and under parts, which are white. But the crown of the head is nearly always black ; sometimes it extends back to the nape, but it never forms a hood, nor is it ever completely lost even in the winter.

As with the Gulls, these birds present some interesting and instructive departures from the type in the matter of coloration. Thus the White-winged Black-tern—a rare British species—in its breeding dress is black, save for the wings, which are pearl-grey, shading into white over the wrist-joint, and the tail and vent, which are white. In its winter dress the head, neck, and under parts are white, the back and wings grey. The tropical Noddy-tern (*Anous*) is another black species, but with a *white* crown, and is further remarkable for the fact that it nests in trees whenever these are available, building a large, flat nest of twigs, grass, and seaweed. Contrasting with this is the Snow-white *Gygis candida*, a bird with a wide range extending from Brazil to the Indian Ocean, the Malay countries, the Sandwich Islands, and Polynesia generally. It lays but one egg, and this is placed on any slight cavity of a branch, or broad leaf-stalk, or on a coral reef.

BEAK OF SCISSOR-BILL (*Rhynchops nigra*).

Some of the Terns, like some of the Gulls, in the breeding season have the breast suffused with a beautiful rose-pink, or in the Sandwich-tern, salmon-pink, which fades soon after death.

The Skimmers, or Scissor-bills (*Rhynchops*), are very near allies of the Terns, but they differ therefrom, and from all other known birds, in the extraordinary form of the beak. This is laterally compressed to the thinness of a paper-knife right up to the gape, where it expands to form the mouth. But more than this, the upper jaw is much shorter than the lower. To say that this extraordinary structure is intimately associated with the bird's method of feeding is merely to state a fact which affords not the slightest clue towards explaining the mode of its evolution. The Terns, it has been remarked, catch small fish and crustacea by a dive from mid-air ; the Scissor-bill, instead, flies low over the water with the beak open and the lower jaw submerged, so that its victims are, as it were, caught in a cleft stick.

In the nestling, it should be remarked, and in the fledgling, the jaws are of equal length; the lower does not start to increase its length until the power of flight has been gained. At first the nestling is fed on regurgitated food by the parents; as it grows older it runs about and forages for itself, which it would not be able to do unless the jaws were of equal length; as soon as the lower jaw has perceptibly lengthened beyond the upper, feeding is only possible when on the wing, after the fashion just described.

Three species of this bird are American, ranging from Virginia and the Carolinas to Argentina. One species extends from Senegal to Damaraland, and from Egypt to the Red Sea and Nyasaland, while there is an Indian species extending into Burma. The plumage is mostly black, and the beak red and orange.

Sub-order *Alcae*

(*Auks*)

Family Alcidae

As examples of the effects of " use," of the results of concentrated and restricted movements in relation to conditions imposed by the external environment, the Auk tribe—the Guillemots, Razor-bills, and Puffins—comprising the above family, are exceedingly instructive.

These birds might be described as gulls in disguise. Among the gulls at least one species, the Kittiwake, is said not only to dive, but to pursue its prey under water. This, however, is but an occasional incident. The Auk tribe, originally given to this mode of obtaining food, became, in consequence, more and more intensively aquatic, flying but little—no farther than from the breeding-ledges to the sea and back in the breeding season and on migratory flight. Swimming and diving, always and continuously, they have gradually undergone a transformation of their skeletal structures which, while fitting them still further for this kind of life, at the same time sapped their ability to move on land.

The most striking of these skeletal changes are seen in the great elongation of the breast-bone and pelvis; and the enormous increase in the length of the ribs, which, indeed, are longer than in any other birds, since they are produced backwards so as to completely reinforce the walls of the abdomen. The thigh has been greatly shortened, so as to bring the leg far backwards, and to cause the body to be held almost vertically when the bird is resting ashore. This backward shifting of the leg has secured greater propulsive power when the bird is swimming at the surface. But at the moment of diving the wings are opened and used as swimming organs, after the fashion of the flippers of the penguins.

We think of birds in terms of land birds; even when we have in mind such aquatic types as ducks and gulls. For these spend no inconsiderable part of their lives on land. But the Auk tribe, like the Petrels, are land-dwellers from necessity rather than choice. Come ashore they must to fulfil their parental duties, but these ended they make for the open sea, and this before their young are fully fledged. The storms of winter must be passed afloat, far out of sight of land, and of shelter they have none. Though after violent and protracted gales the dead bodies of these birds may be picked up on the beach by the dozen, it is not the fury of the waves that have overmastered them, but starvation. For owing to the profound disturbances of the upper layers of the water the fish on which they depend for sustenance have retreated to depths where they cannot be reached. Having regard to the fact that they spend no more than a few days of the whole year on dry land, there is small room for wonder at the profound modifications which the skeleton has undergone to meet these conditions.

But a single egg is laid by any member of this tribe, save the Black-guillemot, and this is of large size and pyriform.

The Common-guillemot is, perhaps, the best-known member of the Auk tribe, for on the Faroes, the chalk cliffs of Bempton and Flamborough, the stacks and crags of Scotland and Wales, they may be seen in serried ranks of thousands. The breeding dress, common to both sexes, differs mainly from the post-nuptial plumage in that the head, neck, and upper parts are of a sooty brown colour, the rest of the plumage being white.

The pyriform shape of the egg is excessively developed in the Guillemots, which make no nest, the egg being deposited on a bare ledge of rock often no more than a foot wide and hundreds of feet above the sea. Owing to its shape it is seldom blown off the ledge, the wind simply turning the egg round on its axis. But great numbers are knocked off by the birds if they leave the ledges suddenly. Another very remarkable feature of the Guillemot's egg is its extraordinary range of colour. No two are ever exactly alike, and some are of rare beauty. They may be blotched, spotted, or streaked with black and brown, some heavily and some slightly marked, on a background of green, or buff, or white; some are almost red in hue.

The much smaller Black-guillemot never associates in hordes such as is the rule with the Common-guillemot, and in no part of its range is it so numerous. But it differs not merely in its habits, but also in its coloration; the summer dress being black, with a large and very conspicuous white wing-patch, and crimson legs. The beak is black, but the inside of the mouth is crimson. It differs again from the Common-guillemot in laying two eggs, deposited in crevices on the cliff face or in a cave. As to its food it differs from both the Razor-bill and the other Guillemots, in that fish form but a negligible part of its diet, which is comprised mainly of small crustacea. There is a further point of interest about this bird, and this is the fact that the nuptial plumage shows a marked tendency to become a permanent dress, since only in some cases is the winter plumage assumed. This is white below and grey mottled with black above.

This little bird may be seen on the north coast of Scotland and the Hebrides, the Isle of Man, and Flamborough, and along the north and west coasts of Ireland.

The Guillemots and the Razor-bill are commonly found closely associated, and this because though so similar in their habits they do not compete with one another for any of the essentials of life. The Razor-bill, a smaller and darker bird, breeds on the same cliffs with the Guillemots, but seeks the shelter of overhanging ledges or crevices as a site for its nursery, though no nest whatever is made. Its egg, in consequence, is less pyriform in shape ; for there is no danger of its falling from the ledge. Yet in spite of the fact that its eggs are better guarded, it is outnumbered by the Guillemot. There

COMMON-GUILLEMOT (*Uria troile*) (Summer dress).

RAZOR-BILL (*Alca torda*) (Summer).

is a curious difference in the brooding methods of the two birds, by the way ; for the Guillemot sits almost upright on the egg, while the Razor-bill assumes a recumbent position.

The two birds do not compete for food, for the supply is inexhaustible. Both pursue and swallow their prey under water ; but when bringing fish to the surface for their young the Guillemot rarely carries in its beak more than one, while the Razor-bill will bring as many as a dozen, commonly small sand-eels. It may be that the very different form of the beak in the two birds accounts for this ; since in the Guillemots it is rather like a slender Gull's beak, while in the Razor-bill it is laterally compressed, but lacking the sharp triangle at the symphysis of the jaw, and marked by vertical grooves, the hindmost and deepest being lined with glistening white. At the autumn moult the raised fillet at the base of the upper jaw, and part of the sheath of the base of the lower jaw, is shed. In the breeding dress the head and neck and back are black, with a greenish gloss ; but in the winter dress the sides of the face and throat are white. It is worth noting that in the juvenile plumage the coloration of the head and neck closely resembles the breeding dress of the adult—a very unusual phenomenon.

The now extinct Great-auk may well be described as a giant Razor-bill, which, for some inexplicable reason, lost the power of flight. Off Newfoundland, and especially on Funk Island, between the sixteenth and seventeenth centuries, these birds were as numerous as Guillemots on our cliffs to-day. But they were mercilessly preyed upon by French sailors, who used to call here and load their boots with their plunder, salting the bodies down for food, till at last the aclonies were wiped out. A few stragglers survived, in various isolated spots, into the nineteenth century.

LITTLE-AUK (*Mergulus alle*).

In 1822 one was captured on St. Kilda, and in 1834 one was taken alive in Waterford Harbour.

While the Great-auk was the largest, the Little-auk is the smallest of the Auk tribe, measuring no more than eight inches in length. Though one of our British birds, it is only found on our shores in a moribund condition after severe storms. Like the Black-guillemot, it feeds mainly on small crustacea ; but it is interesting to note that while these two species agree so closely in the matter of their food they differ in a very striking way in the form of their beaks, for in the Little-auk this is conspicuously short, recalling that of the Adeliae penguin.

Nearly related are the Pacific Pigmy-auks. One of these is remarkable for the fact that the forehead is surmounted by a large and fairly stiff crest of feathers, curled forwards. This is a very singular ornament for a bird which has to swim under water for its food, since one would suppose that it must materially hamper progress, " stream-lining " being the rule in all birds and beasts which swim under rather than on the surface.

The Common-puffin, or Sea-parrot (*Fratercula arctica*), is a peculiarly interesting bird, not only on account of the singular appearance given by its huge, laterally compressed, and gaily coloured beak, and the red, fleshy rosette at the angle of the mouth, but also because, though it leads precisely the same mode of life as the Guillemots and Auks, it is yet less highly specialised. Its legs are placed less far backwards, so that it can walk easily, and when standing it holds the body almost horizontally. In addition to the highly ornamental beak, coloured blue, red, and yellow, the upper eyelid develops at the breeding season a short, triangular, horny process, while embedded in the lower lid is a similar horny plate, oblong in shape. These, with the two gaily coloured triangular plates at the base of the beak, are shed at the autumn moult. Finally the claw of the hind-toe is curiously elongated and curved, though what purpose it serves has yet to be discovered.

PUFFIN (*Fratercula arctica*).

This bird lives in burrows at the tops of cliffs or on turf-covered islands, in thousands. Commonly such breeding-places are covered with masses of pink thrift, and to see these really beautiful birds standing in the sunlight amid this natural flower-garden is an experience never to be forgotten. On the wing the short, orange-coloured legs are held out on each side of the tail, giving a very curious appearance. But one egg is laid, and this is encrusted with a layer of white, chalky material, which when removed reveals below it markings characteristic of the eggs of the Auk tribe. This white layer has probably been evolved to make the egg at least dimly visible in the recesses of the dark burrow. When feeding the young, the bird will bring six or seven fish at a time, commonly sand-eels, held cross-wise in its beak. How the bird manages to catch and hold so many at a time is a mystery.

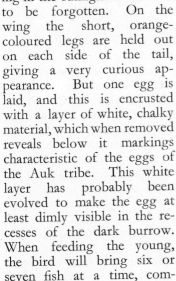

HEAD OF THE PUFFIN, showing the parts of the beak-sheath, which are shed at the autumn moult.

Z 2

Sub-order *PTEROCLES*

(*Sand-grouse*)

With respect to the Sand-grouse and Pigeons, the older ornithologists could do no more than guess at their affinities. But now that a careful study has been made of their anatomy, there can be no more doubt; for it is clear that they are to be regarded as members of the Plover tribe—using this term in its widest sense. But they are "collateral branches" which split off from the main stem at an early period in its development, as may be seen in the Tree of Descent.

The nestling Sand-grouse is of the nidifugous type, in this contrasting with the Pigeons, wherein newly hatched birds are blind and naked, and at no time are more than sparsely covered with a few hair-like threads of down.

The Sand-grouse are all dwellers in desert country, and have short legs and powerful wings; and they are seed-eaters. The Pigeons, on the other hand, are primarily arboreal, and this fact has to be taken into account when considering the condition of the young at birth.

The Sand-grouse form a relatively small group, divided into two sections, one having lost the hind-toe, and one retaining it, though very small. Their phenomenal powers of flight are, so to speak, registered in the form of the sternum, which has

PIN-TAILED SAND-GROUSE (*Pteroclurus exustus*).

an enormously deep keel; but the furcula, or "merry-thought," is reduced to a mere loop of bone widely separated from the keel, a feature also of the Pigeons. Their prowess on the wing is to be attributed to the great distances which commonly have to be traversed night and morning. Indeed, only birds of exceptional wing-power could inhabit these arid wastes. Its importance to the survival of the race is demonstrated in a very striking way during the breeding season.

Though Sand-grouse chicks are able to run about and feed with their parents when but a few hours old, their journeys are of necessity limited, for as yet the wings have not developed; but they *must* drink, and as it is impossible to get the youngsters to the water, commonly many miles distant, it must be brought to them. And this is done by the male, who, after slaking his own thirst, soaks the feathers of his breast and then flies back. The young rush up to receive him, and " drink " by passing his wet feathers through their beaks! There is an element of "reasoning" about this procedure on the part of the male that is worthy of the attention of psychologists.

Pallas's Sand-grouse (*Syrrhaptes paradoxus*) is a sporadic visitor to the British Islands, arriving on such occasions in great numbers. In 1863, 1888, and 1908 there were remarkable irruptions. The largest number came in 1888, when a special Act of Parliament was passed for their protection, in the hope that these aliens would settle down with us. A few pairs, indeed, did hatch out young, but there was evidently some necessary element of their environment wanting, and so by 1892 all had vanished.

Pallas's Sand-grouse, a native of the Mongolian steppes, is one of the handsomest of the group, the upper parts being of a bright sand colour, barred with black. The sides of the face and throat are rust-coloured; the breast is greyish-buff, with a narrow band of black in front and a black patch behind. The wing has buff coverts, and lavender-grey primaries which are produced into long points, while the tail has the middle feathers elongated to form long, slender filaments. The feet, which are feathered right down to the claws, are remarkable for the fact that the toes are set in a large pad, admirably adapted for travelling over sand. But they are not good runners, wherein they differ conspicuously from the Indian Painted Sand-grouse.

Always Sand-grouse seem to live in large flocks. In North-West India the Pin-tailed Sand-grouse (*Pteroclurus alchatis*) may be found, in winter, in tens of thousands. But the common African species (*P. exustus*) is nowhere met with in such numbers.

Sub-order COLUMBAE

(*Pigeons*)

The Pigeons are vastly more interesting birds than most people seem to realise, for they furnish object lessons in evolution of a very striking character. They are, as has already been pointed out, highly specialised members of the Plover tribe; but they have now as completely lost all likeness to the True Plovers as have the Auk tribe or the Gulls. In the Auks we have adaptation to an intensively aquatic life. In the Pigeons we have adaptations to an arboreal life, but displaying many departures therefrom, and developing modifications specially adapted to such departures.

There is no need to describe the general appearance of a pigeon, but its "individuality" has come about mainly, we may take it, as a consequence of the adoption of a vegetarian diet in place of animal food, such as is consumed by the typical plovers. This withdrew them from the seashore and inland waters, and induced a habit of perching in trees, whither a resort is made partly for security and partly for food. As a consequence the legs have become reduced in length, while the hind-toe has retained its primitive position at the level of the front-toes. The vegetarian diet has brought about the development of a conspicuously large, bilobed crop, capable of holding a large amount of broken leaves, seeds, and berries, to be carried from the danger-zone and quietly digested. The beak, which has to collect this food, still retains a plover-like form, the end being noticeably thickened, and the base somewhat constricted.

Finally, they have no down-feathers, nor any visible powder-down patches, though the plumage, especially in species like the Wood-pigeon, is imperceptibly covered with the peculiar smooth, Fuller's-earth-like powder always associated with such patches and their disintegration. Few people seem to be aware of this peculiarity. But take a feather and firmly and evenly press it against a sheet of glass. When the feather is removed an exact impress of its form will be found on the glass, made by this powder the source of which has yet to be discovered.

The nidicolous condition of the young is to be traced to the development of the arboreal habit. Active young, hatched in the tree-tops, would rarely survive till their flight-feathers had grown. By curtailment of the amount of food-yolk within the egg a kind of premature birth results, so that from the consequent helplessness of the chick no endeavour to leave the nest is made till the wings have developed.

THE DODO

If the Dodo, now extinct, is very unlike a pigeon, it is as certainly unlike any other bird. Having at some remote period settled in the Island of Mauritius, and finding there an abundance of food on the ground, no enemies, and an equable climate, it had no inducement to fly, and in course of time became flightless, its wings degenerating to mere vestiges, and the keel of its sternum reduced to the vanishing-point. In this island retreat it found some sort of " Food of the Gods," for it attained to a great size, equal to that of a turkey, while its beak enlarged enormously, though still retaining the characteristic features of its tribe. From the pictures drawn from the living bird by Roelandt Savory, in the early part of the seventeenth century, it would seem that the tail-quills of this bird had become reduced to vestiges, leaving only the large, loose, upper and under tail-coverts, giving a very singular appearance to the hinder end of the body.

The earliest notice of this bird that we have dates from records by the Dutch in 1598, by whom it was known as the *Walgh Vogel*, or Nauseous-bird, from their dislike of its flesh. It was then abundant, but the introduction of pigs into the island seems to have led to its speedy extermination ; for it could not avoid pursuit, nor save its eggs or young from their ravages.

Another and very singular relative of the Dodo is the Solitaire (*Pezophaps*), of Rodriguez. This was also flightless, but very different in appearance, having a long neck and long legs, while the beak was more like that of a gallinaceous bird than that of a pigeon. What were the factors prevailing in this island which could have given rise to the striking physical differences which obtain between this bird and the Dodo ? The Solitaire is furthermore remarkable for the fact that, unlike all the known pigeons, the wrist-joint of the wing was armed with a bony exostosis, " as large as a musket-ball," according to Leguat, who resided in the island from 1691 to 1693, and gave a lively account of its habits.

This cestus-like weapon was used by the males in fighting rivals during the breeding season, and as they stood nearly three feet high, and weighed from forty to fifty pounds, the blows they struck were probably severe. This much, indeed, is attested by the fact that of the innumerable skeletal remains in the various museums of Paris, London, and Cambridge, many

SKELETON OF DODO.

SKELETON OF SOLITAIRE.

show evidence of the wing-bones having been broken and reunited. Such injuries entirely confirm Leguat's descriptions of these duels for mastery, when the birds " whirled round one another," making a loud noise with their wings. It is also to be remembered that pigeons, the world over, use their wings in fighting.

The nest was no less remarkable for one of the Pigeon tribe, since it was formed of a heap of palm-leaves, eighteen inches high, in a hollow of which the single white egg was laid.

Another remarkable pigeon, generally assigned the rank of a family in itself (*Didunculidae*), is the Tooth-billed Pigeon of Samoa ; and this because of its large orange-coloured beak, which, however, is much more like that of some raptorial bird than that of the Dodo. The plumage is of a glossy black colour, with a chestnut back, wing-coverts, and tail. The red legs are conspicuously long, hence marking an adaptation to a terrestrial life. When first discovered in 1839 it was said to be verging on extinction owing to the introduction of cats and rats, its nest being placed on the ground. But it is said to have recovered in numbers, owing to a change of habits, the nest now being placed high up in trees. The fact that it feeds on berries, plantains, and yam-fruits probably accounts for the shape of the beak, which recalls that of the African Plantain-eaters (*Musophagi*).

TOOTH-BILLED PIGEON (*Didunculus strigirostris*).

Family Columbidae

Of the remaining pigeons forming the family *Columbidae*, and numbering round about five hundred species, no more than a general survey can be given. Nor is there need for more, since the differences between them are chiefly those of size and coloration.

They may be divided into Ground-pigeons and Tree-pigeons. The former, in consequence of their terrestrial mode of life, have conspicuously long legs. The large and extremely handsome blue-grey Crowned-pigeons of the genus *Goura*, the largest living pigeons, natives of New Guinea, are very striking-looking birds, owing to

VICTORIA CROWNED-PIGEON (*Goura victoria*).

the huge "crest" of loose plumes which surmounts the head. Two species (*G. victoria*, of Jobi, and *G. beccarii*, of Central and North New Guinea) have spatulate tips to these feathers.

The Nicobar-pigeon (*Calaenas nicobarica*) is another very singular type of these long-legged Ground-pigeons. The whole plumage is of a glossy black, with metallic reflections ; and the splendour of the coloration is further enhanced by the elongation of the neck-feathers, which hang down like the " hackles " of a Game-cock.

We come now to familiar species, such as our native Turtle-dove, Stock-dove, Rock-pigeon, and Wood-pigeon. These are too well known to need description. Special mention, however, must be made of the Rock-dove. Unlike its congeners it is a cliff-dweller. It is, furthermore, the ancestor of our own domesticated pigeons ; hence the fact that they never perch in trees, and nest so readily in " dove-cotes " ; for these are to them the equivalent of the caves and crannies chosen by their wild ancestors as nurseries.

NUTMEG-PIGEON (*Myristicivora bicolor*).

A further point of some importance is the fact that no other species has proved so amenable to domestication, or so plastic. Recall for a moment the amazing variety of types that man has brought into being out of this type, notably the Pouter, with its enormously enlarged crop and upright carriage, and the Fan-tail, with its greatly multiplied tail-feathers. In some breeds the legs have developed long, quill-like feathers, sweeping the ground on each side. All pigeons have a thickened rim to the eyelids, and a soft area of skin forming an operculum to the nostrils. The pigeon-fancier has enlarged these till, in the Carrier-pigeon, they assume enormous rosettes unlike anything ever seen in Nature. These facts deserve more attention than they have yet received.

The Stock-dove, by the way, nests in holes in trees, crevices in a rock face, or in rabbit burrows. Occasionally it will adopt the deserted nests of other birds and squirrel dreys.

PASSENGER-PIGEON (*Ectopistes migratorius*).

A melancholy interest attaches to the Passenger-pigeon (*Ectopistes migratorius*), for this bird is now as extinct as the Dodo. That this fate could ever have overtaken it seems incredible, having regard to its former abundance which far exceeded that of any other known pigeon.

The naturalist Wilson, about 1808, estimated the number of a colony which he saw at more than 2300 millions. As late as 1878 a "roost" of these birds at Petosky, in Michigan, occupied an area twenty-eight miles long by three or four broad. But during the nesting season they were remorselessly netted for the market, and in a few years their numbers were so reduced as to make their capture unprofitable. By this time, however, the species was so reduced in numbers as to make recovery impossible, and the inevitable end followed.

The "Fruit-pigeons" include a formidable number of species. Resplendent colours are the rule among them, though green is the predominant hue. An exception to the rule is found in the beautiful Nutmeg-pigeon (*Myristicivora bicolor*), which is pure white, with black flight-feathers and a black bar across the end of the tail. It is a large bird, a native of the Malay Archipelago.

Of the smaller Fruit-pigeons, perhaps the most lovely is the Fijian *Chrysaenas victor*, the male of which is of a gorgeous and vivid orange colour, with an olive-yellow head and throat, while the female is green, with a yellowish head.

CHAPTER X

Legion *CORACIOMORPHAE*

(*Raven-like Birds*)

WE are to survey now the fourth, and last, "Legion" of the Class Aves. The first included the Divers, Penguins and Petrels; the second the Storks, Swans, Geese and Ducks, and Birds of Prey; the third the Game-birds, Crane tribe, and Plover tribe.

Under the Coraciomorphae are included all the birds which have descended from the lowermost, right-hand branch, shown in the Tree of Descent (see p. 567). They are sub-divided into the Opisthocomiformes, which order includes the Plantain-eaters, Cuckoos, and Parrots; the Coraciiformes, including Rollers, Bee-eaters, Kingfishers, and Hornbills; Night-jars and Owls; Barbets and Woodpeckers; and finally what are known as the Passeriformes.

We must, in short, regard the Coraciomorphae as direct descendants from that primitive arboreal stock, of which Archaeopteryx is the type. No remains have yet come to light of types contemporary with Archaeopteryx, which even then must have begun to swarm out into the waste places of the earth, taking possession of the territory outside the forests and developing, as they became adapted to the varying environments constituted by lakes and rivers, the seashore, and the uplands, into waders, swimmers, and divers, birds of prey, and so on.

The Coraciiformes are possibly of even more ancient lineage than the Galliformes. Valuable connecting links are furnished by that strange bird the Hoatzin and the Plantain-eaters, which, with the Cuckoos and the Parrots, here constitute the Opisthocomiformes, which may be sub-divided into three sub-orders—*Opisthocomi*, *Cuculi*, and *Psittaci*.

Order OPISTHOCOMIFORMES

Sub-order OPISTHOCOMI

(*Hoatzin and Plantain-eaters*)

The primitive nature of the Hoatzin is shown by the fact that by some systematists it has been placed with the Game-birds, by others with the Rails ; but here, for the first time, it is definitely associated with the Plantain-eaters. A discussion as to the reasons for this would be profitless. Let the life-history of the bird explain at one and the same time its essential anatomical characters and the trend of its evolution, as well as the evidence for its association with the Game-birds.

The Hoatzin, a native of the Amazon Valley, is of the size of, say, a wood-pigeon, with a long, broad tail, short legs, enormous feet, and a beak like that of a Touracou, both in its shape and also in having serrations along the cutting edge of the upper jaw. The head is surmounted by a crest ; and the coloration is of a dark olive, with white streaks above and rufous below. It is a strictly arboreal bird, with a slow and laboured flight, and is restricted to trees bordering river banks, where it finds in abundance its staple food, the fruit of an aroid (*Montrichardia*), and the fruit and leaves of the prickly *Drepanocarpus lunulatus*. Instead of being passed, after softening, to the gizzard, the

HOATZIN (*Opisthocomus hoatzin*).

food is retained and broken up in the crop, which, as a consequence, has developed thick, muscular walls, a feature found in no other bird. This transformation of the crop has had a curious sequel, for its slight but persistent pressure, when distended against the anterior border of the keel of the sternum, has reduced the keel to a small bony triangle at the extreme hinder portion of the sternal plate, a process accompanied by declining powers of flight. Here we have an illustration of the "Transmission of Acquired Characters," albeit the process has required unnumbered generations.

We pass now to the consideration of the nestling. This, though hatched in an arboreal nest, is of the nidifugous type—though the pre-pennae are unusually weak and loose for a nidifugous bird—and extremely active, the youngsters leaving the nest and climbing about the trees while awaiting the arrival of their parents with food. Should one fall into the water, for the nest is always overhanging water, it will promptly swim ashore and climb back to the nest, using beak, wings, and feet.

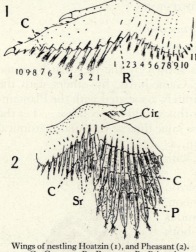

Wings of nestling Hoatzin (1), and Pheasant (2).
C = Covert; R = Remex; P = Primaries;
Sr = Secondaries; Cir = Carpal remex.

The wings, at this stage, present some remarkable features; they have, indeed, preserved conditions which are met with again only in the ancient Archaeopteryx. Briefly, at this stage the hand is longer than the fore-arm, and has the thumb and second finger furnished with a long claw, while the finger-tip forms a sensitive pad which plays an important part in grasping boughs. The wing-feathers are the first to make their appearance, but the growth of the four terminal primaries is inhibited until the inner quills are long enough to break the force of a fall from the tree; as soon as this stage is reached the terminal feathers make their appearance. The claws are then rapidly absorbed, and finally disappear, by which time the hand has slowed down its rate of growth, till, in the adult, instead of being longer it is shorter than the forearm.

The reason for the inhibition of the external primaries is plain. If all the quills grew at the same rate the outermost would soon render the claw of the second digit ineffective, while the inner quills were still too small to serve even as an incipient wing. At the stage immediately preceding the growth of the outermost primaries the wing of the young Hoatzin resembles that of the adult Archaeopteryx; that is to say, the index finger projects beyond the wing-quills. This was the permanent condition of the wing in Archaeopteryx, because, like some modern birds, the wing-quills at the annual moult were all shed at once, so that for a time the wing had to be used as a climbing organ.

More yet has to be told. The wing of the young pheasant or partridge shows a precisely similar sequence of development; that is to say, the outermost remiges have their development held in abeyance till the inner quills have grown large enough to half raise the body from the ground, when the chick is trying to escape to shelter on a threat of danger. But here only the claw on the thumb is present, that of the index finger being absorbed before hatching; but the finger-tip still projects beyond the wing-quills.

Now, this sequence of growth is unintelligible in a ground-dwelling bird, but it acquires a meaning directly we realise that the Game-birds were once strictly arboreal, living in trees, and not on the ground as do the Partridges, for instance. The Pheasants are still partly arboreal. Finally, we find the same order of events in the young of the Plantain-eaters, or Touracous, of Africa; to which, it is contended here, the Hoatzin is most nearly related. The occurrence of the same phenomena in gallinaceous birds, the Hoatzin and Touracous, points to inheritance from a common source, before any of these groups had assumed the forms we know to-day.

Family Musophagi

The Touracous, or Plantain-eaters, are represented by some two dozen species, ranging from fifteen to thirty inches in length, and confined to African forest country, near inland or tidal waters. They have long necks and tails, and short, rounded wings, a short, arched beak, with serrated cutting edges, and semi-zygodactyle feet; that is to say, the outer toe can be turned backwards, when it resembles the permanent condition of the Cuckoos and some other birds. The tops of the trees are their favourite haunts, and their flight is undulatory. When they alight the tail is turned upwards, a characteristic also of the Hoatzin. Their food consists of bananas, tamarinds, paw-paw apples, and other fruits, insects, and molluscs.

WHITE-BELLIED TOURACOU (*Schizorhis leucogaster*).

All save one species are crested, and for the most part they are brilliantly coloured. The East African *Turacus fischeri* is green, washed with blue on the wings and tail, with a crimson hind-neck and white nape, and blackish chest and abdomen. The flight-feathers are crimson, edged with black, and the eyes are red. The Violet Touracou of West Africa is violet-blue, with a crimson crown and hind-neck, and with a broad frontal, horny sheath to the yellow beak. The South African *Schizorhis concolor*, however, is of an almost uniform ash colour.

The crimson coloration of the wings is remarkable for the fact that it yields a pigment, "Turacin," containing copper, which is reducible to a powder, as was shown by the late Sir William Church. Why this strange pigment should be found *only* in the quill-feathers and *only* in the Touracous, yet remains to be discovered.

Sub-order CUCULI

(Cuckoos)

The affinities of the Cuckoos seem unquestionably to be with the *Musophagi*, and more distantly with the Parrots. Like the Touracous they are arboreal, and they have permanently acquired what in the Touracous is a

RENAULT'S GROUND-CUCKOO
(*Carpococcyx renaulti*).

variable character, that is to say, a zygodactyle foot. In this connection it is interesting to note that while some species have adopted a terrestrial mode of life they still retain this "yoke-foot," though they have in every case acquired long legs, for it is to be remembered that short legs are the rule with tree-dwellers, as also with species which spend most of their time on the wing.

The "Road-runner" (*Geococcyx*), of the South-West States of America and Mexico, two species of Radiated Ground-cuckoos of Borneo (*Carpococcyx*) and Sumatra, and the "Coucals" and Crow-pheasants of the genus *Centropus*, numbering more than thirty species, are of this long-legged type, and all have the habit, when alighting after a flight, of jerking the tail upwards, as in Opisthocomes and the Touracous. These birds feed on insects and their larvae, molluscs, reptiles, small mammals, and very young birds.

Since there are more than a hundred and sixty species of Cuckoos known to science, it would be profitless to describe them all, especially since the differences between them in many cases are slight. In the matter of plumage they may be described at large as brownish or grey in coloration, and commonly with barred under parts. But many species of the genus *Chrysococcyx* and *Chalcococcyx* have developed singularly beautiful emerald-green forms, which have a brilliant metallic lustre.

Surniculus lugubris, ranging from India and China and Malay Islands, *Cuculus clamosus*, and the Anis (*Crotophaga*) of America, are black. The

Curly-crested Cuckoo (*Lepidogrammus*) has a very singular crest, shaped like the upper segment of a mill-stone, the side being white, the flat periphery black. *Coccystes*, and several species of *Guira*, are crested. The extraordinary Channel-billed Cuckoo (*Scythrops*), of Australia and Papuasia, has an enormous beak. It flies like a hawk, and is believed to be parasitic. Its note is described as a weird shriek. The American White-ani, *Guira guira*, is brown and buff above, with darker streaks, and paler buff below. In its general appearance it is curiously reminiscent of the Hoatzin, but it has no crest.

What is, for most of us, the typical Cuckoo, is the bird which comes to us each year in the spring, and lends such charm to the days of late spring and early summer by its oft-repeated cry of " Cuckoo-Cuckoo." Of its general appearance there is no need to speak, nor is there any necessity to enlarge upon its habit of foisting its eggs upon other birds, and so evading all parental duties. The cause of this strange behaviour yet awaits solution. The rhythm of the procreative instincts has been broken, and new and puzzling divergencies from that rhythm have been interpolated. The break in the normal sequence occurs with the failure of the instincts to provide a nest for the eggs. They are replaced by a perverted instinct to place the eggs, as they are laid, in some other nest ; but for this the species would have been extinct long since.

The failure of this instinct may be due to the fact that in these parasitic species the males far outnumber the females. As a consequence, apparently, the female pairs first

WHITE ANI-CUCKOO (*Guira guira*).

with one male, then with another ; it can settle down with none. This constant and avid search for a mate kills the normal sequence of behaviour in the male which usually assists in nest-building and the care of the offspring.

This excess of males, or polyandry, it is significant to note, has a parallel in its opposite, or polygamy, where the females are in excess. Here, as in some of the Game-birds, the whole care of the young devolves on the female ; and here, too, we find two females will occasionally lay their eggs in the same nest, sharing the duties, we assume, of incubation. In the American Cuckoos of the genus *Guira* and of *Crotophaga*—known as the " Ani-cuckoos "—a number of females combine to build a large nest which they share in common, each bird deposits about five eggs, and the mothers huddle together to incubate them. But their maternal instincts are evidently crumbling, for they will build so flimsily that the eggs may fall through the bottom of the nest, as they are laid, without exciting their concern, or they will carelessly lay and leave their eggs outside the nest. These aberrant habits, however, are not confined to the Cuckoos. They are shared by some of the Passerine birds to be described later.

The diabolical pertinacity displayed by the young of our Common-cuckoo in ousting its foster-brothers and sisters from the nest is not developed by the young of the Great-spotted Cuckoo—an occasional visitant to Great Britain. This bird lays its eggs in the nests of crows ; and it will lay two or more eggs in each nest. The young cuckoos make no attempt to oust the young crows from the nest. There is good reason for this. For young crows are fed on a highly satisfying food—flesh, in the form of mice and carrion. Small caterpillars and flies, which is all the young of the Common-cuckoo can get, could not be gathered in sufficient quantity to satisfy its demands if the meals had to be shared with three or four other youngsters.

GREAT-SPOTTED CUCKOO (*Coccystes glandarius*).

There are some species of Cuckoos which are only occasionally parasitic. Thus the Hawk-cuckoo (*Hierococcyx sparveroides*), of the Himalayas and East Asia, seems to be usually parasitic, but in the Nilgiris it builds a nest and rears its young. Finally the " Lark-heeled " Cuckoos of the genus *Centropus*—so called because the claw of the hind-toe is elongated like that of a lark—builds a large globular nest with an entrance at one side.

Our Common-cuckoo is perhaps the only bird which has continued to find palatable morsels in the great hairy caterpillars of the Tiger-moth. These hairs are found forming a thick lining, as of felt, in the gizzard.

Sub-order *PSITTACI*

(*Parrots*)

That the Parrots are to be regarded as more nearly related to Plantain-eaters, or Touracous, and the Cuckoos, than to the " Coraciae " to be described presently, there can be no question. Much of the evidence as to their affinities has been masked by the extreme specialisation which they have undergone.

The most conspicuous evidence of the intense specialisation of the Parrots is to be found in the skull, which presents features found in no other birds. The palatine bones, for example, take the shape of great laterally compressed beams, formed in response to the use of the beak as a shearing organ. Their function is to thrust up the upper-jaw, used for climbing purposes, and for seizing and slicing fruits, and hard nuts and seeds; though some of the Cockatoos dig for tubers and bulbs. The modification of the bones of the palate has been accompanied by a very perfect hinge-joint formed between the frontal bones and the beak. The lower jaw, again, is remarkable for its great depth; and in the living bird these jaws are ensheathed in a very dense horny case, the upper jaw terminating in a strong, sharp hook, the lower in a truncated, almost chisel-like plate. Furthermore, the under side of the hook of the upper jaw is curiously striated to form what is known as the " file," the pattern formed by such striation varying in different groups.

OWL-PARROT (*Stringops habroptilus*).

The toes are zygodactyle, and the legs are, as is the rule with strictly arboreal birds, very short. But there are some ground-dwellers, and here the legs are longer. But from the fact that the foot is zygodactyle we may gather that these ground-dwellers acquired their long legs comparatively recently.

All have powder-down feathers on the neck, shoulders, and sides; and in some, as in the African-parrot, so familiar as a cage-bird, the disintegration of these feathers is considerable, investing the plumage and the beak with a " bloom " recalling that of the grape. With one exception all breed in hollow trees, and the young are of the nidicolous type.

More than five hundred species are known, and most are of resplendent coloration. The headquarters of Parrots are in the Australian region and the Malay countries, which possess the majority of genera and species; next follow the tropical areas of South America. India and Africa have but few species.

Probably one of the oldest members of this family is the Owl-parrot, or Kakapo (*Stringops*), of New Zealand. Its coloration, sap-green, with touches of yellow, invests it with a mantle of invisibility, and it is further protected from its enemies by its nocturnal habits. It would seem that the custom of hiding by day in holes has been comparatively recently necessitated by the introduction of new enemies, for this bird is flightless, and the keel of the sternum has almost disappeared, showing that the loss of flight is of very long standing, and could only have taken place when there were no enemies to be avoided. It feeds on mosses, berries, seeds, and even lizards. Alpine districts and open forests are its haunts ; and here, in burrows, under tree-roots and rocks, with no attempt at a nest, it deposits its eggs, two or three in number. The name " Owl-parrot," by the way, has been bestowed from the fact that the feathers of the face have a disc-like arrangement suggestive of that of the owls.

The Australian *Geopsittacus occidentalis* of South and West Australia, and *Pezoporus formosus* of these regions and Tasmania, are nearly related to the *Stringops*, and of similar coloration, but though not flightless they rarely resort to trees, and trust to their great running powers to evade their enemies. They also, like *Stringops*, depart from the usual haunts of Parrots, the forests, and frequent sandy plains or marshy districts, laying two or three eggs on a bedding of grass and rushes, in tussocks of herbage.

The exceptions which prove the rule are always interesting. Further illustrations of this kind, in regard to sites for nurseries, are found in the case of the South Australian Rock-parakeet (*Neophema petrophila*), which breeds in holes in the steep faces of cliffs, near water, and in the South African Love-bird (*Agapornis roseicollis*), which commonly breeds in the nests of Weaver-birds.

No less remarkable is the case of the South American Monk-parrot, or Quaker-parrot (*Myiopsittacus monachus*), which builds a large covered nest of thorny twigs, high up in a tree, with a vestibule and inner chamber in which the eggs, six to eight in number, are laid. This nest, by the way, is also used as a shelter throughout the year, and is sometimes taken possession of by Opossums. A tree may often contain several of these nests, communicating with one another, and containing enough material to fill a cart. No other parrot builds after this fashion.

Commonly the sexes, among the Parrots, differ little in coloration, but in the genus *Eclectus*, extending from the Moluccas to the Solomon Archipelago, the males are green, the females red. In the Red-sided *Eclectus* the male is green and red, the female bright red and blue.

The largest and most gorgeously coloured of the Parrot tribe are the Macaws, of which some fifteen or more species are known. All are birds of powerful flight, and restricted to the great forests of Central and South America. The great Red-and-green, the Blue-and-yellow, and the beautiful Hyacinthine-macaws are some of the many species to be seen in the Gardens of the Zoological Society of London. Their enormous and powerful beaks enable them to break open hard-shelled nuts and stones of fruit with ease.

Near akin to the Macaws are the Cockatoos, restricted to the Australian region, the Philippine and Sulu Islands. The general appearance of such familiar cage-birds needs no description. But special mention must be made of the enormous beak of the Great Black-cockatoo (*Microglossus aterrimus*) of the Aru Islands. It feeds on fruits and seeds of various kinds, but especially on the kernel of the Kanary-nut (*Canarium commune*), the shell of which is so hard as to need a heavy hammer to crack it. But this bird accomplishes the feat with ease by means of its massive beak. Taking the nut, smooth and triangular in shape, end-ways in its beak, and keeping it steady by means of an un- usually slender and fleshy tongue, red in colour and tipped with a black, horny plate, it cuts a transverse notch in the shell by a sawing motion of the chisel-like edge of the tip of the lower jaw. This done, the nut is seized with the foot, and, biting off a piece of a leaf, it uses this to prevent the smooth shell from slipping, and fixes the tip of the lower jaw in the newly made notch, when by a powerful nip it breaks off a piece of the shell. Again transferring the nut to the foot it inserts the long, sharp-pointed tip of the upper jaw into the hole, and picks out the coveted kernel with the long extensible tongue.

RED-AND-BLUE MACAW (*Ara macao*).

The moulding effects of use in producing closely similar modifications of structure in unrelated organisms is well shown in the case of the Lories, or Brush-tongued parrots. For these birds derive a large part of their food by sucking nectar from flowers. And to this end the tip of the tongue has become either fringed or, by an enlargement of the fringe, tipped with a pencil of hairs, such as are found again in the Humming-birds and Sun- birds. It is true that when the tongues of these several types are closely compared there will be found manifest differences, but these are of degree rather than of kind.

HEAD OF GREAT BLACK-COCKATOO (*Microglossus aterrimus*).

But in this matter of the tongue, and in that the " file " of the beak is longi- tudinally striated, they differ from all the other Parrots.

The Lories are divided into three sections, or sub-families—the true

Lories (*Loriinae*), the Lorilets (*Cyclopsittacinae*), and the Kaka-parrots (*Nestorniae*).

The Lories and the Lorilets are, for the most part, of vivid and striking coloration, commonly presenting strongly contrasting masses of red, blue, and yellow. But there are some notable departures from this type, thus *Coriphilus taitianus* of the Society Islands is dark blue, with white under parts ; *C. ultramarinus* of the Marquesas combines dark with light blue.

Of the Parrots of the genus *Nestor* there are but two living species : *N. norfolcensis* of Norfolk Island, and *N. productus* of Philip Island, being now extinct. *N. notabilis*, the Kea-parrot, of the south island of New Zealand, is somewhat soberly coloured for a parrot, the general hue being of an olive-green, with blackish markings ; but there are blue and yellow areas on the wings and tail, and a scarlet rump and under-wing feathers. Of late years this bird has attained an unenviable notoriety. During the summer it lives among the rugged slopes of high, snowy mountains, but descends to the lowlands for the winter. No inconsiderable part of the food seems to be furnished by insects, and before the invasion of the sheep-farmer these were probably its only source of animal matter. But during recent years it has apparently become addicted to attacking sheep, and at times may inflict serious damage. The bird fastens on to the hind-quarters of the victim and, digging through the wool, tears at the flesh of the loins with the formidable beak, inflicting wounds which may ultimately cause death.

KEA-PARROT (*Nestor notabilis*).

Doubtless the extent of the Keas' raids has been exaggerated; nevertheless, their presence on a sheep-farm is undesirable. This unfortunate habit is said to have been acquired by birds which were tempted to peck at sheep-skins hanging outside country stations. Others suggest that they first gained their taste for mutton by digging down into the wool for insects, mistaking the sheep for the large mound-like masses of lichen, native to the country, which were commonly explored for the sake of the insects found there. But be this as it may, the extinction of the species is a foregone conclusion unless the habit can be checked before it spreads to every individual of the species.

Order CORACIIFORMES
(*Rollers, Bee-eaters, Kingfishers, etc.*)

A strangely diverse assemblage is included under this heading, though all are unquestionably derivatives of a common ancestral stock. They are divisible into four more or less distinct groups : the Rollers (*Coracidae*), Bee-eaters (*Meropidae*), Kingfishers (*Alcedinidae*), and the Hornbills (*Upupidae*); the Owls, Night-jars, Swifts, Colies, Humming-birds ; the Trogons, Barbets, Toucans, and Woodpeckers.

But it is rather with the outstanding types of each of these groups that we are concerned here, than with the several species they embrace, for even if each of them could be shown in its natural colours their description would make but barren reading.

The Rollers, Bee-eaters, and Kingfishers are remarkable for the beauty of their plumage, and at the same time they display some striking modifications of structure in relation to their mode of life.

Sub-order CORACIAE
(*Rollers, Motmots, Kingfishers, Bee-eaters, Hoopoes, Hornbills*)

Although one species of Roller (*Coracias garrulus*) is an occasional visitor to Great Britain, this group of birds is unfamiliar to most people. Apparently the most ancient member thereof is the singular Kirombo of Madagascar and the Comoro Islands. The male, which bears a crest, has the upper parts grey, glossed with green and coppery-red reflexions, and white under parts, while the slightly larger female is chocolate-brown above, with buff markings, and spotted below, after the fashion of a mistle-thrush, on a yellow ground. In both sexes there is a powder-down patch on the lower part of the back.

The Kirombo is said to be very noisy during the day, uttering a call-note like " tu-hou " thrice repeated, and either while hovering in the air or in descending, vertical fashion. Meanwhile the wings are struck against the body and the throat puffed out like a bag. It is found in companies of a dozen or more in the forests, and feeding on grasshoppers, chamaeleons, and lizards. The males apparently outnumber the females.

The true or typical Rollers number some twenty or more species, all of which are vividly coloured. Brilliant blues and greens, and washes of red-brown, with here and there touches of black, are the prevailing tones. The sexes are similar, but the young are of duller hues. The beak is somewhat crow-like, save in the genus *Eurystomus*, where it is rather broad and flattened. *Eurystomus* ranges from tropical Africa to India, Manchuria, Australia, and the Solomon Islands. But these richly coloured birds are by no means confined to the tropics. *Coracias garrulus*, which sometimes strays to Britain, has a wide breeding range, extending from Sweden and

Omsk to North Africa and North India. In this species the head, wing-coverts, and under parts are of a light greenish-blue, the back red-brown, the wing-quills blue; the bend of the wing and rump ultramarine, and the tail greenish, with light blue on the outer feathers.

The Rollers are active and noisy birds, and during the courting season the males dart through the air with many turns and twists, expanding and closing the tail; while both sexes have a habit, when excited, of " rolling " or turning somersaults in mid-air, hence the name " Rollers." During these performances, like the Kirombos, the throat is puffed out.

BLUE-TAILED BROAD-BILLED ROLLER
(*Eurystomus calonyx*).

They frequent woodland country and breed in holes, making a bed for the eggs, rather than a nest, of roots, grass, hair, and feathers, wherein four or five glossy white eggs are laid. They feed on small reptiles, frogs, beetles, grasshoppers, and worms.

The Ground-rollers of Madagascar are interesting types, rather less brilliantly coloured and crepuscular in habit. Moreover, they are almost entirely terrestrial, though they will occasionally fly to a low branch, jerking the tail upwards as they alight.

Near allies on the one hand of the Rollers, and of the Kingfishers on the other, are the Motmots and Todies. The Motmots range from South Mexico and the Antilles to Paraguay, and are distinguished by a somewhat loose type of plumage—green, blue, cinnamon, and black are the dominant hues—while the beak, like that of the Rollers, is somewhat crow-like, but with serrated edges, and the tail is long.

They are birds of the dense forests, haunting streams where possible, and feeding on insects caught in mid-air. Live creatures seized on the ground are often rapped against a branch to stun them, as with the Todies, Hornbills, and Kingfishers. This common habit of very different, though related, types is worth noting.

In the best-known species, the typical Motmot (*Momotus braziliensis*), the middle pair of tail-feathers are not only markedly longer than the rest but have a " racquet " at the tip; that is to say, the continuity of the vane is broken at the level of the shorter tail-feathers. And this, it would seem, is not an inherent character of the feather, but is fashioned by the bird itself, which deliberately bites away the vane of the feather right down to the shaft on each side, leaving an oval terminal blade! These feathers are not thus treated in the Red-headed Motmot (*Baryphthengus ruficapillus*).

The Todies, though forming a distinct group, are represented by no more than four diminutive West Indian species from three and a half to four inches long. They have a rather long beak, long legs, and short tail and wings. They are rather handsome little birds, of a vivid green above, with a red throat, yellowish-white or pinkish under parts, and yellow, pink, or green feathers on the flanks, while the beak is of a dull red. Haunting woods in hilly districts they dart out on their prey, insects of various kinds, after the fashion of our Fly-catchers, returning immediately after a capture to the same perch.

RED-HEADED MOTMOT (*Baryphthengus ruficapillus*).

Not the least remarkable thing about these little birds is the fact that they contrive to excavate burrows in sand-banks for the reception of their eggs, driving a tunnel of considerable length, generally with a right-angled turn, and ending in a small chamber containing a slight nest of fibres, grass, moss, or cotton; therein four or five globular, white eggs are laid.

Sub-order *HALCYONES*

(*Kingfishers*)

Other than the Kingfishers it would be difficult to find a group which would serve better to illustrate themes such as the evolution of resplendent plumage, divergence of habit without material change of form, or of physical peculiarities which would seem to render impossible activities which are, in fact, achieved.

More than one hundred and fifty species are known to science, and many of these are remarkable for their great beauty. All, with one exception, have long spear-shaped beaks, and all have extremely short legs and slender toes, which are further peculiar in that, as with the Bee-eaters, Hornbills, and Hoopoes, the front toes are closely bound together, though free at their tips, forming what is known as a " syndactyle " foot. The breast-bone forms a large, oblong plate, notched behind, and with a long keel and shoulder-girdle and a very wide pelvis. These are common heritages, but in the course of their evolution numerous variations or modifications have taken place, serving to break up the group into smaller sections, each with its own distinguishing characteristics.

By the systematists they are divided into two sub-families—the *Daceloninae* or Wood-kingfishers, and the *Alcedinidae*, or Water-kingfishers. Of these the Wood-kingfishers must be regarded as the more ancient group, inasmuch as the whole organisation of these birds is obviously founded on the requirements of an arboreal life. The "Wood-kingfishers" haunt shady forest regions, preferably near water, and they feed upon insects caught in mid-air, caterpillars, crustacea, molluscs, small reptiles, and frogs. They will even eat small mammals and birds. Some, evidently, have become adapted to a more restricted diet, and this has brought about changes in the form of the beak according to the condition enforced by the nature of the diet. Thus the Shoe-billed Kingfisher (*Clytoceyx rex*) of New Guinea has a very short and wide beak, forming a sort of depressed cone. In the genus *Syma* the edges of the jaw are serrated, and in *Melidora* the beak has a

SHOE-BILLED KINGFISHER (*Clytoceyx rex*).

hooked tip. The fact that some of these Kingfishers eat fish occasionally, gives us the source of the mainly piscivorous Water-kingfishers.

In the matter of their coloration the Kingfishers are, if possible, even more interesting and instructive. As a matter of convenience the two sections may be considered together in this regard.

It has already been pointed out that though these birds have many rivals, there are few which can be said to surpass them in splendour, yet there are some which have developed no tendency towards a refinement of their pigmentation, while in others we find evidence that this has begun, and as the survey of the group is followed up the gathering strength of the ability to form resplendent plumage is easily traceable. These drab-coloured types we must regard as more primitive ; that is to say, less removed from the ancestral type.

The Striped-kingfisher (*Halcyon chelicutensis*) will serve as a good example of one of the "primitive" types. This bird is of an ash-grey above, with darker streaks on the crown, the breast is of a dull greyish-white, and the flanks are streaked like the crown, while there is a dark patch of black before and behind the eye.

In the Great Laughing-kingfishers (*Dacelo*), the giants of the tribe, natives of Australia and New Guinea, we find one species, *D. gigas*, without a trace of bright colour ; but in Leach's Laughing-kingfisher the lower back is of a bright "Kingfisher-blue," and the wing-coverts are hardly less vivid, while the tail and the secondaries are dark blue. The colour of the head retains the ancestral striations, recalling those of the Striped-kingfisher.

Blues and greens of various shades were apparently the earliest colours to be developed, and to these were added various shades of buff, passing at last into red. To-day we find four more or less distinct types of coloration, combined in various ways by different species in each group.

The green and white type is illustrated by the handsome Lizard-eating Kingfisher (*Halcyon saurophagus*)—green above and snow-white below—while in *Halcyon lindsayi* we have an earlier phase of this coloration leading in another direction. In this bird the crown and a broad " moustachial " stripe are green, the back is dark green with buff spots, and there is a chestnut-red collar round the neck, while the breast-feathers are white, " laced " with black. In the Shoe-billed Kingfisher the prevailing hue is dark chocolate-brown, with a collar of pale chestnut, a white throat, and a chestnut breast.

Of the blue and white King-fishers the most remarkable are the beautiful long-tailed Tanysipteras of the Papuan Islands and Australia. *Tanysiptera sabrina* of the Moluccas, for example, is pure white, save for the crown and wing-coverts, which are of a rich

HOOK-BILLED KINGFISHER (*Melidora macrorhina*).

bright blue, while the cheeks and back are bluish-black ; the two middle tail-feathers have bluish shafts, which are produced far beyond the level of the rest, and terminate in pure white oval discs. A vermilion-red beak and legs give the finishing touches to a fine scheme of coloration. *Tanysiptera nympha* of New Guinea forms a striking contrast in having a vermilion rump and under parts. In the genus *Ceyx*, which contains the pigmies of the family, red is the dominating colour, some species being entirely red.

Our own Kingfisher is too well known to need description. It is a species of great beauty, and its hues change with the incidence of the light. The white spot on the neck, the white throat, and the chestnut-red under parts, add not a little to heighten the effect of the changing blue and green of the upper parts.

Finally we come to black-and-white types as in *Ceryle rudis*, and the Belted-kingfisher (*Ceryle alcyon*), the only Kingfisher of North America. This is a large white bird, barred with black, a type apparently derived from the green and white stock, represented by *C. amazona*, which is of a dull green colour above and white below.

No more than an indication has been given here of the extraordinary variety and beauty of the colour schemes which the Kingfishers present, and the most elaborate and detailed descriptions would fail to do them justice without the aid of at least a hundred coloured plates.

It should be added that no explanation is yet forthcoming to account for the loss of the second toe in the genera *Ceyx* and *Alcyone*.

That the Common-kingfisher constructs its nursery at the end of a long tunnel, ending in a wide chamber, is a matter of common knowledge, yet few seem to realise the surprising character of this feat. While the long, spear-shaped beak would seem to be admirably adapted for use as a pick-axe, how, with such short legs and feeble feet is the necessary " stance " for the wielding of this axe in the preliminary stages of excavation to be obtained ? And how is the loose earth removed ? Little or no nest is made by any of these birds. That of the Common-kingfisher is formed by the gradual accumulation

BLACK-AND-WHITE CRESTED-KINGFISHER (*Ceryle rudis*).

of the disgorged indigestible parts of the food—fish-bones and the hard parts of crustacea—which become beaten down to form a pancake-like mass on the floor of the brood-chamber. The translucent eggs are almost globular, and white-shelled. Sanitation of the nest is not a matter of concern with these birds. The nest itself is kept clean, but the passage thereto becomes at last extremely foul, though, fortunately, this is attended with no evil results. Young Kingfishers have no down, and in their juvenile, or first plumage, resemble the parent, though with less lustre.

The Water-kingfishers obtain their food—small fish or crustacea—by diving from a stationary perch, such as a post or reed standing in the water. Fish are brought back to be swallowed, and generally are first stunned by being beaten against the bough or post used as a " taking-off " place.

Family Meropidae

The Bee-eaters constitute a small family, comprising five genera and some thirty-five species, and containing no dull-coloured members. They are all, indeed, birds of great beauty, though they display less versatility of coloration than the Kingfishers. In size they range from species of from six and a half to fourteen inches in length.

The beak is moderately long, slightly arched, and pointed, while the feet, as in the Kingfishers, are small and syndactyle. They are all insect-eaters, darting out from a fixed resting-place to seize their victims, and returning to the same spot to devour them, after the fashion of the Kingfishers and the Fly-catchers.

Bee-eaters are confined to the temperate and tropical regions of the Old World, being especially plentiful in the Ethiopian region, somewhat less so in the Indian. One species, *Merops apiaster*, occasionally strays to the British Islands. It may well serve as the type of its tribe in the matter of coloration. Herein the forehead is white, the crown, hind-neck, and back, and most of the lesser wing-coverts, a rich chestnut-red. The secondaries and primaries dark blue, while the under parts are blue, as is the tail, wherein the middle pair of feathers are produced into long filaments. A black bar before and behind the eye, and a golden yellow throat, banded below by a black band, give the final setting to a very beautiful combination of colour.

COMMON BEE-EATER (*Merops apiaster*).

The Nubian Bee-eater (*M. nubicus*) is equally resplendent, but after another fashion. Herein the upper parts are of a crimson-pink, save the lower back, or rump, which, like the abdomen, is light blue, while the head and throat are of a blue-green colour. A rose-pink breast contrasts with the light blue abdomen and throat. The West African *Melittophagus* presents another type, glossy black above, with bright blue on the forehead, rump, wings, and middle tail-feathers, a crimson throat, and black under surface streaked with blue.

The flight of these birds is rapid, and resembles that of the Swallow, since they sometimes skim over the ground, sometimes mount aloft and soar in circles. It is when hawking in the air that their brilliant colours are seen to the best advantage. *Merops* is commonly seen in flocks; *Nyctiornis*, on the other hand, is solitary, and prefers dense forest shades or woods of lofty trees, instead of the open country which most species prefer, whether it be well watered or arid.

The name "Bee-eater" is certainly well bestowed, for when any of these birds discover a beehive they levy a heavy toll on the workers as they leave or return to the hive.

2 A

Like the kingfisher these birds construct their nurseries at the end of long burrows in sand-banks, or even driving their tunnels almost vertically into the ground. And here, as with the kingfishers, one is constrained to marvel at their skill, for they have but small and syndactyle feet, making it impossible to spread the toes, and a long and very slender beak. How do they contrive to remove the sand from a shaft which may be as much as ten feet long, driven down into level ground? No one has yet set himself the task to discover how this feat is achieved.

The eggs, as is the rule in burrowing types, are white, and are deposited on what is at best an apology for a nest in a chamber formed at the end of the tunnel.

Family Upupidae

That the Hoopoes of the above family and the Hornbills presently to be described are closely related there can be no question, nor is there less certainty as to the relationship of both to the Bee-eaters. The Hoopoes form a group of no more than five species, remarkable for their bright hues and the large erectile crest which surmounts the crown. The beak is long, slender, and slightly arched; the legs rather short, while the third and fourth toes are joined at the base.

HOOPOE (*Upupa epops*).

One species, *Upupa epops*, is not only an occasional visitant to our shores, but it has even bred here. Were it adequately protected it might, perchance, become a breeding species, as it is in Southern Scandinavia.

It is a singularly handsome bird, the body being of a delicate vinaceous cinnamon, save the back and wings, which are marked by broad alternating bars of black and white, while a white bar crosses the black tail near its middle. The crest when closed is barred with black along its anterior border; when erected it forms a great semicircular fan, recalling the head-dress of an American Indian, each feather terminating in a black tip and subterminal spot of white.

It feeds largely on dung-beetles and their larvae, hunting for these in manure heaps and in the droppings of animals. Large beetles and worms are hammered on the ground to break them up, and are then neatly tossed into the air and caught, a fashion of feeding which it shares with the Hornbill.

The name of this bird is derived from its peculiar note—"Hoop-hoop"—which is uttered with lowered crest and head and the throat greatly expanded.

Conspicuously coloured as this bird seems to be, when alarmed it throws itself flat on the ground, spreads out the wings and tail, and thrusts the head and beak upwards. As a result the black and white bars break up the contour of the body, which is then described as looking more like a piece of rag casually dropped than a bird. Thus what looks like a possible warning turns out to be a " protective " or " obliterative " coloration.

It nests in hollow trees or crevices, and the hen, while sitting, is fed by the male. The nest material consists of straw, litter, and rags, when procurable, mixed with ordure. As many as ten eggs may be laid, and these are white-shelled. The insanitary and disgusting condition of the nest fits well with the fact that the oil gland of this bird at the breeding season exhales a most offensive odour. Nevertheless, these facts seem strangely out of harmony with the beauty of the plumage.

Far less resplendent are the " Wood-hoopoes " (*Irissor*, *Scoptelus*, and *Rhinopomastus*), which in coloration are of a metallic purple-blue, or greenish, with a white wing-patch and tail markings. The beak is longer and more curved than in the typical Hoopoes, and there is no crest. They are shy, restless birds, travelling about in flocks of six or seven, searching the bark of the highest trees or the ground for insects or their larvae. Their breeding habits are like those of the crested Hoopoes.

These birds are confined to Africa, but there is nothing either in regard to their habits or to the climate which will afford any clue as to the striking differences in coloration of these two types of Hoopoes. The conspicuously longer and more curved beak of *Rhinopomastus* is evidently associated with a more restricted use of the beak as a forceps for extracting insects from crannies.

In the matter of coloration the most striking is Jackson's Wood-hoopoe (*I. jacksoni*), which has a white head and throat.

Family *Bucerotidae*

The Hornbills thus classed may be described as giant-hoopoes, wherein the beak has assumed an enormous size and fantastic shapes. Great size suggests great weight, but their beaks are by no means heavy, for the underlying bony skeleton is but a mere shell supported by an extremely delicate mesh-work of bone, set within a great air-chamber. The horny investment of this beak is also of no great thickness. The cutting edges of the jaws are more or less serrated, and in some species do not touch near the middle of the curve.

In some species the ridge of the beak is raised into heavy corrugations, in others it is surmounted by a casque of strange shape. But there is one species, the Helmet-hornbill (*Rhinoplax vigil*), in which this casque rises steeply from the ridge of the beak, and is formed of a dense mass of tissue, ivory-like in hardness, and the skeletal support behind takes the form of a series of heavy, crossing beams of bone, more or less at right angles to the long axis of the casque. Every feature of the structure of this casque goes to show that it is used as a hammer, but on what occasions and on what material no one has yet discovered.

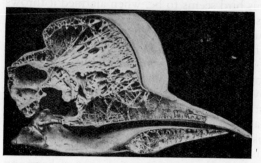

CASQUE OF HELMET-HORNBILL (*Rhinoplax vigil*).

Fruit and berries form the staple diet of these birds, but small mammals and birds are also eaten, as well as fish which are taken when they resort to forest streams to bathe. Their flight is heavy, slow, and extremely noisy, being accompanied by a sound likened to the rushing of an express train.

Ranging from Africa and the Indo-Malayan regions to the Solomon Islands, these birds, with the exception of two species of the genus *Bucorax*, are all confined to dense forests and jungles. These two species, *B. cafer* of South and East Africa and *B. abyssinicus* of North-East and West Africa, live on the ground, and as a consequence have long legs. Small reptiles and mammals probably form their staple diet, and they are said to attack and kill large snakes. They are further remarkable for the fact that in them the casque is open in front. One would have supposed that this would have been a most dangerous innovation since it invites the entrance of parasites, yet no evil effects seem to have attended on this strange modification.

GROUND-HORNBILL (*Bucorax abyssinicus*).

The nesting habits of the Hornbill are remarkable. Incubation and the brooding of the young is performed entirely by the female, who, directly she begins to sit, is made a close prisoner. The male closes up the entrance to the hole in the tree-trunk containing the nest with clay hardened by secretions from his salivary glands. But a slit large enough to permit the passage of the beak is left open, and through this she is fed. And here again is a remarkable thing. The male does not bring food in its natural state, but such as he has recently swallowed, which is regurgitated, enclosed within a bag formed by the lining of his stomach, which has to be renewed before he can feed her again. No wonder that by the time she emerges with her youngster the male is worn to a mere skeleton and sometimes dies from exhaustion.

Sub-order *STRIGES*

(*Owls*)

The Owls are vastly more interesting birds than is generally supposed. By the older naturalists they were designated the " Nocturnal Birds of Prey," under the conviction that they were bound by the closest ties with the Eagles, Falcons, and Hawks, which constituted the " Diurnal Birds of Prey." An intimate study of their anatomy, however, shows that the common likeness which these two present in beak and claw are solely due to adaptation to a raptorial mode of life, furnishing us with a very clear and striking instance of " convergent evolution." The Owls are really near akin to the " Frog-mouths " and Nightjars.

Anatomical characters have been studiously avoided in these pages, but if the real character of the Owls is to be convincingly explained, some of the more important of such characters bearing on this theme of the kinship of the two groups must be enlarged upon.

The plumage of the Owls is peculiarly soft in texture, and this is especially marked in the flight-feathers which are so modified as to produce a " muffled " wing-beat, silence being all important to birds which hunt by night. Again, the feather-tracts are much narrower than in the Hawk tribe, and there are no down-feathers. The nestling-down, again, differs from that of the Hawk tribe in that it consists only of pre-pennae, concerning which more will have to be said presently.

Of internal organs all that need be mentioned are the " caeca." The Hawk tribe, it will be remembered, are almost entirely flesh-eaters, though some of the smaller falcons live largely on beetles. But in all cases, whatever the diet, the blind-gut, or caecum, is represented by a mere vestige. The Owls, which similarly are mainly flesh-eaters, also consume an appreciable number of large beetles; nevertheless, they have surprisingly large caeca, shaped like a " Florence-flask," a peculiarity, be it noted, which they share with the Nightjars. The whole intestinal tract, indeed, of the Owls differs in the character of its convolutions from that of the Hawk tribe, and agrees with that of the Nightjars. It is worth noting that while the bodily shape has been modified in accordance with their predatory habits, the intestinal tract has undergone no corresponding change as between Owls and Nightjars.

The characteristic position of the eyes so that they look straight forward, and the curious arrangement of the feathers of the face to form a disc around each eye, are adaptations to the nocturnal habits of these birds. But no satisfactory explanation is forthcoming for the remarkable nature of the ears. In a few species this aperture is like that of other birds, a mere round hole. But in the majority of species it is not only greatly enlarged, but is associated with the development of peculiar folds of skin and asymmetry in regard to the two sides of the head.

In the Scops-owl the skin, instead of turning inwards around the aperture,

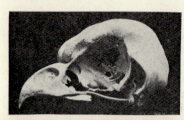

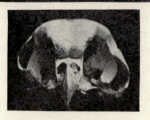

SKULLS OF TENGMALM'S-OWL,
showing asymmetry.

forms a large fenestra surrounding it, and in so doing exposes the outer segment of the eyeball in front and of the skull-wall behind it. In the Brown- or Tawny-owl still more of these areas are exposed, the fenestra being larger on the right than the left side. But more than this, the skin bounding the anterior border of this fenestration is produced into a large, oblong flap, which can be drawn backwards to cover the whole of the exposed region. In the Long- and Short-eared Owls this fenestration attains its maximum, so that when the operculum is raised the greater part of the skull is exposed.

A new feature is here introduced, in the form of a " valve " running from the operculum backwards to the skull wall. On the left side of the skull the aperture leading to the internal ear lies above this valve, and a blind-cave below it. On the right side these positions are reversed, the blind-cave lying above the valve. In Tengmalm's-owl, asymmetry to a very striking degree is found in the skull itself; the tympanic wing of the squamosal extending forwards as a tongue-shaped plate as far as the bony wall of the eyeball on the right side, while on the left it forms a vertical border with a deep notch. So far we have no facts to guide us as to whether these singular modifications of the aperture of the ear are in any way associated with acuity of hearing.

In the matter of the nestling-down, we have in the Owls important data to show that the nestling-down plumage is to be regarded as a degenerate adult plumage. The newly hatched Tawny-owl is clothed in a short, white down composed of umbelliform tufts; that is to say, all the rami of the feathers start from a common base. Presently these are borne out upon the

Pl. 10.

TAWNY OWL (*Strix aluco*).

tips of a second "nestling-plumage." This is composed of feathers of a very loose texture but having a well-defined vane; that is to say, the rami are ranged along either side of a very long shaft, and the complete feather has a transversely barred pattern.

Generally this plumage is confused with what answers to the "juvenile-plumage" of other birds. In the nestling Barn-owl what answers to this second, barred plumage is reduced to umbelliform tufts, and attached to their tips will be found remains of an earlier generation answering to the white, umbelliform tips of the first down-plumage of the nestling Tawny-owl.

When the Owls are surveyed as a whole they are found to present a great range in size; at one extreme are the huge Eagle-owls, and at the other the tiny Scops-owls.

Vivid patches of colour are never developed by the Owls, the plumage being always of some sober tint of buff or grey, with darker markings. The Snowy-owl, however, is pure white, with black markings—a protective coloration to meet the requirements of life amid a snow-clad landscape. In the coloration of the eyes, however, they show striking differences. Thus in the Eagle-owls and Long- and Short-eared Owls they are of a wonderful golden-yellow; in the Barn-owl and Tawny-owl they are of such an intensely dark hazel as to seem black.

BURROWING-OWL (*Speotyto cunicularis*).

The so-called "ears" of the Eagle-owls, Snowy-owls, Long- and Short-eared Owls, are merely tufts of erectile feathers surmounting the crown, and have no relation whatever to the organ of hearing.

The Owls display no skill in nest-building. Some, like the Snowy- and Short-eared Owls, construct a loose platform of sticks and grass on the ground; many, like the Tawny- and Long-eared Owls, are content with the deserted nests of magpies, crows, and squirrels; but there is no invariable rule. Thus the Long-eared Owl, at need, will nest on the ground; the Tawny-owl will use a hollow tree, which is the usual nursery with the smaller species. The Burrowing-owl (*Speotyto*) of South America, a ground-dweller, with long legs and short wings, ranging from British Columbia to Patagonia, shares the burrows of prairie-dogs, ground-squirrels, or badgers, and in South America those of the viscacha, the Patagonia cavy, armadillos, and reptiles.

Sub-order *Caprimulgi*

(*Nightjars*)

Under the generic term " Nightjars " there must be included the singular Oil-bird, and the even more strange " Frog-mouth " (*Podargus*).

Family Steatornithidae

The Oil-bird, or Guacharo (*Steatornis*), is a primitive type standing midway between the Owls and the true Nightjars and Frog-mouths. The beak and feet show this in a very decided way, for the former is large, hooked,

OIL-BIRD or GUACHARO (*Steatornis caripensis*).

and owl-like, but has, further, a pronounced notch near the tip, while the feet have all the toes free.

The Guacharo is of about the size of a crow, and of a chocolate-grey colour relieved by darker bars and white spots. It is a cave-haunting species, spending the day in seaside or mountain caverns, and sallying forth at dusk to search for fruits, which seem to form its only food. In these caves it also breeds, constructing a nest of a clay-like substance placed on ledges or in holes. The eggs, from two to four, are white-shelled, but soon become begrimed with dirt. The nestlings are eagerly sought by the natives, partly for food—though they are said to smell like cockroaches—and partly for the sake of the oil they yield, which is used for illuminating and cooking. They make their raids on the caverns at night by the aid of torches, killing at the same time large numbers of adults.

Most of what we know of the life-history of this bird, which is not much, has been gleaned from the famous caves of Trinidad. But the Guacharo has an extensive range, since it is to be found in suitable areas in the Guianas, Venezuela, Colombia, Ecuador, and Peru.

Family Podargidae

The relationship of the birds known as Frog-mouths to the Oil-birds is indisputable ; and on this account the differences they present ecologically—that is to say, in regard to their life-history—makes them the more interesting.

They have an owl-like appearance, imparted by the soft colouring of the plumage, the erect carriage, and the large beak and eyes. But the feathers of the face do not form a disc as in the Owls. Moreover, when the mouth is opened it proves to be surprisingly large, wherein they resemble the Nightjars. They differ from the latter, however, among other things, in that they have a relatively enormous brush-like tuft of powder-down feathers on each side above the base of the tail.

Their food seems to consist mainly of small birds, reptiles, and frogs, wherein they agree rather with the Owls than with the Guacharo, which is entirely a vegetarian. But smaller Owlet Frog-mouths (*Aegotheles*) approach the Nightjars since they feed upon beetles and other insects, and furthermore have the gape armed with long bristles.

PAPUAN FROG-MOUTH (*Podargus papuensis*).

In the matter of their nesting habits they show interesting differences. For the typical Frog-mouths (*Podargus*) build a flat nest of sticks, loosely packed and placed on the horizontal branch of a tree ; the Eared Frog-mouths (*Batrachostomus*) use moss as a building material, some species being content with a mere pad with a central depression for the eggs. *B. hodgsoni* adds powder-down feathers, and covers the outside with bits of bark and lichen, so as to render it difficult to distinguish the nest from the bough on which it rests. No others among the Nightjars, nor any of the Owls, build so conventional a nest as this, and the circumstances are worth noting. In all cases the eggs are white.

The typical Frog-mouths (*Podargus*) are natives of Australia and the adjacent Papuan Islands ; the Eared Frog-mouths (*Batrachostomus*) inhabit Southern India, the Malay Peninsula, Sumatra, and Borneo ; while the Owlet Frog-mouths, eleven species in all, are distributed over Australia, the adjacent Moluccan and Papuan Islands, and New Caledonia.

One of the largest species is the Great Eared Frog-mouth (*Batrachostomus auritus*), which has a length of about sixteen inches, about twice the size of the smallest of the Owlet Frog-mouths.

Family Caprimulgidae

The true Nightjars are represented by some eighty species of almost world-wide distribution, since they are absent only from the coldest regions, the eastern Pacific and New Zealand. Their coloration is of a highly protective character—consisting of delicate mottlings, vermiculations, and bars of grey, buff, and brown. All have extremely short and slender beaks, but enormous mouths, cleft back to below the eyes, and the gape is enlarged by a fringe of long, stiff bristles.

They are nocturnal in habits, with conspicuously large eyes, emerging at dusk to feed upon moths, beetles, and other insects caught in mid-air. When perching in trees they rest lengthwise, along the bough instead of across, after the usual fashion of birds.

Our own Nightjar, or "Fern-owl" (*Caprimulgus europaeus*), is too well known to need any general description as touching its general appearance. No nest is made, the eggs, two in number, being laid in a slight hollow in the ground. They are, it is to be noted, protectively coloured, the blotches and spots on a creamy ground serving to render them invisible.

Some of the Nightjars develop enormously elongated plumes which are

to be regarded as "Secondary Sexual Characters," equivalent to the gorgeous train of the peacock, or the frills of the Golden-pheasant or the ruff, already described in these pages. Thus in the males of *Heliothreptes anomalus* of Brazil and Argentina, the seventh, eighth, and ninth primaries are produced into long streamers. In the Pennant-winged Nightjar (*Macrodipteryx vexillarius*) the same three feathers are similarly produced, but here the ninth instead of the eighth is the longest, while in the Standard-winged Nightjar (*M. longipennis*) the ninth alone is elongated, and here it takes the form of a long, slender shaft terminating in a racquet-like tip.

PENNANT-WINGED NIGHTJAR (*Macrodipteryx vexillarius*).

Other species have developed excessively long tails. In *Scotornis climacurus* of tropical Africa, for example, it is the middle pair which have thus been raised to the rank of "ornaments"; in four species of South American *Hydropsalis*, all the feathers take part; and in three species of *Macropsalis*, ranging from Panama to Brazil, only the outer pair are affected. These ornaments are commonly regarded merely as among the "curiosities of Nature." But they are really much more than this; for they surely indicate a slowing down of the incidence of the "struggle for existence," a freedom from enemies, or an easier means of obtaining food than is the case with the rest of the Nightjars.

All the true Nightjars, it should be remarked, have the inner edge of the middle claw serrated, forming a comb-shaped organ like that of some herons, but what function it serves is unknown. In the tropical American Nightjars of the genus *Nyctibius*, however, there are no such serrations. And these birds further differ from their tribe in that they breed, not on the ground, but in hollows of branches or stumps of trees.

Finally, it should be mentioned that the true Nightjars are commonly known as " Goatsuckers " from the absurd belief that they suck the milk from goats, just as the Hedgehog is said to suck the milk of cows, a grotesque fantasy which, nevertheless, is still current.

Sub-order *CYPSELI*

(*Swifts and Humming-birds*)

Family Cypselidae

The close relationship between the Swifts and Humming-birds in the above family is unmistakable, and these in turn must be regarded as of collateral origin with the Nightjars. There is but little external evidence to support this interpretation, because they started on their several ways far back in the distant past, each travelling along a line of its own, and changing in accordance with the ever-widening differences of their mode of life. Their common ancestry is revealed only after a study of deeper-seated, anatomical characters. The most superficial of all anatomical characters, it must be remembered, is colour. A blackbird and a thrush are easily distinguished when seen in the garden—by their coloration. Pluck them, and who can tell which is which? Structurally the male and female blackbird are identical, save only in the matter of their reproductive organs, but superficially they are readily distinguishable—by their coloration.

The thrush and the robin are more distantly related, their coloration is different, but the juvenile robin declares this relationship by its spotted plumage. The skeleton and muscles show differences between the two, but they are differences merely of small detail. Just as we succeed in grasping the emergence of ever-widening differences as we compare closely more distantly related species, so we shall be able to grasp the still wider differences which are found when we come to compare nearly related families, sub-orders, and orders.

By the older ornithologists the Swifts were held to be nearly related to the Swallows, but the likeness between the two types is purely superficial, the result of a similar mode of life. We have here, indeed, a case of " convergent evolution," precisely similar to that of the Owls and the Hawk tribe.

The whole energies of the Swifts having been concentrated on flight, the wing, in consequence, has become profoundly modified. As touching its bony framework, it will be found in our Common-swift that the arm, or humerus, has become excessively shortened, till its length scarcely exceeds its breadth ; the fore-arm is also conspicuously short, just as the hand is conspicuously long. No other bird has a wing of these proportions, which stand in strong contrast with those of the albatross, wherein the arm is excessively long and the hand extremely short.

The great span of the long, sickle-shaped wings of the Swift is due to the great length of the long, narrow primaries. No other bird probably spends so much of its life in mid-air as the Swift. Even the Swallows we occasionally see at rest, but the Swift never. It is said even to sleep amid the clouds. But, at any rate, it must come to rest when incubating and brooding, or feeding its young.

The wild, rushing flight, accompanied by screams of ecstasy, which enlivens our summer evenings, makes the Swift one of the most welcome of our summer visitors. But this is not our only Swift, since, on rare occasions, we are visited by the Great Alpine-swift, a much larger species, having a wing-span of nearly two feet, and distinguished at once, apart from its greater size, by its white abdomen.

CRESTED-SWIFT (*Macropteryx mystacea*).

The Swift feeds entirely in mid-air on small flies and beetles, and it breeds under the roofs of houses or, away from human habitations, in crannies, making a nest of straw and other litter, with a few feathers, held together by means of saliva from the salivary glands, which hardens quickly.

The use of saliva is much more extensive in the case of the " Edible-swift " (*Collocalia fuciphaga*), ranging from the Indo-Malayan countries to Australia. These birds build in great colonies in dark caves, constructing a nest of most extraordinary character, since it is formed entirely of saliva furnished by the salivary glands. It hardens rapidly, and forms a saucer-shaped ledge projecting from the wall of the cave. They are often so closely crowded together as to form continuous masses. These are the nests so highly prized by the Chinese for bird's-nest soup. The best-quality nests are translucent; but it would seem that some birds have less active glands, and so are constrained to supplement this saliva by the use of débris, and such nests have no marketable value. Possibly they are second nests, built by birds whose first nursery has been seized, when, naturally, the supply of saliva would be diminished, or they may have been made by birds whose salivary glands were inherently defective.

But be this as it may, this type of nest has other variants. Thus the handsome Crested-swift (*Macropteryx*), ranging from India to Papuasia, fashions a nest of flakes of bark, cemented together by this strange " liquid-glue " and fastened to the bough of a tree. It is the smallest nest of any living bird, measuring no more than one and a half inches across, though the builder is ten inches long. It is fixed to the side of the bough, and the bird has to incubate by sitting across the bough and over the nest, which is only large enough to contain one egg.

The Palm-swifts (*Tachornis*), again, build tiny nests of cotton-down and feathers, attached to the leaves of palms or to the grass roofs of native huts. By way of contrast we have the enormous pendant tubes of interwoven seeds, suspended from overhanging rocks by means of saliva, fashioned by Salvin's-swift (*Panyptila*) of Guatemala. The opening of the tube is below, and the egg-chamber is at the top.

It is interesting to note that the inherent building habits of these several species remain the same throughout a wide geographical range. A further interesting point concerns the eggs, which have white shells, though only in the case of the Edible-swifts and Salvin's-swift are the nests placed in dark cavities. Thus we may infer that the habit of nesting in the open, with the eggs exposed to the light, has been recently acquired. Having regard to the conservative character of their parental instincts, to which reference has just been made, one is at a loss to understand what the factors may have been in inducing these fundamental changes of nesting sites and materials.

Family Trochilidae

The Humming-birds are an extraordinarily interesting group, and surpassingly beautiful in their coloration, which captivates even the most incurious. They disclose, when they come to be closely studied, profoundly interesting structural changes which are intimately associated with their quite peculiar and highly specialised mode of life ; these changes bear directly on that highly controversial theme the " Transmission of Acquired Characters."

The very fact that they are so intensively changed makes it the more remarkable that they should have split up into five hundred or more species ; a fact which makes it impossible to do more than describe them in broad outline in these pages.

Their close relationship to the Swifts is indisputable, and they share with these birds the same striking peculiarities of the wing ; and this, although their mode of flight is very different, for they do not make long excursions in mid-air in search of food, though they feed upon the wing, as will be shown presently.

When we speak of the " evolution " of the Humming-birds, we refer, as in all other cases, to the various lines along which they have developed, presenting ever-widening differences from a standard type, which is that nearest in its general features to the ancestral stock. This, in the case of the Humming-birds, was a bird reminiscent of a Swift. In seeking for this we should look for one or more species which were soberly coloured, and these we find in the genera *Patagona* and *Aglaeactis*.

The Giant Humming-bird (*P. gigas*) is the largest member of the tribe, measuring nine and a half inches in length, while the smallest, found in the genus *Mellisuga*, do not exceed two and a half inches. It is clear that a decrease in size is one of the features of this evolution, and this is noteworthy. For *P. gigas* is of a dull greenish-brown, with a white rump and rufous under parts. In *Aglaeactis* the coloration is brown, dark buff, or black, but with a foreshadowing of the splendours to come in a glittering amethystine or green lower back, and a white or buff tuft on the breast.

GIANT HUMMING-BIRD (*Patagona gigas*).

The evolution of colour in the Kingfishers, it will be remembered, started on the lower back.

Another centre of change is found in the beak and tongue, which have undergone striking and often remarkable modifications in response to the particular modes of feeding and the type of food which is sought. In the Swifts the beak is reduced to extremely small dimensions, but the aperture of the mouth is relatively enormous. These birds capture flies, moths, and beetles in mid-air. In all nestling Humming-birds the beak is swiftlike—an ancestral character; by the time they leave the nest it has assumed the form peculiar to the adult of the species. In all it is long; enormously so, and straight, in *Docimastes*, which uses it to thrust up the long tubes of flowers to obtain nectar, and the small flies also feeding thereon.

In the genus *Avocettula* it is upturned like that of the Avocet among the Plover tribe; in others it may be curved, often in a semicircle. Commonly the edges of the beak are finely serrated.

Some species feed mainly on nectar, supplemented by the small insects they find feeding thereon; they have become, in short, so highly specialised, that they are dependent for their existence on flowers; others feed mainly on small spiders and insects of many kinds obtained from the under sides of leaves, or crevices in the bark of trees, or crannies in rocks. But in all cases they seize their prey as they hover in mid-air, sustained thus by the incredibly swift beating of their wings, which move so fast as to create a haze around the body.

Their flight is more like that of the Hawk-moths than bird-like. Hovering, like a hawk-moth, for a few moments at the corolla of a flower, they dart off the next instant so swiftly that when they are next discovered they are holding a similar position many yards distant. The nectar is obtained by capillary attraction, the tongue being enormously long, and cleft so as to form a pair of tubes by the inrolling of the edges of the two filamentous portions.

One generally associates Humming-birds with the heat and splendours of the tropics, but these living jewels display an adaptability to diverse climatic conditions which is surprising, especially having regard to the nature of their food. Though confined to the New World, they pervade almost every part of it. In the south, *Eustephanus galeritus* has been seen flitting about the fuchsias of Tierra del Fuego in a snowstorm, and in the north-east *Trochilus colubris* charms the vision of Canadians as it poises itself over the Althea bushes in their gardens, and extends its range at least as far as latitude 57° N. *Oreotrichlus chimborazo* and *O. pichincha* live on the lofty mountains whence each takes its name, but just beneath the line of perpetual snow, at an elevation of some sixteen thousand feet, dwelling in a world of almost constant hail, sleet, and snow, and feeding on the insects which resort to the indigenous plants.

HOODED EUSTEPHANUS (*Eustephanus galeritus*).

Peru and Bolivia produce some of the most splendid members of the family. The slopes of the Northern Andes and the hill country of Colombia furnish the greatest number of species, and some of the most beautiful. Many brilliantly coloured species are found in the Brazils, Guiana, and Venezuela, but the great wooded basin of the Amazons seems to be shunned by them. It is interesting to note that the dullest coloured species of the group—the " Hermits " of the genus *Phaethornis*—live in the darkest recesses of the Brazilian forests, as if intensity of light played a more important part in the evolution of their coloration than temperature.

Something has already been said of the coloration of these wonderful little birds, but no words can describe the bewildering combinations of colour they display, which now glisten like burnished metal and now glow as if illuminated by an internal fire. Ruby, sapphire, amethyst, are all outdone in their several degrees of splendour. Even the fire of the opal seems to be challenged. But in addition to these splendours, changing with the incidence of the light, many have developed crests and frills and plumes in amazing variety.

From among the hundreds of species inviting our attention it is difficult to select examples for special mention. One of the most remarkable is the excessively rare Racquet-tailed Humming-bird (*Loddigesia*) of Northern Peru, one of the smallest members of its tribe. It is of a glistening bronzy-green, with whitish under parts surrounding a black central area. The head and crest are of a lustrous cobalt-blue, the throat a shimmering emerald-green, with a black margin, while the legs are encircled with a ring of white plumes like swansdown. But this is not all. The females are by no means so richly clad, and the young males have a tail of ten feathers. In the adult male these are reduced to four, the outermost and the innermost pair. More than this, however, the middle pair is extremely short, so much so that they hardly project beyond the general plumage of the body. What appear to be two very long spike-shaped tail-feathers are really two curiously modified and stiffened under tail-coverts, the rest of which are, as is usual, quite small feathers.

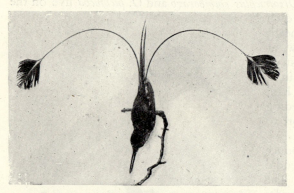

RACQUET-TAILED HUMMING-BIRD (*Loddigesia mirabilis*).

And now as to the outermost pair. These take the form of long, curved, slender rods, terminating in a disc-like expansion. These feathers cross one another, and between the arch thus formed the long, spike-shaped under tail-coverts are framed. While courting, these tail-feathers are made to play a very conspicuous part; now they are spread wide apart, now crossed, and sometimes the tail is brought forward so that the discs stand immediately over the head. During flight, as with most of the small species, the wing-beat is so rapid as to produce a humming sound—hence the name of these birds.

The Central and South American " Sabre-wings," of the genera *Eupeto-mena* and *Campylopterus*, have the shafts of the outermost primaries curiously curved and dilated, and they use these as " castanets " to produce a curious rattling noise during their courtship displays.

As nest-builders these tiny birds are no less remarkable, though they never have to provide for more than two eggs, and some species lay but one. Cotton-down, moss, lichen, and spider-webs are the materials chiefly used. But the nest may be no bigger than the half of a walnut shell, or its tiny cup may surmount a long, more or less cone-shaped mass, a piece of camouflage causing the nursery to blend with the masses of trailing creepers ; or the outside may be masked by flakes of bark and lichen.

The young, about the size of bumble-bees, grow apace, and the parents will sometimes add to the rim of the nest to prevent them falling out.

Sub-order *COLII*

(*Colies, or Mouse-birds*)

Family Colliidae

Outside South Africa, save among expert ornithologists, the Colies, or Mouse-birds, are to all intents and purposes a non-existent group of birds. Yet, though they number no more than eight or nine species, they are extremely interesting types. Their precise relationships have puzzled many. But there can be no doubt that they must be regarded as near relations of the Swifts. This is borne out by the evidence furnished not only by their internal anatomy, but by such striking external features as the character of the toes, which are of the type known as pamprodactylous : that is to say, all are turned forwards, though the hallux, or inner-toe, can be turned backwards at will, as in the Swifts.

Varying in coloration from brown, with darker vermiculations, to grey or ash colour, they are quite inconspicuous, though a well-developed conical crest and long tail furnish something in the nature of ornament. *Colius macrurus*, however, has developed a tuft of blue feathers on each side of the nape. *C. leucocephalus* has a white head. All have red feet and a rather finch-like beak. Though measuring from eleven to fourteen inches in length they are really small birds, for the tail is very long.

Their powers of flight have degenerated, and this because their wings are but little used, since they haunt forest districts where the bush is thick, travelling, except

MOUSE-BIRD (*Colius macrurus*).

in the breeding season, in parties of seven or eight. In climbing trees the sole of the foot is kept close to the bark, giving a mouse-like character to their movements, hence their name. When roosting they pack themselves together in masses and hang by the feet—like the " hanging-parrots," which roost head-downwards after this fashion.

The nest is cup-shaped, and constructed of roots, twigs, and grass, with a lining of wool or finer grass, and placed in thick bushes or near the ground in low trees. The eggs are of a dull white, and unlike those of the Swift and Humming-birds are sometimes streaked with orange or brown. For some curious reason fresh leaves are occasionally placed below them.

In one striking particular they differ from the rest of the Swift tribe, and this in that they are almost entirely fruit-eaters, though green shoots and insects are occasionally eaten.

Sub-order Trogones

(Trogons)

Family Trogonidae

The Trogons are birds of sumptuous appearance and ancient lineage. They must be regarded as having split off from that common stock which, diverging along different lines, gave rise to the Owls, Nightjars, Swifts, and Colies. They present underlying resemblances and evidences of a common ancestry in regard to many of their more deep-seated anatomical characters. If they have a leaning towards one more than others of these several types, it is towards the Nightjars.

Even to-day they have a wide geographical distribution, ranging as they do from Africa through India and the Indo-Malayan region into Central and South America. But in earlier times they lived in Europe, as is shown by the fact that a fossil species, *Trogon gallicus*, has been found in the Lower Miocene of France.

To-day they number nearly fifty species, divisible into eight genera. The majority belong to the New World, but three are found in Africa. They are forest-haunting birds, and sluggish, spending most of their time in the trees. In the structure of their feet they are unique among birds. At first sight the toes would seem to be " zygodactylous," two being turned forwards and two backwards, as in the Parrots, for example ; here, however, it is the hallux, or hind-toe, and the fourth, or outermost, which are turned back; but in the Trogons this " yoke-foot " is formed by the backward turning of the hallux and *second* toe, forming what is known as a " heterodactylous " foot. The beak, which is short and rather wide at the gape, in many species has serrated edges and a notched tip.

They feed principally on fruit and insects of various kinds, but lizards and small crabs are also eaten. The Old-World forms seem to feed chiefly on insects. As a rule, the food is taken by a sudden dart into the air to seize the coveted morsel, when a return is made to the perch.

These are all birds of great splendour, and the " hall-mark " of the tribe seems to be a crimson abdomen, but in some the whole breast is thus coloured. Many have the upper parts of a glorious bronze-green, simulating burnished metal, but blue, purple, and chestnut lend variety to this general scheme of colour. The most famous of all is the superbly beautiful Quezal (*Pharomacrus mocinno*) of Mexico. Of a brilliant iridescent green above, tinged with blue on the tail, and of a gorgeous crimson below, the plumage of this bird gains added splendour by the fact that the upper tail-coverts are produced into long streamers, the middle pair being the longest, three and a half feet long. The wing-coverts, similarly, are elongated to form a great shield on each side of scimitar-shaped feathers, while the head is surmounted by a great crown of loose plumes.

In this matter of coloration of the Trogons some extremely interesting facts are brought out when those of the Indian region are compared with the African and American species. In these two last groups the females are commonly only a little less brilliant than their mates, but the plumage of both sexes in all but two of the Asiatic species resembles that of the immature birds and females of some of the American species, which still wear what we may call the ancestral livery, which is of a russet-hue. Again, the Asiatic Trogons have no serrations along the cutting edges of the jaw, agreeing in this with the young birds of the African and American types, wherein the jaws of the adults are serrated.

These facts seem to point to the Indian region as the original home of these birds which, some-

QUEZAL (*Pharomacrus mocinno*).

how, inhibited the potentiality to develop re-splendent plumage. The extension of the range to Africa on the one hand, and America on the other, allowed this potentiality to find expression.

Sub-order *PICI*

(*Jacamars and Puff-birds, Barbets, Toucans, and Woodpeckers*)

We come now to the last remaining members of the great group " Coracii-formes," among which, probably, they stand nearest to the Rollers and Kingfishers ; but they also serve as connecting links between the Coraciiform and the Passeriform types.

Family *Galbulidae*

The Jacamars, confined to Central and South America, externally are suggestive of the Bee-eaters, but their zygodactyle feet and metallic plumage at once suffice to show that this is but a superficial likeness. They haunt the outskirts of forests, especially in the neighbourhood of streams. Perched on the topmost boughs of trees, and a dead branch for choice, they await insects of all sorts, which are caught by a sudden rush in mid-air, the captor returning to its perch immediately, after the fashion

LARGER PARADISE-JACAMAR (*Jacamarops aurea*).

of the Fly-catchers. Large victims are beaten against the perch before being swallowed.

The general coloration is of a brilliant coppery-green above, with a metallic sheen, and more or less rufous below. They breed, like the Bee-eaters and many Kingfishers, in holes in sand-banks, and lay three, or more, round, white eggs.

Family Bucconidae

The Puff-birds, which constitute the family *Bucconidae*, are closely related to the Jacamars, and like them are confined to Central and South America. They have, too, closely similar feeding habits. Yet they are very different in coloration, and have a short, wide beak. Though forest birds, like the Jacamars, they haunt the recesses of the forest rather than its outskirts. Some forty species, comprising seven genera, are known to science. For the most part they are black, brown, or rufous in hue, relieved by more or less extensive areas of white. The beak is either red or yellow. They also, like the Jacamars, breed in holes in sand-banks. The name " Puff-bird," it should be explained, is bestowed from the habit these birds have of puffing out the plumage of the head.

Family Capitonidae

The Barbets, the exceedingly interesting family which includes the famous " Honey-guides," stand almost at the parting of the ways between the singular Toucans on the one hand and the Woodpeckers on the other. They are a family of small, rather heavily built birds, with a large, stout beak, beset at the gape with long bristles, or " vibrissae," and generally of brilliant plumage. They haunt forests and well-timbered districts throughout tropical Asia, Africa, and America, and are strictly arboreal, hopping from branch to branch, and sometimes climbing up and down the trunk, woodpecker-fashion, in search of insects.

Dull and listless in their habits, they sit motionless for hours on end, and, as if to while away the time, give voice to a noisy ringing note of two or three syllables, variously described as like " Kuttooruk, tok-tok " or " Poo-poo-poop." The likeness of these notes to the sounds of striking metal gives the name of " Copper-smith," " Tinker-bird," and " Iron-smith " to *Xantholaema haematocephala*, *Barbatula*, and *Cyanops faber* respectively. Fruit, buds, and insects form their principal food. From three to five white eggs are laid in a hollow tree, a neat, circular entrance being cut like that made by a woodpecker.

More than one hundred species have been described, and when these are surveyed as a whole a surprising and bewildering series of gradations will be found, both of the form and size of the beak as well as of coloration. No useful purpose would be served by attempting to describe these; such an attempt would be foredoomed to failure, for these differences, though apparent enough to the eye, cannot be set down in words. Suffice it to say that a study of their beaks shows some of simple type, which have not yet assumed the form typical of the Barbets, and it shows some which bridge the gap between the Barbets and the Toucans.

TOUCAN-LIKE BARBET
(*Tetragonops rhamphastinus*).

In the Malayan Hay's Brown-barbet (*Calorhamphus hayi*), for example, the beak is rather finch-like in type, though somewhat heavy, while the plumage is of a dull brown above and greyish-white below. Here we have a " primitive Barbet." In *Tetragonops rhamphastinus*, of Ecuador, and its congeners, we find a beak which may well be the forerunner of that of the Toucans, while in the American *Progonorhynchus* we have what we may call the climax in the evolution of the Barbet beak, the edges of the upper jaw being deeply notched and its base covered with long, stiff bristles.

Sub-family Indicatorinae

There is little in the external appearance of the Honey-guides which would suggest their relationship to the Barbets, save the zygodactyle toes, for they look rather like somewhat thick-billed, drab-coloured finches. But superficial appearances are notoriously untrustworthy. Anatomically this association with the Barbets is completely justified. Save those who have encountered them in their native wild, few people know the Honey-guides at sight; though most of us have heard strange tales of their efforts to lure wayfarers to bees' nests, in anticipation of feasting on the grubs when the nest is rifled.

Their geographical range is curiously interrupted, since it includes the whole of the Ethiopian region, save Madagascar, the Himalayas, and the Malayan and Bornean Mountains. Both sexes are alike in coloration, which is chiefly of a dull brown, while in size they do not exceed that of a lark.

The African Honey-guide may be taken as a type of all, in the matter of leading hunts for honey. Not only man, but that greatest of honey-eaters, the ratel, is pressed into service. On sighting a man one of these birds will

COMMON HONEY-GUIDE (*Indicator indicator*).

call attention by a shrill cry or hiss, and even fly at his face as if enraged at his stupidity in not realising what is required of him. If some response to the invitation is shown the bird keeps a little way ahead, hopping from one tree to another, till the nest to be despoiled is reached. But it leaves it to the man to find the actual spot where it is placed, giving him a sign that he is " hot " by fluttering about ; and it often takes some little time to locate the nest, which is generally cunningly hidden.

Eleven species of Honey-guides are recognised, distributed between two genera—*Indicator*, containing nine species, and *Prodotiscus*, confined to Africa, though three species of the genus *Indicator* are also found there. The eggs, which are white, are laid in a hole in the branch or trunk of a tree, generally, if not always, the deserted nursery of a barbet or of a woodpecker.

Family Rhamphastidae

Externally there would seem to be little to connect the Barbets with the Toucans of the *Rhamphastidae*, save that in both types the toes are zygodactyle. But as a straw is said to show which way the wind blows, so here we have one singular habit that is common to both, and that is the habit of turning the tail upwards over the back when at rest. But when their anatomical characters come to be surveyed that relationship becomes manifest.

The Toucans on their emergence from the ancestral stock would seem to have discovered a source of food which enabled them to escape, in large measure, from the competition of their nearest allies, and the pursuit of this advantage resulted in profoundly changing the form of the beak, which in proportion to the size of the bird is enormous. It is not, however, as massive as it appears to be ; for its horny sheath is of extreme delicacy, and it invests a mere shell of bone enclosing a great air space, a delicate filagree work of body-struts giving the necessary strength. A further peculiarity, which they share with the Parrots, is a hinge at the base of the upper jaw, which gives the beak very considerably increased grasping powers. But the parrot's beak is required to serve as a shearing organ, for the demolition of intensively hard shells of fruits and nuts, hence its smaller size and more dense construction.

The Toucans use this beak like a pair of delicate forceps to reach out for relatively soft fruits growing at the ends of boughs too slender to bear the weight of the body. These, when seized, are crushed by the serrations along the edges of the jaws, though smaller morsels are held by the tip of the beak, dexterously tossed into the air, and caught in the mouth, to be swallowed at a gulp. For the tongues of these birds, however, no ready explanation is forthcoming, for they are of great length, very narrow, flattened, and with serrated edges. Insects, eggs, and, it is said, young birds are also eaten.

Such juicy morsels would be easily and speedily withdrawn from their nests.

It is worth noting that though the feet are of the climbing type—zygodactyle—as in the Barbets, Parrots, and Woodpeckers, they are never used for climbing, since these birds jump from bough to bough like

LAMINATED HILL-TOUCAN (*Andigena laminirostris*).

Hornbills. From this we may gather that the Toucans are descended from a stock which had already become highly specialised in this direction, so that a return to the normal type of foot became impossible.

In the matter of their coloration one finds, as with every other group with a considerable number of species, that there are some which, for quite inscrutable reasons, are relatively drab-hued, while others, so to speak, wear " purple and fine linen."

The dullest are found in the genera *Andigena*, *Selindera*, and *Aulacorhamphus*. In *Andigena laminirostris*, the Laminated Hill-toucan, the crown is black, the rest of the upper parts olive-brown, and the under parts bluegrey, relieved by scarlet under tail-coverts. This bird is further remarkable for the fact that the base of the beak is embellished by a large quadrangular ivory-like plate, or shield. The Green-toucans (*Aulacorhamphus*) are at once recognisable by their uniform green coloration, which may be relieved by a white, bluish, or black throat, and a patch of crimson at the base of the tail. There are about a dozen species in this genus. The most resplendent members of the family belong to the genus *Pteroglossus*, which display vividly contrasting areas of green, scarlet, and yellow, with bands of scarlet and black on the under surface, in thirteen out of the eighteen species.   One of the most singular is the Curl-crested Toucan (*Pteroglossus beauharnaisi*), wherein the feathers of the crown take the form of narrow, shiny-black, twisted laminae, looking like black shavings.

Family Picidae

With the Woodpeckers, which include nearly four hundred species of world-wide distribution—though absent in the Australian region, Madagascar, and Egypt—this review of the Coraciiform birds terminates.   They are a singularly interesting group, since few birds display more clearly the effects of concentrated activities of limited range in modifying the organs directly associated with these activities.

The ancestral Woodpecker may be visualised as a Barbet-like bird, which developed a penchant for ants and insects living in the bark of trees.   Now, ants are insects which few animals will eat with any relish, owing to the formic acid in their bodies.   Nevertheless, some birds, and some mammals, have acquired a fondness for these pungent morsels, and all have adopted the same means for their capture—an excessively long tongue, which can be thrust far out of the mouth among the swarming colonies.   To make the thrust effective the tongue is covered with a very sticky saliva, formed in the specially enlarged salivary glands.   Such is the tongue of the Woodpecker, which is furthermore armed at the tip with barb-like bristles.   The bony supports of this tongue have become enormously lengthened so as to pass upwards and backwards over the skull-roof, where the two rods come to lie side by side, to be continued forward and to enter a special tunnel in the beak.

But more than this : some of the Barbets, it will be remembered, climb up and down the bark of trees, at least occasionally.   The Woodpecker uses no other method of moving about in a tree after once it has closed its wings.   And so the tail-feathers have become modified so that their shafts form long, stiff, pointed spines, which can be used as the third leg of a tripod when the bird is clinging with its feet to the bark and hammering a hole with its beak, or even using its tongue to explore crevices for food.   The beak, again, has become modified, taking on a pick-like form and an extremely dense horny sheath that will resist wear.

But Nature is always presenting us with contradictions.   Animals which have become profoundly modified for some particular mode of life will contrive to materially change that mode of life without any readjustment of their specialised characters.   Thus the Red-headed American Woodpecker (*Melanerpes*) seems to have largely forsaken its diet of insects to feed upon eggs—even hen-roosts being entered and robbed—and on young birds. The skull of the victim is pierced by the pick-like beak, when the tongue is thrust into the wound to extract the brain. Frogs are also killed and eaten. The " Sap-suckers " (*Sphyropicus*) puncture the trunks of trees till the sap oozes out, which they suck up with the long tongue. Insects are attracted by this delectable liquor, and these too are eaten. Such as feed largely by raiding ants' nests have to seek their prey on the ground, as with our Green-woodpecker.

Hence it is easy to see how some other species, such as the African *Geocolaptes olivaceus*, contrive to live out of the forests, breeding in holes in sand-banks after the fashion of kingfishers. What causes brought about the suppression of the hind-toe, so that only the outer toe turns backwards and the two middle toes forwards, as in the Burmese and Indian *Sasia* and

TAIL OF GREEN-WOODPECKER (*Gecinus viridis*).   FOOT OF GREEN-WOODPECKER (*Gecinus viridis*).

the European Three-toed Woodpecker (*Picoides tridactylus*), is unknown. In the matter of size these birds range from the giant Ivory-billed Woodpecker, twenty inches long, to the tiny Downy-woodpecker (*Dryobates*) of seven inches.

Though commonly brightly coloured these birds never have the highly polished, metallic surfaces so conspicuous in the Humming-birds, for example. The prevailing colours are green, yellow, black, and white, in various combinations, relieved by brilliant scarlet on the crown and back, or under parts. The females and young are duller than the males. The great Ivory-billed Woodpecker is black, with a scarlet crown. Our Great-spotted Woodpecker is black above, with a white face, a white patch on the neck, and a larger white patch on each side of the back, while the flight-feathers are barred with white. The under parts are white, save the lower abdomen, which is crimson. In the male the nape has a crimson patch.

Curious changes of coloration take place in this species. The young of both sexes have a crimson crown, the females later lose all trace of this, while the males on assuming adult dress transfer the red from the crown to the nape. In the Lesser-spotted Woodpecker, also one of our native birds, the adult and young male have a crimson crown, like the *immature* stage of the Greater-spotted species, while the young female has a red forehead, which is lost in the adult. It would thus seem that the red area of the head in the Greater-spotted species is in process of disappearing, since it is larger in the young than the adult. The Lesser-spotted differs in other respects from the Greater-spotted species in having the lower back and wings transversely barred with white on a black ground, and no crimson on the under parts.

IVORY-BILLED WOODPECKER
(*Campophilus imperialis*).

In our Green-woodpecker, which is too well known to need a detailed description, the adult male has a crimson crown and moustachial patch, the adult female a crimson crown only, while in the immature birds the crown, though crimson, is duller, and is not continued forwards beyond the eye ; in both sexes in the immature plumage there is a crimson moustachial streak, but this is suppressed in the adult female. Finally, in the immature plumage the upper parts are barred, the under barred, streaked, and spotted.

A conspicuously spotted adult dress is found in the American " Flickers " (*Colaptes*), which has pinkish-brown under parts, enlivened with sharply defined black spots. The upper parts are of a clove-brown, with black streaks, the head lead-coloured, with the crimson patch on the nape which is so characteristic of the Woodpecker, while the under surface of the wing is yellow. *Celeus flavus*, ranging from Mexico to Brazil, is of a canary-yellow, with brown tail and wings, and a crimson moustachial streak.

Our Great-spotted Woodpecker has a singular call-note made by striking a hollow branch with its beak with such amazing rapidity that the head is scarcely visible, producing a strange " drumming " sound. It is *not*, as some suppose, made by the voice.

It has already been remarked that the Woodpeckers' nearest allies are the *Capitonidae*. But in the typical Woodpeckers this relationship is largely masked by the more highly specialised characters which have come into being in the course of their emergence. But in certain diminutive Woodpeckers, known as the " Piculets " (*Picumnus*), we have more primitive types linking up with the Wrynecks presently to be described. In the Piculets the tail is short, and the feathers are not stiffened as in the typical Woodpeckers. Furthermore, they are coloured after a fashion not met with among any other birds, the central tail-feathers having one side of the vane white, the other dark; the outermost feathers are also white, and this peculiarity runs throughout the whole of the species, both in the Old and New Worlds.

Their geographical distribution is also singular. Of the forty known species no fewer than thirty-two are South American. Their coloration is dominantly green. The Indian region and South China have each a similar green species. Other species are found in the Burmese provinces, the Malay Peninsula, Sumatra, and North Borneo. The Rufous-piculets (*Sasia*) are peculiar in having lost the hind-toe. One species is found in the Gaboon, and its two congeners in Northern India and the Malay countries.

Another sign of their primitive character is shown in their small size, the largest species not exceeding five inches, the smallest three inches, in length; this measurement is taken when the bird is fully extended, and includes the tail. A better idea of the diminutive character of the smallest species may be gleaned from the fact that a nest of one of the Rufous-piculets (*Sasia ochracea*)—a Himalayan species—was found within a bamboo stem only two and a half inches in diameter. The bird had drilled a neat hole in the stem about three feet from the ground and about six inches above the joint. The walls of this tube had been cut into grooves by the bird to furnish long strips of fibre to form a bed for the eggs.

HARGITT'S PICULET
(*Picumnus undulatus*).

Family *Iyngidae*

The Wrynecks, in so far as their external appearance goes, do not resemble very closely either the Woodpeckers or the Barbets. But even the most superficial of their anatomical characters will suffice to ear-mark them, since they have the long worm-like tongue and the zygodactyle feet which are the hall-mark of the Woodpeckers. Here, indeed, we have the Woodpecker in the making, which was completed by the spiny tail not yet acquired by the Piculets, and the more intensively arboreal habits.

Our own Wryneck (*Iynx torquilla*) may well serve as the type of the group. Holding the bird in the hand, one of the first things one notices is the singularly beautiful coloration, which recalls that of the Nightjar— a rich buff and brown, powdered all over with minute specks of silver-grey.

It does not climb trees like the Wood-peckers, but like these birds it builds in holes in trees. These, however, must be ready-made; it never hacks one out for itself. It can, it should be remarked, be readily induced to occupy a nesting-box, such as is so often put up on trees for small birds.

Like the Green-woodpecker it feeds largely on ants, which are taken from their nests on the ground. The Wryneck is something of a contor-tionist, and is never seen to better advantage as a performer than when courting, when the neck is out-stretched and the head twisted round to an extent not seen in any other bird. When its nesting-hole is in-vaded protests are made with loud hisses, and this fact, combined with

WRYNECK (*Iynx torquilla*).

the play it makes with its neck, has gained it the name of " Snake-bird." It is also known as the " Cuckoo's-mate." Only four species are known. Our own bird is found all over Europe and Asia; the other three species are confined to Africa.

Order PASSERIFORMES

(*Perching-birds*)

This vast assemblage of birds, numbering more than six thousand species, known as the Passeriformes, has always been, and still is, the despair of the systematist, so closely are they interrelated, so slight are the essential differences between them.

Commonly these birds are spoken of as the " Perching-birds," or " Passeres," and many have doubtless asked what is the meaning of this term, what *are* " Passeres " ? Briefly this term includes birds such as the Crows, Finches, Thrushes, Wagtails, Wrens, Tit-mice, and so on. For the most part they live in trees or undergrowth, and when on the ground hop, though the Starlings, Wagtails, and Crows are familiar exceptions to this rule.

In the more technical, scientific sense the " Passeres " can be less readily defined, for there are a number of types unknown to any but those who have made a life-study of birds, which, having to be included, make any attempt to formulate a crisp definition impossible.

No useful end could be attained in these pages by setting out the evidence on which our conclusions are based as to the affinities, near and remote, of the " Passeres," or of the data in detail on which such and such birds are to be regarded as " Passerine," while others are rejected from that group, especially since this evidence rests entirely on anatomical characters.

The essential facts, however, must be given. In the Passerine birds the hallux, or hind-toe, is well developed, and the front toes are free ; the foot is said to be " eleutherodactyle." None of the Coraciiform birds have a foot of this type. The bones of the skull, and especially of the palate,

share a common plan in the Passeres, and differ from what obtains in the Coraciiformes ; and the same is true of the breast-bone and the shoulder-girdle. More important still, within the group, is the form of the syrinx, the organ of voice at the lower end of the windpipe, about which more must be said. The young are hatched blind, and with a few exceptions, as in the Crows, for example, they develop a loose fragile type of nestling-

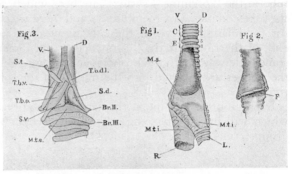

SYRINX OF A JAY.

Fig. 1.—Syrinx after removal of outer wall. *V, D,* Ventral and dorsal borders; *C, E,* Tracheal rings, closed and drawn apart; *M.s.,* Semilunar membrane; *M.t.i.,* Internal tympanic membrane ; *L* and *R,* Left and right bronchus.
Fig. 2.—Shows the fleshy lip, or fold (*F*), on the outer wall.
Fig. 3.—*T.b.d.*1. and *T.b.v.,* Ends of a long muscle running down windpipe for altering length ; *S.d.* and *S.v.,* Muscles of syrinx ; *M.t.e.,* External tympanic membrane ; *S.t.,* Sterno-tracheal muscle; *T.b.o.,* Tracheo-bronchialis obliquus muscle ; *Br.II.* and *Br.III.,* Bronchial rings.

down, which is later borne out upon the tips of the feathers as the fledgling stage is reached.

Nothing is more tiresome in constructing schemes of classification than " exceptions to the rule," and nothing is more exasperating than " annectant types," for they make crisp definitions impossible. But those who take wider views, who regard " Classification " as but a means to an end, find in these " annectant types " the evidence needed to enable one to trace the lines of development leading from lowly unspecialised to highly complex types.

The Passerine syrinx affords a case in point. The accompanying illustration shows these muscles and the essential characters of this all-important type of voice-organ, which attains to its " peak-development " only in the " Song-birds." Herein the last four or five rings which compose the windpipe are fused together to form a solid tube. The " bronchi," or right and left branches of the windpipe to the lungs, are formed each of a delicate tube of membrane, having the outer walls strengthened by three pairs of semi-circular rods. The third pair are more or less isolated, and to the ends of the first two pairs—which are closely applied to the end of the tracheal tube—muscles are attached, which serve to modulate the voice. To the isolated third pair only one muscle is attached, and to its lowest end. A bar across the end of the tube bearing a thin, median, vertical fold of membrane forms a " reed," set vibrating by the rush of air from the two bronchi, and this completes the syrinx or " organ of voice."

In the " annectant types " referred to, the syrinx is simpler in structure, producing a " tracheal " and a " bronchial " syrinx. In the first-named the lower end of the windpipe—the rings which are fused to form the solid tube in the " oscinine " syrinx—are here widely separated, and the walls of the tube completed by membrane ; and there are only a single pair of muscles for modulating the voice, these being attached to the middle, not to the end, of the ring. In the " bronchial syrinx " membranous areas are found some little way down the bronchi, and a long pair of muscles running down the trachea are inserted into the middle of the third pair of these bronchial rings.

Such, in broad outline, is the nature of the organ of voice in the Passeres, which will have to be referred to again when we come to the respective groups concerned.

Sub-order *PASSERES ANISOMYODI*

Families Eurylaemidae (Broad-bills), Cotingidae (Chatterers), and Pipridae (Manakins)

That the Broad-bills, Chatterers, and Manakins are nearly related is beyond a peradventure ; in all the essentials of their structure they agree. The points wherein they differ are those which they have acquired as they drifted away from one another on assuming their distinctive characters.

But the Broad-bills have retained one feature of their ancient heritage of no little importance, since it furnishes a clue to the stock from which they and all the rest of the Passerine tribe have descended. And this is found in the foot. It has already been pointed out that the typical Passerine foot is of the eleutherodactyle type, the hind-toe being well developed, the front toes all free. But in the Broad-bills and the Chatterers the foot is " desmo-dactylous," that is to say, the third and fourth toes are bound together as in the Nightjars.

The syrinx of all these birds is of the " tracheo-bronchial " type, and, furthermore, in one of the Chatterers its main muscle is remarkable for its great massiveness. It would seem, indeed, that the complex muscular syrinx of the true Passeres was derived by the splitting up of such a mass.

The Broad-bills inhabit the forests of Indo-Malaya and the adjacent islands, feeding for the most part on insects, and in some cases on fruit and berries. It is probable, indeed, that these vegetarians represent the primitive members of the group, as this diet helps to explain the great width of the beak from which these birds take their name. The nest, a large, oval structure of grass, moss, and fibres, is suspended from a branch, and has an opening at the side. The eggs in most of the species are white or cream-coloured, but in some the larger end is heavily spotted.

In the matter of coloration some are of great beauty, but in the Indian *Serilophus* we have what must be regarded as an ancestral type, the plumage being

BLACK-AND-YELLOW BROAD-BILL (*Eurylaemus ochromelas*).

of a sombre grey-brown, with a tinge of chestnut on the rump. The Dusky Broad-bill (*Corydon sumatranus*), by an intensification of these melanic pigments, has become black, relieved by a white wing-bar. In this species the beak is so large and wide as to recall that of the Frog-mouths. The Green Broad-bill (*Calyptomena viridis*) is bright green, with a black spot on the neck and black bars across the wings. *Cymborhynchus* is black and crimson, while the beautiful *Psarisomus*, ranging from the Eastern Himalayas to Borneo, is green, with black and blue head and wings, yellow face and throat, and blue tail.

UMBRELLA-BIRD (*Cephalopterus ornatus*).

The Chatterers are New-World types, ranging from South Mexico to Argentina, and they include some very singular as well as some extremely beautiful types, such, for example, as the gorgeous Cock-of-the-Rock (*Rupicola crocea*), which is of a flaming orange colour, with black wings and tail. The head is surmounted by a great semicircular crest, with a narrow sub-terminal border of red; while the greater tail-coverts terminate in a squarely truncate border produced into points. Finally, the inner wing-coverts are produced into long outstanding filaments.   Another most striking species is the Umbrella-bird (*Cephalopterus ornatus*).   This is a large, black bird, with a great crest, which in appearance recalls that of an open umbrella, and a singular pendent wattle down the front of the neck, covered with feathers.

Even more remarkable are the Bell-birds (*Chasmorhynchus*), of which there

are four species: *Chasmorhynchus niveus*, the Bell-bird, or " Campanero," is white, and has a curious wattle, bearing a few short, degenerate feathers.   Normally it hangs down over the beak like the wattle of the turkey-cock, but in moments of excitement, especially when courting, it can be made turgid, when it stands straight up over the beak like a long spine.   *C. tricarunculatus* is chestnut, with a white head, and bears three wattles, a central, above the beak, and one on each side ; and these are coloured blue.   Truly an astonishing form of ornament.   The Bell-birds are famous for the sweet bell-like notes they utter while these wattles are erected.

The Manakins are small, often brilliantly coloured birds, numbering some seventy specimens, and inhabiting thick under-growth near marshes.   They range from South Mexico through Brazil and North Argentina.   Some have the shafts of the

THREE-WATTLED BELL-BIRD
(*Chasmorhynchus tricarunculatus*).

primaries curiously thickened, as in the Bailidor (*Chiroxiphia*), which has a further peculiarity in that the central tail-feathers are produced into long, wire-like filaments.   When courting these little birds perform strange dances, two males facing each other and alternately leaping up into the air and back on to the branch to the tune of *to-le-do*, the first syllable as the upward leap is made, the second at its height, the third on alighting.

Family Tyrranidae

The Tyrant-birds, or " American Flycatchers," are an interesting group, but rather for what they are not than for what they are.   In the first place, they present several significant points of resemblance with the True-fly-catchers and Shrikes.   Thus they stand on the very borderland of the typical Passeres.   They have, however, a " mesomyodean syrinx " ; that is to say, a syrinx of the simple type just described, wherein the voice muscles are limited to a pair, inserted into the middle of the half-rings of the bronchi. Again, though numbering more than four hundred species, there are very few which have developed bright patches of colour, olive or black-and-grey being the prevailing hues, though some display patches of scarlet, orange-red, or yellow, and some have deeply forked tails.

In many the beak is much depressed and wide at the gape, as in the True-flycatchers, and its base is often fringed by bristles. For the most part they are arboreal, and hence short-legged, but some are largely ground-dwellers, and in consequence have relatively long legs. In the genus *Centrites* one finds a conspicuously long hind-toe in accordance with the bird's lark-like habits.

Their range extends from the extreme north to the extreme south of America, and they feed for the most part on insects which are captured by a sudden dart into the air and a return to the adopted station.

YETAPA TYRANT-BIRD (*Cybernates yetapa*).

The best known is the famous King-bird, which is of a blackish ash colour above, white below, but enlivened by a brilliant flame-coloured crown. It is a bird with a dominating personality, and at no time is this more apparent than during the nesting season, when, in defence of its eggs or young, it will attack and drive away crows, owls, and hawks with equal fury, should they approach too near its home.

Family Pittidae

Though the Tyrant-birds and the Pittas are undoubtedly nearly related, they stand as wide as the poles apart in the matter of their coloration, for the Pittas, or Ant-thrushes, are birds of strikingly brilliant plumage. One might fairly describe them as long-legged, short-tailed thrushes, with the splendour of a kingfisher.

Numbering no more than fifty species they are all confined to the Old World, ranging from India and North China to East Australia, New Guinea, and New Britain, while three species are African. Their habits are singularly uniform throughout their range, the birds haunting thick jungle or dense scrub, whether in the rock-strewn glens of India or the damp forests of Malaya. As one would gather from their long legs, they are ground-dwellers, hunting over beds of fallen leaves for molluscs, insects, and worms. Their method of progress is by a series of rapid bounds, so quickly made that the eye can scarcely follow them through the foliage. When hard pressed they will take to flight, though only for a short distance.

The nest is commonly placed on the ground at the foot of a tree or in undergrowth, and is made of twigs, roots, grass, and moss, which may or may not be more or less cemented with mud, and is formed with an entrance at the side. The eggs are of a creamy-white, with brown, reddish-grey, or purplish spots.

The Great-pitta (*P. maximus*), of Gilolo, is glossy black, with blue wing-coverts and a white wing-bar, and green edges to the secondaries. The under parts are white, save the chin, which is black, and the belly, which is crimson. *P. bandi*, of Borneo, is crimson above, with a blue crown and tail, a black nape, and a white wing-bar. The under parts are black, shading into purple and blue on the abdomen. *Pitta coerulea* is bright blue above, with an ashy head, black nape, and greyish-black below. *Coracopitta lugubris*, of New Guinea, is entirely black.

The Wattled ant-thrush (*Philepitta*), of Madagascar, is commonly regarded as nearly related to the Pittas, but it is really closely allied to the Cotingas, or Chatterers. There are two species, one black and one green and yellow. By way of ornament they display a green fleshy wattle above the eye. Little is known of their habits.

Families Pteroptochidae, Conopophagidae, Formicariidae, Dendrocolaptidae and Xenicidae (*The Tapacolas, Ant-birds, Woodhewers, and Bush-wrens*)

Those who make an intensive study of birds find in the families included under this heading some extremely valuable material bearing on the evolution of the Passerine types. But to such as have neither time nor opportunity for detailed research of this kind they are practically non-existent, for even when displayed in a museum they would be passed over unnoticed, since all are small, drab-hued species, belonging for the most part to the American continent, and found only in the recesses of forests or places remote from human occupation. Nevertheless, some, at least, present features of more than passing interest, and these alone of the hundreds of species known will be mentioned here.

But it is to be noted that these birds really form a quite important group in the present connection, since they share between them the possession of one of the three types of windpipe to which reference has already been made in these pages ; they have, in short, a " tracheal syrinx," and hence are known as the " Tracheophonae." The peculiarity of this syrinx, it may be remembered, is that the last few rings at the bottom of the windpipe instead of becoming fused to form a bony box, are, on the contrary, extremely reduced in diameter, and separated by wide bands of thin membrane. But though they share this internal peculiarity they have changed much in outward form in adaptation to various modes of life.

The Tapacolas (*Pteroptochidae*), with which are to be associated the Conopophagas, may be described, with some truth, as a tribe which has failed to make its mark. But if only on this account, it is an interesting tribe. What are the causes which have held them in check? Numbering no more than a dozen genera and fewer than forty species, they are all birds of dull hue, and their haunts are remote from those of man; hence little is known of their habits.

The Tapacolas are small, wren-like birds, with large feet and straight claws. Their range extends from Costa Rica through South America to Patagonia and the Falklands. They haunt thick cover, hopping from bough to bough, or running like mice on the ground, carrying the tail wren-fashion —turned up—in their search for insects, seeds, and buds.

UNDULATED ANT-BIRD (*Grallaria squamigera*).

Of the Conopophagas still less is known. About a dozen species have been described, but those who have sent home specimens to our museums have told us nothing of their habits. They are all of varying shades of brown, with patches of chestnut, deepening into black, chiefly on the crown and throat, in a few species.

We may profitably contrast the slow beat of the pulse of life in the Tapacolas and Conopophagas with the vitality displayed by the Ant-birds, which, though maintaining throughout the whole two hundred and fifty species a monotonously dull-brown coloration of varying shades of intensity, have yet shown themselves to be possessed of a considerable measure of plasticity, whereby they have come to adapt themselves to different modes of life, in the course of which material changes of structure have taken place. These are indicated by the fact that they have split up into three types, or groups. One of these has come to attain a curious likeness to the Thrushes, hence they are known as the " Ant-thrushes," the other as the " Ant-shrikes," from their resemblance to the Shrikes. The third group resembles the long-legged Pittas, but lacking their splendour of coloration.

Though commonly known as Ant-birds they do not, as might be supposed, feed on ants, but on the swarms of spiders and insects driven out by the foraging ants so abundant in South American forests. The " Thrush-like " group (*Formicariinae*) embraces also a number of small species which resemble, not Thrushes, but Wrens and Warblers. The Shrike-like forms (*Thamnophilinae*) are also insect-eaters, but, from their hooked beaks, probably also prey on small birds. But all alike seem to live largely on the ground. The short-tailed, long-legged species (*Grallariinae*), recalling the Pittas, probably live in more open country.

Two species of the *Thamnophilinae* have evidently adopted a very different diet to that of the rest of the tribe. Thus *Neoctantes niger* and *Clytoctantes alixi* have curious upturned beaks.

Much has yet to be learned from travellers and explorers about the habits of these birds. All the information we have, so far, is that they are of shy, retiring habits, creeping silently about among the lower branches or on the ground, searching for insects and larvae amid the densest and thorniest thickets.

The Wood-hewers (*Dendrocolaptinae*), numbering some two hundred and eighty species, like the " Ant-birds," are all dull of hue, though a chestnut tail is a common feature among them. These two groups—the Ant-birds and the Woodhewers— demand a much more intensive study than they have yet received, for in both we find curious parallels with types with which we are familiar. Wrens, Warblers, Thrushes, and Pittas all find their counterparts in the single family of the Ant- birds. Similarly Woodpeckers, Tree-creepers, Nuthatches, Warblers, and Wheatears are, so to speak, personated among the "Woodhewers."

GREAT RUFOUS WOODHEWER
(*Xiphocolaptes major*).

Clearly we have here evidence of the moulding effects of similar modes of life. Why, again, should these two groups have proved so malleable, while the Tapacolas have remained so conservative ?

The characteristics of the five sub-families need not be detailed here, suffice it to say that the Woodpecker and Tree-creeper-like forms belonging to the *Dendrocolaptinae*, *Xiphocolaptes major*, *Nasica longirostris*, and *Dendroplex picus*, are relatively large birds, with long, pointed beaks and spiny tails, giving them a striking likeness to true Woodpeckers, while *Xiphorhynchus trochilirostris* has the slender curved beak and spiny tail of the Tree-creepers. *Glyphorhynchus cuneatus* simulates a Nuthatch. Some half-dozen species of the genus *Sclerurus* have spiny tails. Yet they have relatively long legs and are ground-dwellers.

This remarkable family has produced some wonderful nest-builders.

The " Firewood-gatherer " (*Anumbius*), for example, builds a bulky structure of sticks, with an entrance at the top, and a spiral passage leading down to the nest-chamber, which is lined with grass and contains from four to five white eggs. The Warbler-like *Synallyaxinae*, again, have produced some great architects. Some species of the genus *Synallyaxis*, for example, build enormous nests of sticks and twigs, lined with grass and feathers and generally divided into two chambers. Such nests may be large enough to fill an ordinary wheelbarrow—out of all proportion to the size of the builder.

Next come the nests of the Oven-birds (*Furnarius*). These are huge, globular structures made entirely of mud, and taking long months to build. They have an entrance on one side leading into a spiral passage, which terminates in a spacious nest-chamber. They become baked by the sun till they are as hard as a brick. Finally we have *Geositta curnicularia*, curiously like a Wheatear. Still more strangely, like the Wheatear, it also breeds in a burrow, which it excavates for itself, driving a tunnel as much as six feet long, and lining the nest-chamber with soft grass. The eggs, as is the invariable rule when they are deposited in dark cavities, are white-shelled.

LENATEROS, or FIREWOOD-GATHERER
(*Anumbius acuticaudus*).

The New Zealand Bush-wrens (*Xenicidae*), like the Tapacolas, are interesting examples of types which have failed, so to speak, to make good. We must regard them as side-twigs of the Tree of Descent. If only on this account, however, they are worthy of more attention than they have yet received from ornithologists.

There are but four species of these little birds, peculiar to the highland forests of New Zealand. The best known—and of this even we know but little—is the " Rifleman " (*Acanthidositta chloris*), which is almost entirely arboreal and feeds on insects. It places its bottle-shaped nest in holes in trees or other cavities, and lays from three to five white eggs.

The nearest relations of these birds seem to be the spiny-tailed Ant-birds, but they present rather peculiar features in regard to the external ear, which so far have not been fully investigated.

Sub-order PASSERES DIACROMYODAE

We pass now to the remaining types of the Passerine birds, which, it has already been remarked, are divisible into three main groups, determined by the number of the muscles of the syrinx and the mode of their attachment. These types have already been discussed.

If the Bush-wrens illustrate the evolution of a group with what may be called a " low vitality," these " Diacromyodean " Passeres forcibly demonstrate the very opposite, for they have spread over the whole world, and have split up into more than five thousand species. A moment's reflection will show that this survey would lose both interest and usefulness if it embraced more than the outstanding types.

Here, then, as with every other group throughout these chapters, we have to begin with birds which are on the " borderland."

The Lyre-birds and the Scrub-birds

Of these two the Lyre-bird, at least, is a more or less familiar type. Its place, as is shown by its anatomy, is on the threshold of the " True Passeres," or " Oscines." It cannot be placed with any of the preceding passerine types, because its voice-muscles are attached to the ends of the bronchial semi-rings ; it cannot be placed among the " Oscines," in the strict sense of the term, because it has but three pairs of these muscles instead of seven. Yet it is not unique in this, for right in the very middle of the Oscine-passeres is a genus with only three pairs. This is *Sphenoeacus*, one of the Thrush-tribe. This fact has not received the attention it deserves. A further examination may profoundly change our views as to the systematic position of the Thrushes, or it may show that *Sphenoeacus* has no place in this group.

LYRE-BIRD (*Menura superba*).

But to return to the Lyre-bird ; it is no disparagement to the Peacock or the Birds-of-Paradise to speak of the Lyre-bird as one of the most striking of living birds in the matter of ornament, and this, too, without the added stimulus of vivid colours. The general coloration of both sexes is of dark browns and greys. All the bird's energies, so to speak, have been expended on the development of the tail, which, as will be seen in the accompanying illustration, takes the form of the ancient musical instrument known as the lyre. The frame of the instrument is formed by the outermost tail-feathers, which are curiously notched and delicately shaded with rust-coloured areas on a white ground, while the upper tail-coverts have the webs disconnected to form long, graceful filaments.

In the breeding season each cock makes himself a " playing-ground," and thereon scrapes up little hillocks for " dancing places," where he struts and pirouettes with tail erect and drooping wings, pecking and singing at intervals.

The interesting features of the Lyre-bird, however, do not begin and end with the tail. The great size of the legs and toes suffice to show at a glance that it is a ground-dweller with limited powers of flight. Its haunts are precipitous rocks and gullies in thick forests with tangled undergrowth, where it hunts for worms, molluscs, beetles, and other insects, which are turned up from the ground by the scratching of the powerful feet armed with long claws. Though one speaks of *the* " Lyre-bird," there are, as a matter of fact, three species, but they differ one from another only in relatively unimportant details.

The nest is an oval, domed structure, placed either on the ground or in a tree, and containing but a single egg. The nestling differs from that of all other Passeriform and Coraciiform birds in having a prodigiously thick coat of down.

This bird is but one of the many natural history treasures of Australia which is on the verge of extermination, owing to the deplorable apathy and lack of appreciation of their responsibilities in this regard displayed by the Australian people.

The Scrub-bird (*Atrichornis*) is another rare Australian type, represented by two species, of which the males only are known. They are to be regarded as distant relatives of the Lyre-birds, though by some authorities they are widely separated.

They have extremely short wings, and from the fact that the furcula, or " merry-thought," is wanting, they probably fly but little. The beak is large and the tail long. *Atrichornis clamosa*, of Western Australia, is about eight and a half inches long, brown above, with dark, transverse bars, reddish-white below, with a black patch on the breast. *A. rufescens*, of New South Wales, lacks the brighter coloration of the under parts seen in *clamosa*. They are shy birds, haunting close scrub or grassy and bushy tracts, and feeding on insects. They are said to mimic the cries of other birds with great fidelity, a characteristic also of the Lyre-bird, which has added faithful imitations of a dog's bark and the setting of a saw !

THE SWALLOWS, FLYCATCHERS, SHRIKES, WOOD-SWALLOWS, AND BIRDS-OF-PARADISE

Under this heading a large number of extremely interesting types are included, some of which have been placed elsewhere by other authorities, who have ignored the deeper-seated anatomical evidence, without which no system of classification is worth the paper it is written on.

If the Swallow tribe were not so much in evidence among us, at least during the summer months, we should, perhaps, appreciate them more than we do. The three types constantly before us seem to be accepted for what they are—Swallows, House-martins, and Sand-martins—without comment. Yet, in their coloration and their nesting habits, they present striking contrasts. That they are all living in the same external environment and feeding on the same kind of food, flies and other small insects captured in mid-air and never anywhere else, shows that external conditions of life do not govern their coloration. This, then, must be due to some internal physiological process, whereby precisely similar food material is converted into pigments of very different qualities ; and the same is true of the factors which govern the development of ornament in the form of the long tail streamers which distinguish some.

We get some insight into the problems of coloration when the Swallows of the world are surveyed ; but since they have split up into more than a hundred species, no more can be done here than indicate the broad outlines of the coloration, which may be said to start with the sober-coloured Bourbon Striped-swallow (*Phedina bourbonica*), of the Mascarene Islands and the Congo. Here the upper parts are of a mouse-brown, striated with darker brown, and the under parts are of a pale brown, with striations on the throat, breast, and flanks. These striations have been retained by a number of species which have passed into the " resplendent " stage, as in the Striped-breasted Swallow (*Hirundo puella*).

The beautiful steel-blue of the upper parts of our Swallow has overspread the whole body in the Blue-swallow of South-East Africa ; while the Jamaican-swallow has exchanged blue for green, the upper surface being of a wonderful golden-green with bronze reflexions, while the under surface is pure white. In some species, again, the young birds wear a dull-coloured ancestral livery, as in the White-bellied Swallow (*Tachycineta bicolor*), which in its immature dress is mouse-brown, the adult having a mantle of metallic blue. No more than the barest outlines of this theme have been traced here, but sufficient has been said to show how important is the study of coloration.

THE FLYCATCHERS

That the Flycatchers and Swallows are related is generally admitted, and both show traces of an affinity with the *Tyrannidae* or " Tyrant-birds " already described. They include so formidable a number of genera and species that no more than those which may be called the " expression points " in their evolution can be cited here.

In their habits they resemble one another ; and this is especially true of their mode of feeding, insects being taken in mid-air, not, after the fashion of Swallows, during continuous flight, but by darting out from a convenient perch and returning to the same spot after the capture has been made—or missed.

Our own Spotted-flycatcher, in the matter of its coloration, is one of the more primitive types, being of a hair-brown above, with darker striations on the crown, and white below, with inconspicuous striations on the throat and flanks. Why it was ever called the " Spotted " Flycatcher is a mystery, for it is emphatically *not* spotted. The beak has the typical broad, flat gape, fringed with bristles, characteristic of the Flycatchers, and the legs are short. Our Pied-flycatcher, which does not breed with us, has, so to speak, clarified its pigments. By concentration the brown has become black, which is diffused over the whole of the upper surface, save the forehead and a broad patch on the wings, which are white, while the under parts are pure white. The male of the Red-breasted Flycatcher bears a curious resemblance to our robin, since the throat is red. This little bird visits the British Islands occasionally, though on the Continent it will be found breeding from Denmark to Siberia. Strangely enough, a similar coloration is found again in the scarlet and pink-breasted " Robins " of Australia, as, for example, in *Petroeca rhodinogaster*.

Some species of the genus *Malurus* are conspicuously beautiful. One shows delightful combinations of blue, purple, and velvety-black; another is vermilion, black, and brown above and black below; a third has crimson in place of vermilion; and in these the splendours are displayed only in the males. The Paradise-flycatchers (*Terpsiphone*), so often depicted on Chinese and Japanese fans, contain some beautiful long-tailed, crested birds.

DOBSON'S CUCKOO-SHRIKE (*Artamides dobsoni*).

The males are white. The female has a strikingly different, yet certainly resplendent coloration, being of a rich bay above, with a glossy greenish-black head and throat, and with black markings on the head and tail. In others of this genus the males display maroon, chestnut, blue-grey, or black in place of white.

Whether all the genera included to-day among the Flycatchers are rightly placed here is a matter for investigation, for some of these birds differ very markedly from the typical Flycatchers in their habits. Those of the genus *Smicrornis*, for example, behave like Tits. *Niltara* is a berry-eating genus.

A link between the Flycatchers and the Shrikes seems to be found in the Cuckoo-shrikes (*Campephagidae*), an Old-World family containing some rather striking forms. A common feature is the curiously spiny character of the rump-feathers, the shafts of which slightly project in almost needle-like points.

The " Minivets " (*Pericrocotus*) are predominantly scarlet in the males, yellow in the females.   Azure-blue, cobalt, and black mark the genus *Graucalus;* green and golden-yellow obtain in *Campechaera*, varied by black, white, and grey. Both sexes are resplendent. The Mascarene genus *Oxynotus* is remarkable for the fact that the males of the two species are alike in coloration, while the females are different.

These birds inhabit the wooded regions of India and the Indo-Chinese countries and islands, and generally travel in small flocks, searching for insects.   One species, the Pheasant Cuckoo-shrike (*Pteropodocys phasianella*), is a native of Australia.   It is a ground-dweller, and in consequence has long legs.   The tail, by the way, is long and forked.

The family *Vireonidae*, or " Greenlets," ranging from Winnipeg to Argentina, does not call for special mention. It numbers some sixty species of small birds, greenish or olive in hue, haunting forests up to an altitude of ten thousand feet, as well as swamps and ravines and the streets of towns.   They build neat nests of leaves, grass, bark, and lichens, held together with spider's webs and cottony materials, and lined with fibres. The rim of the nest is commonly turned over on to the fork of the branch in which it is placed, while the eggs, four or five, are white, spotted with red-brown, black, or purple.

We are discussing here, it should be remarked, four fairly distinct groups of inter-related types—the Swallows, Flycatchers, Shrikes, and the " Piping-crows."   The first two of these have just been reviewed.

The Shrikes (*Laniidae*) are by most authorities regarded as constituting five sub-families, which the present writer prefers to regard as entitled to rank as families.   This, however, is a matter of no great importance.

The typical Shrike is well represented by our own Redbacked-shrike (*Lanius collurio*), wherein the beak is notched and hooked at the tip, recalling that of a hawk.   It is the habit of these birds to impale mice, nestling-birds, lizards, and large beetles on thorns, the more easily to take therefrom such morsels as they covet.   This they do because the feet are not strong enough to enable them to hold their victims while they tear them up, hawk-fashion.   They seem, however, never to do more than take a small piece or two from each body, and then leave it.   On account of these unpleasing habits these birds are commonly known as " Butcher-birds."   Insects form the chief item of their food.

The *Prionopidae*, or Wood-shrikes, include a large number of species, for the most part dull-coloured, ranging from Africa and Southern Asia to New Guinea and Polynesia.   They frequent trees and bushes, and feed upon insects, molluscs, and fruits.   As might be supposed from their departure in the method of feeding practised by the traditional Shrikes, these birds have externally little that suggests a Shrike.   The Australian " Magpie-lark " and the Malayan " Jay-shrikes," by their very names, imply likenesses to quite alien forms.

The Drongos (*Dicruridae*), ranging from Africa through India and China to the Malayan Archipelago and Australia, are much more Shrike-like in the form of the beak. While some capture their prey after the fashion of Flycatchers, darting off from some fixed point and returning to the same spot after a capture has been made, others hunt on the ground, or pick their victims from leaves or flowers or from the backs of cattle. Most of the species are black and have excessively long, forked tails, the outermost pair of feathers being drawn out to form, as in *Dissemurus paradisea*, the typical Drongo, a pair of " racquets."

They frequent gardens and open country up to eight thousand feet.

Many have quite melodious notes ; indeed, the Larger Racquet-tailed Drongo has been described as the best singing bird in the East.

The unreliability of external appearances as a guide in the classification of birds is well shown in the case of the Swallow-shrikes (*Artamidae*). They constitute

LARGE RACQUET-TAILED DRONGO (*Dissemurus paradisea*).

but a small group, and are characterised by the pointed greyish-blue beak and long, almost swallow-like wings, and in their actions and mode of life they closely resemble swallows. But structurally they are, without question, Shrikes. With the exception of one West African species, all are found in the Indian and Australian regions and belong to one genus, *Artamus*.

The Piping-crows (*Gymnorhidae*), though comprising several genera and species, are not birds of any very special interest. They seem to be nearly related to the Swallow-shrikes, and like them they have cone-shaped, sharp-pointed blue beaks. The Black and White Australian Piping-crow and the black and white *Strepera*, also of Australia, are the two best-known species. More striking in appearance is the strange *Pityriasis* of Borneo, which is wholly black save for the head, this being featherless and studded with tiny wattles of a flaming red.

THE BIRDS-OF-PARADISE

Of all birds, perhaps these are the most wonderful. Though commonly regarded as glorified crows, they have no relationship whatever with these birds. Their nearest allies, as the present writer has shown, are the

Gymnorhidae—the " Piping-crows " just referred to. No other group of birds includes such an amazing variety of types or such a bewildering galaxy of splendour, a splendour which beggars description ; and, furthermore, this magnificence is associated with displays during the courting season of the strangest and weirdest kind.

In some cases the plumage has the appearance of black velvet rather than of feathers, in others it seems to be made of burnished metal, and yet again, in others, the feathers seem to be made of delicate filaments of silk.

A quite extraordinary form of ornament has been evolved by the rare King of Saxony's Bird-of-Paradise, which bears on each side of the head a long streamer, more than twice the length of the whole bird, which looks as though it was formed of little squares of blue leather, or like a row of small flags attached to a long line. The rest of the plumage may be summarised as velvety-black above and yellow below. The long-tailed Bird-of-Paradise (*Epimachus magnus*), has a dark velvet-like plumage glossed with bronze and purple, while its tail, over two feet long, is tinged with the most intense opalescent blue.

Hunstein's Bird-of-Paradise, when displaying its splendours, is strangely beautiful—a great semicircular shield, looking like golden-yellow spunglass, rises up behind the head, contrasting with a huge breast-shield of dark metallic-green, while the tail is surmounted by a pair of long, stiff shafts looking like curled wires. The Six-wired Bird-of-Paradise has a plumage of a velvet-black, with bronze and purple reflexions. On the back of the head is a broad, recurved band of feathers, glowing with the hues of emerald and topaz of indescribable brilliancy. The throat and breast bear scale-like feathers of an intense, metallic-golden hue, changing with the incidence of the light to green and blue, while the flank-feathers are excessively developed to form, when displayed, a great outstanding shield. Even more singular, however, are the long, wire-like shafts which spring from the head, each bearing at its tip a small vane.

The Superb Bird-of-Paradise is extremely rare, and little is known of its habits ; but it well deserves its name. At first glance one imagines its plumage to have been fashioned out of black velvet, which here and there shimmers with brilliant metallic green and blue reflexions. Its breast bears a wonderful shield of satin-like feathers of a beautiful bluish-green, while from the back of the head springs a huge shield, like a pair of outspread wings, of an intense velvety-black, glossed with bronze and purple.

The long, flowing side-plumes of the Lesser Bird-of-Paradise form an arched, golden cascade when, in moments of sexual excitement, it is raised aloft, and were this the only species known to us we should account it as a superbly beautiful bird ; but it suffers, to a certain extent, when compared with its rivals.

Something, finally, must be said of the King Bird-of-Paradise. Picture a bird no bigger than a thrush, but of a wonderful cinnibar-red, having a sheen as of spun-glass, with the head clothed in short, velvet, orange-hued feathers, and with a white breast having a satin sheen and crossed by a band of deep metallic-green, contrasting with a red throat.   Add a yellow beak, a marvellous apple-green revealed when the mouth is opened during its " display," and legs of cobalt-blue, and you will have the features which arrest the attention at the first glance.   A little closer study will reveal yet other features.   Along each side the flank-feathers are greatly elongated, and when splayed out will form an almost circular shield of delicate ash-grey, bordered with buff and emerald green.   Finally, there is the tail, wherein the middle pair of feathers form a pair of long, wiry stalks, terminating in a coiled disc of emerald-green with a metallic sheen.

The extraordinary display of these splendours during its courtship antics almost beggars description, and would take too long even to attempt it here.

Whether the Bower-birds (*Ptilonorhynchidae*) of New Guinea and Australia are really related to the Birds-of-Paradise is a moot point, and one which cannot be settled till more is known of their internal structure.   By autho-rities to-day, however, they are always regarded as closely associated. Though some species in regard to their plumage may well be called resplendent, they are in no way rivals of the Birds-of-Paradise.   But they are remarkable for the extraordinary habit they have of building " playing-grounds " for the performance of their " courtship rites."   Thus Newton's Bower-bird (*Priondura*) erects an enormous structure of sticks, sometimes eight feet high, and of complicated architecture, the main structure being supplemented by hut-like outbuildings !   The Gardener Bower-bird (*Amblyornis*) builds a miniature cabin of various kinds of moss, and surrounds it with a tiny but perfectly kept lawn of moss, studded with brilliantly coloured flowers, fruits, and insects.   Such as become faded are immediately replaced.

The precise relationships of the beautiful Waxwings cannot, as yet, be determined.   Usually they are regarded as related to the Wood-swallows (*Artamidae*).   They are here included as outstanding members of the larger Swallow—Flycatcher—Shrike series, which we have been surveying.

They are remarkably handsome birds, chiefly northern in their habit, though some range as far as Central America.   Our own Waxwing, which visits us at irregular intervals, and sometimes in great numbers during the winter months, has a curiously silky-brown plumage, enlivened by a singular projection of the shafts of the secondary wing-feathers and the tail-feathers.   Beyond the vane these projections take the form of long, flattened spines of a bright sealing-wax red.   They feed on seeds and berries.

Nuthatches, Titmice, and Tree-creepers

By a general consensus of opinion the Nuthatches, the Titmice, and the Tree-creepers are not only near akin, but are nearly related to the Shrike-tribe. This may well be the case, and here, at any rate, they may be left until their ancestry has been properly studied by an appeal to their anatomy.

These are, at any rate, all strictly arboreal birds, and they present some interesting differences in regard to their mode of life. Thus the Nuthatches and the Tree-creepers spend most of their lives running up and down the trunks of trees, and along and around their branches. Every crevice of the bark is examined for insects lurking there. Nevertheless, in spite of the similarities of their movements, they display striking differences in their external structure. In the Nuthatch the tail-feathers are short and very soft; in the Tree-creepers they are long and spiny, recalling those of the Woodpeckers.

The beak of the Nuthatch is short and pointed, and is used, largely, for breaking open the hard shells of nuts for the sake of the kernel—hazel-nuts, acorns, yew-seed, beech-mast, which are wedged into crevices in the bark before they are split open. One would have supposed that a spiny tail, acting like the third leg of a tripod in supporting the body, when raining blows on a hazel-nut, would have been of immense advantage; but the bird gets on quite well without such aid. Insects and their larvae are also eaten. The Tree-creepers, on the other hand, are entirely insect-eaters, picking up their prey with a long, slender, decurved beak, as with a pair of forceps; yet, as we have remarked, the tail is long and spiny, and used to support the body. These differences, in this regard, are not meaningless, and they will be understood only after a more intensive study of the two birds in a state of Nature.

The Titmice are mainly insect-eaters, but they do not compete with the Nuthatch and Tree-creeper, even when seeking food from the same tree, for they search the outer fringe of the tree, clinging like acrobats to the smallest twigs. Why is the beak of our Great-titmouse (*Parus major*) distinctly longer and more pointed than that of the Great-titmouse of the Continent? This is a problem yet to be solved by scientific investigators.

The genus *Sitta*, to which our own species belongs, has a wide range, extending over nearly the whole of the Palaearctic and Indian regions and throughout North America to Mexico, yet everywhere it shows the same slaty-blue and rust-red, relieved by black and white. Having regard to the extent of its range, though represented by different species and sub-species, it is curious that our own bird should never breed north of Yorkshire or Cheshire. What is the inhibiting factor?

The Nuthatches share a family custom of reducing the size of the hole to the nest—generally in a tree, sometimes in a rock crevice—by means of mud.

The Tree-creepers are a small group, and nearly all soberly clad. · Our own species may well serve as the type of the race, as it is too well known to need description here. A few species have developed bright colours, as in the Wall-creeper (*Tichodroma muraria*), whose haunts are mountain gorges, but which on rare occasions visits Great Britain. Here the coloration is slate-grey, relieved by rich crimson over the wings and splashes of white on the primaries. But it should be noted that the tail-feathers are *not* pointed and spiny, but square-ended.

The Titmice present some sharp contrasts in the matter of coloration, as is shown, indeed, by our own seven species. The Great-tit and the Blue-tit are too well known to need description here. The Coal- and the Mars-tit, though common with us, are yet less well known, and not readily distinguished by the inexperienced. But the white patch on the nape suffices at a glance to distinguish the Coal-tit. The Crested-tit is a peculiarly interesting species, for, though a British bird, it is confined to the pine woods of the Spey Valley. Such as occasionally occur in parts of England seem always to be members of the Continental race. It is a handsome bird, though it boasts no bright colours. The upper parts are of a buffish-brown, the head white, marked by an erectile crest spotted with black, a black triangular bar behind the eye, and a black ring running from the nape of the neck downwards and forwards, where it expands over the whole throat. The under parts are white, tinged with buff on the flanks.

CRESTED-TIT (*Parus cristatus*).

The Long-tailed Titmouse is more in evidence during the winter than in the spring and summer, because after the breeding season it joins nomadic flocks of other tits, or roams in family parties. Since it feeds largely on scale-insects, it is one of the gardener's best friends. Unlike all the other tits it does not breed in a hole in a tree, or a nesting-box, but instead builds a large and most beautiful nest in a bush or hedge. Shredded wool and moss are deftly felted together to form its walls, and externally it is completed by a layer of lichen attached by means of spider-webs. Within, the cavity is lined with feathers ; as many as two thousand have been taken from one nest. The entrance is through a small hole near the top, and within the small chamber thus protected perhaps a dozen youngsters are crowded. The sitting-bird, while incubating, has the tail pulled forward over the back, so that the head and tail project from the doorway.

THE BEARDED-TITMOUSE

Though this bird is regarded as a " Titmouse " by the majority of ornithologists, it is very doubtful whether this is justified. It will probably be found to be more nearly related to the " Babblers," such as *Suthora* and *Paradoxornis*. But be this as it may, it is one of the most interesting of our native birds, and but for vigorous protective measures it would long since have been exterminated by that enemy of ornithology, the egg-collector. The male is a handsome little bird of a rich tawny colour above, relieved by long areas of white on the wings, a blue-grey head, and long,

BEARDED-TIT (*Panurus biarmicus*).

black, moustachial feathers, while the breast is white and the under tail-coverts black. The flanks are coloured like the back. The female lacks the moustache, and is duller. The mouth of the nestling is remarkable for its strange coloration, the roof being of a bright vermilion-red, margined with yellow; and against this background project a number of glistening white papillae resembling teeth.

Since it cannot exist save amid extensive beds of reeds, its range is naturally restricted with us. Drainage still further limited its numbers, till, in 1898, it was estimated that not more than a few pairs remained on any of the Norfolk Broads. Since then, thanks to protection, its numbers have increased. The nest is placed not among reeds, but in beds of reed-mace, or sedge, where it is placed on a platform of dead and decaying stems a few inches above the water, or even on land fringing the water. It is made of blades of sedge or reed, and lined with the flowers of the reed ; occasionally a few feathers are added. In this matter of its nursery, the Bearded-titmouse again differs profoundly from the true Titmice.

THE THRUSHES, WARBLERS, AND WRENS

Under this heading some seven or eight " Families," including a large number of genera and species, must be briefly reviewed. These are mostly species known only to those who make a life-long study of birds. They are not even to be seen in museums, save in the collection of skins reserved for students. In this seclusion they may well remain, for it would require a very big volume to contain descriptions of all.

This much may be said of the group as a whole, that it is a relatively ancient one, among the Passeres representing a stock at least as old as the Shrikes, and perhaps remotely related thereto ; for the nestling plumage of the typical Thrushes recalls that of the nestlings of the Shrike-tribe.

The Bulbuls and the Babblers are primitive members of this great tribe. The Bulbuls (*Pycnonotidae*) are found throughout the Ethiopian, Indian, and Malayan regions, and are characterised by their dull coloration, bristles round the gape, short legs, and short, rounded wings, indicating reduced powers of flight. But there are some singular exceptions in regard to coloration found in the " Fairy Blue-bird " (*Irena puella*), the beautiful green species of the genus *Chloropsis*, and the red-throated, orange-breasted *Rubigula dispar* of Java.

The Babblers (*Timeliidae*) have long been the despair of the systematist. All sorts of birds have been dumped here to await further research. The typical Babblers, at any rate, like the Bulbuls, have bristles at the gape, and short, rounded, concave wings, fitting close to the body, but they are more terrestrial in their habits.

A few species, like the Chinese-robin, a common cage-bird (*Liothrix lutea*), are gaily coloured. *Eupeltes* has the appearance of a long-legged Woodpecker ; while the Scimitar-babbler (*Xiphorhamphus superciliaris*) is remarkable for the shape of its beak, which is very long, slender, and

YELLOW-BILLED CROW-TIT (*Paradoxornis flavirostris*).

curved. The Fluffy- and the Hairy-backed Babblers have the feathers of the lower back excessively developed. Finally come the Crow-tits—though they are neither Crows nor Tits—of the Family *Paradoxornithidae*. The best known of this family are the species of the genus *Paradoxornis* ; tawny-coloured birds with a curiously heavy beak, almost like a parrot's, but without the hooked tip. It is to this group, probably, that our " Bearded-tit " is most nearly related.

The types just referred to may perhaps be regarded as offshoots of a stem which ended in the true Thrushes, the " Chats," and Warblers. Our own Common-thrush and Mistle-thrush, Blackbird, and Ring-ouzel may well stand as types of the " true Thrushes." The streaked and spotted plumage of the immature stages recalls the pattern of birds of similar age among the

Shrike tribe, and this affords part of this evidence which is put forward to establish a kinship between the two groups.

Close allies are the Redstarts and the " Chats," small birds such as the Redstart, Robin, and Nightingale, Stone-chat, Whin-chat, and Wheatear, well known to us all during the summer months. The Shamas, so highly prized as cage-birds, belong to the " Redstart " group, which is typically red-tailed ; between them and the Chats is but a very fine dividing line. Our Hedge-sparrow (*Accentor*) is one of the " Thrush tribe," nearly related, apparently, to the " Redstart " group.

What are known as the *Sialiinae* are small birds, belonging to two genera, one represented by the American " Blue-bird " (*Sialia*), of a beautiful light blue colour, with a patch of chestnut on the breast or back, the other, *Grandala*, found only on the highest ranges of the Himalayas at from fifteen to seventeen thousand feet, of an indigo-blue.

The Warblers include several hundreds of species, of which only a few are known to those who make no special study of birds. The whole of this volume would be required to describe them adequately. Thirty-four species are included in the list of our British birds. Of these, however, only a few are generally recognised, such as the Chiff-Chaff and Willow-warbler, the Reed- and Sedge-warblers, Black-cap, White-throat, and Garden-warbler.

Bright colours are rare among the Warblers, and even where present are not conspicuous, as, for example, in the delicate sulphur-yellow of the Wood-warbler. Their plumage serves as a mantle of invisibility among the foliage, amid which they so assiduously hunt for insects. Exceptions are found in the beautiful little Australian species of *Malurus*, which displays fine combinations of blue, purple, and velvety-black, with a little brown and white. But one of its members, be it noted, is chiefly brown, with a blue tail and a lilac crown, with a black centre ; another is vermilion, black and brown above and black below. Yet another is bluish-black and white. The females are mainly brown, but may have a blue or even a green tail. There are very striking exceptions, and it may well be that a more careful study of their anatomy will show that, after all, these are not Warblers but Flycatchers, as some authorities claim.

Our Gold- and Fire-crested Wrens, with their brilliant crowns, are other apparent exceptions. There seems good reason for regarding them as Warblers, though some regard them as Wrens.

The Warblers include some notable nest-builders, as, for example, our own Reed-warbler and the famous Tailor-birds (*Sutoria*), which sew the edges of one or more leaves together to form a pocket in which they build a nest of fine grass, cotton-down, and hair. The more one dwells upon this achievement the more wonderful it appears. It recalls the almost parallel case of one of the Tree-frogs mentioned elsewhere in this volume, which fastens the edges of a leaf together to form a pocket into which the spawn is shed.

What is the origin of these singular departures from the practice of their tribe : departures which call into play complex activities seemingly the outcome of careful thought ? Science has yet to supply the answer.

Those remarkable birds, the Dippers (*Cinclidæ*) and the Wrens (*Troglodytes*), are, by almost common consent, regarded as allies of the Thrush tribe, using this term in its widest sense. This may be so, but we know too little of their structure to be at all confident on this point, and from their external appearance no very reliable data can be gleaned.

Whatever be the ancestry of the Dipper it has certainly taken a line of its own in regard to its habits, for it alone among the Passeriform types is able to swim and dive with ease, using both wings and feet when submerged. It can also run about on the bed of the stream in its search for aquatic insects and their larvæ ; and this, too, without the slightest structural modification of its legs for swimming purposes, though the toes are conspicuously long. But the feathers are unusually closely packed, and very downy at their bases.

DIPPER (*Cinclus albicollis*).

Our own species, to be found wherever there are rapid, rock-strewn streams as in the west and north of England and Wales, and in Scotland, may be recognised at once by the slate-coloured upper parts, including the short, upturned tail, white throat and breast, and chestnut-red belly ; and its congeners differ in no very marked particulars. They have a wide range, extending over the northern parts of both hemispheres as well as the highlands of Central America and the Andes of South America. They build a domed nest of moss as near to the water as may be ; sometimes, indeed, in a crevice in the rocks in a waterfall, so that the birds have to dive through the falling water to get to the nest.

The Wrens are probably related to the Dippers. They have their headquarters in tropical America, whence they extend northwards to Greenland and south to Patagonia and the Falklands ; eight species inhabit the Himalayas, the hills of West China, the Burmese countries, and Sumatra and Java ; while the genus *Troglodytes*, which includes our own Wren, occupies the northern portions of both hemispheres. Yet, in spite of their wide geographical distribution and the great differences of habitat this implies, nowhere have they developed bright coloration, and they are as conservative in their manner of nest-building as in their sober coloration. Almost always the nest is dome-shaped and of soft materials, but the species of *Campylorhynchus* builds a purse-like structure with a long entrance passage.

THE AMERICAN-WARBLERS (*Mniotiltidae*)

A special heading is given to this group which is one of the most unsatisfactory to be found within the Passerines, since it is made up of such an incongruous mixture of types that a common descent seems almost impossible. No more can be said now to demonstrate the diversity of the forms associated here than that while many are indeed reminiscent of the Warblers, others as closely resemble Tanagers, Flycatchers, Creepers, Titmice, or Pipits.

Ranging from Greenland southwards into South America, they are to be found in country the most varied, to say nothing of climate ; and their food is no less varied. They are mostly insectivorous, but some eat seeds and fruits. All are small, and none are remarkable for the splendour of their coloration, though many display patches of bright colour. As a whole they may be described as olive-green, grey, or slaty-blue, with yellow, or (rarely) orange-coloured under parts. Chestnut markings or white wingbands give further variations.

THE FLOWER-BIRDS

The designation " Flower-birds " is coined here to include six more or less distinct groups or families—*Zosteropidae*, *Drepanididae*, *Meliphagidae*, *Nectarinidae*, *Dicaeidae*, and *Cerebidae*—which depend, some more, some less, on flowers for their food. Some suck up their nectar and have the tongue armed with fringes, after the manner of humming-birds, for this purpose, and some come for the sake of the insects found there ; but the " Honey-suckers " also eat insects. Some are dull-hued, but many are resplendent.

The White-eyes (*Zosteropidae*) are small, olive-coloured birds, some distinctly yellow, while variation is given by patches of fawn, brown, grey, or white ; but all have a white ring round the eye. The straight or slightly curved beak has finely serrated edges. The tongue, which is protractile, has its margins folded and the tip frayed. The outer and middle toes are partially united. They range through part of the Ethiopian region into India and the Australian region, and thence to Amurland and Japan.

The *Meliphagidae*, or " Honey-eaters," rarely exceed a thrush in size, and have the tongue, which is protractile, longitudinally divided into four or more filaments with frayed edges. As in the " White-eyes " the maxilla is serrated, and the middle and outer toes may be partly fused. They are confined to the Australian region.

For the most part they are dull-coloured, but there are some exceptions, as in the Australian " Soldier-bird " (*Myzomela*), which is habited in scarlet and black. In many species parts of the head are bare, and wattles on the sides of the head and throat are often developed. *Ptilotis gracilis* has large, yellow ear-tufts, and the remarkable New Zealand Tui, or " Parson-bird " (*Prosthemadura*), has large outstanding tufts of feathers on each side of the neck. The " Friar-bird " (*Philemon*) has a bare head and a curious horn at the base of the beak.

The Flower-peckers (*Dicaeidae*) and the Sun-birds are probably near allies. The former are small and, in the males, generally brilliantly coloured birds, having a short, broad beak, and the edges of both upper and lower jaws finely serrated at the tip. The tongue is cleft into four semi-tubular sections. Many species display vivid patches of colour—blue or purple, with black, relieved by a scarlet or orange head, or rump-patch, the breast being yellow, greyish, or greenish-white ; but some are dull-coloured.

One or two build remarkable nests. In *Dicaeum* this is domed or pear-shaped, and formed of a wonderful felt-work of cottony material, covered externally with moss or the excreta of caterpillars ; *Pardalotus* chooses old swallows' nests, or even burrows a short distance into banks, and builds therein a spherical nest of roots, bark,

TUI, or " PARSON-BIRD " (*Prosthemadura novae-zealandiae*).

and feathers. These birds are found in West Africa and the Indian and Australian regions.

The Sun-birds (*Nectarinidae*) have much in common with the Flower-peckers, but far surpass them in the brilliance of their coloration, in which they recall the Humming-birds, on account of the metallic appearance of the feathers. The beak is long, slender, and curved, and the extensible tongue is bifid, with each portion frayed out.

There are a large number of species, confined to the Old World, and ranging from Africa and Southern Asia to New Guinea and Australia. Unable to obtain their drink of nectar while poised on the wing, after the manner of Humming-birds, they cling, like Titmice, to the slender stems, while the long tongue is thrust down into the nectaries. And in this way they play an important part in fertilising flowers by transporting the pollen from one flower to another, after the manner of bees. Thus they ensure also their own means of subsistence. As nest-builders they are as skilful as the Flower-peckers, and affect like materials and architecture.

The Hawaiian Honey-suckers (*Drepanididae*) constitute a small family of birds remarkable for their splendid coloration, as well as for the curious diversity they display in the form of the beak, which, by the way, is not serrated along its edges, even when it otherwise resembles that of the Sunbirds. But in some it is finch-like, and in one—*Pseudonestor*—it is parrot-like, while in *Heterorhynchus* it presents the singular feature of having the upper jaw much larger than the lower. These striking differences are doubtless intimately associated with peculiar feeding habits, but as to this no information has yet been gleaned.

The splendid feather cloaks, waist-bands, and mask decorations of the former Hawaiian kings were chiefly composed of the yellow plumage of the " Mamo " (*Drepanis pacifica*), which became exterminated in consequence, and of the scarlet feathers of the " Jiwi " (*Vestiaria coccinea*).

ORIOLES AND STARLINGS

The precise affinities of the Orioles, their relationship to the Starlings, and of these to other groups, have still to be investigated. They are taken here in conformity with our present " knowledge."

The Golden-oriole is one of the most beautiful of birds, the plumage being of a rich orange-yellow, with black wings and tail. Almost yearly it appears in our midst, and has even nested here on more than one occasion. But its beauty invariably ensures its early death, the barbarian with a gun finding it an irresistible target. If these unimaginative marksmen could only be persuaded to leave them unmolested we should probably in a few years have a fair sprinkling enlivening our countryside every summer. Only a few species are known, and in some crimson takes the place of orange-yellow, as in *Oriolus trailli* of Eastern Asia. Though mainly insectivorous, they eat wild fruits in the autumn.

Orioles build very beautiful nests of bark, grass, and fibres, suspended from the fork of a bough, wherein are laid three to five white or salmon-coloured eggs, with brown-pink spots or streaks.

The Starlings are a numerous tribe, and by some are divided into two separate families—the " True-starlings " (*Sturnidae*) and the Tree-starlings (*Eulabetidae*).

Our own Starling may be accepted as the type of the True-starlings. Moreover, it shows some interesting plumage phases. The young birds are of a pale brown colour. Later this becomes exchanged for a dress like that of the parents, but profusely spotted with white, and as age advances these spots disappear.

Another and much more striking species is the Rose-coloured Pastor, which occasionally visits our shores in the autumn. The head, wings, and tail are black, the rest of the body salmon-pink. The immature plumage resembles that of the Common Starling. The Rose-coloured Pastor is a great destroyer of grasshoppers ; our own bird renders us great service as an insect-destroyer, but is most unwelcome in cherry orchards, which unfortunately have a great attraction for it. The curious Ox-pecker, or Rhinoceros-bird, so called from its starling-like habit of settling on the backs of cattle, camels, and so on, for the sake of the flies and ticks which infest them, is also a Starling.

ROSE-COLOURED PASTOR (*Pastor roseus*).

The Tree-starlings, so called because they are strictly arboreal, differ further from the typical starlings in having bristles round the beak, and in laying spotted eggs. They range from Africa through India and the Moluccan Islands to Australia. The Grackles, or Mynas, which make such charming cage-birds and can so easily be taught to imitate human speech, are perhaps the best known of this group. Mention must also be made of the beautiful Glossy-starlings (*Lamprocolius*) and the even more resplendent *Pholidauges*, which is of a rich purplish-violet, with a white belly.

THE HANG-NESTS, WEAVER-FINCHES, TANAGERS, AND FINCHES

We come now to an assemblage, undoubtedly closely allied, including hundreds of species, and a large proportion thereof of lively and often brilliant coloration.

The Hang-nests (*Icteridae*) are confined to the American continent, and derive their name from the enormously long, pendent nests they weave, shaped like a Florence-flask. They are constructed of long, thread-like, and stout vegetable fibres, and often as many as forty may be seen hanging from one tree. But, curiously enough, some species build normal cup-shaped nests. One of the best known is the Baltimore " Oriole " (*Icterus baltimore*), which, like many of its allies, is black, with the breast, belly, lower back, and lesser wing-coverts rich reddish-orange. The nearly allied Caciques are much larger birds, with enormous pointed beaks, their black plumage enlivened by areas of chestnut, yellow, green, and scarlet. The Cow-birds, of the genus *Molothrus*, are remarkable for their parasitic habits, laying their eggs in the nests of other birds, by whom they are hatched, as with the Cuckoos.

The Bobolink (*Dolichonyx oryzivorus*) has the distinction of being one of the finest American songsters; it has also distinct summer and winter plumages, the former a combination of black, cream, and buff, the latter dull brownish-black and buff. Finally, mention must be made of the Meadow-larks (*Sturnella*), which recall our Pipits, even to the elongation of the inner secondaries.

Of the Tanagers some three hundred and fifty species have been described, mostly confined to tropical America, and many of these are superbly coloured. While some are difficult to distinguish from the true Finches, others resemble the *Coeribidae*, and some the *Mniotiltidae* already described.

PARADISE " WIDOW-BIRD " (*Steginura paradisea*).

The Scarlet-tanager (*Pyranga*), like the Bobolink, has a distinct summer, or nuptial, plumage, but of scarlet and black, which is changed for winter into green and black.

The Weaver-finches (*Ploceidae*) range from Africa through India to the Australian region. They take their name from the remarkable nests they construct. This is generally " retort-shaped," that is to say, it is globular, with a spout curving down from the middle or from one side. The Sociable Weaver-bird (*Philetaerus*) builds in colonies, constructing a huge umbrella-shaped mass of sticks and grass, and in this the birds burrow out nests from the under surface. As many as three hundred nests may be found under the roof! In the matter of coloration and ornament these birds are remarkable. The " Widow-birds " of several genera and species, develop during the breeding season long, central tail-feathers, so long as to severely hamper their flight. *Hypochaera* is entirely purplish-blue; one of the " Grass-finches " (*Poephila*) shows a beautiful blending of pale green, blue, lilac, scarlet, yellow, black, brown, and white. Many species are kept as cage-birds, such as the Java-sparrows and the Waxbills.

Of the Finches and Buntings, more than six hundred species have been described. Forty species and sub-species are included among our native birds. Of these the most remarkable are the Cross-bills and the Hawfinch. In the former the upper and lower jaws are produced into points which cross one another, an adaptation to their habit of breaking up pine-cones to extract the seeds. The Hawfinch has a large, cushion-shaped horny pad on the roof of the mouth, and a horny cushion on each side of the lower jaw beneath this pad, whereby the bird is enabled to crush the hard stones of hawthorn and other berries. Many present striking seasonal differences of coloration, which, however, are due to abrasion of the tips of the feathers and not to a change of plumage by moulting. The Brambling, Snow-bunting, and Linnet are conspicuous examples of such changes. Many "foreign finches" are kept by us as cage-birds, of which the beautiful Cardinal of America is a conspicuous example.

The Buntings are distinguished by the presence of a horny knob on the palate. Some, like our Corn-bunting, are dull-coloured, others are bright-hued, like our Yellow-hammer and Cirl-bunting, though these are surpassed by some of the American species, as, for example, the Painted-bunting (*Passerina ciris*), which has the head and neck indigo-blue, the back golden-green, the rump dull red, and the under parts light red, while the wing-coverts are green. The female is duller—a bright olive-green above and white below, with a tinge of greenish-yellow.

The Larks, Pipits, and Wagtails

The Larks (*Alaudidae*) form a tribe numbering a hundred or more species, which are held, by some, to form a connecting link with the Finches. But this relationship is highly problematical. They differ from all the other Passerines in having the back of the tarso-metatarsus covered by three long scales, or plates. These are, however, so completely welded together that they are not readily perceptible. They are found over the whole of the northern hemisphere, as well as the Indian and Ethiopian regions ; only one genus (*Otocorys*), the Shore-lark, occurs in America, and one (*Mirafra*) in the Australian region. The claw of the hind-toe is commonly con-spicuously long, but in some genera, as in *Calandrella*, it may be quite short. The beak is typically short and conical, but it may be almost finch-like or long and curved.

Brilliant colours are nowhere developed among the Larks, though the Shore-lark has a tinge of sulphur-yellow on the head.

Our own Skylark may well serve as the type of this family, and is too well known to need description, either in regard to its appearance or its wonderful power of song. This bird, and the Wood-lark, are the only species which breed here. The outermost primary of the Skylark is considerably longer in the young bird in its first plumage than in the adult; a feature even more marked in the Wryneck, where in the adult the outermost primary is reduced to the condition of a mere vestige shorter than the covert-feathers, while in the juvenile stage it is nearly twice as long as the longest covert. This is not a merely " curious fact," but shows that a reduction in the number of the primaries is slowly taking place. With the exception of a few species of the genus *Mirafra*, all the Larks nest on the ground and lay white eggs, closely spotted with brown and grey.

The Shore-lark (*Otocorys alpestris*), which visits us in the winter, is more conspicuously coloured than the rest of the tribe, being of a pinkish-brown on the back, pale yellow on the forehead and throat, and with a black crown and gorget. The outer border of the black crown-bar is produced backwards to form a pair of short outstanding " horns," while the under parts are white. While the other Larks haunt meadows or deserts, the Shore-lark, as its name implies, prefers the fringe of the sea, where it hunts for insects, small molluscs, and crustacea among the seaweed, and for seeds of marram and other grasses on the beach. It sings during the breeding season, either when on the ground or in the air, like our Skylark, but the song, though melodious, is short.

The Wagtails and Pipits (*Motacillidae*) are generally regarded as near allies of the Larks, mainly because the inner secondaries are much elongated, so much so in the Wagtails and Pipits as almost to conceal the primaries when the wing is closed; in the Larks they are never quite so long.

With the exception of two species found in North-West America, all the Wagtails are confined to the Old World, though they are not found in Australia and Polynesia. They are almost entirely terrestrial in their habits, and frequent the vicinity of water, both fresh and salt, meadows, and damp ground. Graceful in all their movements when on the ground, their undulatory flight is no less pleasing. Four species breed with us—the Pied, the White, the Grey, and the Yellow, or Ray's-wagtail.

The Pipits have long, inner secondaries, like the Wagtails, but in their general appearance they resemble the Larks in being of dull hues, though the curious African genus *Macronyx* affords a striking exception to the rule. Though mainly brown, it displays on the under parts a black gorget, and patches of orange, yellow, and pink. But more than this, *M. crocea* bears a very striking resemblance to *Sturnella magna* and *M. ameliae* to *S. defillippii*. It will be remembered that *Sturnella* is one of the *Icteridae*, and therefore American. How is it, it may be asked, that these two Old-World, African Pipits have come to assume so close a likeness to species resident on another continent?

The Pipits are an Old-World group, and practically cosmopolitan, though they do not occur in the islands of the South Pacific. Of more than forty species, only two are found in North America.

Our own Meadow-pipit, Tree-pipit, and Rock-pipit are too well known to need description here. They breed with us. The Meadow-pipit, like Richard's-pipit, a rare visitant to our shores, has a long hind-claw, like the Skylark.

THE CROWS

Though by almost common consent the Crow tribe (*Corvidae*) are placed at the head of the Passerine birds, no one has yet attempted to justify this on evidence derived from a study of their anatomy. Until this is much more completely known, and until material for comparative purposes has been collected, it is impossible to trace their descent with any degree of accuracy. They may be divided into Crows (*Corvinae*), Magpies, and Jays (*Garrulinae*) and Choughs (*Fregilinae*).

Our Raven may well stand as the head of the family, but it is, unfortunately, now restricted to the wilder parts of the country ; but the Rook, Carrion- and Hooded-crows, and the Jackdaw are still common. Some have contended that the Common- and Hooded-crows are but two forms of the same species, since where the two types overlap, on the breeding grounds, as, for example, in the Clyde and Solway areas, birds displaying the coloration of both species, more or less sharply defined, may be found in the same nest. This, however, can scarcely be admitted as proof that the Common-crow is " dimorphic," for, save where this opportunity for inter-breeding occurs, the two types remain perfectly distinct. Attempts have been made to show that the bare face of the adult Rook is due to denudation of the feather by digging in the soil right up to the base of the beak. There is, however, not the slightest justification for this assumption.

Of the habits of these birds little need be said, but it is important to contrast the nature of their food, since it shows how they have contrived to avoid undue competition. Note that the Raven, even where not molested, is only found in pairs. It is a big bird with a big appetite, and can tolerate no competitors within its territory. The Rook is largely an insect-eater, varying the diet with grain, worms, molluscs, and mice; and, its food being abundant, it breeds in colonies. The Carrion-crow is, like the Raven, mainly a meat-eater, and makes havoc among eggs and young birds during the breeding season. It is a solitary bird. The Jackdaw is eminently sociable, and, again, mainly insectivorous, varying its diet with slugs and worms, occasionally eggs and young birds, while seeds and nuts are also eaten. The Nutcracker (*Nucifraga*), which differs from all our other " Crows " in having a chocolate-brown plumage streaked with white, feeds largely, in its native land, Siberia, on the seeds of pine-cones, hazel-nuts, juniper-berries, and insects, but with us on dung-beetles and grain.

The Magpie and the Jay are too well known to need description, but the conspicuous departure made by the Magpie from the rest of the Crows in the construction of its nest is worth noting. Both this bird and the Jay suffer a merciless persecution with us, and this without adequate reason. One of the most resplendent members of the tribe is the Blue-magpie of Southern Spain (*Cyanopica cooki*), which has the wings and tail of cobalt-blue, an ash-coloured body, and black head. The species of the genus *Cissa*, of India, Burma, and Java, are of a lovely green and blue or cobalt and ultramarine, with a coral-red beak and feet, and a white tip to the tail.

The Jays are a very interesting group whose affinities with the Magpie are shown by the fact that some species present features reminiscent of both.

NUTCRACKER (*Nucifraga caryocatactes*).

HUIA-BIRD (female) (*Heterolocha acutirostris*).

Furthermore, when the tribe as a whole is surveyed they reveal some further evolutionary evidence, inasmuch as we can pass from obvious " Jays " to species like the North American Blue-jay, which displays a very different type of coloration from that usually associated with Jays. The Canada-jay, or " Whisky-Jack," is noteworthy in this connection, since it is of sombre coloration, chiefly sooty-black and grey, while the young birds are still more Crow-like. Here, then, we seem to have a species which has retained much of the ancestral coloration lost by the more resplendent species at all stages of their development.

The Choughs (*Pyrrocorax*), of which there are but few species, are black birds, with a long, curved beak, which, like the legs and toes, are either red or yellow. Time was when the " Cornish-chough " was abundant with us along the coast of Cornwall and the cliffs of Ireland and Scotland, as well as some inland cliffs. But the raids of the egg-collector have nearly wiped it out as a British bird. The Alpine-chough has a shorter beak, of a yellow instead of coral-red colour.

Two or three very remarkable types remain to be mentioned, but whether they are true Crows is open to question ; at any rate, in this group they must remain for the present.

The first of these is the curious Huia-bird of New Zealand (*Heterolocha acutirostris*), the female of which has a very long beak, curved in a semi-circle, while in the male it is comparatively short, conical, sharp-pointed, and nearly straight. He is said to use this in chiselling away the bark of trees containing wood-boring beetle larvae, which the hen then draws out with her " probe." At the base of the beak, in both sexes, is an oval, yellow wattle, rather larger in the female. The nest, of dry grass, leaves, and stalks, is placed in a hollow tree, and the eggs are whitish, with grey or brown spots. It has been suggested that this very remarkable bird is possibly a starling, not a crow, and this may well prove to be the case.

This curious difference displayed by the Huia-bird in the matter of the length and shape of the beak has no parallel among birds. But throughout these pages differences between the sexes in coloration, as well as in structural characters such as spurs, the development of excessively long plumes, caruncles, inflatable air-pouches, and so on, have constantly been recorded. These " secondary sexual characters " are not to be merely tabulated as " facts," but regarded as affording themes for investigation. This survey of the birds of the world, in short, is intended to bring to a focus the essential features which have come into being in the course of the evolution of this Group. A mere record of the name of every known species of bird would have served no useful end. Neither would there be any profit in being able to remember every Order and Sub-order and Family recognised by ornithologists. The real interest in the study of birds—or of any other Group—begins when we set out to inquire into the why and the wherefore of their varied shapes in regard to their shifts for a living, their coloration, changes of plumage, and condition of the young at birth, their migrations, and so on, making a positively bewildering range of choice. In no matter what part of the world one may be, the theme is the same ; only the subjects change.

SECTION XV

CLASS MAMMALIA

By J. G. Dollman, B.A., F.L.S.

CHAPTER I

CHAPTER II

CHAPTER III

CHAPTER IV

CHAPTER V

CHAPTER VI

CHAPTER VII

CHAPTER VIII

CHAPTER I

GENERAL CHARACTERISTICS

The Class Mammalia is the fifth and most highly organised of the vertebrated animals. The group is very clearly defined and sharply marked off from all the other classes, in spite of the presence of some comparatively lowly organised creatures, which, although they exhibit several characters showing an affinity with the Reptiles and Amphibians, are not by any means closely allied to those groups. A well-marked gulf, indeed, exists between the mammals and their nearest-living relations ; which is, however, to some extent, bridged by certain fossil forms which have been discovered during recent years. This evidence from the distant past shows that there has been a gradual transition from certain extinct reptilian types to the most generalised of the mammals.

Mammals differ from the fishes and amphibians, and agree with the reptiles and birds, in the possession, during the early stages of development, of the amnion and allantois, two foetal membranes, the first of which serves as a protective envelope for the developing embryo while the second takes on the function of an embryonic respiratory organ. Further, they are note-worthy for the absence of external gills. They differ from reptiles and resemble birds in being warm-blooded, and in the heart being four-chambered and the circulation double. From both birds and reptiles, mammals are distinguished by the red blood-corpuscles, being without a nucleus and usually circular in shape, and by having the lungs and heart suspended in the chest cavity and cut off from all the other viscera by a stout muscular partition, the diaphragm.

Further points of difference are the possession of but a single arch to the aorta, and in having a more highly developed type of brain and a complete larynx at the upper end of the windpipe. The skin is more or less hairy, and the female is provided with mammary glands which produce the secretion necessary for the nourishment of the young during the immediate post-natal stage. The state of development of the young, at the time of birth, varies very considerably. In the marsupials, for instance, the young are, so to speak, prematurely born, and they exhibit certain structures which can almost be regarded as appertaining to a larval condition. In these types there is no pre-natal connection between the circulatory systems of the parent and embryo ; the young, in such cases, make their way to a special pouch directly after birth, where they are nourished and can complete their development. In other cases, where a connection between the maternal and foetal circulation has been established—that is, in the placentals—the young are born in a more highly developed state. Among the whales we find the young are produced in a very advanced stage, doubtless owing to their aquatic mode of life ; and this is true also of the hoofed animals, wherein the young are able to run about with their parents when no more than a few hours old. In other groups, like the rodents, and in the highest order, the Primates, the young are quite unable to fend for themselves until after a period of careful nursing and nourishment.

The typical mammal may be accepted as a terrestrial animal, with well-developed limbs adapted for terrestrial progression. Many species, how-ever, are arboreal, and their limbs, and sometimes their tails, are specially modified for climbing, while others live largely below the surface of the ground and exhibit special adaptations for this mode of life. Some, like the bats, have become transformed for a life in mid-air, and others, such as the whales and seals, are very specially modified for an aquatic existence.

In some mammals, such as the toothed whales, only one set of teeth, pro-bably answering to the milk-teeth, are developed; these are known as Mono-phydont. In the majority of mammals, however, the permanent, adult, teeth are preceded by a temporary series, the milk-teeth, which may be functional during the first years of life, as in the case of the Primates ; or they may serve no function at all, being shed either before or directly after birth, as in the seals. These mammals with a double set of teeth are referred to as Diphyodont. The mammalian teeth may be extremely simple, as in the many dolphins, where the teeth are all alike, there being no differentiation into front teeth or back teeth ; such a type of dentition is called Homodont. In the greater number of mammals the teeth are differentiated into incisors, canines, premolars, and molars ; this arrangement is known as Heterodont.

Mammals may be considered as representing three main divisions, or sub-classes : (i) Prototheria, including the egg-laying types ; (ii) Metatheria, the marsupials, or pouched-mammals ; and (iii) Eutheria, or placentals, that is, the remainder of the class.

The members of this class are almost universally distributed. They are, however, totally absent from certain oceanic islands ; and no indigenous land mammals, other than a bat, have ever been found in New Zealand.

Sub-class *PROTOTHERIA*

(*Monotremes*)

Order MONOTREMATA

(*Duck-bill, or Platypus, and Spiny Ant-eaters*)

The first and most primitive group, or sub-class, of the Class Mammalia contains the well-known Duckbill, or Platypus, and the Spiny Ant-eaters, or Echidnas ; this sub-class is known by the name Prototheria, and contains a single order, the Monotremata. The Prototherians differ very markedly from the other two sub-classes (the Metatheria including the pouched mammals, and the Eutheria containing all the other mammals, or placentals). The young of these animals are hatched from eggs ; thus in their mode of reproduction the Prototherians, or Monotremes as they are usually called, resemble reptiles.

In certain structural details the Platypus and Echidnas exhibit further reptilian features ; for instance, a plate-like bone (metacoracoid) connecting the shoulder-blade with the breast-bone, and a T-shaped bone (interclavicle) covering the breast-bone and collar-bones, are reptilian characters quite unknown among other mammals. The skeleton is further remarkable for the possession of epipubic or " marsupial " bones, such as are found in the Metatheria. The young, when hatched, are suckled by milk secreted by the mother ; the secretion arises from a number of small pores in the abdominal skin, not from teats as in the pouched mammals and placentals. The name Monotremes has reference to the existence of a single excretory aperture. Both of these primitive mammalian types have modified mouths, resembling birds' bills ; the males are provided with spurs on the hind-legs, and teeth are absent in the adult stages.

These egg-laying mammals, although bearing a superficial resemblance to birds as regards the shape of the mouth, are not so closely related to them as they are to certain extinct orders of Reptiles and Amphibians. The members of the sub-class are found only in the Australian region.

The Duckbill, or Platypus (*Ornithorhynchus anatinus*), is adapted to a semi-aquatic life, as may be concluded from its webbed feet; the latter are furnished with strong claws for burrowing purposes. A full-grown male specimen is about twenty inches in length, the tail occupying about one-third of this measurement. The beak, broad and rather like that of a duck, is bordered behind by a soft membrane, which projects posteriorly as a lappet-like fold over the face and chin. This curious beak-like muzzle is, in the living animal, purplish-black above and mottled yellow and black below. The coat is thick and soft, comprising rather long, crisp, and curly hairs, and a dark woolly under-fur; in colour it is sepia-brown above, silvery-grey tinged with yellow or pink below. There are no external ears and the eyes are quite small. The feet have five toes, each with a

DUCKBILL, or PLATYPUS (*Ornithorhynchus anatinus*).

strong claw; the web of the fore-feet extends beyond the extremities of the claws; in the hind-feet the web only reaches to their bases. A long, horny spur arises from the inner side of the hind-leg of the male Platypus; this is hollow and is connected with a poison gland, and is probably used for offensive purposes. The cheeks are provided with pouches, and in young specimens two or three pairs of cheek-teeth occur in the upper jaw and two pairs in the lower jaw. As the animal grows older these teeth are worn away and replaced by the hard, horny plates which are so characteristic of an adult's mouth.

The Platypus is fairly widely distributed over a great part of Eastern Australia and Tasmania. It lives in burrows constructed in the banks of rivers and pools, and visits the water chiefly for feeding purposes. It lives on a variety of small, freshwater animals, a diet made possible by the specially modified jaws. The breeding burrow is usually a very elaborate piece of work, and although it is seldom more than about a foot below the surface, the tunnel may be as much as sixty feet long, although twenty-four feet is about the average length. The passage to the nesting chamber is usually very tortuous, and, when the nest is occupied, a series of blocks are made by the female to guard the nest and its contents from attack. The nest is rounded and built of grass and leaves; one, two, or three eggs are laid, the usual number being two, the eggs always being joined side by side. The eggs measure about 17·5 by 13 or 14 millimetres in size, and are soft-shelled and dirty-white in colour. The average size of the single eggs is a little larger than that of the twin eggs.

The second family of Monotremes is the *Echidnidae*, containing two genera of Echidnas, or Spiny Ant-eaters. These animals are much more widely distributed than the Platypus, as, in addition to inhabiting Australia and Tasmania, they are also found in New Guinea. They are specially adapted for burrowing and living on ants ; like the true ant-eaters of America, and the pangolins of the Old World, they have elongated, beak-like muzzles, no teeth, and long, extensile tongues. The body is broad and depressed, and clothed in a mixture of spines and hair ; the under parts are hairy. The feet have from three to five toes, each armed with a strong digging-claw ; when walking, the hind-feet have the claws turned outwards and backwards. The tail is reduced to a mere vestige, and there are no external ears. The

ECHIDNA, or SPINY ANT-EATER (*Tachyglossus aculeatus*).

Common-echidna (*Tachyglossus aculeatus*), which is confined to Australia, has a short, straight beak, or muzzle, and the spines of the coat conceal the hair ; the spines are yellowish in colour with black tips. The claws are five in number. In the closely allied Tasmanian-echidna (*T. a. setosus*) the hairs nearly hide the spines.

The second genus, *Zaglossus*, inhabits New Guinea. In these echidnas the beak is long and curved, and the claws three or five in number. The various forms are larger than the Australian echidnas, and most of them are furry, with the spines either completely hidden, as in *Z. bartoni* (five toes), or a few white spines show through the woolly fur, as in *Z. bruijnii* (three to four toes).

Unlike the Platypus, the Echidna is possessed of a pouch into which the egg is deposited and there hatched ; in this pouch the young one is carried about for some weeks, after which it is placed in some safe retreat by the mother, and after a short period it will look after itself.

Sub-class *METATHERIA*

(*Marsupials, or Pouched Mammals*)

Order MARSUPIALIA

(*Kangaroos, Phalangers, Bandicoots, Opossums*)

The pouched mammals of Australia and adjacent islands, and the New World, differ so markedly from the egg-laying mammals (Prototheria), and the more typical placental forms (Eutheria), that they are considered to represent a distinct sub-class, the Metatheria, containing a single order, Marsupialia. These pouched beasts, or marsupials, instead of being born in a more or less perfect state of development, as in the Eutheria, are brought forth at a very early stage and in an embryonic condition. In the Eutheria the pre-natal development is arrived at by a vascular connection, the placenta, between the developing foetus and the maternal uterine tissues ; in the Metatheria there is no such placental connection.

At birth the young marsupials are transferred to the teats of the female, to which they adhere for a long period, their lips being specially modified into sucking organs. In most cases the young at this stage are protected by a fold of skin on the abdomen of the mother ; this fold forms a kind of pouch over the teats. In addition to this peculiarity the front rim of the pelvis, in all cases except one (the Thylacine), bears a pair of splint-like bones, the " marsupial bones," projecting forwards in the form of a V. In nearly all pouched animals the angular part of the lower jaw projects inwards, and there are always large or small cavities in the palate ; both these characters are, however, found in some of the Eutherian Insectivores. The brain and female reproductive organs both display a low grade of organisation. The teeth of the marsupials are very variable ; in some species they bear a superficial resemblance to those of rodents, in others they might be mistaken for the teeth of carnivores or insectivores.

The living marsupials are distributed over the greater part of Australia, New Guinea, and the adjacent islands westward as far as Celebes ; one family of opossums, the *Didelphyidae*, inhabits the New World.

The Order Marsupialia, which is the only Metatherian order recognised, is divided into two sub-orders : (i) the Diprotodontia, which contains all the species having two incisor teeth in the lower jaw ; this sub-order comprises three families : the *Macropodidae*, including the kangaroos and wallabies ; the *Phalangeridae*, including the tree-living Australian opossums, or phalangers, and the Koala ; and the *Phascolomyidae*, which contains about five species of wombat. (ii) The Polyprotodontia, in which there are three or four lower incisors ; this sub-order is also divided into three families : the *Peramelidae*, or bandicoots ; the *Dasyuridae*, containing a large number of carnivorous and insectivorous marsupials ; and the American opossums, or *Didelphyidae*.

Sub-order *DIPROTODONTIA*

(*Kangaroos, Wallabies, Koala, Wombats, etc.*)

The Kangaroos and their allies (*Macropodidae*) are all terrestrial animals, with the exception of the Tree-kangaroos ; they are characterised by their teeth being adapted to a vegetable diet, the large incisors being constructed for cutting purposes.   The great length of the hind-limbs and the peculiar method of progress which these animals display are too familiar to need explanation.   The first toe is absent in all the members of the family except-ing in the Musk-rat kangaroos (*Hypsiprymnodon*), and the pouch is large and opens forwards.   The kangaroos and wallabies (sub-family *Macropodinae*) are distinguished from the other members of the family by having the front molar teeth smaller than the hinder ones, and the first upper incisor but little longer than the others, while the claws of the fore-feet are of moderate size.

Family Macropodidae

The genus *Macropus* contains the true kangaroos, which vary in size from the Great Grey-kangaroo (*Macropus giganteus*) to animals about the size of a hare ; in all these forms the tail is long and tapering.   The Great Grey-kangaroo lives in open forest country of Southern and Eastern Australia. In habits it is gregarious, going about in small or large parties.   These big kangaroos will sometimes make tremendous leaps, covering upwards of twenty-five feet at a single bound ; when travelling slowly, however, the jumps are only about five feet long.   The Grey-kangaroo is the animal known locally as the " Boomer," or " Old Man " ; its distributional range includes Tasmania.   The young of these big kangaroos are very minute at birth, measuring only about one inch in length ; the adults measure as much as nine and a half feet in total length.   For about four months the young one remains fastened on to the maternal nipple, after which it will poke its head out of the pouch and feed on the grass as the mother wanders about ; as it gains strength it will venture out beside her, but will speedily return to the pouch if frightened.

The Great Grey-kangaroo and its allies are distinguished from the other species by the nose being hairy between the nostrils ; *M. fuliginosus*, the Kangaroo-island kangaroo, a close relation of the grey species, is black or sooty-brown in colour, and the coat is much coarser.   The Black-faced kangaroo (*M. melanops*), which extends into Western Australia, is rather smaller than *M. giganteus*, and dark brown in colour with whitish under parts.

Related to the Grey-kangaroo group are three species and several sub-species which have the nose naked between the nostrils : (i) The Antilopine-kangaroo (*M. antilopinus*) is a rufous-coloured species, with very short fur, from the Northern Territory.   (ii) The Wallaroo (*M. robustus*), which has longer and thicker hair, is represented by a number of races varying in colour from foxy-red to smoky-black or grey ; these forms are distributed over the greater part of Australia. (iii) Bernard's-wallaroo (*M. bernardus*) is smaller than the two foregoing species, and the male coat is either black or reddish-black, while that of the female is grey or brownish-grey.

The Red-kangaroos (*M. rufus*) form another group in which the nose is partially naked between the nostrils ; in these animals the fur is soft and woolly, and the face has well-marked white patches at the base of the whiskers. In colour these kangaroos vary from rufous to blue-grey ; they are found over the open country of inland and Western Australia.

RED-KANGAROO (*Macropus rufus*).

The smaller species of kangaroos, of the genus *Macropus*, are known as wallabies ; these have been divided into (i) large wallabies, including about a dozen different forms ; and (ii) small wallabies, containing eleven species. The large wallabies are about half the size of the largest kangaroos, whereas the small species are only about the size of a hare. The tail in these animals is usually more hairy than in the kangaroos, their feet proportionately larger, and their palates more incomplete. The best-known members of the large group are : (i) The Black-tailed wallaby (*M. ualabatus*), from South-Eastern Australia, a species which is still very numerous and much in demand by furriers ; Bennett's-wallaby (*M. ruficollis bennetti*), an inhabitant of Tasmania ; (ii) the Black-striped wallaby (*M. dorsalis*), from Eastern Australia, distinguished by the presence of a dark stripe down the centre of the back and a white thigh mark ; (iii) Parry's-wallaby (*M. parryi*), from New South Wales and Queensland, easily distinguished by its long, slender tail and handsome face markings ; and (iv) the Black-gloved wallaby (*M. irma*), from South-West Australia, in which the feet are yellow and toes black. The small wallabies are a more widely distributed group, being found in New Guinea, the Aru and Kei Islands, as well as in Australia. The Red-legged wallaby is a Queensland species, which frequently has the thighs coloured bright rufous. *M. brunii* is the Aru Island species, and *M. browni* hails from New

Guinea.   The Short-tailed wallaby (*M. brachyurus*) is one of the best known of the group ; it inhabits South-Western Australia.

Another group of wallabies form the genus *Petrogale*, or Rock-wallabies, in which the tail does not taper, but is of the same thickness thoughout its length.   These animals live, for the most part, in rocky surroundings, and are extremely active ; in size they are about equal to the smaller members of the large wallabies.   About a dozen species are now recognised, and they are confined to Australia and a few of the adjacent islands.   The Nail-tailed wallabies form a closely allied group, known by the generic title of *Onychogale ;* they are distinguished by possessing a nail-like appendage at the end of the tail ; the distributional range is confined to Australia.

The small Banded - wallaby (*Lagostrophus*) is distinguished by having very hairy hind-feet and a number of transverse bands on the back.   Only one species is known, and is found in Western Australia and some of the adjacent islands. Another group of small wallabies is included in the genus *Lagorchestes*, popularly known as the Hare-wallabies.   These Hare-wallabies are widely distributed, ranging from Queensland to Western Australia. The last group of wallabies form the genus *Dorcopsis ;* they are distinguished by their shorter hind-limbs, and, like the Hare-wallabies, canine-teeth are present in the upper jaw ; the nine recognised species are confined to New Guinea.

BENNETT'S-WALLABY (*Macropus ruficollis bennetti*).

The last genus of the sub-family *Macropodinae* contains the Tree-kangaroos and is known as *Dendrolagus ;* they are very different in appearance from the true kangaroos and wallabies ; the latter species are almost entirely ter-restrial, whereas the members of this genus have become profoundly modified in accordance with their habit of living in trees.   The fore-limbs are more developed, the hind-limbs proportionately shorter, and the tail longer than in the other *Macropodinae*.   Some of the species are brilliantly coloured ; two are found in Queensland, the remaining forms inhabit New Guinea.

The Rat-kangaroos constitute the second sub-family of the *Macropodidae*, known as the *Potoroinae*.   The Rat-kangaroos differ from the kangaroos and wallabies in having the back molar-teeth smaller than the front ones, the middle claws of the fore-feet much elongated, and the first upper incisor teeth much longer than the others. They are about equal to rabbits in size, and the majority of the species leap like wallabies, though the members of one genus, *Potorous*, use all four feet when moving. These latter animals have prehensile tails which are apparently used in gathering nest-building material. The Rufous Rat-kangaroo (*Aepyprymnus rufescens*), from Eastern Australia, has long ears and a partially hairy nose. The other Rat-kangaroos are included in three genera, *Bettongia*, *Caloprymnus*, and *Potorous*, all confined to Australia and Tasmania.

The Musk rat-kangaroo (*Hypsiprymnodon moschatus*) is the sole member of the third sub-family *Hypsiprymnodontinae ;* it is a rat-like beast with large ears, and has the big toes of considerable size, clawless, and opposable to the other digits. This animal has a very restricted distribution, being found only in North-East Queensland.

Family Phalangeridae

The second family of the sub-order Diprotodontia is the *Phalangeridae*, which contains a number of arboreal species, for the most part vegetarians, but some are insectivorous. The tail is usually well developed and frequently prehensile. The fingers and toes are all, except the big toe, armed with sharp-pointed claws ; the big toe, which is clawless, is opposable to the other digits. The pouch, as in the Kangaroos, opens forwards. The family may be regarded as containing two sub-families, the *Tarsipedinae*, or Honey-mice, and the *Phalangerinae*, including the Flying-phalangers and Australian opossums.

The Honey-mouse (*Tarsipes spenserae*), found only in South-West Australia, is about the size of a common house-mouse, with a long, pointed nose, and very long, extensile tongue ; the tail is long and prehensile. There are three longitudinal, dark stripes on the back ; the general colour above is greyish-rufous and the under parts are whitish. These little animals feed, for the most part, on the nectar of certain flowers and small insects.

In the other sub-family, the *Phalangerinae*, the muzzle is broad and pointed, and the tongue non-prehensile. The teeth, unlike those of *Tarsipes*, are not rudimentary. The species vary in size from the Pigmy Flying-phalangers, which are smaller than a mouse, to the large Australian Opossums and Cuscuses. The former (*Acrobates*) are characterised by the possession of a flying membrane, rather like that of the flying-squirrels and scaly-tails ; the tail is fringed, and acts as a rudder when the animal is gliding. These small Flying-phalangers (*A. pygmaeus*) are insectivorous and entirely arboreal, living amongst the eucalyptus trees of Eastern Australia ; a closely allied species, *A. pulchellus*, hails from New Guinea. Related to *Acrobates* are the Dormouse-phalangers (*Dromicia*) from Australia, Tasmania, and New Guinea, and the Feather-tailed phalangers (*Distaechurus*) from New

Guinea; both are very like dormice in appearance and have no flying membrane. The Dormouse-phalangers have prehensile tails, which accumulate a large mass of fat for the nourishment of the body during the enforced "aestivation," or "summer-sleep."

The Striped-phalangers (*Dactylopsila*) are larger animals than the foregoing genus, being of about the size of a large stoat, with a much longer tail; the various species are confined to New Guinea and Queensland. They are very handsome animals, the body being white, marked with three thick black stripes; they appear to live chiefly on insects.

Allied to the Striped-phalangers are two genera of flying-phalangers (or flying " squirrels "), *Petaurus*, the Lesser Flying-phalangers, and *Petauroides*, the Greater Flying-phalangers. Both groups are remarkable for the presence of a broad, flying membrane, rather similar to that of *Acrobates*. The fur in both genera is very soft and the tail bushy; the flying membrane in *Petaurus* extends from the fingers to the ankle, whereas in *Petauroides* it commences at the elbow and ends at the knee. The Lesser Flying-phalangers are found in Eastern Australia and New Guinea; the large species of the genus *Petauroides* are confined to Eastern Australia and Central Queensland. The Greater Flying-phalangers can make the most astonishing leaps; there is a record of one of the animals gliding for a distance of eighty yards. Both groups are nocturnal and are vegetarian.

STRIPED-PHALANGER (*Dactylopsila trivirgata*).

The next genus, *Pseudochirus*, contains the Ring-tail opossums; the various species are a little smaller than the Australian opossums. They have prehensile, tapering tails, and their coats are woolly and thick. The Ring-tails are mostly arboreal and nocturnal, feeding on a variety of vegetable matter. Upwards of two dozen different forms are now known from Australia, Tasmania, and New Guinea.

The Australian opossums constitute the genus *Trichosurus*; they are stoutly built animals, with tapering, prehensile, hairy tails, naked at their tips on the under surface. The coat is thick and woolly, and extensively used by furriers; it varies in colour from grey to brownish-black. These animals are widely distributed over Australia and some of the adjacent islands, and Tasmania; one species, *T. vulpecula*, the Vulpine-opossum, has been introduced into New Zealand, where it is farmed for its fur.

The last genus (*Phalanger*) of the sub-family contains the typical phalangers, or Cuscuses, of which about twenty forms are now recognised ; they are distributed over North Australia, New Guinea, Timor, Celebes, and some of the adjacent islands. The best-known member of the group is the Spotted-cuscus (*Phalanger maculatus*), a very handsomely coloured species, the coat being a sort of piebald mixture of white, black, and red ; sometimes a grey tint predominates, sometimes the fur is nearly all white. The tip of the tail in this genus is completely naked, not hairy on the upper surface as in the Ring-tails. The Cuscuses are about equal in size to, or little larger than, the Australian opossums, and are distinguished by the soles of

SPOTTED-CUSCUS (*Phalanger maculatus*).

KOALA (*Phascolarctus cinereus*).

the feet being entirely naked, whereas in the genus *Trichosurus* the region under the heels is hairy.

The third and last sub-family of the *Phalangeridae* is the *Phascolarctinae*, containing the Koala, or Native-bear (*Phascolarctus cinereus*). This beast is easily distinguished from all the foregoing species by its stout build, large, furry ears, and vestigial tail. It is entirely arboreal, and confines itself to a diet of eucalyptus leaves. The Koala is about two feet in length and ashy-grey in colour ; it is a very expert climber, and was at one time very common in Eastern Australia ; disease and the furrier, however, have taken a very heavy toll of its numbers.

Family Phascolomyidae

The Wombats constitute a distinct family, the *Phascolomyidae*, the members of which are all heavily built, short-legged animals, with short tails and large claws, specially adapted for digging purposes, on their fore-feet. The teeth are rodent-like, being rootless and with persistent pulps. They live during the daytime in large burrows, coming out to feed in the evening; their diet consists of grass and the bark of young trees and shrubs. Two quite different kinds of wombats may be distinguished, those with naked noses and coarse hair (*Phascolomys mitchelli*, *tasmaniensis*, and *ursinus*), and those with hairy noses and silky fur (*P. latifrons* and *gillespii*). These species are found over South-Eastern Australia, Tasmania, and on Flinders and Deal Islands, Bass Straits.

Sub-order POLYPROTODONTIA

(*Bandicoots, Opossums, etc.*)

The sub-order Polyprotodontia, in which the incisor teeth are numerous, contains, as already mentioned, three distinct families, the *Peramelidae*, or bandicoots, being the one most nearly related to the Diprotodonts.

Family Peramelidae

These animals are all of medium size (large rat or rabbit) and are divided into nine genera, the best known of which are the Rabbit-eared bandicoots (*Thalacomys*) and the Long-nosed bandicoot (*Perameles nasuta*). Their hind-legs are rather long, suggestive of the kangaroo, but their habits are very different, as they are burrowing animals which live largely on insects. These animals are widely distributed over a great part of Australia, Tasmania, and New Guinea. The Rabbit-eared bandicoots, which hail from Australia only, have very pointed snouts, and long ears like rabbits; their tails are long and crested.

RABBIT-EARED BANDICOOT (*Thalacomys lagotis*).

The Long-nosed bandicoot (*Perameles nasuta*) has a rather spiny coat, very different from the soft pelage of the Rabbit-eared bandicoot, which is long and silky. The ears are considerably shorter, and the general colour brownish above, white below. This species is an inhabitant of Eastern Australia. Members of this genus are found all over Australia; one species occurs in Tasmania and another in the Islands of Sharks Bay, Western Australia. The strange Pig-footed bandicoot (*Choeropus castanotis*) is allied to the foregoing species, but its coat, although coarse, is not spiny, and the tail is crested. The name "Pig-footed" refers to the fact that the functional toes are reduced to two on each foot, as in the pig.

Family Dasyuridae

The remainder of the Australian marsupials are included in the family *Dasyuridae*, which contains a number of predatory carnivorous and insectivorous animals, usually with well-developed canine teeth. The various genera and species are widely distributed over Australia, Tasmania, New Guinea, and some of the adjacent islands. The family is sub-divided into three sub-families: (i) the *Dasyurinae*, which contain the more typical members of the family; (ii) the *Myrmecobinae*, containing the marsupial Banded ant-eater, an aberrant animal found only in South and South-Western Australia; and (iii) the *Notoryctinae*, containing two species of marsupial-mole. Possibly these last two groups are quite distinct from the Dasyures and ought to be considered as representing separate families.

The *Dasyurinae* range in size from the Thylacine or Marsupial-wolf to the Pigmy pouched-mice; the larger species are strictly carnivorous, the smaller forms appear to live largely on insects. Most of the species are terrestrial, though a few live in trees; all are more or less nocturnal. The Thylacine or Marsupial-wolf, also known as the Tasmanian-wolf

TASMANIAN-DEVIL (*Sarcophilus harrisi*).

(*Thylacinus cynocephalus*), is the largest member of the sub-order, being about the size of a large, short-legged dog, with a tapering, thinly-haired tail. The colour of the coat is tawny, with a number of transverse, black stripes on the back, those on the hindquarters being most developed. Formerly the Thylacine was an inhabitant of Australia, but it is now only found in Tasmania. The young, four of which are produced at a birth, are carried in the pouch for about three months. In this animal the pouch opens backwards.

The Tasmanian-devil (*Sarcophilus harrisi*) is another large species, being very stoutly built and about the size of a large cat; the coat is thick and black in colour, with a white, crescentic marking on the chest. At the present day this animal is confined to Tasmania, but it was formerly found on the mainland of Australia. The typical Dasyures, or Tiger-cats and Native-cats, of the genus *Dasyurus*, possess the same number of teeth as the Tasmanian-devil, but are more slender in build, and have long and narrow ears, not rounded as in *Sarcophilus*. The pouch, which only appears in the breeding season, opens downwards. These cat-like marsupials vary in colour from olive-grey to blackish-brown ; the coats are usually profusely spotted with white. In two species, the Tiger-cats (*D. maculatus* and *D. gracilis*), the spots spread on to the tail ; in the Native-cats the tails are unspotted, but the tail-tip may be white (*D. viverrinus*) or black, as in Geoffroy's Native-cat (*D. geoffroyi*) and its allies. These Tiger-cats and Native-cats are confined to Australia and Tasmania, except two species from New Guinea which have wholly black tails. Their diet is strictly carnivorous, the large species being able to kill wallabies and large birds.

The Phascogales, representing two genera, *Dasycercus* and *Phascogale*, are smaller than the Dasyures, and usually some shade of grey or brown in colour and unspotted ; some species have one or three black stripes along the back. The tail is either tapering, cylindrical, crested, or tufted. The pouch is only evident when in use ; it is formed of two folds of the abdominal skin. Most of the species are terrestrial, a few are, however, arboreal ; they are carnivorous and insectivorous. About thirty forms are known, mostly from Australia and New Guinea ; a few species extend into Tasmania, while two are known from the Aru Islands.

Closely related to the Phascogales are the Pouched-rats (*Dasyuroides*) and Pouched-mice (*Sminthopsis*), the former being burrowing animals, having the pouch but little developed ; they are inhabitants of Central Australia. The Pouched-mice are entirely confined to Australia ; they are, in appearance, very mouse-like, and terrestrial in habits. The tails of some of these mice become very fat, just before aestivation, or the summer-sleep, and the name " fat-tailed mouse " is often used for the Common pouched-mouse (*S. crassi-caudatus*). The Jerboa pouched-mice (*Antechinomys*) have large ears and hind-feet, and long, tufted tails ; they move by jumping, in much the same way as jerboas and gerbils. The pouch is only visible during the breeding season. The two species are found only in Australia.

The sub-family *Myrmecobinae* contains the single genus *Myrmecobius*, which has been founded for the reception of a remarkable marsupial ant-eater, known as the Banded Ant-eater (*M. fasciatus*). This beast, which is about the size of a rat, has a very elongated nose and a long, extensile tongue, with which it licks up the white ants which form its sole diet. The colour of this ant-eater is very striking, the head, fore-part of the body, limbs, and tail are grizzled rufous, darkening to black on the back, and with a series of transverse white bands between the shoulders and hindquarters. No pouch is developed, and the species is confined to South and South-West Australia.

The last sub-family of the *Dasyuridae* is the *Notoryctinae*, which includes two very remarkable species of marsupial-moles (*Notoryctes typhlops* and *N. caurinus*). These animals are quite unlike all other marsupials, being specially adapted for burrowing underground. Eyes and eyelids are entirely absent, and the ears have no conch; the nose is protected with a horny shield, used in digging operations, for which the fore-feet have developed two enormous, triangular claws, constituting a digging foot quite unlike that of the mole. The tail is short and ringed. The Marsupial-mole appears to travel about just underneath the surface of the sand, searching for various insects on which it lives. The genus is known only from Central, South, and North-Western Australia.

Family Didelphyidae

The last family of marsupials is the *Didelphyidae*, which contains all the well-known opossums of the New World. Although confined to America and adjacent islands at the present day, in former times, during the Tertiary epoch, this family was much more widely distributed, some species being found in Europe. These opossums are distinguished from their Australian cousins by the possession of a well-developed, nail-less, and opposable first toe. Further, there are five incisor teeth in the upper jaw and four in the lower; whereas in the *Dasyuridae* the incisors are $\frac{4}{3}$. The tail is usually long and prehensile; and the pouch, if present, is represented by a couple of folds of the abdominal skin. Most of the species are nocturnal and arboreal, and the majority are insectivorous or omnivorous.

COMMON OPOSSUM (*Didelphys marsupialis*).

The typical member of the family is the Common or Virginian opossum (*Didelphys marsupialis*), which is the largest species of the whole group, being about the size of a cat, with a long, scaly, prehensile tail. The coat is composed of a mixture of under-fur and long, bristle-like hairs. A number of different forms of these large opossums are now recognised, distributed over both North and South America. Closely allied is the South American Rat-tailed opossum (*Metachirus nudicaudatus*), which is about the size of a large rat, and has a long, naked tail; the face in this animal is black and white, and a black streak runs down the back. *M. opossum*, another South American species, is very similar in colour, but has a black, hairy tail, with a white tip. The Thick-tailed opossum (*Lutreola crassicaudata*), from Uruguay, Paraguay, and the

Argentine, is a large, yellow-ochre-coloured animal, with a thick, tapering tail, the proximal half of which is black, with the extreme tip white.

The Philander-opossums (*Philander lanigera* and allied forms) are about two feet in total length, more than half this length being taken up by the long, naked tail, the end portion of which is white. In colour these opossums are frequently brilliant orange above and greyish below ; the face is marked, in some species, with orange eye-stripes, and a black, median stripe on the head. The members of this genus are found over a great part of South and Central America.

The smaller opossums are now placed in several distinct genera, the most important of which are the following : *Marmosa*, including a large number of South American species with long, naked tails and dark markings around the eyes. In size these animals are about equal to rats or large mice. Some of the species (*M. murina*) are very like the common dormouse in colour ; the larger forms are usually of a greyish tint. One species, *M. elegans*, just before entering upon its summer sleep (aestivation) develops a mass of fat around the tail to serve for the sustenance of the body during the long fast. In all the members of this group the pouch is absent. Other small opossums are included in the genera *Peramys, Monodelphis,* and *Notodelphys,* all remarkable for their short and usually non-prehensile tails.

Lastly there is the Water-opossum (*Chironectes minima*), which equals a very large rat in size, and possesses a long, scaly tail with a white tip ; the hind-feet are greatly enlarged and the toes webbed. The coat of this animal is very soft and otter-like, while its coloration takes the form of alternating, transverse bands of dark chocolate and dirty white, with white under parts. In habits this animal closely resembles an otter, living in the water and feeding on various aquatic animals. The female has a well-developed pouch. Its range includes a large part of Central and South America, from Guatemala to Brazil.

CHAPTER II

Sub-class *EUTHERIA*

(*Placentals*)

ALL the remaining mammals are included in the third sub-class, the Eutheria (also known as the Placentalia, or Monodelphia).

The main characters of the Eutheria have already been outlined when dealing with the Metatheria, or pouched animals. The most important difference between this sub-class and the other two divisions concerns the method by which the developing embryo is nourished before birth ; a placental- or umbilical-cord is developed, by means of which a union is affected between the foetus and the mother, and thus nourishment can pass from the latter into the former.

The sub-class is so large and unwieldy that it is necessary to divide it into a number of natural groups, or orders ; some of these orders are very clearly defined and easily distinguished, others are just the reverse, some species appearing to form " annectant types," difficult to dispose of from the systematist's point of view. According to the classification adopted here, the existing Eutheria are split up into nine distinct orders, namely : (i) Edentata, the sloths, armadillos, and ant-eaters ; (ii) Sirenia, the sea-cows ; (iii) Cetacea, whales and dolphins ; (iv) Ungulata, the hoofed animals ; (v) Rodentia, rats, mice, and squirrels ; (vi) Carnivora, cats, dogs, and bears ; (vii) Insectivora, insect-feeding animals such as the hedgehogs, shrews, and moles ; (viii) Chiroptera, the bats ; and (ix) Primates, the lemurs, monkeys, and apes.

Order EDENTATA

(*Sloths, Ant-eaters, Armadillos, etc.*)

The Edentates are characterised by the entire absence of front teeth, or incisors ; in two groups, the ant-eaters and pangolins, teeth are entirely absent. The order contains five distinct groups, or families : the sloths (*Bradypodidae*), the ant-eaters (*Myrmecophagidae*), the armadillos (*Dasypodidae*), the pangolins (*Manidae*), and the aard-varks (*Orycteropodidae*). Those species which possess teeth, in addition to the absence of front teeth, are remarkable for the simple structure of their cheek-teeth, which are made up only of ivory and cement, and are without distinct roots ; functional milk-teeth are, in the majority of cases, not developed.

The members of this order are all of low organisation, the brain being small and of a low type. Some of the species, such as the sloths and ant-eaters, are clothed with hair ; some, like the armadillos, have developed a hard, bony, shield-like shell ; and others have the body protected by a coat of over-lapping scales (pangolins). The first three of the above-mentioned families are confined to the New World ; the fourth group (*Manidae*) is entirely African and Asiatic ; while the aard-varks are found only in Africa. There are no aquatic Edentates, all the species being either terrestrial or arboreal ; among the latter the sloths are entirely vegetarian, the remainder being insectivorous or carnivorous. Three of the groups (ant-eaters, pangolins, and aard-varks) live for the most part on termites, or white ants.

Family Bradypodidae

The Sloths are characterised by their short, rounded heads, very small ears, long fore-limbs, and vestigial tail. Collar-bones are present, and the hair is long and pithy. Their teeth, which number $\frac{5}{4}$ in each jaw, are, like the teeth of the majority of Edentates, more or less cylindrical in form, and of persistent growth. The digits never exceed three in number, and are united together for almost their entire length by skin; the claws are long and very strong. These extraordinary animals are found only in the forests of South and Central America, where they pass their whole lives suspended from the branches of trees, back downwards, the feet having been transformed into curved hooks as an adaptation to their persistent use as suspensory organs. Their diet is strictly vegetarian. In some sloths the hair is coarse, and marked by longitudinal grooves, which lodge colonies of a green alga, giving a greenish tinge to the coat and thereby furnishing a protective coloration.

The sloths with three toes on both the fore- and hind-feet are included in the genus *Bradypus*, which is further distinguished by the possession of nine, instead of the normal seven, cervical vertebrae; the Three-toed sloth is also known by the name of " Ai." The first tooth in the upper jaw is much smaller than the other teeth. These sloths are very variable in colour, some being a uniform dull brown, others a mixture of greyish-brown and white; in many specimens there is a round, short-haired, brown- and orange-coloured patch just behind the shoulders. This curious marking looks, at a little distance, like the stump of a broken bough. The typical species is *B. tridactylus*; several different forms are now recognised.

TWO-TOED SLOTH (*Choloepus didactylus*).

The Two-toed Sloths (*Choloepus*), which are larger than the three-toed species, possess only two toes on the fore-feet; they are further characterised by their much larger skulls, and in having the first tooth in the upper jaw considerably larger than the remaining teeth and shaped like a canine tooth. The cervical vertebrae are seven in number in the typical species (*C. didactylus*); the closely allied *C. hoffmanni* has only six vertebrae in the neck. The former species is known by the native name of " Unau "; it inhabits the forests of Brazil. *C. hoffmanni* is found in Ecuador northwards to Costa Rica. In both forms the coloration is very variable.

A closely allied group is the extinct family of ground-sloths, the *Megatheridae*, which appear to be intermediate between the sloths and ant-eaters, having the teeth and head of the *Bradypodidae*, and the limbs, vertebrae, and tail as in the *Myrmecophagidae*. The typical *Megatherium* was an enormous animal, being between an elephant and a rhinoceros in size. The ground-sloths were herbivorous, and their bodies were clothed in coarse hair. In the genus *Mylodon*, somewhat smaller than *Megatherium*, there were a number of bony plates embedded in the skin. The various species were mostly inhabitants of South America, a few being found in North America.

Family Myrmecophagidae

The Ant-eaters, which live almost exclusively upon ants, are distinguished from the sloths by their elongated heads, long tails, tubular mouths, long, extensile tongues, and absence of all teeth ; in two genera, rudimentary collar-bones are developed. From the Asiatic and African ant-eaters, or pangolins (*Manidae*), they differ in having the body clothed in hair, not horny scales. The tail is, in two genera, prehensile, and the limbs are about equal in length. The middle-toe of the fore-foot is much enlarged, and bears a large claw used for digging. Three genera may be distinguished :

(i) *Myrmecophaga*, containing a single species, the Great Ant-eater (*M. jubata*), which is the largest member of the family, measuring about

GREAT ANT-EATER (*Myrmecophaga jubata*).

eight feet in total length. The head is very narrow and elongated, the skull looking like a long (fifteen inches), slightly curved beak, without cheek-bones or zygomatic arches. The coat is composed of rather coarse, bristly hair, short on the head, and very long on the fore-limbs, flanks, and tail ; on the latter the hairs attain a length of fifteen or sixteen inches. A broad, black stripe, bordered with white, extends from the chest and shoulders to the hindquarters ; the head, mane, tail, and flanks are grey mixed with black ; and the throat, chest, hind-limbs, and markings on fore-limbs black. The tail is non-prehensile, and the animal is strictly terrestrial and largely nocturnal. It is widely distributed over tropical Central and South America.

(ii) *Tamandua*, the Lesser Ant-eater, or Tamandua (*T. tetradactyla*). This animal is rather less than half the size of the Great Ant-eater, from which it is distinguished by its shorter head, larger ears, prehensile tail, and shorter coat. The latter is a mixture of buff and black-coloured hairs, the face, neck, basal portion of the tail, and a median shoulder-stripe being buff-coloured, and a broad, blackish stripe extends from the chest over the shoulders on to the flanks and hindquarters. The tip of the tail, and the whole of its lower surface, are naked. The skull, which is about six inches in length, has the same incomplete zygomatic arch, or cheek-bone, as was noted in the Great Ant-eater. The range of distribution includes the forests of tropical America and Trinidad.

(iii) *Cyclopes*, the Two-toed Ant-eaters. The members of this genus are all small animals, about the size of a rat. The skull, which is only about one and a half inches in length, has a much shorter and more arched muzzle ; the zygomatic arch is, as in the other genera of the family, incomplete. The fore-feet are remarkably modified, only two toes being functional ; the third digit is very large and bears a strong, hook-like claw. The second digit is similarly formed, but much more slender ; the other digits are clawless and more or less vestigial. The hind-feet bear four nearly equal-sized toes, forming a hook-like foot ; the big toe is reduced to the condition of a vestige and concealed beneath the skin. In this genus, unlike *Myrmeco-phaga* and *Tamandua*, the collar-bones are well developed. The coat is soft and silky, and is usually some shade of golden buff or rufous in colour, with a dark, median, ill-defined stripe down the back. The Two-toed Ant-eater (*C. didactylus*) inhabits the northern part of South America, Central America, and Trinidad ; it is entirely arboreal, insectivorous, and nocturnal.

Family Dasypodidae

The next group, or family, is the *Dasypodidae*, which includes the New World armadillos. These animals are characterised by the development of a number of bony plates in the skin, so arranged as to form a hard, bony shield surrounding the body. This shield is, as a rule, composed of three main parts, a more or less solid and inflexible portion over the shoulders and hindquarters, and a middle flexible section, made up of a varying number of rings, covering the trunk. In addition, the head, limbs, and tail are further protected by bony scutes. The under parts are more or less hairy, and hairs often grow in the grooves between the bony plates of the armour ; in some species the hairs are so long and numerous as to almost hide the bony shield. The fore-feet are provided with large claws (five to three in number), and the skull possesses complete zygomatic arches and numerous small, peg-like teeth. The collar-bones are well formed, and the tongue, although elongate, is not so long as in the ant-eaters.

The family is divided into three sub-families : (i) the *Chlamyphorinae*, including a single species of pigmy-armadillo, the Pichiciago, or Fairy Armadillo (*Chlamyphorus truncatus*), from the Argentine ; (ii) the *Dasypodinae*, or true armadillos, representing five different genera ; and (iii) the *Tatusinae*, including the single genus *Tatusia*. The Pichiciago is the smallest member of the order, being only about five inches in length ; the shield covering the body is of a pinkish hue, and the hair on the sides of the face, limbs, and flanks is pure white. The mantle, or shield, is remarkable for the fact that it is only attached along the line of the backbone (except on the head, where it is firmly fixed) ; it is composed of about twenty transverse rows of plates, varying in number from about seven or eight on the head to a couple of dozen on the hindquarters. The abruptly truncated rump is protected by a solid shield of bony plates firmly attached to the pelvis, and comprising five or six concentric rows of plates. From the centre of the segment of a circle, formed by this vertically placed shield, emerges the short, spatulate tail.

The upper surfaces of the feet are covered with horny plates ; the rest of the limbs, belly, flanks, and sides of the body underneath the shield are clothed with long, rather soft, white hair ; the latter forming a well-marked fringe at the junction of the body shield and that of the hindquarters. The eyes are very small, the external ears minute, and the claws of the fore-feet very large and adapted for burrowing purposes. The skull is short and broad behind, and bears two prominent frontal protuberances ; the teeth, which number eight in the upper and eight or nine in the lower jaws, are small, and more or less cylindrical in shape. This species inhabits the sandy plains of the Argentine, spending the greater part of its time underground ; it is a most expert burrower and largely nocturnal in its habits.

The *Dasypodinae*, or true armadillos, are much larger than the Pichiciago, and are distinguished by the bony shield, or carapace, being divided into three sections, a solid scapular and lumbar region, and a variable number of flexible bands covering the middle part of the body. The ears, although much larger than in *Chlamyphorus*, are only of moderate size and set widely apart. The females, as in the Pichiciago, have but a single pair of teats on the breast. The sub-family contains five genera : (i) *Dasypus*, including a number of different species, chiefly distinguished by the number of bands in the central part of the carapace. Teeth $\frac{9}{10}$ or $\frac{8}{9}$. This is the usual and most convenient way of expressing the number of teeth in mammals—the teeth of the upper jaw above, and of the lower jaw below the line. The Six-banded Armadillo (*D. sexcinctus*) is about twenty-two inches in total length, and has a broad, massive skull, with comparatively short muzzle ; it is widely distributed in South America, and four or five geographical races are now recognised. A closely allied but smaller species is the Hairy Armadillo (*D. villosus*) from the Argentine. *D. vellerosus*, a still smaller form, also hails from the Argentine, and another small species, *D. megalolepsis*, with a long, narrow snout, is an inhabitant of Brazil. *D. pastasae* is a large species from Ecuador, with a longer and narrower skull than in the Six-banded Armadillo.

(ii) *Cabassous*, a genus which includes two or three species, which have from twelve to thirteen movable bands in the carapace ; teeth $\frac{9}{9}$ or $\frac{8}{8}$. The best known of the species is the Tatouay (*C. unicinctus*), from Brazil and Paraguay.

(iii) *Priodontes*, the Great Armadillo (*P. gigas*), is the only member of this genus. This animal is at once distinguished by its very large size, the head and body measuring about three feet and the tail nearly twenty inches in length. Further, the skull, which is very large and massive, is remarkable for the large number of teeth, some twenty to twenty-five teeth being developed in each side of each jaw. The claw of the third toe of the fore-feet is very large and powerful, and enables the animal to dig with great facility. This species lives in the forests of Brazil, Paraguay, and adjacent parts of South America; it is, like the rest of the family, largely insectivorous.

(iv) *Tolypeutes*, a genus containing only two or three species of rather small size, with short tails. The armour consists of large scapular and

GREAT ARMADILLO (*Priodontes gigas*).

lumbar-shields, with only three body-rings between them ; these armadillos can roll themselves up into a complete ball. The muzzle is slender, teeth $\frac{9}{9}$ or $\frac{8}{8}$, and the ears long, the latter being set low down on the sides of the head. The best known of the Three-banded Armadillos is the Apar (*T. tricinctus*) ; it is mainly diurnal and widely distributed over the Argentine.

(v) *Zaedyus*, a closely allied genus from Bolivia and the Argentine, possesses a shorter skull than *Tolypeutes*.

The *Tatusinae* are known by their long ears being set close together on the top of the head. The teeth, which number $\frac{8}{8}$ or $\frac{7}{7}$, are very small, and are remarkable in that, with the exception of the last tooth, they are all preceded by two-rooted milk-teeth. The carapace has from seven to nine body-rings, and the genus is further noteworthy on account of the possession of two abdominal teats, in addition to the normal pectoral pair. The Peba Armadillo, *Tatusia novemcincta*, belongs to this genus ; its range extends northwards as far as Texas and south to Paraguay.

During the Pleistocene period there existed in Central and South America a number of different genera and species of gigantic armadillo-like animals, which are grouped together in the family *Glyptodontidae*. The majority of these beasts had the carapace formed of one solid shield, made up of polygonal plates fused together, without any body-rings, while they were further peculiar in having the under surface of the body protected by a bony shield, or " plastron." Some of these glyptodonts were as large as a rhinoceros.

Family Manidae

The next two groups of Edentates belong only to the Old World, and are totally different from the New World families already noticed. The *Manidae*, or Pangolins, are widely distributed over Africa, and the Oriental region as far east as Java, Borneo, and Celebes ; northwards they range into China. These Pangolins, or Scaly Ant-eaters, are characterised by the entire absence of teeth, and by the upper parts of the body and entire tail being covered with a number of over-lapping, horny scales ; the under surface of the body and inner sides of limbs are, usually, sparsely haired. The skull is long and conical in shape, and the cheek-arch is generally incomplete, reminiscent of the condition found in the ant-eaters of America. The eyes and external ears are quite small, and the tongue long and extensile ; collar-bones are not developed.

The family contains but a single genus, *Manis*, which includes a number of different species, all of which can roll up into a ball when danger threatens ; they are mostly burrowing and nocturnal animals, feeding largely on ants and termites, which are captured by their long and sticky tongues. Three well-marked Asiatic species can be distinguished : the Indian-pangolin (*M. pentadactyla*), from India and Ceylon, is about three feet six inches in total length, the tail occupying about one foot six inches of this dimension. This animal agrees with the other Asiatic forms in having the middle upper row of caudal scales continued uninterruptedly to the tip of the tail ; in the African species, to be noticed subsequently, this row of scales divides into two some little distance from the tip. Closely allied to the Indian species is the Chinese-pangolin, another comparatively stoutly built animal, with tail of moderate length ; this form (*M. aurita*) ranges from Nepal into China. The Malayan-pangolin (*M. javanica*) is a more slenderly built animal with a proportionately longer tail. The claws of the fore-feet in *M. pentadactyla* and *M. aurita* are about twice the length of those of the hind-feet ; in the Malayan species the claws of the fore-feet are only slightly larger than the hinder ones.

The African-pangolins include two medium-sized and two large species ; the Giant Pangolin of West Africa, *M. gigantea*, is the largest member of the family (total length five feet four inches) ; it has a long tail, and the scales are of considerable size. As with the other African species, hair does not grow between the scales and there is no trace of external ears ; in the Asiatic forms small external ears are present, and isolated hairs occur on the back between the scales. The other large African species is the Short-tailed Pangolin (*M. temmincki*), which is smaller than *M. gigantea* and has a shorter tail ; its range of distribution spreads right across the middle of the continent from West to East. Both these large forms are strictly terrestrial. *M. macrura* is another West African species, distinguished by its very long tail,

GIANT PANGOLIN (*Manis gigantea*).

which is about twice as long as the body, and by the absence of scales on the lower part of the outer side of the fore-limbs. The White-bellied Pangolin (*M. tricuspis*), also from West Africa, is a smaller species (total length thirty inches), with white hairs on the belly and having the body scales tricuspidate. Both these latter pangolins appear to spend much of their time in the trees.

Family Orycteropodidae

This last family, containing the Aard-varks, or Ant-bears, is to-day restricted to Africa. The members of this genus (*Orycteropus*) are distinguished by their large (total length, six feet) and ungainly bodies, which may be either nearly naked or sparsely haired, their long heads and ears, tubular mouths, and long, cylindrical, tapering tails. The back is arched, and there are four toes on the fore-feet and five on the hind ones. The skull is of considerable length (about ten inches) and the zygomatic arch is complete. The teeth are rootless ; about eight to ten teeth are developed in the upper jaw and eight in the lower jaw. In adult specimens, however, the anterior teeth fall out, and there are not more than five teeth in each side of each jaw ; all but the last three teeth in each jaw have milk predecessors, which do not, however, cut the gum, and are therefore functionless. The Aard-varks, which are widely distributed in Africa, extending from the Cape to as far north as Egypt, are nocturnal, spending the day asleep in their burrows ; they feed exclusively upon termites and ants.

Order SIRENIA

(*Sea-cows*)

The Manatees, Dugongs, and extinct Sea-cow, together with certain fossil forms, constitute the order Sirenia. On account of a superficial resemblance to the whales and dolphins, due to a parallel course of evolution, these animals are frequently and erroneously spoken of as close relations of the Cetacea, or whales. From the evidence at present available it seems probable that the Sirenia have evolved from a primitive, swamp-dwelling ancestor, whose descendants on the one side became more and more aquatic and gave rise to the modern Sirenia, while on the other side, retaining their terrestrial habits, and through such forms as *Moeritherium* and *Palaeomastodon*, they gave rise to the elephants of to-day.

The head in these Sirenians is rounded, and not out of proportion to the size of the body ; the latter is separated from the head by a short and rather indistinct neck. The nostrils, which have separate apertures, are placed on top of the rounded muzzle. The eyes are small and there is no external ear. The tail is flattened and expanded horizontally, forming a broad tail-fin. There is no trace of a fin on the back, and the fore-limbs are paddle-shaped, the fingers being enveloped in a flat skin-sheath. In the modern species the hind-limbs have entirely disappeared. The wrinkled skin is either naked or is scantily covered by bristles. The teats, which are two in number, are placed one on each side of the chest.

The skeleton is very heavily built, especially the skull and ribs ; this may be a special development to assist in keeping the animals under water while feeding on the various aquatic plants which constitute their chief food. The teeth are usually differentiated into incisors and molars, separated by a considerable gap ; the incisors are sometimes large and tusk-like. In one genus, the extinct *Rhytina*, there are no teeth in the adult. The skull resembles in some respects those of the early ancestors of the modern elephants. The lungs are very large, extending back over the abdomen, the diaphragm being oblique ; and horny plates are developed on the roof of the mouth and in the lower jaw.

These animals spend all their lives in the water, never straying very far from the shore ; they frequent bays, lagoons, and the larger rivers, not being found far out at sea. The surviving members of this order are restricted to the warmer regions of the shores of both sides of the Atlantic and the large rivers of those countries, and to the coasts of the Indian Ocean from the Red Sea to North Australia.

The existing genera, together with the extinct Sea-cow, have been referred to three families : (i) the *Manatidae*, containing the Manatees ; (ii) the *Halicoridae*, or Dugongs ; and (iii) the *Rhytinidae*, containing only the extinct Sea-cow.

Family Manatidae

Three species of Manatee can be distinguished, one from South America, one from North America, and one confined to West African waters. They are all medium-sized animals, not exceeding eight feet in length, and are nearly naked. The flippers, or fore-limbs, are oval in shape and bear three nails near the tips ; the tail is rounded, without the notch in the mid-line which occurs in the next family. The upper lip is formed of two swollen, bristly pads, by means of which food is gathered and taken into the mouth, where it is squeezed and pressed by the horny plates inside. Beneath the horny plates in young individuals there are two pairs of incisors in each jaw ; these teeth are never functional and disappear before the animal is adult. There are eleven pairs of cheek-teeth in each jaw, succeeding each other from behind forwards as do the grinders of an elephant, those in the front being shed and their places

AMERICAN MANATEE (*Manatus americanus*).

filled by teeth from behind, so that the first teeth are used up before the last of the series has fully developed. About six of these teeth are functional at the same time.

Manatees are considerably less numerous than they formerly were ; they are, however, still to be found around the West Indies and along the American coast from Florida to Brazil. The African species occurs on the corresponding shores of the West African coast. Occasionally these animals ascend the larger rivers almost to their sources ; there have been reports of Manatees far up the Amazon, and it seems probable that the African animal reaches as far inland as Lake Chad.

Family Halicoridae

There would appear to be only one species of Dugong, *Halicore dugong*, an inhabitant of the Red Sea and Indian Ocean, and as far east as the Philippine Islands and Australian waters. Dugongs are slightly larger than manatees, adult specimens reaching a length of nine feet ; they are also rather paler in colour. The tail, instead of being abruptly rounded, is markedly notched in the mid-line, and the flippers bear no signs of nails. The skull and lower jaws have their front ends bent sharply downwards. In young individuals the incisor teeth number two pairs in the upper jaw and four in the lower. In the adult male the front pair of upper incisors grow into large, rootless tusks ; in the female these teeth, although present, remain small. The lower incisors are functionless, being hidden by the oral plates, and in adult life they are absorbed. Five or six pairs of grinders are present in each jaw, though not all at once, there being the same sort of proboscidian succession as was noted in the case of the manatee.

The Dugong is more marine in its habits than the manatee, feeding, for the most part, on seaweed. Three species have been described, but they are probably all one and the same form.

Family Rhytinidae

Steller's Sea-cow (*Rhytina stelleri*), from Behring and Copper Islands in the North Pacific, is now extinct ; it was by far the largest member of the order, attaining a length of twenty to twenty-five feet. The head of this beast was very small and the flippers short. The tail had two lateral lobes, and no teeth were present in the adult stage, their place being taken by horny plates. This large species was exterminated in the latter part of the eighteenth century, some thirty or so years after its discovery by Behring and Steller.

Order CETACEA

(*Whales*)

In general form Whales are more fish-like than the Sirenia, the head being very large and passing without any visible neck into the body ; the latter tapers off towards the tail, which bears large " flukes," triangular in shape and deeply notched in the mid-line behind. The fore-limbs are in the form of flat flippers or paddles, showing no trace of nails or divisions into hand, fore-arm, or arm ; the hind-limbs have disappeared. Like the Sirenians, fat is accumulated under the skin, and this together with the tissue that holds it is known as the " blubber," which in the great Greenland-whale may be as much as eighteen inches in thickness. The body is naked, except for a few bristles on the snout and chin in very young animals. In the majority of species a dorsal fin is present. The eye has no third eyelid, or " nictitating membrane." There is no external ear, the position of the latter being indicated only by a small hole situated just behind the eye.

The nostrils open either separately, as in the Whale-bone whales, or together, as in the Toothed-whales, the opening being near the top of the head ; the windpipe and lungs are quite cut off from the mouth, so that the animals can proceed under water with their mouths open without fear of drowning ; the opening of the nostrils, or blowhole, is protected by a valvular mechanism, which automatically closes the opening directly after inspiration and before the whale submerges. The " blowing " of a whale is caused not by water taken in through the mouth and blown out through the nose, as is so often and erroneously thought to be the case (we have already seen that there is no communication between the mouth and the nasal openings), but it is the normal act of expiration, the moisture in the exhaled breath forming the well-known " spout." Experienced whalers can tell the different species by their spouts. The organs of scent are but little developed; in fact, in many Toothed-whales the olfactory nerves are not developed. The brain-case is short and the facial region much elongated. The brain is marked by many folds or convolutions. There are no collar-bones, and the pelvis is reduced to two small bones suspended below the front end of the caudal region.

As a rule, one young one is produced at a birth, and is, of course, born at sea. The female has two teats situated far back on the under surface of the body ; these teats communicate with very large mammary glands, and as soon as the teat is seized by the baby whale a copious draught of milk spurts forth.

It seems probable that Whales and their allies have evolved from some ancestral type of terrestrial carnivore. The bristles already referred to as growing on the snout and chin, which remain throughout life only in the Humpback whale, may possibly be regarded as the last remnants of the " whiskers " of their carnivorous ancestors.

The members of the Order Cetacea are found in all known waters, and some species inhabit the larger rivers of South America and Asia. They are all predaceous, living on various types of animal food ; some species feed on fish ; others on minute crustacea, pteropods, and cuttle-fish ; while others, like the grampuses, or " killers," kill and devour not only seals and dolphins but even large whales, which they hunt in packs. Whales are generally gregarious, going about in large " schools," or herds ; a few species are met with singly or in pairs.

The Whales form a sharply defined group; no other group of mammals, indeed, is so distinct or so markedly cut off from the rest of the class. The existing members of the order fall into two sub-groups—the Whalebone- or Baleen-whales, or *Mystacoceti*, and the Toothed-whales, or *Odontoceti*.

Sub-order MYSTACOCETI

(*Whalebone- or Baleen-whales*)

The first of these sub-groups includes three families, which contain the largest mammals that have ever existed. Primarily these families are distinguished by the presence of whalebone, or " baleen," by the nostrils opening separately—the blowhole being double—and by the large size and symmetrical build of the skull, which possesses well-developed nasal bones. The olfactory organ is well formed, and the two halves of the lower jaw are joined together in front by a mass of fibrous tissue. These whales have, for a short period before birth, numerous small teeth in both jaws. After birth the baleen commences to develop ; it arises from the mucous membrane of the palate, and consists of an extensive series of hard, horny, triangular plates growing from the roof of the mouth. The plates are very numerous, two hundred and fifty to three hundred or so on each side, and are placed very close together.   The inner and sloping edge of the plates is frayed out into a hairy margin, so that the inner surface of each set of plates resembles a dense, hairy mat all along each side of the mouth.   This arrangement acts as a filter, or strainer, the water taken in when the whale's mouth is fully open being forced through this filter, when the mouth is closed, by the upward action of the tongue.   The water escapes through the mat-like filter and flows out between the plates, but such small animals as were contained in it remain on the filter.   When the tongue moves down again the collection of minute creatures is jerked off the sieve-like mat on to the tongue ; this latter action is brought about by the sudden straightening out of the baleen plates.

These whalebone-whales are divided into three groups—the Right-whales, the Pacific Grey-whale, and the Rorquals.

Family Balaenidae

The Right-whales (*Balaenidae*), which constitute two genera, have the skin of the throat smooth, not furrowed, and the upper jaw is markedly arched. The vertebrae of the " neck " are fused together.   The first genus, *Balaena*, contains the Greenland, or Arctic, Right-whale (*B. mysticetus*) and the

GREENLAND-WHALE (*Balaena mysticetus*).

Biscay Right-whale (*B. glacialis*).   The head in these whales is of enormous proportions ; there is no dorsal fin, the flippers are short and five-fingered, and the baleen takes the form of extremely long, very narrow plates, black in colour.   The Biscay Right-whale has a relatively smaller head and shorter baleen than the Greenland species ; it is widely distributed in the Atlantic and Pacific, but some regard those inhabiting the Southern waters as representing a distinct species (*B. Australis*).   The Pigmy Right-whale, the second genus (*Neobalaena marginata*), occurs in Australian and New Zealand waters, but does not exceed twenty feet in length.   It is further distinguished by the presence of a small dorsal fin, the flippers being four-fingered and the baleen white.

Family Rhachianectidae

The Pacific Grey-whale (*Rhachianectes glaucus*), which is the sole member of this family, measures from forty to forty-eight feet in length, and has no dorsal fin. Unlike the Right-whales the skin of the throat shows two to four longitudinal grooves, and the vertebrae of the neck are free. The baleen is yellowish in colour, while the plates are few in number and not more than eighteen inches in length. This whale inhabits the North Pacific.

Family Balaenopteridae

The Rorquals, constituting the third family, differ from the Right-whales in having relatively smaller heads and free neck-bones ; further, there are but four digits in each flipper. In these whales the whole of the throat and chest is furrowed by a number of longitudinal pleats. Two genera of Rorquals may be distinguished—the Humpback-whales (*Megaptera*) and the Rorquals (*Balaenoptera*). The Humpback, which is widely spread over the

HUMPBACK-WHALE (*Megaptera nodosa*).

Atlantic and Pacific, reaches as far north and south as the Arctic and Antarctic regions ; it is a very strongly built whale and reaches a length of about fifty or so feet. The flippers are of great length and curiously scalloped along their outer margins. They are white, while the body is black. A small dorsal fin is developed, and there is a longitudinal series of tubercles on the head. The throat is marked by from twenty-five to forty pleats, and a sprinkling of bristles is developed on the front of the chin.

The Fin-whales, or true Rorquals (*Balaenoptera*), have the body longer and more slender than the foregoing genus, more numerous throat furrows and smaller flippers. A dorsal fin is present. Some, like the Lesser Rorqual, are comparatively small, not exceeding thirty feet in length. The Common

Rorqual is a much larger animal, whales of eighty feet or more having been recorded. This whale is of slender build and has a small dorsal fin set well back. The throat pleats are from sixty to one hundred in number, and the baleen bluish-grey in colour and about three feet in length.

Lastly we have Sibbald's-rorqual, which is the largest of all mammals,

COMMON RORQUAL (*Balaenoptera physalus*).

specimens from the South Atlantic measuring as much as one hundred feet in length ; in the North Atlantic they are about ten or twenty feet smaller. The dorsal fin is smaller than in the Common Rorqual, the flippers rather longer, the baleen black, and the throat pleats about sixty in number.

Sub-order ODONTOCETI

(*Toothed-whales*)

The second group, or Toothed-whales, contains a large variety of forms, such as the sperm-whales, dolphins, killers, and porpoises, in which teeth are usually present in one or both jaws, and whalebone is never developed. The nostrils, or blowhole, have a common opening which is situated asymmetrically, and the nasal bones are very small. The olfactory nerves are often absent. The species are widely spread over the various seas, and also occur in the rivers of Asia and South America.

Family Physeteridae

The Sperm-whales (family *Physeteridae*) have no functional teeth in the upper jaw, but numerous teeth are developed in the lower jaw. The cranium forms an elevated crest behind the nostrils and is strikingly asymmetrical in this region. The Sperm-whale, or Cachalot (*Physeter macrocephalus*), is remarkable for the fact that the female is only about half the size of the male ; the latter may reach to a length of sixty feet. The head is very large and obliquely truncated in front, with the blow-hole on the left-hand side of the end of the snout. This whale is an inhabitant of the warmer waters throughout the world, passing into the colder zones during the summer months. The Pigmy Sperm-whale (*Cogia breviceps*), from Indian and Australian waters, is only about ten feet in length and has from nine to thirteen pairs of mandibular teeth; in the upper jaw teeth are either absent or reduced to a vestigial pair. This species has also been recorded from the Cape and North Pacific.

SPERM-WHALE, or CACHALOT (*Physeter macrocephalus*).

Family Ziphiidae

The next family, the Beaked-whales (*Ziphiidae*), is characterised by the presence of two pleats on the throat, a crescentic, transversely placed blow-hole, and by the teeth all being reduced to vestiges, with the exception of one or two pairs in the lower jaw, which are greatly enlarged and present only in the males. These Beaked-whales appear to live largely on cuttle-fish. There are four different genera now recognised. The Bottle-nosed whale (*Hyperoödon*), which inhabits the North Atlantic, has all the neck vertebrae fused together. It is remarkable for the large bosses that develop in old males on the front of the skull; one or two pairs of teeth are con-

CUVIER'S BEAKED-WHALE (*Ziphius cavirostris*).

cealed near the tip of the lower jaw. Arnoux's-whale (*Berardius arnuxi*), another member of this group, is typically from New Zealand waters; it has the posterior vertebrae of the neck fused together, and there is a pair of large teeth in the front of the mandible, with a smaller pair behind. This rare species has recently been recorded from Alaska and South Georgia. Of the remaining Beaked-whales, Cuvier's-whale and Sowerby's-whale are the most important. The latter is about fourteen feet in length and has a single pair of teeth near the middle of the lower jaw.

Families Platanistidae and Delphinidae

There remain the River-dolphins (*Platanistidae*), and Dolphins and Por-poises (*Delphinidae*). The former group contains only four genera and species. These animals are all of small size, have free, cervical vertebrae, and long, beak-like jaws furnished with numerous teeth. The La Plata dolphin (*Pontoporia blainvillei*), from near Buenos Ayres, is only about five feet in length and has about sixty pairs of teeth in each jaw. The Inia

(*Inia geoffroyensis*), from the Amazon, is another member of the group, rather larger in size (seven feet in length), with fewer teeth (twenty-six to thirty-three pairs in each jaw). The Yangtze-dolphin

LA PLATA DOLPHIN (*Pontoporia blainvillei*).

(*Lipotes*) is about nine feet in length, has a large dorsal fin and about thirty-three pairs of teeth in each jaw. The last genus of the family *Platanista* contains the Gangetic-dolphin (*P. gangetica*); it is about eight feet in length, quite blind, the dorsal fin is very small, and about thirty pairs of teeth are present in each jaw. This dolphin is found only in river water, inhabiting the Ganges, Indus, and Brahmaputra.

The *Delphinidae* form the largest of the Cetacean families; the genera may be grouped in two sections, those which, like the dolphins, have a distinct beak and those which have no distinct beak, like the porpoises. The Common-dolphin (*Delphinus delphis*) grows to a length of from seven to eight feet, and carries from forty to sixty pairs of teeth in each jaw. All

COMMON-PORPOISE (*Phocaena phocaena*).

the members of this group have a fairly well-developed dorsal fin, excepting *Leucorhamphus peroni*, Peron's-dolphin of the South Seas, and another form, *L. borealis*, from the North Pacific, in which the dorsal fin is absent.

The beakless, or second, group contains the porpoises, "killers," beluga, and narwhal. The typical representative, the Common-porpoise (*Phocaena phocaena*), reaches a length of five to six feet, and has about twenty-five pairs of teeth in each jaw. Dorsal fins are found throughout this group with the exception of the black Indian-porpoises, from Chinese and Japanese waters and the Indian Ocean. The common species is sometimes encountered as far west as the coasts of the United States, and in the south reaches the Atlantic coast of France.

The Killer, or grampus (*Orca gladiator*), is a large species (thirty feet in length) with a dorsal fin which in the male may attain to a height of six feet. The teeth number twelve pairs in each jaw. This animal is very widely distributed, ranging from the Arctic to the Antarctic. The False-killer (*Pseudorca crassidens*) was, up till 1927, regarded as a very rare whale. It was originally described by Owen from a sub-fossil skull found in a Lincolnshire fen. In 1868 it was recorded from off the Danish coast and from Tasmanian waters. Later it was reported from Venezuela, California, and Florida ; but in 1927 a large school of these whales was left stranded on the coast of Sutherlandshire, and upwards of one hundred and twenty specimens were secured for the British Museum. It resembles a Killer in

NARWHAL (*Monodon monoceros*).

the great size of its teeth, but is entirely black in colour, while the flippers recall those of the Pilot-whale, being quite unlike those of the Killer. The dorsal fin is relatively small, and in each jaw there are from eight to ten pairs of large teeth. These whales live almost entirely upon cuttle-fish.

The Pilot-whale, or Ca'ing-whale, attains a length of about twenty feet and, like the False-killer, is black in colour, but with a white patch on the chest. The genus *Globiocephalus* is widely distributed in the North Atlantic and Australian waters. The dorsal fin is low and triangular, and the flippers are very long and narrow and have a strongly curved front border. There are from eight to twelve pairs of teeth in each jaw, and the head is enormously swollen and rounded, owing to the large fatty cushion on the rostrum.

The Beluga, or " White Whale " (*Delphinapterus leucas*), is distinguished at once by its white colour, rounded flippers, eight to ten pairs of teeth in each jaw, and by the dorsal fin being absent. It grows to about twelve feet in length, and it is an inhabitant of the Arctic regions. Lastly comes the Narwhal (*Monodon monoceros*), which sometimes reaches fifteen feet in length and also has no dorsal fin, while the flippers are short. The teeth are reduced to a single pair of incisors. One of these, usually the left, grows into a very long, spirally twisted and horizontal tusk, which may attain to a length of over nine feet; the other tooth remains a mere vestige within the jaw-bone, as they both do in the female. Occasionally both tusks are developed, when they present the remarkable peculiarity of having the spiral twist running in the same direction in both teeth, differing in this from spiral horns, where the twist is opposite in each horn. The Narwhal is an inhabitant of the Arctic, occasionally coming as far south as the Wash.

CHAPTER III

Order UNGULATA

(*Hoofed Mammals*)

THE animals belonging to the Order Ungulata have their limbs adapted solely for progression, that is to say, for walking or running only, and the toes are usually enclosed in hoofs or protected by hoof-like nails. They are all, with the exception of the tree-climbing hyraces, terrestrial in habits and herbivorous. The number of digits varies from one to five, and the toes are usually free. Collar-bones are never developed. The cheek-teeth have either low or elevated crowns, and the grinding surface of the teeth is either in the form of small hillocks or flattened and ridged, the latter type being characteristic of the ruminants. The group is widely distributed over both the Old and New World, exclusive of Australia and New Zealand.

Formerly the order was considered to contain only the " odd- " and " even-toed " ungulate mammals, the elephants and hyraces being regarded as representing distinct groups. The discovery of a number of extinct intermediate forms has led, however, to a readjustment of this classification, and, at the present day, the Proboscidea (elephants) and Hyracoidea (hyraces) are accepted as sub-orders of the Ungulata. We thus have four sub-orders: (i) Artiodactyla, or even-toed ungulates, including the cattle, sheep, goats, chamois, musk-ox, antelopes, pronghorn, giraffes, deer, chevrotains, camels, llamas, pigs, and hippopotami; (ii) the Perissodactyla, or odd-toed ungulates, including the horses, zebras, asses, tapirs, and rhinoceroses; (iii) Hyracoidea, the hyraces, or dassies; and (iv) Proboscidea, the elephants.

Sub-order *ARTIODACTYLA*

(*Even-toed Ungulates*)

The even-toed Ungulates differ from the odd-toed group in never having more than four toes to each foot; moreover, the two middle toes—that is, the third and fourth toe of the five-toed type—are of the same size and placed symmetrically. In some cases these two middle toes are the only ones developed.

The sub-order is divided into four sections : (A) the Pecora, or true ruminants ; (B) the Tragulina, or chevrotains ; (C) the Tylopoda, including the camels and llamas ; and (D) the Suina, or pigs, peccaries, and hippopotami. In the first section, the Pecora, we can distinguish four family groups : the *Bovidae*, including all the cattle, sheep, goats, and antelopes found over nearly the whole range of the order, exclusive of South America ; the *Antilocapridae*, the pronghorn of North America ; the *Giraffidae*, the giraffes and okapi of Africa ; and the *Cervidae*, or deer tribe, common to Europe, Northern Africa, Asia, and the New World.

Section A.—*Pecora*

(*True ruminants*)

The true ruminants have no front teeth in the upper jaw, the cannon-bones are complete, the feet furnished with hoofs, and the stomach is composed of four separate chambers ; the group includes all the hollow-horned ruminants, such as oxen, sheep, goats, and antelopes, the American prongbuck, the giraffe, and all the animals known as " deer."

Family Bovidae

This family includes all the hollow-horned ruminants in which the horns are hollow sheaths investing bony cores, both the core and the horn being permanent and not shed annually ; these horns are always present in the males (in the wild species), and in many cases the females also bear horns. There is no canine-tooth in the upper jaw, and the molars are usually remarkable for the height of their crowns. The family includes the oxen and their allies, goats, chamois, sheep, and antelopes. Owing to the number of different groups it is convenient to regard this family as composed of sixteen sub-families, the first of which is the *Bovinae*, and includes oxen and other cattle.

In this group the size is usually large, the tail long and tufted, and the muzzle bare and undivided ; face-glands and foot-glands are not developed, and horns are present in both sexes. The typical representative of the sub-family is the extinct Aurochs, or Wild-ox of Europe (*Bos taurus*), represented to-day by some of the half-wild cattle of Western Europe ; the remaining species of existing *Bovinae* are classified in four genera, the first of which, *Bibos*, contains the Gaur and Banteng. The Gaur (*Bibos gaurus*) is a very large animal, standing about six feet at the shoulder ; the horns are massive, markedly curved, and are pale-greenish in colour with blackish tips. It is distributed throughout the hill-forests of India, Burma, and the Malay countries, but is not found in Ceylon. The Burmese and

Malayan Gaur are now referred to distinct races. The other member of the genus, the Banteng, is a smaller beast than the Gaur, with more slender horns. In old bulls the latter are connected together by a shield-like growth. Whereas the Gaur is nearly uniformly black in colour, the Banteng is blackish or red, with a large white rump-patch. The Banteng, of which several races have been described, ranges through the East Indies and Malay Peninsula to Burma, Assam, Siam, and Cochin China.

The second genus, *Poëphagus*, includes only the Yak (*P. gruniens*), a large, ox-like animal found on the mountains of Tibet and adjacent Chinese districts; the shoulder height is about five and a half feet, and the largest horns on record measure thirty-eight inches along the outside curve. The hair on the flanks, shoulders, chest, thighs, and tail is of exceptional length, and in the wild state the coat is uniformly brownish-black; in the domesticated speci-mens white markings occur.

EUROPEAN BISON (*Bison bonasus*).

The European and North American Bison constitute the third genus (*Bison*); both are remarkable for the high withers and sloping hind-quarters. A kind of mane and mantle of long hair are de-veloped, and the h o r n s are much smaller than those of the Yak. Bison, as really wild animals, have been practically exterminated in both continents; formerly the European species (*B. bonasus*) was found over a considerable part of Europe; it is now confined to the Lithuanian forests. The American Bison (*B. bison*) originally roamed over a vast extent of North America; it is now repre-sented by a few large herds preserved in a state of semi-domestication in Yellowstone Park, U.S.A., and in the North-west of Canada.

The Asiatic buffaloes represent a fourth genus, *Bubalus*, in which the outline of the back is nearly straight, and the horns are triangular in section; in the Bison and Yak the horns are rounded, while in the Gaur and Banteng they are elliptical. In these Asiatic buffaloes the ears are of moderate size only, and the hair in the middle of the back is directed forwards from the hindquarters to the nape. The largest of the three species is the Indian-buffalo (*B. bubalis*), an animal standing about six feet at the shoulder and

Pl. 11.

MOUFLON (*Ovis musimon*).

carrying immense horns. The latter may measure as much as seventy-seven inches in length, and are either crescentic in form or nearly straight. This species is found throughout parts of peninsular India and Assam. A smaller form occurs in the Philippine Islands (*B. mindorensis*), possessing short and stoutly built horns. The third species, the Anoa (*B. depressicornis*), from the Island of Celebes, is the smallest of the buffaloes, the shoulder height being only about three feet three inches. The horns are of medium length and are directed upwards in the plane of the forehead; the record pair of horns measure $12\frac{3}{8}$ inches on the curve.

Lastly, the African buffaloes are grouped together in the genus *Syncerus*; these animals resemble their Asiatic cousins in many respects, but have broader, fringed ears, and the hair from the nape to the hindquarters is directed backwards. Two species may be distinguished, one large and black, inhabiting the plains (*S. caffer*), and a smaller, usually red-coloured animal found in the equatorial forest-zone (*S. nanus*). The large species frequently carries very large and massive horns, which are, typically, greatly expanded and meet one another at their bases.

The second sub-family of the hollow-horned type is known as the *Caprinae*, and contains the sheep, goats, ibexes, markhors, and tahrs. They are all of smaller size than the oxen and carry their heads higher. Both sexes bear horns, those of the females being small. They are marked with transverse ridges, and are usually in the form of an open spiral. The tail is, as a rule, quite short, and is never tufted. The muzzle is hairy and grooved, and face-glands and foot-glands are sometimes present. The members of this group are widely distributed, ranging over Europe, Asia, Northern Africa, and North America. The sheep, which constitute the genus *Ovis*, are all very much alike as regards coloration, and chiefly differ in the form and size of their horns. These animals all agree in having face-glands and foot-glands and in the absence of a beard. The horns of the females are small and spike-like. The facial region of the skull is bent downwards. The sheep are found over most of the area inhabited by the *Caprinae*, exclusive of peninsular India, Arabia, and North East Africa. About six species of sheep can be distinguished, and many races have been described.

The Mouflon (*O. musimon*), from Sardinia and Corsica, is a medium-sized, dark-coloured animal, standing about twenty-seven inches at the shoulder, and reddish-brown in coloration, with a grey saddle-marking in the winter coat of the males. The Red-sheep of Cyprus (*O. orientalis*) is an allied species which has a bright rufous summer coat; it ranges through Asia Minor to Persia. The Urial (*O. vignei*) is a rather larger species, standing about thirty-four inches at the shoulder, with strongly ridged horns, which form an open spiral on each side of the face. Four races of Urial are recognised; they are distributed over a large part of Central Asia.

The Argali (*O. ammon*) is the largest of the Asiatic sheep, measuring as much as forty-eight inches at the shoulder. The horns are very large and, in some races, have a very beautiful spiral twist. The distributional range includes Kamchatka and Bokhara, extending through the Altai and Tibet to Mongolia. The horns of the various races vary considerably in form; those of the typical Argali are comparatively short and very heavy, the spiral twist of the horn describing little more than a complete circle. In the Pamir-argali (*O. ammon poli*) the horns are sometimes of very great size, the record pair measuring some seventy-five inches along the front curve. This latter race appears to have carried the matter of horn development to excess; most of the really large-horned specimens seem to find the weight of their horns too much for their strength, and encumbered with these ponderous weapons they are easily overtaken and killed by wolves.

The American-sheep, or "Bighorns," may be all grouped together under one specific name, *O. canadensis.*

AMERICAN BIGHORN SHEEP (*Ovis canadensis*).

These sheep are spread over a large part of North America, extending from Mexico northwards to Alaska, and eastwards to Kamchatka and North-East Siberia. They are of fair size, standing about thirty-eight to forty inches at the shoulder. The horns are smoother than in the Asiatic species, and have the front angle well marked. No throat ruff, such as is seen in the Urials, is developed; the horns of the females are ribbed at the base and slightly curved. The Kamchatkan race is named *O. c. nivicola*, and the East Siberian sheep *O. c. borealis.*

The Arui, or Barbary-sheep, is the type of a second genus, *Ammotragus*, in which the horns are strongly wrinkled, and may measure as much as twenty-eight inches in length; the tail is long; face-glands and foot-glands are absent; and no beard is developed. The horns of the female are larger than in the true sheep. The height at the shoulder is about thirty-nine inches. It has a brownish-grey or rufous coat, and is found only in North Africa. Intermediate between the sheep and the goats we have the Bharal (*Pseudois nahoor*), in which the large, nearly smooth horns curve backwards over the neck, and the tail is rather longer than in the true sheep. No beard is developed. This species is confined to the mountains of Central Asia.

The true goats, ibexes, and markhors form the genus *Capra*, in which the horns are either scimitar-shaped or form an open or close spiral; in the males they are frequently strongly ridged, in the females they are smaller and smooth. The tail is about as long as in the Bharal, and a beard is present in the male, which sex diffuses the characteristic goat-like smell. The group is widely distributed over the more mountainous parts of Southern Europe, North-East Africa, and through Asia Minor and Persia to the highlands of Central Asia. The species most like the Bharal are the Eastern Turs (*C. caucasica*), in which the horns are nearly smooth and directed backwards. These sheep-like goats occur in the Central Caucasus. The Western Tur (*C. severtzowi*), from the Western Caucasus, shows a greater advance towards the ibex-type of horn.

The Ibexes may be regarded as representing five species— the Pyrenean-ibex (*C. pyrenaica*) from the Pyrenees, the Alpine-ibex (*C. ibex*) from the Italian Alps, the Asiatic-ibex (*C. sibirica*) from the mountains of Central Asia, the Nubian-ibex (*C. nubiana*) from Nubia and South Arabia, and the Abyssinian-ibex (*C. walie*). In the Pyrenean species the horns form a very open spiral, and do not possess such well-marked knobs on the front as do the horns of the other species; in the Alpine-ibex the horns are scimitar-like and carry a number of knobs on their front surfaces. The Asiatic-ibex resembles the Alpine species, but is considerably larger (shoulder

CIRCASSIAN GOAT (Domesticated).

height, forty-two inches) and the horns are bigger, the record pair measuring some fifty-eight inches along the front curve.

The Wild-goat, or Pasang (*C. hircus*), is allied to the Ibexes, but is distinguished by the front edge of the horns, which are scimitar-like in form, being sharp and angular. The beard is very long and the general build slender. These goats are found in the Caucasus and Asia Minor; a race has been described from Sind and Baluchistan. From the wild goats we pass on to the Markhors (*C. falconeri*), which may be regarded as goats with spirally twisted horns. The size of these animals is large, some being forty-one inches at the shoulder and carrying immense horns. They are distributed over the high mountainous districts of Central Asia. The Astor-markhor has the horns twisted in a loose, open spiral, widely divergent; in the Cabul race (*C. f. megaceros*) they are somewhat like a corkscrew in form, and in the Suleman-markhor (*C. f. jerdoni*) the spiral formed by the twisted horns is straight and screw-like. In the Circassian domesticated goat the horns are vertically placed and of considerable length.

The *Caprinae*, or goats, appear to be connected with the *Rupicaprinae*, or Chamois, by means of the Tahrs (*Hemitragus*) found in the Himalayas (*H. jemlahicus*), Arabia (*H. jayakari*), and Southern India (*H. hylocrius*). In this group the horns are short and regularly curved, being nearly as large in the females as in the males. The chin is beardless, and the males possess a strong and fishy smell. The Himalayan and Indian species are of considerable size (thirty-eight to forty-two inches at the shoulder); the Arabian-tahr is smaller (twenty-four and a half inches) and has more slender, less knotted horns.

The sub-family *Rupicaprinae* contains five different types—the Chamois, Serows, Gorals, Takins, and the White-goats of North America. They are typically goat-like beasts, with horns which in both sexes are either hook-shaped or bent outwards and then upwards. Foot-glands and face-glands may be present or absent, and there is a bare spot on the muzzle. The distributional area includes Southern Europe, Asia Minor, the Himalayas eastward to China and Japan. The Chamois (*Rupicapra*) may be recognised at once by its simple, vertically placed horns, with their tips sharply hooked backwards; the members of this genus are found in the mountains of Southern Europe eastward to Asia Minor. The Serows (*Capricornis*) are more heavily built animals, with the horns directed in the plane of the face and curving backwards and outwards; unlike the chamois-horns they are marked with transverse ridges. The range extends from the Himalayas into China and south to the East Indies.

The Gorals (*Nemorhaedus*) are very like the Serows, but smaller, with smaller horns, and usually paler in colour. The various species extend from the Himalayas into Central China. The Takins (*Budorcas*) are much larger than the other members of the sub-family, being more like an ox in build (height at shoulder, three and a half feet). The horns are massive and are directed outwardly at the base, then downwards, and the tips upwards. The species are three in number, and extend from the Himalayas (Mishmi Hills) into Western China. One of the Takins (*B. bedfordi*) has a beautiful golden-coloured coat; the other forms are brownish or blackish in colour. The White-goats, also known as the Rocky Mountain-goats (*Oreamnos*), are distinguished at once by their thick, white coats, elevated withers, and simple, conical-shaped horns. The latter are never very large, eleven and a half inches being the record length. These animals, which stand about forty inches at the shoulder, occur on the Rocky Mountains northwards along the coast to Alaska.

The sub-family *Ovibovinae*, which contains the Musk-ox (*Ovibos moschatus*) only, is apparently related to the chamois-takin group ; the dentition is goat-like, the horns, which in old males grow close up to one another at the base, are directed first outwards and downwards, curving upwards in the apical portions. The coat is long and coarse, the body large and ox-like, and the horns massive, the record horns measuring twenty-seven and three-quarter inches in length. Several races have been described, distributed over Arctic America, Greenland, and Melville Island.

Many large-, medium-, and small-sized animals belonging to this group (*Ungulata*) are popularly referred to as " Antelopes." The name " antelope " is apparently derived from Anthalops, the name of the fabled unicorn. The Indian-blackbuck, a very graceful and handsome beast, is, strictly speaking, the only animal that is entitled to the name of antelope, but it is customary to refer to a large number of African and Asiatic hoofed animals by this name. No true antelopes are found in America ; the American " antelope," or Prongbuck, belongs to quite a distinct group, and the Rocky Mountain-goat, which is occasionally referred to as an antelope, has really more relationship with the goats than with the antelopes. All of these animals have narrow, upper molar teeth like sheep, and their muzzles are hairy. There is frequently a gland below the eye, and the horns are usually compressed and lyrate or recurved, or cylindrical and spiral. No fewer than twelve groups or sub-families of antelopes are now recognised, the great majority of which are confined to Africa, where these animals exist in great variety.

The first group, the *Bubalinae*, contains four distinct types : (i) the Hartebeests (*Bubalus*) ; (ii) the Bontebok, Blesbok, etc. (*Damaliscus*) ; (iii) the Gnu (*Connochaetes*) ; and (iv) the Brindled-gnu, or Blue-wildebeest (*Gorgon*). The Hartebeests are remarkable for their long, ugly faces, ungainly bodies, and curiously twisted horns, which instead of arising directly from the head, as in an ordinary horned animal, are mounted on a boss, or pedicle ; they are strongly ringed, bend first forwards and then sharply backwards. The general shape of these animals is by no means pleasing, as the shoulders are considerably higher than the hindquarters.

About eight different Hartebeests can be distinguished, the most distinct of which are the following : the Bubal-hartebeest (*Bubalus boselaphus*), from North Africa, is the smallest member of the group (forty-four inches at the shoulder) and the horns rarely exceed fifteen inches in length ; the Western-hartebeest (*B. major*) is larger than the Bubal and has longer horns ; the Tora-hartebeest *(B. tora)*, from Abyssinia and Somaliland, is a rather paler coloured animal, with more divergent horns. The Cape-hartebeest (*B. caama*) is much darker in colour than the other species, and has the horns mounted on a conspicuously high pedicle ; this is the animal originally christened " hartebeest " by the early Dutch settlers in Cape Province, where it was formerly a common animal. It is now extinct in the Province, being found only to the north of the Orange River as far as Southern Rhodesia and Bechuanaland. The Lelwel-hartebeest (*B. lelwel*), from East and Central Africa, is another species with a very pronounced horn-pedicle, and has an exceptionally long face ; this is the largest member of the genus, standing about fifty-two inches at the shoulder and carrying horns measuring about twenty inches in length. Lastly there is Lichtenstein's-hartebeest (*B. lichtensteini*), from South-central and parts of East Africa, with a very short horn-pedicle and having the horns curved sharply inwards.

In the second group or genus, *Damaliscus*, the horns arise directly from the head, and the withers are less elevated. The Bontebok (*D. pygargus*) and Blesbok (*D. albifrons*) are two closely allied species, which once existed in South Africa in herds great beyond counting ; they can now no longer be regarded as truly wild animals, the thousands upon thousands of these two beautiful antelopes which once roamed the African plains being reduced to a few hundred specimens preserved on various South African farms. In general colouring the Bontebok and Blesbok are very similar, being dark rufous, with white face-markings ; in size they are smaller than the Hartebeests, standing about forty-two inches at the shoulder and with horns of about fifteen to eighteen inches in length. Other well-known members of this genus are the Hirola, or Hunter's-hartebeest (*D. hunteri*),

HUNTER'S-HARTEBEEST (*Damaliscus hunteri*).

from Jubaland, East Africa ; the Sassaby (*D. lunatus*) from South Africa ; and the Korrigum (*D. korrigum*) from West, Central, and East Africa. Hunter's-hartebeest is coloured very like an ordinary hartebeest, but has a white chevron-like marking on the forehead.

The Gnu, or Black-wildebeest (*Connochaetes gnu*) differs from the Hartebeests in having smooth horns, not ringed, and in possessing four teats instead of two. Further, the muzzle is very broad, the tail horse-like, and tufts of hair are present on the face. This grotesque-looking animal was formerly very common on the plains of Cape Province and the Orange Free State ; as a truly wild animal it no longer exists, but it is preserved on a number of South African farms. In general appearance the Gnu is rather reminiscent of an ox, hence the name of " wildebeest," or " wild ox," given it by the early Dutch settlers. It stands about forty-six inches at the shoulder, and is dark umber-brown in colour with a black face ; the long hairs of the tail are dirty white in colour, and the mane upright.   Good horns measure as much as thirty inches in length.   The Brindled-gnu, or Blue-wildebeest (*Gorgon taurinus*) is considerably larger than the Gnu, standing some fifty-two inches at the shoulder, and is grizzled-roan or grey in colour, with dark vertical stripes on the neck and shoulders, and a black tail tuft.   The withers are higher than the hindquarters, and the horns, instead of curving forward over the face, spread out sideways like those of a buffalo.   The various races of this species are widely distributed, ranging from Kenya Colony to south of the Zambesi River.

The second group, the *Cephalophinae*, contains the Duikers, or Duikerboks, of Africa, small- or medium-sized antelopes characterised by their spike-like horns, naked muzzles, and large face - glands ; the females have four teats. Three different kinds of Duiker may be distinguished : (i) the Forest - duikers (*Cephalophus*), with short, stout horns and uniformly coloured coats ; (ii) the Blue-duikers (*Guevei*), small, grey-coloured animals with very small horns ; and (iii) the Bush-duikers (*Sylvicapra*),* with long, slender horns

GNU, or BLACK-WILDEBEEST (*Connochaetes gnu*).

and speckled coats.   The first of these genera, *Cephalophus*, contains about thirty-four species and sub-species, of which a few are comparatively large, like *C. sylvicultrix*, the Yellow-backed duiker (thirty to thirty-four inches at the shoulder) ; but the majority of Forest-duikers are small animals, from about sixteen to twenty-four inches in height.

All the members of this group of antelopes are confined to Africa and some of the adjacent islands, the Forest- and Blue-duikers being found in the great equatorial forests ; the Bush-duikers are widely distributed over the more open parts of the country to the south of the Sahara.

The next group (*Oreotraginae*) includes but a single genus and species, the Klipspringer (*Oreotragus oreotragus*) ; this animal differs from all other antelopes in having coarse, pithy hair and narrow cylindrical hoofs.   The horns, which are usually present only in the male, are short and spike-like, and arise almost vertically above the eyes. This species is to be found in the more mountainous districts of Africa, from Abyssinia and Nigeria southwards to the Cape. The fourth sub-family, the *Neotraginae*, contains six kinds of medium-sized and small antelopes which inhabit the greater part of Africa to the south of the Sahara. The largest members of this group are the Oribis (*Ourebia*), which stand about twenty-five inches at the shoulder, and are easily distinguished from their allies by the presence of bare, glandular patches of skin beneath each ear ; their horns are slender and ringed in the basal-half.

The Grysbok (*Nototragus melanotis*) and Steinbok (*Raphicerus campestris*) are two closely allied forms ; the former possesses small side-hoofs and is found only in South Africa, whereas the Steinboks, in which the small lateral hoofs are absent, are more widely distributed, extending northwards to Kenya Colony ; both these antelopes are fawn-coloured, and the coat of the Grysbok is marked with white speckling. In general size they are rather less than the Oribis. The remaining genera are all very small : the Sunis (*Nesotragus*), from East Africa, standing from thirteen to fourteen inches at the shoulder and having very beautifully ringed horns, from three to five inches in length ; the Pigmy-antelopes (*Hylarnus*), from West and Central Africa, about equal in size to the Sunis, but with the horns nearly smooth and shorter ; and the Royal-antelope (*Neotragus pygmaeus*), which is not only the smallest member of the group but also the smallest of all true ruminants, being only ten inches in height and having very small horns ; it is confined to West Africa.

KLIPSPRINGER (*Oreotragus oreotragus*).

Nearly related to the *Neotraginae* is another sub-family of small antelopes known as the *Madoquinae*, containing the well-known Dik-diks of East and South-West Africa, which represent two distinct types, those with long and rather trunk-like noses forming an enlargement of the nasal-chamber, whose function is so far unexplained (*Rhynchotragus*), and those with normal muzzles (*Madoqua*) ; these little antelopes are distinguished by the presence of a tuft of hair on the crown of the head and the very beautiful horns of the bucks. Dik-diks stand a little over a foot at the shoulder and are frequently very handsomely coloured, some species having silvery-grey backs, chestnut flanks and faces, and white under parts. Included in this group is the Beira (*Dorcotragus melanotis*), a curious antelope found only in Somaliland and

Abyssinia ; it is considerably larger than the Dik-diks (twenty-three inches at the shoulder), and has spike-like horns and very large ears.

The Reedbucks and their allies form the sixth group, the *Reduncinae.* Five distinct genera can be recognised : (i) *Kobus,* including the Waterbucks and Defassa, the largest members of the group, being about the size of a pony, and bearing long, lyrate horns, and having the lateral hoofs well developed. The typical Waterbuck (*K. ellipsiprymnus*) is found over the greater part of Eastern Africa. (ii) *Onotragus,* the Lechwes, which are rather smaller than the Waterbucks, and (iii) *Adenota,* the Kobs, which are still smaller with shorter horns. The Lechwes inhabit parts of South, Central and East Africa, and the Kobs are confined to equatorial Africa and Rhodesia. (iv) *Redunca,* the Reedbucks, have shorter tails, small lateral hoofs, and, like the Oribis, a bare patch of skin under each ear ; the height is from twenty-seven to thirty-seven inches, and the various species are widely spread over the greater part of Africa south of the desert region. (v) *Pelea,* which contains but a single species, the Vaal-rhebok (*P. capreolus*), of South Africa, distinguished by its grey-coloured, woolly coat and spike-like horns. Associated with this group is the remarkable antelope known as the Dibatag (*Ammodorcas clarkei*), which is found only in Somaliland ; in appearance it is rather like a cross between a reedbuck and a long-necked gazelle.

WATERBUCK (*Kobus ellipsiprymnus*).

The next three groups contain only a single species each ; the first of these, the *Aepycerotinae,* is an African sub-family of fairly large antelopes called the Impalas, or Pallas (*Aepyceros melampus*), characterised by their long and beautifully shaped lyrate horns, and the absence of lateral hoofs. The other two groups are Asiatic, the *Saiginae,* from the Kirghiz steppes, containing the well-known and very ugly Saiga (*Saiga tartarica*), a sheep-like beast, having the nose much inflated and the nostrils opening downwards ; and the *Pantholopinae,* containing the closely allied Chiru (*Pantholops hodgsoni*) from the high plateau of Tibet. This latter antelope is remarkable for its long and graceful horns, and, like the Saiga, its nose is inflated. The Saiga was, in Pleistocene days, an inhabitant of Great Britain.

The tenth sub-family is a very large one, containing the typical antelope, or Blackbuck (*Antilope cervicapra*), the Gazelles (*Gazella*), the Gerenuk (*Lithocranius walleri*), and the Springbuck (*Antidorcas marsupialis*). The Blackbuck is found only in peninsular India, and is easily recognised by its long, spirally twisted horns. The Gazelles are much more widely distributed, being found over a great part of Asia and North and Eastern Africa. Unlike the Blackbuck, most of the Gazelles have horns in both sexes; some of the Asiatic species, however, have hornless females. They are mostly of medium size, though a few of the African species are larger (thirty-five inches at the shoulder). The Gerenuk is a fairly large animal, with massive horns and greatly elongated limbs and neck; it is confined to the desert regions of East Africa.

SUDANI-REEDBUCK (*Redunca redunca cottoni*).

The Springbuck, which inhabits South Africa, is very like a gazelle in general appearance, but is distinguished by the presence of an evertible fold of skin, lined with long, white hairs, situated in the hinder part of the animal's back; horns are present in both sexes. In the middle of the nineteenth century Springbuck existed in countless thousands, and their periodical migrations were a great menace to the Boer farmers. These antelopes are in the habit of making great leaps, jumping to a height of eight to ten feet; this they do repeatedly before running away from danger.

The next, or eleventh, sub-family (*Oryginae*) contains a variety of large antelopes, with horns present in both sexes. Three genera can be distinguished: (i) Oryx, with straight, spike-like horns in the Gemsbuck (*O. gazella*), Beisa (*O. beisa*), and Arabian-oryx (*O. leucoryx*), and sabre-shaped horns in the White-oryx (*O. algazel*). The first of these species is found only in South Africa, the second inhabits the eastern side of the continent, and the White-oryx is confined to the deserts of Western Africa and the Sudan. (ii) *Hippotragus*, which includes the Sable-antelope of South and East Africa, the extinct Blaaubok of Cape Province, and Roan-antelope of Africa, south of the Sahara, in which the horns are scimitar-shaped and sometimes of great length. The Roan-antelope is a very large beast, standing four feet nine inches at the shoulder, but with shorter horns than the Sable ; in the latter, some of the Angolan, or Giant Sable-antelopes carry horns of sixty-four inches in length. (iii) *Addax*, including only the Addax, is distinguished by its long, spirally twisted horns ; it inhabits the desert regions of Northern Africa.

The last group, the *Tragelaphinae*, contains some of the most beautiful of all the antelopes. The species vary in size from nearly as large as a bison to as small as a duiker. The typical genus, *Tragelaphus*, contains the Bush-bucks, or Harnessed-antelopes, which are frequently brilliantly coloured, the body being bright rufous, marked with longitudinal and transverse white stripes. The Bushbucks (*T. scriptus* and races) are widely distributed over a large portion of Africa. Closely allied to the Bushbucks are the animals known as the Nyala (*T. angasi*), the Mountain-bushbuck (*T. buxtoni*), and the Situtungas (*Limnotragus spekei* and sub-species). The Nyala is rather like a large bushbuck (height, three feet six inches), with beautifully shaped horns ; the male is slaty-grey in colour, and the female bright chestnut, with the white, harness-like markings of a bushbuck ; it is confined to a comparatively small area in South-East Africa. The Mountain-bushbuck is distinguishable from all the other members of the genus by its much bigger and more massive horns and larger size, standing nearly as high as a Kudu at the shoulders ; this species has, at present, been recorded only from the Sahatu Mountains in Gallaland.

The Situtungas, which about equal in size the Nyala, are easily distinguished by their conspicuously elongated hoofs, by means of which the animals are enabled to walk upon the soft mud of the swamps in which they live. The various races of Situtunga spread from West Africa eastward to Uganda and south as far as Northern Rhodesia. The Kudus, represented by two distinct species, if not genera, are easily known by their spirally twisted horns ; the Greater-kudu (*Strepsiceros strepsiceros*) is a very large beast, with magnificent horns, the record horn-length being seventy-one and a half inches along the outside curve and fifty-one and a quarter inches in a straight line. These animals enjoy a very wide distribution, being found over the greater part of Africa south of the Sahara and north of the Zambesi ; to the south of that river, southwards to Cape Province, the Kudu was formerly a common beast, but it is now rare in many of its former haunts. The other is the Lesser-kudu (*S. imberbis*), which is much smaller in size (only about forty inches at the shoulder instead of nearly sixty inches), and carrying very much smaller horns, the best specimen on record measuring only about thirty-six inches in length. This antelope is confined to the northern part of Tanganyika territory, Kenya Colony, Somaliland and Abyssinia.

The Bongo (*Boöcercus euryceros*), of which three forms have been described, is one of the most strikingly coloured of all antelopes, being a rich, rufous-red in colour, and having the body marked by a series of white, vertical stripes, ten to thirteen in number, and possessing exceptionally massive horns (height at shoulder, four feet ; record horn-length, thirty-nine and a half inches). It is widely distributed over a great part of equatorial Africa, living exclusively in dense forest-country ; it extends south as far as Katanga, in the Southern Congo. The Elands are the largest of all the antelopes, adult bulls standing nearly six feet at the shoulder. Two well-marked species can be distinguished—*Taurotragus oryx*, the Common-eland, and *T. derbianus*, Lord Derby's Eland. The latter is distinguished by the larger and heavier

Lord Derby's Eland (Congo race) (*Taurotragus derbianus congolanus*).

horns and the broader ears. *T. oryx* is distributed over the greater part of Ethiopian Africa, while *T. derbianus* spreads across Africa from Senegambia to the Sudan and southwards to the Congo.

The Nilgai, or Blue-bull (*Boselaphus tragocamelus*), is easily distinguished from the other members of the sub-family by its ungainly build (height, four feet six inches), bluish-grey coloured coat, and short horns. This animal is found only in peninsular India. The other Indian representative of the group is the Four-horned Antelope (*Tetracerus quadricornis*), which is readily recognised by the possession of four horns, and is thus quite distinct from all its relations. In size it is much smaller than the other members of the sub-family, standing only twenty-five inches at the shoulder.

Family Antilocapridae

The second family of Ungulate mammals, containing the Pronghorn, or Prongbuck, although closely allied to the cattle and antelopes, differs in that the horns are forked and shed annually ; furthermore, they are smooth and the main branch of the fork is curved backwards. The muzzle is hairy, except for a narrow line between the nostrils, and face-glands are absent; scent-glands occur in both fore- and hind-feet. The coat is stiff and harsh, the tail very short, and the lateral hoofs are not developed. The genus contains but one species, *Antilocapra americana*, widely distributed over North America ; it stands about three feet at the shoulder, and the horns average fourteen to fifteen inches in length.

Family Giraffidae

This group includes two species of Giraffe and the Okapi. Both animals —which appear to be distant cousins—have short, skin-covered horns (present in both sexes in the giraffe). The upper canine teeth and lateral toes are not developed. The range is restricted to Africa south of the Sahara. The neck and limbs of the Giraffe are very long, the total height of an old male reaching as much as eighteen feet. In addition to the normal pair of horns arising from above the orbits, there is frequently a large anterior horn, and sometimes a pair of occipital horns are developed at the back of the skull.

GIRAFFE (*Giraffa camelopardalis*).

Giraffes are found over a great part of Africa, from Nubia southwards to the Orange River, except in the great Congo-forest zones. The Somali- or Reticulated-giraffe (*Giraffa reticulata*), from Somaliland, Kenya Colony, Sudan, and Abyssinia, is one of the handsomest species, being liver-red, overlaid by a fine buff-tinted network. The other species of Giraffe, *G. camelopardalis*, is spotted and blotched with brownish or blackish markings on a light ground colour. Numerous races have been described, differing chiefly in the colour and pattern of the body-markings and the development of the horns ; they are distributed over the greater part of Africa, from the Sudan to the Orange River.

The Okapi (*Okapia iohnstoni*) is smaller than the giraffes, with shorter neck and legs. The males alone carry a single pair of frontal-horns, which are capped with bare bone. The ears are broader and the tail shorter. The coloration of this animal is remarkable and on a very different plan to that of the giraffes, most of the upper parts being a sort of plum colour, the sides of the face pale, pinkish-buff, while the sides of the hindquarters and the upper parts of the limbs are white, with dark transverse bars. Here we have a " protective coloration " affording concealment in the dark forests of the eastern part of the Congo, wherein alone the species is found.

Family Cervidae

The animals belonging to this family—the Deer tribe—usually possess, in the males, peculiar branched appendages known as antlers. These antlers arise from the crown of the head, and are in some cases simple spikes, in others they are complex and branched, the branches being termed " tines." They are usually shed once every year, and with the exception of the reindeer and caribou are present only in the male sex ; they arise from a pair of bony pedicles situated on the skull above and behind the eyes. These pedicles are sometimes of considerable length, sometimes quite short ; they form part of the skull itself, and when the antlers have been recently shed these pedicles form small, skin-covered prominences. When the new antlers commence to grow, small velvety knobs, richly supplied with blood-vessels, appear on the surface of the pedicles. These knobs, which are formed of bony matter, increase very rapidly in size, and in the more typical kinds of deer develop into antlers with many tines. When the growth is nearly completed the whole antler is invested in a soft, vascular skin, called " the velvet," and a deposition of bony matter takes place at the base of the antler in the form of a prominent ring. This constricts the blood-vessels supplying the " velvet," which eventually dries up and is rubbed off in due course.

The different tines borne by the antlers of the various species of deer have received distinct names. In the Red-deer group the shaft, or beam, of the antler carries three tines on its lower front edge, of which the lowest is termed the " brow "-tine, the second the " bez "-tine, and the third the "trez"-tine, or sometimes the " royal "-tine. The top of the beam may either be divided into two or three tines, or divided up into a number of internal snags. From this it is clear that the " horns " of deer differ fundamentally from those of the " hollow-horned " ruminants, since they have no horny invest-ment, or sheath, and are periodically shed and renewed. Moreover, they increase in size and complexity of branching every year from the assumption of the first pair of simple spikes up to full maturity. In very old animals the antlers tend to become smaller and have fewer tines.

The members of this family are widely distributed over a great part of Europe, Asia, and America ; one species, related to our Red-deer, inhabits

Northern Africa. The family is divided into two groups, or sub-families : (i) the *Moschinae*, which contains only the musk-deer ; and (ii) the *Cervinae*, which includes all the other deer.

The Musk-deer, or Kastura (*Moschus moschiferus*), differs from all the true-deer and their allies in having a gall-bladder, and in possessing, in the males, an abdominal-gland in which the famous musk-scent, so much in demand by perfumers, is secreted. Further, there are *no antlers*, face-glands, or foot-glands. In place of antlers the upper canine-teeth are, in the bucks, greatly enlarged, projecting from the mouth for a considerable distance ; similarly enlarged teeth are found in the Muntjaks, the Tufted-deer, and the Chinese Water-deer. One specimen has been recorded which carries exceptionally long teeth, projecting from the jaw a distance of more than three and a half inches ; these sabre-like teeth are

MUSK-DEER (*Moschus moschiferus*).

chiefly used for fighting with during the pairing season, when the bucks indulge in terrific combats. The Musk-deer stands about twenty inches at the shoulder, and has a thick, pithy coat ; the ears are large and the tail very short. The various races are distributed over Central and North-Eastern Asia ; the Himalayan form is the one most often met with.

The other group, the *Cervinae*, differs in having no gall-bladder or abdominal musk-gland, and foot-glands are, with one exception (*Pudu*), developed in, at least, the

CHINESE WATER-DEER (*Hydropotes inermis*).

hind-limbs. Antlers are characteristic of most of the genera, being absent in the Chinese Water-deer (*Hydropotes*). A large number of different kinds of deer are now known, the most important of which are the following :—

The Muntjaks, or Barking-deer (*Muntiacus*), are small animals (shoulder height usually about twenty-one inches) with tusk-like upper canine-teeth in the males, and having small and simple antlers (which, as with all the *Cervidae*, excepting the reindeer and caribou, are developed in the males only), arising from a bony prolongation of the skull. The various species are widely spread over the Indo-Malayan region, and extend eastward to China. The Common-muntjak, a Javan animal known as *Muntiacus muntjak*, carries fairly large antlers, sometimes measuring nearly ten and a half inches in length ; the largest species is *M. crinifrons* from China, which stands above twenty-four inches at the shoulder. Next there is the Chinese Tufted-deer (*Elaphodus cephalophus*), the only member of the genus. This deer is about equal in size to the larger species of Muntjak, and has similar tusk-like teeth in the males ; but the antlers are smaller, and scarcely project from the tuft of hair on the crown. The coat is rather like that of the Musk-deer, being coarse and pithy, and is usually some shade of chocolate-brown in colour ; the species is entirely confined to China.

The first of the more typical deer is the Fallow-deer, representing the genus *Dama*, two species of which are now recognised. In these deer, as in all true deer, the canine-teeth are never large, and the antlers are large and supported on short, bony bosses, or pedicles. The main branch of the antlers, or beam, is expanded, or palmated, and the coat is normally spotted with white in the summer and is dark brownish in the winter, without spots. In size these deer are considerably larger than the genera just dealt with, the shoulder height of the bucks being about three feet. Fallow-deer were at one time restricted to Persia and the Mediterranean countries, they have, however, been introduced into Central and Western Europe. The giant Irish-deer, commonly called the " Irish-elk " (*Megaceros gigantea*), now extinct, is related to the Fallow-deer ; this beast probably stood six feet at the shoulder, and carried enormous antlers, sometimes exceeding eleven and a half feet in spread.

The typical deer of the genus *Cervus* and their allies are now considered to represent six different genera ; the one most nearly related to the Fallow-deer is probably the genus *Axis*, which contains the Indian Spotted-deer, or Chital, a handsome beast, with a fawn-coloured coat spotted with white. The antlers of this deer are quite unlike those of the Fallow-deer, being very long and not palmated ; fine antlers measure over three feet in length, and are three-tined, or have three branches, one tine, called the " brow-tine," arising at right angles from the beam just above the burr, or base, and the other two being formed by the division of the beam into a short inner-tine and a long outer one. In general dimensions these deer are rather larger (height at shoulder, thirty-eight inches) than Fallow-deer, and are found only in the Indian Peninsula and Ceylon. Allied to the Chital is the

Para, or Hog-deer (*Hyelaphus*), in which the antlers are mounted on longer bases, or pedicles. Hog-deer are found over a large part of India, and eastward to Siam and Annam ; one species occurs in the Philippines.

The Sambars, of the Oriental region, form the third genus, *Rusa*, distinguished by their shaggy coats and three-tined antlers, the brow-tine of which forms an acute angle with the beam. The typical Sambar of India is a very large animal, standing some fifty-four inches at the shoulder and carrying horns which may measure as much as fifty inches in length. Another group of large species is included in the genus *Rucervus*, in which the brow-tine arises either at right angles to the beam or curves outward in the same line as the latter. The best-known members of the Rucervine group are the Barasingha, or Swamp-deer (*R. duvaucelli*) from India, Schomburghk's-deer (*R. schomburghki*) from Siam, and the Thamin (*R. thamin*) from Burma and adjacent countries ; the latter species has very simple antlers, and Schomburghk's-deer is remarkable for its very complex and many-tined antlers.

The Japanese-deer, or Sikas, form the next genus (*Sika*), containing a number of medium-sized animals, which are spotted like the Fallow-deer in the summer season. The antlers, which are usually four-tined, are smaller and more simple than those of the true deer. These deer are found in Japan, Formosa, and Northern China. The sixth and last genus of this group is *Cervus*, which contains six different species, all very closely allied. The antlers are usually five-tined and of considerable size, and the tail shorter than in the foregoing genus. Furthermore, the coat is uniformly coloured in the adult phase. The Red-deer (*C. elaphus*) is probably the best known of this group ; it is widely distributed over the greater part of Europe and extends eastwards to Persia. The largest race is the Maral, which stands nearly four and a half feet at the shoulder. The Wapiti (*C. canadensis*), of North America and Asia, is still larger (five feet four inches in height) and sometimes carries enormous antlers (record length, sixty-six inches). The Hangul (*C. cashmiriensis*), which is about equal to a Red-deer in size, inhabits the forest-clad slopes of Northern India.

Probably allied to the true deer is the remarkable Père David's-deer, or Mi-lu, only known from a herd formerly kept in gardens of the summer palace in Pekin and their descendants. This species, known as *Elaphurus davidianus*, has curiously shaped antlers, which divide a short distance above the burr, the front branch curving forwards and again dividing.

The White-tailed deer, Mule-deer, and Black-tailed deer, of America, are included in the genus *Odocoileus*. The White-tailed deer extend into South America, while the two latter forms are restricted to North America. The Marsh-deer and Pampas-deer are nearly related species, which are regarded as representing a distinct genus, *Blastocerus*. Both are inhabitants of South America, the Marsh-deer being about the size of a Red-deer and the Pampas-deer not much bigger than an English Roe-deer. The genus

Hippocamelus, also confined to South America, contains two species with small antlers in the form of a single fork, the front branch of which is the

ROE-DEER (*Capreolus capreolus*).

shorter. The Brockets (*Mazama*) are small-sized relations of *Hippocamelus*, standing only from about nineteen to twenty-seven inches at the shoulder, and having antlers in the form of simple unbranched spikes. As a general rule, the coat is bright rufous; the various species and subspecies are confined to Central and tropical South America. Still smaller are two South American deer belonging to the genus *Pudu*; these animals are only thirteen and a half to fifteen inches in height, and have very small, spike-like horns.

The Roe-deer of Europe and Asia constitute a genus of small species (twenty-six to thirty-four inches in height) known as *Capreolus*; they are distinguished by the antlers arising almost vertically from the head, the beam dividing into two nearly upright branches, the hinder one of which divides again.

The largest members of the family are the Moose of North America and the Elk of Northern Europe, which vary in height from five and a half to six and three-quarters feet, carry enormous palmated antlers, and have broad, overhanging muzzles. These two animals are included in the genus *Alces*. The record horn-spread for the American species is seventy-eight and a half inches, and for the European animal some fifty-two inches.

(MOOSE (*Alces alces americanus*).

The Reindeer and Caribou (*Rangifer*) differ from the other *Cervinae* in that the females as well as the males bear antlers, and in having completely hairy muzzles.   In size they are large or medium, and the antlers may be palmated as in the Newfoundland race, or long and slender as in the Barren-ground type ; the various races are spread over a considerable part of North America and Northern Europe.   The males sometimes measure as much as four feet ten inches at the shoulder.

The last member of the family is the Chinese Water-deer (*Hydropotes inermis*), in which, as has been noted, no antlers are developed and the upper canine-teeth form long tusks.   Standing about twenty inches at the shoulder, this little deer is similar in colour to the Brockets ; it is found only in China and Korea.

Section B.—*TRAGULINA*

(*Chevrotains*)

The Chevrotains, or Mouse-deer, are placed in a separate section, the Tragulina ; they are all small, even-toed, hoofed animals, which resemble the Pecora in the absence of upper front teeth, but differ in the entire absence of horns, or antlers, and in the stomach having three, not four, chambers. The upper canine-teeth, in the males, are very long.   The section contains a single family, *Tragulidae*, which consists of three genera.   Firstly, *Tragulus*, the typical group of true Chevrotains, is found in South-Eastern Asia.   These animals are quite small (height about twelve inches), and have the cheek-teeth of true ruminants, and also the bones of both fore- and hind-feet are fused to form " cannon-bones."   In this group the skin under the lower jaw is naked and the coat is unspotted ; the colour is usually some shade of rufous, with light markings on throat and chest.

Three species and many races are recognised ; the one most commonly met with is the Javan-chevrotain, *T. javanicus*.   Secondly, the Chevrotain of Southern India and Ceylon, the Memina, is now considered to represent a distinct genus, *Moschiola*, on account of the chin being hairy and having the back spotted with white.   The African Water-chevrotain represents the third genus, in which only in the hind-limbs are cannon-bones formed ; this species, which is known as *Hyemoschus aquaticus*, is confined to equatorial Africa ; it is a little larger than the Asiatic chevrotains, measuring about thirteen to fourteen inches at the shoulder, and the coat is olive-brown in colour, spotted and striped with dirty-white.

Section C.—*TYLOPODA*

(*Camels and Llamas*)

The Tylopoda comprise the Camels and Llamas, animals easily distinguished from all the foregoing species by the presence of upper incisor-teeth, one pair in the adults and three pairs in young animals.   Other dental differences are the presence of a gap between the first premolars, when present, and remaining cheek-teeth, and the lower canine-teeth are not set horizontally with the incisor series. No horns or antlers are developed, and the feet are two-toed and furnished with nails, not hoofs. The camels are strictly Old World animals, while the llamas are found only in South America; both are contained in the Family *Camelidae.* The camels are characterised by the presence of the well-known humps; the one-humped camel, or Dromedary (*Camelus drome-darius*), is unknown in the wild state. The two-humped camel, or Bactrian-camel (*C. bactrianus*), is now found as a wild animal only in the Gobi Desert in Central Asia. The Llamas (*Lama*) are distinguished from the camels by their smaller size, the absence of humps, longer ears, narrower feet, shorter tail, and more woolly coat. Two species are differentiated, the wild llama, or Guanaco (*L. glama*), which is a large species (height at shoulder, about three feet

BACTRIAN-CAMEL (*Camelus bactrianus*).

seven inches) with bare callosities on the limbs, and the Vicugna (*L. vicugna*), which stands only about two feet nine inches at the shoulder and has no callosities on the limbs. The former inhabits Tierra del Fuego, Patagonia, and Chili, and the Vicugna is found in Peru, Ecuador, and Bolivia.

Section D.—*Suina*

(*Pigs, Peccaries, and Hippopotami*)

This section embraces the pigs and hippopotami, animals which lack the power of rumination, and have cheek-teeth with hillock-like crests on the crowns, very unlike the crescentic-shaped columns of which the ruminant teeth are composed. Further, the two main digits of the feet are distinct, not fused together to form cannon-bones. There are no horns or antlers, and the skin is either scantily clothed in harsh hair or nearly naked. The members of this section are distributed over practically the whole world; no truly wild pigs of any kind are, however, inhabitants of Australia or New Zealand. The pigs form one family, the *Suidae*, and the two species of hippopotamus are included in a second group, the *Hippopotamidae.* The former is further divided into two sub-families—*Suinae*, the pigs, and *Dicoto-lynae*, the peccaries.

The true pigs, representing the genus *Sus*, are grouped together in about seven species, the best known of which are the European Wild-boar (*S. scrofa*), the Indian Wild-boar (*S. cristatus*), and the Wild-boar of the East Indies (*S. vittatus*). The European species extends into Central Asia and southwards to Northern Africa. Formerly it was, apparently, abundant in Great Britain, the species not being exterminated until the sixteenth century. It is one of the largest members of the group, measuring about thirty-six inches at the shoulder, and is clothed in a dense coat of long, rather harsh hair. The general colour is brown or brownish-grey, and, as is the case with nearly all this genus, the young are striped. In this and the closely allied species no warts are developed on the face; the wild pig of Java, *Sus verrucosus*, has three pairs of warty knobs on the face, and the young are unstriped. The Indian Wild-boar is distinguished from the European species by the greater development of the crest on the neck and shoulders.

GIANT FOREST-HOG (*Hylochoerus meinertzhageni*).

The Pigmy-hog (*Porcula salvania*) is the smallest member of the family, standing only some eleven inches in height; the tail is exceptionally short (one and a quarter inches). This little pig is found only in the Eastern Himalayas. One of the most striking members of the family is the Babirusa (*Babirussa babyrussa*) from Celebes. In the males of this pig the upper canines, which are large and recurved, pierce the skin of the face; the lower canines are also set in a vertical recurved direction, and both upper and lower are devoid of enamel. The incisors and cheek-teeth are reduced in number, and the tail has no terminal tuft.

In Africa, apart from the European type of Wild-boar, we can distinguish three different kinds of pig, the Bush-pigs and Red river-hogs (*Cheiropotamus*), the Forest-hogs (*Hylochoerus*), and the Wart-hogs (*Phacochoerus*). Bush-pigs have small canines and forty-two instead of forty-four teeth; the ears are fringed and the coat is frequently brightly coloured. The distributional range extends throughout the greater part of Africa, south of the desert region, and Madagascar. The Forest-hogs, the largest of the pigs, are probably intermediate between the Bush-pigs and Wart-hogs; the canines are comparatively small, and the upper incisors, as in the Wart-hogs, reduced to a single pair.   The coat is black and much more hairy than in the latter beasts, and a pair of gigantic warty excrescences are situated below the eyes ; these extraordinary pigs inhabit equatorial Africa, from the Cameroons to Kenya Colony.   The Wart-hogs are smaller beasts, less hairy, and have the canines enormously enlarged, and three pairs of warts on the face.   These pigs occur over nearly the whole of Africa south of the Sahara.

The second sub-family, containing the Peccaries, is distinguished from the pigs by the hind-feet having only three complete toes, and by there being only thirty-two teeth instead of the normal forty-four ; the upper canines are smaller and directed downwards, and the tail is vestigial.   The distributional range includes a large part of South America, extending north to Texas.   The mane and dorsal crest in some species are long and extend back on to the rump (*Dicotyles pecari*), in other forms the hair on the back is shorter (*D. (Pecari) tajacu*).

HIPPOPOTAMUS (*Hippopotamus amphibius*).

The Hippopotami (*Hippopotamidae*) are distinguished from the pigs and peccaries by the massive build, the broad muzzle, and the position of the nostrils, which are on top of the rounded snout.   The incisors and canines, which grow from persistent pulps, are directed downwards in the upper jaw ; the lower incisors are set horizontally.   At the present day the group is entirely African.   Two genera may be distinguished, the common large Hippopotamus, *Hippopotamus*, and the pigmy species from West Africa, *Choeropsis*.   In addition to the difference in size, the latter genus has only a single pair of lower incisors, whereas the large species has two pairs in each jaw.   The Common-hippopotamus (*H. amphibius*) is found throughout most of the large rivers of Africa south of the Sahara.   When fully adult this animal measures some fourteen feet in length, whereas the pigmy species (*C. liberiensis*) does not exceed six and a half feet.

Sub-order PERISSODACTYLA
(*Odd-toed Ungulates*)

The " odd-toed " ungulates possess four, three, or one toes on the fore-feet, and three or one on the hind-feet, the first toe of the ancestral five-toed types being entirely suppressed.   The second, third, and fourth toe are represented in the three-toed types ; the third toe when one only is present, and in the case of four toes, sometimes found on the fore-limb, the additional digit corresponds to the fifth toe of the five-toed types. The toe corresponding to the third toe is longer than the second and fourth, when these are present. The stomach is simple, and such cranial weapons as are present are situated on the muzzle, not the crown of the head, and are placed in the median line.

Three families of existing Perissodactyla may be distinguished : (i) *Equidae*, the horses, asses, and zebras ; (ii) *Tapiridae*, the tapirs ; and (iii) *Rhinocerotidae*, the rhinoceroses.

Family Equidae

The horse family is characterised by the length of the head and limbs ; the latter, in existing types, have only one functional toe to each foot, the two side toes being reduced to small splint-bones. The hoofs encase the terminal segment of the digit, and the skull has the eye-sockets completely surrounded by bone. The present-day *Equidae* represent a single genus, *Equus*, which is now entirely confined to the Old World, the range extending from Asia Minor through Syria and Persia to Central Asia and a large part of Africa south of the Sahara. In the past the group was represented in both North and South America.

The genus *Equus* may be regarded as representing four groups : (i) the horse group (*Equus*), with unstriped bodies, short ears, and broad hoofs ; (ii) the ass group (*Asinus*), with unstriped bodies, longer ears, and narrower hoofs ; (iii) the Grévy's zebra group (*Dolichohippus*), with striped bodies and broad ears ; and (iv) the zebra group (*Hippotigris*), with the head and neck and, in most cases, the body striped, and narrow ears. These groups may be regarded as of subgeneric value. The Wild-horse of Mongolia (*E. caballus przewalskii*) is found in the Gobi Desert district ; it is a pale, dun-coloured animal, with a large head, convex profile, no fore-lock, and a long, short-haired tail terminating in a long-haired tuft.

The Kiang, Chigetai, and Onager are close allies of the horses ; they are found in the desert regions of Asia, extending from Syria and Persia to Central Asia. These so-called " wild asses " are of fair size, standing about three feet eight inches to four feet at the shoulder ; the black colour of the mane is continued down the back as a dark stripe. They differ from the true horses in having no callosities on the hind-limbs, and in the tail being long-haired at the tip only.

The Kiang (*E. hemionus kiang*), from Tibet and Ladak, is bright or dark reddish in colour, and the stripe down the back is remarkable for its narrowness. A near relative of the Kiang is the Chigetai (*E. h. hemionus*), from Mongolia and Turkestan ; it is, however, less red in colour. The Ghorkhar, or Onager (*E. onager*), is an allied species from Syria, Persia,

Baluchistan, and Western Mongolia ; it is smaller and paler than the other forms, and has a broad, dorsal stripe.

The next group (*Dolichohippus*), which contains only a single species, Grévy's-zebra (*E. grevyi*), has the broad ears thickly haired on the inside, and the coat is marked by numerous narrow stripes ; this animal is found only in Abyssinia, Somaliland, and Kenya Colony. The last group (*Hippotigris*) contains all the remainder of the zebras, that is, the Bonte-quaggas and mountain, or true, zebras, and the extinct Quagga. The latter animal, which was formerly very common in South Africa, was striped only on the neck and shoulders, the rest of the upper parts being brownish and the limbs pale. The true zebras (*E. zebra*) are found only in South and South-West Africa ; they are remarkable for the transverse striping or gridiron pattern on the posterior back. The Bonte-quaggas, which do not possess the gridiron marking on the rump, are widely distributed over Africa south of the Sahara.

GRÉVY'S-ZEBRA (*Equus grevyi*).

The true Wild Ass (*E. asinus africanus*) comes from North-East Africa. It differs from its Asiatic cousin in having longer ears, a shorter mane, and less hairy tail. The colour lacks the rufous tinge of the Kiang, and the shoulder-stripe is usually well marked.

Family Tapiridae

The Tapirs form the second family of the Perissodactyla ; the group is characterised by the possession of four front and three hind toes. The cheek-teeth are simple and low-crowned. These animals are further distinguished by the elongation of the snout into a short trunk. The distribution is somewhat remarkable, one species being found in the Malay while the other four are confined to Central and South America. The Malayan-tapir (*Tapirus indicus*) is the largest member of the family, standing nearly three and a half feet at the shoulder. In colour this animal is as strange as the giant panda, the head, fore-part of body, and limbs being black, while the body behind the shoulders to the rump is white.   The newly born young are, however, striped and spotted with yellowish-white.   The distributional range extends from the Malay Peninsula to Tenasserim, and also includes the Islands of Borneo and Sumatra.

The American tapirs, of which four species are recognised, are uniformly coloured when adult, the coat being a dark, brownish tint, but the young are striped and spotted in the same manner as is the juvenile coat of the Malayan species.   The common South American-tapir (*T. terrestris*) has a shorter snout than the Asiatic animal, and there is a stiff, upright mane on the neck. Roulin's-tapir (*T. roulini*) is an allied species from the mountains of Ecuador and Colombia, and two further species occur in Central America—Baird's-tapir (*T. bairdi*) and Dow's-tapir (*T. dowi*).   These American tapirs are, by some authorities, referred to different genera.

Family Rhinocerotidae

The Rhinoceroses constitute the third family of Perissodactyla, the *Rhinocerotidae*, the members of which are easily recognised by their massive proportions, by the toes being reduced to three in number on both the fore- and hind-feet, and to the presence, at least in the male sex, of one or two median horns on the head ;   these horns are composed of horny fibres arising from the skin, and are not connected with the skull, although the latter develops a bony boss on which the horns rest.   One of the reasons why the Asiatic rhinoceroses have been nearly exterminated in many of their former haunts is because of the demand for rhinoceros-horn for medicinal purposes in China.

Three of the species are Asiatic, two African.   Commencing with the great Indian-rhinoceros (*Rhinoceros unicornis*) we have a very large, one-horned animal ;   the horn is comparatively short, twenty-four inches being the record horn-length for this species.   In large specimens the shoulder height is nearly six feet, this rhinoceros being the largest of the Asiatic species.   The skin exhibits a number of deep folds around the neck and three on the body, one in front of the shoulders, which does not extend across the back, one behind the shoulders, and one in front of the thighs ; the latter two folds are continued across the back.   The skin of the sides of the body is thickly studded with rounded tubercles, and that of the limbs is composed of many-sided, scale-like scutes.   The distributional range was at one time quite extensive ;   it is now restricted to Nepal, Assam, and some of the adjacent territory.

The Javan-rhinoceros (*R. sondaicus*), which is also a one-horned species, is distinguished from the Indian-rhinoceros by its smaller size, standing about five and a half feet at the shoulder, and by the mosaic-like pattern of the skin.   In addition, the male of this species alone carries a horn ;   the latter is smaller than that of the Indian species, the record specimen measuring only ten and three-quarters inches in length. Formerly it was widely distributed in South-Eastern Asia, occurring in the Sanderbans and other parts of Eastern Bengal, Sikkim, and Assam, and through Burma to the Malay Peninsula and Java ; it has, however, been exterminated in most of these localities. The skin-folds differ from those of the Indian species in that all three folds are carried across the back.

The Sumatran-rhinoceros is the only species in Asia possessing two horns ; it resembles the other Asiatic rhinoceroses, however, in having teeth in the front of the jaw, and cannot be considered as a near relation of the two-horned African species. It differs from the Indian and Javan rhinoceroses in having only a single pair of lower incisors, the small, central pair of the other two species being absent. It is the smallest of the rhinoceroses, measuring only about four and a half feet at the shoulder ; it is also the most

WHITE RHINOCEROS (*Rhinoceros (Diceros) simus*).

hairy of the existing species, and may be distinguished from all the members of the family by the fact that it has got two horns and also a folded skin. The skin is not marked in the same mosaic-like manner as in the Javan animal, nor are the rounded tubercles, or polygonal scutes, of the Indian species developed, but the skin has a granular texture. This species is found in Sumatra, Borneo, and the Malay Peninsula northwards to Assam and Siam. Its scientific name is *Rhinoceros (Dicerorhinus) sumatrensis*.

The African rhinoceroses represent two species, the White-rhinoceros (*R. (Diceros) simus*) and the Black-rhinoceros (*R. (Diceros) bicornis*). The former is a very large animal (height at shoulder about five feet six inches), and the females often carry longer horns than the males, the record horn-length being sixty-two and a half inches. Both the African rhinoceroses carry two horns. They are distinguished from one another by the shape of the muzzle ; in the white species this is large and square-shaped, whereas in the black rhinoceros the muzzle is pointed and the upper lip prehensile. The Black-rhinoceros is a smaller animal than its square-mouthed cousin, and is more of a browser, whereas the white species usually grazes. In colour both forms are dirty-brown, the " white " rhinoceros appearing rather paler than the black species.

The horns of the latter are never as large as the largest White-rhinoceros horns, forty inches is a good length for a horn, and fifty-three and a half inches is the record length for the front horn; the rear horn is nearly always the shorter of the two, rarely exceeding twenty inches in the black species or fifteen inches in the white. The cheek-teeth of the two animals differ considerably, those of the White-rhinoceros being specially adapted for chewing grass, whereas those of the black variety are modified for masticating twigs and leaves. The skulls of both the African species are easily distinguished from those of the Oriental rhinoceroses by the entire absence of front teeth. A well-marked external difference between the two groups is the absence, or slight development, of the folds in the skin in the African species, these folds never being so well marked as they are in the Asiatic forms.

The black species enjoys a wide distribution, extending from Nyasaland and Northern Rhodesia northwards to Abyssinia and Somaliland, and in the west it reaches Nigeria and the drier parts of Central and West Africa. The Black-rhinoceros, like its white cousin, was formerly a very common animal in South Africa, but these animals have nearly all been shot down, a few remaining where protection is afforded them. The White-rhinoceros is now practically exterminated in South Africa; north of the Zambesi this species again occurs in the Sudan, Uganda, and Northern Congo.

Sub-order HYRACOIDEA

(Hyraces, or Dassies)

This sub-order contains a group of small animals whose affinities have long been a puzzle to the systematic zoologist. From their size and general appearance they were formerly thought to be allied to the rodents. At a later date they were placed in the Order Ungulata, associated with the rhinoceroses; the group is now considered to represent a distinct sub-order, the Hyracoidea, and is usually placed between the rhinoceroses and elephants. These animals are remarkable for their rodent-like teeth; the upper incisors, which are reduced to a single pair, grow from persistent pulps and are curved as in rodents. Instead, however, of being fashioned on the chisel plan, they are prismatic and terminate in sharp points. There are two pairs of lower front teeth, both being rooted, and therefore very unlike the true rodent-type; the outermost pair are set rather horizontally and have their crowns divided into three lobes. The cheek-teeth, which are separated from the incisors by a considerable space, are seven in number, and resemble the teeth of Perissodactyle ungulates.

The tail is quite short and collar-bones are not developed. The ears are small and rounded; the colour of the coat is usually brownish-grey, mixed with black; and there is a light or dark glandular spot near the

centre of the back.   The brain resembles that of an ungulate more than a
rodent, and the intestinal canal is remarkable for possessing supplemental
caeca.   The fore-foot has four functional toes, the first digit being rudimentary ; the hind-foot has three toes, the inner (or second) digit being furnished
with a curved claw; all the other toes, of both fore- and hind-feet, resemble
those of rhinoceroses in having short nails.   The various species and races
of Hyrax are widely distributed over Africa, the range extending into Arabia
and Syria.

Family Procaviidae

The sub-order contains the single family *Procaviidae* and two genera,
Procavia, the terrestrial hyraces, and *Dendrohyrax*, the tree-climbing species.
The Cape-hyrax, or Dassie (*Procavia capensis*), is one of the best-known
species ; it has a dark spot marking the dorsal gland and lives among rocks.

BRUCE'S HYRAX (*Procavia brucei*).

This species, which has
been subdivided into about
six races, is found in Cape
Province and South-West
Africa.   In Abyssinia we
find the allied *P. brucei*,
and other closely related
forms occur in the Congo,
East   Africa,   Transvaal,
Sudan, Nigeria, Angola,
Senegal, and the Cameroons.
In Syria there occurs a pale-
coloured species (*P. syriaca*);
this animal is the one referred to in the Scriptures
as the " coney."   Local races of this Syrian-hyrax are found in Palestine
and Southern Arabia.

The tree-hyraces are a much less numerous group, only about twenty
forms being known.   Of these the South African Tree-hyrax is named
Dendrohyrax arborea, and the East African species is *D. crawshayi*.   The
majority of these tree-living hyraces are more or less confined to the equatorial regions, the range embracing the greater part of the equatorial forest
zone as well as the islands of Fernando Po and Zanzibar.

Sub-order PROBOSCIDEA

(Elephants)

Elephants are quite unlike all the other ungulates, their general structure
differing widely from that of the allied types ; the evidence in favour of
considering the Proboscideans as belonging to the Order Ungulata is chiefly

founded upon the discovery of various extinct types which appear to connect the modern elephant with some of the Ungulata. The group is characterised by the great size of the body, the possession of a mobile trunk, at the end of which the nostrils are situated, and by the possession of five toes to each foot, the toes being enclosed in a common covering of skin, and usually furnished with short hoofs. They are further distinguished by their teeth being quite different from the ordinary mammalian dentition, the incisor-teeth in the existing species being reduced to two very large, cylindrical, ever-growing and curved tusks, situated in the upper jaw ; no canine-teeth, or lower incisors, are developed, and the molars are large and transversely ridged. The tusks are composed of solid dentine, enamel being formed only near the tip ; in the very young elephant there is a small pair of milk-tusks, which are normally shed early in life.

Reports have been received from time to time of the existence in Africa of four-tusked elephants ; apart from the possibility of injury or disease leading to the bifurcation of a tusk, it is possible that such a four-tusked condition might arise through the retention of the milk-incisors along with the permanent tusks. The real four-tusked elephant (*Tetrabelodon*)—that is, an animal with lower as well as upper tusks—is a beast of the distant past, which played an important part in the ancestry of the modern elephants.

The mode of succession of the cheek-teeth is quite unique amongst land-mammals ; the teeth (usually six in number) are never all in place at the same time, there being a gradual forward movement of the whole series from below upwards and forwards, so that only one or portions of two teeth are ever in use on either side of both jaws at once. As the front teeth become worn away and cast out, so the development of those behind goes on. The cheek-teeth appear to represent three milk-molars in front and three molars behind ; the number of ridges on the grinding surface of the teeth increase with each successive tooth, the first milk-molars being small teeth with only a few transverse ridges, whereas the last tooth to come into action may be made up of as many as twenty-four ridges (in the Indian species).

Elephants are exclusively vegetable-feeders ; they prefer to browse, but will frequently graze, having to spend a large portion of their time gathering food with their trunks in order to fill their capacious stomachs. They are very fond of the bark of young trees and fruit of all kinds. In parts of East Africa they are very partial to the nuts of the dome-palm ; the soft rind of the nuts is alone devoured, the hard kernel being ejected.

Family *Elephantidea*

The family *Elephantidea* is, at the present day, reduced to two species contained in the single genus *Elephas*. The distributional range is now limited to the Ethiopian and Oriental regions ; the group was, however, very much more widely spread over the surface of the world in former days.

2 E

The earliest-known animal of this group is a comparatively small, tapir-like beast, which was found in a fossil state in the Upper Eocene deposits of the Fayûm, the lake province of Egypt ; the Fayûm lies about sixty miles south-west of Cairo to the west of the Nile valley. This early Proboscidean has been named *Moeritherium ;* it probably had a short, trunk-like nose, and the second pair of upper incisor-teeth were considerably enlarged, foreshadowing the development of the tusks of the modern elephant. *Moeritherium* was, apparently, a shore- or swamp-dwelling animal, which, doubtless owing to the continuation of conditions favourable to its environment, was enabled to persist until the Upper Eocene days, when it was accompanied by another and still more elephant-like animal, known as *Palaeomastodon.* This creature was about the size of a half-grown Indian-elephant and was remarkable for the possession of two pairs of tusks, the incisor-teeth being reduced to a single pair in each jaw and large and tusk-like in form. The trunk in this animal was not freely flexible as we know it in the modern elephant, but formed part of the upper jaw, so that only its extreme tip could have been free or prehensile.

In the four-tusked elephant (*Tetrabelodon*), of the Miocene and Lower Miocene, we have a still more elephant-like beast, the early forms of which had long, lower jaws ; in the later types, as the lower jaw commenced to shorten, so the trunk began to lengthen till it came to hang down as in modern elephants.

The Indian- or Asiatic-elephant (*Elephas maximus*) averages rather smaller than its African cousin, the height at the shoulder rarely reaching as much as ten feet ; as a general rule, big male Indian-elephants do not exceed nine feet in height and females are about a foot shorter. Of course, as regards wild-killed animals, we must remember that a dead elephant is a very difficult animal to measure, and an error of several inches in attempting to calculate the height of the beast, as it stood in life, is quite understandable. A good old African bull elephant (*E. africanus*) will measure as much as eleven feet four or five inches at the shoulder, although ten feet six inches is a very fine specimen. The rule that is applicable to the Indian-elephant that twice the circumference of the fore-foot will equal the height of the animal, cannot be applied with accuracy to the African beast, because, generally speaking, the height exceeds this dimension.

The ivory, or tusks, of the Asiatic-elephant are both smaller and lighter than those of the African-elephant ; good Indian tusks weigh from fifty to one hundred pounds and measure six to eight feet in length ; the record length for an Indian tusk is eight feet nine inches, an exceptionally large tusk for an Oriental specimen. The tusks of the African-elephant are both larger and heavier than those of the Indian species ; the longest tusk on record is one in the American National Collection, which measures eleven feet five and a half inches, and the heaviest tusk known, which is one in the British Museum, weighs over two hundred and twenty-six pounds. These are, however, exceptionally large tusks ; good African ivory will measure eight to ten feet in length and weigh from one hundred to one hundred and eighty pounds.

There are a number of other external differences deserving of note ; firstly, the outline of the backbone is distinctly convex in the Indian-elephant, whereas the African species has a well-marked depression between the shoulders and the hip, giving the animal a rather broken-backed appearance. Secondly, the ears of the Indian animal are much smaller than those of its African cousin, the former measuring only about five feet across (from tip to tip) when fully extended, and the latter as much as nine feet across. In the Indian-elephant there are usually five nails on the fore-foot and four on the hind-foot ; in the African species the nails on the hind-foot are reduced to three. The females in Africa carry long and slender tusks ; in India they are either tuskless or are provided with quite small ones. The foreheads of the two animals are markedly different, the Asiatic beast having a flat, almost vertical forehead, whereas the African-elephant's head is sloping and convex. Lastly, the trunks of these two animals differ very considerably : the Indian species has a simple, trunk-like tube, terminating at its extreme tip in a single finger-like process ; the African-elephant's trunk is, on the other hand, more like a series of telescopic rings, and terminates in two finger-like points.

There are a large number of internal differences, one of the most important of which concerns the molar teeth ; in the Indian species these are composed of a series of flat plates, the enamel folds cemented together and forming small and narrow wavy ridges on the grinding surface of the teeth. The African-elephant's cheek-teeth are similarly formed, but the ridges are less in number and widen out into a diamond- or lozenge-shaped pattern. In the Indian species the successive cheek-teeth present the following average number of ridges : 4, 8, 12, 12, 16, and 24. The ridge-formula for the African forms shows a marked falling off in number of plates in the later teeth : 3, 6, 7, 7, 8, 10.

The Indian-elephant inhabits the wooded districts of India, Ceylon, Assam, Burma, the Malay Peninsula, Siam, Cochin China, Sumatra, and Borneo. In the latter island it is possible that the animals are not really indigenous, having probably been introduced by man many years ago. The Ceylon, Sumatran, and Malayan elephants have all been described as different races of the typical Indian-elephant, the type locality of which may be taken as Mysore.

The African-elephant, like its very early predecessor, *Moeritherium*, is not found outside Africa ; a number of local races have been described, but, with few exceptions, these have been founded on unsatisfactory characters. The elephants from the Cape northwards to the Zambesi, and from there up the eastern side of the continent to Kenya Colony and Southern Sudan, may perhaps be regarded as the Cape-elephant (*E. africanus capensis*).

This animal is now very rare in the Province, only a few remaining in the Knysna and Zitzikama forests. The two most distinct races are the Cameroons-elephant (*E. a. cyclotis*), which has large, oval ears, and the Abyssinian sub-species (*E. a. oxyotis*), in which the ears are very large and triangular in shape.

Whether the elephant of Kenya Colony and Tanganyika Territory is different from that of South Africa is, at present, not definitely known, but there appears to be a small race (*E. a. orleansi*) in Somaliland. The tusks of

AFRICAN ELEPHANT (*Elephas africanus*).
(Photograph taken i n the Lorian Swamp, Kenya Colony, by Mr. Marius Maxwell, by whose permission it is reproduced.)

the Somali-elephant are considerably smaller than those of its near neighbours in the Lorian-swamp district of Kenya Colony ; in the former about fifty pounds a pair is the average weight, while in the Kenya and Masai elephants tusks of over one hundred pounds apiece are met with.

Elephants are possessed of a very keen sense of smell ; with a suitable wind they can smell a white man from a distance of several miles, and in stalking these animals it is essential to keep on the right side of the wind. Their eyesight, compared with that of carnivorous animals such as the lion and tiger, is very deficient, both by day and by night. Their sense of hearing is fairly well developed, sufficiently so, at any rate, to warn them of danger at close quarters.

CHAPTER IV

Order RODENTIA

(*Rodents*)

RODENTS are mostly small-sized animals, the majority of which are terrestrial ; there are, however, a number of tree-living rats and mice, while the squirrels are almost entirely arboreal in habits ; a few forms, such as the beaver and water-rats, are aquatic. The members of the Order Rodentia are easily distinguished by their large, chisel-shaped incisor-teeth, and the absence of all trace of canine-teeth ; the former, which grow from persistent pulps, are reduced to a single pair in the lower jaw and one or two pairs in the upper jaw. The cheek-teeth form an unbroken series situated a considerable distance behind the incisors ; the premolars are usually only a single pair in each jaw, or they may be altogether absent. These cheek-teeth may be either rooted or rootless, and have their crowns studded with tubercles, or flat and laminated. The orbits, or eye-sockets, are not cut off from the temporal region of the skull, and collar-bones are usually developed. The order is widely spread over both the Eastern and Western Hemispheres.

Sub-order *SIMPLICIDENTATA*

(*Single-toothed Rodents*)

Rodents are divided into two groups, or sub-orders : (i) those which have only a single pair of incisors, or front teeth, in the upper jaw, known as the single-toothed Rodents (*Simplicidentata*), and including all the squirrels, rats, mice, voles, porcupines, and their allies ; and (ii) those which have two pairs of incisors in the upper jaw, known as the double-toothed Rodents (*Duplicidentata*), including the hares, rabbits, and picas. The first group is by far the largest, and is further subdivided into three sections : (A) the squirrel-like rodents (*Sciuromorpha*), which have the angular part of the lower jaw arising from the lower surface of the root of the sheath of the incisor-tooth, while the two bones of the lower leg (tibia and fibula) are separate and distinct ; (B) the rats, mice, and voles (*Myomorpha*), in which the angular process of the lower jaw is usually as in the squirrels, but the two bones of the lower leg are united ; and (C) the porcupines and their allies (*Hystricomorpha*), which have the angular portion of the lower jaw arising from the outer side of the incisor socket.

Section A.—*SCIUROMORPHA*

(*Squirrels*)

Commencing with the squirrel-like rodents (*Sciuromorpha*), we find in Africa a very curious family of flying-squirrels, or scaly-tails (*Anomaluridae*), in which a flying or gliding membrane is developed, much as in the flying-phalangers of Australia and the true flying-squirrels.

Family Anomaluridae

These animals are distinguished from the true flying-squirrels by the flying membrane being supported in front by a cartilaginous spur arising from the elbow, whereas in the flying-squirrels the spur comes from the wrist. The name " scaly-tail " has reference to a row of overlapping scales situated at the base of the under side of the tail ; in the larger scaly-tails (*Anomalurus*) these scales are of considerable size, and have their sharply pointed ends directed backwards, thus forming a series of climbing irons. In the smaller species (*Idiurus* and *Zenkerella*) the scales are quite small and are ridge-like in pattern. Some of the species of *Anomalurus* are very handsomely coloured, *A. peli* from West Africa being a large, black-and-white animal, and *A. fulgens* from the Cameroons being a uniform orange-red tint. The larger scaly-tails (*Anomalurus*) vary in size, some being little larger than a squirrel, while others are nearly equal to a small cat ; the species extend across equatorial Africa, from Liberia to as far east as Kenya Colony and southwards to Northern Rhodesia. The Pigmy Flying scaly-tails (*Idiurus*) are only about the size of a small rat or mouse, and are confined to West and Central Africa. The Flightless scaly-tail (*Zenkerella insignis*), which is only known from the Cameroons, has no parachute-like membrane, being a grey-coloured, rat-like animal with a bushy tail. All the members of this family are arboreal.

Family Sciuridae

The second family, the *Sciuridae*, containing all the true squirrels and marmots, is very much more widely distributed than the scaly-tails, the species being found in both the Old and the New Worlds ; they are distinguished from the *Anomaluridae* by the absence of scales on the tail, and the presence of a bony process (the post-orbital process) behind the orbit, or eye-socket, of the skull. This family is divisible into two groups, the true squirrels and their relations forming the sub-family *Sciurinae*, and the prairie-dogs and marmots, which are included in the sub-family *Marmotinae*. In the first of these groups the animals are usually of slender build, with long, bushy tails, and the great majority of species are arboreal ; in the *Marmotinae* the build is more massive, the tail shorter, and their habits terrestrial.

The squirrels are a very large group of rodents, and it will only be possible to give a brief account of the more important species. In Africa alone there are thirteen different genera, some being arboreal, like the common European-squirrel, others (the ground squirrels) being largely terrestrial in habits. Many of the African-squirrels are very strikingly coloured, one species (*Aethosciurus lucifer*) from Nyasaland is bright orange, with a dark stripe running down the back ; another very brilliantly coloured species is *Paraxerus palliatus*, the coat being a mixture of silvery grey and bright orange. Closely allied are the African Side-striped squirrels, belonging to the genus *Funisciurus*, which are found in the forests of West Africa. The common squirrels of equatorial Africa are grouped together in the genus *Heliosciurus ;* they are mostly grey-coloured when the coat is new, turning rusty-brown as the black on the hairs gradually bleaches. Specimens of these squirrels are frequently met with in which the coat is partly grey and partly rufous, giving the animals a very patchy appearance.

There are two genera of African Giant-squirrels, animals quite half as big again as the common squirrel ; for the most part these large species are confined to West and equatorial Africa. The head and body measurement is about eleven inches, and the general build more massive than in the smaller genera. *Protoxerus*, the Bar-tailed Giant-squirrels, extend from the Gold Coast eastwards as far as Kenya Colony and southwards to Angola ; some of the races are very brightly coloured, varying from greyish-buff to bright orange. In striking contrast to these Giant-squirrels are the African Dwarf-squirrels, two groups of which may be distinguished: (i) the Striped Dwarf-squirrels of Uganda (*Tamiscus*), which have two or four black stripes along the back, and are usually some shade of green in general colour; and (ii) the West African Pigmy-squirrel (*Myosciurus*), a little animal, smaller than a house-mouse, which is found only in the Cameroons and Gaboon.

Related to the above groups are four different types of the so-called Ground-squirrels, terrestrial animals distinguished by their very harsh and scanty coats, the hairs being almost spiny. The largest of these is the North African Ground-squirrel (*Atlantoxerus getulus*), a large (head and body, eight inches), brownish-coloured squirrel, with four dark stripes on the back. The East African Ground-squirrels (*Xerus*) are rather smaller, reddish in general colour, and with unstriped coats. The South African Ground-squirrel (*Geosciurus capensis*) has a light stripe on each flank. Lastly, the equatorial Ground-squirrels (*Euxerus*) have longer and narrower heads; they are confined to equatorial Africa.

In Europe, Asia, and America squirrels are found in great variety, the number of different genera being very large. The common European-squirrel (*Sciurus vulgaris*) is widely distributed, and about a dozen different races are recognised from Europe alone ; the genus *Sciurus* is found over the greater part of the forested area of the northern hemisphere. The common British-squirrel (*S. vulgaris leucourus*) is remarkable for the seasonable change of coat, the greyish-brown winter coat bleaching to chestnut-red in the summer, when the tail and ear-tufts turn white; as the new coat appears in the late summer and autumn, a black streak develops down the centre of the bushy tail, and the white hairs of the tail and ear-tufts, and the red ones of the coat, gradually fall out and are replaced by the greyish-brown hair of the new coat. In many parts of England the squirrel has become a comparatively rare animal ; this appears to be largely due to the introduction of the American Grey-squirrel, which has increased in some localities to such an extent as to become a regular pest, driving out and killing off the indigenous species.

In North America there are a large number of different genera and species of squirrel closely allied to the European animal. The Grey-squirrel (*S. carolinensis*), mentioned above, is very widely distributed over the continent, and has established itself in many other parts of the world. The Red-squirrels, or Chickaris, are other well-known North American species, which represent a distinct group, or sub-genus, *Tamiasciurus*. Some of the North American genera extend down into Central America; Hoffman's-squirrel, for instance, from Costa Rica, belongs to the sub-genus *Guerlinguetus*, a group of typical North American species.

In Central America and South America a number of pigmy tree-squirrels occur; these animals are much smaller than the average species, and are classified as representing a distinct genus, *Microsciurus*. In addition to the pigmy squirrels there are a number of larger forms in South America, which have been grouped together into nine genera; some of these South American squirrels are very brilliantly coloured and of considerable size. The genus *Urosciurus*, for instance, contains the giant South American squirrels, which are very large, and have long, broad tails; in colour they are a mixture of bright orange and black. Squirrels of equally large dimensions are included in the genus *Simosciurus*; *S. stramineus* is a very handsome animal, having the fore-part of the body greyish, hindquarters orange, fore-feet white, and hind-feet black.

The Asiatic squirrels show a similar range of variation, both as regards size and colour. Some, like the Great-eared squirrel of Borneo and the Giant-squirrels of India, are of very large size, equalling the largest of the African and South American genera; others, like the pigmy Asiatic squirrels, are only about the size of a mouse. The Great-eared squirrel of Borneo (*Rheithrosciurus macrotis*) is over two feet in total length, and has a very large and bushy tail and long, black ear-tufts; the colour of the coat is very striking, being chestnut-red and brownish-buff above and white below, the two areas being separated by a dark, flank stripe.

The Asiatic Giant-squirrels are equally handsome in colour and nearly as large; they are grouped together in the genus *Ratufa*, which is distributed over India, Ceylon, Assam, Burma, Siam, Malay Peninsula and Islands, eastward to Celebes. *R. indica* is a brilliant chestnut-red coloured species, from the India Peninsula, and the Giant-squirrel of Ceylon (*R. macroura*) is a long-tailed species with a black and white coat. In addition to these large squirrels, a great number of rather smaller forms also occur in Asia, representing a number of distinct genera. Of these the genus *Callosciurus* contains a large variety of highly coloured species, about equal in size to the common squirrel; they are widely distributed, ranging from India eastwards to China and south to Java and Borneo. Some genera of Oriental squirrels are distinguished by their elongated snouts; in the genus

Dremomys, the range of which extends from the Himalayas to China and southwards to the Malay Peninsula and Borneo, there are included a number of long-nosed, brown and white-coloured squirrels.

Closely allied, long-nosed species are Berdmore's-squirrel (*Menetes berdmorei*), from Burma and Siam, and the Chinese Long-nosed squirrel (*Rupestes forresti*), both of which forms are distinguished by having a pale stripe along the flanks. In the Dutch East Indies and Malay Peninsula there occur a number of other long-nosed squirrels, which are distinguished by their shorter tails and the presence of three dark stripes down the back ; these squirrels are included in the genus *Lariscus*. The well-known Palm-squirrels of India are an allied group, differing from the other Oriental species in having three pale stripes down the back ; these squirrels are included in the genus *Funambulus*, which is confined to peninsular India and Ceylon. Related to the palm-squirrels is a genus known as *Tamiops*, distinguished by having one or three black stripes on the back ; the members of this group inhabit the country from Assam to Yunnan and Siam.

The Pigmy-squirrels of Asia are included in the genus *Nanosciurus ;* they are very similar to the West African pigmy-squirrel, but have larger and more numerous teeth ; they inhabit Sumatra, Malacca, Borneo, and Philippines. A pigmy-squirrel from Guianas of South America is considered to be related to these Oriental species ; it is rather larger than *Nanosciurus* and is named *Sciurillus pusillus*.

CHIPMUNK (*Tamias quadrivittatus*).

Related to the true squirrels are the Chipmunks (*Tamias* and *Eutamias*) of North America and Eastern Asia ; these small striped-squirrels may possibly be regarded as a connecting link between the *Sciurinae*, or squirrels, and the *Marmotinae*.

The *Marmotinae*, the second sub-family of the family *Sciuridae*, includes the Prairie-dogs (*Cynomys*), Spermophiles and Sousliks (*Citellus*), and Marmots (*Marmota*). The prairie-dogs are entirely confined to the New World, and have very short tails, usually not exceeding five inches in length (head and body about one foot), and small ears. These animals associate in large companies ; they are, like the other members of the sub-family, strictly terrestrial in habits, living together in burrows, those of a community of prairie-dogs occupying a very large area of ground. The sousliks, spermophiles, or pouched-marmots, are smaller than the prairie-dogs and are more widely distributed, the species being found in Europe, Asia, and North America. They resemble prairie-dogs in appearance, though the tail is, in some forms, longer, and the cheek-pouches are much larger.

Marmots are also found throughout a large portion of the northern hemisphere; they resemble prairie-dogs in form, but are much larger and more massively built, and cheek-pouches are but little developed. The Alpine marmot (*Marmota marmotta*) is a large European species, the body measuring about twenty inches in length; the Bobac, another marmot found in Siberia, is a smaller form (length of body, fifteen inches), while in the Woodchuck (*M. monax*), from North America, the length of the body does not exceed fourteen and a half inches.

Family Petauristidae

The third family of Rodents, the *Petauristidae*, includes the true Flying-squirrels of Europe, Asia, and North America; in shape these animals are like squirrels, but they have the fore- and hind-limbs connected by a para-chute-like fold of the skin, which is attached in front to a cartilaginous spur arising from the wrist. A number of different genera are now recognised, the most important of which are the following: *Eupetaurus*, containing a single, very large species, *E. cinereus*, from Northern India; *Petaurista*, the giant flying-squirrels of Asia, which extend from the Indian Peninsula and Ceylon eastwards to Japan and the Malay Peninsula and Islands, many of these large flying-squirrels being brilliantly coloured, and having long and silky hair; *Sciuropterus*, small flying-squirrels found in Scandinavia and Russia, and extending eastward to Japan.

BURMESE FLYING-SQUIRREL (*Sciuropterus phayrei probus*).

The species known as the Pigmy Flying-squirrels (*Petaurillus*) are quite small, *P. emiliae* from Borneo being only the size of a mouse; whereas in the larger members of the family (*Eupetaurus* and *Petaurista*) the body measures about eighteen inches in length and the tail about two feet. These squirrels are mostly nocturnal, and are capable of making very considerable leaps; when jumping from one tree to another the parachute-like membrane is fully extended, and the animals jump downwards to commence with, gradually flattening out into a horizontal glide towards the finish.

Family Aplodontidae

The fourth family, the *Aplodontidae*, contains the North American Swellels, terrestrial animals of medium size, with rootless cheek-teeth, short tails, and very small eyes; only one species, *Aplodon rufa*, is known, divisible into a number of races. In habits it resembles the prairie-dog, living in communities, but their burrows are usually constructed adjacent to water.

Family Castoridae

The beavers constitute the fifth family of Rodents, the *Castoridae*; these animals occur in both North America and Europe, two species being recognised—the American- or Canadian-beaver, *Castor canadensis*, and the European-beaver, *C. fiber*; the latter is now confined to Scandinavia and a few of the larger European rivers. The beaver is known at once by its very flat and scaly tail, webbed hind-feet, short ears, rounded head, and thick, soft coat. The weight of a fully grown beaver is from forty-five to

EUROPEAN-BEAVER (*Castor fiber*).

sixty pounds, and the total length of the body, thirty inches; the tail is about ten inches in length. The habits of this truly aquatic animal are too well known to need description. It was, in former times, an inhabitant of England, where its fossil remains have frequently been found.

Section B.—MYOMORPHA

(*Rats and Mice*)

The next family, the *Muscardinidae*, or dormice, fall into the second section of the Simplicident Rodents, the Myomorpha, in which the angle of the lower jaw arises as in the squirrels, the two bones of the lower leg (the tibia and fibula) are united at their ends, and in the cheek-arch of the skull the jugal, or cheek-bone, rarely extends far forward.

Family Muscardinidae

Dormice are confined to the Old World, where they are found from England eastward to Japan; in the south they extend as far as Cape Province. They are all of small or medium size, the largest being rather smaller than a squirrel. They have bushy tails, and the blind part of the intestine, or caecum, is absent. The common British-dormouse (*Muscardinus avellanarius*), an animal about the size of a mouse, is the smallest member of the group ; its bright, yellowish-buff coat and large black eyes make it one of the most attractive of this handsome group of rodents. The largest member of the family is the Squirrel-tailed or Edible-dormouse (*Glis glis*),

EDIBLE-DORMOUSE (*Glis glis*).

inhabiting Southern-Eastern Europe ; it is easily distinguished by its large size and smoke-grey colouring.

Two other kinds of dormice are found in Europe : (i) *Eliomys*, in Southern Europe, extending into Asia Minor and Africa ; and (ii) *Dyromys*, which is found over a considerable part of Europe and Central Asia. In Africa there are three genera, *Graphiurus*, containing but a single species, *G. ocularis*, a large, grey-coloured dormouse from South Africa ; *Claviglis*, containing a large number of small species widely distributed over Africa, south of the Sahara ; and *Gliriscus* from South Africa. In India there occurs a very striking member of the group, the Spiny-dormouse (*Platacanthomys lasiurus*), a medium-sized mouse with a coat of spines. Lastly, in China there is found a small, ashy-grey-coloured species, with a plumed tail (*Typhlomys cinereus*), and in Japan we find a small dormouse which bears the name *Glirulus japonicus*.

Family Muridae

With the next family we commence the largest mammalian family, the *Muridae*, which contains all the true rats and mice, voles, gerbils, and hamsters. In the group there are only three pairs of cheek-teeth in each jaw ; these teeth are either rootless, as in the voles, or furnished with roots, as in the true mice. The number of species is so great that it will only be possible to mention the more important ones. The family is very widely distributed, occurring even in Australia.

The first sub-family of this group is the *Hydromyinae*, which contains a number of large Australian water-rats and various strange rat-like animals inhabiting the Philippines. The former are large (total length, twenty-three inches), water-living rats, with very soft fur and curiously compressed tails, which no doubt assist them in swimming ; many of the species are brightly coloured, *Hydromys chrysogaster*, the Golden-bellied water-rat, being an orange-buff tint on the under side of the body. These large water-rats, together with the closely allied genera *Xeromys*, *Leptomys*, and *Crossomys*, are inhabitants of Australia and New Guinea. The Philippine species belong to three genera, the most striking of which is the striped *Chrotomys* of Luzon, an animal about equal in size to the common rat, and having its back striped.

Another important sub-family is the *Gerbillinae*, which contains the African and Asiatic gerbils, in which the incisor-teeth are usually grooved and the hind-feet elongated. In Africa these gerbils are represented by at least eleven different genera ; some of these have long tails, frequently plumed at the tip (*Taterillus*), others have short and fleshy tails (*Microdillus* and *Pachyuromys*). The common Gerbils of Africa are grouped in two genera, *Taterona* and *Gerbillus*, in which the tail is long and hairy ; in colour these animals are usually bright buff or yellowish above and pure white below.

Some of the members of this sub-family are the size of a large rat ; others are little larger than a small mouse (*Microdillus*). The Fat-tailed Gerbils of South Africa (*Desmodillus*) and North Africa (*Pachyuromys*) are smaller animals than the common Gerbils, with fat and fleshy tails ; *Desmodilliscus* is a pigmy, fat-tailed form from the Sudan and Northern Nigeria. The Indian Gerbil, which is closely allied to the African genus *Taterona*, has been recognised as representing a distinct genus, *Tatera*, confined to the Indian Peninsula and Ceylon.

Two sub-families are confined to Africa, namely the *Otomyinae*, or African Swamp-rats, and the *Dendromyinae*, containing the African Tree-mice, Tree-rats, and Fat-mice ; both groups agree with the gerbils in having the incisor-teeth grooved. The Swamp-rats are about the size of a common water-rat, with rather short tails, and thick, soft fur ; the various species are distributed over the greater part of Africa, from the Cape northwards to Abyssinia. The Tree-mice (*Dendromus* and *Prionomys*) and Tree-rats (*Deomys*) are remarkable for their long tails, which, at least in the genus *Dendromus*, appear to be semi-prehensile. The Tree-rats are further characterised by their spiny coats ; they are found only in West and Central Africa. The Tree-mice are widely distributed over a great part of Africa, south of the Sahara. The Fat-mice (*Steatomys*) have quite short tails and fat bodies ; they are inhabitants of South, East and West Africa.

The typical sub-family, the *Murinae*, is by far the largest group, containing all the true rats and mice, which vary in size from the minute harvest-mice to the large rats of Africa (*Cricetomys*) and Asia (*Bandicota*), and the still larger New Guinea-rats of the genus *Mallomys* (total length, thirty inches). The sub-family is characterised by the molar-teeth being rooted, and in having the tubercles of the teeth arranged in three longitudinal rows, while the incisor-teeth are smooth in front, not grooved. The best-known members of the *Murinae* are the Common-mouse, or House-mouse (*Mus musculus*), the Black-rat (*Rattus rattus*), and the Brown-rat (*Rattus norvegicus*). The genus *Mus* is now considered to contain only a comparatively few species, such as *M. muralis* from St. Kilda, whereas the genus *Rattus* includes over a hundred different forms. In addition to the genera *Mus* and *Rattus*, two other groups are represented in Great Britain—the Field-mice (*Apodemus sylvaticus*) and Harvest-mice (*Micromys minutus*). The former are very widely distributed from Ireland to Japan; the Harvest-mouse extends from England to Central Europe and Asia.

The Giant-rats of Africa (*Cricetomys*) are of very large size, measuring some two feet six inches in total length; the various species and races are remarkable for having a very long tail, with a white tip. Another striking genus is *Acomys*, which includes the Spiny-mice, animals which have a harsh, spiny coat, almost as spiny as a hedgehog; in colour they are either reddish or slaty-grey above and white below. These spiny-mice come for the most part from Africa, but certain species are found in South-Western Asia, Cyprus, and Crete. Other closely allied African murines are the Crest-tailed rats (*Lophuromys*), Field-rats (*Arvicanthis* and *Lemniscomys*), and the Red-nosed rats (*Aenomys*).

AFRICAN GIANT-RAT (*Cricetomys gambianus*).

In Northern Australia there occur the Jerboa-rats, representing the genus *Conilurus*, characterised by their tufted tails and long hind-limbs; somewhat similar but smaller animals are the Kangaroo-mice of Australia (*Notomys*).

Some most remarkable animals, the East African Crested-rats (*Lophiomys*), are now classified as representing a distinct sub-family; these rats are of large size, long-haired, and have a well-marked crest of long hairs down the back; another curious feature is found in the skull, the temporal region being roofed over with bone.

CRESTED-RAT (*Lophiomys ibeanus*).

The Hamsters form another sub-family, the *Cricetinae*, the members of which have rooted teeth like the *Murinae*, and are widely distributed, being found over America, South-East and Central Europe, Central Asia, and South Africa. The well-known hamster *Cricetus cricetus*, of Europe, belongs to the typical genus ; the African representative is *Mystromys albicaudatus*, and among several American Cricetines are the well-known mouse-like forms of the genera *Peromyscus* and *Oryzomys*. Allied to the hamster-group are the voles and lemmings, forming the sub-family *Microtinae*, distinguished by the molar-teeth being flat-crowned, prismatic, and rootless. This is a very large group, widely distributed over both hemispheres ; in Great Britain we have three well-marked Microtines, the Field-vole (*Microtus agrestis*), the Bank-vole (*Evotomys glareolus*), and the Water-vole (*Arvicola amphibius*) ; as with so many British mammals, these voles are absent from Ireland.

Families Spalacidae, Geomyidae, and Jaculidae

Of the remaining families the most important are the *Spalacidae*, the Mole-rats, *Geomyidae*, the American Pocket-gophers, and the *Jaculidae*, the Jerboas. The *Spalacidae* occur in South-Eastern Europe, Asia, and Africa. The blind mole-rats of Europe (*Spalax*) are some of the most specialised members of this group ; this genus is also found in Asia and Northern Africa. In East Africa we meet with the long-haired mole-rats of the genus *Tachyoryctes*, some members of which are very handsomely coloured, having golden or rufous coats. The pocket-gophers are found only in America, the species being grouped into two genera, *Geomys* and *Thomomys*.

ARMENIAN JERBOA (*Alactaga williamsi*).

The jerboas have the body modified for jumping, the hind-limbs and feet recalling those of the kangaroo, while the fore-limbs are usually extremely small and the tail long and plumed. The true jerboas (*Jaculinae*) are found in the Palaearctic and Ethiopian regions, one genus, *Alactaga*, spreading as far north as Southern Russia. The Three-toed jerboas are included in the genus *Jaculus*, and the Long-eared jerboa of Central Asia is known by the generic name of *Euchoreutes*. The *Sicistinae*, another sub-family, penetrates as far west as Norway. The American *Jaculidae* form a distinct sub-family, the *Zapodinae*, including the single genus *Zapus*, small jumping-mice, with orange- or buff-coloured backs and white under parts.

Section C.—*HYSTRICOMORPHA*

(*Porcupines*)

The third and last section of the Simplicident Rodents is the *Hystrico-morpha*, in which the angle of the lower jaw arises-from the outer side of the lower incisor-socket. The *Pedetidae*, or Jumping-hares, the first family of this section, is very difficult to classify ; some authorities consider it to belong to the Myomorphic rodents, but, on the whole, the affinities of the group appear to be rather with the present section than with the Myomorpha.

Families Pedetidae, Ctenodactylidae, etc.

The Jumping-hares (*Pedetes*) are found over a large area of South and East Africa. They are as large as a common hare, and have long hind-limbs and rootless molars. The next family, the *Ctenodactylidae*, includes four genera of small species, the Gundis (*Ctenodactylus*, *Massou-tiera*, and *Pectinator*), short-tailed, g e r b i l - coloured animals found in North, North-West, and East Africa, and the Rock-rat (*Petromys*) of South-West Africa, dis-tinguished by its long, black, t u f t e d t a i l. Closely allied are the families *Octodontidae*, containing the well-known genus *Ctenomys*, i n h a b i t i n g South America, and the *Capro-myidae*, in which are placed two very distinct genera, *Thryonomys*, the African Cane-rats, and the West Indian *Cap-romys*. The former have harsh, almost spiny coats and very large incisor-

MERIDA TREE-PORCUPINE (*Coendu pruinosus*).

teeth. In this family we may, perhaps, place the Coypu (*Myocaster*) ; this is a large South American rodent, with enormous incisors, long, naked tail, and webbed hind-feet.

Families Hystricidae and Erithizontidae

The porcupines are classified in two families, the *Hystricidae*, which is entirely confined to the Old World, and the *Erithizontidae*, containing the American porcupines. In the typical porcupine (*Hystrix*) the skull is inflated and the tail quite short; it inhabits Mediterranean Europe and Africa. A closely allied genus, *Acanthion*, occurs in Asia. The Brush-tailed porcupines (*Atherurus*) of West Africa and Asia are distinguished by their longer, brush-shaped tails. The American family contains short-tailed, hairy forms (*Erithizon*), and a Central and South American group (*Coendu*), which have long and prehensile tails and are arboreal.

Families Chinchillidae, Dasyproctidae, etc.

The Chinchilla (*Chinchilla laniger*) and Viscachas (*Viscaccia*) represent another South American family-group, the *Chinchillidae*. The Chinchilla is a medium-sized rodent, with long legs and very soft fur; the Viscachas are large editions of the Chinchilla. The *Dasyproctidae* contains two large South American animals, the Agouti (*Dasyprocta*) and Paca (*Coelogenys*); both are furnished with hoof-like toes, and the tail is short or obsolete. Another South American family, the *Caviidae*, contains the largest of all living rodents, the Capybara (*Hydrochoerus capybara*), the body being about four feet in length and very strongly built; the feet are webbed, the animal leading a semi-aquatic existence. On the plains of Patagonia there is to be found the Patagonian cavy, *Dolichotis patagonica*, another member of this family; it is almost equal in size to a hare, and has a short tail and enormous ears. Lastly, the typical members of the group, the Cavies, or wild guinea-pigs, are all small animals, with short legs and ears; five genera are now recognised.

Sub-order DUPLICIDENTATA

(Double-toothed Rodents)

The second division of the Order Rodentia, the Duplicidentata, contains all those rodents which possess two pairs of upper incisor-teeth, the second pair being very small and placed close behind the front pair. Of these the Picas, or tail-less hares, may be regarded as representing a distinct family, the *Ochotonidae ;* they are much smaller than rabbits, with smaller ears and no tails, and are widely distributed, the range including South-Eastern Europe, Central Asia, and North America.

Family Leporidae

The second family, the *Leporidae*, contains all the Hares and Rabbits, a very large group in which the ears are long and the tail short. The former (*Lepus*) are widely distributed over Europe, Asia, North America, and Africa. The species are very numerous, some twenty odd forms occurring in Europe alone. The Varying-hares of Northern Europe (*L. timidus*) are represented in Scotland by a distinct race (*L. timidus scoticus*); these hares are distinguished from the Common-hare (*L. europeus*) by the tail being shorter, and its upper surface never being marked with a conspicuous black area, but being either white or clouded with greyish-brown.

Another difference lies in the fact that the Varying- or Mountain-hare changes the colour of its coat to white in winter, whereas the ordinary species never turns white, but sometimes grey. In the Scottish Mountain-hare the coat never turns completely white in winter, there always remaining a certain amount of grey on the back. A closely allied species, *L. hibernicus*, is found in Ireland; this Irish Varying-hare differs from the Mountain-hare of Scotland by being dull russet in colour, and the white pelage is never so wholly white as in the latter form.

The Common-hare (*L. europaeus*) ranges from Great Britain eastward into Russia, and from the Baltic southward to the Pyrenees, Italy, and Greece; about seven sub-species of this hare are recognised.

In India we have a curious hare, *Caprolagus hispidus*, which has an entirely brown tail, and the ears are shorter than the head; in the genus *Lepus* the tail is always white below, and the ears are longer than the head. The "Cotton-tails," of North and South America, are now placed in a distinct genus, *Sylvilagus*; they are rather smaller in size than the typical hares, being about equal to a rabbit. The Red-hares (*Pronolagus*), of South and South-East Africa, are still more rabbit-like in form; the tail in this group is usually bright reddish-buff.

The true rabbits are included in the genus *Oryctolagus*, and were originally restricted to Northern Africa and South and Central Europe; they have, however, been introduced into many other parts of the world, sometimes, as in Australia, becoming a regular pest. Rabbits differ from hares in having their young born blind and naked; in addition, the hind-limbs and ears are considerably shorter.

CHAPTER V

Order CARNIVORA

(*Carnivores*)

THE cats, dogs, hyaenas, bears, seals, etc., are grouped together in the Order Carnivora, the name having reference to their most characteristic habit, that of living very largely upon animal food. They may be regarded as very highly organised types, perhaps almost as high in the scale as the monkeys.

All members of the order have the toes furnished with claws, and there are never fewer than four toes to each foot. Unlike the monkeys, the first toe is never opposed to the other digits. The teeth are specially adapted for seizing and devouring the prey ; the canine-teeth are large and tusk-like, and one pair of cheek-teeth in each jaw is frequently modified for biting purposes, these teeth being called " carnassial," or flesh-teeth. Collar-bones, if present, are never complete, and the hinge, or condyle, of the lower jaw is semi-cylindrical in form and set in a transverse direction. Carnivores are widely distributed over nearly the whole world, excepting Australia and New Guinea. The order is divided into two sub-orders : (i) the terrestrial carnivores, known as the Carnivora Vera, or Fissipedia, including all those forms adapted to a terrestrial life ; (ii) the Pinnipedia, or seals, specially modified for an aquatic existence.

Sub-order *Carnivora Vera*

(*Cats, Dogs, and Bears, etc.*)

The Carnivora Vera always possess the carnassial-teeth. The group is subdivided into three sections : (A) the cats (*Aeluroidea*) ; (B) dogs (*Cynoidea*) ; and (C) bears (*Arctoidea*). The first of these sections contains four distinct families : (i) the *Felidae*, or cats ; (ii) *Viverridae*, the civets ; (iii) *Proteleidae*, the aard-wolf ; (iv) the *Hyaenidae*, or hyaenas.

Section A.—*Aeluroidea*

(*Cats*)

Family Felidae

This group is remarkable for the large size of the canine-teeth ; there is only one upper molar, a small tooth transversely expanded behind the last premolar. The members of this family may be regarded as representing the ideal carnivorous type, showing many special adaptations for the pursuit, killing, and eating of their prey. They are found over nearly the whole area inhabited by the Carnivora vera ; they are, however, not found in Madagascar, nor do they extend as far north as do the foxes and bears.

Sub-family *Felinae*.—The Lion (*Felis leo*), of which several races have been described, stands as much as three feet eight inches at the shoulder and measures some ten feet six inches in total length—that is, from the nose to the tip of the tail. The Indian-lion has frequently quite as full a mane as the best African specimens. The tail, in the males, terminates in a well-marked brush, or tuft, in the middle of which, at the extreme end of the tail, is a hard, horny nail.

The Lion is, at the present day, found throughout a large part of Africa, from South Africa northwards to Abyssinia and westward across the Sudan up the west coast to Algeria; whether any lions still exist in the Mediterranean littoral is extremely doubtful. In Asia the lion is now a comparatively rare animal; it is still found in Mesopotamia and parts of Persia. One of its last strongholds in India is the peninsula of Kathiawar, in the Guzerat district; the lions are apparently confined to the forests on the Gir hills, situated about twenty miles from the coast.

The Tiger (*F. tigris*) is about equal in height to the lion; a really big tiger will measure three feet six inches at the shoulder and about ten feet seven inches in total length. The tail averages about three feet four inches in length and tapers gradually towards the tip. No mane is developed, but in old males there is a kind of ruff of long hair around the neck and throat. The range of distribution is fairly extensive, tigers inhabiting the greater part of India and extending north to the Caucasus and Persia; in the south-

LION (*Felis leo*).

east they are found in the Malay Peninsula and Islands, and northwards reach to China, Manchuria, and Korea. Several distinct races of tiger are now considered to be recognisable, the typical form being the sleek-coated animal of Bengal. In the Caspian provinces and the Caucasus there is a rather smaller race with a rougher coat (*F. tigris virgata*); the Manchurian-tiger also bears a name (*F. tigris longipilis*), the distinguishing character being the long, thick fur, pale colouring, and massive build. Another race has been named from Central China, and a small form from Java is known as *F. tigris sondaica*.

The Leopard (*F. pardus*) is closely allied to the lion and tiger, and, like the lion, it occurs in both Africa and Asia. In general dimensions it is considerably smaller, standing only about two feet four inches at the shoulder and measuring about eight feet four inches in total length.

Pl. 12.

MANCHURIAN TIGERS (*Felis tigris longipilis*).

Leopards vary very greatly in size, and this fact has, in India, given rise to the idea that there are two distinct species, a large one called the " panther " and a smaller animal known as the leopard ; both forms, however, represent one and the same species, the leopard.

Unlike the tiger, leopards are found in Ceylon ; they are widely distributed over India, the range also including the Caucasus, Asia Minor, Afghanistan, a large part of Central Asia, Assam, Burma, Siam, China, Manchuria, the Malay Peninsula, Sumatra, and Java. In the west they reach Africa through Persia, Arabia, and Syria ; in Africa they are found over the greater part of the continent, from Algeria and Abyssinia southwards to the Cape. Several different geographical races of the leopard are now recognised, but they are all very much alike, differing chiefly in colour and the size and arrangement of the spots. In Somaliland there occurs a dwarf race (*F. pardus nanopardus*), which, in addition to being smaller, is much paler in colour.

TIGER (*Felis tigris*).

The Snow-leopard, or Ounce (*F. uncia*), differs from the leopard in having a much longer and softer coat, and in being much paler in colour. The spots are much larger and rosette-shaped, the central area being rather more richly coloured than the ground colour ; the latter is a kind of stone-grey, washed with pale buff. The tail is of great length and very thick, not tapering to any marked extent towards the tip ; the size of the body is less than in the common leopard, an adult specimen measuring about seven feet in total length, of which about half is occupied by the tail. This leopard is an inhabitant of the high mountain ranges of Central Asia, living at elevations of six to twenty thousand feet.

The Jaguar (*F. onca*) is the largest New World member of the *Felidae*, being a little larger in size than the leopard, and having a distinctly larger head. The ground colour of the coat is usually richer, being more like that of a tiger, and the spots larger. The latter are in the form of rosettes, with one or more spots in the centre. This cat is very largely arboreal in its habits, and is distributed over a great part of Central and South America, from Northern Mexico to Patagonia.

The Puma, or Cougar (frequently referred to in American publications as a " lion " or " panther "), comes next in size to the jaguar amongst the American cats, and is the only large unspotted species in the New World. The body is very long, and the height at the shoulder about two feet. The range of distribution is very extensive, pumas occurring nearly all over South America and spreading northwards as far as British Columbia.

To return to the Old World species, there exists in part of the Himalayan region, and in Assam, Burma, the Malay Peninsula, and Dutch East Indies, a large and very beautifully marked cat known as the Clouded-leopard (*F. nebulosa*). The body markings are in the form of irregular blotches outlined with black, and the ground colour fulvous-grey or buff. The tail is of considerable length, the head elongated, and the canine-teeth of great length ; this species appears to live an entirely arboreal life. Closely allied to the Clouded-leopard is a smaller species known as the Marbled-cat (*F. marmorata*), which inhabits much the same area and is very similar in markings and colour.

CLOUDED-LEOPARD (*Felis nebulosa*).

The Fishing-cat (*F. viverrina*) is a medium-sized, spotted cat from India and Ceylon, the species extending into Lower Burma, Tenasserim, and Assam. It feeds largely upon fish and snails, and lives mostly in marshy localities. One of the commonest among the small spotted-cats of Asia is the Leopard-cat (*F. bengalensis*) ; it is rather smaller than the domesticated cat, and is widely distributed over India, China, and the Malay countries. The Manul-cat (*F. manul*), from Tibet and Mongolia, is another small species, measuring about twenty-one inches in length (head and body), with a ten-inch tail. This short-tailed cat is quite unlike any other wild species, having a very soft, thick coat of a yellowish-grey tint, marked on the hindquarters and tail with some indistinct dark stripes. One of the commonest and most widely distributed species is the Jungle-cat (*F. chaus*), which occurs in North Africa and Central and Southern Asia. This cat is rather larger than the domestic cat, and is distinguished from its relations by the shortness of the tail and uniform tawny coat.

The African Serval (*F. serval*) is a large, spotted species, distinguished by its long legs, small head, large ears, and short tail ; it stands about twenty inches in height and measures about forty inches in length (head and body), with a tail of fifteen inches. The general colour of the coat is tawny-buff, marked with solid spots and streaks of black ; it is found practically all over Africa. The African Wild-cat (*F. ocreata*) and the Wild-cat of Europe (*F. silvestris*) appear to be two closely related species ; the latter is distinguished by its thicker and longer coat, and shorter, more bushy tail. The Wild-cat is now extinct over the greater part of Britain ; it is still to be found in the extreme north of Scotland, however, where it is reported to be increasing in numbers in certain districts ; the Wild-cat has never been an inhabitant of Ireland.

The Bay-cat (*F. temmincki*) of Asia and the Golden-cat (*F. aurata*) of West and Central Africa are two nearly allied forms ; in these cats the body markings are nearly or quite obsolete, and the colour of the coat is either golden-tan or dark greyish-brown. Other uniformly coloured species are the Bornean Bay-cat (*F. badia*) and the Flat-headed cat (*F. planiceps*) from the Malay countries.

WILD-CAT (*Felis silvestris*).

In South America there occur two handsomely marked cats, the Ocelot (*F. pardalis*) and the Margay (*F. tigrina*). The former extends northwards into Mexico, and in the south reaches Paraguay ; the body markings are in the form of elongated blotches, with their centres rather darker than the surrounding tawny-yellow of the ground colour. The Ocelot is, for the most part, arboreal, and measures from three to four feet in total length, the tail being about a root long ; the Margay is considerably smaller, rarely exceeding three feet in total length. Another South American species is the Pampas-cat (*F. pajeros*), an animal about equal in size to the European Wild-cat, but having a still shorter tail. The coat is long and yellowish-grey in colour, the body being marked with pale brown oblique bands ; it is found only in the arid regions of the Argentine and Patagonia.

The Caracal and Lynxes form a group of the *Felidae*, closely allied to the true cats ; some authorities regard them as representing quite distinct genera, but they may conveniently be considered as sub-genera of *Felis*. The Caracal (*F. (Caracal) caracal*) is quite unmistakable, the uniformly coloured upper parts, lynx-like ears, and comparatively long tail distinguish it from all its relations. The coat is a rufous-fawn tint above, paler below, with traces of rufous spots on the belly. In Africa the Caracal is found over nearly the whole continent, while in Asia it ranges through Palestine, Arabia, Syria, and Mesopotamia, down through Persia into India; it is unknown in Ceylon.

Lynxes are characterised by their long legs, black ear-tufts, soft, thick coats, and short tails; further, a kind of ruff is developed around the throat. They are widely distributed, being found throughout the northern forested areas of both the Old and New Worlds. Two species occur in Europe, the Northern-lynx (*F. (Lynx) lynx*), of Sweden, Norway, and Russia, and the Pardine lynx (*F. (L.) pardella*), from the Iberian Peninsula. The former is a

NORTHERN LYNX (*Felis (Lynx) Lynx*).

large animal with a long coat, which is sometimes spotted, sometimes plain. The Pardine-lynx is a smaller animal, and has a shorter, richer-coloured coat, profusely spotted with black. The Asiatic-lynx (*F. (L.) lynx isabellina*) is a close ally of the northern species, and the Canadian-lynx (*F. (L.) lynx canadensis*) may also be regarded as a race of the typical form. The Bay-lynx (*F. (L.) rufa*) is, however, referable to a distinct species; in this lynx the colour is usually uniformly red, but some specimens are spotted.

The second sub-family of the *Felidae* is the *Acinonychinae*, containing the Chita; it is distinguished from the *Felinae*, or cats, by the long legs, slender body, small head, and by the fact that the claws are non-retractile, so that the points of the claws are always exposed. The Chita, or Hunting-leopard, is further remarkable for the development of an incipient mane; three species are recognised: *Acinonyx jubatus* and *A. rex*, from Africa, and *A. venaticus*, from India, Persia, Transcaspia, and Palestine. A full-grown animal will stand as much as three feet at the shoulder and measure seven feet from nose to tip of tail, the latter being about two feet six inches in length.

Family Viverridae

This family contains a number of different genera and species, some, like the Civets, Fossa, and Binturong, being of medium size, while others, such as the Linsangs and lesser mungooses, are small. The members of this group differ from the cats in having longer faces and bodies, shorter limbs, and a larger number of cheek-teeth; the premolars are never fewer than three in number, and, with the exception of the Fossa, two molars are always present on each side of the jaws.

Sub-family *Cryptoproctinae.*—The Fossa (*Cryptoprocta ferox*), of Madagascar, can be regarded as a connecting link between the cats and civets. The claws are cat-like in number and action, and only a single molar-tooth is present on each side of both jaws. The premolars, however, are four in number, and thus the dentition resembles that of the civets more than the cats. It is a medium-sized animal, measuring about five feet in total length, and is a uniform brown in colour.

Sub-family *Viverrinae.*—The true Civets are now regarded as representing two genera : *Civettictis*, the African species, and *Viverra*, the Asiatic civets. In these animals the carnassial, or " flesh-teeth," are more of the dog type. Their bodies are long and the limbs short ; the toes, which are five in number, are furnished with semi-retractile claws. The coat is long and shaggy, and marked with black spots or stripes, the general colour of the fur being grey. They are further characterised by the development of abdominal scent-glands. The African-civet (*C. civetta*) is about fifty inches in total length, the tail occupying some eighteen inches. The Common Indian - civet (*Viverra zibetha*) is about the same size as the African species, but is browner, and the sides of the coat are either uniformly coloured or transversely marked with indistinct dark stripes.

AFRICAN-CIVET (*Civettictis civetta*)

The next group of importance to notice is the genus *Genetta*, which contains a large number of small, spotted animals, with slender bodies and longer tails than are found in the civets. They are mainly African, one species alone reaching South-Western Europe and South-Eastern Asia ; in Africa the number of forms recognised is very large, and they are widely distributed over the continent, from Northern Africa to the Cape. Closely allied to the Genets we have the Linsangs, rather smaller animals than the former with still more slender bodies, and having but a single upper molar on each side of the jaw. The African species are included in the genus *Poiana ;* they are confined to West and Central Africa, and have smaller spots than their Asiatic cousins ; the latter (*Prionodon*) come from the East Indies (*P. gracilis*) and Burma and Tenasserim (*P. maculosus*).

The genets and linsangs are, for the most part, terrestrial animals ; the next group, the Palm-civets, are arboreal in habits. Some of the Palm-civets are Asiatic (*Paradoxurus* and *Paguma*), others are confined to West and Central Africa (*Nandinia*). The former are like civets in colour, being grey with black markings, whereas the African species are more like genets, being brownish-buff with brown markings. The African Palm-civets are rather smaller than the Asiatic forms, and have two light-coloured spots behind the shoulders. The dental formula of these animals is the same as in the true civets, but the teeth are smaller and the carnassials less specialised. The Asiatic species are very widely distributed, being found throughout a large part of Southern Asia and the Indo-Malayan Archipelago, extending eastwards into Southern China and the Philippine Islands.

The Hemigales (*Hemigale*) form a closely allied group, distinguished by their curious colouring, the greyish-brown back being marked with five or six broad, blackish, transverse bands. The typical species hails from the Malay Peninsula, Borneo, and Sumatra. Another curious ally of the palm-civets is the Binturong (*Arctictis binturong*), a large, civet-like animal found in the forests of Assam southwards to the Malay Peninsula, Sumatra, and Java. The length of the body is about thirty inches, and that of the tail some twenty-six inches; the tail is bushy and prehensile, in the latter feature being reminiscent of the tails of some of the American monkeys. The coat is long and coarse and blackish-grey in colour, and the ears bear long tufts of hair. It is entirely arboreal and nocturnal in its habits.

Lastly, there is the Cynogale, or Otter-civet (*Cynogale bennetti*), a semi-aquatic member of this group; it is easily recognisable by the otter-like build, having a blunt muzzle, webbed toes, and a very short and blunt tail. The head and body measure about two feet in length, and the tail another six inches; it is an inhabitant of the Malay Peninsula, Borneo, and Sumatra.

INDIAN-MUNGOOSE (*Herpestes mungo*).

Sub-family *Mungotinae*.—This group contains all the Mungooses, Cusimanses, and Meerkats. In this sub-family the socket of the eye is frequently surrounded by a ring of bone; in the Civets and Palm-civets the orbits are open behind. Further, the bony capsule of the ear (auditory bulla) is very prominent in this group, and the toes are straight and furnished with non-retractile claws. The species extend over a great part of Africa and Asia; one form is found in Europe. The true mungooses (*Herpestes*) are weasel-shaped animals, with long, tapering tails and short legs. The ears are small, and the nose naked and grooved below. The tail is the same colour as the body, and usually black at the tip. One of the largest of these beasts is the Egyptian-mungoose (*H. ichneumon*), measuring some thirty-five inches in total length. Closely allied to this species is the Spanish-mungoose (*H. Widdringtoni*) and *H. caffer* of Africa, south of the Sahara.

There is another African group, the so-called Slender-mungooses (*H. gracilis*), which are considerably smaller than the above-mentioned species, and frequently brilliantly coloured; some forms, from desert countries like Somaliland, are bright yellowish-buff all over, except the tail-tip, which is black. The White-tailed mungoose (*Ichneumia albicauda*) is the largest of the African species, exceeding in size the Egyptian-mungoose ; in this form the colour is blackish-grey, except the tail, which is white. The Indian-mungoose is about thirty inches in total length, the tail being about equal in length to the body ; the general colour is uniformly brownish or grey, there being no black tail-tip ; this species is found in peninsular India and Ceylon. Other forms occur in the Malay countries and eastward to Southern China. The Marsh-mungoose of Africa (*Atilax paludinosus*) is a large, brownish-red coloured animal, which is widely distributed across the equatorial region of the continent.

The Four-toed mungooses (*Bdeogale*), Smooth-nosed mungooses (*Rhyncho-gale*), Striped-cusimanses (*Mungos*), and Unstriped-cusimanses (*Crossarchus*) are allied African genera. The Four-toed mungooses are restricted to West and Central Africa and the Island of Zanzibar. The species from the latter locality is a uniform dark brown, while the mainland form (*B. nigripes*) is creamy-white with black limbs. The Striped-cusimanses, from South and East Africa, have the back washed with buff or tawny and marked with eight or ten dark, transverse bands. The unstriped species (*Crossarchus obscurus*) inhabits West and Central Africa. The Smooth-nosed mungoose (*Rhyncho-gale melleri*) is a large, dull, brown-coloured animal from South-East Africa.

The Bushy-tailed meerkats (*Cynictis*), of South Africa, agree with *Bdeogale* in having four toes ; the coat in these meerkats is bright yellow or buff throughout.

The Meerkats (*Suricata*) also possess only four toes ; they agree with the Smooth-nosed mungoose and Cusimanses in the absence of the groove between the nose and the upper lip. The tail is only about half the length of the head and body, and the hind-part of the back is transversely striped; the species are confined to the Cape, the Orange Free State, and Namaqualand.

In Madagascar there occur some curious mungoose-like animals which may be referred to this group. One of these forms (*Galidictis striata*) has the back marked with dark, longitudinal stripes, and another, *Galidia elegans*, has the tail ringed with black. *Eupleres goudoti* is another remarkable mungoose, having a short tail, uniformly speckled coat, and very feeble jaws and small teeth. From the size and structure of the teeth it is fair to assume that this animal subsists largely upon insects.

Family Proteleidae

This family contains but a single species, the Aard-wolf (*Proteles cristata*), allied on the one hand to the civets and on the other to the hyaenas. In general appearance it resembles a small striped-hyaena, the coat, which is long and woolly, being a pale stone colour, marked with about eight black transverse stripes on the flanks and black bars on the legs. The ears are longer than in the hyaenas and the muzzle more pointed. The tail is thick and bushy, and the animal stands about twenty inches at the shoulder; it has five toes on the front-feet and four on the hind-feet, whereas the hyaenas have four toes on both the fore- and hind-feet. The teeth are quite small and very unlike the massive dentition of the hyaenas. These Aard-wolves are found over a large area of the African continent, extending from Somaliland southwards to South Africa; in the west they reach as far north as Angola.

Family Hyaenidae

This is another Old World family, distinguished by the enormous size of the teeth, especially the canine- and carnassial-teeth. Both the fore- and hind-feet are four-toed and furnished with non-retractile claws, and the tail is shorter than in the Aard-wolf and the general build more massive. Two genera are recognised : *Hyaena*, including the Striped- and Brown-hyaenas, and *Crocuta*, containing a single species, the Spotted-hyaena (*C. crocuta*). The Striped-hyaena (*H. hyaena*) is an inhabitant of peninsular India, and extends westwards through Persia and Mesopotamia into Palestine, Syria, Arabia, and North-East Africa. It resembles the Aard-wolf in possessing a crest of dark hair down the neck and back; the black striping is also rather similar, but heavier. This hyaena is a good deal larger than the Aard-wolf, standing about twenty-nine inches at the shoulder.

The Brown-hyaena (*H. brunnea*), which used to be a very common animal in Africa, is now comparatively rare; it inhabits South-West Africa north as far as Angola, and in the eastern part of the continent reaches the equatorial regions. It stands about twenty-eight inches at the shoulder, and is distinguished by the long mantle of brown hair draping almost the entire body; there is a dirty-yellow marking on the throat, the limbs are barred with black, and the tail is bushy. The Spotted-hyaena is a very different-looking animal to the other members of the group; it is the largest of the hyaenas (shoulder-height, thirty-one inches) and has rounded and smaller ears. There is no crest, or mantle, and the tail is shorter and less bushy. The coat is buffy-brown, marked with burnt-sienna spots; this species is found throughout the greater part of Africa to the south of the Sahara.

Section B.—CYNOIDEA

(Dogs)

The second section of the Carnivora Vera, the Cynoidea, contains the single family of the *Canidae*, or dogs and their allies.

Family Canidae

The members of this family usually have moderately long legs, tails, and muzzles ; the feet are so fashioned that the animals walk on the toes only (digitigrade), and the claws are non-retractile and nearly straight. The teeth are, with few exceptions, forty-two in number ; and there are five toes on the fore-feet and four on the hind-feet, except in the hunting-dog (*Lycaon*), which has four toes on each foot. These animals are widely distributed over both the Old and New Worlds. Most of the *Canidae* are gregarious, and all are terrestrial, their feet not being suitable for tree-climbing. So large a number of different species have been described that it will only be possible to refer here to the most important of them.

Commencing with the wolves, the common European-wolf (*Canis lupus*) is the largest member of the family, and with the other wolves, American Prairie-wolves, Old World Jackals, and domesticated dogs, constitute the genus *Canis*, though some authors regard the wolves as representing a distinct group, which has been named " *Lupus.*" In this genus the teeth are the typical number of forty-two and are arranged as follows : incisors $\frac{3}{3}$, canines $\frac{1}{1}$, premolars $\frac{4}{4}$, and molars $\frac{2}{3}$ on each side ; the teeth are all heavy and large, but the canines are not specially elongated. The tail is usually in the form of a moderate-sized brush, and the pupil of the eye is, in the more typical species, rounded.

Wolves are found over most of the country occupied by the *Canidae ;* they are, however, absent from Africa, the Malay Archipelago, and South America, and have long been extinct in the British Isles, Holland, and Denmark. The teeth of the wolf are relatively larger than in any other breed of dog, domestic or otherwise. The wolves of Northern Europe are usually paler in colour than those of the southern part of the continent ; they stand about two feet four inches at the shoulder and measure about five feet in total length, the tail occupying from fifteen to sixteen inches. The Common-wolf is widely distributed, extending across Europe and a large part of Asia, where the coat gradually becomes more woolly in texture and paler in colour ; this latter form is known as the Tibetan race (*C. lupus laniger*). The wolf of America may also be regarded as a geographical race of the European animal. The Indian-wolf (*C. pallipes*) is a rather smaller and browner-coloured beast, and, unlike the common species, does not collect in large packs.

The Prairie-wolf, or Coyote (*C. latrans*), of North America, is distinguished by its smaller size, more hairy coat, and much more bushy tail ; it ranges from Central America to Hudson Bay. A somewhat similar animal is found far away in the distant Falkland Islands ; it has been named the Antarctic-wolf (*C. antarcticus*). This wolf is rather smaller than the coyote and less hairy ; the tail is black in the middle and has a white tip.

The Jackals are all smaller than the wolf, and, as a rule, more richly coloured. One of the largest of the group is the Abyssinian-wolf, or Cuberow (*C. simensis*), an animal intermediate between the wolves and jackals. The colour of the coat is bright foxy-red, with white under parts, and the tail black-tipped. The Indian-jackal (*C. indicus*, or *aureus*) and its relatives are distinguished from the wolves by their smaller size and teeth ; the Indian species measures about thirty inches from the nose to the root of the tail. In colour it varies considerably, sometimes being pale yellowish, sometimes brown or greyish. It is found over the greater part of India and Ceylon, and spreads westwards into South-Eastern Europe and North-Eastern Africa ; a number of local races have been described.

Several other species are found in Africa, the most noteworthy being the Egyptian-jackal (*C. lupaster*), a large, pale, red-coloured form, found in Northern Africa, and the Black-backed jackal (*C. mesomelas*), distributed over the greater part of the continent south of the Sahara ; this jackal is very handsomely coloured, the sides of the body and limbs being red, and the back black, speckled with silver-grey. Another African species is the Side-striped jackal (*C. adustus*), which usually has an oblique, light-coloured stripe on the flanks. A small desert form is found in Somaliland (*C. mengesi*) ; in this species the coat is pale sandy in colour.

CHINESE FOX (*Vulpes hoole*).

The Australian Dingo is probably a descendant of some of the wild dogs of Asia, introduced into Australia by human agency. Of the true wild dogs the best known is the Indian species, the Dhole (*Cuon dukhunensis*). All the wild dogs lack the last molar-tooth of the lower jaw, a difference that is considered to be of generic value. Other species occur in the Malay Peninsula and East Indies (*C. rutilans*), and in Java (*C. javanicus*). The Racoon-dog (*Nyctereutes procyonoides*) is a Far-Eastern species, an animal with short legs and tail, rounded ears, and a very long coat.

The vulpine series, or foxes, represented by four or five genera, have less massive teeth than the canine branch, and the canines are proportionately longer. The Arctic-foxes (*Alopex*) appear to be a connecting link between the two groups ; they are found in the Arctic regions of the Old and New Worlds, and are distinguished from the true foxes by their short, rounded ears. In summer the coat is brownish-drab, in winter entirely white.

The true foxes (*Vulpes*) are distributed over most of the northern part of the northern hemisphere, extending southwards to Mexico, Morocco, and India. They are mostly solitary animals, not gregarious like the dogs. In colour they vary from buff to grey, the Chinese fox (*V. hoole*) being pale buff in colour. Closely allied to the foxes are the Fennecs of North-East Africa and Arabia (*Fennecus zerda*), small, fox-like creatures, with very large ears and very pale, sandy-coloured coats. Another large-eared species is the Great-eared fox of South and East Africa (*Otocyon megalotis*), a larger and darker animal than the Fennec, remarkable for having four lower and three or four upper molar-teeth on each side.

Lastly, the Cape Hunting-dog (*Lycaon pictus*) is distinguished from all the rest of the family by possessing only four toes to each foot, and in the curious, irregularly blotched coat, the blotches being of buff, or orange, white, and black. These dogs, which are found over the greater part of Africa south of the Sahara, are gregarious and terribly destructive.

Section C.—*Arctoidea*

(*Bears, Racoons, Skunks, etc.*)

The third section of the Carnivora Vera, the Arctoidea, contains the bears (*Ursidae*), the pandas and racoons (*Procyonidae*), and the weasels, skunks, badgers, and otters (*Mustelidae*). All the members of this section agree in having five completely developed toes on each foot, and in the absence of a caecum, or blind-gut.

Family Ursidae

The bear-family is characterised by having two upper and three lower molars on each side; the crowns of these teeth are longer than they are broad. Of the four premolars in each side of both jaws the front three are often reduced to mere vestiges, and may fall out. The tail is very short, and the toes are armed with long, non-retractile claws. These animals are " plantigrade "—that is to say, the sole of the foot is applied to the ground, and not raised above it as in the dogs. The Polar-bear (*Thalarctos maritimus*), of the Arctic regions, is the most distinct of the *Ursidae*, being remarkable in that the coat is white at all times

POLAR-BEAR (*Thalarctos maritimus*).

of the year, the head and neck longer than in the other species, and the molar-teeth very small and narrow.

The Typical- or Ursine-bears (*Ursus*) include a number of different species widely distributed over the northern hemisphere, extending southwards as far as Mexico in the New World, and the Atlas Mountains and Himalayas in the Old World. The Brown-bear (*U. arctos*) was formerly an inhabitant of Great Britain, being exterminated about the eleventh century ; it is found in the larger forests of Europe, and ranges east into Asia as far as Japan (*U. arctos yesoensis*). Although, perhaps, inferior in size to the Grizzly-bear, the brown species is a very powerful animal, measuring some seven to eight feet in length and standing three feet or more at the shoulder. The Alaskan-bear (*U. a. dalli*) and Kodiak-bear (*U. a. middendorffi*) may be

BROWN-BEAR (*Ursus arctos*).

considered as geographical races of the Brown-bear.

The Grizzly-bear (*U. horribilis*), of North America, is a very close ally of the European species ; as a rule, it is rather larger, greyer in colour, and the coat is shorter. The American Black-bear is distinguished from the above species by its smaller size, much shorter hind-foot, and black coat ; these bears rarely exceed five feet in length. The Himalayan Black-bear (*Selenarctos thibetanus*) is about the same size as the American species ; it is distinguished by the white chevron-like marking on the chest. The Japanese and Formosan Black-bears are closely related species (*S. japonicus* and *S. formosanus*), while other allied forms inhabit China. The Malay-bear, or Bruan, represents yet another genus, *Helarctos ;* it is very like the Himalayan species, but smaller, and with a shorter coat.

Lastly, we have the Sloth-bear, or Aswal (*Melursus ursinus*), found only in peninsular India and Ceylon, and distinguished from all the other bears by its longer tail (four to five inches), mobile snout, coarse shaggy coat, long extensile tongue, and very powerful claws. The cheek-teeth are of quite small dimensions, and the upper incisors reduced to two pairs. The coat is black, with a white patch on the chest ; the nose and claws are also white.

Family Procyonidae

The pandas, racoons, cacomistles, coatis, and kinkajou form the Family *Procyonidae*, all the members of which, except the Great-panda, have two molar-teeth on each side of both jaws ; the latter animal has the same number of molars as in the bears, $\frac{2}{3}$. The tail is usually long and ringed. The range includes America and a part of the Oriental region.

The Great-panda (*Ailuropoda melanoleuca*) is remarkable for its bear-like form, short tail, and black-and-white coat, the general colour being white, while the ears, rings around the eyes, limbs, and a transverse bar from the shoulders to the fore-limbs, are black. Formerly classified as a bear, the Great-panda measures about six feet in length. It is confined to the mountains of Tibet and Sze-chuan. The Panda (*Ailurus fulgens*), from the South-East Himalayas, is about equal to a cat in size, and has a rounded head, with large ears and a long tail. The coat is thick and bright red in colour above, and the under parts are blackish-brown. The face is white, except for a red-coloured eye-stripe, and the tail ringed. The claws of this beast are partially retractile.

The Racoons (*Procyon*) are exclusively American, and differ from the pandas in having a sharply pointed muzzle, small ears, and non-retractile claws. The Common-racoon (*P. lotor*) is about three feet in total length, the tail measuring about ten inches. It is brownish-grey in colour, and has black face-markings and bars on the tail. The Cacomistles (*Bassaris*) are further American species, inhabiting the United States southwards to Central America. The ears are large and the claws partially retractile; in size they are about equal to a cat, and are brownish in colour.

The Coatis (*Nasua*) are at once distinguished by their very long muzzles; the tail is frequently barred, and the colour of the coat varies from rufous to grey. These animals are found in South America, extending northwards into Mexico.

The last member of the family is the Kinkajou (*Cercoleptes caudivolvulus*), remarkable for having a prehensile tail. The tail is as long as the head and body, the muzzle short, and, owing to the loss of a pair of premolars in each jaw, there are only thirty-six teeth. The coat, which is soft and short, is uniformly yellowish-brown in colour. The range extends from the northern part of South America into Mexico.

Family Mustelidae

In this family most of the animals have long bodies and very short limbs; the molar-teeth are reduced to a single pair in the upper jaw and usually two pairs in the lower jaw; in one genus (*Mellivora*), however, there is only a single pair of lower molars. Three sub-families may be distinguished: *Lutrinae*, the otters; *Melinae*, skunks and badgers; and *Mustelinae*, the stoats, weasels, and allied forms. The otters are characterised by their short, rounded feet (except the hind-feet of the sea-otter), webbed toes with blunt claws, and broad, flattened heads. The coat is soft, short, and thick, and is of a uniform brownish-tint above, greyer below; the upper molars are large and square-shaped. All the species are aquatic, and are widely

2 F

distributed in both the New and Old Worlds.   The European-otter (*Lutra vulgaris*) is a medium-sized species, measuring some forty-five inches in total length ; it is found throughout the rivers of Europe, and extends far into Asia.   The North American-otter (*L. canadensis*) is a very closely allied form, as are the species described from India and the Malay countries.

The largest species of otter is the Brazilian-otter (*L. brasiliensis*), which is over five feet in total length.   The African and Asiatic otters, with rudimentary claws, are placed in the genus *Aonyx*.   The Sea-otter (*Latax lutris*) is a heavily built, short-tailed species, measuring a little more than four feet in total length ; the hind-feet are very large, more like seals' " flippers " than the feet of a true carnivore.   The incisor-teeth are reduced to only two pairs in the lower jaw, and the cheek-teeth have smooth and rounded crowns.   The sea-living otter is found only on the coasts of the North Pacific, from Oregon to Alaska on the American side, and on the Asiatic side it occurs along the Kamchatkan coastline.

In the sub-family *Melinae* the feet are elongated, the claws non-retractile, and the members of the group terrestrial and fossorial in habits.   The Skunks (*Mephitis, Conepatus,* and *Spilogale*) are found only in America, ranging from Hudson Bay southwards through Central America into

BRAZILIAN-OTTER (*Lutra brasiliensis*).

South America, as far south as Patagonia.   They are remarkable for their bushy tails, soft coats, black and white coloration, and for the nauseous secretion which these animals can eject from a pair of caudal glands ; an infuriated skunk can squirt this evil-smelling fluid for a distance of four or five yards.

In Africa we meet with a somewhat similar group of animals known as the Striped-muishonds ; these skunk-like beasts are found over a great part of the continent to the south of the Sahara.   The South African form is named *Ictonyx capensis ;* it is black below and white above, with three broad, irregular, black lines on the back and a whitish tail.   In North Africa there are two smaller and less hairy species, representing the genus *Poecilictis.*

The remaining members of the sub-family are less slender of body and more massively built.   The Ferret-badgers (*Helictis*) have longer tails and longer bodies than the true badgers, and possibly form a connecting link between the skunks and badgers.   These animals inhabit the country from Nepal to China, southwards to Java.   The Ratels (*Mellivora*), represented by two species, one Indian and one African, are heavily built, short-legged, and short-tailed animals; they have black faces, limbs, flanks, and under parts, and silvery-grey backs. In size they equal a large badger, and are strictly nocturnal, sleeping during the day in earths. The American-badger (*Taxidea americanus*) and the European-badger (*Meles meles*) are both very like the ratels in general build; they may be distinguished by possessing thirty-eight teeth instead of the thirty-two which the ratels have. The American-badger has a proportionately larger upper carnassial-tooth than the European species, and the upper molar is smaller and triangular in shape; in the Common-badger the upper molars are very large and oblong in shape.

There remain two further kinds of badger, the Malayan-badger (*Mydaus meliceps*) and the Sand-badgers (*Arctonyx*). The former is only about fifteen inches in length, with a very short tail; it is dark brown in colour, with a median, dorsal white stripe. The Sand-badgers come from Northern India, Assam, and Burma; they are easily recognised by their longer tails; the head and body measuring about thirty inches, while the tail is nearly a foot in length.

EUROPEAN-BADGER (*Meles meles*).

The sub-family *Mustelinae*, or weasel group, is, with the exception of the wolverine, remarkable for the long, weasel-like bodies, short, partially webbed toes, sometimes armed with semi-retractile claws, and the transversely expanded upper molars. The range of the group is very extensive, embracing a large part of both the Old and New Worlds.

The Grison (*Galictis vittata*) and Tayra (*Tayra barbara*), two South American mustelines, have non-retractile claws; the latter is as large as an otter and dark brown in colour; and the Grison, which is about the size of a large ferret, has a shorter tail and is coloured rather like the ratels. The Martens (*Martes*) are comparatively large animals, being about equal in size to a medium-sized cat (thirty inches in total length). The fur is extremely soft, and in some forms, such as the Russian and Canadian " sable," of great value in the fur-market. The British representative is the Pine-marten (*M. martes*), now a rare animal in most parts of Britain. The martens are distributed over North America, Europe, and a large part of Asia. The polecats, stoats, and weasels form the typical genus *Mustela*. Of these, the Polecat (*Mustela putorius*) is the largest, and the Weasel (*M. nivalis*) the smallest. The polecats are smaller than the martens, and have proportionately shorter tails. In general colour these animals are dark olive-brown mixed with black, the head, feet, and under parts being blackish, and the ears and face-markings white or light brown. The Ferret is a domesticated variety of the polecat. Polecats range throughout Europe, Asia, and America.

Closely allied to the polecats are the Minks; one species (*M. lutreola*) is found in Europe, and another (*M. vison*) is confined to North America. The Stoat (*M. erminea*) and Irish-stoat (*M. hibernica*) are distinguished from the weasel by the tail being longer and having a black tip. Both the Common-stoat and the Weasel turn white in winter. These two species range throughout the greater part of Europe and Asia ; the latter form is also found in most of the Mediterranean Islands.

Finally, in the Glutton, or Wolverine (*Gulo gulo*), of the forest areas of Northern Europe, Asia, and America, we have a musteline dentition that suggests that of the hyaenas. This animal resembles a small bear in appearance, large specimens measuring three feet in length from the nose to the root of the tail, which, with the long, terminal hairs, is over a foot in length. The coat of the Wolverine is much used by the furrier.

Sub-order PINNIPEDIA

(Seals)

In this sub-order, which includes the eared-seals, walruses, and seals, the limbs are modified for an aquatic life, the feet having become transformed into " flippers," and the tail is very short. The incisor-teeth are never as numerous as in the typical Carnivora Vera ($\frac{3}{2}$, $\frac{2}{2}$, or $\frac{2}{1}$, never $\frac{3}{3}$), and the cheek-teeth are uniform, there being no carnassial-teeth differentiated. The members of this group are all marine, some of them occasionally entering rivers. Three families can be distinguished : the *Otariidae*, or eared-seals ; the *Odobaenidae*, or walruses ; and the *Phocidae*, or true seals, sea-leopards, and elephant-seals.

Family Otariidae

The members of this group are distinguished from all the other seals by the presence of small external ears, and from the true seals by the fact that the hind-feet, when the animals are on land, turn forwards, not backwards as in the seals. Further, a distinct neck is observable, and there are three pairs of incisors in the upper jaw and two pairs below, there being thirty-four or thirty-six teeth altogether. These Eared-seals, or Sea-lions, may be regarded as something approaching a connecting link between the terrestrial carnivores and the typical Pinnipedia. The males are very much larger than the females, and all the species are gregarious.

The southern Sea-lion (*Otaria jubata*), from the Falkland Islands and Patagonia, differs from the other species in having a kind of mane ; it is smaller than the northern form, measuring some seven feet in length, whereas Steller's Sea-lion is sometimes twelve feet in length. The latter (*Arctocephalus stelleri*), from the North Pacific, is the largest of the sea-lions. *A. ursinus* is an allied form ; it is the common Sea-bear, or Fur-seal, of the North Pacific, the skins of which are used very extensively by furriers. Around the shores of South Africa we meet with another form, *A. pusillus*, and in Australian waters *A. forsteri* is found. The Californian Sea-lion *A. gillespii* is the species most commonly kept in captivity.

Family Odobaenidae

This family contains two species only, the Pacific (*Odobaenus obesus*) and Atlantic (*O. rosmarus*)

CALIFORNIAN SEA-LION (*Arctocephalus gillespii*).

Walruses ; they may be regarded as intermediate between the eared-seals and the true seals. There are no external ears, and the hind-feet turn forwards when on land, though not to the same degree as in the eared-seals. Two pairs of incisors are present in both jaws, and the upper-canines are in the form of long and massive tusks ; in the record specimen these tusks have a total length of thirty-seven and a quarter inches. All the other teeth are small and simple of structure, the molars being

ATLANTIC WALRUS (*Odobaenus rosmarus*).

flat-crowned. The tail is rudimentary and the coat short. One of the most striking features of these animals is the enormous size and thickness of the vibrissae, or " whiskers." Walruses are gregarious, and, as a general rule, are not found far away from land; they subsist chiefly on bivalve molluscs.

Family Phocidae

The true seals are divided into a number of genera, all of which agree in the absence of external ears, and the hind-limbs, when the animals are on land, are extended out behind the body. Further, the soles of the fore- and hind-feet are hairy; in the eared-seals and walruses the soles are naked. The upper incisors are $\frac{3}{2}$, $\frac{2}{2}$, or $\frac{2}{1}$; they have simple crowns, not grooved as are the first two upper teeth of the *Otariidae*. The coat is harsh, without the woolly under-fur of the eared-seals. In *Halichaerus*, the Grey-seal (*H. grypus*), and the typical seals (*Phoca*), the incisor-teeth number three pairs in the upper jaw and two pairs in the lower jaw. In the former the crowns of the cheek-teeth are simple, and, with the exception of the last one or two

COMMON-SEAL (*Phoca vitulina*).

in the upper jaw and the last lower tooth, all are single-rooted. In *Phoca* the molar-crowns are more pointed, and, excepting the first in each jaw, the teeth are all two-rooted.

The species are widely spread throughout the northern seas; they include the Common-seal (*P. vitulina*), the Bearded-seal (*P. barbata*), Ringed-seal of the North Atlantic (*P. hispida*), the Greenland-seal (*P. groenlandica*), and the Lake Baikal-seal (*P. siberica*) from Siberia. The Common-seal is found in European waters, around the Atlantic coast of America, and also in the North Pacific. The Grey-seal, the larger of the two British species (length about eight feet as against four to five feet in the Common-seal), appears to be restricted to the North Atlantic.

The Monk-seal (*Monachus albiventer*) and its allies form the sub-family *Monachinae*, in which there are two pairs of upper and lower incisors. The first and fifth toes of the hind-feet are much longer than the other toes; in the *Phocinae* the toes are about equal. All these seals, excepting the Monk-seal, are found in the southern hemisphere; the various genera include *Monachus*, the Monk-seal, from the Mediterranean and adjacent parts of the Atlantic Ocean; *Ogmorhinus*, the Sea-leopard (*O. leptonyx*); *Lobodon*, the Crab-eating seal (*L. carcinophagus*); *Leptonychotes*, Weddell's-seal (*L. weddelli*); and *Ommatophoca*, the Ross-seal (*O. rossi*).

Lastly, the sub-family *Cystophorinae*, containing the Bladder-nose or Hooded-seal (*Cystophora cristata*) from the Polar regions, and the Sea-elephants, or Elephant-seals (*Mirounga*), from Californian and southern waters. In this group the incisors number two pairs above and one pair below. The first and fifth toes of the hind-feet are very long, and the males have an inflatable nasal-organ. In the Bladder-nose seal the last molar usually has two roots; in the Elephant-seals they are all one-rooted. The nasal appendage in the Bladder-nose seal forms a kind of hood over the head when it is inflated; in the Elephant-seal it is more like a trunk.

The Northern Elephant-seal (*M. leonina*) was, at one time, common on the shores of the island of Juan Fernandez and Lower California, a herd inhabiting the waters of Guadalupe Island. It is rather a smaller beast than the southern form (*M. patagonica*), bulls of which

NORTHERN ELEPHANT-SEAL (*Mirounga leonina*).

measure as much as twenty-one feet in length, and has a longer and more slender proboscis. The Southern Elephant-seal was formerly found around the shores of Patagonia, the Macquarie Islands, Kerguelen, Marion, Heard, Tristan-da-Cunha, Falklands, South Georgia, South Shetlands, and the Inaccessible Islands. It has, however, in common with the northern species, been exterminated in many of its former homes; this species has been reported from the Cape, and it occasionally visits the Antarctic pack-ice. A number of sub-species have been described.

CHAPTER VI

Order INSECTIVORA

(*Insectivores*)

THE members of this order are for the most part small-sized animals, with long snouts and numerous small, sharp-pointed teeth. The body is usually covered with a soft coat of fur, but there are sometimes spines mixed with the hair, while in other cases the spines are so developed as to form a protective armour. The toes are all furnished with claws, and the thumb and great toe are not opposable to the other digits. Internal characters include the almost universal presence of collar-bones (absent in the otter-shrew, or potamogale, of Africa), and the lobes of the brain are smooth, not thrown into folds.

These animals are apparently most nearly allied to the bats and lemurs. They are widely distributed over both the Old and northern half of the New World. No insectivores are found in Australia, and only a few species of shrews extend into South America (*Blarina micrura, thomasi,* and *equatoris*).

The order may be divided into two groups, or sub-orders, the Dermoptera, containing the flying-cobegos, or colugos (*Galeopithecus* and *Galeopterus*), and the Insectivora Vera, containing all the other members of the order— that is, the typical insectivores.

Sub-order *Dermoptera*

(*Cobegos*)

The Cobegos are included in the family *Galeopithecidae*, and differ from all

COBEGO, or "FLYING-LEMUR" (*Galeopterus variegatus*).

true insectivores in feeding upon leaves and in possessing a flying- or gliding-membrane connecting the limbs and tail, reminiscent of the flying-membrane of the flying-squirrels and scaly-tails; in these flying rodents, however, the parachute-like membrane does not extend backwards to include the tail. The fingers and toes are webbed as far as the claws, which are curved and very sharp; these sickle-like claws doubtless assist the animals to catch hold of the boughs and tree-trunks at the termination of their flight, or glide. A Cobego has been known to glide a distance of seventy yards from one tree to another; when gliding through the air, the limbs and tail are stretched out so that the parachute-like membrane is fully extended.

These animals are clothed in short and very soft fur, and coloured to look as much like the bark of a tree as possible, so that when resting against a tree-trunk they are very difficult to make out.

As might be expected from their diet, the teeth are very different from those found in the insect-eating insectivora, the lower front teeth being quite unique in the whole Animal Kingdom, resembling small combs more than teeth. These animals are found over the greater part of the Malay Peninsula and Islands, extending from Tenasserim and Siam to Borneo, Sumatra, and Java. One species occurs in the Philippine Islands, *Galeopithecus philippinensis ;* the Cobegos of the Malay Countries belong to the genus *Galeopterus,* of which *G. temmincki,* from Sumatra, *G. peninsulae,* from the Malay Peninsula, and *G. variegatus,* from Java, are the most distinct species.

Sub-order *Insectivora Vera*

(Shrews, Moles, Tenrecs, etc.)

The true Insectivora (Insectivora Vera) have been divided into nine families, two of which (*Tupaiidae,* tree-shrews, and *Macroscelididae,* jumping-shrews), are distinguished by the fact that the two halves of the pelvis are fully united, and the eye-socket, or orbit, is differentiated from the hinder-part of the skull, either by a ring of bone (*Tupaiidae*) or by a bony process (post-orbital process) in the jumping-shrews. The tree-shrews are further characterised by the larger size of the brain-case and the normal development of the ankle region (tarsus).

Family Tupaiidae

The typical Tree-shrews (*Tupaia*) very closely resemble squirrels, from which they are distinguished externally by the possession of a light-coloured stripe on the shoulder and by having the snout sharply pointed.

In general size the Tree-shrews are mostly rather smaller than squirrels, and have long, bushy tails. The species, which are very numerous, are found in Borneo, Siam, China, and the Malay Peninsula and Islands ; some of them are very brightly coloured, *T. ferruginea,* from the Malay Peninsula, being chestnut-red, and the Painted tree-shrew, *T. pictus,* from Borneo, is a mixture of chestnut and olive above, with a black stripe down the middle of the back. In the Natuna Islands there occurs a brilliant burnt-sienna coloured form, *T. lucida ;* the majority of the species, such as the Pigmy Javan tree-shrew, are olive-brown or greenish in colour, speckled with buff.

In India and Borneo there is found a closely allied group of this family, the genus *Anathana,* and a somewhat similar tree-shrew, *Urogale cylindura,* hails from the Philippine Islands ; the latter species is a small, olive-brown animal, with the shoulder stripes only faintly developed. A further group of these animals, from Borneo and Sumatra, is included in the genus *Tana,* some of which are very handsomely coloured, one species being olive-brown in the front part of the body, with chestnut-red limbs, back, and tail, and bright orange under parts.   The smallest of the tree-shrews are placed in the genus *Dendrogale ;* in size these shrews are about equal to a small rat, and the tail is less bushy than in the allied genera.   These pigmy tree-shrews inhabit Siam, Annam, Cochin China, and Borneo.

Lastly, the Pen-tailed shrew (*Ptilocercus lowi*) may be included in this family ; the tail in this animal is very long, and bears a feather-like fringe on its terminal portion.   In colour it is greyish-brown above and yellowish below.   It hails from the islands of Borneo and Sumatra, and parts of the Malay Archipelago.

Family Macroscelididae

The second family of the first group of the Insectivora Vera, the *Macroscelididae,* in addition to the orbital character mentioned above, differs from the tree-shrews in having the ankle region (tarsus) of the foot greatly elongated.   These Jumping-shrews leap like jerboas, and move about more on their toes than on the soles of their feet.   Seven genera are now recognised, of which the typical genus, *Macroscelides,* containing two South African species, is distinguished from the nearly allied genus *Elephantulus* (North, East, and South Africa) by the bony capsule of the ear (auditory bulla) being much enlarged, and the colour of the coat being greyer ; in *Elephantulus* the coat is usually yellowish or buff-coloured.   The Short-nosed Jumping-shrews (*Nasilio*) differ from both the foregoing genera in possessing three lower molar-teeth ; in *Macroscelides* and *Elephantulus* there are only two lower molars.   The members of this genus extend all over South Africa, on the eastern side of the continent reaching as far north as Kenya Colony.

LONG-NOSED ELEPHANT-SHREW (*Rhynchocyon petersi*).

The next genus, *Petrodromus,* is distinguished from the three groups just dealt with in having four, instead of five, toes on each front foot ; in size they are considerably larger, being as big as a rat, and instead of being greyish or buff-coloured they present a mixture of olive-green and rufous. These shrews inhabit South Africa northwards to the Congo.   Two closely allied genera, *Mesoctenus* and *Cercoctenus,* from East Africa, are very similar, except that the lower surface of the tail is furnished with a number of club-headed hairs.

The largest members of the family are the Long-nosed Elephant-shrews (*Rhynchocyon*) (total length, fifteen inches), which have only four toes to each foot; the snout is much longer, and the ankle-joint still more elongated. The species, which are confined to Central and East Africa and Zanzibar Island, are frequently very brightly coloured, some being chestnut-and-black (*R. petersi*), others having a sort of chessboard pattern on the back (*R. cirnei*). One species, *R. chrysopygus*, from East Africa, has the body and limbs deep chestnut-red, and the hindquarters orange-buff in colour.

The second group of the Insectivora Vera, in which the two halves of the pelvis are either not united or only partly so, and the orbital region of the skull is not differentiated from the hinder part, contains seven different families.

Family Talpidae

The first of these, the *Talpidae*, or Moles and Mole-shrews, are characterised by the bony capsule of the ear (auditory bulla) being bladder-like, the cheek-arch (zygoma) complete, and the lower front teeth vertical. Most of the species have become profoundly modified for a subterranean life, the eyes being small and sometimes functionless, the ears short, and the fore-limbs transformed for digging. The distributional range of the family comprises a large part of the temperate regions of the Old and New World.

The *Talpinae*, or true moles, have the upper bone of the arm and collar-bone very short and massive, while the conspicuously broad fore-foot is made still broader by an additional sickle-like bone developed on its inner side. The Common-mole (*Talpa europea*) is widely distributed over Europe and Asia; different species are found in Spain, Italy, and Switzerland. The Asiatic

RUSSIAN DESMAN (*Desmana moschata*).

genera, *Parascaptor*, *Scaptochirus*, and *Mogera*, are closely allied to the typical genus; *Mogera* extends as far east as Japan. In North America we meet with a number of different types of mole; one genus, *Scalops*, having webbed toes, being adapted for an aquatic mode of life. The Star-nosed mole (*Condylura cristata*) is the best-known of these New World moles, its popular name having reference to a number of fleshy appendages around the tip of the snout; the tail in this mole is considerably longer than in the Common-mole and the general colour browner (head and body, four inches; tail, four and a half inches).

The *Desmaninae*, the second sub-family of the *Talpidae*, contains the Mole-shrews, the Water-mole, or Western Desman, and the Russian Desman. The mole-shrews, as their name implies, are intermediate between moles and shrews, the fore-feet never being so modified for digging as in the true moles. The mole-shrews of Japan belong to a species known as *Urotrichus talpoides*, small shrew-like animals with very hairy tails, and having the fore-feet but slightly enlarged. Another Japanese species is named *Dymecodon pilirostris*, in which the tail is longer and less hairy. A Chinese species, *Uropsilus soricipes*, is a long-nosed form with a long, short-haired tail. *Nasillus* and *Rhynchonax* are closely allied Chinese genera.

The Water-mole, or Western Desman (*Galemys*), is a much larger animal than the mole-shrews (head and body, five inches ; tail, five inches), and adapted for an aquatic life. The feet are webbed, the tail long and flattened, and the fur long and soft. The snout is of considerable length, and the general colour brownish-grey above but greyish-buff below. These water-moles are found only in South-Western France and the Iberian Peninsula. The last genus of this group is *Desmana*, which includes but a single species, *Desmana moschata*, the Russian Desman, an animal very like a large edition of the Water-mole, measuring about sixteen inches in length; it is an inhabitant of South-East Russia and entirely aquatic in its habits.

Family Soricidae

The next family, the *Soricidae*, or shrews, includes a very large number of genera and species widely distributed over both the Old and the New World. The members of this group are distinguished from the *Talpidae* by having the auditory region of the skull flat and ring-like in shape ; the cheek- or zygomatic-arch incomplete, and the first lower incisor-teeth set horizontally. The typical genus *Sorex* extends over a large area of Europe and North America and the temperate regions of Asia. The teeth in this and the allied genera are tipped with a red-brown stain, the ears well developed, and the tail evenly haired. The Common Shrew-mouse of Europe, *Sorex araneus*, extends from England eastward into Asia ; in common with so many other British mammals it is not found in Ireland. The Pigmy-shrew (*S. minutus*) is very similar to the Common-shrew, but smaller, the head and body measuring only about fifty-two millimetres in length as against sixty-five to eighty millimetres in *S. araneus ;* this small shrew ranges from Ireland eastwards into temperate Asia. In addition to the Common- and Pigmy-shrews, about fifteen others occur in Europe, and numerous members of the genus are found in Asia and North America.

The name *Soriculus* has been given to a closely allied genus in which the tail is sometimes very long, sometimes comparatively short ; the longest-tailed species is the Chinese *S. irene*, in which the tail measures nearly ninety millimetres. *S. nigrescens*, from India, has a much shorter tail (forty milli-metres). Still shorter tails are met with in some of the American shrews ; *Notiosorex crawfordi*, from New Mexico, a pale, ash-grey-coloured species, has a tail of only about twenty-six millimetres in length, and in *Blarina*, a genus which extends southwards into Central and South America, the tail is equally short.   In Western China there occurs the closely allied *Blarinella*, in which the tail is a trifle longer (thirty-three to forty-eight millimetres).

The Water-shrews of Europe (*Neomys*) are very distinct, the fur being very soft and mole-like in colour, and the feet and tail fringed with white hairs.   These shrews live, for the most part, in the water ; they extend from England eastward through Europe to Asia Minor.

The second group of Shrews, those with *white* teeth, are distributed throughout a great part of Europe, Asia, and Africa.   In the African genus *Sylvisorex* the tail is evenly haired, and in some forms is much longer than the body ; in other species it is about equal in length to the body. Another white-toothed African genus is *Surdisorex ;* in *S. norae* the tail is very short (less than a quarter of the body dimensions), and the fore-feet large and rather mole-like ; this species is an inhabitant of Kenya Colony. In the genus *Crocidura* the tail is clothed in two distinct types of hair, the normal, short caudal-hairs and a number of long, bristle-like hairs.   Some members of this genus are the size of a small rat, others are extremely minute, one species, *C. pasha*, from the Sudan, being amongst the smallest of the whole mammalia (head and body, fifty millimetres).   This genus is very widely distributed, being found over nearly the whole of Africa and a large part of Europe and Asia.   A species has recently been described from the Scilly Isles.   The Crocidurine shrews, with a second upper-premolar, are grouped together in the genus *Pachyura ;* these shrews occur in the Mediterranean region, Africa, and Asia.

In Sze-chuan and Tibet we meet with a very short-tailed shrew, *Anourosorex squamipes*, the body measuring about eighty millimetres and the tail only about fifteen millimetres in length.   There remain two genera of Water-shrews, *Chimarrogale*, from Northern India, and *Nectogale*, from China, Tibet, and Sikkim, in both of which the tail bears a well-developed fringe on the lower surface.

Family Erinaceidae

The next family, the *Erinaceidae*, includes the hedgehogs and gymnuras, or rat-shrews ; it differs from the *Soricidae* in having a complete zygomatic arch ; this cheek-arch is much more solidly built than in the moles.   The existing members of the family are found only in the Old World.   The hedgehogs, or *Erinaceinae*, are characterised by their spiny coats and short, stumpy tails ; the pelvis is very broad, and the long palate is perforated in much the same manner as occurs among the marsupials, or pouched-mammals, of Australia.   Five genera of hedgehogs are now recognised, in four of which a median parting is developed among the spines on the crown of the head.   Of these, *Erinaceus*, the typical genus, has the coronal parting narrow and inconspicuous.

About a dozen different forms of *Erinaceus* are now known, ranging over a considerable part of Europe and Asia eastwards as far as China. The common European hedgehog (*E. europaeus*) is a member of this genus ; it is found over a large part of Western Europe, from the Mediterranean coast northwards to Scotland and Southern Scandinavia ; and westward it reaches Ireland. Geographical races have been named from Spain, Italy, and Sicily, and the hedgehogs of Roumania and the Island of Crete are considered to represent distinct species. The Common-hedgehog has the fur on the under surface of the body yellowish-white in colour ; in the Roumanian species (*E. roumanicus*) the colour of the furred parts is usually much darker and the chest is frequently white. The hedgehog hibernates during the winter months ; it is mainly a nocturnal animal, coming out from its hiding-place as dusk falls and feeding on a variety of insects, slugs, and worms. It will eat eggs, snakes, frogs, and other small animals, and also has a great liking for cockroaches.

The closely allied genus *Aethechinus*, from Africa and Southern Europe, has a wider parting on the head, and some of the species are smaller and darker than the common hedgehog. Another genus of this group which occurs in Northern and East Africa is *Atelerix*, which contains a number of small, light-coloured or brown species, in which

WHITE RAT-SHREW, or GYMNURA (*Gymnura rafflesii*).

the great toes are absent. In the genus *Hemiechinus* the coronal-parting is not developed ; the Long-eared hedgehog of India (*H. megalotis*) belongs to this group, it being a large species with big ears.

The second sub-family, the *Gymnurinae*, contains the rat-shrews, distinguished from the hedgehogs by the coat being hairy, not spiny, the palate being complete, not perforated, and, in the typical genus, the tail long and rat-like. The largest members of the group are the Gymnuras of the genus *Gymnura*, the bodily size being greater than in a large rat ; the various species inhabit Tenasserim, the Malay Peninsula, and some of the islands. *G. rafflesii* is a white- or cream-coloured animal, and *G. gymnura* is white in front and black behind, with black eye-stripes and under parts. The Lesser Rat-shrews (*Hylomys*), from Borneo, Sumatra, Annam, and Siam, are of much smaller size, and with shorter tails. *Neotetracus*, a Chinese genus, is very similar to *Hylomys*, but has a longer tail. In the Philippine Islands the sub-family is represented by a long-footed species known as *Podogymnura truei*.

The remarkable Otter-shrew (*Potamogale velox*), from West and Central Africa, is the sole member of the family *Potamogalidae*, in which the cheek- or zygomatic-arch is wanting, and the bones of the lower leg are united at their lower ends. In general appearance this animal resembles a small otter, the fur being very soft, otter-brown above with light-coloured under parts. Dimensions : head and body, eleven inches ; tail, eleven inches.

Family Centetidae

In the next family, the *Centetidae*, or Tenrecs, the cheek-bone of the skull is also wanting, and the upper cheek-teeth are narrow and V-shaped, not broad-crowned as they are in the *Potamogalidae*. The members of this family are found only in Madagascar, and they are divided into two sub-families, the *Centetinae* and the *Oryzorictinae*. The Common-tenrec (*Centetes ecaudatus*) is a large-sized insectivore (length, fifteen inches), with no tail and a harsh, almost spiny coat ; the young of this tenrec are striped. The Lesser-tenrecs, representing the genus *Hemicentetes*, are striped both in the young and the adults, and the pelage is more shiny. The Hedgehog-tenrecs (*Ericulus*) have the entire upper sur-face of the body clothed in spines.

COMMON-TENREC (*Centetes ecaudatus*).

The second sub-family, the *Oryzorictinae*, contains four genera, of which the most important are *Microgale*, the Long-tailed tenrecs, and *Oryzorictes*, the Rice-tenrecs. The former are small, shrew-like animals, with long tails and furry bodies, devoid of all spines ; the tail is, in one species, more than double the length of the head and body. The Rice-tenrecs are burrowing animals, with very short tails and long snouts ; they do considerable damage in the rice-fields of Madagascar. *Limnogale mergulus* is a large aquatic member of this group, having webbed toes and a laterally flattened tail.

Allied to the tenrecs are two animals known as Solenodons, from the West Indies ; they form a very distinct family group, the *Solenodontidae*, the two species being the Hayti-solenodon (*Solenodon paradoxus*) and the Cuban-solenodon (*S. cubanus*). These animals look like very large, long-snouted rats, with long and nearly naked tails and large ears, and have the body clothed in long, coarse hair. The Cuban species has the head, neck, and chest yellowish, and the rest of the body, from the shoulders to the tail, blackish; the Hayti form is brown in front and blackish behind. In the Solenodons the skull is narrowed in the orbital region, and, unlike the rest of the order, the mammae, instead of extending on to the pectoral region, are post-inguinal in position. The snout is long and trunk-like, and has the nostrils situated one on either side of its tip. The head and body measurement of these animals is about twelve inches, and that of the tail eight inches.

Family Chrysochloridae

Lastly, there is a curious group of mole-like animals found in South, East, and Central Africa, known as the *Chrysochloridae*, which contains a number of different genera of the so-called " Golden-moles." In these animals the skulls are conical in shape, and the zygomatic-arch well developed. As in most burrowing animals, the ears are small, and the forefeet specially adapted for digging purposes, the two middle claws of the hand being greatly developed. The eyes are small and hidden beneath the skin. Four genera are now recognised: *Bematiscus*, the Giant Golden-moles of South Africa ; *Chrysospalax*, the Natal Golden-moles ; *Amblysomus*, containing a number of smaller forms from South, East, and Central Africa ; and *Chrysochloris*, the typical Golden-mole, from South and Central Africa. The name " Golden-moles " refers to the coats of these animals, which present a brilliant sheen rather like some forms of " shot " silk, the lustre varying in colour from blue, green, or violet to golden-bronze.

CHAPTER VII

Order CHIROPTERA

(Bats)

BATS are distinguished from all other mammals in having the fore-limbs transformed into wings capable of true flight. Some marsupials, rodents, and insectivores can, by means of parachute-like membranes, glide from tree to tree, but the power of true flight is possessed only by the bats among the mammalia. These animals may be regarded as insectivores specially adapted for an aerial existence. The fore-limbs greatly exceed the hind-limbs in length, and carry the greater part of the flying-membrane ; the fore-arm is very long and bears four long, exceedingly slender digits, resembling rods of bone, which support the membrane of the wing. The thumb is short and is not enclosed in the wing ; it bears a claw, and is used for climbing or to suspend the body when at rest. The wing-membrane is continued along the arm and extends down the sides of the body to the hind-limbs, which are joined to the tail by a similar membranous development. The knee-joint is directed backwards, and the toes are not included in the flying-membrane, but are free, and usually bear strong, sharply pointed claws. The interfemoral-membrane is usually supported by a cartilaginous spur (the calcar), arising from the inner side of the ankle.

The insect-feeding bats have small cheek-teeth, furnished with sharp cusps ; the fruit-eating species have larger and smooth-crowned teeth. The former group are mostly small animals, and are included in the sub-order Microchiroptera, while the latter are, for the most part, of large size, and form the sub-order Megachiroptera. The ears of the Microchiroptera are often of considerable size, and the " earlet," or tragus, is frequently excessively large. In addition to the sensitive nature of the wing-membrane, some members of this group of bats possess special tactile organs in the form of leaf-like expansions, or " rosettes," of skin around the nose. The Microchiroptera are distributed over nearly the whole world, even reaching New Zealand ; the Megachiroptera are confined to the tropical and sub-tropical regions of the Old World.

Sub-order *Megachiroptera*

(*Fruit-bats*)

The fruit-bats (Megachiroptera) are generally large-sized bats, with smooth-crowned cheek-teeth ; the index-finger is composed of three joints, the third phalange generally terminating in a claw, and the tail, when developed, is situated below the interfemoral-membrane, not included in it.

Family Pteropodidae

The members of this sub-order are grouped together in a single family, the *Pteropodidae*, which is divided into two sub-families, the *Pteropodinae*, containing the typical fruit-bats, and the *Macroglossinae*, in which are placed a few species of pollen-eating bats, with curious tongues. Three groups may be distinguished among the *Pteropodinae* : (i) the Rousettine section, containing the typical fruit-bats (*Pteropus*) ; (ii) the Epomophorine section, which includes the " epauletted "-bats of Africa ; and (iii) the Cynopterine section, or short-nosed fruit-bats of Africa and Asia.

The great majority of fruit-bats are included in the Rousettine section, being members of the genus *Pteropus*, the well-known fox-bats, or flying-foxes, some ninety species of which are now recognised. These fox-bats are widely spread over the eastern hemisphere ; although they extend westward as far as Madagascar and the Island of Pemba, no species of *Pteropus* is found in Africa. In the latter continent their place is taken by bats of the genus *Eidolon*. The fox-bats, or flying-foxes, are nearly all of large size, the largest of them measuring as much as five feet across the wings; they usually have reddish-brown or pale, buff-coloured bodies and black wings. These bats are further characterised by the entire absence of a tail and by their long, fox-like muzzles. They are gregarious, living together in large communities, many hundreds roosting in a single tree. Closely allied genera (*Acerodon, Pteralopex*, and *Styloctenium*) occur in Celebes, Timor, the Solomon and Philippine Islands.

The African fruit-bats belonging to the genus *Eidolon* are rather smaller than the majority of the fox-bats, and quite different in colour, the fur of the body being straw-yellow rather than rufous. These bats extend from the Sudan southwards to South Africa; the genus is also found in Madagascar and Southern Arabia. The bats of the genus *Rousettus*, which are smaller than *Eidolon* or *Pteropus*, are found in Africa and eastwards as far as

COLLARED FRUIT-BAT (*Rousettus collaris*).

the Solomon Islands; both *Rousettus* and *Eidolon* are distinguished by the possession of a tail.

The Epomophorine section contains a number of different genera and species of the so-called "epauletted"-bats, which are distributed over a very large area in Africa, ranging from the southern borders of the Sahara south to the Congo. They are remarkable for their large heads and expanded lips. In many species tufts of light hair are developed on the shoulders of the males. The tail, when present, is quite short, and is not connected with the interfemoral-membrane. One of the most striking members of this group is the Hammer-headed bat (*Hypsignathus monstrosus*), in which, in the males, the head is very large, and the muzzle greatly enlarged and truncated; it inhabits West Africa, extending eastwards as far as Uganda.

The bats belonging to the Cynopterine section are distinguished by their shortened muzzles; they are mostly of small size, and the majority of the species are Oriental, the typical genus (*Cynopterus*) ranging from India eastward to Celebes and Timor and southwards to Java.

The pollen-eating bats (*Macroglossinae*) are distinguished from the other fruit-bats by the great length of their tongues and their sharply pointed faces. They range from West Africa eastward to Australia and New Guinea. In one genus, *Notopteris*, the tail is of exceptional length for a member of the Megachiroptera.

Sub-order MICROCHIROPTERA

(Insect-eating Bats)

The insect-eating bats (*Microchiroptera*) are mostly of small size, and usually have teeth of an insectivorous type. The angular part of the lower jaw is more developed than in the fruit-bats, and the margin of the ear does not form a ring as it does in the latter group ; the index-finger is always clawless ; and the tail, which is frequently of considerable length, is either included in the interfemoral-membrane or lies on the upper surface of the membrane.

About six hundred different species and sub-species of these insect-feeding bats are now known. These are divided into sixteen families, the most important of which are the following :—

Family Rhinopomidae

The Mouse-tailed bats of this family are so called on account of the long, free tail, the greater part of which is outside the interfemoral-membrane. These mouse- or long-tailed bats are widely distributed across North-East Africa and Asia, eastwards as far as Burma and Sumatra. They are, in addition to the long tail, characterised by the broad snout, surmounted by a rudimentary " nose-leaf," and the index-finger has two joints.

Family Emballonuridae

This family comprises another group of free-tailed bats, but with shorter tails than the mouse-tailed species. In this group are included the well-known Tomb-bats of India (*Taphozous melanopogon*) and a closely allied species (*T. mauritianus*) from Africa. These tomb-bats are fair-sized animals, and the males have a glandular sac on the throat. The African tomb-bat is very beautifully coloured, being pale buff, marked on the back with wavy lines of silver and black. This family is widely distributed throughout the tropics of both the Old and the New Worlds ; in tropical America the group is represented by three small species of almost pure white-coloured bats belonging to the genus *Diclidurus*.

Family Noctilionidae

In this family of Fish-eating bats the legs are very long and the feet large. These bats appear to live mainly on small fish and other aquatic animals, and doubtless their long legs and feet are special adaptations for this mode of life. The fish-eating bats are found only in tropical America and Trinidad. Owing to their curiously wrinkled lips, they are sometimes referred to as the " hare-lipped bats."

Families Nycteridae and Megadermidae

In the above families are included the False-vampire bats and their allies. These two groups both contain a number of large-eared species which possess pointed nose-leaves. All the members of the *Nycteridae* are included in the single genus *Nycteris*, and are distinguished from the second group by having the tail of considerable length and entirely enclosed within the tail-membrane. These bats occur principally in Africa, but certain species are found in the Malay Peninsula and Dutch East Indies. The *Megadermidae* are distinguished by the absence of the upper incisor-teeth and the extreme shortness of the tail ; the species are distributed over Africa, Southern Asia, the Philippines, and Australia. Many are very handsomely coloured, the African genera *Lavia* having the fur greenish-grey and the wing-membrane bright yellow. The largest of this group is the Australian *Macroderma gigas*, a very large bat with long ears ; the Asiatic genera are *Megaderma* and *Lyroderma*, while *Cardioderma* is another African genus.

Family Rhinolophidae

This group of Horseshoe-bats is represented by the single genus *Rhinolophus*, the members of which are inhabitants of the temperate and tropical regions of the Old World. They are remarkable for their complicated nose-leaves and large ears ; the latter are without the tragus, or " earlet." The majority of the species are of some shade of greyish-brown in colour and vary a good deal in size ; some, like the Lesser Horseshoe-bat (*Rhinolophus hipposideros*), being quite small (head and body, two inches) ; others, such as the Greater Horseshoe-bat (*R. ferrum-equinum*), being considerably larger (head and body, three inches). Some of these Horseshoe-bats vary greatly in coloration, sometimes being of a bright orange-buff, sometimes greyish or snuff-brown. Upwards of one hundred different forms of this genus are now recognised.

Family Hipposideridae

This group, known as Leaf-nosed bats, is closely allied to the Horseshoe-bats, with similar nose-leaves and large ears, but having the toes with only two joints, not three as in the *Rhinolophidae*. The various genera and species are confined to the warmer parts of the Old World, extending northwards as far as Northern Africa and the Himalayas. Some forms, like the common African Leaf-nosed bat (*Hipposideros caffer*), are only of small size, the head and body not exceeding two inches in length ; others, such as *H. gigas*, are about five inches in length. In colour these bats very closely resemble the Horseshoe-bats, some being orange-buff, others greyish-brown. One of the most remarkable members of the family is a small species (*Anthops ornatus*) from the Solomon Islands, which has been called the " Flower-nosed bat." It possesses a very large and complicated nose-leaf in the form of a rosette extending from eye to eye, and adorned above with three stalked balls, the appendage covering almost the entire face.

Family Phyllostomidae

This family of American and West Indian Leaf-nosed bats is a very large one, containing a number of different sub-families and genera which inhabit the tropical and sub-tropical parts of America northwards towards the Southern United States and Bahamas. Most of the members of this family possess a simple nose-leaf; in one group (the *Chilonycterinae*) this organ is absent. In all the species the molar-teeth are well developed and there are three joints to the third finger. These American Leaf-nosed bats are frequently referred to as " Vampire-bats," but they are not blood-suckers. One of the best-known species is the common South American Leaf-nosed bat, the Javelin-bat (*Phyllostomus hastatus*). It has a body of medium size (head and body, four and a half inches), with a dark red or black coloration. In other forms (*Artibeus*) there are white stripes on each side of the head, and in *Uroderma*, in addition to the white head markings, a white stripe extends down the back.

Family Desmodontidae

The blood-sucking Vampire-bats, thus grouped, are the true " Vampire-bats " which feed, apparently, exclusively upon blood. Their teeth are specially modified for cutting or shaving through the skin of the animals upon which they prey, the incisor, or front teeth, having chisel-like edges. The premolars are also adapted for the same purpose, whereas the molars, or crushing-teeth, are greatly reduced in size and number. In addition, the stomachs of these vampires are considerably modified for the absorption of this peculiar diet. The Vampire-bats are confined to tropical America, extending northwards into Mexico. Three genera are now recognised, *Desmodus*, *Diaemus*, and *Diphylla;* the Common Vampire-bat, *Desmodus rufus*, is about three inches in length, and of a reddish-brown tint above.

Family Vespertilionidae

The typical bats (*Vespertilionidae*) form a very large family, the members of which are distinguished by the possession of a two-jointed third finger, long tails, and

LONG-EARED BAT (*Plecotus auritus*) (Back view).

well-developed earlets, or tragi. The group is divided into six sub-families, the typical one, the *Vespertilioninae*, containing all the well-known European species, such as the Long-eared bat (*Plecotus auritus*), the Common-bat, or Pipistrelle (*Pipistrellus pipistrellus*), the Noctule (*Nyctalus noctula*), the Serotine (*Eptesicus serotinus*), and Daubenton's-bat (*Myotis daubentoni*). The Serotine and the Noctule are two of the largest of the British bats, the spread of the wings being about fourteen inches. Both these species are very widely distributed. The Common - bat, or Pipistrelle, has a

LONG-EARED BAT (*Plecotus auritus*) (Underside).

spread of wings of about eight and a half inches ; it is the smallest of the British species, and is widely distributed over Europe, North Africa, and parts of Asia.

Family Molossidae

In this group the wing-membrane is much reduced in size. One of the most interesting of these bats is the Naked-bat from the Malay Peninsula and the East Indies (*Chiromeles torquatus*). This is a large species, the body measuring about five and a quarter inches in length, and, with the exception of some hairs upon the neck, its thick and wrinkled skin is almost entirely naked, and the wing-membrane is greatly reduced in size. Somewhat similar are the Mastiff-bats (*Molossus*), which usually have the tail partially free ; they are found in the warmer parts of the New World. Similar free-tailed bats belonging to this group are found in Africa, Asia, and Australia.

CHAPTER VIII

Order PRIMATES

(*Lemurs, Monkeys, and Apes*)

THE Order Primates includes the lemurs, monkeys, apes, and man, which are grouped in two sub-orders, the lemurs constituting the Lemuroidea and the three latter groups forming the sub-order Anthropoidea. In some systems of classification the lemurs are considered as a distinct order ; in others the Tarsier is grouped with the Anthropoids in a special section, the Haplorhini.

The Primates, exclusive of man, present the following characteristics. The skin, as in most mammals, is furnished with a hairy or woolly coat, and the tail is long, short, or externally invisible; in many New World species the tail is prehensile. The teeth are differentiated into the normal four sets (incisors, canines, premolars, and molars), and the permanent series is preceded by a set of milk-teeth. There are usually two pairs of incisors in both the upper and lower jaw, and, except in the marmosets and tamarins (*Hapalidae*), the molars are arranged in three pairs in each jaw. The orbit, or eye-socket, is always surrounded by a ring of bone (a character found in some Insectivores and in the Horse family *Equidae*).

The stomach is usually simple (in the guerezas and langurs the stomach is extraordinarily complex), collar-bones are always present, and the two bones of the fore-arm, the radius and ulna, are never united. There are usually five fingers and five toes, furnished, in most cases, with well-formed nails; the thumb may be quite small or absent, and the great toe, unlike that of man, is opposable to the other toes. The skull has, as a rule, a large brain-case containing a very highly developed brain, and, with the exception of the aye-aye, there are always two teats, or mammae, situated in the pectoral region (in the gentle lemurs there are, in addition, two abdominal mammae). The young are born in a very helpless condition, and are entirely dependent on the milk secreted by the maternal mammae.

The various species of the order range over the greater part of the tropical and sub-tropical regions of both the Old and the New World, extending in America northwards as far as Mexico and south to thirty degrees below the equator. In the eastern hemisphere some species extend as far north as Japan and Tibet, while in the south they reach nearly to the southernmost point of Africa. No indigenous member of the order is found in Australia, New Zealand, New Guinea, the Pacific Islands, or West Indies.

Sub-order *Lemuroidea*

(*Lemurs*)

The Aye-aye, Tarsier, and Lemurs, collectively known as Lemuroids, form the sub-order *Lemuroidea*. These animals are much more lowly organised than the monkeys and apes. The following are the chief distinguishing characters of the group. The muzzle is usually pointed and dog-like, and the external ears, which are sometimes very large, have no distinct margins, or hems, such as occur in the apes. The tail, which is never prehensile, may be long, short, or entirely absent, and the teats are either on the breast, the abdomen, or both. The eye-sockets are usually directed more forwards than in other mammalian orders; they are not, however, closed in behind by bone, as in the monkeys and apes, but communicate freely (except in the tarsier) with the temporal region. The second toe of the foot is always provided with a claw, and the lower bones of the arms and legs are not joined together, except in *Tarsius*. There are, as a rule, thirty-six teeth; the lower front-teeth in the majority of species are set horizontally, and there is usually a gap between the upper front, or incisor, teeth.

The Lemuroids are now confined to the Old World and predominate in Madagascar, where from thirty-five to forty different species occur. In Africa the group is widely spread to the south of the Sahara, and in the Oriental region these animals enjoy an extensive distribution, spreading throughout a great part of India and Ceylon eastward to Annam, Siam, the Malay Peninsula and Islands to as far east as Celebes and the Philippine Islands.

Family Chiromyidae

The first family, the *Chiromyidae*, contains but a single genus and species, *Chiromys madagascariensis*, the well-known Aye-aye. It was first brought to Europe in the year 1780, and long remained a puzzle to zoologists, some thinking it was related to the squirrels, some to the quadrumana ; even now very little is known about its exact systematic position. The Aye-aye is about the size of a cat, and has a short-snouted, rounded head, large eyes and

AYE-AYE (*Chiromys madagascariensis*).

ears, and a long, bushy tail ; the fingers and toes (except the big toe) are long and have pointed claws, but the third finger has assumed the form of a long, delicate-jointed rod of bone, comparable with one of the long fingers of a bat. The thumb and great toe are opposable to the other digits, the great toe being furnished with a flat nail. The teats are two in number, and occupy an abdominal position. The skull has a dome-shaped brain-case and a short muzzle ; the two halves of the lower jaw are not joined together in front by bone, but are united by fibrous tissue. The incisor-teeth of this animal are quite unlike those of any other member of the order, being more like the gnawing teeth of rats and squirrels, the teeth growing up as fast as they are worn away; they are provided with enamel only on their front surfaces. Another rodent-like character is the long gap between the incisor-teeth and the cheek-teeth, of which there are four above and three below.

The Aye-aye is nocturnal and arboreal, and builds a large nest in which to rear its young. It feeds, for the most part, on insects. With its large ears it is, apparently, able to detect the presence of wood-boring insects, or their burrows, when the branches are tapped ; its large, rat-like teeth assist in tearing open the branches and exposing the burrows, when the wire-like finger is used to extract whatever insects may be inside.

This curious lemur, which is regarded as an object of superstition by the natives, is found only in the forests on the eastern side of Madagascar.

Family Tarsiidae

The second family of the Lemuroids is the *Tarsiidae*, which contains the single genus *Tarsius*, seven species of which are now recognised. These strange little lemurs, known as the Tarsiers, are about equal in size to a rat, and have rounded heads and enormous eyes. The ears are large, and the hind-limbs longer than the front ones ; the fingers and toes terminate in sucker-like discs, and all carry flat nails, except the second and third toes, which are clawed. The tail is long and has a tufted end. The skull possesses very large eye-sockets, which are nearly separated from the hinder part of the skull by a bony plate, a feature which distinguishes this animal from all the other Lemuroids, and in which it shows a resemblance to the monkeys and apes. The incisor-teeth differ from those of the true-lemurs in that there is no gap in the middle of the upper jaw, and the lower teeth are vertical, not horizontal.

Like the Aye-aye the Tarsiers are nocturnal and arboreal. They move from branch to branch by leaping, their sucker-like fingers and toes enabling

TARSIER (*Tarsius spectrum*).

them to hold on to the boughs with amazing facility. They are distributed amongst the islands of the East Indian Archipelago, having been recorded from Borneo, Sumatra, Java, Celebes, and some of the smaller islands, and the Philippine Archipelago.

Family Lemuridae

The third and last family of the Lemuroids is the *Lemuridae*, including all the true lemurs. In these animals there is always a gap between the front pair of upper teeth, and the lower incisors and canines (the dog-teeth) are set horizontally. The family is divided into the following groups, or sub-families : (i) the *Lorisinae*, or slow-lemurs ; (ii) the *Galaginae*, the galagos (bush-babies) ; (iii) the *Chirogalinae*, the mouse-lemurs ; (iv) the *Lemurinae*, or typical lemurs ; and (v) the *Indrisinae*, or endrinas, sifakas, and avahi. The members of this family are widely distributed over Africa, Madagascar, India, and the Far East.

(i) The Slow-lemurs (*Lorisinae*) are characterised by their soft, woolly coats and large eyes, and the limbs are nearly equal in length ; the index-finger is either vestigial or very diminutive, and the thumb is set at right angles to the other digits. The tail is either absent or quite short. Four genera can be distinguished, two African (*Perodicticus* and *Arctocebus*, the Pottos), and two Oriental (*Nycticebus*, the Slow-lorises, and *Loris*, the Slender-lorises). The species range throughout a great part of equatorial Africa and over a large area of the Oriental region.

SLENDER-LORIS (*Loris gracilis*).

Bosman's-potto (*Perodicticus potto*) was first described in 1704, since when four further species have received names. The genus extends across equatorial Africa from Sierra Leone to Kenya Colony. One remarkable feature about these animals, which are rather smaller than a rabbit, is that the spines of the backbone, in the region of the shoulders, project through the skin. The index-finger is reduced to a mere vestige, and the tail, although short, is not hidden by the fur. The fur on the body is brownish in colour, and interspersed are numbers of long, black, bristle-like hairs. Pottos are nocturnal and arboreal, being very slow-moving animals. The other type of Potto, or " Angwantibo " (*Arctocebus*), is very closely allied to *Perodicticus ;* it is found only in Old Calabar and the Cameroons. In this genus the spines of the vertebrae do not penetrate the skin.

Related to the pottos are the Slow-lorises of the genus *Nycticebus*, which are rather smaller, but not so small as in the slender-lorises. The fur is thick and soft, and the head rounded, with large eyes, as in the pottos. The index-finger, although not vestigial, is quite small, and the tail concealed by the body-fur. About eleven forms are now recognised, distributed over Bengal, Assam, Burma, Siam, Annam, the Malay Peninsula, and the East

Indies eastward to the Philippines. These animals feed, like the pottos, on insects, leaves, and fruit; their movements are very slow, and they are entirely arboreal and nocturnal.

The smallest member of the *Lorisinae* is the typical *Loris*, or Slender-loris, from Southern India and Ceylon. The body is about the size of a small rat, thinner in build than the Slow-loris, and with more slender limbs. The eyes are large, and the muzzle prolonged into a sharp-pointed snout. The index-finger, although quite small, is well-formed, and there is no external tail.

(ii) The *Galaginae* may be regarded as containing only the Galagos, or " bush-babies," of Africa. These Galagos (*Galago* and *Hemigalago*) are widely distributed over the African con- tinent, from south of the Sahara to as far south as South Africa. They are nocturnal and arboreal, and feed, for the most part, on insects, fruit, and birds' eggs; unlike the slow-lemurs, they are very active. Some species are no larger than a small rat (*Hemigalago demidoffi*), others (*Galago crassicaudata*) are nearly as large as a cat. All have large eyes, extremely soft fur, and long, bushy tails, and the ankle region of the leg is markedly elongated. A large number of species and sub-species are now recognised.

(iii) The *Chirogalinae*, or Mouse-lemurs, con- tain the smallest members of the whole order, some being little larger than a dormouse. Four genera may be distinguished: *Microcebus*, the dwarf-lemurs; *Chirogale*, the true mouse- lemurs; *Opolemur*, the fat-tailed lemurs; and *Mixocebus*, the Hattock. All are restricted to the Island of Madagascar. The dwarf-lemurs

DWARF-LEMUR (*Microcebus myoxinus*).

resemble dormice in having buff- or grey-coloured coats and large, black eyes, surrounded by dark eye-stripes. The mouse-lemurs (*Chirogale*) have the ankle-joint, or tarsus, elongated, in this respect resembling the African galagos; the muzzle is longer than in the dwarf-lemurs, and in one species (*C. trichotis*) the ears are tufted.

(iv) The fourth sub-family, the *Lemurinae*, contains all the true lemurs, in which the head is usually rather dog-like, the eyes being directed outwards. The hind-limbs do not greatly exceed the fore-limbs in length, as they do in the next sub-family, and the ankle-joint is not elongated as it is in the galagos. The group embraces three genera: *Lemur*, the typical lemurs, of which a number of forms are now recognised; *Hapalemur*, the gentle- lemurs (three species); and *Lepidolemur*, the sportive-lemurs, about six or seven of which have received names. They are mostly gregarious and arboreal, and many are diurnal; all the species are confined to Madagascar and the adjacent islands.

The typical lemurs (*Lemur*) are all animals of the size of a cat, or larger, clothed in thick, woolly coats, with hairy and tufted ears. The teats are two in number, and are situated in the pectoral region; the angle of the lower jaw does not extend downwards. Some of the species are very handsomely coloured, and many are very variable, some specimens of the Ruffed- or Variable-lemur being bright red in colour, and others being a mixture of black and white. The well-known Ring-tailed lemur (*L. catta*) is less arboreal than many of the species, sometimes living in rocky localities. In the Gentle-lemurs (*Hapalemur*) the head is rounded and the muzzle short; the hind-limbs are rather longer than the fore-limbs, and the female has four teats, two pectoral and two abdominal. These lemurs are the smallest of the group, and have the angle of the lower jaw greatly expanded. The Sportive-lemurs (*Lepidolemur*) closely resemble the Gentle-lemurs in size and general appearance, but have no upper incisors and rather shorter tails.

RUFFED-LEMUR (*Lemur varius*) (Black and white phase).

(v) The last sub-family, the *Indrisinae*, contains the highest members of the Lemuroids; in these lemurs the length of the hind-limbs considerably exceeds that of the fore-limbs, and the thumb is set far back on the hand, and but little opposable to the other digits. The species are confined to Madagascar and are divided into three genera: *Avahis*, containing the single species *A. laniger*, the woolly-lemur, or Avahi, the smallest member of the group, with a shorter and hairy face; the tail (fifteen inches) is longer than the body (eleven and a half inches), and the fur thick and woolly, concealing the ears. The eyes and eye-sockets are exceptionally large, and the lower jaw of considerable depth.

The Sifakas (*Propithecus*) are much larger than the woolly-lemur, the body being equal in size to a large cat. Their coats are more hairy than woolly, and the face more fox-like; the tail is of considerable length. The colour varies immensely, some species being white with yellowish, red, or black markings, while others, apparently of the same species, are entirely uniform in colour. Unlike the woolly-lemur and the majority of lemurs, the sifakas are most active in the mornings and evenings. The last genus, *Indris*, contains but a single species, *I. brevicaudata*, distinguished from the sifakas by its larger size, much larger hind-limbs, large tufted-ears, longer face, and short tail. The colour of the coat is black and white, and the species is gregarious and diurnal. It is popularly known as the Endrina, or by the native name of " babakoto."

Sub-order *ANTHROPOIDEA*

(*Monkeys and Apes*)

The Sub-order Anthropoidea contains all the remaining members of the Primates—that is, the Marmosets, New and Old World Monkeys, Apes, and Man. The characters which distinguish Anthropoids from the Lemuroids are briefly as follows. The eye-socket, or orbit, is, in the Anthropoids (except in the New World *Aotus*), completely cut off from the temporal region behind by a vertical plate of bone, and the index-finger is always well developed. The thumb, however, is sometimes reduced to a vestige, or entirely absent ; and the second toe always bears a flat nail, never a claw. The hemispheres of the brain exhibit many folds, or convolutions, and the mammae, or teats, are never abdominal. The nasal region of the face is shorter and less dog-like, and the eyes are directed forwards. There is never any gap between the upper incisor-teeth, and the lower canines do not resemble the incisors, nor are they set horizontally.

In the New World the members of this sub-order (excluding man) extend from thirty degrees below the equator northwards as far as Mexico ; in the Old World they are found over the greater part of the warmer regions. Some species extend as far north as Tibet and Japan, while in the south others reach nearly to the Cape. No indigenous forms have ever been found in New Guinea, Australia, the Pacific Islands, or the West Indies.

The Anthropoids, exclusive of man, are classified in five families, three from the New World (*Hapalidae* and *Calimiconidae*, the marmosets and tamarins, and the *Cebidae*, the New World monkeys), and two Old World groups (*Cercopithecidae*, the Old World monkeys, and *Simiidae*, the apes). In the New World types the nose is flat and broad, with the nostrils opening outwards and separated from each other by a broad division (Platyrrhine) ; in the Old World species the nose is narrow, and the nostrils open downwards, as in man, being set close together (Catarrhine). The teeth in the New World monkeys are thirty-six or thirty-two in number, there always being three premolars and two or three molars on each side of each jaw, whereas the Old World forms resemble man in having thirty-two teeth, two premolars and three molars being present on each side of the jaws.

The tail in the New World species is frequently prehensile, which is never the case in those of the eastern hemisphere. The latter, however, often have large cheek-pouches, and callosities, or bare patches, are commonly developed on their hinder parts ; both of these features are invariably absent in the American monkeys.

Family Hapalidae

Commencing with the marmosets and tamarins of the family *Hapalidae*, we have a large number of highly coloured species representing some seven genera. All agree in having only two molars on each side of each jaw— that is, thirty-two teeth in all, instead of thirty-six as found in the *Cebidae*, or American-monkeys ; further, the digits, with the exception of the great toe, do not bear nails but claws, and the thumb is not opposable to the fingers, the hand being, as it were, a paw rather than a hand. The best known of the marmosets are the common White-eared and Black-eared species (*Hapale jacchus* and *H. penicillata*), distinguished by their tufted ears and ringed tails ; the members of this genus are inhabitants of Brazil. The smallest of the marmosets, and the smallest Anthropoid, is the Pigmy-marmoset (*Cebuella pygmaea*), being only as large as a small rat. It also hails from Brazil, where it is widely distributed.

The tamarins may be considered as representing four genera. The Panama-tamarin (*Oedipomidas geoffroyi*) is a highly coloured species with a bright chestnut-coloured nape. The Silky-tamarin (*Leontocebus rosalia*) represents another group ; it is a very beautiful monkey, with a long, silky coat like unspun silk. This tamarin inhabits South-East Brazil. The Moustached-tamarins form another group, *Mystax ;* the most extreme development of the moustache is seen in *M. imperator*, from the Brazilian Amazons. These animals are all diurnal and arboreal, climbing trees more like squirrels than monkeys.

Family Calimiconidae

Formerly considered to be of sub-family rank, this South American family is here created for the reception of a single species of tamarin-like monkey, *Calimico goeldii*, an animal that appears to be intermediate between the true tamarins and the American monkeys proper. It has the hands and feet of a tamarin, but the teeth of a member of the *Cebidae*—that is, six cheek-teeth on each side of the jaws.

Family Cebidae

The third and last family of New World Anthropoids, the *Cebidae*, contains all the true monkeys of the western hemisphere. They all have thirty-six teeth (six cheek-teeth on each side of the jaws), and the fingers and toes bear nails, not claws. The tail is always present, usually long, and frequently prehensile ; in one genus (*Cacajao*) it is quite short. These monkeys are all arboreal, and are found throughout the forests of tropical America.

The family is divided into four sub-families : (i) the *Aotinae*, the night-monkeys, titis, and squirrel-monkeys ; (ii) the *Pithecinae*, or saki-monkeys ;

(iii) the *Alouattinae*, or howling-monkeys ; and (iv) the *Cebinae*, containing the capuchins, woolly-monkeys, and spider-monkeys.

(i) The *Aotinae* are all small animals with long, bushy, and non-prehensile tails. The Squirrel-monkeys (*Saimiri*) are remarkable for their rounded heads, short thumbs, and very large brain-case ; the angle of the lower jaw is not expanded. They are frequently very brightly coloured, with black or grey heads, yellow or orange limbs, and greyish or orange backs. The distributional range extends from Costa Rica in Central America southwards into Brazil, Peru, and Bolivia. The Squirrel-monkeys are gregarious, diurnal, and subsist largely upon insects. The Titi-monkeys (*Callicebus*) are equal to, or rather larger than, the squirrel-monkeys, and their coats are considerably longer. The brain-case is not markedly enlarged, but the angular part of the lower jaw is greatly expanded. In habits they are very similar to the squirrel-monkeys, and many of the species are very handsomely coloured, some being deep chestnut with black foreheads, fore-arms, and feet, and yellow hands (*C. torquatus*), while others are brownish-grey above and bright rufous-orange below (*C. cupreus*). The numerous species are widely distributed from Guiana and Brazil southwards to Paraguay ; in the west they extend as far as Colombia, Ecuador, Peru, and Bolivia.

The Night-monkeys (*Aotus*) are about equal in size to the smaller titis, and have rounded heads and large eyes. The thumb is very short, and, as in the other members of the sub-family, the tail is long and non-prehensile. The skull is remarkable for the enormous size of the eye-sockets, the large canine-teeth, and the lower incisors which project forwards ; the partition between the orbital and temporal regions is nearly as imperfect as in the well-known tarsier. The forehead is usually marked with three black bars, these giving the name of *A. trivirgatus* to the best-known of the species. These monkeys are nocturnal and gregarious ; they range from Nicaragua southwards to the north-eastern Argentine, reaching Guiana in the east and Peru in the west.

(ii) The sakis, or *Pithecinae*, are distinguished by having their lower incisor-teeth set more horizontally, suggesting the condition found in the lemurs. The tail, which is non-prehensile, is either long or quite short, and the ears are large. Three genera are now recognised : *Cacajao*, the uakaris, and *Pithecia* and *Chiropotes*, the sakis. The uakaris are easily distinguished by their short tails and dilated lower jaws. The coat is comparatively short and silky, and in two of the species, *C. rubicundus* and *C. calvus*, the face is bright scarlet in colour ; in the third species, *C. melanocephalus*, the face is black. In the latter form the coat is chestnut-brown on the back and sides of the body, with black shoulders and extremities. This monkey is found in the forests around the Rio Cassiquiare, Rio Negro, and Rio Branco. The Red-uakari (*C. rubicundus*) is chestnut-red in colour, and the Bald-uakari (*C. calvus*) is dirty-white above and brownish below. The latter species is confined to a small area of country to the west side of the Japura River, while *C. rubicundus*, the Red-uakari, is found only in the forests adjacent to the Japura delta.

In the Long-haired sakis (*Pithecia*) the hair is long and harsh, especially on the head, where it frequently hangs over the face. The tail is long, curly, and bushy. Considerable colour variation is found in these monkeys, about eight species of which bear names. They abound in the forests of the valleys of the Orinoco and Amazon, extending eastwards to the Guianas and westwards as far as Ecuador and Peru. In the Hairy-saki (*Pithecia monacha*) the general colour above is black, washed with yellowish-grey, and browner below ; the hands and feet are grey. The White-headed saki (*P. pithecia*) has the hair on the head shorter, and, in the males, white in colour ; in the Golden-headed saki (*P. chrysocephala*) the males have the head buff-coloured. The third genus, *Chiropotes*, contains three species : the Black-saki (*C. satanas*), the White-nosed saki (*C. albinasa*), and the Dusky-saki (*C. chiropotes*) ; the hair on the head forms a sort of cap, and the tail is bushy without being curly. *C. satanas* and *C. albinasa* are black, and *C. chiropotes* a mixture of vandyke-brown and brownish-buff ; the White-nosed saki has a scarlet nose, with a white patch in its centre.

RED HOWLING-MONKEY (*Alouatta senicula*).

(iii) The Howling-monkeys (*Alouattinae*) are a very easily recognised group, containing but a single genus, *Alouatta*. They are the largest of the South American monkeys, and are remarkable for their very ugly faces and enlarged throats ; the tail is prehensile, the lower surface of the tail-tip being sensitive. The females in this monkey are considerably smaller than the males. The skull exhibits a very low type of brain-case and an enormously developed lower jaw to accommodate the greatly inflated hyoid bones, the larynx being developed to an extraordinary extent. By means of this strange vocal apparatus, possessed by the male howlers, the voice is greatly augmented, and is audible at a distance of several miles. These monkeys extend from Mexico and Guatemala through Central America into Ecuador, Peru, and Bolivia in the west, and to the Guianas in the east ; southwards they range through Brazil into the Argentine and Paraguay. Island forms are known from Coiba Island and Trinidad. Some species are very handsomely coloured, being a mixture of bright golden-orange and deep coppery-red, as in the Red Howling-monkey

(*A. senicula*), while others are black (*A. niger*). Some fourteen species are now known; they are gregarious and, to some extent, semi-nocturnal, uttering their loud cries before sunrise and late in the evening.

(iv) The remaining New World monkeys are grouped together in the sub-family *Cebinae*, the typical members of which are the Capuchins of the genus *Cebus ;* they are widely spread over tropical America, ranging from Mexico to Paraguay. The Capuchins, which extend from Costa Rica to Paraguay, are stoutly built monkeys with rounded heads. The tail, although prehensile, to a certain extent, has no naked area at the tip. The members of this genus are the monkeys most commonly met with in a state of captivity; about two dozen species are recognised which vary in colour from pale-brown to black. The Woolly-monkeys (*Lagothrix*) are larger than the capuchins, the limbs longer, and the coat extremely dense and woolly; the tail is perfectly prehensile, the lower surface of the tip being naked. In colour these monkeys are ashy-grey or brownish-red, with darker-coloured heads, extremities, and under parts. About seven species have been described; they are confined to the north-western part of South America.

The Woolly spider-monkeys (*Brachyteles*) are very similar in appearance to the Woolly-monkeys, but the limbs are longer, and the thumb is often wanting or represented only by a vestigial digit. But a single species of this genus is known, *B. arachnoides ;* it is found in South-Eastern Brazil. The Spider-monkeys (*Ateles*) are remarkable for their slender bodies and limbs, long and perfectly prehensile tails, and coarse coats; the thumb is either entirely absent or reduced to a vestige. There are about a dozen different species of Spider-monkeys, ranging over nearly the whole of the distributional area of the *Cebidae*.

Family Cercopithecidae

The Old World monkeys may be considered as representing the single Family *Cercopithecidae ;* the characters wherein these monkeys differ from the American species have already been dealt with (see *Cebidae*). They fall into two natural groups, or sub-families : (i) the *Cercopithecinae*, which contains a number of genera such as *Papio* (baboons), *Cercocebus* (mangabeys), *Macaca* (macaques), and *Cynopithecus* (black apes of Celebes) ; and (ii) the *Colobinae*, containing *Colobus* (guerezas) and *Pithecus* and allied genera (langurs). Sometimes the Colobus monkeys and Langurs are considered as a separate family, *Colobidae*. The first of these groups is remarkable for the universal presence of cheek-pouches, and the stomach is fashioned on a simple plan. The bare patches, or callosities, on the buttocks, are prominent features, and the tail is either long, short, or externally invisible.

The baboons may be regarded as the lowest of all the Catarrhine (Old World) monkeys ; the facial region is greatly developed, giving the animals a dog-like appearance. The limbs are about of equal length. These

2 G

monkeys walk on all fours, the palms and soles being in contact with the ground.   Baboons are mostly terrestrial, but they occasionally take to the trees in search of food.   The African baboons include the typical baboons (*Papio*), the Mandrill, and Drill (*Mandrillus*), and the Geladas (*Theropithecus*). The typical baboons are further sub-divided into the true baboons, in which the body is more or less evenly haired, and the hamadryas-baboons, in which a long mantle covers the fore-part of the body.   The tail in these baboons is of medium length and is sometimes tufted at the tip ; the common-baboons are usually yellowish-brown in colour, while the hamadryas-baboons are stone-grey in tint with bright pink callosities.   The former are distributed all over Africa south of the Sahara, while the latter are confined to East Africa and Arabia.

The Mandrill and Drill are easily distinguished from the baboons by their short, pig-like tails.   The male Mandrill develops longitudinal and bright-coloured swellings along each side of the muzzle, and has enormous canine-teeth.   In general colour it is darker than the baboons, and the callosities are violet in tint ; the nose and anal region are scarlet.   The range of distribution extends from Senegambia to the Congo.   The Drill (*M. leuco-phaeus*), another West African type, is rather smaller than the Mandrill, has the ridges on the muzzle less developed, the face wholly black, and scarlet callosities.   The Geladas, two species of which are known (*T. gelada* and *T. obscurus*), are distinguished from the true-baboons by their nostrils opening on the side of the snout, not at its end ; further, a heavy mane, or mantle, is developed ; the tail is tufted like a lion's, and there is a nude, scarlet-coloured patch on the chest ; both species are confined to Abyssinia.

In the Island of Celebes there occurs a small, black monkey, known as the Celebean black-ape (*Cynopithecus niger*) ; this monkey is considerably smaller than the baboons, and has the nostrils directed downwards and out-wards.   The tail is only about one inch in length, and the coat is a uniform black, while the callosities are flesh-coloured.

The macaques differ from the baboons in having shorter faces, and the nostrils open before the end of the muzzle and are directed outwards and downwards.   The tail is very variable; in some cases it is long or of medium length, in others it is tufted like a lion's, while in other species it is so reduced in size as to be externally invisible.   Probably a number of different genera could be distinguished ; they may, however, conveniently be grouped in the single genus *Macaca*.   Some of the forms are terrestrial ; the majority are, however, inhabitants of forests and bush country.   A great number of different species and races have received names, mostly from the Oriental region.   One species (*M. sylvana*) inhabits Morocco and Algeria and extends into Northern Spain and Gibraltar, while other species reach as far north as Tibet and Japan.   In South-Eastern Asia these monkeys abound in the islands of the East Indian Archipelago and Celebes.

The Barbary-ape (*M. sylvana*) is one of the most important members of the genus; it inhabits Morocco, Algeria, Gibraltar, and Spain, and is distinguished by its massive build and entire absence of external tail. Other species with rudimentary tails are the black Celebes-macaque (*M. maura*), the Brown-macaque (*M. speciosa*) from Cochin China, Assam, and Burma, and the rufous Short-tailed macaque (*M. rufescens*) from Tenasserim. Then there are a number of species with short tails, like the Japanese-macaque (*M. fuscata*), an animal with a thick, soft coat, and others with rather longer tails (eight to twelve inches in length). Among the latter we have the well-known Pig-tailed macaque (*M. nemestrina*) from Burma, Tenas-serim, the Malay Peninsula and Islands of the East Indian Archipelago; this monkey is very heavily built, and has the head and back washed with a blackish tint.

Another important member of this group is the Rhesus-monkey (*M. rhesus*), a golden-grey-coloured species from Northern India. There is a further group in which the tail is over twelve inches in length, but not as long as the head and body; in this group we have the Bonnet-macaque (*M. sinica*) of Southern India. The hair on the crown in this species radiates from a central parting, and the tail is nearly as long as the head and body. Lastly, there are the typical macaques with long tails, a very numerous group, widely spread over a great part of South-Eastern Asia, the range embracing the Philippine Islands.

The Mangabeys (*Cercocebus*) are an entirely African group, ranging across the centre of Africa from Guinea to Kenya Colony; they are more slender in build than the macaques, with long limbs and tails. These monkeys may be regarded as intermediate between the macaques and the guenons, having the build of the latter, but the teeth of the macaques, the last lower molar being five-cusped, not four as in the guenons. The digits are webbed, the second and third toes being connected for nearly their entire length. They are all arboreal, dwelling in the dense forests of tropical Africa. The White-collared mangabey (*C. torquatus*) is one of the most handsome species, having a chestnut-coloured crown, and pure white markings on the sides of the head and neck. The Sooty-mangabey (*C. aethiops*) is a sooty-black coloured monkey, and the Crested-mangabeys (*C. albigena*), from the Congo and Cameroons, are blackish in colour, or brown, mixed with grey.

The Guenons (*Cercopithecus*) are the typical members of the family; they differ from the foregoing species in having shorter, less dog-like faces, narrower loins, and longer hind-limbs. The tail is very long, nearly as long as in the next sub-family, the callosities are small, and the colour of the coat is frequently very brilliant, and usually speckled with black and grey. Unlike the macaques and mangabeys the last lower molar-tooth has only four cusps, not five. They are very largely arboreal in their habits, and are confined to the African continent and certain small islands off the coast, ranging from the Gambia eastward to Abyssinia and southward through the equatorial forest zone to the Cape.

The species are very numerous, and vary very greatly in colour ; they have been sub-divided into several groups, or sub-genera ; some, like the White-nosed guenon (*C. petaurista*), of West Africa, have a white spot on the nose. Other white-nosed species are Schmidt's-guenon (*C. schmidti*), from the Congo, and the Red-bellied guenon (*C. erythrogaster*), from Nigeria. In others, such as *C. whitesidei*, the nose-spot is buff-coloured. A green group includes the Vervet-guenon (*C. pygerythrus*), from Cape Province, and the Grivet-guenon (*C. sabaeus*), from North-East Africa. Then there are a number of species with brightly coloured ear-tufts, such as Wolf's-guenon (*C. wolfi*), from the Congo, with bright orange ear-tufts, and Dent's-guenon (*C. denti*), from the Eastern Congo, with long, white ear-tufts. Some species (*C. kolbi*, from Kenya Colony) have a white collar around the neck, while another group (*neglectus-diana* group) have an oblique white stripe on the thighs ; *C. neglectus*, from West and Central Africa, has a prominent rufous band across the forehead, while *C. diana* is remarkable for a black-and-white forehead band, and a prominent white beard.

Closely allied to the true guenons are the Talapoin-guenons. These monkeys are very much smaller than the guenons, and are greenish-yellow in colour. Two species are known : *C. talapoin*, from the Gaboon, and *C. ansorgei*, from Angola.

The Patas-guenons are grouped together in a separate genus, *Erythrocebus*, the members of which are larger than the true-guenons, have longer limbs, flatter heads, and the general colour of the coat is foxy-red mixed with grey or black, while the nose and brow-band may be either black or white. The various species are distributed from Senegal in the west to as far east as Uganda and Kenya Colony ; they are rather more terrestrial in their habits than the true guenons, and are gregarious.

The second sub-family, the *Colobinae*, containing the langurs (*Pithecus*) and guerezas (*Colobus*), is distinguished from the *Cercopithecinae* by the tail being very long, the ischial callosities small, the stomach large and complex, while cheek-pouches are either small or absent, and the last lower molar five-cusped. Their food consists largely of leaves, and they are entirely arboreal in habits. The langurs are Asiatic, while the guerezas are entirely confined to equatorial Africa and the adjacent islands.

In the langurs, cheek-pouches are absent, but the thumb, although short, is always developed. The species are very numerous, and varied. The largest of the whole group is the Himalayan-langur (*P. schistaceus*), a large, brownish-grey-coloured monkey, with a white head ; closely allied is the Sacred Hanuman-langur (*P. entellus*) of India. In these langurs the young are coloured much like the adults (*entellus* group) ; in another group the immature pelage is golden-yellow (*auratus* group), while in other specimens (*aygula* group) the young are parti-coloured, having a dark, spinal stripe down the back. Some of these monkeys are bright chestnut-buff in colour (*P. rubicundus*, from Borneo, and *P. nobilis*, from Sumatra) ; others, like

P. aygula, are uniformly grey in colour, while there are some species black all over. One of the most handsome members of the *aygula* group is the Cross-bearing langur (*P. cruciger*) of Borneo; this animal is of a bright rufous colour, with a black, cross-shaped marking on its back.

Closely allied to the typical langurs are two large monkeys known as the Douc-langur (*Pygathrix nemaeus*) and the Black-footed langur (*Pygathrix nigripes*); they hail from Cochin China and Annam. The former is an iron-grey-coloured animal, with black thighs, chest, hands and feet, and shoulders, yellowish-white fore-arms, and maroon-coloured legs.

The Snub-nosed langurs (*Rhinopithecus*) are fairly closely related to the true langurs; they are heavily built monkeys, with short, snub noses and plumed tails. *R. roxellanae*, from Eastern Tibet, is a brightly coloured species, having orange-buff frontal-band, sides of face, under parts and extremities, and a greenish-grey-coloured tail. Another species (*R. bieti*) comes from Yunnan, and a third one (*R. brelichi*) has been described from Central China. Nearly allied to *Rhinopithecus* is the genus *Presbytiscus*, which contains a single species (*P. avunculus*) from Tonkin; it is a smaller monkey than the true Snub-nosed langurs, black above and yellowish below. The tail is long, and is black with a creamy-white tuft.

A monkey from South Pagi Islands, Sumatra, has been described as representing a genus related to the Snub-nosed langurs.

SIAMANG (*Symphalangus syndactylus*).

This animal has been named *Simias concolor*, and, in addition to possessing a snub nose, it has a short, naked tail, tufted at the end, and its coat is jet-black in colour. The Proboscis-monkey (*Nasalis larvatus*), from Borneo, is the last of the langurs. This species is very easily distinguished by its proboscis-like nose, which reaches quite fantastic proportions in the male, and by its bright rufous colouring; in general size it equals the largest of the langurs.

The guerezas may be considered as representing one genus, *Colobus*, including the Black, Black-and-white guerezas, and Red-colobus monkeys, in which the thumb is nearly obsolete, small cheek-pouches are developed, and the tail is frequently tufted. The Black-guereza (*C. satanas*) is black all over, and the tail is untufted; this monkey is a West-African species.

Farther east, white hair appears on the thighs, forehead, back, and tail, one of the most easterly forms known, *C. caudatus*, from Kenya Colony, having the centre of the back black, surrounded by a mantle of long, white hair, falling down like a great white sheet on each side of the body, while the tail, which is black at its base only, takes the form of an enormous white brush. The various species of guereza are confined to equatorial Africa, ranging from Senegambia to Kenya Colony. The excessive development of this white hair constitutes a singularly effective protective coloration, one of the most remarkable to be met with among the monkey tribe, for it causes the animal to blend

EASTERN GORILLA (*Gorilla gorilla beringeri*).

ORANG-UTAN (*Simia satyrus*).

perfectly with the long masses of lichen hanging down from the boughs of the trees of the damp forests where it lives.

The Red-colobus monkeys have more or less evenly haired tails, without well-marked terminal tufts. In colour they vary considerably; some, like *C. ellioti*, are deep chestnut-red in the fore-part of the body and greyish-brown behind, others, such as *C. ferrugineus*, are black above and bright red on the flanks and ventral surface. The range of the species extends across equatorial Africa; it also includes the Islands of Fernando Po and Zanzibar.

Family Simiidae

The last family of the Primates is the *Simiidae*, or " Man-like " apes, which contains the largest and most highly developed members of the order. They are all arboreal, but when on the ground they can assume a semi-erect position ; their front limbs being sufficiently long for the fingers to reach the ground while in this attitude. Cheek-pouches and external tail are wanting, and, except among the gibbons, ischial callosities are absent. The stomach is simple, not sacculated as in the *Colobinae*, and the brain shows a very high state of development, closely resembling in general structure that of man. The cranial capacity of the skull, although large, is never as great as in the human being ; the canine-teeth, especially in the males, are large, and the two halves of the lower jaw are always firmly ossified together.

Commencing with the Gibbons, which are sometimes regarded as forming a distinct family, the *Hylobatidae*, we have two distinct types to consider : the true Gibbons (*Hylobates*) and the Siamangs (*Symphalangus*) ; the former are smaller and of more slender build than the latter, standing about thirty inches in height, whereas the Siamangs exceed three feet in height when standing upright. The second and third toes of the Siamangs are joined together by a web, and a kind of pouch is developed in the skin of the throat. These Gibbons and Siamangs are, perhaps, the most perfectly arboreal of all the Anthropoid apes ; the fore-arm is longer than the arm, and the hand longer

CHIMPANZEE (*Anthropopithecus troglodytes*).

than the foot. Furthermore, they are the only apes which, when on the ground, walk upright. The head is small and rounded, and the body clothed in soft, woolly fur.

The genus *Hylobates* contains about a dozen very closely allied species, some of which are entirely black (*H. nasutus*), or black with white face-markings (*H. hoolock* and *H. lar*), while others are grey (*H. leuciscus*) or pale brown (*H. agilis*). These various forms are widely spread over a considerable part of the Oriental region, from Bhutan and Annam eastwards to Cochin China, Yunnan, Tonkin, the Malay Peninsula, and Islands of the East Indian Archipelago. The Siamangs, which are black, are apparently confined to Tenasserim, the Malay Peninsula, Sumatra, and South Pagi Island.

The Orang-utan (*Simia satyrus*) is found only in the Islands of Borneo and Sumatra. The males are very much larger than the females, an old male standing as much as four feet six inches, while the female rarely exceeds three feet six inches in height. The arms are of great length, reaching to the ankles in the erect position, and the legs are quite short and bandy. The sides of the face, in old males, are bounded on each side by a massive, outstanding fold of skin, and a long moustache is frequently developed. The coat is long and harsh, and varies in colour from deep chestnut-red to yellowish-red. The brain of this ape has the convolutions very strongly marked, resembling very closely in general structure that of man. Another very remarkable feature of the orang is the enormous air-sac, or pouch, which, opening from the larynx, extends between the skin and the muscles, around the front of the neck and over the breast to the arm-pits, on each side. It serves as a voice-resonator.

The Gorillas represent a third genus of Anthropoid ape, *Gorilla*, containing one or more species and several sub-species. Gorillas are distributed across equatorial Africa, from the Cameroons and Gaboon eastward as far as the Birunga Mountains in the eastern Belgian Congo. These apes are the largest members of the family, and in many ways approach more closely to man than any other Anthropoid; the brain, however, exhibits a comparatively low state of development and weighs some ten ounces less than that of a normal human being. The fore-limbs greatly exceed the hind-limbs in length, and both the hands and feet are broader than in the Orang-utan. A really big male gorilla will stand about five feet four inches; the female does not exceed four feet two inches in height. The skull of an old male has enormously developed ridges above the eye-sockets, and very large canine teeth. The Western-gorilla is blackish-brown in general colour, with a grey back and reddish or black crown; the Eastern form (*G. gorilla beringeri*) is black, with a sharply contrasted pale-grey back.

The Chimpanzees (*Anthropopithecus*) are considerably smaller than the gorillas, and the difference in size between the sexes is not so marked. The legs are proportionately longer, and the skull does not normally exhibit the excessively marked orbital and central crests which occur in the gorilla. The brain is very highly organised, and the majority of zoologists consider this ape as the one nearest to man. The coat is long and black or brown in colour, and the face either black or flesh-coloured. These apes are entirely confined to the equatorial forest zone of Africa, ranging from the Gambia and Sierra Leone eastward across the Congo to Tanganyika Territory and Lake Tanganyika.

INDEX

2 G 2

PRINTED IN GREAT BRITAIN BY WILLIAM CLOWES AND SONS, LIMITED, LONDON AND BECCLES.